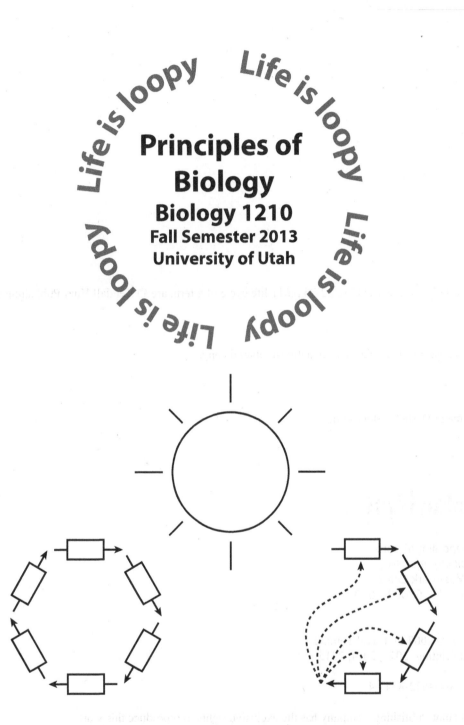

Principles of Biology
Biology 1210
Fall Semester 2013
University of Utah

Life is loopy · Life is loopy · Life is loopy · Life is loopy · Life is loopy

David H. Temme

Kendall Hunt
publishing company

Fig 7-2 p.182 forelimbs and Fig 22-26 p.611 life cycle of a fern. are © Kendall Hunt Publishing Company

This book was printed directly from author-prepared copy.

Cover image © Shutterstock.com

www.kendallhunt.com
Send all inquiries to:
4050 Westmark Drive
Dubuque, IA 52004-1840

Copyright © 2007 by David Temme
Revised Printing: 2013, 2014, 2015

ISBN 978-1-4652-8347-4

A Brief Discussion of Approach

Have you ever noticed in the Roadrunner cartoons (if you have never seen one, I apologize) that the coyote does not immediately fall after running off a cliff. So long as he keeps looking forward, he keeps right on running across thin air. Falling only happens after he looks down.

I think this describes me at a certain juncture in my own education. I was running along, looking forward, and by all classical standards doing quite well. But little things kept hinting to me that things were not as stable or as put together as they seemed. Finally, I looked down and found that I had long passed the cliff. After the fall I realized that, in some extremely fundamental ways, I needed to start over. Most important, I realized that understanding the foundation underlying the basic workings of Life is what intrigued me the most. In other words, I wanted to figure out how to best unify this subject that we call biolog .

Over the years I have found that teaching introductory biology classes and trying to figure out how to best unify biology go hand in hand. The repeated cycle of going back and studying the various pieces of the puzzle, attempting to explain them, and getting feedback from students has helped clarify my vision of biology. I have come to see how some relatively simple concepts reach their fingers through the entire workings of Life. This in turn has made it possible for me to present Life more and more as interwoven concepts and less and less as an enormous compilation of facts.

But as my view of Life evolved, I also found that what I wanted to discuss in class was significantly dive ging from standard textbooks. Initially I tried to compensate by providing lecture outlines and using a traditional text as a required backup. Finally, I decided that the gap was becoming too great. I needed to write my own book. Not a textbook per se, for I had no interest in trying to capture all the information found in standard biology textbooks. I am trying to write a book that captures a way to think about biology. More specificall , I am trying to develop a conceptual framework based on relatively few core ideas that makes it possible for students to begin to see how to understand the various aspects of Life. Information is still presented, but the information is always secondary to the ideas that allow one to understand the information.

Where does this approach fit into the ongoing debate on how to best design an introductory textbook? It seems like much of the discussion is centered around questions such as: Should the order of topics go from small to big, or big to small? Should it contain lots of detail (a so-called major's book) or less detail (a so-called nonmajor's book)? Should it try to capture the students' attention by first discussing seemingly more relevant issues such as cancer, drug addiction, or species extinction? Does it need to be accompanied by a Web- and CD-based computer extravaganza to get the attention of students raised largely by TVs? Although I think that these are all good questions, they all seem to contain an underlying assumption: The debate is over style and not substance. What should be to be taught is clear because obviously to teach introductory biology is to introduce (in more or less detail) what is known about biology. The issue of debate is how to best present it.

My approach is different because I disagree with the substance. I think introducing biology by introducing what is known about biology is a major educational mistake. To paraphrase an old parable, telling students what is known is to give them fish (that will last through the next test), instead of teaching them how to fish. One respons to this type of criticism is to focus on teaching students how we know what we know. That is, to base the discussion of biology on how biologists have used the scientific method of inquiry to gain insight into the ways of the living world. Although potentially a worthy approach, I have gone in a different direction. As I stated earlier, my goal is to try to cultivate a way of thinking about biology. I focus on providing students with images instead of just words. In the process, I try to show students how to understand things that they don't really believe they could ever understand. Perhaps I am naive, but I believe that education in its truest form is enticing.

A Warning

Most books start with a preface. My preface is that this book could still be more complete. Multiple topics could be expanded further, and in each case doing so would show how the basic themes of Life can be used to organize even more.

Moreover, I also have no doubt that in the pages to come you can find examples of typing errors, awkward sentence structures, and ideas presented in convoluted ways. In the years spent putting this together, feedback from many people, but especially Dan Weinstein, Kiana Sarraf, Shauna Horne, and my wife Katina Temme, have helped me use fewer conceptually twisted passages and more complete sentences, as well as pointing out many instances where what I had thought I had put on paper, and what was actually written, were not in agreement. But nonetheless, errors persist because I have always been more interested and concerned about the nature and organization of the ideas presented, than with adding all the extra coats of polish needed to give an impeccable shine to the presentation. Admittedly, this is one of my faults that falls under the broader categories of time, trade-offs, and priorities.

Despite all its flaws, I believe strongly in the novel approach to biology being developed within these pages. Why? The first is personal. As I developed the framework presented here, it helped me make sense of Life in a deeper, more meaningful way. It was, and still is, exciting! Second, despite the fact that it starts out feeling quite foreign to most students, in my years of teaching biology from this perspective, I have seen many students embrace the transition. The reason is simple; they began to see that it was helping them to better think about, question, and understand Life overall. And, as a consequence, they realized that they were becoming more prepared to take on further challenges, not just in biology, but in anything they wished to pursue. Following is one of my favorite notes from a former student that reflects this

> My sister took your class her junior year of college. A year before I came to the U, when I was registering for my freshmen classes, she pushed me off the computer and said, "I am going to change your life!" When I looked at what she was doing, it was signing me up for your class! She told me it was a hard class, but you will actually learn something and it will stick. She said she wished she would have taken it her first year, because you learn to think.

Contents

An important question for your

Is it seeking training or education?

Scenario 1a: (trained or educated)

Scenario 1b: (trained or educated)

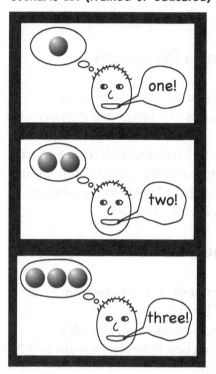

Scenario 2a: (trained or educated)

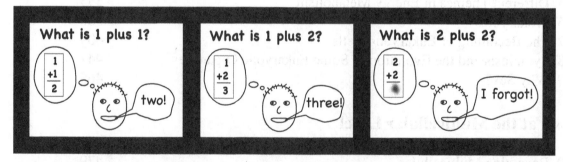

Scenario 2b: (trained or educated)

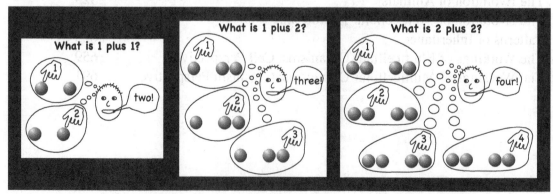

Science and the Rational Program

I suggest that the human mind—as well as the minds of other organisms—is set up to look for *patterns*. Specifically, we tend to notice whenever one event seems to be followed by another event. It stirs our curiosity. For instance, you may have asked yourself questions like this before: Am I feeling sick now because of what I ate at Joe's restaurant this morning? Did it rain today because I washed my car yesterday? Did my favorite basketball team lose last night because I decided to watch them on TV? And it seems that the potential patterns that pique our curiosity the most are those that we can imagine being useful in some way.

This search for useful patterns occurs by carrying on a conversation with Nature. By Nature I mean everything in the world around us, including us. The idea of carrying on a conversation with Nature, however, might raise a few eyebrows. How can we carry on a conversation with something that cannot talk? The most succinct answer is: We can do it easily. In fact, we do it all the time. I explain by using an example.

Conversing with something that cannot talk

Suppose you encountered the following sequence of events: You clapped your hands, and then a short while later a ten-dollar bill fell from the sky. How would you respond?

Two possible responses are to ignore it or to check to see if the pattern is repeatable. That is, you might pose a question to your surrounding world. How would you ask the question? You would clap again. How is the surrounding world going to give an answer? By whether or not a ten-dollar bill again falls from the sky.

Let's suppose that you choose to clap again, and the answer to your question was yes—another ten-dollar bill falls from the sky. Would you now have enough confidence to go into a fancy restaurant with an empty wallet and order a $10 meal (just one clap), a $20 meal (just two claps), . . . a $100 dollar meal (just 10 claps)? Perhaps, but two times in a row may not be sufficient to convince you that clapping really does lead to ten-dollar bills falling out of the sky.

Yet my guess is that your interest would be aroused, and you would likely explore further. How could you go about doing so? For one, you could keep asking the same question; that is, you could keep clapping. But you may not want just to keep clapping in the same spot under the same conditions. You might want to go inside a building and see if it still works there. You could also clap at night, on sunny days, on cloudy days, and so on. You may even want to travel to other parts of the world to see if it is just a local phenomenon. The more times in a row under many varied circumstances that the answer to your question was yes, the more confidence you would gain in the pattern.

Alternatively, you could try to understand the underlying basis of this pattern. Here you might want to explore questions such as: Where are the ten-dollar bills coming from? How did they get up there? How many are up there? How did clapping cause one to fall? By asking such questions, you begin to focus on the *mechanism* by which clapping leads to ten-dollar bills falling from the sky.

The goal of inquiring about any suspected pattern further—whether checking for repeatability or looking for a mechanistic understanding—is to establish whether the pattern seems real. In other words, does the pattern appear to be *reliable* or *trustworthy*? In many cases the answer will quickly prove to be "no". A gust of wind could have blown a ten-dollar bill from someone's hand, and you may have clapped right before it settled down in front of you. Repeated clapping would quickly show the absence of any connection between the two—the timing of the two events was nothing more than a coincidence. Alternatively, the answer will keep coming back "yes" whenever the suspected pattern is actually part of how Nature works. Gravitational attraction is a noteworthy example because it shows that both demonstrated repeatability and a mechanistic understanding are not needed to establish reliability. I honestly have no understanding of the mechanism by which the earth pulls on objects from a distance (and it is not clear to me that any one else really does either). Yet I trust that when I let go of a pencil, it will fall to the ground. Why? Because every pencil, or any other weight-bearing object that I have ever released, has done so. Even our language underlies the reliability of such an event. We refer to something slipping out of our hand as "dropping it" because we anticipate what is going to happen next; it is going down. Furthermore, my trust of gravity has come from more than just my experience with dropping things. Every aspect of my life has been accompanied by the pull of gravity—so far it has never let up, even for a moment.

Of course, there will be some considered patterns that we are, to at least some degree, still uncertain about. In such cases, Nature has yet to give what seems to be a definite yes or no answer, which sets the stage for further exploration to be part of every day.

Recognizing trustworthy patterns makes prediction possible and prediction may be useful

Recognizing patterns as being trustworthy is not a useful property in and of itself, but trustworthy patterns carry predictive information. Returning to the gravity example: Right before I let go of something from my hand, I cannot say for certain that it will fall to the ground because it has not happened yet. What will happen in the future always has an element of uncertainty. But because I trust gravitational attraction to be a reliable pattern, I can predict with a great deal of confidence that it will fall to the ground. And the ability to predict is potentially useful to any organism. For instance, it can help an organism survive because having some idea what is going to happen allows an organism to better anticipate what to avoid and what to pursue. In fact, using prediction to make life-promoting decisions is often phrased in terms of using common sense. We might say that it is a "wise idea" to move out of the path of a tumbling boulder or that it is "smart" to avoid a potential predator because we can predict what would happen otherwise.

Being able to predict patterns of occurrence also sets the stage for one to manipulate their surroundings. If I know that on arranging the external world in a certain way a certain type of event will follow, then I can use this pattern to do something useful for me. It is this simple thought pattern that forms the basis of **technology**—from making and using rock hammers and spears to computers and microwave ovens.

Two fundamental questions

To search for patterns in Nature is to ask two fundamental questions:

• What can happen (i.e., what is possible and what is not)?

• What controls these happenings (i.e., what regulates when possible happenings will happen)?

These questions are common to all types of endeavors. For example, psychologists are interested in what human behaviors are possible, and what regulates when these possible behaviors will occur. On the other hand, businesspeople are interested in what people will buy and what regulates when they will buy. I even suggest that all your personal endeavors fit into this framework. Suppose, for instance, you see someone today that "strikes your fancy." The two questions become: Is it possible that she/he could be interested in someone like me? If so, what sort of things should I do to help sway his/her interest?

What Is Science?

Science is nothing more than the endeavor to uncover consistent patterns in the workings of Nature. Which means that we are all scientists because we all engage Nature in an ongoing conversation. This realization leaves little room for hating science. In fact, this definition even places organisms other than humans into the ranks of being scientists. For example, every dog I have ever known has sought and found all sorts of consistent patterns associated with getting fed and going on walks.

If we are all scientists, what distinguishes professional scientists from anybody else? The difference is that professional scientists take this natural pattern-looking behavior to another level. They do not just rely on casual observation to uncover patterns. Instead, they employ much more systematic means and methods to ask Nature questions about its ways. The whole notion of doing an experiment is to set up a situation where Nature more clearly answers posed questions. This more rigorous approach makes it possible to find patterns that could not be discovered otherwise.

The general basis of the scientific method: searching for differences that make a difference

The purpose underlying the scientific method is straightforward. Scientists are interested in understanding what factors must be present for a specific event to occur. In other words, science attempts to understand causation. The idea is that every occurrence is an outcome structured by components of the situation that preceded it. The goal of science is thus to assess which of the many factors surrounding any occurrence actually played a role in determining the outcome.

The scientific method is how scientists answer the question: How should one go about trying to determine what factors lead to a certain outcome? In other words, the scientific method is a guide to ways to ask questions of Nature that lead to the most unequivocal answers. The guidelines include discussion of setting up control groups and experimental groups, and other such things. These details are important, but how straightforward the scientific method truly is can get lost in such discussions. All the various means by which scientists go about their work are built from one fundamental idea: Change *one and only one* factor at a time and then see if *this difference makes a difference in the outcome*. By holding all but one factor constant across experiments you can screen off all other factors. The altered factor is thus isolated for scrutiny. So, if a difference in outcome shows up, you can, with some confidence, assert that you have found a **causal factor**—a factor that can make a difference in the outcome. On the other hand, varying two or more factors within an experiment makes interpretation of an observed difference more difficult. One cannot be sure which of the altered factors made a difference in the outcome. The details of the scientific method concern ways to isolate one factor at a time.

A side note: Do not confuse the discovery of a causal factor with the discovery of **the cause**. The difference between a causal factor and a cause has to do with *sufficiency*. A causal factor will contribute to the occurrence of an outcome, but it alone is not sufficient. In other words, more than one factor influences the outcome. In contrast, if something is the cause, it is, in and of itself, sufficient. The alteration or removal of any other factor will not under any circumstance affect the nature of the outcome. Single causes are probably rare, if they exist at all. It seems that Nature works through interactions, and interactions, by definition, involve the interplay of more than one factor.

Science demands that all observations be measured

Many observations about Nature are **subjective**—that is, the observer makes a difference. Or put in another way, in many instances changing the observer can lead to a change in the nature of the observation. Consider, for instance, the question: Does asparagus taste good? The first person you ask says yes, the next two say no, and it continues to flip-flop back and forth as you ask more and more people. So which is it: Does asparagus taste good or bad? There is no right answer, which really means that there is no universal answer. Tastes of any form, whether they concern food items, movies, paintings, poetry, novels, or anything else, are always personal preferences. When individual preferences are involved, differences in the observer can make a difference in the outcome. And as we know, humans are not all identical.

Yet despite the subjective nature of many of our observations, Nature seems to work, at least at times, in universal ways. In other words, patterns, such as gravitational attraction, seem to exist independent of the observer. You may like or dislike the constant pull of gravity, but the presence of the pull does not depend on what you think about it. And clearly the goal of science is to escape our subjective tendencies and discover more universal patterns in the workings of Nature. But still the observations made by individual scientists can be tainted by personal preferences. The fact that scientists often want or hope to demonstrate that Nature works in a particular way can cloud or bias their observations. The scientific method attempts to counter this problem in several ways. Perhaps the most basic means (and the only one I will mention here) is the requirement that all observations be measured (i.e., converted to length, volume, weight, or presence/absence). If I ask several people to lift some object and then tell me how heavy it is, I will likely get several different answers (depending in part on the relative strength of each observer). To some it might be pretty heavy, to others it might be really heavy, and still to others it might be pretty light. But their answer should all be the same if I ask them to measure the weight of the same object. As long as each uses an accurate scale, the recorded weight will be independent of whomever put it on the scale. Put in another way, measuring helps make the observation **objective**—that is, the observer does not make a difference. Science depends on objective observations.

Applying the scientific method

Some years back I moved to a new house. Because I like to grow things, I quickly went to work preparing a new garden plot in a sunny area of the backyard. After considerable effort—due to the rocky nature of the soil—the area was prepared, and I planted tomatoes of several varieties, eggplant, peppers, zucchini, and green beans, along with other things. To my delight, everything began to grow marvelously. My tomato plants, in particular, were growing tall and bushy. But strikingly, as the tomatoes started to grow and ripen, most were ruined when they turned hard and brown at the flower end. I subsequently found out that my tomatoes suffered something known as blossom-end rot.

The widespread development of blossom-end rot raised an obvious question: What caused it? I had grown tomatoes many times before without incident. So something had to be different about this new garden site. But what was it? Unfortunately a lot of possibilities came to mind. There could be something unique about the composition of the soil, the exposure to wind, the types of insects or fungi present, the fact that the garden was positioned near a drop off, among many other things. With all these different possibilities, how would I ever determine which were causal factors?

Here is what I did. The following year I tried a few new things that I thought might make a difference. The result: My tomatoes got blossom-end rot. The next year I made a few more changes. The result: Once again my tomatoes had blossom-end rot. After three years of tinkering I still had no real idea what was going on. Finally I gave up and quit growing tomatoes in that area. But after a six-year hiatus, I thought I would make a few changes and give it another shot. The result: The tomatoes did *not* have blossom-end rot.

After all this so-called experimentation, do I feel confident that I understand what caused blossom-end rot in my tomatoes? The answer is no! Am I confident that my tomatoes will not get blossom-end rot this year? Again, no! Why? There were just too many variables for me to come to any firm conclusion. Just the fact that every year was different adds one more variable on top of any other changes I made. How could I solve this problem? Employ the scientific method. The experimental design would be straightforward. Within the same year, divide tomatoes into different groups and then control the growing conditions so that each group is different from another group in only one way. For instance, two groups composed of the same tomato variety could be grown in conditions with one difference. Perhaps the soil calcium levels could be maintained at a higher level in one group than the other. Alternatively, two different varieties of tomatoes could be planted in the same growing conditions. Furthermore, having replicates of each group would increase the confidence in the results.

Did I ever do this? No, and here is why! First off, my garden would need to be much larger to set up all these different groups. Plus, even if I had sufficient space, it would take a tremendous amount of time and resources to set up and implement this experimental design. In situations where there are many possible causes, using the scientific method to try to discover which ones make a difference is extremely laborious and time consuming. Personally, my inability to grow a few backyard tomatoes did not justify that type of effort. Yet if blossom-end rot was found to be a widespread problem, then it may make more sense for someone to go through all the needed time and effort. Any person performing such a systematic investigation could be considered a professional scientist.

The cause of certain types of human disease has captured more attention than blossom-end rot, and once again the scientific method can play an important role. For example, go back a few years and consider people beginning to question whether a relationship existed between smoking and lung cancer. To discern the nature of this relationship by casual observation would be difficult for one simple reason. Some people smoke heavily their entire life without getting lung cancer, whereas others get lung cancer despite the fact that they never smoked. Clearly, if smoking causes cancer, it is not like gravity where the object falls every time you let it go. It could, however, be more like rolling a weighted dice. With a weighted dice all possible numbers still show up, but any weighted number will show up more often than expected by chance alone (which would be 1/6th of the time with a fair dice). Similarly, although smoking may not guarantee that you will get lung cancer, it may increase your chance of getting lung cancer (over what it would be if you had not smoked). But how would one ever show this to be the case?

To determine whether a dice is weighted, you need to roll the dice a large number of times. From this large sample size, one can then compare whether any numbers show up more often than would be expected by chance. Statistical methods (which beyond mention will not be addressed here) can be used to help interpret this comparison. Similarly, the idea that smoking increases one's chance of getting lung cancer (in comparison to if you did not smoke) can be tested by coupling the scientific method with a large sample size. Divide a large number of people into two groups with only one known difference between them—whether or not they smoke, and then see if the incidence of lung cancer is higher in the group that smokes in comparison to the group that does not smoke. Again statistics can help interpret the comparison. Just to get you to address the obvious, tell me what is wrong with the experimental design in Figure 1-1.

As long as someone is willing to make the effort, the scientific method can be used to investigate many of the more subtle patterns in Nature. And to date, it has. Researchers have begun to explore the workings of subatomic particles to distant stars and galaxies, and most things in between. Of course, much of this effort cannot continue without society's support. Which raises an interesting question that we all participate in: What types of science should we, as

Group 1:

- Born in 1945.
- Lived entire life within a certain geographic area, call it area X.
- is a male.
- smoked 2 or more packs a day for 20 or more years.

Group 2:

- Born in 1945.
- Lived entire life within a certain geographic area, call it area X.
- is a female.
- has never smoked

Figure 1-1. Something is wrong with the above experimental design. What is it, and how could this problem be fixed?

a society, support? None at all? Just research that seems directly applicable to current human problems—what is often termed **applied research**? Or should we venture beyond and support scientific exploration driven by simply being curious about the way Nature works? So-called **basic research** may someday discover something applicable to human problems, but that is not its driving force. For example, in biology many trained scientists focus their entire careers on learning more about the different types of organisms with which we share this planet. For many of these organisms there is no obvious direct connection with humans. So should we study their ways?

Consider the following experiment: In many bird species adult males have strikingly different plumage than females. For example, in an African bird named the long-tailed widowbird (*Euplectes progne*), the five-inch-long body of a male is adorned with a twenty-inch-long tail, whereas females have only around a three-inch-long tail. Mating in these birds occurs when males set up territories and females somehow choose to nest in one of the male's territories. A scientist named Malte Andersson wondered whether females paid attention to male tail length when choosing among territories, which if true would help explain why these males had such long tails. So he performed the following experiment. He took 36 males and divided them up into four groups: Group 1—he left as normal males; Group 2—he created males with much shorter tails by cutting their tails to around 6 inches; Group 3—he created males with extra long tails (around 30 inches) by supergluing the extra tail feathers from Group 2 onto normal males; and Group 4—he cut and superglued on tail feathers without altering the overall tail length. Group 4 is a necessary part of the experiment design because otherwise Group 3 would be different from the first two groups in two ways: increased tail length and the presence of cut feathers superglued on to the tail.

Group 4 corrects that problem because now there is only one difference between Group 1 and Group 4 (the presence of cut feathers superglued onto the tail), and one difference between Group 3 and Group 4 (differences in tail length). Figure 1-2 presents a sketch of the four different groups. Andersson then counted the number of females nesting in each male's territory. It turned out that the males with the extra-long tails had about twice as many active nests in their territory as the normal males. His results thus supported the suggestion that females in this species seem to prefer males with longer tails.

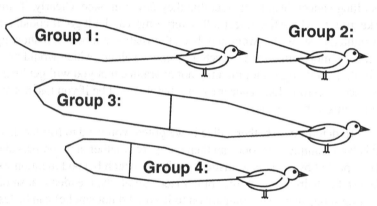

Figure 1-2. A sketch of the four different groups of male Long-tailed Widow Birds created in the experiment described in the text. In groups 3 and 4, the vertical line through the tail indicates the use of superglue to attach tail feathers. Given that the tail-length in group 1 and group 4 are the same, can you explain why the scientific method requires that the Group 4 treatment be part of the experiment? (See text for further discussion.)

It is not obvious that better understanding the ways of long-tailed widowbirds will directly contribute to solving pressing human problems. Yet personally I support this type of inquiry because I find joy in knowing more about how the living world works. I guess I am curious that way (double meaning intended). Is that a sufficient reason? I don't know. Maybe it is also true that increasing understanding can lead to increased appreciation of the living world that we are a part of. And maybe that increased appreciation will help us make wiser decisions about how we attempt to manipulate our surroundings. Again, I don't know. I do, however, believe that these questions are worth considering.

Some terms of science

A few terms were left out of the preceding discussion of science and the scientific method that I still want to introduce. It seemed best to wait and group them all together. Note that many of these terms are commonly used in everyday language. I define how they are used in science, and it is important for you to understand the distinction.

fact—a measured property of the surrounding world. For example, the measured weight of an object, or the number of nesting females in a male long-tailed widowbird's territory would be facts.

data—the collection of numbers that result from a set of measured observations. For example, if we take a group of people and measure each individual's height, the recorded height for each individual would be a fact, and the entire set of measured heights would be a data set.

statistics—means of summarizing and analyzing data sets. For example, if I measured the height of one hundred people I could report on this group's height by reading each individual number. That, however, would be too much detailed information for anyone to process. More likely, I would use statistics to help summarize the data. The most common statistic is the average. There are many other statistics, such as the variance and standard deviation, that help describe the overall distribution of numbers. Statistics can also be used to compare data sets. For instance, I mentioned earlier that certain forms of statistical analysis could be used to compare the recorded incidence of lung cancer in a smoking and a nonsmoking group. Any such analysis attempts to determine the probability that differences in the two data sets are simply a result of chance. Which means that the lower this probability is, the more confident one can be that the experimental difference was what made a difference in the outcome.

hypothesis—an educated guess about the existence of some type of pattern in Nature. For example, in the long-tailed widowbird experiment described earlier, the hypothesis was that male tail length was at least one of the factors that females used to decide which male's territory to nest in. Generally, hypotheses are based on prior observation or are formulated by rationally extending current scientific working knowledge. In other words, a hypothesis is not just a random guess, although creativity can play an important role in its formulation.

Although a hypothesis is often presented as the starting point of the scientific method, recognize that some hypotheses are not amenable to testing by the scientific method, whereas other potentially testable hypotheses have never been tested because so far no one has been willing to put in the time and effort to do so. Furthermore, some scientific experiments have no more of a hypothesis than "let's change something and see what happens."

law—a regular pattern of occurrence in Nature. When our ongoing conversation with Nature reaches the point that a suspected pattern is accepted as completely trustworthy, this pattern takes on the character of a law. The *universal law of gravitation* is an example. There are no known exceptions to the idea that any two bodies of matter generate a pulling attraction toward each other. The universal law of gravitation also points out that laws do not necessarily explain the facts that they describe; they just state the regularity. As I said earlier, it is not exactly clear how gravity actually works.

theory—a general idea that aids in conceptually unifying, hence explaining, many and diverse phenomena of Nature. (Note that in biology the many and diverse phenomena of Nature are all the different types of organisms found on this planet.) In other words, a theory makes sense of and explains a vast body of scientific knowledge. Theories are generally too vast to be subjected to direct testing by experimentation. Unlike a hypothesis, a theory may not hinge on a single point that is directly falsifiable. However, any theory may be modified or even rejected over time because a new or modified theory seems to have greater explanatory power.

induction—the process by which specific bits of information and logic are used to build a more general statement of a pattern. Induction, in addition to creativity, is used often in the formation of hypotheses.

deduction—the process by which a general statement of a pattern is used to generate a more specific statement of a pattern. Deductive reasoning is often used in devising testable predictions from hypotheses (i.e., if–then statements for which the relevant components can be measured).

control group—the group within the context of a scientific experiment (where two or more groups are set up) with the least number of manipulations. In terms of two earlier discussed experiments, the nonsmoking group and the group of long-tailed widowbirds whose tails were left alone would be the control groups. In an experiment designed to test the effects of some medication, the control group would be those given a sugar pill. In such an experiment the control group has been manipulated— each individual was instructed to take a pill—but it is the least manipulated because the pill did not add any new ingredients to each individual's body.

experimental group—the group or groups within the context of a scientific experiment that have one additional manipulation—one thing either added or subtracted—in comparison to the control group. It is the combination of experimental and control groups that make it possible to test whether some factor is a causal factor—that is, whether it makes a difference in the outcome.

Some goals of science education

One part of a science education is to learn from the work of scientists before you. That is, to learn what patterns in Nature have been uncovered so far by scientific exploration. Unfortunately, a burdensome aspect of this task is learning the terminology that has been invented to discuss these patterns.

But you must also realize that scientific knowledge is continually evolving! Any pattern taught in a science class is not considered to be the absolute truth; it is just the best working model for the moment. Each pattern is only as good as the evidence that supports it and the intellectual framework through which the pattern was interpreted. New evidence or new intellectual perspectives may thus lead to a change in what patterns are considered to be reliable. In other words, *scientific discovery is a building, self-correcting process*. Scientific explanations of today should be better than those of the past, but not as good as those in the future. As a consequence, science education creates the freedom to question and critically examine whatever you are told. Part of being a scientist is to have a healthy dose of well-reasoned skepticism.

Finally, you need to work on those abilities that will help you pursue patterns on your own. With such skills in hand, you can go out and explore those aspects of Nature that you find most compelling. Such abilities include the following:

• Opening wide your curiosity to the types of patterns that might exist in Nature

• Using accepted patterns to speculate further about the workings of Nature

• Opening your senses and intellect to the observation of new patterns

• Knowing how to test critically whether a pattern that you speculate to exist is a reliable pattern

Forming More Connections

So far I have used the realization that humans are *pattern crazy* to set up a fairly standard introduction of science and the scientific method. At this juncture you may be ready to move to the next subject. If so, skip ahead to Chapter 2. But our pattern craziness is so immersed in the way that we think, learn, and communicate that it seems important to try to cast a wider net. I start by introducing the analogy of mental maps and then proceed from there. The discussion of education sits at the heart of my teaching philosophy and, consequently, how I have tried to organize this book. During that discussion I introduce the notion of *embracing confusion*, which I believe stands as a prerequisite for all truly educational experiences. I then finish this section by trying to incorporate rational thought and language into the mix. In the process, I discuss why mathematics is commonly considered the language of science.

Mental maps

As each of us carries on an ongoing conversation with Nature, we are constantly formulating our view of how Nature works—what patterns we think exist, what patterns we think don't exist, and where uncertainty still exists. I find it useful to think of anyone's current view on how Nature works as a map. In other words, inside our heads we constantly carry around our most up-to-date "map of Nature."

Why call it a map? For one, we are not carrying around the real thing, just our representation of Nature and how it works. Similarly, a map is at best a bare-bones representation of some area. Just think of the difference between being in a place and looking at any map of the same place. Or put in another way, you may look at a map of your home state or country and say, "Hey that is where I live!" But, as you know, it is not a literal statement.

What is more important to realize is that we use what is inside our head and printed maps in essentially the same way—to help us navigate by expectation. For example, when using a map, we think in terms like, "*If we are here and traveling in this direction, then we should see such-and-such next.*" On a road trip the expectation might be something like, "*The next intersection should be highway 61,*" or on a hiking trip, the expectation might be something like, "*Over that next ridge we should find a small lake.*" Similarly, our mind helps us navigate through life by constantly using storage of past experience to create an expectation of what should happen next. For example, every time you walk out your front door, you have an expectation of what you are going to see, hear, and smell (as well as what you are not going to see, hear, and smell). The expectation will include all the nuances of this familiar place, such as the size, shape, and location of trees, sidewalks, and others buildings. With each new step your view changes, but as long as you remain on familiar turf, the map in your head adjusts to create a new set of expectations and keeps you on course. Problems do arise when something unexpected pops up. Perhaps a dog that you have never seen before darts out from behind a house and comes running toward you. Yet although this particular dog is unknown, past experience with other dogs will have generated a general dog map that can be quickly pulled out. This map may include something like—dogs wagging their tails tend to be friendly, whereas dogs baring their teeth tend to be aggressive. Given that this dog is wagging its tail, you stop briefly to pat its head as it approaches and then proceed on your way.

The typical reaction to instances where reality does not meet our map-based expectation clearly illustrates our ongoing dependence on mental maps—we tend to get engulfed in the panic of feeling lost. Prodded by this discomfort, our focus tends to quickly narrow to the task of finding out where we are. With a printed map we continually flip back and forth between the map and the surrounding landscape intensely trying to match map-based expectations with our surroundings. The scenario is similar with mental maps as we quickly search for an explanation—something that connects our current perceptions back to some aspect of our mental map. If you have seen the movie *The Wizard of Oz*, just imagine what was going on in Dorothy's mind when she first stepped out her front door into the land of Oz and exclaimed, "Toto, I don't think we are in Kansas anymore."

Navigation and education

Here I propose that we can use the concept of a mental map to help us envision how we think and learn. But first I need to add some more background.

Different forms of maps and different types of navigation

Maps come in both spatial and temporal forms. A road map is a spatial map, as is our conception of what we will see when we walk out our front door. Both of these are configurations of where things will be located in relationship to each other in the environment. In contrast, the expectation that a pencil will drop when you let go of it is perhaps better described as a temporal map—an expectation of what will happen next. Any written story involving cause and consequence is also a temporal map, for it is a discussion of this leading to that. But the fact that movement across space always takes time and temporal sequences of events tend to move across space muddles this distinction. In other words, time and space are probably best thought of as two parts of the same map. It is the time–space continuum stuff that physicists prattle on about and science fiction writers wrap their story lines around in a number of mind-twisting ways.

Map-based navigation also seems to occur in two distinct ways. The flavor of one of these forms, which we could call **topographic navigation**, is captured in the statement—I knew the area like the back of my hand. Topographic navigation starts with becoming familiar with the topography of an area through past experience—that is, in a detailed and accurate way you know numerous local landmarks along with their relative position to each other. Navigation occurs whenever you use this knowledge to move from where you are to where you want to go by constantly keeping track of your position in relation to local landmarks. This is clearly how we navigate around our home, the local market, or any other place where we spend a lot of time. The preceding description of you navigating past your front door was an example of topographic navigation.

Orienteering stands in stark contrast to topographic navigation. With topographic navigation your position in relation to the navigational landmarks used changes as you move. For example, that oak tree in your front yard could be in front of you or behind you depending on where you are and what direction you are moving. With orienteering, the relative position of the navigational features do not change as you move. The magnetic fields used to establish compass directions are an example. The directions *east* or *west* remain the same no matter where you move within any local environment. The same is true of *north* and *south* (at least until you travel all the way to either the North or South Pole, where these directions then flip-flop). Other distant objects like the North Star, the position of the sun at given times of the day, or distant mountain ranges can also be used in the same fashion.

Using and changing our map of Nature

Let's start with a question: What is thinking? From a map-based perspective, to think is to navigate through the mental landscape inside your head (in search of something). Each thought pattern moves along the spatial and temporal patterns that exist in your map of Nature, and the same navigational alternatives would seemingly be present. Topographic thinking would be moving around among a set of related and familiar details. Mental orienteering, on the other hand, would make use of broad universal concepts. Details would be less important because the basic ideas should apply in any circumstance.

Learning, on the other hand, is the adding to and refining of your current map. Although learning may be motivated in a variety of ways, confusion can be a particularly strong impetus. *To seek out and embrace confusion* is to admit that your current map is inadequate—that you are at least somewhat lost. The associated uncomfortable feeling will then in turn prod you to search for some form of resolution. One alternative would be to quickly back away from what is causing the confusion, and return to a comfortable, familiar place. That, however, has nothing to do with learning. *Learning, by definition, is an adventure*. New ideas, new revisions, need to be introduced creating new places to explore. The search is for revisions that help to clarify—that is, help you to formulate a seemingly acceptable explanation (at least for the moment).

Of course, how you tend to think—how you tend to navigate within your mind—will influence how you explore the world around you. For instance, thinking topographically tends to bias your exploration toward paying attention to the local details. This creates an important limitation to consider: Topographic thinking will tend to lead to the formation of many disconnected maps. Like the topographic map you use to move around your neighborhood won't help you navigate anywhere else, the landmarks generated in each revision will be unique to the (subject) area being explored. Furthermore, it may prove difficult to keep a whole mental closet full of topographic maps from getting messed up and even lost (forgotten). We can only keep track of so much, and when each new map addition is a special case, that limit can easily be surpassed.

Educational exploration by orienteering—that is the use of broad concepts to guide our thinking—creates a striking contrast. When concepts head the exploration, we seek out new places that can be understood by already familiar principles. Connections and analogies will thus always be at the heart of how we amend our map. Additions to our map will not be more special cases to memorize (and then quickly forget), but an increasingly larger body of knowledge connected by the same conceptual framework. Furthermore, exploration by orienteering will trigger us to always be on the lookout for better guides—that is, even broader, more general concepts— that make it possible to cast an even larger web of connection across the informational terrain.

Exploration by orienteering may also make the whole task of educational exploration less daunting. Although the discomfort of feeling lost is part of the education process, topographic exploration may maximize this discomfort. Due to its disconnected nature, each new bout of topographically guided exploration tends to start with the feeling of being completely lost. Past experience is not much of a guide when you immerse yourself in the details of a new area. Orienteering, on the other hand, always keeps you anchored to something familiar—the concept or concepts guiding the exploration. Plus, although navigating by orientation can truly be exploratory—keep heading west, and you will come to areas where you have never been before—you are never really lost. Although you may not be able to find what you are looking for, you can always find your way back "home." It is no more complicated than if you travel due west for a ways, you can return home by simply traveling due east.

Although the last couple of paragraphs portray conceptual thinking in a more favorable light, it's clear that thinking and learning work best when both forms of navigation are combined. Details can be important, but they are so much more useful when they are embedded in a broad conceptual framework. When details fit into a bigger picture, we can go beyond just recognizing each detail's unique features and see its connection to other details. Alternatively, although broad concepts may connect us to different areas, if we never get down and get our hands dirty exploring the details, we will never come to know the nuances of any area.

Let me finish this section with one last thing to consider. Suppose you are presently located at point A in Figure 1-3, and you want to get to point B. The shaded area represents familiar terrain, and so it is possible to get from Point A to Point B via topographic navigation. The only issue is that this route is not the shortest or most efficient route possible. But how could you ever discover this shortcut without converting all the surrounding area into a topographic map by exploration? One way would be to combine both forms of navigation. You may be able to envision the shortest route from point A to point B by visualizing your topographic map in the context of a larger orientation scheme (such as the position of the afternoon sun). In other words, navigation by orientation can be used to create new connections among existing topographic maps. This suggests that learning involves not only exploring new places, but also finding new connections between areas with which you are already familiar.

Science, rational thought, and language

Rational thought is nothing more than how we make and use our map of Nature. In other words, it is the system by which we construct and use mental patterns that seem consistent with our perceptual dialogue with Nature. The point I add here is that the creation of **language** underlies the increased capacity of humans to convert perceived patterns into thought patterns. We can put our maps in story form, and as a consequence, the pieces are easier to manipulate. We can play out different scenarios in our mind in an attempt to determine which scenario is best without going through an actual trial-and-error process. The better our map is, the better we will be able to decide the best course of action—that is, the better we will be able to think rationally.

Any form of language has two components: the formation of symbols (e.g., words), and the formation of the rules delimiting how the symbols can be manipulated (e.g., rules of grammar). For a language to effectively guide rational thought, the symbols and the rules of usage need to mimic the objects, patterns, and relationships observed in Nature. Stated differently, the language must delimit what can follow from a given set of conditions in accord with what is observed to happen.

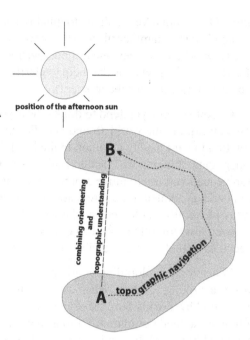

Figure 1-3. One could topographically navigate from A to B by moving through previously explored areas (the gray area). Alternatively, a shorter, but never before traveled route, could be devised by combining orienteering (such as using the position of the afternoon sun) and topographic understanding. (See text for further discussion.)

Mathematics is often considered to be the language of science. You may even hear the claim that Nature is written in the language of mathematics. But what do such statements really mean? The key is that mathematics can act as the thread that connects two previously mentioned statements: (1) Science attempts to find trustworthy patterns in the workings of Nature, and (2) the discovery of trustworthy patterns makes predictions possible. The easiest way to uncover the nature of this thread is to use an example. Let's again consider gravity.

There is more to the trustworthiness of gravitational attraction than the fact that my pencil will drop once I let it go. The strength of the pull is also a reliable pattern, which in turn means that the *rate* that my pencil (or any other object) will accelerate due to the pull of gravity is a reliable pattern. Now the key point: The language of mathematics is set up to make statements that keep track of how different variables connected by some form of rate change across time. Start keeping track of time right now, and that statement of how things will change becomes a prediction. So, whenever a trustworthy rate is discovered in Nature—such as the acceleration due to gravity—any mathematical expression that accurately describes the relationship between this rate and other variables can be used to make very exact predictions. Figure 1-4 provides a couple of examples. Also note that although the focus here is not on how mathematics can be used in the study of Life, discussion of rates will be a predominant theme. So keep in mind that any rate discussed could be incorporated into the language of mathematics to make predictions.

An aside: Earlier I implied that the temporal rates—how something changes across time—associated with reliable temporal patterns underlie the use of mathematics to make predictions. There is, however, another aspect of the story. In Nature, things can also change across space, and reliable spatial patterns would also come with spatial rates—how things change across some aspect of space, such as area or volume. So just like temporal rates, known (or at least estimated) spatial rates could be incorporated into the language of mathematics to make predictions about how certain things are expected to change across changes in spatial dimensions.

Rational thought is abstract

I often hear comments like "I can't learn this because it is too abstract." Here I want to convince you that abstraction is always part of language-based thought, which means that you do it all the time.

The task of converting our observations of Nature into a language involves simplification. Given the limitations of our brain and sensory capabilities to compare, contrast, and organize the immense variety of sensory experiences, we cannot take all features into account. Instead we must concentrate on those features yielding a consistent, understandable picture. As a consequence, the formation of language, as well as any other form of mental map-making, always involves abstraction. We are separating our conception from the real thing, and removing as much as seems possible in the process.

Consider, for instance, the very beginning of language, creating symbols—what we call words— to represent categories or classes of perceived objects. The word *chair*,

A mathematical statement or expression:

$$d = \tfrac{1}{2}\, a\, t^{2}$$

description: this statement connects the rate that an object accelerates (**a**) with two other variables:
   t = the time the object has accelerated
   d = the distance the object has traveled

A trustworthy rate:

acceleration due to the pull of gravity = 9.8 m/s^{2}, where:
   m = meters
   s = seconds

Combining the mathematical expression with the known rate can be used to make accurate predictions:

Example 1: How far will a rock dropped from 100 m above the ground have traveled after 3 seconds?

$$d = \tfrac{1}{2}\, a\, t^{2}$$

$$d = \tfrac{1}{2}\, (9.8 \text{ m/s}^{2})\, (3 \text{ s})^{2}$$

$$d = 41.1 \text{ m}$$

Example 2: How long will it take for a rock dropped from 2 meters to hit the ground?

$$d = \tfrac{1}{2}\, a\, t^{2}$$

can be algebraically arranged to:

$$t = \sqrt{\frac{2\,d}{a}}$$

$$t = \sqrt{\frac{2\,(2 \text{ m})}{(9.8 \text{ m/s}^{2})}}$$

$$t = 0.64 \text{ s}$$

Figure 1-4. Two examples of how the combination of the language of mathematics and a known rate can be used to make predictions.

for instance, is an abstract symbol used to designate a class of similar-shaped objects that we sit on. Its abstract nature is first made evident by the fact that you cannot sit on the word *chair*; you can only sit on those objects that we call chairs. Plus, the word *chair* screens off much of reality because all the things that you or I call chairs are similar, but they are not identical. Which raises a question: Why don't we have a unique word for every different shape and color of things that we make to sit on? Why shouldn't our language include new symbols for every nuance of variation? The practical answer is that it seems too cumbersome. There would be just too many words to try to master. Furthermore, such detail is often not needed to convey the important points. When the word chair (or some other general term) is used in a sentence, what color it is, what materials it is made out of, or some other detail may be irrelevant to the main idea trying to be conveyed. So there is no need to add more clutter. Once recognizing this, it makes sense that the more relevant an aspect of Nature is to one's livelihood, the more sophisticated the language designed to describe it will become. Less can be left out without significantly impairing the message. Eskimos, for example, have more words for snow than we do, and each profession has its own associated jargon.

Recognizing Limits

I suspect that most of us do not pay as much attention to warning labels as might be warranted. But nonetheless I finish this chapter with a warning: One should always be cautious about any rational conclusion that one draws about the workings of Nature. The process of simplifying Nature to the point of being understandable comes with no guarantee of accuracy—that is, our maps will not always be accurate guides. Important things may be left out, as it may be difficult if not impossible to screen off only irrelevant features. Plus, parts of our map could be just plain wrong. For example, connections may be present that either do not exist in Nature or connect the wrong things together.

I take this warning seriously. Only through understanding the limitations associated with rational thought can we attempt to embrace its strengths while avoiding its pitfalls. So next I further discuss where some problems can arise.

Nature to perception

We can perceive only a small portion of Nature's rich, diverse, and mysterious "reality." Such limited access occurs in part because we are constantly being provided with too much information. All our different senses are constantly, hence simultaneously, engaged. Yet our conscious brain can pay attention to at most a few sensations at a time. Most sensory input is thus constantly being filtered out. More important, however, is the fact that much of Nature cannot even be detected by our senses. Human senses operate within a very limited range, so any phenomenon that occurs on too small or too large a spatial scale, or on too short or too long a temporal scale, will be imperceptible.

Of course, the impetus for human technology typically centers on getting around limits to human function, and the case of sensory limits is no exception. Instruments such as microscopes allow us to see even smaller things, and telescopes make it possible to see things even further away. And science has taken full advantage of such technology. The underlying theme of basically every instrument found in scientific laboratories is that they in some way, shape, or form increase our range of perception. Recognize, however, that technology will never allow us to escape limits to perception; it will only change what constitutes "too large" or "too small."

The perceptions of scientists are also constrained by the fact that only measurable aspects of perceivable phenomenon are open to study. Thus, the scientific method cannot be used to meaningfully address whether a poem is good, whether a landscape is beautiful, or any other question where the relevant observations cannot be accurately measured. Qualities such as goodness and beauty have a subjective component, and unbiased measurements cannot be made when the observer makes a difference. The question of how far science can delve into the observable world boils down to the question: What portion of our observable world is subjective? This is an interesting question.

Perception to mental conception: Mental processing

Mental conception further filters reality. Mental conception is the process of interpreting one's perceptions in terms of one's current map of Nature. Cognitive psychologists suggest that we have the greatest tendency to take notice of those things that reinforce our preexisting conceptual patterns and to ignore perceptions that do not. In other words, we tend to screen off perceptions that would require us to modify our current map. Perhaps this is why indoctrinating someone in a certain way of thinking, especially at an early age, is often successful.

As an educator, this tendency to resist modifying our map concerns me. One of the goals of education is to generate the best working map possible, which may at times require some major revisions. So I often wonder how do we motivate ourselves to continually fight against this tendency to become intellectually stagnate?

Mental conceptions back to perceptions: Communication

Through its connection to language, rational knowledge is teachable. I can tell you about an experience that you have not shared. And in the process, you may incorporate that experience into your map. This raises an important question: Are we taking advantage of the experience of others, or are we being deluded by the experience of others? Two reasons to worry:

First, the speaker may convey an inaccurate reflection of Nature. They may be wrong because of ignorance, or the speaker may deliberately choose not to communicate clearly. As George Orwell once put it: "The great enemy of clear language is insincerity." Why would anyone want to deceive someone else? The most likely reason is to manipulate them. I imagine that you could think of a few cases where you attempted deception through muddled clarity.

Second, whatever is said is always reinterpreted by the listener (in context of the listener's current map of Nature). Reinterpretation opens the door for a striking difference to exist between the intended communication and the actual communication. I know from many years of teaching that how students interpret what I say is often far from my intent.

This problem is accentuated by the fact that we are comfortable with nonliteral interpretation based on shared experience. For instance, if I said to you: "He flew after the bus," you would not think that someone actually flew. Nor did I think that I saw someone fly. You and I both know from experience that people cannot fly. Instead, your mind converts this expression into the image of someone running to try to catch a bus before it leaves, which is what I was attempting to communicate. Problems arise, however, whenever nonliteral expressions are not based on a foundation of shared experience. Here the listener may interpret things literally, even though that was not the speaker's intention.

Some additional problems with rational thought

So far I have made mention of three general forms of problems linked with rational thought: incompleteness of our perceptions, our tendency to be indoctrinated into one worldview, and problems associated with learning via language. Here I want to add three more to the list:

• A tendency to believe in logical extensions in both spatial and temporal scales. Consider for instance the process of multiplication. If I asked you: What is three times two? I'd guess that you would answer six. What if I asked you to prove that six, and not five or seven, was the correct answer. Could you do it? Here is how I would answer the proof question. Multiplication is, in essence, combining a certain number of sets of a certain size. For instance, three times two is combining two sets of three objects each. So I would get two sets of three objects, say oranges, and combine them. Next I would follow the rules of counting to come up with a total. There will be six oranges. Similarly, I could prove that 10 x 10 = 100. But what if I was asked to prove that 10,000 x 10,000 = 100,000,000. Could I do it? The answer is no. I would die before I could create and then count 10,000 sets of 10,000. Yet I do not, and I suspect that you do not, doubt that 10,000 x 10,000 = 100,000,000. Why? Because we believe that the rules of multiplication can be logically extended to numbers beyond those that we can experience. Why do we believe that? Because we believe that multiplication meets the basic rule for logical extension: That found within the range of experience will stay the same beyond that range. In other words, those factors that result in a trend will not change nor will any new factors be added beyond the range of experience.

The problem with logical extensions is that in many cases it is dubious at best to think that some important factor will not change outside the range of experience. If we are susceptible to believing in logical extensions, then we are susceptible to being deluded. I have often heard the argument, for instance, that maintaining the current American lifestyle into the future depends on continuing past trends of economic growth. This is a clear case of logical extension. But is it true? You should hope for you and your descendants that it is not because in a finite world—like the one we live in—continual expansion of scale is impossible.

• We tend to focus on the most immediate and direct effects in attempts to ascertain causation. In other words, causal factors less immediate and more indirect tend to be screened off. Consider, for instance, the following scenario: Two children are playing catch when a somewhat errant throw sends the ball crashing through a house's window. Immediately afterward the homeowner comes running out of the house to inform the children, in not the kindest of ways, that they should have played catch elsewhere. And the homeowner makes sense. If they had played elsewhere, the window would not have been in the path of the errant throw. One of the children, however, had a different view. He calmly told the homeowner, "It is not our fault, it is yours. You should have built your home in a different place." And the child's argument is also valid; the same errant throw would not have intersected the window if the house had been built elsewhere. The question, however, is: Which person would you side with?

People to whom I have posed this scenario seem most inclined to side with the homeowner. Their reasoning is that the decision on where to build the home was made before the decision on where to play catch. In other words, the house was already present before the children began to play catch nearby. It was thus the children's responsibility "to be responsible." Consider, however, a similar scenario: A river fueled by recent heavy rains swells beyond it banks, subsequently flooding many of the surrounding homes. We could conclude that the heavy rains caused the houses to be flooded. The heavy rains were the most recent difference that made a difference. However, building houses in the river's flood plain was what made them vulnerable to flooding in the first place. So should the heavy rains, just because they were the most recent, be given the full weight of responsibility? Hopefully the obvious answer is no. Maybe the child had a point after all.

• We tend to avoid paradoxes. Paradoxes arise whenever two or more connected things make perfect sense in isolation, but either contradict, or in some other way seem nonsensical, when viewed together. Here is a simple example of a paradox:

The below statement is true.
The above statement is false.

Each statement is potentially valid, yet the combination creates an irresolvable loop. (If the above statement is false, then it is not true that the below statement is true, which means that the above statement is true, which leads us back to the above statement being false, and so on.) Similarly many M. C. Escher paintings capture paradoxes in that he arranges pieces of the world in ways that contradict the common conception of how the world works.

So why wouldn't it make sense to avoid paradoxical observations? To do so would be to avoid things that do not make sense, and doing that makes sense, doesn't it? I suggest that in certain ways it does not. I, however, will wait to discuss the crux of my argument for not avoiding paradoxes until the end of Chapter 5, where it can be placed in a biological context.

The asymmetry between power and vision

Rational thought's bottom line is that it has extended our means to manipulate the world around us. Through rational thinking, we have increased our power. In fact, we now have the power to destroy the world as we know it. This power increase, however, comes with a trade-off—the associated screening off tends to make us both shortsighted and short-termed in our perspective. I tend to think of the loss of fa-reaching vision as a loss of wisdom because wise decisions depend on taking as much as possible into account. This leaves us with an important question: Is it possible to use power wisely?

An ecological perspective of rationality attempts to better balance this trade-off between power and wisdom. It is the recognition that a complex world cannot be summarized too simply. In other words, an ecological perspective takes the afore-mentioned limitations of rationality seriously.

Confronting the rational program: Zen Buddhism

Zen takes an ecological perspective of rationality to its extreme. It says that true understanding can only occur if one does not screen off at all. Or put in more Zenlike terms: The world cannot be meaningfully divided into parts, for in doing so one is deluded and therefore misses enlightenment. An enlightened state is where the borders between oneself and the rest of the universe dissolve. In other words, enlightenment is transcending dualism— the perceptual and corresponding conceptual division of the world into categories. What is wrong with dualism? When you perceive or conceive of an object, you draw a line around it, separating it from the rest of the world. That is, you artificially divide the world into parts. Doing so precludes you from seeing the world as it is.

Correspondingly, a Zen understanding is not teachable because whatever one understands cannot be put into words and communicated. What is wrong with words? Each word represents a conceptual category, and therefore words are inherently dualistic. Thus, although words can lead you to see some truth, they do so at the expense of missing so much else.

This is not a Zen biology book. We will take a rational approach to the study of life. But this does not mean a Zen perspective should be completely discounted. There is at least one obvious and important Zen aspect to Life. Life, as we shall see, can be viewed as occurring across a hierarchy of levels. From a rational perspective we can consider only one level at a time. Yet if we actually isolate any one level, the Life within it disappears. For example, if we separate you from the rest of the living world by putting you in a plastic container, you will soon die. Similarly, if any organ is removed from the context of being a part of a body, the organ will quickly cease to function. Life, whatever it is, is the culmination of all these different levels of organization operating simultaneously.

I personally use a Zen perspective as a constant reminder that there is always much more to what I think I rationally understand.

Some key terms:

science - the search for consistent patterns in the workings of Nature. (Modern science requires those searching for patterns to use a systematic means called the scientific method.)

fact - a measured property of the surrounding world (e.g., the weight of an object). Or put in the perspective of the observer, a measured observation.

data - a set of facts.

hypothesis - an educated guess about the existence of some type of pattern in Nature.

law - a regular pattern of occurrence in Nature (e.g., the universal law of gravitation).

theory - a general idea that aids in conceptually unifying, hence explaining, many and diverse phenomena of Nature.

rational thought - the system by which we construct and use mental patterns that seem consistent with our pattern-seeking conversation with Nature.

Some study questions:

1. *What are the two basic ways that we establish whether a suspected pattern in Nature is trustworthy?* Why do we try to uncover patterns in Nature in the first place? What are two fundamental questions in terms of searching for patterns?

2. Provide a general explanation of how the scientific method is used to test a suspected pattern. *Be able to evaluate an experimental setup in terms of whether it follows the guidelines set by the scientific method.* Explain the difference between something being the cause of an outcome and something being a causal factor in an outcome.

3. Modern science attempts to be an "objective" way of knowing. Why is this important? *What is one way that the scientific method attempts to do this?*

4. Is our understanding of patterns (i.e., rational knowledge) a completely accurate depiction of Nature? Explain. In what ways does the scientific method limits the types of phenomenon that scientists can study?

The Physics of Change and Arrangement

You may find it curious that I begin a discussion of Life by discussing physics. But the two striking features of living organisms are their ongoing activity and their complex arrangement. Just think of yourself. Everything you have done, everything you are doing right now, and everything you might do in the future involves change. And whether you realize it or not, your most striking accomplishment to date is developing, from simpler beginnings, this intricately complex arrangement called your body. Furthermore, ongoing change and formation of complex arrangements are not unique to humans; they are found in all Life forms. So, to think more clearly about Life, we must first be able to think clearly about change and arrangement—something physicists have been trying to do for a long time. The physical patterns we uncover here form a backdrop for all further discussion.

Bouncing Balls and the Changing Arrangement of Motion

Here is a common everyday observation: A bouncing ball will not bounce forever. Even so-called superballs are no exception. They take a little longer to settle down, but still the height of each bounce falls short of the one before, and the ball's motion eventually disappears as it settles to the ground (see Figure 2-1). Here, in the first part of this chapter, I explore why a ball cannot hold on to its motion and become, in essence, a perpetual motion machine. In other words, I consider the question: Why does the arrangement of motion change across time? The goal in exploring a familiar observation is to develop ideas that we will later apply to much less familiar circumstances within the working of Life. Our brains seem to like it when we go one step at a time.

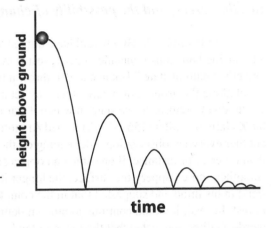

Figure 2-1. This graph of a bouncing ball shows that both the maximum height and the time interval between each successful bounce decreases until the ball stops bouncing altogether.

Refining the question

Envision someone standing on a concrete floor holding a tennis ball in his or her hand. Via gravity, this mysterious but trustworthy pattern mentioned in the previous chapter, the considerably bigger ball that the person is standing on—called earth—is pulling on the tennis ball. The tennis ball is also pulling back, although due to the infinitesimally smaller mass, the strength of the pull is infinitesimally smaller. So when the tennis ball is let go, allowing these two balls to move toward each other, for all practical purposes it is the tennis ball that does all the moving. We perceive it as the ball falling to earth. It continues to fall, accelerating all the way, until it collides with the concrete floor below. However, due to its compliant and elastic nature, the tennis ball then rebounds from the collision. The compliance is that the upward push of the rigid concrete floor on the ball stretches or deforms it into a more flattened shape. The ball's elastic nature then acts to pull the ball back into its original round shape and in the process creates the push (against the floor) that lifts it back into the air. It has retained motion, although it is now traveling in the opposite direction (see Figure 2-2). Of course, the relentless pull of gravity continually reins in the upward moving ball until it decelerates to the point that it stops. Here, with nothing to hold it in place, the constant gravitational pull reverses the ball's direction, and it once again begins to fall toward earth. Or to think about it in another way, a bouncing ball (or any other bouncing object) uses its elasticity to reset its falling to earth. The force in the spring back comes from the motion that it gathered falling to earth the last time, which then sends it back to a height from which it can fall again.

However you look at it, the question of why a ball cannot bounce forever is thus a question of why this oscillating cycle created by an elastic push upward and the constant pull of gravity downward cannot settle into a perpetual arrangement of motion. In other words, what else interferes that causes this oscillating movement to continually dwindle into no movement at all?

I start by fleshing out some basic ideas on the ways and means of motion and develop some terminology along the way. In the process, we will slowly develop the conceptual tools needed to answer the bouncing ball question, along with understanding any other related issue.

Inertia, forces, and the possibility of change

Aristotle (384–322 BC) would have argued that a bouncing ball stops bouncing because rest is every object's "'natural state." Bounce a ball, throw a ball, roll

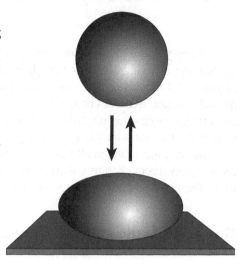

Figure 2-2. The two forces involved in the oscillatory movement of a bouncing ball.

a ball along the ground, or in any other way set a ball (or any other object) into motion, and eventually it always returns to the state in which it started—that is, it comes back to rest. Nearly 2,000 years later, Galileo Galilei (1564–1642) turned Aristotle's idea on its head. He realized the significance of another everyday observation—depending on the circumstance, some objects come to rest sooner than others. For instance, if one starts an object sliding across a surface with the same size push, the smoother, more slippery the surface, the longer it takes for the object to stop. He then extended this trend in his mind and suggested that in the complete absence of friction, an object would never slow to rest. Instead, it would continue to move indefinitely in a straight line at the same speed. In other words, Galileo suggested that the inherent tendency of any object is to maintain its current velocity. If an object is at rest (velocity equals zero), its tendency is to stay at rest, and if an object is moving, its tendency is to continue to do so. Physicists today continue to think that Galileo got it right and refer to the tendency of objects to retain their velocity as **inertia**.

Thus from Galileo's perspective, change, such as a ball slowing down, was not an internal or natural property of the object, but a result of outside interference. Stated differently, change happens—that is, inertia is interrupted—only when a force, such as friction, intervenes. In general, a **force** is any kind of push or pull experienced by an object.

Issac Newton (1642–1727) coined Galileo's insight as the first of his three laws of motion, which is sometimes also called the law of inertia. In Newton's words: *Every body continues in its state of rest or of uniform speed in a straight line unless it is compelled to change that state by forces acting on it.* In essence, this law states that what *is* will continue to *be* unless some force intervenes.

Newton's other two laws of motion further clarify the concept of force. For instance, his second law is a rather obvious extension of his first. If velocity stays the same in the absence of a force, then the effect of a force is to change velocity or accelerate an object in the direction of the force. This could involve the acceleration of an object at rest or along the direction that it was already moving, the deceleration of an object—which is simply the acceleration of an object in the opposite direction of its current movement—or the acceleration of an object in some other direction due to a force applied at an angle other than its previous path of movement. In the latter, the object turns to a new path of motion. (Note: His second law also incorporates that the effect of any force, that is how much it will accelerate any object, is also influenced by the object's mass. Specifically, more massive objects are harder to accelerate than smaller ones. Stated mathematically, this statement becomes the amount of acceleration (*a*) is equal to the force (*F*) divided by the object's mass (*m*). Rearrange this and it becomes the familiar equation *F = ma*.)

Newton's third law makes it explicit that forces are both external and interactional. Although an object can never apply a force on itself (e.g., a ball cannot throw itself), it can only apply a force on another object, and in the process the other object applies a force back. Furthermore, force-applying interactions are always symmetric. Or as stated by Newton: *Whenever one object exerts a force on a second object, the second exerts an equal and opposite force on the first.* The reciprocal nature of this interaction is the source of the common phrase, "for every action there is an equal and opposite reaction."

A taxonomy of forces

A bat colliding with a ball is a good example to use when we think how forces are generated. **Contact forces** happen whenever the paths of two (or more) objects moving at different velocities intersect. During the duration of the contact the two objects exert equal but opposite forces on each other.

Although not as obvious as bats and balls colliding, pressure (such as air pressure) is also a contact force. It is the collective force generated by the constant collisions between some surface and the randomly moving molecules making up a surrounding medium. Although we can measure and personally experience pressure generated by such mediums as air or water, we cannot see the individual collisions behind it because molecules are so small.

More puzzling than contact forces are **field forces**. Two striking features underscore their peculiar nature.

• First, field forces can be applied at a distance—that is, objects interact in force-generating ways even when they are not in direct contact with each other. Gravity is the classic example. As mentioned in Chapter 1, the earth pulling on objects not in direct contact with it (and the objects pulling back) is part of our everyday experience. But think about how curious gravity is, two objects pulling on each other without any strings attached. The only thing I find intuitive about field forces is that the strength of the force diminishes as the distance separating interacting objects increases.

• Second, the strength of the force that one object applies on the other object does not weaken over time. In other words, *field forces never tire*. (And be glad that they do not. Just imagine if the gravitational attraction that holds you to earth at some point got tired and let go.) As long as two objects remain a set distance apart, the strength with which these two objects push or pull on each other through a field force interaction remains constant across time. In contrast, when we push or pull on something, we tire because the fuels our muscles need to generate force are being used up. Energy demand eventually exceeds energy supply, and the force weakens. This suggests that the tireless nature of field force interactions is due to their ability to generate force without ever using anything up. Stated differently, there is a conservation of force because there is a conservation of all needed to generate the force. I have no idea how this occurs.

Physicists invented the concept of "fields" to talk about these tireless interactions at a distance. Fields are not matter, but rather something that surrounds objects that interact. The result is the application of forces on each object whose fields are interacting. Physicists now believe that the basis of field interactions is an exchange of some form of particles between objects.

There are four types of field forces currently recognized: **gravitational**, **electromagnetic**, **strong nuclear**, and **weak nuclear**. In the topics that we discuss, we will only use the first two, so I briefly describe only those. With gravity, the interaction between objects is somehow based on each object's mass, and the resultant forces are attractive. Alternatively, electromagnetic interactions are based on charge with interactions among like charges being repulsive, and interaction among opposite charges being attractive. In some ways, electromagnetic interactions are even more curious than gravity. Mass at least I can see. But what exactly is charge? For example, what does it means to say that an electron has a negative charge and a proton has a positive charge? With charge, that generating a field appears as invisible as the field that it generates.

An aside: Although four types of field forces are recognized, many physicists suggest that these four are merely special cases of a single, more general form of interaction. The idea is striking because if correct it means that a single form of interaction unifies the universe and all its workings. Pursuit of this unified theory is a major goal of today's physicists.

Energy is another way to talk about forces and inertia

Instead of forces and inertia, energy is commonly used as the mental construct to talk about the motion of an object. More specifically, the concept of energy is separated into two basic forms:

• **Kinetic energy** (KE)—the energy associated with the current velocity of an object of a certain mass. Kinetic energy increases whenever the velocity of an object of a given mass goes up, the mass of an object of a given velocity goes up, or some overall increasing combination of both. Note that the concept of inertia can now be restated as the tendency for objects to retain their kinetic energy.

• **Potential energy** (PE)—the energy associated with the potential of an object to increase its velocity, or accelerate, in the future. Because acceleration requires a force, an object has PE whenever a force is being applied. It may not, however, be accelerating at the moment. Its velocity will remain constant so long as an equal but opposite force is also being applied on the object. A book held stationary in your hand is such an example. The gravitational attraction between the book and the earth is counterbalanced by the upward lift of your arm muscles. Remove, or just lessen, either of these two forces, and acceleration begins. The presence of imbalanced forces establishes the potential for the object to accelerate in the direction in which the force is strongest.

Change always involves the transformation of energy

Energy is transformed whenever PE is converted into KE, or vice versa. The transformation of PE to KE is simply the acceleration of an object in a certain direction due to a force acting on it. On the other hand, transforming KE into PE occurs whenever the directional movement of one object somehow generates a force in the same direction on another object (see Figure 2-3). The most easily envisioned scenario is one object colliding into another object and thereby pushing it in the same direction. Connected by a field force, a moving object can also pull or push another object in the same direction. For instance, any ball headed skyward is pulling at the earth to move along with it. But as mentioned earlier, due to the huge difference in mass, the equal and opposite pull of the earth on the ball has a much more noticeable effect—continually decelerating the ball until it finally stops and then begins to accelerate in the opposite direction.

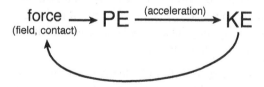

Figure 2-3. Potential energy (PE) is transformed into kinetic energy (KE) as an object accelerates due to the application of a force, whereas KE is transformed to PE whenever a moving object introduces a force on another object.

Later I consider the nature of these transformations solely in terms of one object colliding into another. Realize that when we speak of an object's velocity being positive, then anything moving in the opposite direction has a negative velocity. The choice of which direction to call positive is arbitrary.

Two objects can collide if and only if they are moving at different velocities because otherwise one could not catch up with the other. Consider the direction of the faster object to be the positive direction. On contact, the faster object exerts a positive force on the slower object. The application of this force increases the slower object's PE, which is then transformed into KE as the slower object accelerates in the positive direction (until all the PE is transformed into KE). Conversely (by Newton's third law), the slower object exerts an equal and opposite force on the faster object, which increases the faster object's PE in the opposite direction. The transformation of this opposite or negative PE into KE occurs for as long as the faster-moving object **decelerates**. In sum, *the collision between two objects always results in the faster object moving slower and the slower object moving faster.*

The significant pattern underlying these reciprocal transformations is that, in total, they all balance out. None of the energy around prior to the collision is lost. All the KE either stays as KE or is transformed to PE. Similarly, all the PE either stays as PE or is converted to KE. In fact, this pattern of energy transformation without energy loss is thought to be such a universal pattern that it gained the status of being a law. The **first law of thermodynamics** states that energy can neither be created nor destroyed only transformed from one type of energy to another.

Usable versus unusable energy

Perhaps you have heard the comment that we—as a human society—are running out of energy. What does that mean? We all know that our cars use gasoline. Similarly, our bodies continually require inputs of fuels. But how can one reconcile these observations with the first law of thermodynamics? One cannot run out of something that cannot be destroyed. Are all the reports of future energy shortage wrong? Or more generally, is it impossible to ever run out of energy to use? The answer to both questions is no.

The problem is that the first law of thermodynamics does not distinguish between **usable energy** and **unusable energy**, but we must. Although energy is present whenever matter is in motion, not all patterns of motion are usable.

I just made a leap that I need to back up and discuss. So far motion has been discussed in terms of the movement of a single object, or one object colliding into another. But in the last paragraph I mentioned that not all patterns of motion are usable. The idea of different patterns of motion is, however, hard to reconcile with a single object because a single object can move in at most one direction at a time. In contrast, the pattern of motion among a group of simultaneously moving objects can range from completely random to completely directional motion (see Figure 2-4). Completely random motion is the absence of any directional bias—that is, at any given time the probability of finding an ob-

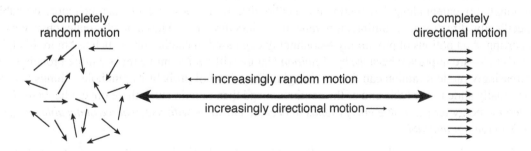

Figure 2-4. The pattern of motion continuum.

ject moving in any one direction is the same as any other direction. Completely directional motion is reached when all objects are moving in the same direction. As one moves from completely random to completely directional, the continuum in between is filled in by an increasing tendency for objects to be moving in some directions over others.

An aside: A single moving object continuously bouncing off other objects in its surroundings can be characterized along a continuum of movement patterns *across time*. If each new postcollision direction is no more likely than any other possible direction, then the object is moving randomly around its environment—sometimes referred to as a "random walk." On the other hand, the degree to which some postcollision directions are more likely than others is the degree to which the pattern is increasingly directional.

Where does the distinction between usable and unusable energy fit into this continuum? As I have asked this question to students over the years, their intuition commonly leads them to the correct answer: Directional motion is usable, and random motion is not. But why is this correct? Just think about the expression "*to make use of.*" To make use of something is to use it to do something, which is to change something. Recall that to a physicist change is acceleration, so a pattern of motion is usable only if it can accelerate something else. For instance, place any object amid complete random motion, and what happens? In essence, nothing. Collisions occur, but because randomly moving bodies tend to move equally in all directions, they tend to apply forces equally from all directions. In total, the object may be jostled around a bit, but it is not consistently accelerated in any one direction (see Figure 2-5). Random motion is thus unusable. In contrast, any degree of directional movement (from not quite random to completely directional) is usable because the potential forces generated are not equal in all directions. Place any object in the path of directionally moving bodies, and the collisions will accelerate the object in the same direction (see Figure 2-6).

Figure 2-5. An object placed in a field of random motion.

Figure 2-6. An object placed in a field of directional motion.

Why does usable energy tend to become unusable with use?

This distinction between usable and unusable energy sets us up to discuss one of the more important patterns found in Nature. As objects in motion collide into other objects, patterns of motion can change up and down this continuum. That is, more random (or less usable) patterns can become more directional (or more usable), or vice versa. But there is a striking asymmetry in the relationship. Although movement along this continuum in either direction is possible, one is much more probable. Specifically, directional becoming more random (or less directional) has a much greater chance of occurring. And notions of probability—commonly expressed in catchphrases such as "more likely" or "tends to"—are important because by *definition* Nature will *tend to* move toward more probable states. Increasingly random motion can thus be thought of as a kind of probability sinkhole—things *tend to* continually slide toward this end of the continuum and then remain stuck there once it happens. Or stated in energy terms, *usable energy tends to become unusable with use, whereas unusable energy tends to remain unusable.*

It is one thing to state that one type of event is more probable than another and quite another to understand why it is so. Here we work on the latter. The task is to explain why directional motion (or net directional motion) tends to become increasingly random as it collides into, and hence direction-ally accelerates, other objects.

Maintaining the direction of movement across collisions could proceed forever. Each object propelled by a collision need only be sent off in the same direction that the object colliding into it was moving. The newly accelerating object could then, in turn, apply the same directional force on some-thing else, starting the cycle anew. For example, envision an infinite number of balls arranged in a per-fect line. Once set into motion, the first ball collides with the second ball, which then hits the third ball, and so on—a perpetual cycle of collisions rolling endlessly across the universe (see Figure 2-7).

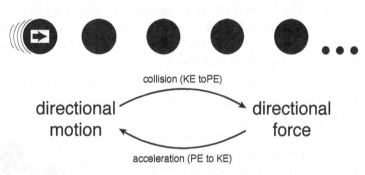

Figure 2-7. Once the first ball (in and endless line of balls) is set into motion, directional motion could be maintained across collisions by the cycle shown.

Probability does, however, complicate the seeming ease of this scenario. Each ball could strike the next ball in a variety of ways. Yet among these many potential contact points, only one will conserve the same direction of motion—the type of collision that is commonly referred to as a "square hit". (Perhaps you have observed in a game of pool that when one ball collides right into the center of another ball, the first ball stops and the second ball takes off in the same direction. In contrast, if the two balls collide at any of the other possible angles, the first ball careens off the other ball, and a single direction of motion splits into two.) In other words, when it comes to conserving the direction of motion across collisions, there is only one way to get it "right," but many ways to get it "wrong" (see Figure 2-8(a)). One out of a lot of possibilities is by definition an improbable event. Ex-pressed as a fraction or proportion, the probability is one (the one way to get it right) over all the nu-merous possible angles of collision. One over a very large number is a very small number (see Figure 2-8(b)). (Playing pool can quickly reinforce the underlying probability issue, as one finds that square hits are difficult to achieve, even when aiming.) This leads us back to why it would be difficult for a direction to be maintained across many colli-sions. An endless line of balls will maintain the same direction only if each collision is a square hit. One even slight miss, and the chain will be interrupted as balls stray off in more than one direction (hence increas-ing the overall randomness of motion). Plus the unlikely event of a square hit to occur again and again is even more unlikely. (Note: The probability of more than one independent event having the same outcome can be calculated by multiplying

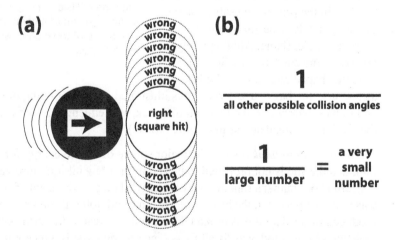

Figure 2-8. (a) Of all the angles that one ball could collide into another, only one—a perfectly head on collision known as a square hit—will maintain direction. In other words, when it comes to conserving direc-tion across a collision there is only one way to get it 'right', and enumer-ous ways to get it 'wrong'. (b) The general method of calculating the probability of a square hit.

the probabilities of each event together, and whenever fractions less than one are multiplied the result is even smaller.) All of which leads to a simple conclusion: Although maintaining a constant direction across many collisions is possible, it is extremely improbable.

Although the preceding scenario involves an endless line of balls colliding into each other, the same logic applies to a group of objects all moving in the same direction colliding into another group of objects. The direction will be conserved only if each object in the first group collides squarely with an object in the second group. Due to the more ways of getting it wrong than right logic developed earlier, the probability of *one* collision being a square hit is very low, and probability of *all* the collisions being square hits is even lower.

Considering groups of objects colliding into each other also raises another issue missing in the endless line of balls. Once objects within the two groups become too packed together, all sorts of angled collisions become unavoidable. Envision, for instance, a tightly packed cluster of balls all moving in the same direction colliding into a second cluster (see Figure 2-9(a)). Due to the arrangement, at least some balls in the first group cannot be lined up to collide squarely with the second group of balls without one or more other balls being in the way. As a consequence, collisions will occur at various angles causing balls, as they careen off each other, to accelerate in many new directions. These balls may in turn collide with other balls in the cluster, which, except in the unlikely case of a square hit, will send balls off in other (and most likely new) directions. In other words, each new collision tends to further scatter the initial single direction of motion into increasingly random motion (see Figure 2-9(b)). In the process, a usable source of energy tends to become increasingly unusable. (Note: Although only one ball—the cue ball—collides into a triangle-shaped cluster of 15 balls known

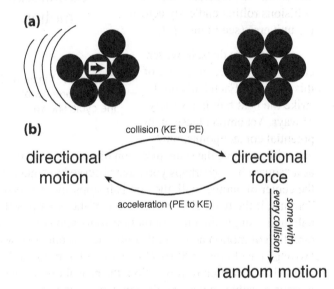

Figure 2-9. (a) A tightly packed cluster of balls heading toward a collision with another tightly packed cluster of balls (b) After the collision, the second cluster may retain some of the same direction of motion, but due to impossibility of all square hits, some of the motion will also be scattered. (See text for more details.)

as the rack, the basic idea described is illustrated at the beginning of every pool game. Even if the cue ball rams squarely into the first ball of a rack, subsequent collisions will occur at new angles, causing the motion to spread across many directions.)

Something to think about: The major source of usable energy for Life on earth is solar radiation, and the sun is not projected to burn out for a few billion more years. So why is there increasing concern about humans running out of energy? The concern stems from two historical twists. The first was a unique period in the history of life—around 300 million years ago—when plant material was produced faster than it was broken down, and as a result the earth accumulated a *finite* layer of fatlike molecules known today as fossil fuels. The second twist is a recent upsurge in technological devices that run either directly (e.g., cars using gasoline) or indirectly (e.g., a microwave using electricity generated by a coal-burning power plant) on fossil fuels. So now the lifestyle of many seems hooked to the continued use of fossil fuels, yet due to their finite nature the supply of fossil fuels cannot last forever. Evidence suggests that some forms of fossil fuel shortages may begin to show up in the next 50 to 100 years or even sooner.

Why does unusable energy tend to remain unusable?

Just to be complete, I need to spend some time explaining why once energy becomes unusable it tends to remain unusable. Of course, there is nothing really new in the explanation, as the distinction between what is possible versus what is more probable remains the underlying theme. In fact, the only difference is that the focus shifts from unlikeliness of square hits to the unlikeliness of a collision at any specific angle.

To start, consider the following scenario. Six objects moving in different directions are all headed on a collision course with one of the other objects. In other words, six objects moving in six different directions are all about to engage in three separate collisions. After the first collision, the two objects bounce away in two new directions of motion. The second collision also results in the two objects bouncing away in the same two directions as the objects from the first collision. And the same is true for the third collision. In total, six directions of motion have been reduced to two, and in the process the energy within this motion has become increasingly usable (see Figure 2-10).

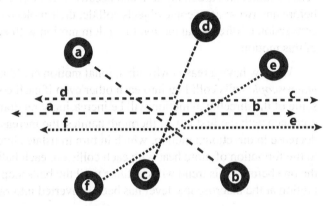

Figure 2-10. A scenario in which the energy contained within the motion of six balls becomes more usable. Each ball collides with one other at just the right angle that all pairs bounce off each other in the same direction of motion. Six directions of motion are thus changed to only two.

Is this scenario possible? Absolutely! It is just not very probable. The number of possible angles in which any two objects moving from two different directions can collide into each other is huge—ranging from the glancing blows to various degrees of much more blunt contact. Yet, there will only be one collision angle that will send any two objects off along two specific directions. In other words, the logic is the same as with a series of square hits—there is a lot more ways to get it wrong than to get it right. As a consequence, the probability of the second collision sending objects off along the same two directions as the first collision is one over a very large number. The same would be true for the third collision. Furthermore, multiplying these two probabilities together would calculate the probability that both the second and third collisions would send objects off in the same direction as the first collision—which is an even much smaller number. Add even more objects, hence more collisions to the mix, and the probability continues to become progressively smaller. So although it is possible for motion to become increasing directional among a group of randomly moving objects bouncing off each other, probability suggests that it won't occur very often or for very long. The unusable energy of random motion will thus tend to remain unusable.

Another twist

You and I live in a macroscopic world. Not only are we relatively huge, but even the smallest objects that we can see are relatively huge in the sense that they are composed of many minutely smaller objects called molecules. (Note: Molecules are made up of even smaller objects called atoms, which are composed of even smaller objects called protons, neutrons, and electrons, and what makes up these subatomic particles, as well as how they interact to form atoms, is not exactly clear.) This fact is significant given that what is perceived as a single object colliding into another object, such as a cue ball hitting one of the other pool balls, is actually a tightly packed cluster of molecules colliding into another tightly packed cluster of molecules. So even in the case of a square hit at the macroscopic level, the collisions at the molecular level will not all be square hits (due to the reasons described previously). As a consequence, some directional motion will be converted to increasingly random molecular motion during each collision. Random molecular motion is also known as **heat**. This means that in every macroscopic collision, the two objects become hotter. Heat's accomplice, **temperature**, is a measure of the average pace of random molecular motion.

An aside: We live in a **thermal world**, which is another way of saying that the temperature is above absolute zero (estimated to be –273 degrees centigrade). At any temperature above absolute zero all molecules are in motion, and because it is more probable, the motion tends to be random. So before any two macroscopic objects collide, their molecules are already randomly jostling about. The conversion of directional motion to random motion with each collision only quickens the average pace of this motion.

We now have a reason why directional motion could not be conserved across an endless line of *macroscopic* balls colliding into each other even if each collision was a square hit. In each collision, some of the directional motion will be increasingly randomized at the molecular level. So, in accordance with the first law of thermodynamics, the increase in random motion must be equaled by a decrease in directional motion, which in turn translates into a decrease in velocity. In other words, due to the formation of more heat with each collision, each ball in the line will not travel quite as fast as the one before. This trend will continue until the balls stop altogether—that is, when all the directional motion at the macroscopic level has been converted into random motion at the molecular level.

Another aside: Of course, unless the balls are moving through a vacuum, collisions will occur with more than the next ball in line. Any moving ball will be constantly running into surrounding air molecules as well as those molecules lining any surface that it is rolling along. Such collisions further contribute to the conversion of directional motion to heat, and thus cause the directional motion to dissipate even more quickly.

Thermal gradients are a source of usable energy

In many ways, this would be a good place to stop this discussion. The reasons that collisions carry the unavoidable consequence of increasingly randomizing directional motion have been covered. But stopping here may also leave a mistaken impression. Although heat can be thought of as unusable energy, a **thermal gradient**—a change in temperature across distance—puts the notion of usable energy back on the table. When an object is positioned within a thermal gradient, molecules on the higher temperature side will collide into the object with collectively greater force than molecules on the cooler side. As a consequence, the object will accelerate away from the higher temperature (see Figure 2-11). Internal combustion engines, such as those commonly found in cars, are an example of a heat engine. Gasoline (or some other fuel) is ignited in a chamber enclosed by a movable piston on one side and an unmovable cylinder on all the other sides. The resultant higher temperature on one side of the piston creates a thermal gradient that pushes the piston down the cylinder. Through a series of other connections the movement of this piston is then eventually transferred to the car's wheels, which as they spin push the car down the road.

Like directional motion, any thermal gradient will not last across collisions. Consider, for example, a

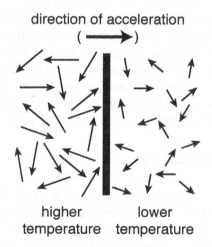

direction of acceleration
(——➤)

higher   lower
temperature   temperature

Figure 2-11. A graphic that shows why thermal gradients are a source of usable energy. The relatively faster-moving molecules on the left-hand side of the object will exert a higher pressure, causing the object to accelerate to the right.

thermal gradient created by lighting a match and holding it in the air while it burns—the air surrounding the burning match will become hotter than air further away. To make this example simpler to think about, suppose the burning match creates a distinct patch of air ten degrees warmer than its surroundings. Within this hotter patch of air, the randomly moving molecules are constantly colliding into each other, but such collisions do not change the temperature. When all colliding molecules are, on average, traveling at the same speed, collisions do not alter the collective pace. The situation is different at the borders of this hot patch. Molecules near the edge tend to be moving faster than those just beyond. As these molecules from each side begin to collide, the difference in pace begins to even out. Amid random collisions, faster-moving molecules begin to move slower, and slower-moving molecules begin to move faster. In the process, the cooler surroundings become warmer, and the hot patch becomes cooler. The trend continues until the thermal gradient disappears completely. Once reached, this temperature equilibrium does not reflect any loss in energy—that would violate the first law of thermodynamics—only a loss in usable energy.

Hotter spreading toward cooler is referred to as **conduction**. In the preceding example, heat is conducted through air. Heat spreading through a metal rod warmed at one end is another example. **Diffusion** is a more inclusive term. It refers to the redistribution of either velocity (discussed presently) or materials (discussed further in Chapter 12) from regions of high concentration to regions of lower concentration. Conduction is thus the diffusion of heat.

An aside: When sufficiently extreme, thermal gradients can result in a movement distinct from conduction called free convection. **Free convection** is a mass migration of molecules all moving in the same direction, powered by density differences within a fluid. Wind is a familiar example. Through differential heating by the sun, various places within the atmosphere come to have different densities. As warm, less-dense air masses rise, cooler denser air masses move in to replace them. Convection can also be seen readily in a heated pot of water. Water near the bottom becomes warmer than the water higher up. Once this gradient becomes sufficiently extreme, the warmer, less-dense water moves cohesively upward, and water molecules from the top fall down to fill the void. The water in the pot begins to roll—or as a physicist would say it, convection cells form. Watch for this the next time you boil a pot of water.

The second law of thermodynamics

Both the tendency for directional motion to become random and the tendency for thermal gradients to equilibrate are often said to occur spontaneously. The notion of spontaneous changes has two important and interconnected attributes.

First, spontaneous generally implies that something will "just happen." For example, directional motion changing to random motion is said to just happen because the conditions underlying this occurrence—that anything moving will eventually collide with something else, and once a collision occurs the probability of changing direction is much higher than maintaining a specific direction—are unavoidable. Similarly, disappearance of a thermal gradient just happens because randomly moving objects will always collide with other randomly moving objects at the edge of a thermal gradient.

Second, and perhaps more significant, *spontaneous changes are never spontaneously reversible*. In essence, this means that if probability favors something to move in one direction, then it cannot simultaneously favor it to move in the opposite direction. To consistently counter the tendency to move toward more probable states would thus require some additional form of intervention. For instance, randomly moving objects will not consistently change toward increasingly directional motion unless some means to steer randomly moving objects intervenes—such as you or I pushing randomly moving pool balls in a common direction. The same is true for disappearing thermal gradients. A hot spot spreading out until the pace of random molecular motion evens out is change toward a more probable state. As a consequence, one should never expect a room of equal temperature to spontaneously change to a room where one-half is warmer than the other (or to any other pattern of an unequal temperature distribution). Something more would need to intervene to sort the faster-moving molecules into one region of the room and the slower-moving molecules into a different region.

The **second law of thermodynamics** is the law embracing this asymmetric pattern. Specifically, it recognizes that change tends to proceed in a particular direction, and that direction is toward increasing randomness. And once you think about it, it is easy to understand why this pattern exists—increasing randomness is movement toward an increasingly probable state. Furthermore, the second law is the underlying foundation for many other more specifically stated patterns—such as the tendency for usable energy to become unusable with use, or the tendency for things to fall apart with time (a topic discussed further later).

To quickly glance at the second law's pervasiveness in the workings of Nature, try to imagine a world without it. A world where change in opposing directions would always be equally likely. Barns spontaneously arising from a pile of lumber would be as likely as barns spontaneously falling apart. Films played backward would portray reality as well as those that are run forward because of the absence of any consistent direction of change. Even the whole concept of time would lose any meaning because moment by moment getting younger would be as likely as getting older. And you can extrapolate further. The bottom line is that it would completely disrupt much of what you know and trust about the world.

Back to bouncing balls

Now it is time to return to our original question: Why can't balls bounce forever?

The general answer is that as a ball accelerates toward earth due to the pull of gravity, it will collide into other things (and other things will collide into it), and during the course of these collisions it is much more likely for the ball's directional motion to become increasingly random than vice versa.

But for clarity, let's look a little closer. As a released ball begins to accelerate toward earth due to the constant pull of gravity, it will be continually running into and accelerating air molecules along the way. As soon as these accelerated air molecules begin to collide with other air molecules (which in turn collide with other air molecules, and so on), the improbability of square hits quickly creates the tendency for the motion to become increasingly random. Of course, these air molecules were already moving randomly about prior to the collision (due to the temperature being above absolute zero), but collisions with the passing ball will up their average pace—that is, the column of air through which the ball just passed will be just a bit warmer than the surroundings. This newly formed thermal gradient will not last as the faster-moving molecules collide into slower-moving molecules along the ever-expanding edge. In other words, the energy transferred from the ball to the air tends to literally diffuse away and thus can never be transferred back to the ball. Due to the conservation of energy, this lost energy shows up as a reduced final velocity as the ball reaches the floor.

Once it hits the floor the remaining kinetic energy is converted into potential energy as the ball decelerates to zero. Some of this potential energy is stored in the elastic deformation of the ball's shape, but not all of it. The collision with the floor is a collision of ball molecules with floor molecules. Floor molecules at the point of contact are thus accelerated, and due to their tightly clustered arrangement, probability strongly favors the quick conversion of directional motion to random. The point of contact will thus become warmer, which will then tend to spread to the surroundings by diffusion. All of which continues to contribute to the bottom line: more of the ball's directional motion is being lost.

So as the ball begins to accelerate upward due to the ball's elastic recoil, the amount of potential energy being converted into lift is less than what the ball started with. Furthermore, collisions with air molecules on the way up continue to slow the ball even further. So by the time that the pull of gravity reins in the upward-moving ball to the point that it stops, the height reached will be less than from where it was initially dropped. And for the same reasons, that trend will continue for each bounce until the ball comes to rest on the floor. By then, all the directional energy within the ball has been converted into heat diffusing through the surroundings.

Arrangements of Matter

Because Life constantly uses usable energy, understanding Life requires an understanding of the nature of energy transformation—that is how arrangements of motion tend to change across time. But the living organisms that make up Life are more than just the constant motion within them. At each slice of time they are distinct arrangements of matter. Yet across time these arrangements are constantly changing. How do these arrangements form? Why and how do these arrangements continually change? These are important questions. And although they cannot be quickly or easily answered, taking some time here to set up a basic framework with which to consider arrangements will prove useful later.

Furthermore, I also want to introduce some language used to discuss arrangements. The ideas underlying terms like **emergent properties**, **order**, **complexity**, and **organization** are all applicable to Life.

Factors that influence arrangements of matter

Any arrangement is defined by relative position of each of the parts. The question of how any arrangement came to be is thus the question of how each part came to be in its current position. Three basic possibilities exist: (1) it was pushed or pulled there by the nature of its interactions with surrounding objects, (2) something selectively placed it in that spot, or (3) it just happened to end up there as a result of random movement. Because the distinction between these options is important, let's discuss each a bit further.

The first is called **self-assembly**. It occurs whenever any sort of field force interactions among objects acts to influence how the parts come to be arranged. Stated differently, it is the tendency of certain objects, due to field force interactions, to take on and/or stay in certain arrangements. Water and oil separating is an example. Each water molecule has regions of both positive and negative charge, whereas oil molecules are neutrally charged. So when mixed, the opposite charged regions of water molecules pull toward each other pushing intervening oil molecules out of the way. Eventually by this process all the water molecules group together forming distinct regions of oil and water. The formation of crystals is another example of self-assembly. And as we will discuss later, many aspects of biological structure, such as the distinct shape of each type of protein and cell membranes, come together by self-assembly.

An alternative to self-assembly is what I call, for lack of a better term, **differential placement**. Like self-assembly, different types of objects end up in distinct locations, but that doing the arranging is not the interaction among the objects per se, but something external that somehow recognizes different types of objects and places them in different places. Cleaning one's room is a familiar example. My pairs of socks tend to gather in my socks drawer not because they have a natural affinity for each other, but because I recognize them and treat them differently than my wife's socks, or shoes, or shirts, or anything else that I arrange within our room. Following the old adage "a place for everything, and everything in its place" is all about differential placement. As is anytime we build anything, from a model car to a house or airplane. Building involves following a plan that specifies both the order and position in which the different types of parts are arranged. We will see examples of differential placement in the workings of Life, such as DNA replication and protein synthesis, but there are some fundamentally different twists. Differential placement is part of the repertoire used by living things, such as cells, to build more of themselves, which means they are building things that can continue to build more of the same thing, and so on. In contrast, I have never seen an airplane, once constructed, build or even participate in building another airplane.

Earlier the notion that we live in a thermal world was introduced, which means that all molecules are in constant motion, and because it is more probable, this motion tends to be random. In terms of arrangement, random motion, whether occurring at molecular level due to the temperature being above absolute zero or due to some other form of shaking or stirring, introduces the possibility of unplanned changes in position among parts. In other words, it adds a mixing component. The magnitude of the effect depends on the **level of agitation** or random motion present. More specifically, arrangements will begin to undergo random rearrangements whenever mixing forces begin to exceed the strength of any forces holding parts in a specific arrangement. For example, if you shake a jar containing separated layers of oil and water hard enough, the molecules will mix. Heating up the same arrangement to a high enough temperature would have the same effect.

Energetics and stability of different arrangements

Consider a system of parts that are currently configured into an arrangement. Suppose this arrangement just encountered a sudden fluctuation in the level of agitation high enough to jostle the parts about. Once this fluctuation subsides, the system may return to the same arrangement as before, or it may rearrange into one of the other possible configurations.

Whether or not the system switches arrangements depends in part on whether the disturbance was of sufficient magnitude to reach an **instability**. An instability occurs when parts have been so knocked about that when they resettle, they resettle in a new arrangement. The amount of force needed to reach an instability is termed the arrangement's **activation energy**.

If the arrangement returns to its previous state, the amount of energy released as it settles back together will equal that added by the disturbance. Twanging a rubber band is a familiar example. As a rubber band returns to its equilibrium shape, the energy released through vibrations equals that added initially.

This may not be the case if the arrangement changes. The energy released may either exceed or be less than that put in, which raises two related questions: In the case where more energy is released, where did the additional energy come from? And, in the case where less energy is released, where did the lost energy go? The first law of thermodynamics rules out one possible answer. The additional or the lost energy was not created or destroyed. The only option remaining is that the energy was stored in the arrangement, and different arrangements have different amounts of stored (potential) energy.

For example, a book could be resting on a table or the floor, and being on the table stores more energy. As a consequence, whenever the book falls from the table to the floor, energy is released—that is, PE is converted into KE. All **fuels** are arrangements that can be readily converted into other lower energy arrangements. On the other hand, moving the book from the floor to the table stores energy. Part of the activation energy (the energy needed to move it up to the table) is converted into PE held within the new arrangement.

Whenever two possible arrangements have different relative energy states, the higher energy arrangement will be less stable because the conversion from a higher energy arrangement to a lower energy arrangement always has a smaller activation energy than the opposite conversion. Continuing with the book example, it takes a greater input of energy to lift the book from the floor to the table than to knock it off the table. So a disturbance will come along more often that is able to knock a book off the table, than one able to lift the book from the floor to the table.

Emergent properties

Do properties ever emerge from specific arrangements of matter? The answer is yes. In fact these so-called **emergent properties** are extremely pervasive. That a television works, that a painting is a work of art, and that you are living are all examples.

How can you tell whether any property is an emergent property? Just rearrange the parts and see if the property disappears. For example, the weight of a television set is not an emergent property because if you weigh your television then rearrange its parts and then weigh it again, the weight remains the same. On the other hand, a similar rearrangement will typically disrupt a television's ability to generate pictures and sound. These abilities are thus emergent properties. Similarly, you could rearrange the spots of color making up a painting and see if it continues to be a work of art. In fact, art of any form could be defined as an emergent property. If rearranging the paint within a painting, or the choreography within a dance performance, or the acts within a play does not make a difference, then the so-called creative process would not seem all that creative. Like art, the act of living can be defined as an emergent property. Rearrange the parts of your body and you will die. And the same is true for any other type of living organism.

Order

An arrangement is ordered whenever the parts are arranged in a **pattern**. A checkerboard, for example, has a spatial pattern of alternating red and black squares. The planets revolve around the sun in a specific temporal pattern. Your body is composed of a spatial pattern of tissues and organs. The simple test for whether a pattern exists, hence whether it is an ordered arrangement, is predictability. Cover up part of a checkerboard, and where red or black lie underneath can be accurately predicted. Similarly, astronomers can accurately predict where the earth will be in relation to both the sun and other planets a day, a month, or a year from now. And if you know your anatomy, you can accurately predict where different parts will be located within a body without first looking. The bodies of all types of living organisms are ordered arrangements.

Alternatively, random arrangements are disordered because they lack a pattern. In a random array of colors, for example, one could not predict which color was at any specified location without first looking.

When the second law of thermodynamics is applied to arrangements, the claim is that ordered arrangements will tend to become disordered with time. You will hear statements like the following:

• Natural processes tend to move toward a state of increasing disorder.

• Every system that is left to itself will on average change toward a less-ordered state.

To state it more completely: Any system at a temperature above absolute zero will encounter disturbances, in particular thermal agitation. Such disturbances tend to result in random rearrangements, which tend to lead an ordered system toward more disorder.

Applying this idea to you leads to an interesting conclusion. As an ordered arrangement in a thermal world, you are probably constantly falling apart. And the evidence makes it clear that you are. This raises the question: How are you constantly putting yourself together again?

Complexity

Complexity adds another dimension to the description of any ordered arrangement. As makes sense intuitively, checkerboards are ordered but not that complex, whereas airplanes, especially modern ones, are both ordered and complex. This intuition is formalized by defining complexity in terms of the probability that such an arrangement could come together by chance assembly of parts. The more improbable that chance assembly is, the greater the complexity. Complexity is thus affected by factors such as: (1) the total number of parts to be arranged, (2) the total number of different types of parts to be arranged, (3) the number of sequential steps that must occur for the arrangement to come about, and (4) the uniqueness of the order of sequential steps that must occur for the arrangement to come about. A standard checkerboard with a total of 64 parts (squares) of only two types (red or black) arranged in an alternating sequence is thus much more likely to arise than an airplane. Although from our earlier discussions of probability, it is clear that even a checkerboard is a hopeless improbable arrangement via chance. Using the analogy of each red or black square as being heads or tails of a coin, the probability of flipping a coin 64 times and coming up with a perfectly alternating sequence is the same as coming up with 64 heads or tails in a row. Which in either case is 0.5 raised to the 64th power—considerably more than a rather small number.

The importance of understanding complexity in reference to thinking about life is that even the seemingly simplest extant life forms, such as single-celled bacteria, are incredibly complex structures. This means that there is virtually no chance that these or any other organisms were initially assembled by chance events alone.

Putting it together

To both summarize and synthesize, I finish by addressing how ordered and complex arrangements can arise and be maintained. In the process I twist some familiar ideas around some new terms, and I hint at where we will be going next.

As we have seen, arrangements come about in one of two ways: random rearrangement, or something specifically positioning different parts in different places. In the latter, something is ordering or **organizing** the arrangement. Such differential positioning of parts can occur via one of two means:

• *Imposed organization* is when something external to the system acts on the system such that it nonrandomly arranges the different types of parts in the system. Whenever we build, repair, or clean something are all examples. We are the external thing imposing order on a system by placing different types of objects in different places in accord with some plan—what I earlier called differential placement. And note that what motivates us to impose organization is emergent properties. We build things like houses and watches to take advantage of the properties that they offer. We repair things to maintain these useful properties in the face of the constant random rearrangement of a thermal world. And we clean things (some of us more than others) to basically make what we have easier to find and thus use.

• *Self-organization* is when the objects within a system interact in a way that directs nonrandom arrangement of parts. The easiest form of self-organization to envision is what I earlier called self-assembly, where field force interactions among parts tend to pull the parts into certain arrangements. Water and oil separating and crystal formation were mentioned examples. In such cases, the cooler the temperature, the more stable the arrangement because the less heat the less agitation.

But there is a second form of a self-organization. One where plans and differential placement work alongside self-assembly, and energy flowing through a system becomes necessary for the action and interaction of the system's parts to act in organizing ways. In considering this form of self-organization, we begin to step into the realm of biology. Life is an example of energy-driven self-organization.

Some key terms:

inertia - the tendency for the velocity of any object to stay the same (i.e., if an object is at rest—velocity equals zero—it tends to stay at rest, and if an object is moving at a certain velocity its tendency is to continue to move at that velocity).

force - any kind of push or pull experienced by an object.

contact force - the push or pull that one object experiences as a result of colliding with another object.

field force - the push or pull that an object experiences as the result of an interaction with another object at a distance.

energy (classic definition) - what an object has when it is in motion.

kinetic energy (KE) - the energy that a moving object has, where the amount depends on both the mass and the velocity of the object. (The higher the velocity of an object of a given mass, or the larger the mass of an object of a given velocity, the higher the kinetic energy.)

potential energy (PE) - the energy associated with the potential—due to the presence of one or more forces—of an object to increase its velocity, or accelerate, in the future.

first law of thermodynamics - energy can neither be created nor destroyed, only transformed from one type of energy to another. (PE to KE or KE to PE)

heat - random molecular motion.

temperature - a measure of the average pace of random molecular motion.

diffusion - the redistribution of velocity or materials from regions of higher concentration to regions of lower concentration.

spontaneous change - the requirements for a change to occur are met without any external intervention, so the change just happens.

second law of thermodynamics - (in terms of motion) a nonrandom pattern of motion among objects undergoing collisions tends to become an increasingly random pattern of motion, but not vice versa. (in terms of arrangement) a nonrandom (ordered) arrangement of objects subjected to disturbance tends to become an increasingly random arrangement of objects, and not vice versa.

self-assembly - the tendency of certain objects, due to field force interactions, to take on and/or stay in a nonrandom arrangement.

emergent property - any property of a system that results from the arrangement of the system's parts.

ordered arrangement - when the parts of system are arranged in a pattern—that is, they have a nonrandom arrangement.

complex arrangement - an arrangement that is unlikely to come about by just chance (random) rearrangement. The smaller the chance, the more complex the arrangement.

imposed organization - the actions of something external to a system rearranges its parts in a nonrandom way.

self-organization - a system's parts interact in a way that results in these parts taking on a nonrandom arrangement.

Some study questions:

1. Discuss change in terms of inertia, forces, and energy (both kinetic and potential).

2. *What is the difference between usable energy and unusable energy? Explain why usable energy tends to become unusable with use, and not the other way around.*

3. What three factors can affect how the parts of system come to be arranged? Know the difference between each of these.

4. How would you test whether some property of a system is an emergent property? What are some examples of emergent properties?

5. What will happen to an ordered arrangement if it is randomly rearranged? *Explain the connection between temperatures above absolute zero and random rearrangements.*

6. *Explain how nonrandom arrangements ever come about.*

A View of Life

Biologists study Life. But in a sense, this is a funny notion. Research biologists do not wake with the thought, "Gee, I think I will go study Life today." Instead they are much more focused. Life is made up of lots of parts, and different biologists study different parts. Some focus on specific types of single-celled organisms such as certain types of bacteria or protists. Some go even smaller and study the parts inside single cells, such as enzymes and mitochondria. Others study the parts inside multi-cellular organisms, such as hearts or kidneys or other organs. Entire populations of a specific type of organism, be it single-celled or multicellular, sway the attention of other biologists, whereas still others try to examine the workings of entire biological communities. When it comes down to it, the focus of biologists can be as diverse as Life itself.

Here, I am not as interested in the diversity so much as in the similarity. What shared characteristics link enzymes, cells, organisms, populations, and communities? What unifies these parts into Life itself? I am intrigued by how to best answer the big question: What is Life?

A common response to the "what-is-Life?" question is a listing of characteristics such as growth, metabolism, response to stimuli, and adaptation to the environment. I find this response lacking in the same way that listing symptoms fails to answer the question: What is the disease? Characteristic symptoms aid one in telling when a disease is present, but not what the disease is. Similarly, growth, metabolism, and other characters help us identify when something is living, but do not define what Life is. Life has a more fundamental nature that I see as hidden in the riddle: *How can something continue to persist even though the parts that make it up continually fall apart?*

The various means by which geologists' date rock layers embedded with fossils all have one basic assumption: Past rates are the same as present rates. Certain materials are now observed to change from one form to another at a certain rate. Geologists assume that these material transformations took place at the same rate in the past. If this assumption is accurate, then calculating a reasonably accurate age is as straightforward as multiplying the rate of change times the measured amount of change in the item (or the surrounding substrate) to be dated. Using this method, the oldest discovered remnants of organisms (some bacteria-like organisms) goes all the way back to 3.5 to 3.8 billion years ago, and there is no evidence of an interruption in the presence of living forms since then. I must admit that I have no conception of how long 3.8 billion years is. I have trouble enough envisioning a month or two, and past a decade or so my time concept becomes quite fuzzy. I just think of 3.5 billion years as an inconceivable amount of time, times a million or so. The important point is that it seems like living forms have persisted across a great time expanse—and may well continue to do so for a long time into the future.

Life's riddle emerges from the fact that the parts making up Life last but a blink-of-the-eye in comparison. Some of the oldest organisms known are several thousand-year-old bristle-cone pines (*Pinus aristata*), but that means they have lived only a millionth of the time Life has been on earth. In contrast, you have an outside chance of living only 90 plus years, and humans are relatively long-lived organisms. The life span of many organisms is best measured in months or even days.

A Closer Look at Life's Riddle

So what has made it possible for Life as a whole to persist despite the ongoing demise of its parts? What is the answer to Life's fundamental riddle? My most basic answer is only three words long: *Life is loopy.* Of course, such a short and somewhat wacky sounding answer needs further explanation. That explanation is the focus of this chapter.

Something to consider: The study of Life is filled with a dizzying amount of information discussed through a dictionary-size array of multisyllabic terms. For introductory students, it is extremely difficult just to keep all the terms straight and next to impossible to actually understand what is going on. Faced with what seems frustratingly hopeless, I have found that students quickly lapse into education's worst enemy—they try to memorize a bunch of seemingly unconnected bits of information, and hope that this will somehow get them through the exams. Not only does the whole experience seem relatively worthless, it is simply no fun. There is no good reason (except for the fear of a low grade) to work very hard because there is nothing really to be gained. If I am describing you, then I suggest that it is time to try something new.

In this chapter, I introduce a new way to learn about Life. Here we uncover Life's basic features, and then in subsequent chapters, we use this conceptual framework to organize Life's details. Although this approach still requires hard work, your effort will be well spent. Master the conceptual tools developed here, and you will have put in place a framework that can help you understand any aspect of biology that you would ever care to consider. In the words of a former student: "I finally realized that you were not trying to teach me biology, but to teach me how to understand biology." (Note: You may find yourself, at least initially, a bit unnerved by the broad conceptual nature of the following discussion. Although memorizing a bunch of disconnected facts may seem relatively worthless, you probably have had more practice memorizing details than thinking conceptually. So you may find yourself being pushed out of your student comfort zone and thus feel less sure-footed in terms of how to proceed to succeed. Although this may sound trivial, my best advice for now is to keep up and spend time trying to connect the dots.)

All of Life's parts are processors

If you have had any background in biology, you have heard lots of terms: Enzymes with names like hexokinase and glyceraldehyde 3-phosphate dehydrogenase; metabolic pathways with names like glycolysis and the Krebs cycle; components of protein synthesis with names like DNA transcription and RNA translation; components of energy metabolism with names like the light phase of photosynthesis, oxidative phosphorylation, and aerobic respiration; cell organelles with names like mitochondria and chloroplasts; cells with names like prokaryotic and eukaryotic; tissues with names like epithelium and connective; organs with names like kidneys, spleens, and hearts; and species with names like peregrine falcon (*Falco peregrinus*) and humans (*Homo sapiens*). If you lack much background, just know that these are some of the dizzying array of terms that I mentioned earlier.

The key point here is that all these terms, no matter how fancy or complicated their names sound, are simply parts of Life, and *all parts of Life share one fundamental and extremely simple similarity*— what goes in is different than what comes out. The way I will typically say it is that: INPUTS ARE DIFFERENT THAN OUTPUTS.

For convenience, I refer to anything that converts inputs into different outputs as a **processor**. This means that all of Life's parts, regardless of how hard their name is to remember, qualify as processors. And it should be obvious that the concept of a processor extends beyond what is typically considered parts of Life. For example, a car converts gasoline and oxygen (a car's inputs) into motion, heat, carbon dioxide, and water (a car's outputs); or a lightbulb converts electricity into light and heat. Other things around your house or apartment, such as a television or a stereo, would also qualify as processors.

Basic features of processors

Any processor is simply an agent of change. It changes inputs into something else. In a sense, inputs are the processor's resources—what it needs to run—and outputs are the processor's products— what the processor converts the inputs into.

Processors can vary in three ways: the **nature of its inputs** (what it can take in and alter); the **nature of its outputs** (the final rearrangement of it inputs); and the **rate** that inputs are converted into outputs (where rate is measured by the amount of inputs converted to outputs per unit time). Figure 3-1 shows the generic way the processors will be illustrated.

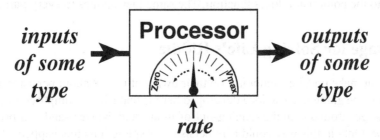

Figure 3-1. Throughout this book processors will be illustrated as a rectangle (box) with inputs entering and different outputs leaving. The simplicity of a box points to the fact that the details of how inputs are converted into different outputs is not the focus of the processor concept. The focus is the nature of the change (what is converted into what), and the rate that the conversion occurs. Changes in rate will be indicated by the presence of a rate meter (whose look is modeled after a car's rate meter, which is more commonly known as a speedometer).

The combination of a processor's inputs and outputs defines what type of processor it is. In other words, any two processors are different if they have different inputs and/or outputs. Figure 3-2 depicts several different examples. Use the biological examples (Figure 3-2(b), (c), and (d)) to practice seeing the bigger picture without being caught up in the details. Although you may not know what some of the inputs or outputs are (such as NADH or activated ribonucleotides), you can still see that each different part of Life can be characterized in terms of its unique combination of inputs and outputs.

A universal problem

The fact that all of Life's parts are processors helps to clarify why the persistence of Life truly is a riddle. A processor by definition is not set up to last (to continue to convert inputs into different outputs). First of all, any processor will be an ordered material arrangement, and ordered material arrangements can be disrupted. In fact, recall from the last chapter that the second law of thermodynamics states that for any processor existing in a thermal world (temperature is above absolute zero), the disruption is inescapably relentless. The random rearrangement at the molecu-

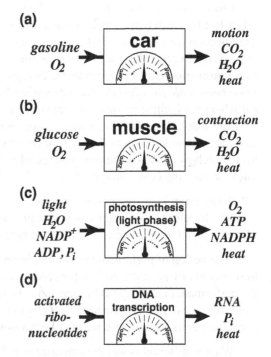

Figure 3-2. Several examples of different types of processors.

lar level caused by heat is always pushing ordered arrangements toward disorder. Furthermore, each processor plays an active role in its own demise for two reasons. First, as any processor converts its inputs into outputs, it is continually dipping into its input (resource) supply. Unless more inputs are continually made available, the input supply will eventually run out. Second, any processor will suffer wear and tear as it runs. With time, this wear and tear can accumulate to the point that the processor breaks down.

Cars provide a familiar—and often costly and annoying—example of a processor contributing to its own demise. As a car runs, it is continually using up its gasoline supply, and once the gas tank is empty, the car will stop (until more gasoline is added). Furthermore, a running car continually adds wears and tear to each of its parts. Eventually the car suffers a breakdown, as some essential component finally wears to the point that it loses function. The same idea applies to every part of Life.

Setting the Stage for Solving Life's Riddle

If processors that make up Life cannot last on their own, yet Life is about persistence, then something more must be going on. The idea developed here is that Life is composed of processors that interact in ways that get around both the running-out-of-inputs and the wear-and-tear problem *for each and every processor*. Only in this way could Life persist. To explore how this happens, I first build the concept of a performance. We will then find that Life is comprised of performances with a distinctive twist: Life's performances are loopy. What makes loops so special? *Only loops are finite in length, but have no ending.*

The concept of a performance

Processors can be said to interact whenever the actions of one processor affects the actions of another. But how can that happen? Here a processor's rate becomes the focal point. Two processors form a connection (or interaction) whenever the rate that one processor converts inputs to outputs somehow plays a role in controlling another processor's rate. In other words, processes interact when a **regulatory connection** exists between them. *To regulate is to control rate, so a regulatory connection is one thing being able to adjust the rate of another.* For example, I form a regulatory connection with my car whenever I adjust its speed (its rate of converting gasoline into motion) by changing the amount of pressure that I place on the accelerator. You form a regulatory connection with a radio whenever you turn the volume knob up or down. Your parents even form a regulatory connection with you whenever they somehow influence the time you spend performing any activity such as partying (your partying rate), or studying (your studying rate).

A key point is processors tied together by regulatory connections become parts of a larger whole. I choose to refer to this larger whole as a **performance**. Inherent in this notion of a performance is the idea of a *division of labor,* as each distinct type of processor contributes to the whole in different ways.

The notion of performance does not, in and of itself, solve the persistence problem. Pay attention only to any performance's inputs and outputs (and not the details of the interactions that make up the performance) and any performance meets the definition of a processor—outputs will be different from inputs. So, just like the processors that make it up, the processor nature of any performance will contribute to its own demise for the two reasons outlined earlier.

What is different is that performances can have emergent properties, and as a consequence they can do something in addition to contributing to their own demise. Recall from the last chapter that emergent properties are properties that arise from arrangement. A performance is an interactional arrangement of processors, and certain arrangements generate abilities that go beyond a simple summing of the parts. Consider, for example, the computer that I am currently using to write. As it operates, it is converting electricity into electromagnetic radiation and heat, and it is wearing down its parts. That is its processor nature. But also while running, the regulatory arrangement among the different processors make it so the computer can do word processing, computer graphics, and video games, along with a host of other activities. Similarly, although a car has a processor nature, it displays emergent properties because the nature of the interaction among the parts makes it possible for a car to transport you from one place to another. The list of performances that have emergent properties goes on. A stereo, a microwave oven, and yourself are all wonderful examples.

So how does the fact that performances can do something in addition to contributing to their own demise, crack open the possibility of persistence? Suppose that when a performance is running, it acts to restore the conditions it needs to keep running. If so, the performance would act to keep itself going by doing things that *counteract* the constant degradation of the conditions it needs to continue to run. A performance using its current supply of usable energy to somehow gather more usable energy captures this flavor. To explore this theme further, however, we need to better understand how performances can be assembled. This means that we need to understand the specific ways that one processor can form a regulatory connection with a different processor. So hang on because this takes a moment to explain

The ways and means of regulatory connections

To understand how the rate of one processor could influence the rate of another, one must first understand what controls a single processor's rate. So we begin there, and then build on this understanding to show the various ways that regulatory connections can form. (Note: I am going to go through the next section in what may seem like painful detail because it is not just about information, but about a way to think. And I need to make sure that you can follow and use all the nuances.)

What controls a single processor's rate?

Let's start with a simple truth: Every processor has an upper limit in terms of how fast it can convert inputs into outputs. This upper limit is referred to as the processor's maximum velocity, or **Vmax** for short (see Figure 3-3). Each processor's Vmax is set by details of that specific processor. For example, I once owned a car whose Vmax made it nearly impossible to get a highway speeding ticket because 65 mph was reachable only when the car was traveling downhill with a tailwind. Why did this car have a relatively low Vmax (as compared to most cars)? The answer lies in the car's design details. Change some aspect of the details, such as put in a larger, more powerful engine, or make the car lighter, or rearrange the car's body into a more aerodynamic shape, and the Vmax would increase. Similarly, your running Vmax (the fastest speed that you can run) is set by many aspects of your body's shape, including the length of certain leg bones, the position that muscles attach to these bones, and your specific distribution of muscle fiber types within these muscles (some muscle fibers contract faster than others). And like with cars, change some of those details, and your running Vmax will likely change—as demonstrated by the fact that humans overall display a wide range of top end speeds. Fortunately, we do not need to be concerned here about the details that set any processor's Vmax. We just need to keep in mind that each processor has a Vmax.

Figure 3-3. A processor that is running as fast as it can (as indicated by the fact that the rate meter has topped out at Vmax).

Once a processor is operating at Vmax, the only way for inputs to be converted to outputs at a faster rate is to have more than one processor of the same type operating simultaneously (see Figure 3-4). Several lawnmowers, for example, can cut a given area of grass faster than just one. Similarly, a large population of similar processors (organisms) can eat through resources faster than a small population.

On the other hand, two factors could keep any single processor from operating at a rate below its Vmax: input limitation or the presence of some form of throttle/sensor. Let's discuss each in turn.

Input limitation is when the processor could go faster but the availability of inputs holds it back. A car that has run out of gasoline is a blatant example of input limitation. The car cannot move because it lacks a supply of an essential input—gasoline. You experience input limitation whenever you run as fast as you can for a far enough distance. Input limitation kicks in after you reach your

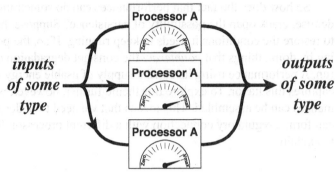

Figure 3-4. This figure makes the simple but important point that the simultaneous operation of more than one copy of the same processor (**Processor A**), each operating at Vmax, will convert inputs into outputs faster than a single processor (operating at Vmax).

Vmax early in the run. Even as you continue to push yourself, your speed begins to slow because you cannot continue to supply resources fast enough to allow your muscles to work at their maximum rate. Stated in everyday terms, your speed drops as you begin to tire. Tiredness is input limitation.

Figure 3-5(a) and (b) illustrates the basic way to determine whether any processor is input limited—add more inputs and see if the process speeds up. Increasing the supply of some input allows a processor to run faster only if the previous level of input availability was holding back its rate. (This is simply employing the scientific method—change one factor and see if it makes a difference.) Figure 3-5(c) also shows that an input limited processor will slow down even further if the input supply is reduced.

The term **throttle** is used to describe the valve that regulates the rate of an internal combustion engine (the type of engine found in most cars, motorbikes, or lawn mowers) by controlling the rate that fuel enters into the engine. Here, I use this term more generally. I use throttle to indicate any mechanism that can adjust the speed at which a processor converts inputs into outputs. By this definition, examples of throttles are commonplace. A car's accelerator, the volume control on a radio, cook settings on a

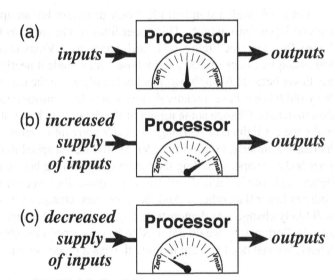

Figure 3-5. How changing the input supply will affect a processor's rate if it is input limited. In (a), a processor is running at a rate below its Vmax. In (b), the processor's rate speeds up as the input supply increases, demonstrating that input limitation was what was holding the processor's rate below Vmax in (a). In (c), the input limited processor slows down even further as the input supply is decreased.

microwave oven, and the speed control on a blender are all examples. The key point is that a processor with a throttle can operate at speeds below Vmax. In fact, a processor with a throttle will run at Vmax only when the throttle is set at full speed (and it is not input limited). Any setting below full throttle and a processor's rate is reined in. Sufficient resources are available for the processor to go faster, but the throttle's setting keeps the processor from using these resources at the maximum possible rate.

Although throttles such as the volume control on a radio or a car's accelerator are familiar, I introduce what may be a new way of thinking about them. A throttle is a **sensor**. Just check the dictionary—sensors are generally defined something like "a device that detects and responds to some change in conditions." That is what a throttle does. It detects the presence of whatever can change a throttle's setting. The response is the change in the processor's rate. In fact, the idea of a **response** can *always* be framed in terms of a rate change. For example, a car's accelerator is a pressure sensor. The speed of the car's engine responds to changes in pressure on the accelerator. Figure 3-6 adds the concept of a sensor on to our previous illustration of a processor.

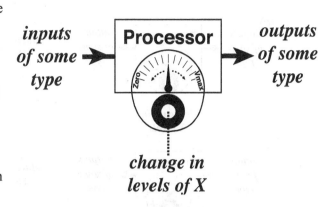

inputs of some type → **Processor** → *outputs of some type*

change in levels of X

Figure 3-6. A processor with a sensor. The sensor is represented as an "eyeball" attached to the rate meter. The sensor detects changes in levels of **X**, where **X** could represent anything. For example, **X** could be pressure, temperature, a chemical such as glucose, or some specific wavelength of electromagnetic radiation. The key idea is that the sensor converts changes in **X** levels into changes in the processor's rate.

Think about all the responses your body makes. To name just a few: Your heart rate goes up as you start to run; certain muscles contract while others remain at rest when your hand jerks back after placing it on a scorching hot surface, and you go search for water when you feel thirsty. The operation of sensors makes these responses possible, along with every other response that you or any other organism makes. It is thus important to understand the nuances of the sensor concept. Specifically, we need to understand the difference between a positive and negative sensor.

So far, we have specified a sensor as any type of device that can convert changes in the levels of something (call it **X**, where **X** is whatever a particular sensor detects) into a change in a processor's rate. Such a notion, however, does not specify how a processor's rate will change in response to change in **X** levels. For example, does the processor's rate increase or decrease if **X** levels increase? Both options are possible. Furthermore, sensors tend to work in a consistent fashion as **X** levels change in opposite directions. For instance, if a sensor *turns up* a processor's rate whenever **X** levels increase, then the same sensor would be expected to *turn down* a processor's rate whenever **X** levels decrease. The question that remains is: What is the nature of the relationship between changes in **X** levels and changes in a processor's rate?

A positive relationship is when a processor's rate and **X** levels change in the *same way*—as **X** levels increase, the processor's rate increases and vice versa. Correspondingly, any sensor that operates in this fashion is called a **positive sensor** (see Figure 3-7). A car's accelerator is an example. Increasing pressure causes the car to go faster, and decreasing pressure causes the car to go slower. The sensors located on all your skeletal muscles, such as your biceps and triceps, are a biological example (see the second half of Figure 3-7). They detect levels of a molecule known as **acetylcholine**. Increase acetylcholine levels, and a muscle will contract faster and with more force (until each reaches its Vmax). Decrease acetylcholine levels, and the speed and force of contraction will slow. In fact, in the absence of any acetylcholine, a skeletal muscle is at rest (does not contract at all). (Note that the basis for controlling the pattern in which your skeletal muscles contract is to somehow control acetylcholine levels around each and every muscle. As we will discuss more later, the nervous system is all about doing just that.)

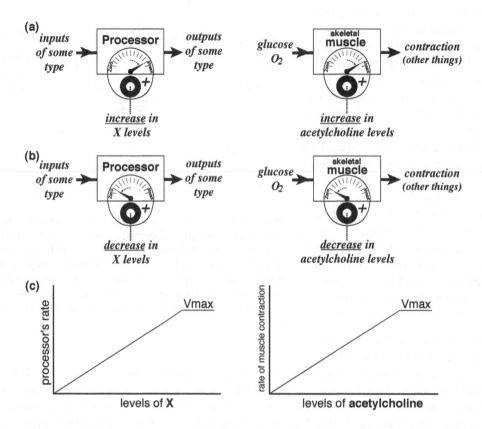

Figure 3-7. A **positive sensor**—as designated by the positive (+) sign in the corner of the "eye"—is one that forms a positive (or same) relationship between **X** levels and the processor's rate. That is, if **X** levels increase, the rate the processor converts inputs to outputs also goes up (a), and if **X** levels decrease, the processor's rate also decreases (b). In (c), this positive relationship is shown graphically. The right half of this figure shows a biological example that is discussed further in the text.

In contrast, a negative relationship is when a processor's rate and **X** levels change in the *opposite* way—as **X** levels increase, the processor's rate decreases and vice versa. Correspondingly, any sensor that operates in this fashion is called a **negative sensor** (see Figure 3-8). Your heart provides a biological example. Like your skeletal muscles, your heart (which is made up of a muscle type known as cardiac muscle) also has sensors that detect acetylcholine levels. But interestingly, acetylcholine affects the heart in completely the opposite way. Heart rate *decreases* as acetylcholine levels *increase* around your heart. In fact, high enough acetylcholine levels can actually cause your heart to stop beating (but only for a few seconds). Alternatively, your heart rate continues to increase as acetylcholine levels decrease, reaching somewhere around 90 to 100 beats per minute in the absence of acetylcholine. (As you are probably aware, your heart's Vmax is greater than 90 to 100 beats per minute. This means that more than just acetylcholine levels control your heart's rate. Specifically, your heart also has a positive sensor to two molecules, epinephrine and norepinephrine—which are also known as adrenaline and noradrenaline, respectively. Increasing levels of these molecules can cause your heart rate to increase to somewhere around 200 beats per minute or more.)

A warning: Do not confuse what a sensor detects with a processor's inputs. Pressure on a car's accelerator is **NOT** an input. Pressure is not converted into motion. The pressure just opens the flow of a gasoline (and oxygen) into the engine so that these inputs can be converted into outputs (motion, heat, water, and carbon dioxide) at a faster rate. Similarly, acetylcholine is **NOT** an input to either skeletal or cardiac muscle—it is not used in any way to power a muscle's contractions. Instead, its presence influences the rate that contractions occur. Or consider a light fixture with a photocell. A

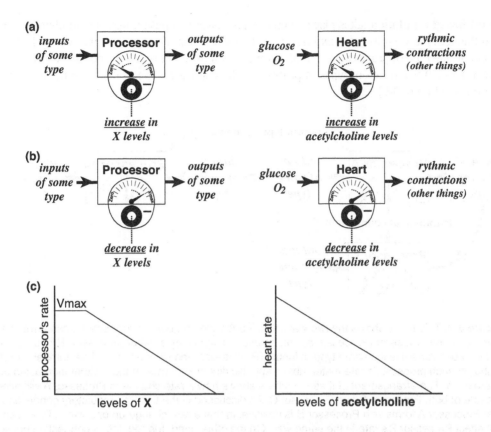

Figure 3-8. A **negative sensor**—as designated by the negative (–) sign in the corner of the "eye"—is one that forms a negative (or opposite) relationship between **X** levels and the processor's rate. That is, if **X** levels increase, the rate that the processor converts inputs to outputs goes down (a), and on the other hand, if **X** levels decrease, the processor's rate increases (b). In (c), this negative relationship is shown graphically. The right half of this figure shows a biological example that is discussed further in

light is a processor that converts electricity into light and heat. Photocells are sensors found on many outdoor light fixtures, such as streetlights and porch lights, that cause the light to turn on when it gets sufficiently dark. In other words, photocells open the flow of electricity into a light when the absence of light—darkness—reaches a certain threshold. If darkness was an input, instead of that detected by a sensor, then darkness could be converted by a lightbulb into light and heat. Darkness, however, does not power lights; electricity does.

Building regulatory connections

The preceding discussion was long enough that it would be easy to forget why we needed to discuss concepts like input limitation and sensors. We need these concepts to illustrate how to build regulatory connections—where one processor's rate somehow affects the rate of a different type of processor. And we need to understand regulatory connections to see how to build performances that can persist.

Input-based regulation and **sensor-based regulation** are the two basic means by which regulatory connections can form. We next discuss each in some detail. But note up front that each has a basic similarity: One type of processor affects the supply of something that affects the rate of another processor. Changes in supply happen because whenever a processor runs, its supply of inputs is being continually decreased, whereas the supply of outputs is continually being increased. Continue to keep that in mind.

Input-based regulation takes place when one processor is input limited and another type of processor influences *the supply of the limiting input*. This could happen in one of two ways: (1) an output or outputs of one type of processor are used as inputs by a different type of processor (output–input connection), or (2) two different types of processors share at least some of the same inputs (same-input connection; see Figure 3-9).

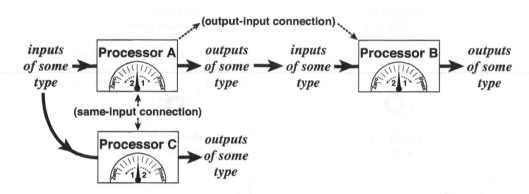

Figure 3-9. This figure shows the two ways that input-based regulatory connections can form: the outputs of one processor (Processor A) can be used as inputs by another processor (Processor B), or two processors use the same type of inputs (Processor A and Processor C). The number 1 or 2 found on each processor's rate meter label a specific direction of rate change: either increasing or decreasing. The arrangement of these numbers shows how a rate change in Processor A will effect the rate of both Processor B and Processor C. As discussed in the text, the regulatory connection that Processor A forms with Processor B is positive, in that a rate change up or down in Processor A will affect Processor B's rate in the same way. On the other hand, the regulatory connection between Processor A and Processor C is reciprocally negative, in that a rate change up or down in either of these processors will affect the other processor's rate in the opposite way.

Output–input connections can be seen as a form of **positive regulation** because by producing outputs that can be used by another processor as inputs, the action of one processor "benefits" another. It is also positive in the same sense as was described earlier for a positive sensor. A rate change in one processor will result in the *same* type of rate change in the connected processor. For example in Figure 3-9, decreasing Processor A's rate slows the rate that its outputs become available to be used as inputs by Processor B, which in turn can slow the rate that Processor B can convert inputs into outputs. Due to a similar chain of events, the opposite can also occur—increasing the rate of Processor A can lead to Processor B increasing its rate.

To begin to get you to see that output–input connections are an integral part of Life, just take a deep breath. Really, do it! You probably know that the purpose of that breath is to gather in a type of molecule known as molecular oxygen (although we normally just call it oxygen). Where did that molecular oxygen come from? It is an output of a process called water-splitting photosynthesis. In other words, when you breathe in a so-called breath of fresh air, what you are really breathing in is a waste gas produced by plants and other things that do water-splitting photosynthesis. Makes you pause and think, doesn't it? In fact, what we find later in this chapter is that one of the essential features of Life is that every type of molecule that is an output from one of Life's parts is an input to another of Life's parts.

In contrast to an output–input connection, a same-input connection creates a form of **negative regulation**. Whenever the input supply is limiting, two (or more) different types of processors that use the same inputs are "competitors." As a consequence, the success of one (in terms of gathering inputs to convert to outputs) will have an *opposite* effect on the other's rate because it reduces the supply of the shared input. For example in Figure 3-9, if Processor A can increase the rate that it gathers inputs, then less inputs will be available to Processor C, slowing its rate. (*A side note*: Although not directly connected, Processor C forms an indirect regulatory connection with Processor B. For instance, if Processor C is able to increase its rate, Processor A's rate will decrease, which in turn reduces the rate of Processor B. As we will discuss further in Chapter 5, indirect regulatory connections play important roles in the structure of Life.)

Sensor-based regulation takes place whenever one processor has a sensor that detects either an input or an output of some other processor. Sounds simple enough. What makes sensor-based regulation a bit more complicated is that whether the overall regulatory effect is positive or negative depends on the interaction of two factors: (1) whether that detected by the sensor is an input or an output, and (2) whether the sensor is positive or negative. Figure 3-10 goes through the four possible ways that this interaction can play out. Study them carefully, as Life uses them all.

Two forms of positive sensor-based regulation:

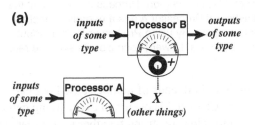

(a)

As Processor A's rate increases, X levels will tend to increase (because X is an output). The positive sensor responds to rising X levels by increasing Processor B's rate.

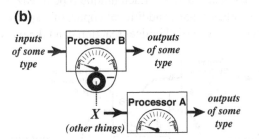

(b)

As Processor A's rate increases, X levels will tend to decrease (because X is an input). The negative sensor responds to falling X levels by increasing Processor B's rate.

Two forms of negative sensor-based regulation:

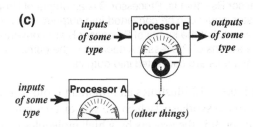

(c)

As Processor A's rate increases, X levels will tend to increase (because X is an output). The negative sensor responds to rising X levels by decreasing Processor B's rate.

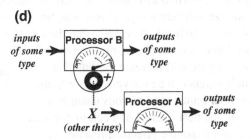

(d)

As Processor A's rate increases, X levels will tend to decrease (because X is an input). The positive sensor responds to falling X levels by decreasing Processor B's rate.

Figure 3-10. The four possible combinations of sensor-based regulation. The nature of the effect that Processor A has on Processor B—that is, whether it is positive or negative—depends on the combination of two factors: whether the actions of Processor A increase **X** levels (**X** is an output) or decrease **X** levels (**X** is an input), and whether Processor B's sensor is positive ("+" in the corner of the sensor) or negative ("-" in the corner of the sensor). Below each example is a brief description of the interaction starting with Processor A's rate increasing. The basic nature of these interactions are most easily described from this perspective.

There is a second theme in how regulatory connections can form. How many copies of a specific type of processor are present can influence the current rate that inputs are converted into outputs. For example, I previously mentioned that several lawn mowers can cut a field of grass faster than just one. So a regulatory connection exists whenever the action of one type of processor somehow alters the present copy number of a different type of processor. How could such **number-based regulation** happen? There is nothing in the basic description of a processor that rules out one processor using a different type of processor as an input. Similarly, there is no rule against the output of one type of processor being a different type of processor. And as shown in Figure 3-11, both of these actions would change the number of a specific type of processor.

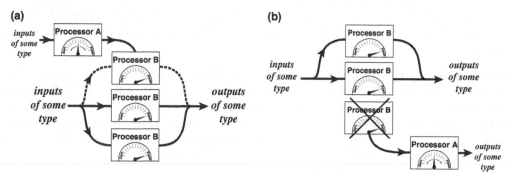

Figure 3-11. Processor number regulation. In (a), the action of Processor A has a positive effect on the rate that the inputs of Processor B are converted into outputs. Processor A produces more Processor Bs—that is, Processor B is an output of Processor A—and the more Processor Bs present the faster inputs can be converted into outputs. In (b), the action of Processor A has a negative effect on the rate that the inputs of Processor B are converted into outputs. By using Processor B as an input, the actions of Processor A decreases the number of Processor Bs. Fewer Processor Bs slow the rate that inputs are converted into outputs.

Figure 3-12 illustrates an important biological example of both ends of number-based regulation. Protein synthesis (which we will discuss much more in Chapter 12) occurs in every living cell on this planet. It is the process by which molecules called amino acids are strung together to form larger molecules known as proteins. Many different types of proteins can be made through protein synthesis, and each distinct type potentially functions as a distinct type of processor. For example, some forms of proteins, known as **enzymes**, can facilitate specific chemical reactions. Each unique type of enzyme will catalyze a different type of reaction. So, if protein synthesis makes additional copies of a specific enzyme found in a cell, it is increasing the rate that a specific type of chemical reaction can take place.

Or stated in processor terms, more copies of a specific enzyme will increase the rate that this enzyme's inputs can be converted to outputs. On the other hand, as conditions change, it may be in the best interest of a cell to decrease the rate that a specific chemical reaction is taking place. One way to do this would be to reduce the number of enzymes that facilitate this specific reaction. Many cells create a processor known as a **proteasome**, that takes proteins identified for destruction by a certain form of tag, and breaks them back down into their component parts—amino acids. Right now in cells throughout your body, the copy number of different types of enzymes is being controlled by the interplay between protein synthesis and proteasomes.

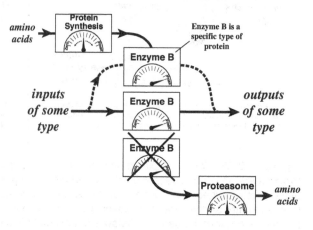

Figure 3-12. A biological example of the two sides of number-based regulation. Details are discussed in the text.

Predation is another well-known example of negative number-based regulation. Both a rabbit and a coyote qualify as processors (inputs are converted into different outputs); so when a coyote eats a rabbit, one processor is using another processor as an input. As a consequence, the rabbit population size is reduced by one, which in turn reduces the rate that rabbit inputs are converted into rabbit outputs.

A final comment: As you try to sort through all these little boxes, eyeballs, and arrows and such I envision eyes glossing over as heads are asking: Why is he telling us this? Repeating myself, Life consists of certain types of performance, and performances are made by regulatory connections. So understanding the basic ways that regulatory connections can form is a big deal. Many biologists throughout the world dedicate their careers to understanding the details of specific biological regulatory connections. Big fat biological textbooks are literally filled with example after example of these regulatory connections. All these examples, each with their own nuances of detail, can make the whole topic of regulation seem mind-bogglingly complex. But you know what? Every regulatory connection found in biology fits into one of the basic patterns outlined in the past few pages. And that is a big deal. Understand the logic underlying each now, and you may surprise yourself with what you may be able to understand later.

The basic structure of performances that can persist

We are now ready to tackle the issue of how to build performances that can persist. Recall that we are looking for performances whose emergent properties act to counteract the constant degradation of the very conditions that the performance needs to keep running. It is here that we find the basic structure of Life. Life has persisted not because something has kept it going, but because *Life keeps itself going*.

To begin to see how a performance that contributes to its own persistence could be structured, envision (without getting caught up in the details of how this could work) two or more processors that collectively act to maintain another processor's running conditions. Now, let's play this idea out further in two different ways: one way that doesn't work and one that does.

Let's use Figure 3-13 to explain the idea that does not work. In this figure, Processor A can persist as long as Processor B and Processor C maintain its running conditions. Yet Processor B and Processor C will persist if and only if they too are accompanied by other processors that collectively restore their running conditions (Processor D and Processor E for Processor B, and Processor F and Processor G for Processor C). Similarly, Processors D, E, F, and G will persist only if even more processors collectively restore their running conditions, and so on, ad infinitum. Clearly we have backed ourselves into a dead end. An infinite number of processors would be needed to keep just one type of processor (Processor A) running. This is an impossible scenario. The universe is simply not large enough.

Figure 3-13. The structure of a performance in which the basic unit of a persistent performance is present—processors act to maintain the running conditions of other processors—yet the performance as a whole fails to solve the persistence problem. See text for further discussion.

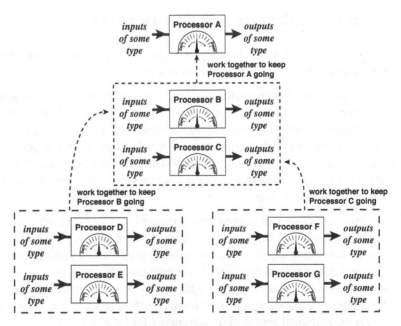

And so on, ad infinitum...

Let's take another tack. Like in the previ-ous example, in Figure 3-14 the combined action of Processor B and Processor C works to maintain Processor A's running condi-tions. The difference is that the interaction is always reciprocal. For example, the action of Processor A in combination with Processor C works to maintain Processor B's running conditions, and Processor A in combination with Processor B works to maintain Proces-sor C's running conditions. Such mutual dependence is better known as interdepen-dence, and interdependence connects these three processes into a loop. The processes in total create a full circle of interdependence. From the perspective of each processor, the rest of the loop acts to counteract its tenden-cy to disrupt itself. From the perspective of the entire performance, the performance acts to maintain the running conditions for the entire performance (by contributing to the persistence of all the processors making up the performance). Overall, the performance can be aptly described as a **self-perpetu-ating** or **self-promoting performance**—a performance whose emergent property is to keep itself going. And this all happens with a finite number of processors. Loops of in-terdependence, like any other form of loop, have no ending but are finite in length.

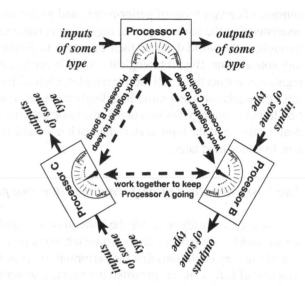

Figure 3-14. The basic structure of a self-perpetuating performance—a performance whose emergent property is to keep itself going. Each dashed lines signifies a proces-sor that acts to maintain the running conditions of another processor. Note that in this performance every processor is connected with every other processor. Furthermore, note that while this figure consists of only three proces-sors, its is easy to extend the logic and envision a larger performance containing many processors where each acts to maintain the running conditions for every other processor. See text for further discussion.

A View of Life: One Sun and Two Loops

I said earlier that Life is loopy. Now we are starting to zero in—by loopy, I meant that Life is composed of self-perpetuating performances.

Two forms of loopy performances, in particular, form the basic structure of Life: nutrient cycling and reproduction. Each of these counters one of the two basic ways that processors contribute to their own demise. Nutrient cycles play an important role in countering each processor using up its supply of needed inputs. Reproduction acts to counter the deterioration of processors through wear and tear (as well as other forms of disruption). So instead of saying that Life is loopy, it would be more accurate to say it is two-loop loopy. Any process must be a part of each of these two types of performance to have any chance of persisting.

But before we look at these two forms of loopy performances somewhat closer, realize that there is one fundamental limit to the self-perpetuating nature of Life. Both nutrient cycling and reproduction require a constant supply of usable energy, yet neither can counter the pattern (discussed in the last chapter) that usable energy tends to become unusable with use. So, for both of these loopy perfor-mances to continue, a supply of usable energy must be continually supplied from elsewhere. Although there are some extremely rare exceptions (such as some thermal vents found deep in the ocean), the sun is the continual source of usable energy for Life on earth.

Life, thus, has three basic components: nutrient cycling, reproduction, and the sun as an external source of usable energy. Life will stop if any of these three are absent. But of these three, only the sun has a foreseeable stopping point. The sun is not part of a loopy performance. It is simply a processor with a finite fuel supply. Someday the sun will burn out, and all life forms still present on this planet will go with it. But the sun's fuel tank is thought to hold enough fuel for billions of more years, so currently it is not Life's most pressing issue.

Nutrient cycling

Along with usable energy, Life processors use up material inputs. Materials in certain arrangements are taken in and rearranged. Chemists call these material rearrangements chemical reactions. The atoms making up molecules are rearranged to form different types of molecules. So, as each processor converts its needed molecular inputs into a different type of molecule, the supply of these input molecules will eventually be used up.

Loopy performances that counteract this problem are commonly termed **nutrient cycles**. They are material cycles, or more specifically chemical cycles, that are built through a specific form of regulatory connection—output–input connections. Specifically, a molecular arrangement that is an output of one processor is used as an input by another processor. Nutrient cycles form whenever one simple condition is satisfied: Every molecular arrangement that is an output of one processor can also be used as an input by another processor. If so, these output–input connections come full circle (see Figure 3-15). And once the circle forms, the performance as a whole is self-perpetuating in nature. Every material arrangement is constantly being lost (as it is used as an input to a chemical reaction) and constantly being regenerated (as it is an output of a chemical reaction). So, from the perspective of any processor within such a cycle, all the other processors in the loop convert the material arrangement it outputs back into a material arrangement that it can use again. In other words, the actions of all other processors within the loop continually regenerate a supply of needed material inputs.

One example of nutrient cycling within Life is the counteracting nature of two biological processes called photosynthesis and aerobic respiration (discussed much more in Chapter 16). These two processes sit at the heart of the continual cycling of material arrangements (molecules) composed of the three elements most commonly

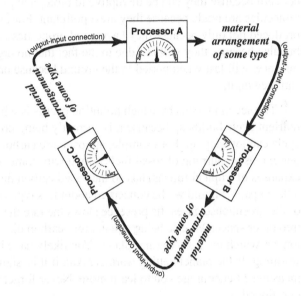

Figure 3-15. The basic structure of a nutrient cycle. The material outputs of each processor can be used as inputs by some other type of processor.

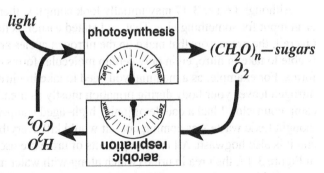

Figure 3-16. A nutrient cycle showing how the processes of photosynthesis and aerobic respiration are involved in the cyclic rearrangement of three elements: oxygen, hydrogen, and carbon.

found within living organisms: oxygen, hydrogen, and carbon (Figure 3-16). Photosynthesis removes hydrogen atoms from water, freeing molecular oxygen, and then adds these hydrogen atoms to carbon dioxide to form sugars. On the other side of the coin, aerobic respiration takes hydrogen atoms from sugars, freeing carbon dioxide, and adds hydrogen atoms back on molecular oxygen to form water.

Overall, nutrient cycles set a boundary condition for Life. For a processor to be part of Life, other processors must exist that can convert every one of this processor's material outputs back into its needed material inputs. Otherwise, it will eventually run out of needed material inputs and stop.

Understanding nutrient cycles sheds light on the topic of **pollution**. A pollutant, in its strictest sense, is any output whose concentration builds up in the atmosphere, the water, or the soil. Pollution occurs via two means. First, some processor generates an output that is not used as an input by anything else. In other words, the outputs of any processor that are not hooked into nutrient cycles are pollutants. Many human-produced molecules fall into this category. Furthermore, the buildup of some of these man-made pollutants, such as radioactive wastes or chemicals like dioxins, has caused concern because they can be disruptive to biological processes. Curiously, some human-produced molecules are made because they are a pollutant. For example, many different forms of plastic are produced not only because they have good properties for forming pipes, containers, toys, and so on, but also because they will last due to the fact that no organism can use them as an input. PVC pipe, for instance, will last when buried in the ground because none of the abundant soil-dwelling organisms can feed on it.

The second means by which pollution occurs is when the concentration of some output within a nutrient cycle builds up because it is currently being produced at such a fast rate that the rest of the cycle cannot keep up. For example, atmospheric carbon dioxide levels are currently rising because our extensive burning of fossil fuels (along with some other factors like such as destruction of vast expanses of tropical forests) has so increased carbon dioxide outputs that biological input is failing to keep pace. Should we be concerned about this type of atmospheric change? Carbon dioxide is one of the greenhouse gases. Its presence slows the rate that the incoming heat from the sun escapes back into outer space. All else being equal, more carbon dioxide in the atmosphere means heat hangs out longer, which means a warmer planet. You likely have heard of this phenomenon by the name global warming. Is the planet getting warmer? And if it is, should we be concerned enough to take preventive measures? I encourage you to learn more. Never forget that it is the nature of your future that is being questioned.

Nutrient cycles also force us to see that not only are we part of something bigger, but that we are intimately connected with organisms that we scarcely even consider. Let's use the basic workings of the nitrogen cycle (see Figure 3-17) to make these points.

Although Figure 3-17 may initially look complex, there is an underlying simplicity—every output is an input for something else. That, as I stated earlier, is the defining feature of a nutrient cycle. Overall, the processors that make up the nitrogen cycles are many different types of organisms. Each is able to take in nitrogen in only certain molecular forms and outputs nitrogen in other molecular forms. For example, as a mammal you need to take in nitrogen mostly in the form of amino acids, and nitrogen leaves your body during urination mostly as urea. I remember years ago while working as a camp counselor, I had a couple of junior high–aged campers who did not want to urinate outside. They thought toxic waste was coming out—it would kill everything that it touched. It is a ghastly thought, and it is also hogwash. All the components of urine are useful inputs to other organisms. As shown in Figure 3-17, the urea in urine (which along with water and salts are urine's major constituents) is converted by certain types of bacteria into ammonia, which is converted by other types of bacteria into nitrite then nitrate, which is taken into plants and converted into amino acids. So whenever you feed on plants or on other animals that feed on plants, you become a link within the nitrogen cycle. As amino acids brought in through your diet are broken down, the nitrogen is converted to urea to be excreted once again. Clearly, we are just one dependent part of a much larger performance.

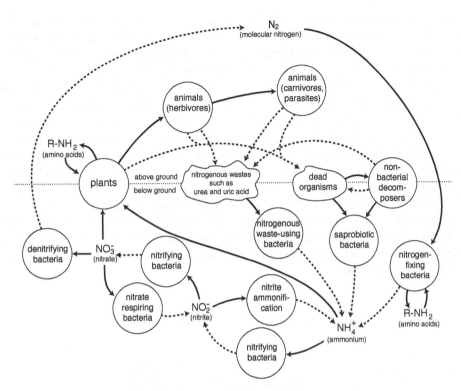

Figure 3-17. The basic structure of the nitrogen cycle. Each type of organism enclosed in circles are the different types of processors involved. Solid lines are inputs, dashed lines are outputs.

The nitrogen cycle is also a good place to try to sway opinion of bacteria. Bacteria generally carry a bad rap as those nasty little creatures that make us sick. It is true that you may even die one day from a bacterial infection. But place that possibility against the backdrop that in the absence of bacteria you would not be here in the first place. In Figure 3-18, I removed all the different types of bacteria found in Figure 3-17. Notice any problems? It breaks the cycle, and the absence of a nitrogen cycle would spell the end to all the remaining organisms, including us. Part of the problem is that without bacteria the molecular forms of nitrogen found in plants and animals and their wastes would never get converted back to nitrate. Without nitrate, plant growth would be severely depressed because for many types of plants it is the strongly preferred nitrogen source. All animals either directly or indirectly feed off plants, so animals are similarly doomed. Perhaps you should thank a bacterium today!

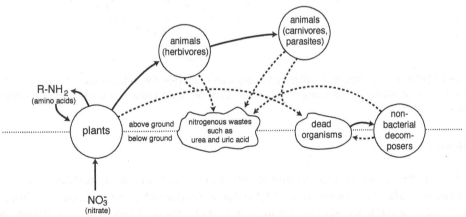

Figure 3-18. What is left of the nitrogen cycle when all the bacteria are removed. It is not a cycle anymore.

Let's make this point about bacteria a bit more subtly. A quick comparison of Figure 3-19 with Figure 3-17 finds only nitrogen-fixing bacteria removed. Nitrogen-fixing bacteria are the only organisms on the planet able to use molecular nitrogen (which makes up around 78% of the molecules that comprise the atmosphere) as a nitrogen source. So although a loop of nitrogen conversion is still present, in the absence of nitrogen-fixing bacteria all the nitrogen converted to molecular nitrogen by denitrifying bacteria is permanently lost. With less and less nitrogen available to be recycled, the overall biological productivity will steadily decline. If nitrogen availability ever reaches zero, then the biological community as a whole will become extinct. Nitrogen-fixing bacteria are thus a key part of the nitrogen cycle. I mention this in part because of a local issue. In the southern Utah deserts (as well as other deserts in the southwest) a fuss is starting to be made over a crusty soil covering called cryptogamic soil. Repeated trooping over this stuff destroys it, and evidence being gathered suggests that it takes a long time for it to form again. One aspect of the biological significance of such destruction, especially if it is wide ranging, is that cryptogamic soil houses all the nitrogen-fixing bacteria found in these areas. Its destruction spells the demise of these bacteria, which breaks a critical link in the nitrogen cycle. As a consequence, the entire desert community will suffer. So as you enjoy the desert, it makes sense to watch your step.

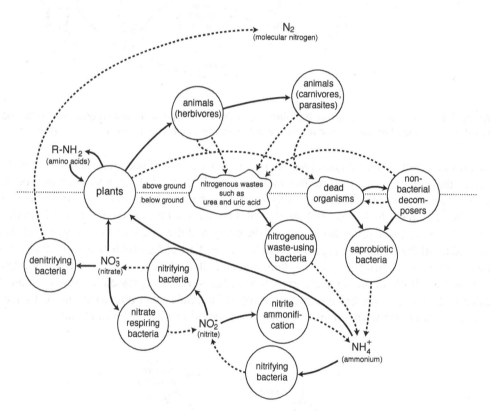

Figure 3-19. What is left of the nitrogen cycle when nitrogen-fixing bacteria are removed. The conversion of nitrate to molecular nitrogen removes more and more nitrogen from the remaining cycle.

Repositories

To flesh out this general understanding of nutrient cycling being developed here just a little further, I add one additional factor. Typically, an output produced by one processor (within a nutrient cycle) will not be instantaneously brought in as an input by the next processor. Yet, the presence of a time delay between outputs becoming inputs can cause a problem. During this time delay, a material output could somehow move beyond the "reach" of those processors able to use it as an input. If so, this material arrangement would be lost from the cycle. Each unit of loss reduces the overall biological productivity because fewer materials are available. As a consequence, a well-functioning nutrient cycle depends on some means to keep outputs around. For convenience, I generically call any such means of temporary storage a repository.

Many nutrient cycles form within the confines of a single cell. In such cases, the repository is the boundary formed by the cell membrane. Nutrient cycles can also form on a much larger scale. Here, components of the environment commonly function as the repositories. The atmosphere, bodies of water, soils, and rocks are the prime examples. In some nutrient cycles, important chemical transformations also occur outside the confines of an organism—that is, the chemical transformations are geochemical instead of biochemical. This fact, plus the nonbiological nature of many repositories, is why large-scale nutrient cycles are commonly called *biogeochemical cycles*.

Through gravity holding huge reservoirs of constantly mixing gases, the atmosphere acts as a repository by keeping biologically useful output gases from drifting off into space. Carbon dioxide, molecular oxygen, and molecular nitrogen are all important examples. Bodies of water such as lakes and oceans can act similarly by holding things in solution, although water is not a great repository. Too much slips through water's "fingers" (through precipitating out of solution) to maintain high levels of nutrient cycling. This is why the ocean's most productive areas are upwellings and estuaries where nutrients levels are kept higher by the continual addition of nutrients from elsewhere. Certain constituents of soils can also hold on to outputs that are useful nutrients for other organisms. In fact, the better a soil is able to hold on to released nutrients, the more fertile the soil is considered to be. And finally, on a longer (geological) time scale, many rocks act as repositories. The weathering of rocks continually makes molecular forms of elements such as phosphorus, potassium, and calcium available to certain life forms. In the other direction, these elements are also being made continually into rocks, mainly though oceanic deposition. A geological process called uplifting completes the loop. Through uplifting, rocks move to the surface, where their contents can again be released by weathering.

Reproduction

Although a nutrient cycle is a self-perpetuating performance, nutrient cycles alone cannot solve Life's riddle. We have yet to discuss a performance that can counteract the problem of processors falling apart. As mentioned previously, the inescapable effects of wear and tear and heat-generated random arrangement, along with other potential forms of disruptive conditions, makes it impossible for a single individual (processor) to last forever. Reproduction, however, can counter this problem.

Although details can vary extensively, the essence of reproduction is a performance that somehow acts to regenerate more copies of itself. The production part of reproduction is the production of offspring. The prefix *re-* signifies that something is being done again. Specifically, that the offspring produced grow up to be the same type of organism that produced them. This familiar notion of parents producing offspring that grow up to be parents of the same type is the easiest way to see reproduction as a loopy performance (see Figure 3-20). Stated in terms developed here, *reproduction is a collection of connected processors (a performance) acting to make more copies of the <u>same</u> processors with the <u>same</u> connections.*

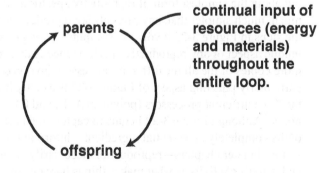

Figure 3-20. The loopy nature of reproduction.

Reproduction counters the deterioration of individuals (processors) by simply making more of the same type. By reproducing, an individual can become a population of like-individuals, which creates more chances that at least one individual will not fall apart at any given time. So long as this is true, the type will persist. Or stated differently, *as long as new individuals of the same type are produced at least as fast as old individuals fall apart, some individuals of this type will continue to exist* (see Figure 3-21).

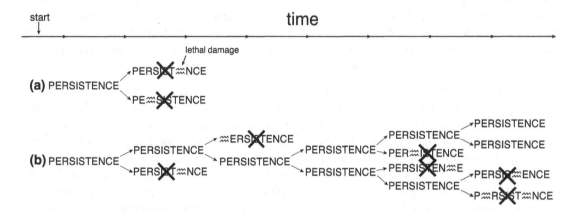

Figure 3-21. The word PERSISTENCE represents a reproductive performance that makes two copies of itself at each reproductive bout. The ability to reproduce, however, is blocked when any letter falls apart—which occurs regularly but randomly. In (a), PERSISTENCE fails to persist because it falls apart faster than it can reproduce. In (b), however, the table is turned. Despite the fact that it is constantly falling apart, PERSISTENCE is able to persist because the rate of reproduction relative to the rate of falling apart has increased.

That reproduction can act to maintain types across time is illustrated by a simple but often-unappreciated truth: *Every living organism that currently inhabits this planet is connected to the past by a chain of reproductively successful ancestors.* It has to be true because otherwise you, along with every other type of current living organism, would not be here. This realization is definitely worth spending some time pondering.

Understanding how a reproduction performance can take place is to understand how a performance could duplicate itself. To be truthful, reproduction is not nearly as easy to understand as a nutrient cycle—which is simply composed of output–input connections coming full circle. The reproductive details found in even the simplest of present-day organisms can be mind-boggling. But to begin to set the stage for later, more extensive discussions on the ways and means of reproduction, I sketch out about the simplest form of reproductive performance imaginable in Figure 3-22. This is much, much, much simpler than any present-day reproductive performance. Like nutrient cycles, some of the steps in Figure 3-22 involve the outputs of one processor being inputs to another processor. But a unique aspect of any reproductive performance is that somewhere processors must output (produce) more copies of the all the different processors involved (polymers A, B, and C in Figure 3-22). A particularly puzzling aspect of Figure 3-22 is exactly how the outputs of polymer C would come to be the three different processors (polymers A, B, and C). It appears to just happen, which is too simplistic. Although Figure 3-22 begins to capture the basic structure of a reproductive performance, it omits completely an essential ingredient—information. As we shall see—as these ideas are developed further in later chapters—reproduction necessarily entails an ongoing interaction between information and activity. Activity is what makes things happen, and information is what guides activity to happen in the *same way* across generations.

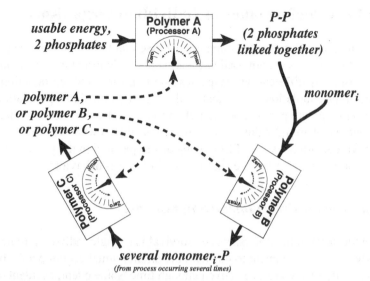

usable energy,
2 phosphates

Polymer A
(Processor A)

P-P
(2 phosphates
linked together)

polymer A,
or polymer B,
or polymer C

monomer$_i$

Polymer C
(Processor C)

Polymer B
(Processor B)

several monomer$_i$-P
(from process occurring several times)

Figure 3-22. A simple reproductive performance. It is a loopy performance because the actions of each processor (polymer A, B, and C) form regulatory connections with each of the other processors. It is a reproductive performance because the performance as a whole makes more copies of all the processors making up the performance. Additional copies of each processor makes it possible for additional copies of the performance as a whole to be set up. (Note: The subscript I in monomer$_i$ designates that the monomer is any of several different types. A polymer is several monomers linked together. Each different type of polymer (A, B, or C) is different in that it is a different sequence of monomers. Do not, however, worry that terms such as polymer and monomer may be unfamiliar to you, and the explanation just given is insufficient. It is seeing overall reproductive pattern, not the specifics of each step, that should be your present focus.)

A brief summary

Figure 3-23 illustrates the simple conception of Life developed earlier. Each component **counteracts** one of the ways that Life could fail to persist. The sun counteracts the tendency for all parts of Life to deplete their supply of usable energy by continually supplying a new source of usable energy. Nutrient cycles counteract the tendency for all parts of Life to deplete their supply of needed material arrangements by converting the outputs of each part of the cycle back into the arrangement needed as inputs. And reproduction counteracts the tendency for all parts of Life to fall apart with time by continually making new copies of each part. Or stated differently, for any process to be a part of Life, it must be plugged in to an external usable energy source (which is almost exclusively the sun), and it must be part of two types of performance: reproduction and nutrient cycles.

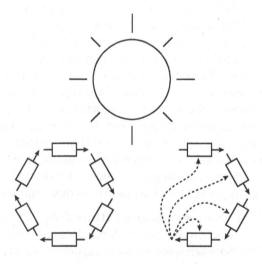

Figure 3-23. Life's three components: (starting at the top and going clockwise) the sun, reproduction, and nutrient cycles. The linear flow of usable energy from the sun powers the cyclic flow of all material nutrients and the production of more copies of all of Life's processors.

The Nature of the Performance of Individual Organisms

Although reproduction and nutrient cycling are the essential loopy performances of Life, they operate at a level that most of us are not used to thinking about. Nutrient cycles commonly operate across a community of many different types (species) of organisms, and reproduction is a counteracting performance at the population level—that is, through reproduction a population containing individuals of a certain type can persist even though individuals die. We, however, tend to think about Life from the perspective of an individual organism because that is what we are. Here, I more fully incorporate the individual into the view of Life being developed and in the process develop a simple and powerful dichotomy that describes the nature of all individual behaviors.

All aspects of survival involve counteracting responses

Survival is *not* the same thing as persistence. Survival is a single individual remaining alive. Individuals can survive from one moment to the next, but an individual cannot persist because no single individual can potentially survive forever. Given enough time, some event, accident or otherwise, will take an individual's life. Yet in the greater scheme of persistence, survival is no trivial matter. As you probably are aware, dead things cannot reproduce. So individuals acting in ways that help them survive could in turn facilitate reproduction.

If you are reading this, then you are currently alive. The question of survival is: What needs to happen for you to still be alive a minute from now, an hour from now, or even longer? To be alive at this moment, every part of you (e.g., heart, brain, liver) that needs to be operating correctly is doing so. And each of your parts can currently function because each is experiencing the conditions it needs to keep running. The same must be true if you are going to still be alive an hour from now. In other words, the key to survival is *to keep things the same.* The conditions needed for all your parts to keep working must be maintained. The difficulty of this task is that like every processor, each of your body's parts is constantly disrupting the conditions it needs to keep running. Needed inputs are being used up, and waste products are accumulating. Plus, external sources of danger such as predators, parasites, or being hit by a bolt of lightning can disrupt running conditions. So to survive—that is, to keep things the same—an individual must continually act to counter all disruptions to its running conditions. Think about yourself. You go to work so you can get money to buy food so you can eat to counteract your always-diminishing supply of usable energy and nutrients. Each breath you take helps to counteract the increasing shortage of oxygen and increasing buildup of carbon dioxide in your body. Each drink you take helps counteract water loss. Running away from a speeding car or other forms of danger is a counteraction aimed at moving you to a safer location. The healing currently going on where you cut yourself yesterday is a means by which you continually restore disruptions to your arrangement. The list goes on and on, yet the basic point stays the same: To survive you must keep things the same by making **counteracting responses**.

The phrase **maintaining balance** along with the term **homeostasis** are commonly used to describe the actions of keeping things the same. Loss must be balanced by gain. Gain must be balanced by loss. So when someone speaks about an organism maintaining energy balance, carbon dioxide balance, water balance, or any other balance, recognize two things: First, the discussion is about an organism attempting to survive. Second, counteracting responses are the means used to do so. *Counteracting responses are trend-reversing,* and to act in ways that reverses any trend of change is to push things back toward where they were prior to the change (see Figure 3-24). The response to levels of something going down is to act in ways that will increase levels. The response to levels of something going up is to act in ways that will decrease levels.

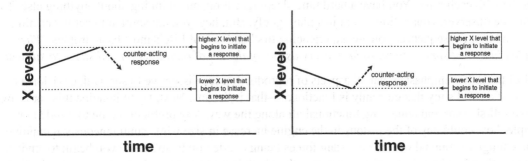

Figure 3-24. The two sides of a counter-acting response—responding to either rising **X** levels or decreasing **X** levels in trend-reversing ways, where X represents anything relevant to an organism's survival.

All aspects of reproduction (at the individual level) involve coacting responses

In contrast to counteracting responses, **coacting responses** will work against an organism's survival. *Coacting responses are trend maintaining;* they respond to change in ways that keep the change going (see Figure 3-25). And maintaining (or even accelerating) any direction of change is to exacerbate any form of disruption to an organism's running conditions.

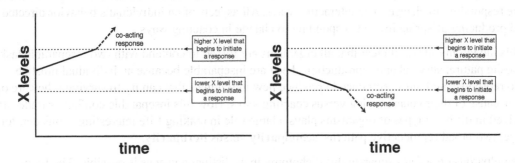

Figure 3-25. The two sides of a co-acting response—responding to either rising **X** levels or decreasing **X** levels in trend-maintaining ways, where X represents anything relevant to an organism reproducing.

But curiously, organisms do not avoid all coacting responses. Why? In the larger scheme of things, it comes back to the fact that survival is not the same as persistence. As convoluted as this may sound, the chain of logic goes as follows: First, survival is useful because organisms must remain alive to maintain the opportunity to reproduce. Second, any type of organism can persist only if it reproduces. And third, from the perspective of an individual organism, the performance of reproduction runs opposite to the performance of survival. Just think about it. Producing an offspring is not about keeping things the same, it is about generating something new, and to make something new is to change things. Generating change underlies every step of reproduction from finding a mate, to ovulation in females, to sperm production in males, to both males and females finding a mate, to giving birth, to parental care, to the offspring's growth and development. And the means to generate change is to employ coacting responses.

It is the explosive, risk-taking, inherently unstable nature of coacting responses that makes reproductive behaviors seem so incredibly crazy in other species and so exciting within ourselves. Just think about the first stages of romance. In a coacting way, you and your partner each act to accelerate an initial trend of mutual attraction. You write poetry when you've never done so before. You buy presents that you cannot afford and perhaps do not even like. You forgo other activities that you enjoy just to be with each other. You have a hard time sleeping, eating, and thinking about anything else. To the outside observer, your actions seem just plain goofy. But, hey, you are smitten to act in coacting ways. And as a consequence, you are experiencing firsthand one of Life's most basic ironies: *Whereas an individual must survive to reproduce, every aspect of the act of reproduction will strive to kill you.*

Just to further emphasize that all aspects of reproduction are disruptive to survival, envision a car the size of a child's toy that currently is functional—that is, it runs. Next, try to imagine this car growing to a full-size car and remaining functional all along the way. Any problems come to mind? For example, how could any of the pistons in the engine increase in size while simultaneously remaining strong enough to contend with the constant forces being exerted on them? Once you begin to envision problems, then you have just realized that growth, which is a part of reproduction, is constantly disruptive to survival. Growth is change, and survival is all about keeping things the same. Furthermore, recognizing the disruptive nature of growth gives you one more reason to be amazed and impressed with yourself (along with every other living organism). From a very small size, you have grown to your present stature and remained alive every moment along the way. How did you ever accomplish such a feat?

The dichotomy: Survival versus reproduction, reproduction versus survival

We have just created a powerful, but simple dichotomy in terms of understanding the behavior of individual organisms. All aspects of an individual's behavior directed toward maintaining its own life involve responding to change in counteracting ways. All aspects of an individual's behavior directed toward producing offspring involve responding to change in coacting ways.

This dichotomy makes it clear that all organisms are forced to contend with two inseparable tasks of opposite nature: survival and reproduction. They are inseparable because an individual must be alive to reproduce and must reproduce to produce new individuals that can try to survive. They are opposite because of their counteracting versus coacting ways. How this inseparable conflict or trade-off is resolved in different types of organisms plays a large role in making Life interesting. Consider, for instance, two broad reproductive patterns: **semelparity** versus **iteroparity**.

Semelparous organisms separate this dichotomy in as distinct a way as is possible. The focus initially is on growth and survival, and then they undertake a single episode of breeding. During this single reproductive attempt, as many resources as possible are shifted away from survival and toward reproduction. As a consequence, the breeding effort is large, but the individual dies shortly thereafter. Salmon of several different types (species) are a classic example of semelparity. Because of the extreme effort involved in swimming upriver to reach spawning grounds, it makes sense for any individual salmon to attempt the trip only once. But when constrained to a single reproductive attempt, it also makes sense not to hold back. Each salmon ensures its death by converting as much of its body's resources as possible into reproduction.

Alternatively, iteroparous organisms never make such a complete switch from survival to reproduction. During each breeding attempt resources are allocated away from survival, and consequently, individuals are more susceptible to death during this time. But enough resources are still allocated to survival during the breeding period that an individual has a reasonable chance to survive to breed again in the future. In other words, iteroparous organisms never completely trade off reproduction for survival, and as a consequence they set up the possibility of breeding more than once. There are many examples of iteroparous breeders. You, as a human, are one of them.

Designing counteracting and coacting responses

The idea that all behaviors of all individual organisms can be captured by two simple patterns (counteracting or coacting) is exciting because it makes the goal of understanding how Life works in a deep and meaningful way seem that much more attainable.

What we need to add to this simple framework is an understanding of the basic ways to design a counteracting or coacting response. Once you have the basic design features down, you are equipped to understand every one of the literally millions of examples of counteracting and coacting responses among the living forms inhabiting this planet. The conceptual power comes from the fact that although there is a huge range in the details of how different organisms orchestrate survival and reproductive behaviors, there are only six basic ways to design a counteracting response and six more ways to design a coacting response. Furthermore, once you understand just one of these possible designs, you are well on your way to understanding all of them.

These basic designs are presented in some detail in an appendix at the end of the chapter. Putting them in an appendix is not a statement of importance, but a way to separate this discussion from the rest of the chapter.

A Potpourri of More Philosophical Topics

I finish this chapter with a bit of a potpourri of more philosophical topics that emerge from the view of Life being developed. Each topic helps fill in some cracks in this general view of Life, but they do not all hang together in a distinctly cohesive way. Perhaps more important, the focus is not so much to present more information on biology, *but to give you a chance to ponder some topics that are fun to think about.*

Next-level reversals

Perhaps you noticed something that at first sounds odd. Counteracting responses are defined as trend reversing, yet it is through counteracting responses that organisms as a whole maintain a trend—they maintain their survival by keeping things the same. Stated differently, all the various body parts that generate counteracting responses combine to become coacting (trend maintaining) at the next level of organization—the whole organism.

This same pattern of reversal came up when we discussed the fact that individual organisms are caught in a trade-off between survival and reproduction. Although the coacting aspects of reproduction can be disruptive to individuals, reproduction counteracts the fact that no individual can survive forever. And like with survival at the individual level, this counteracting aspect of reproduction forms a coacting aspect at the level of the population as a whole. It makes it possible for a population to maintain a population across time; or in other words, it allows the population to persist. And it is because of this next-level reversal that reproduction should, when necessary, take precedence over individual survival.

This raises an intriguing question: Are next-level reversals important components of Life at even higher levels of organization? Let me provide one example that suggests that the answer is yes.

Another coacting aspect of reproduction is the potential for compounding growth. The larger a population becomes, the more individuals there are to reproduce, which makes it possible for next generation to be larger than the last, and the next even larger, and so on. Stated differently, given a sufficient supply of needed resources, the size of any population can grow explosively (exponentially). (Note: The potential for populations to grow exponentially is discussed further in Chapter 5.)

This explosive potential again generates a next-level reversal. It forms a larger-scale counteracting response that helps keep nutrient cycles from clogging up. Let me explain. The inputs and outputs of individual populations form the links of larger-scale nutrient cycles. To keep a nutrient cycle flowing, each link must continually process inputs (into outputs) as fast as they are becoming available—that is, as fast as the previous link in the cycle is generating outputs. But what is to maintain this balance? In other words, if one link begins to fail to keep up, how can an increasing buildup of the previous link's output be averted? A buildup will slow the flow through the whole cycle just as a clog at one part of a drain slows the flow through the whole drain. The answer is that any such buildup is potentially countered by a corresponding buildup in those populations that use this output as an input. Overall, the constant adjustment in population size at each link acts to keep nutrient cycles clog free, which in turn keeps the environmental supply of different chemical forms being cycled relatively constant. Once again counteracting responses act at the next level to keep things the same.

The extent to which this type of performance operates on a global scale has recently enjoyed considerable debate. Originators of what has been termed the Gaia hypothesis have taken this idea to one extreme. They see Life, as a whole, being like a single organism. Just as single organisms maintain running conditions by a coordinated collection of counteracting responses, they suggest that Life has come to do the same thing. Specifically, the counteracting responses of population size increases (and decreases) are sufficiently powerful for Life to maintain its needed running conditions on a planetary scale.

Although this is an intriguing idea, I am not sold on the biosphere as a single organism metaphor. My basic problem is that although such a metaphor can aid clarity, it can also generate confusion. The clarity comes from inspiring focus on counteracting performances operating at such a large level of organization. We need to understand the extent that interactions among all the different populations that make up Life on this planet influence the nature of the planet. The confusion comes from the ease by which we take comparisons too far. The different counteracting responses within a single organism are often coordinated by intricate means of chemical communication among different body parts. As we discuss further in Chapter 7, the evolution of this intense degree of coordination is channeled by the fact that the only route for each body part to persist is to help the organism as a whole to survive and reproduce. The same, however, cannot be said for the different populations that make up Life as a whole. Although different populations constantly interact, the persistence of each is not tied directly to the persistence of all other populations. This greater autonomy among parts makes the evolution of the same degree of cooperation (with the same underlying means of coordination found in individual organisms) impossible. Yet, if we take this metaphor too seriously, we might presume that they work the same.

Living versus Life

Let me ask a couple of somewhat strange sounding questions: Is it possible for organisms to be living but not be part of Life? Is it possible for something nonliving to be part of Life? I can make an argument for a yes answer to both.

Living is what responsive, metabolically active organisms are. As I once found in a dictionary, living is the opposite of being dead. But a living organism is part of Life if and only if it is part of Life's two loops. It must be able to reproduce, and nutrient cycles must be in place that rearrange all its chemical outputs back into needed chemical inputs. Otherwise, it may not be currently dead, but in terms of persistence it is a dead end—a condition that (along with vampires) has been termed the "living dead". A mule is an example. These hybrids of horses and donkeys are vigorous living animals. But they are not part of Life because they are sterile. The same would be true for a plant species whose reproduction relies solely on an animal pollinator that just went extinct. The individuals making up this plant species are all still very much living, but in the absence of reproduction the species as a whole is headed for extinction. Links broken in a nutrient cycle result in a similar fate. Certain species will go extinct as they eventually run out of their needed inputs.

Some biologists have suggested that viruses are not living. They are basically little chunks of a molecule called DNA or RNA that use the machinery of metabolically active (living) cells to make more viruses. In other words, they do not metabolize on their own. So according to the preceding definition of living, they are not alive. But as reproductive entities potentially hooked into nutrient cycles, they surely could be a part of Life.

Scaling Life's performance hierarchy

As mentioned earlier, whether something is seen as a processor or a performance is often a matter of perspective. When attention is paid only to the inputs and outputs, any performance will appear to be a processor because outputs will be different from inputs. However, closer inspection may reveal the presence of many different connected processors—the characteristic features of a performance. Consider yourself. I pointed out earlier that you are a processor because what goes in is different from what goes out. Yet you are also a performance. All your different parts (e.g., liver, muscles, and eyes) are different types of processors connected into the performance that you call yourself.

That something can simultaneously be both a process and a performance makes a **performance hierarchy** possible. A performance hierarchy forms whenever units of performance become processors joined by regulatory connections into a higher-level performance.

Such a performance hierarchy is found in Life and is often called the *hierarchical organization of Life*. Each level of organization is a new level of performance (see Figure 3-26). Strikingly, Life exists only within the context of the entire hierarchy. Life's two essential loops—reproduction and nutrient cycling—round into a complete form across the various levels of performance.

To form a loop, interdependent processors must remain close enough to interact. A straightforward means to increase such linkage is to enclose different processors within a single container—that is, to lock them all together within a cell. This is what a biological cell is all about. Different processors making up a reproductive performance are enclosed within a

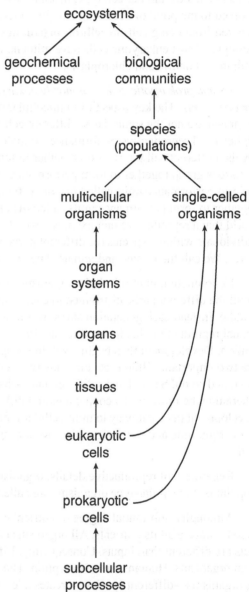

Figure 3-26. Life's performance hierarchy (see text for further discussion).

container. *In fact, cells are Life's fundamental reproductive unit.* Cells reproduce by **cell division**. Cell parts are duplicated and then pulled to each side before the container divides into two.

Two basic cell types are found on this planet: prokaryotic cells and eukaryotic cells. **Prokaryotic cells** have the most basic cell form. You probably know them as bacteria. **Eukaryotic cells** tend to have a more complex structure. Individual cells of either type are known to exist as an organism—a single-celled organism. Yet a trend in the history of Life is that different types of cells have formed reproductive alliances. These alliances have formed in two distinct ways:

• *Cells living inside other cells.* Although there are many examples of one cell type taking up residence inside another cell type, in some cases it seems that the cells living inside another cell have evolved to the point of becoming a highly integrated part of the host cell. In other words, they have evolved from being cells to **cellular organelles**. Mitochondria and chloroplasts are thought to be two examples. Most eukaryotic cells have mitochondria, whereas a smaller subset of eukaryotic cells have both mitochondria and chloroplasts.

• *Some prokaryotic cells, but mostly eukaryotic cells, have also joined together to form multicellular organisms.* The key aspect of multicellular organisms is cellular differentiation. All cells within the organism are not the same. These different cell types are the different types of processors linked into a higher-level reproductive performance. Actually, the performance hierarchy proceeds through several levels. Different cell types group together to form performance units called **tissues**. Different types of tissues group together to form performance units called **organs**. Different organs group together to form performance units called **organ systems**. And finally, different types of organ systems group together to form performance units called **organisms**. In addition, it is common in the multicellular world that a reproductive unit extends beyond a single individual. Reproduction can be sexual, and individuals within a species (or different parts of the same individual) can differentiate into one of two sexes. We call them male and female. The pair is the reproductive unit.

Reproduction in multicellular organisms is not like cell reproduction. Duplicates are not made of all the different parts, distributed to each side, culminating with splitting the organism down the middle. Instead each generation starts over as a single cell and proceeds through **development**. In sexual reproduction this first cell results from a fusion between two cells—a process known as fertilization. Development then begins with this single cell dividing in the basic way that cells do. But there are two important differences. First, the two cells remain attached, as they do in the next division, and next, and so on. Second, cells differentiate—that is, from one cell various different types of cells arise. There may be upward of a couple hundred different cell types within a single organism. The details of development (as a pathway to multicellular reproduction) center around how different cell types form at the right time and in the right place to reform the same type of organism that produced the initial cell.

Regardless of reproductive details, organisms able to reproduce can form **populations**. Distinct populations of similar-type organisms are called **species**.

Although a substantial degree of nutrient cycling occurs within organisms, no organism can completely recycle all its nutrients. All organisms exhibit the characteristic features of a processor—outputs are different than inputs. Consequently, Life depends on nutrient cycles forming on a scale larger than organisms. Humans are no exception. The flow of outputs-turned-inputs between different types of organisms—different species—creates a level of performance know as a **biological community**. As discussed earlier, however, nutrient cycles commonly extend beyond resource flow among species to include abiotic (nonliving) components. An **ecosystem** is all the biotic and abiotic processors and repositories involved in the cyclic flow of all materials used to build organisms.

All levels of performance are complex

All these levels of this hierarchical performance are complex. At the cellular level, prokaryotic cells have thousands of different types of processors, and eukaryotic cells have even more. Multicellular organisms can have hundreds of cell types, and biological communities have thousands to perhaps millions of different species.

This complexity makes one wonder: Why so complex? Or stated differently: Why not simpler? The answer is not readily apparent. The effects of complexity can range from being bureaucratic (wherein all the different types of interactions impede the effectiveness of the total performance), to redundant (wherein certain parts exist because they can fit into the loopy performance, but their absence would not be missed), to adaptive (wherein the complexity tends to enhance performance, especially in terms of making it possible for the loop to continue to perform effectively under a wider range of circumstance), or probably many other nuances in between. Biologists often envision biological complexity as being adaptive, but bureaucracy and redundancy may well be present in the structure of Life.

The mirage of teleology

The Aristotelian notion of final cause is synonymous with the concept of teleology. Final causation is the idea that an action occurs *in order to accomplish* something later in time.

Many scholars have held the notion of teleology in disrepute because it flip-flops the most easily accepted view of the relationship between cause and effect—an effect is the result of previously occurring actions (causal factors). Furthermore, these causal factors resulted from actions that preceded them, and so on back in time. Therefore every occurrence can be explained solely by the events that preceded it.

Teleology, on the other hand, muddies this generally accepted time course. It suggests that an action was initiated to bring about some desired effect. In other words, the notion of final cause claims that the effect of a cause plays a causal role in initiating the cause of the effect (huh?).

Where teleological thinking has made its greatest inroads is in thinking about living organisms. The actions of living organisms often appear to be teleological. For example, it appears that coyotes chase after rabbits *in order to* get food. Or, each step in development occurs *in order for* the organisms to become a sexually mature adult.

All this confusion stems from a simple fact: A loop seems to go somewhere if one observes only part of the loop. Life being composed of self-promoting performances means that present actions of individual organisms are repeats of performances that kept themselves going in the past. Coyotes that caught rabbits in the past, for example, produced the coyotes trying to catch rabbits now. Living things are like a race car running a circular track. They travel in temporal circles—that is, loops that form across time. Although at any one time they appear to be moving in order to get somewhere, they are only heading back to where they have already been. So to see the ways of living organisms we have to see the whole loopy track. Otherwise, a self-promoting performance appears to be organized by what it is attempting to accomplish in the future.

Appendix: Designing Counteracting and Coacting Responses

All counteracting and coacting responses have four basic components. First, they employ a *sensor* responsive to some aspect of the organism's internal or external environment, such as internal water levels, internal usable energy levels, presence of predators or potential mates, temperature, and so on. Here I refer to this sensor generically as an **X**-sensor, where **X** is any such component. Second, the organism must have a processor or set of processors whose actions work to change **X** levels. Third, a connection must exist between the **X**-sensor and those processors able to alter **X** levels. Fourth, this connection must be such that **X** levels are altered in either a trend-reversing way (counteracting re-sponse) or a trend-maintaining way (coacting response). For example, in a counteracting response rising **X** levels must be met with rate changes that act to decrease **X** levels. Alternatively, falling **X** levels must be met with rate changes that act to increase **X** levels. The overall effect is to act to maintain **X** at a constant level. (Exactly what level that might be, and how accurately that level is maintained, depends on the details of the counteracting response. Details such as how sensitive the **X**-sensor is, and how rapidly and forcefully the **X**-changing processes can counter movement in either direction.) Coacting responses would work in the opposite manner. Rising **X** levels would be met with rate changes that act to further increase **X** levels. Alternatively, falling **X** levels would be met with rate changes that act to further decrease **X** levels.

Counteracting responses: Direct connection

Figure 3-27 illustrates the simplest means to set up such a counteracting response. In both cases, the sensor that responds to changing **X** levels (an **X**-sensor) is located on a processor able to alter **X** levels (because **X** is either an input or an output). Although the details are different, each of these generates a counteracting response because they combine a positive and negative relationship. So overall the response to changing **X** levels, whether they are rising or falling, is one that opposes (acts to decelerate) the trend

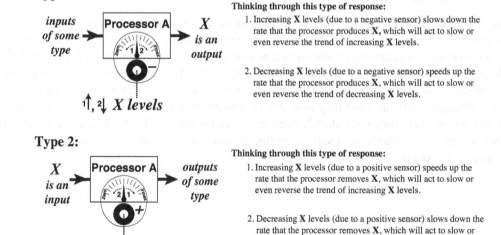

Type 1:

inputs of some type → Processor A → **X** is an output

↑1, 2↓ **X levels**

Thinking through this type of response:
1. Increasing **X** levels (due to a negative sensor) slows down the rate that the processor produces **X,** which will act to slow or even reverse the trend of increasing **X** levels.

2. Decreasing **X** levels (due to a negative sensor) speeds up the rate that the processor produces **X,** which will act to slow or even reverse the trend of decreasing **X** levels.

Type 2:

X is an input → Processor A → outputs of some type

↑1, 2↓ **X levels**

Thinking through this type of response:
1. Increasing **X** levels (due to a positive sensor) speeds up the rate that the processor removes **X,** which will act to slow or even reverse the trend of increasing **X** levels.

2. Decreasing **X** levels (due to a positive sensor) slows down the rate that the processor removes **X,** which will act to slow or even reverse the trend of decreasing **X** levels.

Figure 3-27. The two most basic ways to set up a counteracting response.

Coacting responses: Direct connection

Any counteracting response is easily converted to a coacting response—that is, a response that acts to maintain or even accelerate any trend of change. The graphics in Figure 3-27, for instance, can be converted into coacting responses by simply switching each sensor to the opposite sign (see Figure 3-28). Once switched, the response to rising **X** levels is to either increase the rate **X** is produced or decrease the rate that **X** is used as an input, and the response to lowering **X** levels is just the opposite.

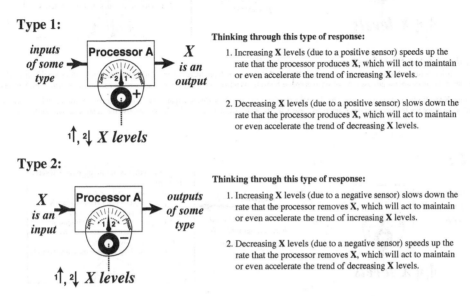

Type 1:

inputs of some type → **Processor A** → **X** is an output

⬆,²⬇ *X levels*

Thinking through this type of response:

1. Increasing **X** levels (due to a positive sensor) speeds up the rate that the processor produces **X**, which will act to maintain or even accelerate the trend of increasing **X** levels.

2. Decreasing **X** levels (due to a positive sensor) slows down the rate that the processor produces **X**, which will act to maintain or even accelerate the trend of decreasing **X** levels.

Type 2:

X is an input → **Processor A** → outputs of some type

⬆,²⬇ *X levels*

Thinking through this type of response:

1. Increasing **X** levels (due to a negative sensor) slows down the rate that the processor removes **X**, which will act to maintain or even accelerate the trend of increasing **X** levels.

2. Decreasing **X** levels (due to a negative sensor) speeds up the rate that the processor removes **X**, which will act to maintain or even accelerate the trend of decreasing **X** levels.

Figure 3-28. The two most basic ways to set up a coacting response.

Counteracting responses: Indirect connection

Most counteracting responses found in organisms are not structured as simply as those shown in Figure 3-27. The basic difference is that **X**-sensors are not always located on the processors that can directly alter **X** levels. In such cases, the generation of a counteracting response depends on the presence of some form of regulatory connection through which a rate change in processors with **X**-sensors will lead to rate changes in processors that can alter **X** levels. I refer to counteracting responses involving such regulatory connections as **indirect counteracting responses**. Figure 3-29 illustrates the four possible ways that such responses can be arranged when the regulatory connection is forged through the output of the processor with the **X**-sensor. Spend some time trying to find the relatively simple logic that underlies each type.

Type A:

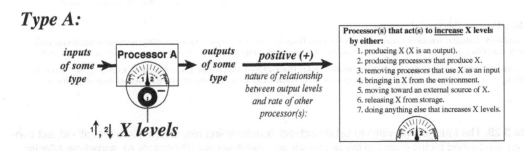

inputs of some type → **Processor A** → outputs of some type → *positive (+)*

nature of relationship between output levels and rate of other processor(s):

⬆,²⬇ *X levels*

Processor(s) that act(s) to <u>increase</u> X levels by either:
1. producing X (X is an output).
2. producing processors that produce X.
3. removing processors that use X as an input
4. bringing in X from the environment.
5. moving toward an external source of X.
6. releasing X from storage.
7. doing anything else that increases X levels.

Thinking through this type of response:

1. Increasing **X** levels (due to negative sensor) slows down the rate that Processor A produces outputs. Due to the positive relationship this, in turn, slows the rate of the processor (or processors) that act to increase **X** levels, which overall acts to slow or even reverse the trend of increasing **X** levels.

2. Decreasing **X** levels (due to negative sensor) speeds up the rate that Processor A produces outputs. Due to the positive relationship this, in turn, speeds up the rate of the processor (or processors) that act to increase **X** levels, which overall acts to slow or even reverse the trend of decreasing **X** levels.

Type B:

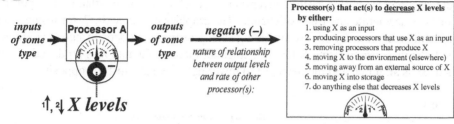

Thinking through this type of response:

1. Increasing **X** levels (due to negative sensor) slows down the rate that Processor A produces outputs. Due to the negative relationship this, in turn, speeds up the rate of the processor (or processors) that act to decrease **X** levels, which overall acts to slow or even reverse the trend of increasing **X** levels.

2. Decreasing **X** levels (due to negative sensor) speeds up the rate that Processor A produces outputs. Due to the negative relationship this, in turn, slows the rate of the processor (or processors) that act to decrease **X** levels, which overall acts to slow or even reverse the trend of decreasing **X** levels.

Type C:

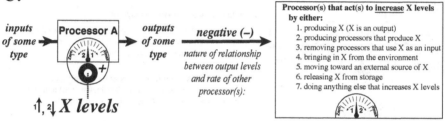

Thinking through this type of response:

1. Increasing **X** levels (due to positive sensor) speeds up the rate that Processor A produces outputs. Due to the negative relationship this, in turn, slows the rate of the processor (or processors) that act to increase **X** levels, which overall acts to slow or even reverse the trend of increasing **X** levels.

2. Decreasing **X** levels (due to positive sensor) slows down the rate that Processor A produces outputs. Due to the negative relationship this, in turn, speeds up the rate of the processor (or processors) that act to increase **X** levels, which overall acts to slow or even reverse the trend of decreasing **X** levels.

Type D:

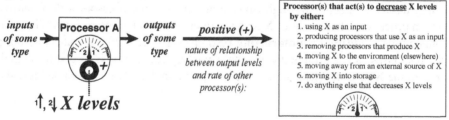

Thinking through this type of response:

1. Increasing **X** levels (due to positive sensor) speeds up the rate that Processor A produces outputs. Due to the positive relationship this, in turn, speeds up the rate of the processor (or processors) that act to decrease **X** levels, which overall acts to slow or even reverse the trend of increasing **X** levels.

2. Decreasing **X** levels (due to positive sensor) slows down the rate that Processor A produces outputs. Due to the positive relationship this, in turn, slows the rate of the processor (or processors) that act to decrease **X** levels, which overall acts to slow or even reverse the trend of decreasing **X** levels.

Figure 3-29. The four general ways to set up indirect counteracting responses. Note that all indirect connections are formed by the output of the processor with the **X**-sensor (Processor A), somehow affecting the rate of **X**-changing processors. A positive relationship means that as output levels change the rate of effected processors changes in the same way—increasing output leads to increasing rate, while decreasing output leads to decreasing rate. A negative relationship is just the opposite—increasing output leads to decreasing rate, while decreasing output leads to increasing rate.

What is still missing in Figure 3-29 is a better explanation of how the output-based regulatory connections could occur. Of course, we have already covered that in our discussion of output-input based connections, number-based connections, and sensor-based connections. The following three figures (Figures 3-30 through 3-32) illustrate how each of these regulatory connections can be used. In Figures 3-30 and 3-31, there is only one and two examples shown, respectively. It turns out that these types of regulatory connections cannot be used to construct each of the four possible types illustrated in Figure 3-29.

Type A:

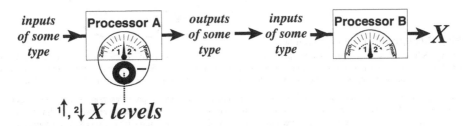

Thinking through this type of response:

1. Increasing **X** levels (due to a negative sensor) slows down the rate that Processor A produces outputs. This change slows the rate that Processor B needed inputs become available thus the rate that these inputs can be converted into **X,** which will slow or even reverse the trend of increasing X levels.

2. Decreasing **X** levels (due to a negative sensor) speeds up the rate that Processor A produces outputs. This change speeds up the rate that Processor B needed inputs become available thus the rate that these inputs can be converted into **X,** which will slow or even reverse the trend of decreasing X levels.

Figure 3-30. The one way an output-input based connection can be used to form an indirect counteracting response. It follows the basic design laid out in Type A in Figure 3-29. We will see biological examples of this form of regulation when we discuss enzyme-level metabolic regulation in Chapter 14.

Type A:

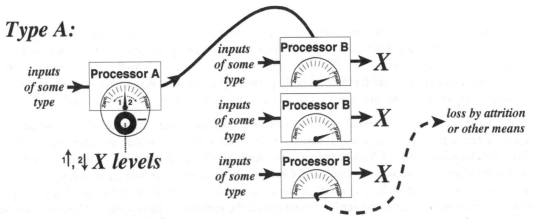

Thinking through this type of response:

1. Increasing **X** levels (due to a negative sensor) slows down the rate that Processor A produces more copies of Processor B. Once the rate of Processor B production dips below the rate of loss, the number of Processor Bs will be reduced, which will slow or even reverse the trend of increasing **X** levels by decreasing the rate that **X** is produced.

2. Decreasing **X** levels (due to a negative sensor) speeds up the rate that Processor A produces more copies of Processor B. Once the rate of Processor B production exceeds the rate of loss, the number of Processor Bs will increase, which will slow or even reverse the trend of decreasing **X** levels by increasing the rate that **X** is produced.

Type D:

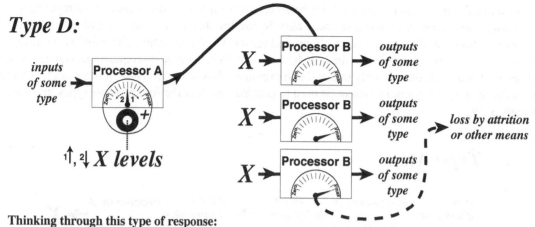

Thinking through this type of response:

1. Increasing **X** levels (due to a positive sensor) speeds up the rate that Processor A produces more copies of Processor B. Once the rate of Processor B production exceeds the rate of loss, the number of Processor Bs will increase, which will slow or even reverse the trend of increasing **X** levels by increasing the rate that **X** is used as an input (thus converted into something else).

2. Decreasing **X** levels (due to a positive sensor) slows down the rate that Processor A produces more copies of Processor B. Once the rate of Processor B production dips below the rate of loss, the number of Processor Bs will be reduced, which will slow or even reverse the trend of decreasing **X** levels by decreasing the rate that **X** is used as an input (thus converted into something else).

Figure 3-31. The two ways a number-based regulatory connection—where the output of one processor is another processor—can be used to form an indirect counteracting response. They follow the basic design laid out in Type A and Type D in Figure 3-29. We will see biological examples of this form of regulation when we discuss gene-level metabolic regulation in Chapter 14.

Sensor-based connections (Figure 3-32) introduce the notion of communication into the realm of counteracting responses. Communication, in any form, depends on one thing generating something that something else can detect via a sensor. Those conditions are met whenever one processor has a sensor that detects an output of another processor. The output can be said to be a "signal," and the sensor that detects this signal could be said to be a "receiver," a "receptor," or a "signal-sensor." In Figure 3-32, the signal is an output of the processor with an **X**-sensor. The signal-sensor is on an **X**-changing processor.

The basic scheme of signals and receivers illustrated in Figure 3-32 creates the possibility of locating an **X**-sensor in a different place than the processors that respond to changing **X** levels. For example, with a means to transport a signal, an organism could locate a sensor to some aspect of its environment in a different location than the body parts most capable of responding to such change. This idea, however, raises the questions about when such separation would be beneficial.

One reason has to do with (what I call) the **optimal vantage-point** and **optimal effector-point** being in different locations. The optimal vantage point is the best place within an organism to put a lookout for changing levels of **X**. Alternatively, the optimal effector-point is the location that a processor can most effectively respond to changing **X** levels. For example, consider an animal reacting to an external source of danger such as an approaching predator. At the very least, the optimal vantage point to detect an external source of danger is somewhere on the surface of the organism. How else would a sensor be able to detect what is going on outside? And most likely, some surface locations would be better than others. In contrast, muscles need to be sandwiched inside the organism to effectively move an animal away from danger. However, putting each of these parts in their best location would work only if three conditions are met. First, the sensor that detects an approaching predator must change the rate that a signal is produced. Second, the muscles used in mounting an escape must have a sensor that detects this signal. And third, the signal must travel fast enough to start a response before the predator gets there. We address this issue again in Chapter 25.

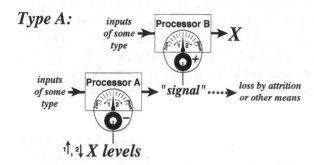

Type A:

Thinking through this type of response:

1. Increasing **X** levels (due to a negative sensor) slows down the rate that Processor A produces the output designated as a "signal". Once the rate of signal production dips below the rate of loss, the total amount of signal will be reduced. Decreasing signal levels (due to a positive sensor) slows down the rate that Processor B produces **X**, which will slow or even reverse the trend of increasing **X** levels.

2. Decreasing **X** levels (due to a negative sensor) speeds up the rate that Processor A produces the output designated as a "signal". Once the rate of signal production exceeds the rate of loss, the total amount of signal will be increased. Increasing signal levels (due to a positive sensor) speeds up the rate that Processor B produces **X**, which will slow or even reverse the trend of decreasing **X** levels.

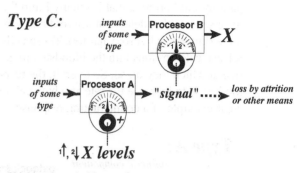

Type C:

Thinking through this type of response:

1. Increasing **X** levels (due to a positive sensor) speeds up the rate that Processor A produces the output designated as a "signal". Once the rate of signal production exceeds the rate of loss, the total amount of signal will be increased. Increasing signal levels (due to a negative sensor) slows down the rate that Processor B produces **X**, which will slow or even reverse the trend of increasing **X** levels.

2. Decreasing **X** levels (due to a positve sensor) slows down the rate that Processor A produces the output designated as a "signal". Once the rate of signal production dips below the rate of loss, the total amount of signal will be decreased. Decreasing signal levels (due to a negative sensor) speeds up the rate that Processor B produces **X**, which will slow or even reverse the trend of decreasing **X** levels.

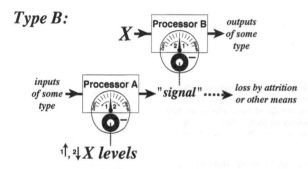

Type B:

Thinking through this type of response:

1. Increasing **X** levels (due to a negative sensor) slows down the rate that Processor A produces the output designated as a "signal". Once the rate of signal production dips below the rate of loss, the total amount of signal will be reduced. Decreasing signal levels (due to a negative sensor) speeds up the rate that Processor B uses **X** as an input (thus is converted into something else), which will slow or even reverse the trend of increasing **X** levels.

2. Decreasing **X** levels (due to a negative sensor) speeds up the rate that Processor A produces the output designated as a "signal". Once the rate of signal production exceeds the rate of loss, the total amount of signal will be increased. Increasing signal levels (due to a negative sensor) slows down the rate that Processor B uses **X** as an input (thus is converted into something else), which will slow or even reverse the trend of decreasing **X** levels.

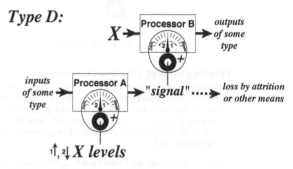

Type D:

Thinking through this type of response:

1. Increasing **X** levels (due to a positive sensor) speeds up the rate that Processor A produces the output designated as a "signal". Once the rate of signal production exceeds the rate of loss, the total amount of signal will be increased. Increasing signal levels (due to a positive sensor) speeds up the rate that Processor B uses **X** as an input (thus is converted into something else), which will slow or even reverse the trend of increasing **X** levels.

2. Decreasing **X** levels (due to a positive sensor) slows down the rate that Processor A produces the output designated as a "signal". Once the rate of signal production dips below the rate of loss, the total amount of signal will be reduced. Decreasing signal levels (due to a positive sensor) slows down the rate that Processor B uses **X** as an input (thus is converted into something else), which will slow or even reverse the trend of decreasing **X** levels.

Figure 3-32. The four ways a sensor-based connection can be used to form an indirect counteracting response. They correspond to Type A through Type D in Figure 3-29. The common feature of all four examples is that they have two sensors: one that detects **X** levels, and one that detects an output of the processor with the **X**-sensor. This output is called a "signal", and the signal-sensor can also be called a receiver or receptor. This arrangement makes it possible for one processor to "communicate" with another. The processor with an **X**-sensor (Processor A) sends out a message whenever **X** levels change by producing more or less of the signal. The message is received by an **X**-changing processor because it changes its rate in response to changing signal levels (due to the presence of a signal-sensor).

As a last word on signal-based communication and counteracting responses, I briefly discuss a specific example that is operating within your body and then in Figure 3-33 show how this example can be illustrated using the same format created in Figure 3-32. For reasons having to do with the proper operation of your heart and other forms of muscle, your body tries to maintain a fairly constant level of calcium ions within your blood. A group of cells in your body known as the parathyroid gland monitors the levels of calcium ions in your blood. Whenever blood calcium ion levels decrease past a certain point, the parathyroid gland increases the rate that it produces a signal molecule known as parathyroid hormone that is released into the bloodstream. Osteoclasts, which are a specific cell type, have sensors that detect parathyroid hormone. They are found in and around the mineral component of bone (known as hydroxyapatite). These cells can (in essence) ingest hydroxyapatite and in the process release calcium ions into the bloodstream, and increasing levels of parathyroid hormone increases the rate at which they do so. So overall, the response orchestrated to blood calcium ion levels becoming too low is to increase the rate at which calcium ions are pulled out of storage within bones. This is a clear example of a counteracting response.

Type A:

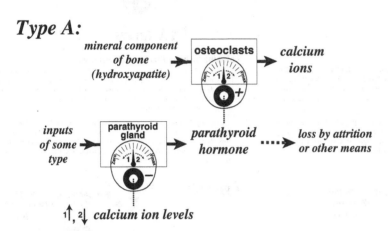

Figure 3-33. A biological example of counteracting response using a sensor-based regulatory connection. It follows the basic design laid out in Type A in Figure 3-32.

Thinking through this type of response:

1. Increasing **calcium ion** levels (due to a negative sensor) slows down the rate that the **parathyroid gland** produces **parathyroid hormone**. Once the rate of parathyroid hormone production dips below the rate of loss, the total amount of parathyroid hormone in the blood stream will be reduced. Decreasing parathyroid hormone levels (due to a positive sensor) slows down the rate that **osteoclasts** break the mineral component of bone into **calcium ions** (among other things), which will slow or even reverse the trend of increasing **calcium ion** levels.

2. Decreasing **calcium ion** levels (due to a negative sensor) speeds up the rate that the **parathyroid gland** produces **parathyroid hormone**. Once the rate of parathyroid hormone production exceeds the rate of loss, the total amount of parathyroid hormone in the blood stream will be increased. Increasing parathyroid hormone levels (due to a positive sensor) speeds up the rate that **osteoclasts** break the mineral component of bone into **calcium ions** (among other things), which will slow or even reverse the trend of decreasing **calcium ion** levels.

Coacting responses: Indirect connection

Figure 3-34 shows once again that any counteracting response is easily converted to a coacting response. Figure 3-34 is identical to Figure 3-29 except that each sensor is switched to the opposite sign. Once switched, the response to rising **X** levels is to speed up the rate that **X** is produced, and the response to lowering **X** levels is to slow **X** production.

Type A:

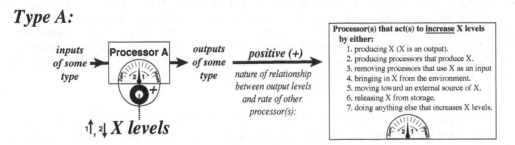

Thinking through this type of response:

1. Increasing **X** levels (due to positive sensor) speeds up the rate that Processor A produces outputs. Due to the positive relationship this, in turn, speeds up the rate of the processor (or processors) that act to increase **X** levels, which overall acts to maintain or even accelerate the trend of increasing **X** levels.

2. Decreasing **X** levels (due to positive sensor) slows down the rate that Processor A produces outputs. Due to the positive relationship this, in turn, slows the rate of the processor (or processors) that act to increase **X** levels, which overall acts to maintain or even accelerate the trend of decreasing **X** levels.

Type B:

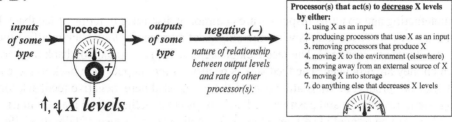

Thinking through this type of response:

1. Increasing **X** levels (due to positive sensor) speeds up the rate that Processor A produces outputs. Due to the negative relationship this, in turn, slows the rate of the processor (or processors) that act to decrease **X** levels, which overall acts to maintain or even accelerate the trend of increasing **X** levels.

2. Decreasing **X** levels (due to positive sensor) slows down the rate that Processor A produces outputs. Due to the negative relationship this, in turn, speeds up the rate of the processor (or processors) that act to decrease **X** levels, which overall acts to maintain or even accelerate the trend of decreasing **X** levels.

Type C:

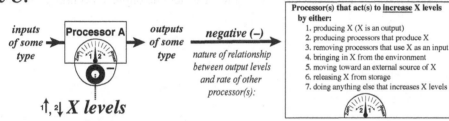

Thinking through this type of response:

1. Increasing **X** levels (due to negative sensor) slows down the rate that Processor A produces outputs. Due to the negative relationship this, in turn, speeds up the rate of the processor (or processors) that act to increase **X** levels, which overall acts to maintain or even accelerate the trend of increasing **X** levels.

2. Decreasing **X** levels (due to negative sensor) speeds up the rate that Processor A produces outputs. Due to the negative relationship this, in turn, slows the rate of the processor (or processors) that act to increase **X** levels, which overall acts to maintain or even accelerate the trend of decreasing **X** levels.

Type D:

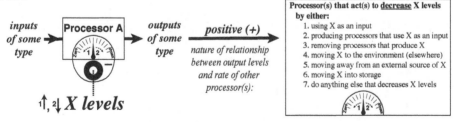

Thinking through this type of response:

1. Increasing **X** levels (due to negative sensor) slows down the rate that Processor A produces outputs. Due to the positive relationship this, in turn, slows the rate of the processor (or processors) that act to decrease **X** levels, which overall acts to maintain or even accelerate the trend of increasing **X** levels.

2. Decreasing **X** levels (due to negative sensor) speeds up the rate that Processor A produces outputs. Due to the positive relationship this, in turn, speeds up the rate of the processor (or processors) that act to decrease **X** levels, which overall acts to maintain or even accelerate the trend of decreasing **X** levels.

Figure 3-34. The four general ways to set up indirect coacting responses. Note that all indirect connections are formed by the output of the processor with the **X**-sensor somehow affecting the rate of **X**-changing processors. A positive relationship means that as output levels change the rate of effected processors changes in the same way—increasing output leads to increasing rate, while decreasing output leads to decreasing rate. A negative relationship is just the opposite—increasing output leads to decreasing rate, while decreasing output leads to increasing rate.

Feedback loops

Both counteracting and coacting responses are commonly discussed in terms of feedback loops. The classic notion of a feedback loop is when the outputs of a processor loop back to affect the rate at which these outputs are produced. The feedback is negative if the outputs loop back to decrease the rate at which they are produced. The feedback is positive if the outputs loop back to increase the rate at which they are produced. Translating over to the terms used here, negative feedback loops are counteracting (trend reversing), and positive feedback loops are coacting (trend maintaining). Thus, the claim that Life can be framed in counteracting and coacting terms is also a claim that Life can be framed in terms of negative and positive feedback loops.

Here, I have chosen to use the terms counteracting and coacting for one simple reason—it is easier to understand. Here is a simple example. It is easy to think of an organism running away from a potential predator as a counteracting response. Running away is an attempt to counteract the increasing danger created by an approaching predator. On the other hand, try to use negative feedback loops to frame the same idea. Now one is stuck putting it in terms of an output that loops back to negatively affect the rate at which more outputs are produced. It can be done—the output of running, if all goes well, increases safety, which negatively affects the rate at which the organism continues to run—but it is awkward.

Some key terms:

process - that which occurs when something (a processor) alters inputs, such that outputs are different than inputs.

performance - that which results from two or more processes being linked together by regulatory connections.

input limitation - whenever a processor's rate (the rate that inputs are converted to outputs) is slowed by the availability of inputs. (Input availability is the most limiting factor.)

sensor - any device that adjusts a processor's rate as a response to detecting some change in conditions.

positive regulatory connection - whenever one process increases a limiting factor of another, resulting in the other process speeding up.

negative regulatory connection - whenever one process decreases a limiting factor of another, resulting in the other process slowing down.

input-based regulation - whenever one processor is input limited, and the actions of another processor influences the supply of the limiting input.

sensor-based regulation - whenever one processor has a sensor that detects changing levels of some condition, and the actions of another processor influences the level of those same conditions.

nutrient cycle - the cyclic flow of materials that results whenever each processor's specific form of material outputs become inputs for some other type of processor. This is because the only way for all outputs to become inputs is if the output-input connections come full circle. (From the perspective of each processor in the cycle, the actions of all the other processors take its material outputs and convert them back to useful inputs.)

reproduction - a performance where processors act to make more copies of the same processors.

counter-acting response - when a sensor that detects some trend of change initiates rate adjustments that act to reverse the trend.

co-acting response - when a sensor that detects some trend of change initiates rate adjustments that act to maintain or even accelerate the trend.

homeostasis - the act of maintaining similar conditions despite constant disruptive fluctuations.

Some study questions:

1. *Explain why all parts of life can be thought of as being a process.*

2. Explain the statement: All processes contribute to their own demise.

3. What is meant by the expression "a processor's rate"? *What are three ways a single processor's rate may be limited?*

4. By definition, performances form when processes are linked by regulatory connections. Be sure that you understand how each of these types of regulatory connections work. Furthermore, be able to explain, in some detail, the workings of each of the four basic forms of sensor-based regulation illustrated in Figure 3-10.

5. Explain how counteraction is a key component of persistence. More specifically, explain how nutrient cycles and reproduction can both be considered counteracting performances.

6. *Besides nutrient cycles and reproduction, the sun must continue to shine for life to persist on this planet. Briefly explain why?*

7. Explain how counteracting responses can help an individual organism survive.

8. Explain how responses by an organism that enhance survival can at times be at odds with responses that aid reproduction. *Next explain why (in terms of persistence) reproductive behaviors should, when necessary, take precedence over individual survival.*

9. *Be able to explain how any of the counteracting responses diagrammed in Figures 3-27, 3-29, 3-30, 3-31, 3-32, and 3-33 work.*

10. *Be able to explain how any of the coacting responses diagrammed in Figures 3-28 and 3-34 work.*

Different Shapes and Different Species

Any organism at any moment has a distinct shape or form. This is not a shocking statement. But I must make clear exactly what I mean by this. When I say shape, I mean more than just an organism's outline; I mean everything about the way the organism is put together. Clearly limb length and other features of external morphology are components of shape. But so are aspects of external appearance such as its coloration. Two individuals that only vary in color pattern have different shapes. Internal morphology is also included. For instance, the relative size and arrangement of an animal's internal organs are features of its overall shape. In fact, the concept of shape goes down to the type and arrangement of molecules making up an organism.

Have you ever heard it mentioned that Life is incredibly diverse? This means that the organisms inhabiting our planet come in a huge diversity of shapes. Just think about squirrels, oak trees, elephants, earthworms, grasshoppers, bacteria, and all the other different organisms that you have encountered. Equally striking is the fact that this huge variety of shape does not form a continuum. Shapes of individual organisms, although not necessarily identical, often (but not always) cluster into distinct groups. In other words, instead of the living world being a blend of living things, each only slightly different than the next, Life's tapestry seems to be punctuated by gaps (see Figure 4-1). The presence of distinct groups suggests the notion of **species** may be applicable to Life. In general, a species is defined as more than one object grouped by virtue of common attributes and assigned a common name. (Note: In case you never really noticed gaps, look! Can you find, for example, organisms with a continuum of shapes between elephants and hippopotamuses, or hippopotamuses and rhinoceroses? You won't on this planet. Or pay attention to the birds you see in the next week. Do you see a continuum of shapes or do individuals cluster into groups of shapes? The next time you take a walk, pick a leaf from different trees; then try to arrange these leaves into a continuum of changing shape. Although no two leaves will be identical, you will likely find it is hard to do. Actually, I encourage you to look at anything you want to. Just look!)

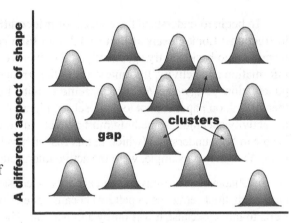

Figure 4-1. A graphic illustrating the idea that if the shape of lots of individual organisms were measured along two (or more) dimensions, the data points would not fill up the entire area (representing an evenly distributed continuum of shapes), but would group into clusters of more similar shaped organisms separated by gaps—regions where the measurements of few if any individuals landed.

Here we begin to explore this pattern of diversity: a wide variety of shapes punctuated by gaps. This chapter begins to lay some groundwork. I take on two tasks. First, I consider how an individual organism comes to take on its particular shape. Second, I look more closely at the idea of species, paying particular attention to what effect different forms of reproduction—asexual versus sexual—have on the formation and maintenance of distinct clusters of organisms.

Further exploration of the differences in shape spills into subsequent chapters. For example, Chapter 5 looks at how shape differences affect the interaction among species, whereas Chapters 6 and 7 begin to approach the question of how all these different-shaped life forms came to be.

A Brief Lesson in Growth and Development

One of the most puzzling aspects of biology is that individual organisms build themselves from simpler beginnings. Consider yourself. You started out as a single, somewhat amorphous cell. Although for the first nine months of your development your mom housed you in a supportive environment, your mom had nothing to do with the actual construction. From that first cell, you built yourself into the individual that emerged from mom at birth. You have continued to build and rebuild (as you repair damage) yourself ever since. Using a term introduced in Chapter 2, you are an example of self-organization.

Although the details are quite complex and not fully understood, organisms build themselves via an interaction of several factors: their genetic information, their activity, and their environmental circumstance. Here I touch on the nature of this interaction. In doing so, I skip over as much as I think I can get away with while still hitting some fundamental points.

A spiraling loop between information and activity

To begin to understand the concept of **information** being developed here, just follow these instructions: **Look closely at Figure 4-2, and then return to here**. Did you do it? (If not, I recommend you go back and try again.) If you did, then you were an example of an interaction between information and activity. Information is in the arrangement—the *sequence* of letters, spaces, and punctuation—that *codes for* some specific activity, but *cannot* perform the activity itself. An arrangement of ink on paper cannot look closely at Figure 4-2. For any set of instructions to be converted into the activity specified, something must actively interpret the code. By interpret I mean that something is able to both understand (which in this case means be able to read English) and carry out the instructions. You, in this example, were the active interpreter.

In Chapter 1 we discussed the existence of causal patterns. Specifically, events or actions often occur in a distinct sequence (a pattern) because one event causes the next to occur. For example, one ball starts to move because it was hit by another ball. The addition of information, however, can add a new twist. What comes next can be steered by not only the current activity, but also what activity the next set of information to be interpreted codes for. Consider, for example, someone following a chocolate chip cookie recipe. At one point the person adds brown sugar. Next, in following the recipe, they add eggs. Although the act of adding sugar did precede the act of adding eggs, adding sugar did not cause the addition of eggs. This sequence of events occurred because it was specified by the recipe (the information). The presence of information thus greatly expands the options of what can come next. Any activity potentially coded for lies within the realm of possibility.

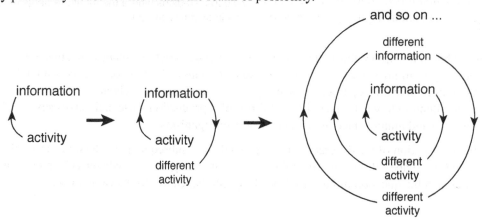

Figure 4-2. From a simple beginning a spiraling interplay between activity and information can lead to a complex pattern of activity.

Among these many possibilities is the potential for activity and information to form a loopy inter-action. It starts with activity and a set of instructions (information). The initial activity interprets some portion, some chunk, of this entire set of instructions. In doing so, a new type of activity is added to the mix. The loopy interaction starts to form when one aspect of this new activity is the interpretation of a different part of the information package. Again new activity is added, which continues the spiral if it leads to the interpretation of another new—that is, so far unused—part of the instructions. Continue to repeat these steps and a spiraling interplay between activity and information continues to unwind (see Figure 4-2). Such a spiraling interplay opens the door to a unique possibility: A potential complex pattern of activity can emerge from seemingly simple beginnings—some initial activity and an information package.

How organisms build themselves

What does this spiraling interaction have to do with how organisms build themselves? In a simple-minded way, perhaps a lot. Regardless of the reproductive details, all newly formed individuals start off as a relatively simple amorphous form. These starting forms, however, all share two common ingredients: the ability to carry out certain forms of activity, and a whole set of information. Further-more, all available evidence suggests that individuals grow and develop from their initial form (build themselves) through an ongoing interplay between action and information. Is the spiraling interaction shown in Figure 4-2 an accurate representation of this interplay? No, it's too simple. But it is not the details that are important here. What is important is whether the notion of a spiraling interaction cap-tures the essence of how organisms come to construct themselves from simpler beginnings. I suggest that it does.

Whether an individual will develop into a form that we call frog, cat, dog, grasshopper, human, etc., is set from the start. Envisioning development as a spiraling interaction helps clarify why this is true—the information package is set from the outset. Because the pattern of activity is being steered by the information present, the sequence of forms that each individual moves through is at least some-what predetermined. If something starts with the information to make a certain type of frog, it could not develop into anything else.

That is not to say that development is *completely* predetermined or deterministic. An organism's starting point *is <u>not</u> the sole determinate* of how it will develop throughout its life. Development is much more interesting than that. Whereas an organism's basic body plan is constructed via a spiraling interaction between information and activity, developmental details—such as how large any particular muscle should become, how strong any particular bone should be, how the nervous system should be assembled—are, to at least some extent, constantly fine-tuned to mirror their use in daily life. The common expression, "use it or lose it" captures some of what I am talking about. Yet taken at face value, this is a strange statement because it implicitly presumes that some aspect of a body will just develop, but only be kept around if the organism uses it. Perhaps "use it to develop it" would be bet-ter because body parts in constant use tend not only to be maintained, but also to develop further. In contrast, underused parts either never develop as fully or begin to atrophy. A striking example is that under conditions of weightlessness, where support structures are much less needed, bones of astro-nauts begin to deteriorate. The logic underlying this type of fine-tuning is straightforward. Body parts are expensive to build and to maintain, so unless an organism demonstrates a need by continually using a specific part, the resources needed to maintain it or even develop it further, will be allocated elsewhere.

What determines how an organism uses its body?

Two things influence how an organism uses its body: its environmental circumstance and its developmental history (see Figure 4-3).

Every organism is constantly engaged in an ongoing interaction with its environment. Consequently, the specific nature of each organism's environment continually influences what it must do to get needed resources, avoid various forms of danger, and (if sexual) eventually find a compatible mate. To list just a few examples: The type of predators around influences what a prey needs to do to escape; a predator's hunting efforts and tactics will need to change as prey abundance changes; and whether your environment includes schooling will change the way you use your developing mind. It is no wonder that zoo-raised animals have a difficult time returning to the wild. A zoo's environment, where food is brought and predators are absent, does not push animals to develop their potential skills more fully.

Although environmental circumstance sets the context, it is an organism's developmental history—that is, how an organism has developed so far—that determines what tools an organism has available to accomplish specific tasks. For instance, you can only use your hands and arms to gather food if you develop them first. Furthermore, an organism's developmental history becomes self-reinforcing. The act of making use of some existing body part will influence how that part develops in the future, which in turn sets the stage to continue to engage in activities that take advantage of that development. For example, if you develop strong arms through a past interaction of activity and information, you are going to be more inclined to take on activities that involve considerable arm strength in the future (which in turn acts to maintain or even further develop arm strength).

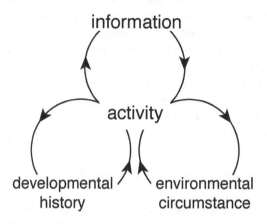

Figure 4-3. The relationship between development's four interactants: information, activity, history, and environment. Activity sits at the crossroads. It connects to information through the spiraling interplay discussed earlier. Developmental history and environmental circumstance enter the mix by setting the tone for how an organism uses its developing body by limiting what is currently possible and what is currently useful. These in turn indirectly influence how information is interpreted, which then affects how the organisms puts itself together. (Note: The arrow going from activity to environment recognizes that an organism's actions can modify its environmental circumstance. While important, it is not a topic emphasized here.)

Play and practice

Actually, it is too simple to think that all organisms initiate possible actions (via their developmental history) only when current environmental circumstance directly forces their hand. In addition to running when being chased by a predator or in pursuit of a prey, organisms seem to run at times because they simply "feel" like running. These whims of activity, however, likely serve a purpose. They may help an organism hone their skills before their environment ever puts them to the test. For example, there are no second chances with predators, so preparation makes sense. The playfulness seen in many younger mammals may be the classic case. Their play mimics the activities and skills needed to be successful later. Here is a personal example. When my friends and I were beginning to drive, my friend named Bob stood out as the seemingly most reckless driver. He commonly pushed closer to the edge than I was ever comfortable with. His justification for taking on seemingly needless risks has, however, long stuck with me. He said he pushed himself to develop his driving skills so that he would be ready when it really mattered—when skill could make a difference between being involved in or avoiding a serious accident. As it turned out, I am likely alive today because Bob (instead of me) was driving when we barely—and I mean barely—escaped a highway head-on collision. He made all the right moves, moves that required skills that I had never developed, to avoid the accident. Years later I was reminded of Bob's driving as I watched a couple of red squirrels (*Tamiasciurus hudsonicus*) take seemingly unnecessary risks with a dog of mine. Instead of just staying in a safe perch high in a tree, they repeatedly came back down only to be chased again. Maybe there was some other factor involved, like trying to get to a food source or attempting to return to a more secure long-term shelter. But I wondered whether it was all about practice. Were they taking on some risk with a predator of known location, to be more ready when they encountered a different predator in a less-controlled, and thus more dangerous, situation?

Let's put these ideas in the context of your own life. Have you ever heard a statement like: "Andy has the potential to be a great basketball player." Maybe it was said about you and playing the piano, or your friend Betty's ability in mathematics. No matter who it is, or what skill is being discussed, let's make sure you understand what is being said because there is a deterministic notion in such a claim. Although it suggests that a person's initial information has steered its development toward certain skills, it is *not* a claim that development is completely deterministic. If it was, then all Betty would need to do to realize her potential in mathematics is to sit back and wait. Under complete determinism, claims of potential are simply statements about what will happen in the future. What an individual does or does not do makes no difference because one cannot be any better or any worse at any skill than what they were set out to be. Which, of course, is not true.

Instead, we all have the potential of being better at anything that we do. We just need to do it— repeatedly. Performing an activity repeatedly essentially tells our body that these skills seem like they will be important, so the needed body parts should be developed more fully. In this way, our body's development is always being fine-tuned by how we use our body. Where determinism again enters this scenario is by imposing limits on the degree to which our body can change with use. My personal spiraling interaction between information and activity, for example, resulted in a slender build, which is a polite way of saying that I'm kind of skinny. Had I lifted weights more throughout my life, my muscles would have developed further. However, there is no way that I could have ever gotten as big as Arnold Schwarzenegger or any other massive body builder. Similarly, I could have practiced basketball morning, noon, and night for my whole life and never have become as good as Michael Jordan (or have even come close). Some may find such limits depressing. I like to focus on the other side. Instead of lamenting that I may never be the best, I realize any improvement in my skills opens the door for me to do things that I have never been able to do before. In other words, measure yourself against yourself, and an unexplored frontier exists all around you. Adventure awaits all of us; we just must be willing to do the work needed to enter.

A last note: Repeating an activity to prepare for the future that goes beyond the joyous self-initiation of play seems distinct enough to demand a new term—we call it practice. And the discipline underlying practice may be a uniquely human trait. Yet, practice still seems to be rooted in play, as truly disciplined practitioners (of whatever) still seem to be motivated by a more bound form of joy, which we call passion. Within any discipline, those without the underlying passion seem more likely to lose their way.

Information is genetic

The information contained within individual organisms is commonly termed **genetic information**. As stated before, it is information because it encodes instruction. But what is it about this information that makes it genetic?

The term *genetic* could be construed in three ways. First, it indicates that it is information found within organisms. Second, it indicates that the information is encoded in molecular arrangements known as nucleic acids. **Deoxyribonucleic acid**, or DNA, is the particular form of nucleic acid used most commonly. Third, it indicates that the information can be copied and then passed from parents to offspring. The most basic avenue of such transmission occurs when one cell divides into two. The starting cell's information is copied, and then one copy ends up in each of the two daughter cells.

The word **heritable** often shows up in any discussion of genetics. Heritable is the term used to describe features of a parent that can be passed to offspring. Genetic information is thus heritable.

Four new words: Genes, genome, genotype, and phenotype

Implicit in a spiraling interplay between information and activity is the idea that the information present from the outset is not interpreted all at once. The spiral is set up by new activities leading to interpretation of previously unused information. Biologists use two terms—genes and genomes—to better express this notion. **Genes** are individual instructions within this entire package of information. In other words, a gene is a unit of information that codes for a specific task. So each time a new activity leads to the interpretation of new information, one or more previously unused genes are being interpreted. A **genome** is a set of genes that, in total, has enough information to guide the assembly of a fully functional organism. Stated differently, for development to result in a potentially reproductive individual, the action–information interplay must start with a full deck of information—that is, an entire genome.

Genotype and phenotype are two other words commonly thrown around by biologists when discussing development. Let's start with genotype. As stated earlier, any newly formed individual capable of developing into a functionally reproductive adult contains a genome. (Actually, many organisms have more than one genome, but we will take up that issue later.) All individuals, however, do not have the same exact genome. In fact, the specific details of genomes vary widely. An organism's **genotype** is, thus, its specific genetic constitution. All individuals have one or more genomes, but they do not necessarily have the same genotypes.

An organism's **phenotype** is the other side of a matched set. Commonly, an organism's phenotype is seen as being the organism's body or, more specifically, the organism's current shape (what it looks like). But conceptually, such a view is less than satisfying because it fails to grab onto the phenotypes dynamic nature. If organisms are built by a constant interplay between information and activity, and the genotype is the information, then the phenotype must be activity. The phenotype (or body shape) of an organism is what is directly involved in the activities of living, which range from internal activities such as growing more, developing further, and repairing damage, to external activities such as capturing food, avoiding predators, and finding mates.

Furthermore, seeing the phenotype as activity makes you realize that genotype and phenotype are not separable—neither exists without the other. Yet, sometimes you will hear people refer to the process of growth and development as the development of a phenotype. This implies that a phenotype is not present until a body develops into (presumably) the adult form. But such view does not reflect biological reality. From start to finish—that is, from first cell to death—an organism must always have both information and activity, which means that they always have both a genotype and a phenotype. What is striking is that during the course of this lifelong journey, one changes and the other does not. As stated earlier, an organism's genotype is set from the outset—that is, an organism's genotype does not change (at least in any systematic way) over an organism's life. In contrast, an individual's phenotype is in constant interaction with both its genotype and its environment, and, in accordance with these interactions, undergoes continual change. Growth and development is the process by which the activity of the current phenotype results in the phenotype changing. In you, your initial phenotype was your first cell (supplied by your mom) that started going about the work of interpreting your information (supplied by both your mom and dad). This interaction has built the phenotype that you have today, which will be different, in at least some ways, than the phenotype that you will have tomorrow.

And your phenotype will continue to change until the day you die. (Note: In the (somewhat esoteric) terms of the last chapter, an organism's phenotype is the current set of processors that collectively generate its performance. An organism's phenotype changing is, thus, a change in the set of processors.)

A side note: Some people (including me) think that the concept of an organism's phenotype should include all involved in an organism's performance, irrespective of whether it is a direct product of its growth and development. For example, I consider a bird's nest to be a part of its phenotype. It is used in the performance of raising offspring. Other examples include tools used by humans, dams built by beavers, or even another organism. Some parasites manipulate host behavior to the extent that the host acts in ways good for the parasite but totally detrimental to themselves. At that point, the host is doing the parasite's work, so it becomes part of the parasite's phenotype.

Shape constrains performance ability

One of the fundamental concepts in biology is the relationship between shape and performance, which is also referred to as the relationship between form and function. An organism's shape—its current phenotype—makes it possible for it to perform certain activities well, but at the cost of not being the best shape to perform well in other ways. Stated more succinctly, there exists a **shape–performance trade-off**. Examples of shape–performance trade-offs are as abundant as there are differently shaped organisms. Look for yourself. Watch birds fly the next time you are out. Birds with differently shaped wings fly differently. Watch differently shaped dogs run. Some run faster, some turn faster, and some, like dachshunds, are slow at both. Still dachshunds can do some things that other dogs cannot do. I once read that dachshunds were bred to go down badger holes. (This may be true, but it is still unclear to me what exactly is supposed to happen if the dachshund actually finds a badger when it gets down the hole.) Or if you like plants or ants or anything else, just look, and you will see evidence of shape–performance trade-offs everywhere

As a kid I used to watch blue jays and cardinals come to my mom's feeders. Both would eat sunflower seeds, but they did so in strikingly different ways. As you may know from personal experience, the trick of eating sunflower seeds is managing to extract the seed from the outer shell. (I am not very good at this. I tend to just swallow shell and all.) Blue jays, which have a fairly long and somewhat slender beak, had trouble breaking open the shell. They would take each seed one by one to a close-by branch, place the seed between their toes and the branch, and then use their beak to chisel the seed open. A blue jay's beak shape made them rather poor sunflower seed feeders, so they had to spend a lot of effort to break open each shell. Cardinals, on the other hand, had short, thick, powerful beaks. They easily pulverized the shell with a sewing-machine-like-action to get to the seed. Never get into a sunflower seed-eating contest with a cardinal. You will lose. Yet the thick squatty bill of a cardinal could never probe for insects inside cracks in a tree's bark, forage for nectar in long tubular flowers, or feed in many of the other ways that other birds do. Their bill is just not the right shape.

We tend to think about the shape–performance trade-off as it applies to different individuals. Two individuals, for instance, of different shape will not perform equally. Each will tend to be better than the other at some activities and worse at others. But the same is true within an individual. As I have stressed, an individual's phenotype changes throughout its life. Accordingly, performance abilities change also. And as dictated by this trade-off, some abilities improve whereas others get worse. I, for example, could run faster during my early 20s than I can now, many years later. On the other hand, certain aspects of my mental abilities seem to be much better now (at least within the confines of my own delusions).

Distribution of gaps and the species concept

The idea of species is easily applied to Figure 4-4(a). Although individuals are not all shaped identically, the individual objects can easily be put into three distinct groups, each which could be labeled with a distinct name. Thus if the gaps found among organisms are clear cut and evenly spaced like Figure 4-4(a), then applying the notion of species is easy and likely meaningful. Individuals organized into distinct clusters suggest that there is something about the way the living world works that leads to such distinct groupings. But what about the distribution of shapes found in Figure 4-4(b)? Is the idea of species applicable here? The great range in shape clearly lends itself to this idea. It is difficult to imagine that diamond-shaped and circular-shaped objects should be considered part of the same group. Yet a dilemma emerges because there are no distinct gaps—all the objects can be arranged into a continuum. Some system could be devised to break these 19 individual objects into different groups, but wherever the lines were drawn would have a sense of being arbitrary (hence seemingly meaningless).

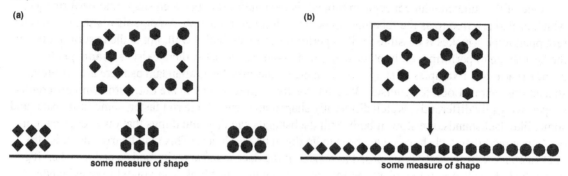

Figure 4-4. In both (a) and (b) a collection of differently shaped objects are sorted by shape. In (a) individual objects sort into three distinct groups. In contrast, the different shaped objects in (b) align into one continuum of changing shape.

The issue raised by Figure 4-4(b) would be biologically moot if all living organisms cluster into distinct groups. But the real world seems to not always be so simple. Although gaps are apparent, their distribution often makes assigning individuals into distinct species difficult. Figure 4-5 summarizes some of these difficulties. Our inadequacies as observers may be one source of such trouble. What may seem to us as a broad continuum may actually be punctuated by gaps not readily apparent through our available means of observation (or at least how we have viewed them so far). The other real possibility is that the living world is not always broken up into distinct species. In such cases, trying to organize organisms into species would be a misrepresentation. It all comes down to realizing that just because some organisms seem to distinctly cluster into species does not mean that all individuals can be readily assigned into a distinct species. There is no reason, other than our own mental stubbornness, to think that one size must fit all.

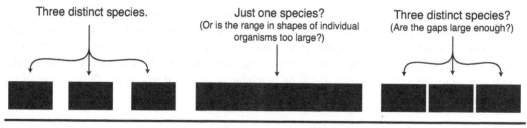

Figure 4-5. Some of the difficulties potentially encountered when attempting to assign individuals into species. Each block represents a region of shape filled by a continuum of individuals.

Except for the frustration often felt by those biologists called taxonomists who expend considerable effort trying to sort individuals into species, the fact that the living world may not always be punctuated by distinct and regular gaps poses no problem. The world is simply the way it is. Our job (if we choose to accept it) is to see the world as it is—that is, to see the true patterns—and then try to understand why the patterns came out the way they did.

Although there may be much more involved, differences in the way individuals reproduce may have a large effect on whether individuals cluster into distinct species. I consider, in particular, the two most general categories of reproduction: asexual and sexual reproduction. First, I discuss how asexual reproduction can generate and maintain a broad continuum of shapes. In other words, I argue that asexual reproduction is not necessarily conducive to the formation and maintenance of species. Next, I focus on how sexual reproduction works in the opposite manner—that is, how it acts to shape the distribution of organisms into distinct groups.

Species and asexual reproduction

Asexual reproduction is reproduction in the classic sense of the word. The prefix *re-*, indicating something happening again, is combined with the production of offspring. Each generation potentially starts over at the same place. In the absence of errors, one parent passes an intact copy of its genome to its offspring. Evidence suggests that the same starting phenotype is also passed to offspring. Starting development with the same genotype and phenotype as their parent (or any siblings) sets the stage for an asexually produced offspring's growth and development to follow the same course as their parent or any siblings (see Figure 4-6). Only differences in each individual's interaction with their environment potentially nudge the development of parents and offspring to move along slightly different paths.

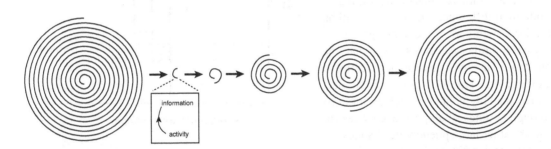

Figure 4-6. A view of asexual reproduction. It begins with a reproductive individual represented by a well developed spiraling interplay between activity and information. This individual then produces an offspring that starts over at the same place—that is, it has the same genotype and the same starting phenotype. The same starting point generates the tendency for this offspring's development to unfold like its parent's did.

At first glance, asexual reproduction seems conducive to the maintenance of distinct species. Any individual with a unique genotype can, across generations, become a **clonal population**—a group of individuals all having the same genotype. It only takes one individual producing offspring with the same genotype, which in turn produce more offspring with the same genotype, and so on. Members of the same clone would clearly be members of the same species.

Introducing mutations

No matter how much effort goes toward prevention, mistakes happen. The act of copying genomes to be passed to offspring is no exception. Inevitably copy errors will occur. Whenever such errors crop up during offspring production, the information package passed to offspring is modified. Most of the information remains as it was, but one or a few small portions of the overall content are altered by error. Such modifications are commonly called **mutations**.

Mutations are significant because even slight changes in a genotype can alter how an organism develops by altering the spiraling interaction between activity and information. The degree to which development is changed depends on what information was modified and how it was modified. Accordingly, the effects of mutations can vary from being lethal—development of a functional organism is disrupted—to effectively neutral—development is not altered in any significant way. Somewhere in between lie individuals that, as a result of a mutation, develop a somewhat different shape but are still reproductively competent.

Introducing complications

Mutations can complicate the species notion. Suppose that one individual within a clone produces an offspring with a slightly altered genotype via mutation. Further suppose that due to this modification of information, this offspring develops a noticeably different shape but is still able to reproduce. With time, this one individual can give rise to its own distinct clonal population. Finally, suppose that environmental conditions are such that individuals from both clones—the original and the one that arose via mutation—are able to coexist in the same general area. Should the individuals making up these two clonal populations be considered members of the same species or two distinct species?

Here are some reasons to suggest that, despite their differences, they should still be considered members of the same species. They have similar genotypes, given that one clone arose via slight genetic modification of the other clone. Due to their genetic similarity, their phenotype likely develops similarly (although at times small genetic changes can result in rather large phenotypic changes). Plus, the species notion does not imply that all members of the group must be identical. Furthermore, we may want to not only consider how similar the two clones are to each other, but also how similar they are in relation to what else is around. Despite somewhat marked phenotypic differences, if these two clones are markedly distinct from anything else around, the temptation would be to lump them into a single species. They form a cluster surrounded by a noticeable gap. Yet even if these suggestions make sense to you, recognize that the guidelines are still fuzzy. There is no clear way to answer the questions: What is similar enough to be considered the same species? What is different enough to be considered different species?

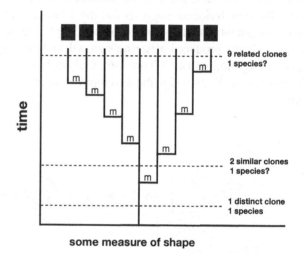

Figure 4-7. One way that asexual reproduction makes application of a species concept confusing. This figure starts off with a single clone persisting across time. At that point it makes sense to say that all members of this clone are members of the same species. But across time certain mutations (m) occurred that persisted. Each of these events gave rise to a new clone with both slight genetic and phenotypic differences from the clone from which it arose. After one episode of a mutation that persisted occurs, a question arises as to whether members of these similar and closely related (due to recent common ancestry) clones should be considered members of the same species? How to best answer this question becomes increasingly fuzzy as more episodes of mutation followed by persistence occur leading to an increasingly broader range (both genetically and phenotypically) of clones. Should the members of the nine related clones at the top of this figure be considered members of the same species? See text for further discussion.

The issue becomes even more complicated if these two clones exist within a broader continuum of shapes. And when reproduction is asexual, the formation of a broad continuum of shapes over time is possible. Just continue to repeat the preceding scenario—mutation resulting in a slight but noticeable shape change, followed by reproductive competence and coexistence. With each new episode the original clone blossoms into an even broader continuum of shapes (see Figure 4-7). When does this continuum become too large to consider all the clones members of the same species? It is a good question, but there is not a good answer.

The bottom line is that concept of species is hard to apply in asexual organisms for three reasons: (1) There is nothing about asexual reproduction that forces an initial distinct population of types to remain so; (2) as long as modified types arising in the population are able to persist, the range in shapes can become an increasingly large continuum; and (3) at some point in the process the term *species* ceases to be meaningful.

Species and sexual reproduction

In striking contrast to asexual reproduction, a sexually reproducing individual is often not a reproductive entity. Except in the case of self-reproducing hermaphrodites (which are relatively common among plants), it "takes two to tango." It is both the requirement of a partner and what it takes to pull off reproduction with a partner that makes underlying dynamics quite distinct from those found in asexual reproduction.

The question we begin to explore here is: Do these different dynamics contribute to the formation of species? But before we discuss this further, we need to develop some general background on the nature of sex and sexual reproduction.

Sex, sexual reproduction, and gender

What is sex? Many respond to this question by kind of shaking their heads, shrugging their shoulders, having an excited but somewhat embarrassed glimmer in their eye, and simultaneously uttering: "Well, you know." People making that type of response, however, are confusing sex with sexuality. Our sexuality is all the feelings and emotions that accompany the fact that we are sexually reproducing organisms. As you may have experienced, sexuality can be confusing.

Sex is straightforward. It occurs whenever genetic information from more than one individual is combined into a single individual. Notice that sex's definition does not state that the single individual is a new individual. In other words, sex can and does happen without reproduction. Bacteria and other types of single-celled organisms provide numerous examples.

Although sex is defined easily and occurs commonly, why sex takes place is not an easily answered question. Think for a moment. Reproducing asexually is hard enough, so why complicate it by making it a cooperative affair? In addition to the effort needed to produce and nourish offspring, sexual reproduction requires that energy be spent finding a suitable mate. Consider yourself. How much of your life have you already spent preoccupied with finding and keeping a mate? I remember a friend of mine once bemoaning this expense. Apparently one time while stopping his car to gaze at a female, it dawned on him how much more he might have accomplished with his life—like gone on adventures throughout the world, studied many disciplines, written a book or two, and still had some time left over to relax—if he had been freed of his sexual preoccupation. At times it seems that my biggest obstacle to teaching biology is that most people are too busy being biological, especially being sexual, to study biology.

What adds to the intrigue is that the answer to the question of why many organisms reproduce sexually is not obvious. Many ideas have been put forth, but biologists still debate which, if any, is correct. In Chapter 19, I return to this issue and present a view that makes the most sense to me (at least right now).

Continuing with another question: What is gender? In other words, what is it to be male or female? This is another question that commonly evokes the somewhat embarrassed, "Well, you know" type of response. We tend to think about gender in terms of certain anatomical features that we cover in public such as breasts and penises. Focusing on certain anatomical features, however, misses the boat. Most sexually reproducing organisms have gender. Yet across living organisms there is no anatomical feature that consistently defines an individual as either male or female. Looking for a penis will not get you far in looking for maleness in plants.

At the most basic level, male and female is a division of labor. Sexual reproduction occurs by the fusion of two cells—each commonly called **gametes**—into a single cell—commonly called a **zygote**. The zygote is the start of the new individual (containing both a genotype and an initial phenotype). The event is sexual because genetic information within the zygote is a combination of that received from the two fusing gametes. Two basic elements are needed to make this fusion work. Gametes must be sufficiently mobile to find each other, and once combined there must be an ample supply of nutrients to get this new individual out of the starting block. There are two basic ways these two requirements could be met:

• These two tasks could be split equally among gametes. Each could be equally mobile and carry an equal supply of nutrients. In other words, all gametes are the same size—a condition termed **isogamy**. A potential advantage of isogamy is that any gamete could potentially fuse with any other gamete. But there is a potential disadvantage. A trade-off may exist between being stuffed full of supplies and being mobile. A larger nutrient-filled cell may be more difficult to propel around. If so, splitting both roles thus leads to gametes that are not very good at either.

• The second option involves gametic specialization. Some gametes have shed their nutrient supply to become small and mobile. Others become larger so they have ample nutrients. Sexual reproduction now involves a small, mobile gamete finding and fusing with a large, fully supplied gamete. Under at least some types of conditions, gametic specialization makes the whole process more efficient. The presence of two gamete types is called **anisogamy** or **heterogamy**. *This differentiation of gametes into two types is the emergence of gender.* Regardless of what other anatomy accompanies them, **males** are those individuals in a sexual population that make relatively small, much more mobile gametes. **Females** are those individuals that make large, nutrient-rich gametes. In animals, these two distinct forms of gametes are better known as **sperm** (small mobile gametes) and **eggs** (large nutrient-laden gametes). In many plants, they are referred to as **pollen** (small mobile gametes) and **ovules** (large nutrient-laden gametes). In both plants and animals, some individuals are **hermaphrodites**—single individuals that produce both gamete types. The male portion of a hermaphrodite is the portion making the small mobile gametes, whereas the female portion is that making large gametes. Some organisms are even sequential hermaphrodites, changing from one sex to another during the course of their life.

Unsurprisingly, the behavioral and morphological differences between males and females are underscored by their gametic differences. For example, in addition to producing the nurturing gamete, females tend to be more involved in other phases of nurturing offspring, and the mobile-gamete males tend to be more involved in pursuing the opposite sex. And why this is particularly striking is that while different genders may have evolved initially because it increased efficiency with which gametes could fuse and form a functional zygote, it has since sprouted a whole new mix of complications. Each sex, by the fact that they are different, approaches reproduction from a different perspective. As a result, although sexual reproduction is a cooperative venture, gender can skew the terms under which each sex will cooperate. We discuss this further in Chapter 6.

Sexual reproduction and species: An initial look

Sexual reproduction divides the living world into groups. Each male needs a female to reproduce, and not all females will do. Similarly, each female needs a male, and not all males will do. Every male and female on this planet demarcates a group containing those opposite-sexed individuals with which they are reproductively compatible. Reproductive compatibility, in its most basic sense, means that a male and female produce gametes that can fuse to form a cell that can potentially build itself into a sexually competent adult. Viewed another way, reproductively compatible individuals produce gametes containing what each other's gamete is missing, so that after fusion their combined contents form a functional whole.

The notion of reproductive compatibility can also include recognition as a potential mate. Two individuals may produce complementary gametes, but unless they recognize each other as a potential mate, it is unlikely their gametes will ever get together.

Let's use these ideas to build the idea of a sexual population (see Figure 4-8). First consider a male and female that are reproductively compatible. This male is also reproductively compatible with a larger group of females. This female is also reproductively compatible with a larger group of males. This raises an interesting question: Are all the males in this female's group reproductively compatible with all the females in this male's group? Stated differently: Does sexual compatibility neatly overlap? At least in principle, it seems the answer could be yes. For all to be reproductively compatible with a single female, the group of males must share traits. Specifically, this female must recognize them all as a potential mate, and they must produce gametes complementary to this female's gametes. By the same logic, the female group must share these same traits. Seemingly, both groups would thus share the traits needed for all members of one group to be sexually compatible with all members of the other group. If so, the two groups become parts of a single sexual population.

Sexual populations may be the most clearly delimited groups within the living world. That is not to say, however, that sexual compatibility always draws clear and easily recognized lines (see Figure 4-8). First off, sexual compatibility is not always black or white. Among the pairings that can potentially produce viable offspring, some pairings may be more successful at doing so than others. Second, reproductive compatibility may not always perfectly overlap. Think about domestic dogs. A midsize dog may be able to mate (and the mating result in viable offspring) with dogs over some size range.

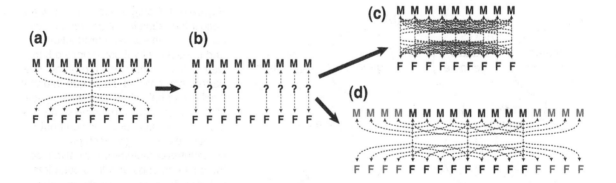

Figure 4-8. Does sexual reproduction always lead to distinct sexual populations? In (a) the group of females (F) that one male (M) is reproductively compatible with (which includes being able to physically mate with and producing viable offspring) is aligned with the group of males that one female is reproductively compatible with. In (b) the question is raised as to whether all the males and females within these two groups would be reproductively compatible with each other. In (c) the answer is yes, which means that sexual reproduction has created a distinct group in nature—a sexual population. However, as shown in (d), it is possible that reproductive compatibility does not overlap perfectly. In such cases sexual reproduction still forms groups, but a distinct sexual population does not exist. See text for further discussion.

Due to size issues alone, however, the largest size within that range may have difficulty breeding with the smallest size within the same range. To push this idea to its extreme, size differences will prevent pocket-sized poodles and Great Danes from successfully breeding. And finally, as outside observers, it is not always easy for us to recognize who is reproductively compatible with whom. Nonetheless, reproductive compatibility does impose structure on life. It should come as no surprise that a species is commonly defined as a group of potentially interbreeding individuals. That is, males and females that can potentially produce viable offspring are members of the same species, and if not, they are members of different species. This notion of species is commonly referred to as the **biological species concept**.

We could stop our discussion of species here having presented a commonly accepted notion of species, but to do so would ignore the notion of species that we started with—the presence of clusters of distinctly shaped organisms. The question thus remains: What, if anything, does sexual reproduction and sexual compatibility have to do with the formation of these distinct groups?

Sexual reproduction continually stirs up genetic information

Whether small and mobile or swelled with a nutrient supply, every functional gamete within a sexual population has an equal amount of genetic information. This means that each offspring receives an equal genetic contribution from each parent, which in turn means that the zygote has twice the genetic information as either gamete prior to fusion.

This raises a question: How can an offspring get one-half of its genetic information from each parent and end up with a whole genome?

First, let's go through the obvious but *incorrect* answer: One parent contributes one-half of the genes that makes up a complete genome, and the other parent contributes the other half. Yet with such a scheme, how do the parents "decide" which half to give? Unless each provides exactly complimentary halves (see Figure 4-9(a)), the total contribution will not equal a whole. Even a slight overlap among each parent's contribution would result in the offspring receiving two copies of some genes and zero copies of others (see Figure 4-9(b)). The genetic information of the offspring would be incomplete. Each sex attempting to supply offspring with complementary halves of a genome is thus a dubious proposition. Mismatches between parents may be hard to avoid. The consequences of mismatches will likely be fatal for the offspring.

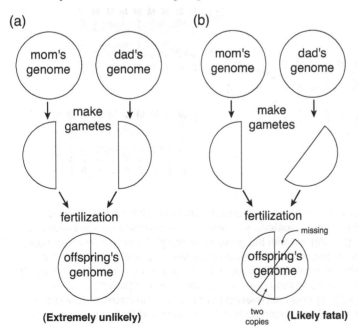

(a)

(b)

(Extremely unlikely)

(Likely fatal)

Figure 4-9. A diagram showing how genetic information is <u>not</u> passed across generations in sexual reproduction, and a reason why it could not work this way. In this scenario each reproductive partner starts with a single genome that it splits into half when it produces gametes. The offspring's genome is, thus, a fusion of the half genomes contributed by each parent. In (a) each parent contributes complementary halves, so the offspring ends up with a complete genome. In contrast, (b) shows what happens if parents do not contribute perfectly complementary halves. The offspring ends up with two copies of some portions of the genome, and is missing completely other portions. Such offspring would not have all information needed to develop into a reproductively competent individual.

The unobvious but *correct* answer: Each half contributed by each parent is actually a whole. Each parent contributes an entire genome. This means that fusion of two gametes results in a cell with two genomes—one from each parent.

Before I go on, let me slip in a few new terms here. **Ploidy level** is the number of complete genomes contained within a cell. **Haploid** is the term used for any cell that contains one complete genome. **Diploid** is the term used for any cell that contains two complete genomes. Commonly, a number followed by the letter n designates ploidy level. For example, 1n = haploid, 2n = diploid, and so on. Put in these terms, fusion starts with two haploid cells that join to form one diploid cell.

What happens next varies considerable among sexual organisms, although there is one other constant. Diploid cells must be converted back to haploid cells before the next round of fusion. Otherwise the number of genomes would double with each fusion—two fusing diploids would result in a cell with four genomes (a tetraploid), which in turn would fuse to form a cell with eight genomes (an octoploid), and so on. Although the details are not important here, the means by which diploid cells become haploid cells is called **meiosis** or **meiotic cell division**. Together fusion and meiosis form a sexual cycle (see Figure 4-10). Sexual organisms vary in terms of what happens between fusion and meiosis or between meiosis and fusion. In humans

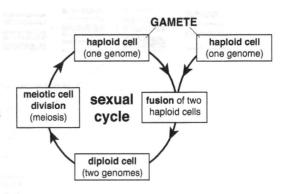

Figure 4-10. The cycle of events common to all organisms that reproduce sexually.

and other animals, the diploid cell formed by fusion develops into a multicellular organism where each cell remains diploid. Upon sexual maturity, meiosis occurs only among the cells within the body—the **germ cells**—that give rise to gametes. Fertilization, the fusion of gametes, starts the whole cycle over again.

Sexual reproduction mixes genetic information across generations. Mixing can happen in two places: during the formation of gametes and as males and females choose their sexual partners. Let's use the life cycle found in animals (multicellular forms are diploid) to help visualize this mixing.

To produce gametes, diploid germ cells (within the diploid multicellular organism) must undergo meiosis to form haploid cells. Gamete formation could occur without mixing as long as the two genomes are kept separate so that each gamete contains either the genome this individual got from its mom or the genome it got from its dad. This is not what happens. Instead, these two genomes are typically mixed during the formation of gametes, so that each gamete gets one genome that is a mixture of the two genomes it got from its parents. These genomes are reshuffled each time a germ cell undergoes meiosis to make gametes, so each gamete formed (within the same individual) may have a unique combination of genetic information (see Figure 4-11). This explains why you and any of your siblings most likely have genetic differences. Your dad's sperm and your mom's egg that fused to form you and the ones that fused to form any of your siblings are most likely different.

The second form of mixing is more obvious. As individuals of opposite sex pair into reproductive couples, information unique to each partner is potentially blended together within their offspring (see Figure 4-11).

Reasons that sexual reproduction creates clusters

This mixing is of no consequence if all the genomes within a sexual population are identical. Continually mix the parts of identical objects, and one continually gets identical objects.

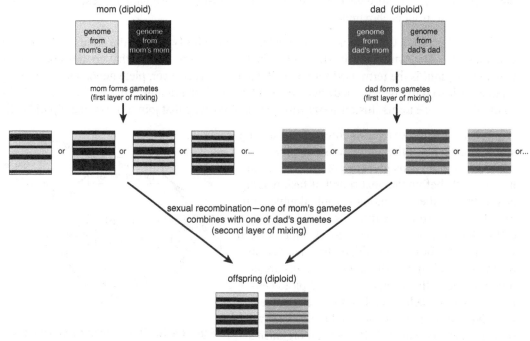

Figure 4-11. The two ways sexual reproduction mixes genetic information across generations. First, each sexually mature diploid individual (a square represents a complete genome) forms haploid gametes by shuffling the genomes received from each of its two parents into one complete genome. Each gamete formed within one individual is, thus, a potentially unique mixture of information received from its two parents. The second layer of mixing comes when gametes from two sexually mature individuals of opposite sex fuse to form a new diploid offspring.

But as in asexual reproduction, mutations will steadily be introduced into sexual populations, which can lead to noticeable phenotypic changes without fouling up the individual's ability to reproduce. What is different, however, is what happens afterward. Remember that in asexual reproduction, mutations give rise to genetically distinct individuals, and each new combination can remain intact (persist) as long as individuals bearing this combination continue to reproduce. In other words, asexual reproduction acts to maintain genetic combinations that work. Sexual reproduction, on the other hand, is a different scenario. Mutations within sexual populations still can give rise to genetically distinct individuals. Furthermore, any changed bit of genetic information—that is, any mutation—will persists so long as it is being copied and passed to offspring. But sexual reproduction does not maintain distinct genetic combinations across generations. In each new generation, the specific genetic combinations found within the reproductive individuals are broken up and then assorted into new combinations. By new, I don't mean that combinations in one generation are never repeats of combinations found in past generations. Repeatedly mix a collection of parts, assort them into combinations, and by chance some combinations will be repeated. Such mixing can also generate combinations that have not existed before, especially as new mutations continually enter the mix. But each individual's genetic combination is most distinctly new in the sense that parents produce offspring that are genetically distinct from either parent.

The important point here is not the details of how the mixing occurs, but the fact that this continual genetic mixing tends to stir the shapes of a sexual population's members into a cluster. To see how, envision a population made up of individuals with a range of different genetic combinations. These genetic differences translate into a similar range of phenotypic differences. For the sake of argument, let's start with a uniform distribution within this range of shapes—that is, the frequency of each shape is the same (shown in Figure 4-12). Further assume that the environment is such that across this con-

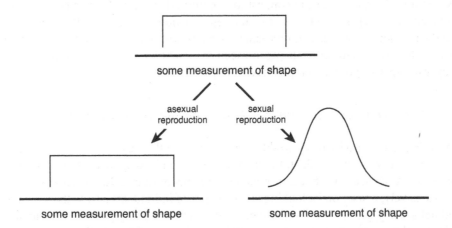

Figure 4-12. A diagram showing how asexual and sexual reproduction affects the distribution of individual shapes. Asexual reproduction has no effect on the distribution (shown here as a uniform distribution remaining a uniform distribution). In contrast, the mixing of sexual reproduction tends to pull any starting distribution into a bell-shaped distribution.

tinuum of shapes, each type is equally capable of reproducing. In other words, the environment itself is not going to have any influence on the distribution. The question, then, is under these conditions, what will happen to this uniform distribution with time?

If reproduction was asexual instead of sexual, the expectation would be that the distribution remains uniform across generations (see Figure 4-12). As long as each of the clones making up this uniform distribution are equally successful at reproducing, the frequency of each clone would remain essentially the same across generations. The mixing of sexual reproduction changes all that. Sexual mixing tends to pull the distribution of types toward the middle, just as any form of mixing does. It is an issue of probability. The closer a genetic combination is toward the middle of the range, the more ways the combination can arise. So by chance alone, combinations closer to the middle become more common, and combinations closer to the edge become rarer. Sexual reproduction thus tends to pull the distribution of possible types into a bell shape (see Figure 4-12).

In principle, it is no different than rolling two dice. Two dice totals range from 2 to 12. But each total within this range does not have an equal probability of coming up. The totals at the two edges—2 and 12—tend to come up most infrequently; the middle total—7—has the highest probability of being rolled; and the probability of rolling each of the numbers rises steadily as one progresses from either edge toward the middle (see Figure 4-13). The reason for the probability distribution, as mentioned earlier, has to do with the number of ways each of these totals can come up. Each edge total has the smallest probability of being rolled because there is only one way these totals come up. Two happens only when both dice come up 1, and 12 happens only when both dice come up 6. Seven, on the other hand, has the highest probability of being rolled because it has the most ways of coming up—6. Distinguishing between first dice and second dice, the six ways are: (6, 1), (5, 2), (4, 3), (3, 4), (2, 5), and (1, 6). Probabilities decline away from the middle because the ways to roll each total declines. There are 5 ways to roll 6 or 8, 4 ways to roll 5 or 9, and so on.

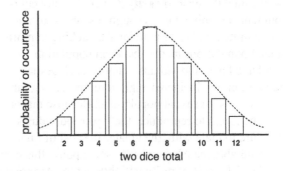

Figure 4-13. The probability distribution of the possible outcomes from rolling two dice.

94   Chapter 4

I think that it is obvious, at least in contrast to a uniform distribution, that a bell-shaped distribution is more a cluster of types. The fact that sexual reproduction, in and of itself, tends to generate bell-shaped distributions is why sexual reproduction can be viewed as something that creates clusters. And if individuals within a cluster of shapes are seen as members of the same species, this is a good reason to layer the species notion on top of sexual populations.

One reason that sexual reproduction may help generate distinct clusters

In terms of producing easily recognizable species, the fact that sexual reproduction tends to produce a cluster of shapes is not sufficient. Figure 4-14(a) illustrates why this is true. Five distinct sexual populations exist (A–E) that form five clustered distributions of shape. But because these clusters overlap so extensively, a taxonomist looking at the shapes of individuals across these sexual populations would not see any gaps in the distribution. So, despite there being gaps in who can mate with whom, a close look a morphology would not reveal the existence of five distinct sexual populations. For shape to reveal distinct sexual populations, the overlap in shape must be minimal (see Figure 4-14(b)).

Does sexual reproduction help minimize such overlap (help maintain distinct clusters)? There may be one reason that it does. To explain, however, I need to set a particular stage. The best way to take advantage of an environment where resources exist in a broad continuum is to have a matching broad continuum of individual shapes. That way some individuals have the shape best suited for every slice of this resource continuum. The tendency of sexual populations to form clusters, however, makes it difficult for one sexual population to generate such a broad continuum of shapes. Sexual populations that overlap extensively, as shown in Figure 4-14(a), could take full advantage of this environmental opportunity. The question I now ask is: Even when environmental conditions favor extensive overlap, is there anything about sexual reproduction that would tend to act in the opposite direction, that is, tend to reduce the amount of overlap? Envision, for example, Figure 4-14(a) losing two sexual populations to become Figure 4-14(b).

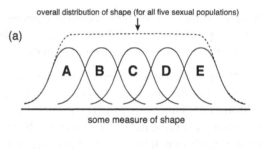

(a)

overall distribution of shape (for all five sexual populations)

some measure of shape

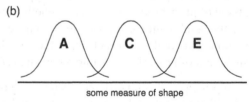

(b)

some measure of shape

Figure 4-14. The difference between extensively overlapping (a) and distinct clusters (b). In both (a) and (b) each bell-shaped curve is meant to represent the distribution of individual shapes within a sexual population. In (a), however, the shapes of the individuals making up each sexual population overlaps so extensively that, except for observing who mates with who, it would be difficult for an observer to tell which individual is a member of what sexual population. In contrast, the sexual populations in (b) would be much easier to distinguish by shape differences alone.

The answer is yes. It has to do with what has been called the **cost of rarity**. Given that any environment can only supply enough resources to support a finite number of individuals, packing in more sexual populations means that each population will have fewer individuals—that is, each sexual population will be increasingly rare. Increasing rarity has a cost in sexual populations. Because mates must be found to reproduce, the fewer individuals there are to mate with, the greater the cost of finding a suitable mate becomes. At some point, this cost of rarity will outweigh the benefits of increasing overlap. The cost of rarity will thus act to keep sexual populations more distinct. In other words, even when environmental conditions do not favor distinct clusters, sexual reproduction acts to maintain distinct clusters anyway.

A new twist: Sexual reproduction can generate bimodal clusters

So far I have argued that sexual populations and a shape-based species concept may often be compatible notions, due to the fact that the mixing component of sexual reproduction along with the cost of rarity could act to generate shape-based gaps between different sexual populations. It is a reasonable sounding argument, which may just contain some truth. There is one aspect of sexual reproduction, however, that potentially confuses this alignment.

Males and females within any sexual population are never phenotypically identical—there are always at least some anatomical differences. This means that males and females have at least minor developmental differences. (Either the information present is somewhat different, or something triggers the same packet of information to be read somewhat differently.) This opens the possibility that the same mechanisms used to trigger small developmental differences could also be used to trigger a whole cascade of developmental differences. And this possibility has been exploited. Males and females within the same sexual population often have noticeably different shapes; a condition generally termed **sexual dimorphism**. Humans are an example. Although there is considerable overlap, male humans (*Homo sapiens*) are on average larger than females. Elephant seals (*Mirounga angustirostris*) are a much more extreme example. Males tend to weigh around four times as much as females (males weigh up to 8,000 lb., whereas females weigh up to 2,000 lb.). In birds, the plumage often develops differently in males and females, with males commonly having the gaudier plumage. Plumage differences range from small patches of feathers being a different color to utterly striking contrasts. Whereas the females are plain and brown, male peacocks (*Pavo cristatus*), with their ornate coloration and yard-long tails, and the males of different species of birds of paradise, whose feathers, in total, are colored with every hue of the rainbow and are gathered, lengthened, and twisted into a bizarre assemble of arrangements, are classic examples of extraordinary differences. Further examples can be found throughout the sexual world, from insects to plants.

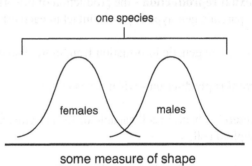

There is something illogical about classifying male elephant seals or male peacocks as being members of a different species than their respective females. Yet that could happen if species were sorted by shape alone. So in cases of sexual dimorphism, it only makes sense that the notion of species as clusters of distinctly shaped individuals be extended to include the possibility of bimodal clusters (see Figure 4-15).

Figure 4-15. The bimodal shape distribution of a sexually dimorphic population.

Some key terms:

information - what any arrangement that can code for some activity has. (Something that has information can be interpreted, where the interpretation is the conversion of the coded activity into the activity.)

genome - a set of information that, in total, has sufficient information to guide the development of a reproductively competent organism.

gene - a single instruction within a genome.

genotype - an organism's specific constitution of genetic information.

phenotype - the performing (active) part of an individual organism, which is generally thought of as the organism's body. (Geneticists commonly use the term phenotype to refer to specific features of an individual's body.)

shape-performance tradeoff - the notion that because an organism has a particular shape (at any point during its life) it cannot be great at doing everything. Any shape makes certain activities possible, but at the cost of not being the best shape to perform well in other ways.

asexual reproduction - the production of offspring by a single parent, where, in the absence of errors, the parent's genotype is passed intact to each offspring.

sex - when genetic information from more than one individual is combined into a single individual.

sexual reproduction - when sex is coupled with the production of new individuals.

gamete - a haploid cell capable of fusing with another gamete—typically of the opposite sex—to form a diploid cell.

zygote - diploid cell produced by the fusion of two gametes.

anisogamy - when an sexual population produces two distinct types of gametes—generally a small mobile gamete (male) and a larger nutrient-laden gamete (female).

ploidy level - the number of genomes contained within a cell.

haploid - a cell that has one genome.

diploid - a cell that has two genomes.

biological species concept - two individual organisms of the opposite sex are members of the same species, if and only if, they recognize each other as potential mates (hence may attempt to mate), and if they do mate they can produce viable offspring; the largest unit of populations within which the mixing genetic information through sexual reproduction occurs or could occur.

sexual dimorphism - when males and females within the same sexual population develop distinctly different shapes.

Some study questions:

1. Explain why every organism must start its growth and development with both a genotype and phenotype. How does an organism's genotype and phenotype change during the course of its development?

2. Explain how an organism's development is, in some sense, deterministic, but it is not completely deterministic.

3. *Understand the notion of a shape-performance tradeoff.*

4. Explain what is meant by the statement: Asexual reproduction is reproduction in the classic sense of the word.

5. Explain how a mutation in one individual in a clone could give rise to a different clone.

6. Discuss one way that sexual reproduction complicates reproduction. *Could sexual reproduction occur without gender? What is the most basic difference between males and females? Discuss one way that gender facilitates sexual reproduction.*

7. *Discuss two ways that sexual reproduction mixes up the genetic information within a sexual population.* Next discuss how such mixing could result in a bell-shaped distribution of shapes within a sexual population.

8. Be able to explain how sexual reproduction forms groups—so called sexual populations. What do sexual populations have to do with the biological species concept?

The Nature of Biological Communities

Part of my aim in the last chapter was to get you to realize that the species concept and the ways of the living world are not always in perfect alignment. Individual organisms inhabiting this planet are not always arranged into nice distinct clusters, each of which can be assigned a different name—a species name. Yet, the species concept does not demand absolute clarity. A wide variety of distinctly shaped organisms inhabit this planet, which for the most part cluster into distinct groups. So, despite some fuzz around some edges, the most accurate way to talk about all these different types of organisms is to speak about different species. Here we frame discussion of how these different organisms interact with each other in terms of how species interact with other species. In other words, we begin to focus on the nature of biological communities.

A biological community forms whenever resources flow between different species. Or put in terms introduced in Chapter 3, each species can be viewed as a processor that forms regulatory connections with other species through a flow of resources, and the performance built through these regulatory connections is the biological community. The focus of this chapter is to examine more closely the nature of this performance. I start by developing further the idea of species as processors.

Species as Processors

In Chapter 3, I introduced the idea that individual organisms can be viewed as processors because outputs are different than inputs. Any species can be viewed as a processor for the same reason. The inputs and outputs of each member collectively add up to form the inputs and outputs of the species as a whole. Furthermore, what types of resources can be processed (what are the inputs) and how they are processed (what are the outputs) are constrained for each species by the coupling of two facts: members of the same species have similar shapes and the existence of a shape–performance trade-off.

To better link the processor concept with species, however, I need to distinguish between two forms of outputs: growth and waste. In general, any processor grows whenever outputs loop back to become part of the processor that produced them. At the species level, two forms of growth take place. First, individual members grow. Throughout the course of development, resources are continually processed into outputs used to build larger, often more complex, organisms. Second, the species' population size can grow via reproduction. Wastes, on the other hand, are outputs freely released to the environment (see Figure 5-1).

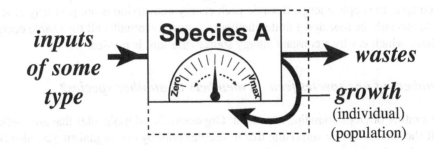

Figure 5-1. A diagram of a species—named here Species A—as a processor. Two forms of outputs are distinguished: (1) Outputs that loop back into the species as growth in terms of individual members getting larger and/or the population as a whole getting larger. Such growth is illustrated by the dotted line expansion of the Species A box. And (2) outputs released freely into the environment as waste.

The Formation of Regulatory Connections between Species

Species form regulatory connections between them by a *flow* of resources (although the word flow may conjure up too tame of an image). The flow of resources through different species is not like water flowing peacefully through a river channel. Resources generally flow between species by members of one species either feeding on members of another species or by using the wastes of another species. This raises a question: Why do these types of connections form? As it turns out, it all has to do with building and breaking.

Building and breaking

All organisms build themselves. Interestingly, the chemistry underlying this construction involves both building and breaking. Organisms are composed of certain types of molecules called, in general, **biological molecules** or **biomolecules**. Part of building themselves involves building these molecules by rearranging other, generally simpler, molecules available in the environment. The breaking side of the story comes from the fact that building anything, including biomolecules, requires an input of usable energy, and organisms get this needed energy by breaking other molecules apart. Briefly, here is how it works. All molecular arrangements contain potential energy (PE) (often termed **chemical energy**) within their structure. Some arrangements store more than others do. Potentially usable energy is thus released whenever a molecule is converted into arrangements containing less PE. It all goes back to the conservation of energy (the first law of thermodynamics); the difference in PE between the initial and the final arrangements must be transferred somewhere. Organisms have come up with ways to funnel some of the energy released toward the task of building needed molecules, as well as powering other activities of living such as motion.

The whole concept of building and breaking is thus an energetic one. Building takes place whenever rearrangement results in arrangements containing more PE than the starting arrangements. Breaking down or breaking apart occurs whenever rearrangements result in arrangements containing less PE than the starting arrangements. And this dichotomy is coupled within the workings of Life as organisms commonly break apart certain molecules to supply the energy to build others.

You may be saying, now wait a minute: The energy used to run Life comes from the sun, not from breaking down molecules. Actually both are true. Although the sun is the ultimate energy source, solar energy is first plugged into Life when it is used to build more PE containing molecules. These molecules in turn are broken apart to release energy to power other activities. An interesting twist is that whenever this released energy is used to build other high-energy molecules, some of this usable energy is stored again. So, molecules built using energy supplied by breaking apart molecules could later be broken apart to supply energy. Because each energy conversion is not perfectly efficient, however, this cycle can only be repeated a finite number of times. Eventually, all the usable energy will be degraded to heat, which is why a constant energy source (the sun) is needed.

Why do members of one species feed on members of another species?

To make a rather obvious-sounding statement: Organisms build molecules that are useful to themselves. It should also not be surprising that molecules built by one organism may also be useful to another organism. For one, such molecules may be used as an energy source—that is, an organism is able to break apart molecules built by another and harvest some of the energy released. A second potential use stems from the fact that organisms of all types are basically composed of the same types of biomolecules. So, although an organism may get a needed biomolecule by building it itself, this biochemical similarity creates the possibility that an organism can get a needed biomolecule already assembled from another organism (see Figure 5-2). It all comes down to the old adage: Why do something if you can get someone else to do it for you? The advantage of doing so boils down to energetics. By getting a biomolecule from another organism, one saves the expense of having to build one itself.

There is still the question of how one organism actually gets molecules built by another. Organisms do not tend to just hand out molecules they build. Typically, these are the molecules of growth and repair, so to give them up is to give up part of their body.

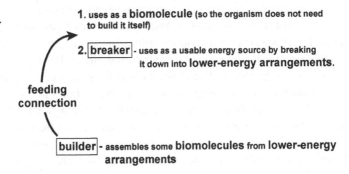

Figure 5-2. The two reasons that a biomolecule built by one organisms would be a useful input to another organism.

Two ways, in general, exist to pry something away from someone unwilling to give it up freely: Either steal it or barter for it. When it comes to biomolecules, both means are used.

Biomolecular theft occurs whenever one organism captures and feeds on another organism. This is an output–input connection as the growth output of one organism is the input of another. And as I am sure you are aware, having one's body fed on is hazardous to one's health—commonly to the point of death. Basically, for biomolecular-thieving organisms to live, others must die. It is called **cannibalism** when a biochemically thieving organism feeds on a member of the same species. **Predation** is when a member of one species feeds on a member of a different species—the prey (see Figure 5-3). Many distinguish between a predator and a parasite. A **predator** is something that captures and kills its prey either before or during the course of feeding, whereas a **parasite** lives on or in another organism and drains resources from its still living **host**. **Decomposers** are quite similar to predators. Both feed off the molecules formed by another organism, and both depend on the death of the other organism to get access to those molecules. The difference is that unlike predators, who take the death of their prey into their own hands, decomposers must wait for the organisms that they feed on to die.

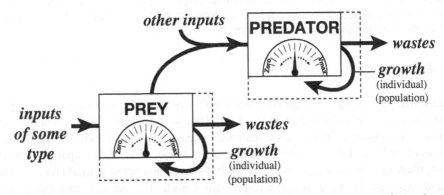

Figure 5-3. A processor-based diagram of members of one species—some form of predator—feeding on members of another species—the prey. Predators, in essence, feed on the outputs of their prey that loop back as growth.

What I always find humbling is that we are part of this scenario. Humans are a biochemically thieving species. Just because what you ate today was purchased from a grocery store and wrapped neatly in some form of container does not change the fact that you feed on other organisms. Those organisms had to die for you to live.

The member of one species swiping molecules from a member of another species can even form into a chain of theft—organisms stealing molecules from others that previously stole molecules from others. Every species creates opportunities for other species. Biologists call a chain of theft formed by different species feeding on each other a **food chain**. Perhaps, the most easily recognized food chain centers on usable energy. The chain starts with species called **photosynthetic** organisms or **producers**, who are able to use the sun as an energy source to build high-energy molecules. The first link forms when other species feed on sun-using species, breaking apart some of their molecules for energy. General names used for all energy-thieving species are **heterotrophs** or **consumers**. More links form when heterotrophic species swipe molecules to break down from other heterotrophs. Each link in this energy chain is called a **trophic level**. Through this chain, species other than those able to use solar energy directly plug into the sun as a power source (see Figure 5-4).

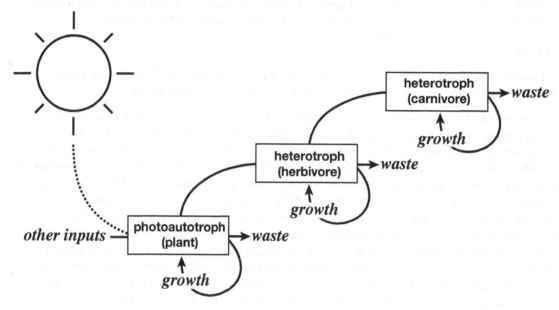

Figure 5-4. A processor-based diagram of an energy food chain. To simplify the picture the rate meter and size-changing aspect of each processor is omitted. Note that through this chain, biomolecules synthesized in a plant could end up in a carnivore.

A brief interlude

Like all organisms, photosynthetic organisms need usable energy 24 hours a day every day of their life. The sun, however, only shines part of every day (and in most parts of the world the duration and intensity changes seasonally). Therefore sun-using organisms must build and *store* high-energy molecules when sunlight is available that can be pulled out of storage and broken apart for energy when it is not. So, photosynthetic organisms are on the sun side of an energetic food chain during daylight hours and swiping side of the energetic food chain at night. Of course, because they are getting these molecules from themselves it is not, by definition, thievery, yet the energetic principle is the same. The fact that sun-using organisms must store high-energy molecules also makes them more vulnerable to theft by other species. It is no different than someone's vulnerability to theft going up as they store more money.

Although energy-thieving species have an underlying similarity with sun-using organisms at night, there is often a striking difference. Sunlight goes basically everywhere, so being mobile is not such a big deal for sun-using organisms. In contrast, mobility is clearly an asset to organisms attempting to go around and steal molecules from others. And although there are exceptions (such as mobile photosynthetic organisms), we find this pattern in the multicellular organisms with which we are most familiar. Plants (and many forms of multicellular algae that live in water) are nonmobile, sun-using organisms. Animals are mobile, thieving organisms. A familiar energetic food chain starts with plants at the base and animals elsewhere. Animals that feed on (are predators or parasites of) plants are termed **herbivores**, animals that feed on other animals are called **carnivores**, and **omnivores** are animals that feed on both plants and other animals.

Continuing on

The pathway by which molecules move among different species is not confined to a single chain. Food chains branch whenever more than one species feeds on the same species. Branch points are places where **competition** occurs—different species feeding on the same species compete for that resource. Food chains can also converge. They do so whenever one species can feed on more than one species. With branching and convergence, more and more species become connected through the flow of resources. Different food chains become interconnected into a **food web** (see Figure 5-5).

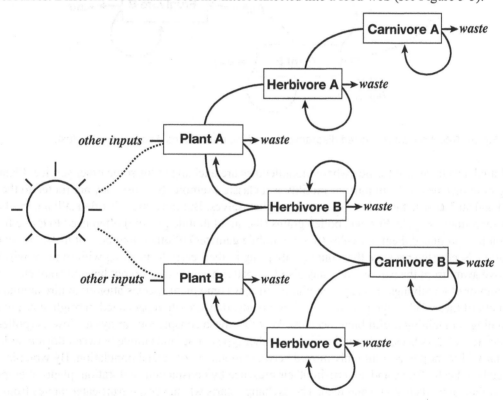

Figure 5-5. A processor-based diagram of a food web.

In addition to theft, links in food chains are at times formed by trading or barter. Biologists call such relationships **mutualisms**. Many plants, for example, establish a molecule exchange with certain types of bacteria. Plants require a nitrogen source to grow, but are unable to use the most abundant nitrogen source—the 78% or so of the atmosphere composed of molecular nitrogen (N_2). Certain types of bacteria—generally called nitrogen-fixing bacteria—are able to change molecular nitrogen to ammonia—a form of nitrogen that can be used by plants. Conversely, these bacteria are unable to synthesize their own sugars; hence, they must get them from some organism—such as plants—that can. Plants and nitrogen-fixing bacteria could thus benefit by establishing a tightly coupled exchange. Many plants, in fact, form root nodules where they house and feed sugars to nitrogen-fixing bacteria in exchange for ammonia (see Figure 5-6).

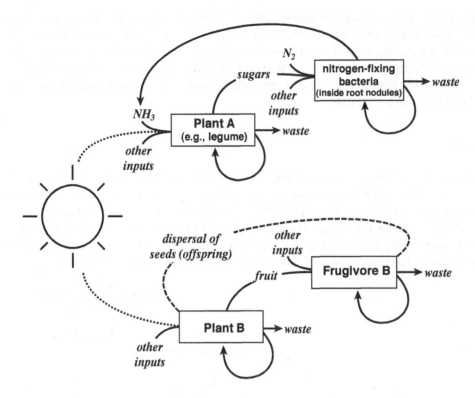

Figure 5-6. A processor-based diagram of two of the mutualisms discussed in the text.

Mutualisms have also formed where biomolecules are exchanged for some other service. Plants trading biomolecules with animals for motility is a classic example. Because they are rooted to the ground and stiff in structure, plants cannot move themselves. But movement is often still a part of a plant's reproductive cycle. For one, pollen grains (the small mobile gamete) often need to move from the plant that produced them to ovules (big nonmobile gametes) of other members of the same sexual population. Seeds (the package that contains offspring in their early form along with some provisions) that move away from the parent plant may also fare better because they do not have to compete with their mom or other siblings. There is a similarity in how some plant species attempt to hire animals to move both of these. When the pollen or seeds are ready, they are often packaged in bright conspicuous surroundings containing useful biomolecules. We know these conspicuous arrays as flowers (pollen) and fruits (seeds). As bees, or hummingbirds, or other types of animals move between flowers to feed on nectar within, pollen is commonly moved between members of sexual population. By wrapping their seeds in fleshy fruits, and advertising their presence by conspicuous coloration, plants attempt to entice mobile animals to come and feed. The exchange starts whenever the fruit-eater moves from the parent plant before it spits or defecates out the seeds within the fruit. The exchange comes to fruition whenever these seeds fall in a good spot for germination and growth (see Figure 5-6).

Why would one species' waste be another species' resource?

Organisms tend to release as waste—that is, release freely into the environment—molecules that they cannot use. Here I focus on the question: Why would a molecule that one organism cannot use be useful to another? In other words, why would **waste connections** (see Figure 5-7) between species ever form?

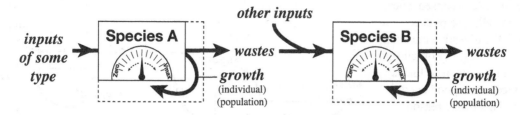

Figure 5-7. A processor-based diagram of two species form a waste connection—that is, something freely released by members of one species is a useful input to members of another species.

One reason is relatively easy to see. Whenever one species swipes a certain molecule to break apart for energy, the lower-energy molecules left over are released back into the environment because otherwise they would accumulate to excessive levels. But these lower-energy wastes will be useful inputs to those species able to build the higher-energy molecule in the first place (see Figure 5-8). For example, herbivores swipe sugars and other high-energy carbon-containing molecules built by plants, and when these molecules are broken down, carbon dioxide (CO_2) is one of the leftover lower-energy molecules. For herbivores, this accumulating carbon dioxide is a waste released to the atmosphere. Plants, on the other hand, grab carbon dioxide from the atmosphere to once again use it to build high-energy carbon-containing molecules (see Figure 5-9).

Another reason one species' waste is another species' resource is that many species release molecules that can still be used as an energy source (see Figure 5-10). This sounds a bit odd because why would an organism release a molecule until all the potentially harvestable energy is squeezed out? It boils down to the shape–performance trade-off. Organisms often lack the means to completely break apart every molecule built by organisms they feed on. For example, animals feeding on plants ingest cellulose (a higher-energy molecule plants build to use as a structural material) but often lack the tools

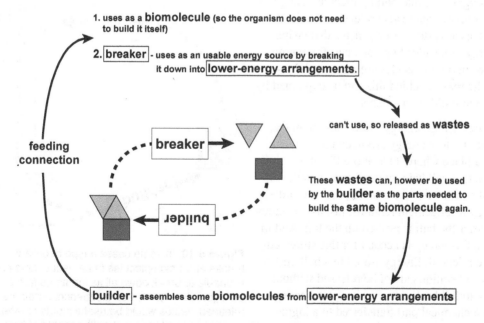

Figure 5-8. Feeding connections set the stage for waste connections to form (that complete a nutrient cycle). The lower energy molecules released as waste when biomolecules are broken to harvest usable energy will become usable inputs for any organism able to build the biomolecule from lower-energy arrangements. Note that this idea is presented both visually (center) and as a written flow chart (outside).

to digest it. As a consequence, ingested cellulose passes through the digestive tract coming out in feces. For organisms able to break down cellulose, such feces are a good energy source. This is one reason that dung to a dung beetle is *not* a "useless piece of s__t." Similarly, when animals break down amino acids for energy, they fail to squeeze out all the energy available. Ammonia (NH_3) is a molecular leftover removed by excretion that still has a fair amount of chemical energy. Certain bacteria and other small organisms subsequently use it as an energy source. (There is one other reason that organisms release higher-energy molecules. Certain tasks organisms need to accomplish demand building a molecule that they have no further use for. However, I know of no quick way to explain why this is so, so I won't try. But like with anything else, this creates opportunities for other species to break these molecules down.)

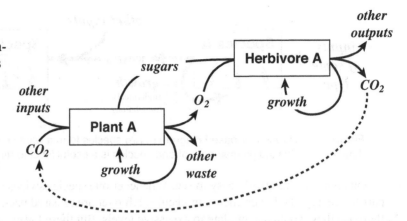

Figure 5-9. A diagram showing that waste connections form in both directions between plants and herbivores (as well as all other animals that indirectly get their energy from plants). Carbon dioxide (CO_2), which is freely released by herbivores, is a useful input to plants. Molecular oxygen (O_2), which is freely released by plants, is a useful input to herbivores. The reasons behind these waste connections are discussed in the text.

The final reason sounds odd until you think about it. Organisms that build molecules using the sun as an energy source also release low-energy molecules as a waste. For organisms that swipe high-energy molecules to break apart for energy, these low-energy molecules are an essential resource. The reason behind this can be explained by thinking about hills and valleys.

Whenever high-energy molecules are made, some part of a low-energy arrangement is transferred to a place where it has more PE. It is analogous to a ball being moved from a valley to the top of a hill. After the transfer, the rest of the low-energy arrangement remains, just as the valley remains after the ball is pushed up the hill. And in both cases this valley is needed for this stored energy to be released. Energy stored in a ball pushed to a higher elevation cannot be released without the valley to fall back into. Similarly, the energy stored in a chemical part transferred to a higher-energy arrangement cannot be released without the lower-energy arrangement to transfer back to.

Photosynthetic organisms such as plants use solar energy to transfer the hydrogen in water molecules (H_2O) to a higher-energy molecular

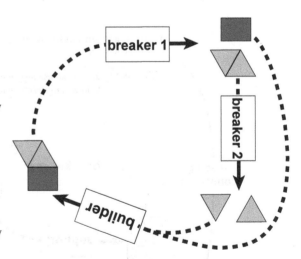

Figure 5-10. In some cases a type of organism that breaks apart biomolecules to harvest usable energy is unable to break down all its inputs as far as possible (breaker 1). As a consequence, certain freely-released wastes would be useful inputs to other organisms (such as breaker 2) capable of breaking down these molecules even futher. A nutrient cycle still forms as long as organisms capable of rebuilding biomolecules out of the remaining lower energy arrangements are present. (See text for more details.)

arrangement. In other words, the molecule to which hydrogen is added is the hill, and the oxygen atoms left behind (which combine to form molecular oxygen—O_2) are the valley. Molecular oxygen is, in fact, a deep valley, for it is an extremely low-energy molecule. So, for a plant to ever break any of these high-energy molecules back down (such as to provide energy during the night) molecular oxygen must be present. It is no different than the fact that wood cannot be burned without molecular oxygen. In the process, hydrogen atoms once again combine with oxygen atoms to form water molecules (see Figure 5-11). Overall, plants still release oxygen because more building occurs than breaking apart during growth, so these low-energy oxygen molecules ac-

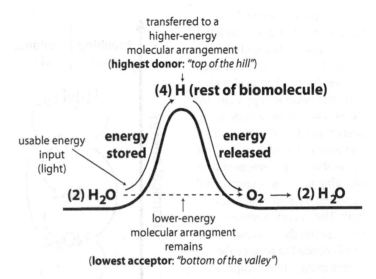

Figure 5-11. A diagram showing the movement of hydrogens from water to a higher-energy arrangement and then back to the leftover low-energy molecule (molecular oxygen) to form water again. The numbers in parenthesis are there to balance the equation (the number of hydrogens and oxygens remain constant throughout). (See text for further discussion).

cumulate and are released as a waste. This waste becomes an essential input for herbivores feeding on high-energy molecules built by plants (or any other organisms in the food chain breaking down swiped high-energy molecules for energy) because without this molecular valley, the energy stored in high-energy arrangements (such as sugar molecules) cannot be released (see Figure 5-9). There cannot be a hill unless there is a valley. This is why you are presently breathing in molecular oxygen. If you need to convince yourself of its importance, just stop breathing for a while.

Nutrient cycles and the principle of reciprocal opportunity

In Chapter 3 we discussed what nutrient cycles are and why they are fundamental to Life. Now we are ready to address the impetus for nutrient cycles to form. What is interesting is that it is so simple.

The basic foundation of material cycles is what I term the **principle of reciprocal opportunity**. The principle is composed of two tenets:

• Every time an organism builds a molecule, it creates the opportunity for an organism (itself or some other organism) to break the same molecule down to harvest energy.

• Every time an organism breaks down a molecule, it creates the opportunity for an organism (itself or some other organism) to use the parts left over to build another biologically important molecule.

Although these two ideas should already be familiar, here I emphasize that their tightly coupled nature explains why every species' outputs are potentially useful inputs for some other species. Nutrient cycles form whenever this potential becomes reality. As this occurs, the basic elements found in both the higher-energy and lower-energy molecules—such as carbon, nitrogen, hydrogen, and oxygen—will be continually recycled (see Figure 5-12).

Couple the principle of reciprocal opportunity with the second law of thermodynamics, and why the sun must keep shining for nutrient cycles to continue becomes apparent. In the absence of an outside energy source, nutrient cycles could continue indefinitely only if *all* the usable energy released when breaking molecules apart could be stored back in molecules built. But energy transfers are never perfectly efficient, so the sun is needed to replace the usable energy that escapes as heat (see Figure 5-13). Without such an outside energy supply, nutrient cycles would eventually grind to an energy-starved halt.

This coupling also explains why nutrient cycles cannot occur solely within the confines of a single organism. Although nutrient cycles can and do form within individual organisms (inside organisms certain molecules are constantly being broken apart and put back together), the energetics of food chains dictate that some nutrient cycles must extend across species. Even if the same organism that breaks down molecules swiped from others has the tools to use the molecules' leftovers to build the same molecule again, the inefficiency inherent in energy transfers means that it must break apart more molecules than it builds. Leftover molecules will thus be in excess and released as waste. Only the photosynthetic species at the bottom of the food chain, which can access incoming solar energy, have an adequate power source to assemble all these accumulating wastes back into more high-energy molecules. This, in fact, is the means by which solar energy keeps nutrient cycles spinning.

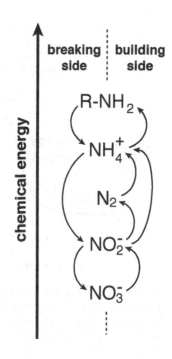

Figure 5-12. The five major nitrogen-containing molecules within the nitrogen cycle (return to Figure 3-11 if you need to review) are arranged in terms of the amount of relative potential energy within their structure. Each arrow represents the different ways that different species either break these molecules into lower-energy forms, or build them into higher-energy forms. That arrows both enter and leave each molecule indicates that the output of every conversion is an input to another conversion. Breaking and building coming full circle forms a material cycle—which in this case is the nitrogen cycle.

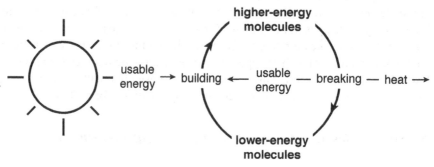

Figure 5-13. A diagram showing that inputs of solar energy are needed to replace the energy lost as heat in any building-breaking cycle is to continue.

What Is Regulated?

So far we have discussed how different species form regulatory connections with each other. What we have yet to mention is what exactly within biological communities is being regulated. This turns out to be a matter of perspective. Focus on the resources, per se, and what is being regulated is the amount, the rate, and the efficiency in which usable energy moves and material resources are recycled throughout the community. Focus on species, and what is regulated is species size—both in terms of the population size of each species and the number of species (often termed species richness) making up a community.

Here I steer the focus toward the species size aspect of regulation. But due to their intertwined nature, one cannot divorce these two perspectives. All aspects of resource movement influence both aspects of species size, and vice versa. So resource movement will still come up repeatedly. I focus on three questions:

• What regulates the population size of any species within a community?

• What regulates the number of species within a community? In other words, why aren't there more or less species present?

• Within a community, how will changing the population size of any one species affect the rest of the members of the community?

Population regulation (Question 1)

Every species' population can potentially grow in a compounding way—as population size increases, there are more individuals to produce offspring, making it possible for the population to grow even faster. This compounding growth is known as **exponential growth**. Each species' population within a community is potentially explosive in terms of scale. Exactly how explosive is influenced by the **life history** of the members making up a species' population. Life history is an organism's reproductive schedule: how often (generation time), how much (number of offspring per reproductive bout), and with what degree of success (proportion of offspring that survive to breed in the next generation) an organism reproduces. Decreasing generation time and/or increasing the other two life-history components always increases a population's potential rate of increase. Yet, even the population size of a species with a long generation time and that produce few offspring per reproductive bout can still increase quickly. For example, a single pair of elephants (one of the slowest reproducing organisms on earth) can become a population of 15 million in only 500 years.

To look closer at the power of exponential growth, consider the population growth of an organism with a particular life history. The organism is asexual, it reproduces once in its lifetime, it has two offspring per reproductive bout, and both offspring survive to breed. Under this scenario a single individual could potentially become a population of 6.34×10^{29} individuals in only 100 generations. In certain bacteria that have as short as a 20-minute generation time, that is approximately a day and a half.

Generation: 1   2   3   4   5   6   7   8   9   10 ... 20 .... 50 100

Population: 1   2   4   8   16   32   64   128   256   512   524288 5.6×10^{14} 6.34×10^{29}

The final population size of unchecked exponential growth in any species is infinity. There are, however, no species on this planet with an infinite population size. Something must be limiting the population size of each and every species. The question is: What is that something? There are two options: external regulation and internal regulation.

In **external regulation** each population member tries to put as many offspring into the next generation as possible. Their success, however, is regulated by external factors such as food availability, living space, and predators. In other words, external regulation occurs when a population internally pushes toward infinity, but environmental circumstance pushes back, eventually holding the population size to the maximum that environmental conditions can currently support.

In **internal regulation** a population's upper limit is not set by environmental conditions, but by the members of the population themselves. Each member has some mechanism by which they sense when population levels are starting to get too high, and they slow their reproductive rate to the point that the population stabilizes before reaching the externally set maximum.

Which of these two is better? One could surely argue that internal regulation has an advantage. In a population pushing up against external resource limits, individuals as a whole are pushed to the edge. Each individual must struggle just to get (on average) sufficient resources to survive and to produce a replacement number of offspring. Internal regulation, however, does not let a population reach that level of resource limitation. Each individual enjoys access to resources beyond those needed just to squeeze by. With fewer individuals, the same size pie can be divided into bigger pieces. Accordingly, life for each individual would not be as difficult or as risky.

The question though is not what sounds better or even is better for the population as a whole. The question is which one is found in Nature. The logic developed later in Chapter 7 suggests that, except under special circumstances, external regulations will be prevalent. The available evidence backs this up. Populations of many different species have been observed to grow until limited resources hold them back. Thus, our discussion of population regulation will focus on factors that constrain a population's access to resources.

Constraints associated with materials

We live in a finite material world. The earth's mass is not growing or contracting because no appreciable amount of materials is coming or leaving earth. A few meteorites enter, some space shuttle trash among other odds and ends leave, but these inputs and outputs are trivial. Furthermore, at temperatures found on earth, the basic forms of materials—elements such as carbon, oxygen, and gold—do not change into different elements. The amount of carbon, gold, or any other naturally occurring elements found on earth today is the same as it was 100 years ago, a million years ago, and presumably will remain the same into the future.

Material limits alone make it impossible for any population to continue to expand toward infinity. Because organisms are made of certain materials, a finite material world means that only a finite number of organisms can be built.

A finite material world also reemphasizes the importance of nutrient cycles. Just consider what would happen to Life on earth if the materials used to build organisms could be used once only. At some point all the materials available to build organisms would be used up. Beyond that point, no more organisms could be built. Life would cease to exist.

Materials, however, can be and have been used over and over. This means that the materials making up your body right now (and all other organisms) have been used to build other organisms in the past. Put differently, the materials making you up were not born with you, but are just being temporarily borrowed. Their birth can likely be traced back to the origin of the universe. Have you ever wondered how many different organisms your present materials were once part of, and what they were? Think, for instance, about the apple you ate for lunch. Some of the carbon atoms from that apple are now part of your body. Now narrow the focus to just one of those carbon atoms. What organism was it part of prior to being part of an apple tree? And before that? And before that? And so on. If that carbon atom was on average part of one organism per year since Life emerged on this planet, then it has already been part of around 3.5 billion different organisms. And given that even long-lived organisms are in a constant state of material flux, one organism a year seems likely to be an underestimate. I can envision a scenario where a carbon atom goes from the apple, to you, and into another plant within hours. Imagine if this carbon atom could tell the tale of where it has been. "Well, let see, I think it was about 75 million years ago when I was lodged in the liver of a young brontosaurus when all of sudden it got gobbled up by a *Tyrannosaurus rex*. Now that was cool, being part of one of those big beasts. . ."

Constraints associated with energy

In contrast to materials, the amount of usable energy is not finite in amount, at least for a few billion more years. Until the sun burns out, it will continue to bathe the earth with usable energy. That does not mean, however, that availability of usable energy does not impose constraints on population size.

First, solar energy has a limited flow rate. Only a finite amount of solar energy reaches the earth at any moment, so only a finite amount can be captured into the living world at any moment. This sets an upper limit to how much Life is potentially supported. Furthermore, not all the solar energy entering can be captured by photosynthesis. In fact, photosynthesis is able to capture only an astoundingly small amount—less than 1/10th of 1%—of the incoming light. Next, only a small amount of the captured energy is actually incorporated into growth. Up to 70% or so of the light captured by plants is used to power a plant's continual operation, so only that remaining is available for growth. Thus, only a very small percentage (perhaps as low as 0.03%) of the solar energy reaching the earth's surface is ever incorporated into plant biomass. The rest is degraded to heat. A finite amount of plant biomass can only build a finite amount of plants.

Second, the efficiency in which usable energy flows through the food chains enters the picture. As discussed earlier, food chains form when herbivores eat plant biomass, carnivores eat herbivore biomass, and so on. Or, put in another way, herbivores are those things that convert plant biomass into more herbivores; carnivores are those things that convert herbivore biomass into more carnivores, and so on. For example, mountain lions (*Felis concolor*) are those things that convert mule deer (*Odocoileus hemionus*), and whatever else they eat, into more mountain lions. How efficient are such conversions? Can the biomass consumed by one trophic level be converted with 100% efficiency into biomass at the next trophic level? That is, can 100 kilograms of plant be converted into 100 kilograms of deer, which could then be converted into 100 kilograms of mountain lion? The answer is no. The reason comes back to the tendency for usable energy to become unusable with use. This inherent inefficiency in energy transfers means that each link in a food chain will have less usable energy to build organisms than the link before. Less building means at each trophic level the total biomass must be less than the previous trophic level. This dwindling usable energy supply eventually becomes too little to support another trophic level. So, the starting energy supply and conversion efficiency always frame an upper limit to the number of trophic levels. Whether this energy-based limit is reached in any community depends also on other factors.

The actual **gross production efficiency**—the efficiency with which biomass at one trophic level is converted into biomass at the next trophic level—varies widely among different species, ranging from around 1% to 30%. As a result of these low efficiencies, the trophic level in which any species feeds can have a large effect on its population size.

Let's consider an oversimplified example. Suppose an area exists where mountain lions feed exclusively on mule deer, and mule deer are eaten only by mountain lions. Further, suppose that the efficiency with which mountain lions convert mule deer into mountain lions is 10% (which is probably too high, but it makes the math easy). How would the population sizes compare? Given that mountain lions and mule deer are roughly the same size, a 10% conversion efficiency means that around 10 deer would need to be consumed to build one mountain lion. Which means that the mountain lion population can only be around one-tenth the size of the deer population. Reduce this gross production efficiency to 1% (which is probably more accurate because it is close to what has been observed in large mammals), and there would be 100 times more deer than mountain lions. Details aside, the take-home point is that energetics alone explains why you are more likely to see a deer than a mountain lion. Add in a mountain lion's tendency to be elusive, and it is easy to see why people who spend a lot of time outside in mountain lion country rarely, if ever, see one. The same argument also can be made for any link in the chain. You are more likely to see a member of a plant species that mule deer typically eat than a mule deer.

Low gross production efficiencies result from a combination of four factors. First, some usable energy is lost because some of that eaten cannot be digested and is passed through the organism. Second, the PE contained within the molecules digested and then absorbed cannot be used directly by the organism. Instead, this energy must be transferred into molecular arrangements that the organism can directly use as fuels. And, as with all energy transfers, usable energy is lost as heat during the conversion. Third, some portion of the energy stored in these fuel molecules must be used to power activities other than building biomass—such as keeping an animal's heart beating. And finally, again due to inefficiency associated with energy transfers, some energy used to build biomass will also be lost as heat.

Constraints associated with an organism's shape

Consider a single herbivore species, say some type of insect. Can it feed on every plant species? Due to basic similarities in the structure of all plant species, it seems possible that something able to eat one plant species could eat them all. The answer, however, is no.

Plants may look like passive organisms, just growing to be fed on, but don't let appearances fool you. Plants do all sorts of things to protect themselves. Some of the defenses they build—such as sharp spines around leaves and stems, or wrapping their offspring in tough seed coats—are easy to see. But most plant defenses lie invisibly tucked inside their cells. They build molecules, often termed **secondary compounds**, which help a plant function better in the sense that they make herbivores consuming them function worse. Some can kill the organism feeding on its tissue outright—that is, they are poisonous or toxic. Others slow an herbivore's growth by somehow interfering with its ability to use plant tissue. In part, slowing growth acts as a defense because the worse herbivores are at converting plants into more herbivores, the fewer the number of herbivores that will be around to feed on plants. But there is a second issue. Herbivores should selectively feed on those plant species that they can grow best on. So a plant can reduce the extent that it is fed on by becoming a poorer-quality food than an herbivore's other choices,

Despite each plant species' efforts to stop herbivory, every plant species is fed on to at least some extent. This vulnerability stems from the fact that every defense system has a weakness and hence can be circumvented. One just needs the right tools to do so. The tropical tree *Dioclea megacarpa*, for example, packs its seeds with a whole lot (13% of its dry weight) of a toxic molecule. Due to its similarity to another molecule used to build proteins, this toxic molecule can interfere with an organism's ability to make proteins correctly. Circumventing this defense, however, is as straightforward as having a means to discriminate between the two molecules. In fact, not only can the insect species that feeds on these seeds sort the useful molecule from the impostor, but it also has the tools to convert the impostor into useful molecular forms. So, from this insect species' perspective, this impostor molecule is not only not lethal, but it is also a food source.

So what is the basic point? *That the shape–performance trade-off is always setting limits on trophic interactions.* In terms of plants and herbivores, although plant species have defenses, the shape–performance trade-off makes it impossible for a plant to have every type of defense. On the other hand, no herbivore can circumvent all defenses. A plant's defense system will protect it from most but not all herbivores—which is clearly better than having nothing. Alternatively, each herbivore species' diet is generally restricted to those plant species whose defenses it can best handle. This basic story is repeated as one goes up the food chain. Whether it's herbivores feeding on plants, or carnivores feeding on herbivores, or carnivores feeding on other carnivores, the shape–performance trade-off makes it impossible for any species to feed profitably on all species at the next lower trophic level. In fact, many species are so specialized that they are constrained to feed only on one other species.

Similarly, the shape–performance trade-off tends to restrict the range of environmental conditions that any species can handle. A species whose shape is able to handle cold temperatures, for example, may die from overheating in warmer climates.

What this has to do with the regulation of each species' population size is hopefully obvious. Performance limits translate into specific requirements. An herbivore species able to feed on only certain plant species, for example, needs those species around to persist. A plant unable to handle frost is confined to live where temperatures do not drop below freezing. And requirements translate in population limits. An upper limit to any species' population size is set by the relationship between what a species requires and how much is available.

Each species' requirements are multidimensional in the sense that each specific requirement (e.g., temperature range, rainfall, food resources, and so on) adds another dimension to its needs. Biologists often refer to this multidimensional overlay of all of a species' requirements, both biological and physical, as its **niche**.

A species' niche can be viewed as a glass half-filled with water. Whether you view the glass as half full or half empty depends on your perspective. If you focus on where the water is not, then the glass is half empty. Alternatively, if you focus on where the water is, then the glass is half full. Similarly, focus on where a species *is not*, and one sees its niche in terms of its limits—what a species cannot do, hence where this species cannot be. In contrast, focus on where the species *is*, and one can see its niche as a representation of what a species can do—what are the set of conditions that it can handle, hence where can this species persist. This half-full perspective describes, in essence, what role a species plays within the performance of a biological community. The best view is to see a species' niche from both perspectives.

The concept of carrying capacity

As long as the sun keeps shining and every material output of one species is also an input for another species, a biological community is a sustainable performance—it can keep going. A sustainable performance as a whole creates the opportunity for sustainable parts. Any species whose resource use (inputs and outputs) potential fits into this larger performance may be able to divert a limited but sustainable flow of resources its way. Species convert resources into populations, so the idea of a limited but potentially sustainable resource flow rate translates into a limited but potentially sustainable population size. This maximum *sustainable* population size for each species in a community is known as its **carrying capacity**.

The emphasis on being sustainable divorces the concept of a species' carrying capacity from the maximum population size achieved at any point in time. Species' population sizes can and sometimes do exceed their carrying capacity. But if they do, the outcome is predictable. Once carrying capacity is exceeded, at some point in the future the population will crash. Furthermore, any species' carrying capacity is not immutable. It potentially changes whenever the biological community as a whole changes. In fact, the actions of a species itself can alter its carrying capacity either up or down. Change within a species that allows it to better take advantage of resource opportunities will increase its carrying capacity. Alternatively, at times when a species' population exceeds its carrying capacity, the excessive population may pull so hard for resources that the very community on which species depend is altered. Such alteration may reduce the species' carrying capacity in the future.

Human population trends

A general theme in human history is the continual development of novel means to push back the constraints operating on the human population. This effort has been particularly successful in the last couple of hundred years. As a consequence, the human population has been growing exponentially during that time. The recent expansion—1 to over 7 billion in the last 180 years or so—is particularly striking (see Figure 5-14). Specifically:

• Prior to the advent of agriculture (around 10,000 years ago) the total human population is thought to have been around 5 to 30 million.
• By the time of Christ the population is thought to have increased to around 200 to 300 million.
• The first billion took from the dawn of humanity until 1830.
• The second billion took only 100 years.
• The next four billion took only 70 years.
• The last billion to be added (so 7 billion in total) only took 12 years.
• If this current trend continues, the next billion may arrive by 2025, or in just another 13 years (currently the world population is growing by around 74 million people per year).

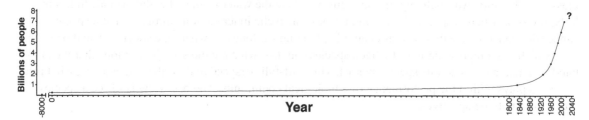

Figure 5-14. Human population growth over the last 10,000 years—although to make the scale somewhat readable only the last 2,000 years is plotted continuously. Note that most of the expansion in human population size has occurred in the past 100 years or so. The question mark indicates the uncertainty as to how the population will change in the future.

How have we accomplished this feat? Basically, humans have found means to bust through all three of the afore-mentioned constraints operating on populations:

• *Energy.* Human agriculture involves changing an area's species composition toward those better used by humans. Agriculture, in its various forms, has thus increased our biological food base. Furthermore, we have tapped another energy source—fossil fuels. Although fossil fuels—which represent past storage of solar energy—are limited in amount, their availability has increased greatly the rate at which humans can utilize a source of usable energy.

• *Materials.* Many novel materials (e.g., iron, plastics) have been incorporated in the performance associated with human life. That is, they have been used to build human-used tools and machines.

• *Shape.* Humans are the **consummate shape changers**. We change shape every time we put on different clothes or pick up a different tool. Just think of a carpenter building a house. Each time one tool is put down and another picked up, the carpenter's performance ability changes. With one shape, he/she can saw wood, with another he/she can pound in nails, and so on. The combination of manipulative hands, upright posture, and a creative brain underlies the human ability to wander through a broad landscape of shapes, changing back and forth with great rapidity. As a consequence, we are not nearly as constrained as other species by the shape–performance trade-off, making niche expansion possible.

What is the human carrying capacity?

What constitutes a sustainable human population is a slippery number. First off, both the level of resource throughputs potentially maintained across time and the efficiency in which those resources are used influence carrying capacity. And both of these factors—through changes in climate, biological aspects of environment, and technology—have and will continue to be changed by the actions of human hands. Another difficulty in sizing up the human carrying capacity is deciding exactly what we would like to carry onward. Are we trying to maximize the number of people that we can squeeze on this earth, or should considerations of carrying capacity factor in a particular lifestyle? If our intent is to maximize lives, then maybe 20 billion or more people could be sustained if all arable land was cultivated, all people lived on a minimum grain diet, and all other forms of resource consumption were kept to the absolute minimum level. But, if issues of lifestyle come into play, for instance everyone living up to average American standards, the number is less, likely considerable less. Just consider the fact that the global harvest would need to increase by 2.6 times just to feed those presently on this planet like average Americans. Can we sustainably produce that much more food? If not, then our current population has already exceeded this measure of lifestyle carrying capacity.

Other factors will also play a role in determining carrying capacity. Consider, for instance, that although much of our current lifestyle is powered by fossil fuels, the finite nature of the fossil fuel supply makes sustainable use impossible. So at some point we will need to switch to sustainable energy sources. This raises the question: How will such a switch affect carrying capacity? Although the rate that affordable energy can be harvested using sustainable options is not yet clear, it is distinctly possible that it will be less. But even so, how such reduction would influence any measure of carrying capacity is complicated by the fact that increasing energy-use efficiency reduces the amount of energy needed to sustain a certain lifestyle. In other words, the effect that energy has on carrying capacity depends on the answer to two questions: How much energy can we sustainably harvest? And how much more efficient can we become? The same argument could be applied to any other potentially limiting resource, such as fresh water supplies.

The bottom line is that the question of the human carrying capacity is confusing because we have just come through a unique period in human history, a period of seemingly unbridled expansion. Population increased fast, but, until recently, food supplies and the supplies of other resources increased even faster (see Figure 5-15). In fact, if you assume that past trends predict future possibilities, you may choose not to worry about an ever-increasing human population. The idea is that the resource supply can potentially increase forever because human ingenuity will always figure out a way to push back any limits encountered. Maybe it is being pessimistic, or maybe its because all other aspects of Life always encounter trade-offs and limits, but I do not accept the view that human population can continue to comfortably expand forever, or to even much higher levels than are currently present. Despite our recent success in increasing our resource supply, humans, like ever other creature on this planet, will face limits to growth. As a consequence, the nature of our future depends on how we face these limits. Will we continue to focus our ingenuity on trying to squeeze even more resources out of an increasingly resistant and disrupted

	1950	factor of increase	1990	factor of increase	2012
human population (billions)	**2.55**	2.07	**5.28**	1.33	**7.0**
oceanic fish (million tons)	**19**	4.54	**86.3***	1.04	**90**
grain production (million tons)	**631**	2.71	**1715***	1.31	**2241**
fertilizer use (million tons)	**14**	10.2	**142.3***	1.26	**180**

* - a three-year average with the date indicated being the middle year.

Figure 5-15. Some statistics concerning human population and food production. Note that while the population more than doubled between the years of 1950 and 1990, measures of food production such as harvest of oceanic fish and grain production increased even faster. That trend, however, has not continued since 1990.

planet (until the whole system collapses in exhaustion), or will we come to accept that limits do exist and focus our ingenuity on how to live both comfortably and sustainably within these bounds? It is our future to make.

The number of species within a community (Question 2)

Why does a community have the number of species that it does? This question is important in terms of understanding the workings of communities. It is not, however, an easy question to answer.

Number of species

First off, there are some important practical problems associated with this question. To begin to access the number of species within any community, one needs to know the number of species found within any area. The number of species inhabiting any area of any part of the planet, however, is unknown. Why? Because even in relatively species-poor areas, many of the small inconspicuous organisms have yet to be described. And the incompleteness of this record is only magnified in high-diversity areas.

Bottom line: We still have a largely unexplored planet in terms of the number of species that accompany us. How unexplored? Well, as of 2013, taxonomists have at least nominally described somewhere around 1.9 million different eukaryotic (nonbacterial) species—although due to potential redundancies in such a large effort, the actual number of valid described species could be considerably less (perhaps 1.5 million). And, curiously, of the described species roughly

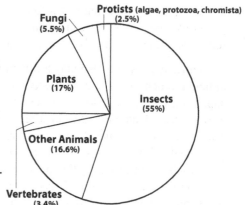

Figure 5-16. Proportional representation of currently described eukaryotic (nonbacterial) species broken into major groups.

three-quarters are animals, and more than two-thirds of animals are insects (see Figure 5-16). However, these figures, both in terms of total numbers and proportional representation, do not appear to be accurate reflections of the truth. Modern estimates of species number range from 3 to 100 million, and evidence suggests that those still to be discovered and described do not fall proportionately among the different groups. For instance, a 2011 study headed by Camilo Mora, a marine ecologist, employed a new innovative method to estimate that 8.7 million eukaryotic species—give or take around 1.3 million—currently reside on this planet. Furthermore, they estimated that although 72% of the plant species may have already been documented, the same may be true for only around 12% of all land animal species, 7% of land fungi species, and 9% of all marine species. Intuitively, it makes sense that plants (which live on land and are rooted—so they can't run away) would be the most thoroughly sampled so far. But this sampling bias suggests that plants are overrepresented in the pie chart. For example, Mora's estimates suggest that plants make up only around 3% of the total species diversity, whereas animals, especially invertebrates, compose around 89%.

An aside: In 1982, Terry Erwin, an insect (especially beetles) taxonomist working in the tropics published a brief paper that used a "back-of-the-envelope" type approach to estimate that there may be as many as 30 million insect species just within tropical forests alone (see Figure 5-17). Of course, this simple-minded estimate may be (and probably is) wildly inaccurate for a whole host of reasons. For instance, subsequent studies have found that one of the assumptions underlying this estimate—that each tropical tree species has a fairly unique set of beetle species—may not be as accurate as first thought. But that is not the point. The point is that as taxonomists continue to look, speculate, and extrapolate, the world around them keeps relaying the same message: There are still lots and lots of unknown species out there.

Furthermore, these estimates of species diversity have not taken into account the prokaryotic world. As of April 13, 2013, there are only 12,035 named prokaryotic species in the published record (11,584 Eubacteria, 451 Archea). So, in contrast, eukaryotic species numbers seem relatively inconsequential—in essence, a drop in the bucket.

But, it would be incredibly naive to assume that these numbers reflect reality. Why? It starts with the fact that prokaryotes are really small, thus are hard to study and, hence, characterize. For instance, single-celled prokaryotic organisms are commonly 200 times smaller than what we can see with the naked eye, with a mass of somewhere in the range of one-billionth (1×10^{-9}) gm. For prokaryotes that can be cultured in a laboratory, microbiologists have worked effectively around this small size, but most prokaryotes don't fare well under standard laboratory conditions.

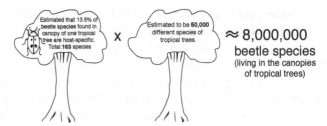

Beetles make up around 40% of insect species:

$$\frac{4}{10} = \frac{8,000,000}{X} ; \qquad X \approx 20,000,000$$

insect species
(living in the canopies
of tropical trees)

Around twice as many insect species living in canopy as compared to the ground:

$$20,000,000 + 10,000,000 \approx 30,000,000$$

insect species (living in the canopies of tropical trees)   insect species (living on the ground of tropical forests)   insect species (living in tropical forests)

Figure 5-17. The information and logic used to estimate that tropical forests may contain as many as 30 million different insect species.

Next, consider the fact that prokaryotes exist in mind-boggling numbers. For instance, based on sampling, it has been estimated that in the upper 200 meters of open ocean every milliliter of water is inhabited by around 500,000 (5×10^5) prokaryotes. In other words, fill a liter (quart) jug with ocean water, and there is approximately 500 million (5×10^8) single-celled prokaryotic organisms living in there. Fill the same jug with fresh water, and the number appears to double, to around 1 billion (1×10^9). Double that again to 2 billion (2×10^9), and that is approximately the number of prokaryotic cells that inhabit each gram of soil, which means that if you place a small pinch of soil in your hand (around 3.5 grams or 1/8th of an ounce), you now hold roughly the same number of prokaryotic organisms as there are currently humans on the planet. And 7 billion may be in the range of the number of prokaryotes that live in a healthy human mouth, and a healthy human colon may be home to around 10,000 times more (somewhere in the 10^{13} range).

In 1998, after estimating prokaryotic densities in the major habitat types, along with the overall amount of each habitat, William Whitman and colleagues calculated that we may share this planet with $4–6 \times 10^{30}$ prokaryotes. To better try to wrap your head around such a large number, consider the fact that the total biomass of such a large number of such tiny organisms would roughly equal the biomass contained in all plants found on planet Earth. In other words, a major portion of Life's mass is simply invisible to us! Strange to think about!

So, in a sense, the prokaryotic species number question comes down to: How many species do $4–6 \times 10^{30}$ individuals divide up into? Of course, that assumes that the prokaryotic world divides up into meaningful species groups—that is, by some relevant biological parameter (such as genetic, phenotypic, or ecological similarity) each individual is part of a distinct cluster of individuals. For reasons that we started to touch on in the last chapter, that may not be true. In fact, lack of distinct clusters may even be common. Furthermore, for humans to ever be aware of underlying diversity, we must have some means to identify the distinct groups that do exist. Again, that seems problematic. Consider the fact that it has been a common practice to consider two prokaryotes members of different species if their underlying DNA structure differs by more than 30% (as measured by a technique known as DNA–DNA hybridization). Although the 30% line is a pragmatic and universally applicable standard, its meaningfulness is quite suspect. For instance, if we used the same measure in the eukaryotic world, all members of the class Aves (or more generally known as birds)—which ranges from pelicans to hummingbirds to eagles, and so on—would be right on the border of being considered members of the same species. Members of the same order of birds—such as ravens and house finches, which are both members of the order Passeriformes—would clearly be the same species, as they differ by less than 13%. Or to put it on more familiar terms, humans and olive baboons—as a representatives of great apes and old world monkeys, respectively—would also be members of the same species, as they differ by less than 8%.

Bottom line: From a species number perspective, prokaryotes are confusing. Perhaps there is a billion or more (which would still make the average population size in the range of 10^{21}), or maybe there is really not all that many. Huge numbers of tiny organisms, can, and do, disperse basically everywhere—things like mountain ranges or oceans are not dispersal barriers—so it is feasible that the same environmental circumstance spread out in different locations across the globe may be occupied by effectively the same type of prokaryote—the one best suited to utilize that habitat. If so, the diversity issue may be more about the number of distinct habitats. Yet, from the perspective of tiny prokaryotes, it seems reasonable that the number of unique combinations of conditions would still be immense. Plus, members of the 4–6×10^{30} or so prokaryotes are found in every medium and on every surface that in any way, shape, or form can support Life. In fact, the range of conditions and situations in which Life can exist is defined by prokaryotes. They have diverged metabolically to the point that they can utilize inputs (such as certain forms of sulfur and iron) and withstand environmental conditions (such as low pH and high temperatures) that extend way beyond the eukaryotic range. In the process, they have extended the range of outputs that can be used as inputs and thus have become the drivers of one of the key self-promoting performance of Life—nutrient cycles. So, how diverse is the prokaryotic world? Diverse enough to take advantage of a huge range of opportunities in a way that collectively sustains Life. The eukaryotic world cannot make the same claim.

Spatial scale

In addition to the difficulty of knowing all the different types of organisms within an area, it is hard to know a community's spatial scale. That is, it is difficult to know how far apart two species can be and still have a resource connection. Food connections must be close by because an individual of one species can eat an individual of another only if they reside in the same area. On the other hand, waste can be carried by rivers or by wind for great distances. Waste connections, thus, potentially form between species far apart. And at least some of these distance connections may be important.

Consider, for instance, the movement of sulfur. Sulfur is a necessary ingredient of every organism. Two protein building blocks (amino acids) contain sulfur, and proteins are essential to the function of any organism. When people first started to trace sulfur's flow, they found a puzzling discrepancy. It appeared that sulfur was being washed from land via rivers to the sea at a faster rate than it was being made available on land. In other words, a link appeared to be missing in the sulfur cycle. The link being the means that sulfur flowed back from the sea to the land. At least in part, the missing link was found to be a waste product—dimethyl sulfide—formed by many species of marine algae. One near-shore alga, *Polysiphonia fastigiata*, is particularly effective at converting sulfide ions in seawater to dimethyl sulfide. Once formed, some dimethyl sulfide escapes into the atmosphere where the wind can escort it back over land. *Polysiphonia fastigiata*, along with other dimethyl sulfide producing marine algae, are, thus, an important part of the biological community of all terrestrial organisms—which, of course, includes us.

Yet, regardless of not knowing the exact dimensions of any community, two aspects of community species numbers seem clear: all communities are made up of a large number of species, and some communities are more diverse than others. The most diverse communities are tropical forests. Although they only cover around 6% of the earth's land area, tropical forests may contain up to half the species on this planet. This raises two fundamental questions: Why do communities have so many species? And, why are there more species in some areas than other areas?

To me the best way to approach either question is to first ask the opposite question: Why not fewer species? The poignancy of this question arises from the simple-minded observation that the backbone of a community—the food web—seems by its very nature to be vulnerable to contraction, perhaps even to the point of a total collapse. Food webs are chock full of species negatively affecting other species. Within trophic levels, species compete for resources. Why don't competitors outcompete, hence eliminate, other competing species? And if it can happen once, why doesn't it happen to the point that there is only one remaining species in each trophic level—the food web shrinking back to a food chain? Predator–prey interactions between trophic levels seem just as vulnerable. Why aren't predators able to catch their prey to the point that they catch them all? This in turn would lead to the extinction of the predators due to the absence of a food supply. Take this to its logical extreme, and the end result would be the food chain toppling link by link.

Coexistence among competitors

Interspecific competition is when individuals of different species compete with each other for resources. The more similar their resource demands, the more intensely they compete. However, there seems to be a limit to the extent that the resource use of two species can overlap and still coexist. Two species are not thought to be able to share the same most-limiting resource. If so, the superior competitor for this resource is expected to drive the other species to extinction. This concept is known as the **competitive exclusion principle**. Often it is defined in terms of niches: Two species cannot occupy the same niche in the same place for long. Or, there is a limited amount of niche overlap compatible with coexistence among different species. A corollary to this idea is that similarity makes coexistence difficult. Similarly shaped species, due to their similar performance abilities, will be more likely to share the same most-limiting resource.

Coexistence thus boils down to competing species not sharing the same most-limiting resource. Two factors can contribute: *the ability of species to be different and the opportunity for species to be different.* The shape–performance trade-off sets the stage for abilities to be different. Differences in shape necessarily result in differences in performance ability. Yet, in a homogeneous environment, performance differences alone may not translate into resource use differences. When conditions are the same everywhere, the opportunity for individuals of different species to utilize a common environment differently is limited. The opportunity for species to be different, thus, depends on **environmental heterogeneity**—environmental differences within the area that both species reside. Each competing species can be better at using different aspects of their common environment.

An example of coexistence based on physical heterogeneity of an environment:

The intertidal zone is the region along an ocean shoreline between that exposed at lowest tide to that inundated with water at the highest tide. One component of physical heterogeneity within this zone is the percentage of time that a surface is covered by water. The higher a surface is positioned in this zone, the smaller the percentage of time that it is covered with water.

A classic study done in a coastal area in Scotland looked at how two species of barnacles (*Balanus* and *Chthamalus*) were able to coexist. Although initially thought to be a type of mollusk (e.g., snails, clams, and scallops), barnacles are unusual crustaceans (e.g., crabs, lobsters). Barnacles hatch from the egg into a free-swimming form, similar to the larval form of other crustaceans. After swimming around for some time and passing through several molts, a barnacle settles onto some solid surface within the intertidal zone and attaches by the head end. Overlapping calcareous plates are then formed around the attached animal, creating a sturdy surrounding wall, and two more pairs of calcareous plates are attached at the top to form a doorlike structure that can open and close. The door opens when the barnacle is submerged, and its feet extend out of the opening, kicking in a manner that brings in food particles. The door shuts when exposed to air at low tide. Because solid surfaces on which to attach are often limited within the intertidal zone, the sessile adult forms compete for space.

It turns out that the smaller *Chthamalus* can grow and survive as adults on surfaces in the entire intertidal region. The larger *Balanus*, on the other hand, are able to grow and survive as adults only in the lower part of the intertidal zone (surfaces covered with water more of the time). Furthermore, where *Balanus* can grow, it tends to be able to competitively exclude *Chthamalus*. That is, given sufficient periods of water coverage, it is a better competitor for the limiting surface area on which to reside. However, even if *Chthamalus* is excluded by *Balanus* in this lower region, it can still persist. Its ability to survive in conditions in which *Balanus* cannot (area higher in the intertidal, hence covered with water less often), frees it from being excluded by such competition. The combination of different performance abilities and physical heterogeneity is thus what makes it possible for both types to persist within the same intertidal zone.

Predation can enhance coexistence among competitors

Predators can influence the outcome of competitive interactions among prey species. Their means of doing so is straightforward. By feeding mostly on members of competitively dominant species, they prevent the population of these species from growing to the point that they exclude other species. In other words, predators add another dimension to the environment of competing species and therefore potentially increase the environmental heterogeneity.

One of the first experimental demonstrations of this effect occurred again in the intertidal zone. The attraction of the intertidal zone for competition experiments is that in small areas a diverse collection of species, such as barnacles, mussels, limpets, chitons, tunicates, bryozoans, and algae, all compete for one limiting resource—space to attach. This study focused on 15 species of mussels, barnacles, limpets, and chitons all competing for space and one predator, a starfish (*Pisaster ochraceous*) in an intact intertidal community along the Washington coast. These starfish mainly feed on one species of mussel (*Mytilus californianus*), which is the dominant space competitor in the community. So, when starfish were experimentally removed from an area, this mussel was able to monopolize more of the area, and the number of species contracted from 15 to 8.

A side note: *Pisaster*, like many other starfish, feeds in a peculiar way. A two-part hinged shell surrounds a mussel's soft, digestible body parts. *Pisaster* moves on top of a mussel and then everts its stomach into the mussel through either imperfectly sealed edges or through a small gap created by the pull exerted by the starfish. Digestion begins outside the body as the soft parts of the victim are reduced to a thick broth, which is then passed into the body.

Succession–disturbance coexistence

Succession is the changing of the species composition of a biological community across time. That is, species replace other species within a locale over time. Two underlying reasons that succession occurs are

- *Modification of habitat*. The way species interact with their surroundings (inputs and outputs) may modify conditions in a manner that aids the growth of other species and/or hinders their own growth.

• *Competition.* Each new group of species outcompetes the preexisting species. Here we will focus more on the competitive aspect of succession.

A **disturbance** is anything that removes the present community of organisms from an area to at least some extent. It could be as small as a single tree falling within a forest, or as large as an extensive forest fire.

Succession–disturbance coexistence is possible whenever a trade-off exists between competitive ability and the ability to colonize new disturbance sites. In other words, whatever makes a species a good competitor also makes them a poor colonizer and vice versa. As a consequence, the better colonizing species will tend to move into any new disturbance quickly, reproduce, and then move on to another site of disturbance before being outcompeted by slower colonizing, but better competing species.

A classic early successional species is a good colonizer for two reasons: It can grow fast and reproduce quickly, which means that it can quickly take advantage of available resources; and when it reproduces it makes numerous small, highly mobile offspring, increasing the odds that at least one offspring will find a new disturbance site. Because it is also a poor competitor, its persistence depends on continual disturbance. Otherwise it would eventually run out of new places to colonize.

Later successional species, on the other hand, play the trade-off the other way. They are better at persisting in their present location due to increasing competitive ability coupled with increased life span, but are slower at establishing in disturbance sites. Their fewer, larger, and relatively more immobile offspring are not as apt at finding disturbance sites, and they grow slower and reproduce later once colonization has occurred.

Succession–disturbance coexistence is common feature of terrestrial plant communities. Part of the explanation for this is that individuals of all plant species potentially compete with each other for sunlight, and the way to win this competition is to grow taller. Because sunlight comes down from above, taller plants can put their leaves up above smaller plants and intercept sunlight first. But growing taller always comes at the cost of being a slower grower (one part of being a poor colonizer). To grow taller and not be blown over by the next gust of wind, a plant must also be sturdy. To be sturdy, however, requires increased investment of resources in support structure. With more resources going toward support structure instead of leaves and roots, which capture the resources needed for growth, growth rate must decline. The general trend is that the larger a plant species' maximum height, the slower that individual members grow.

This trade-off, in combination with disturbance, creates opportunities for shorter but faster growing plants to persist. They come to a newly disturbed area, grow fast, reproduce, and then get out before they are overgrown by taller, sturdier plants. This trade-off, along with the fact that there is always room to grow even taller, also helps explain why plants come in a variety of growth forms. Consider herbaceous plants (plants without any woody tissue), bushes, and trees. The fundamental difference between these three growth forms is the amount they invest in support tissue. Herbaceous plants are defined as plants without woody tissue. In other words, they are plants without any significant investment in support structure. As a consequence, they can grow relatively fast but not very tall. Bushes can grow taller than herbaceous plants because they have some woody tissue, but they cannot grow as fast. So, given enough time (and adequate growing conditions) bushy plant species can outcompete herbaceous plants for sunlight. But that is not the end of the successional story. Bushes can eventually be overgrown by slower growing plants called trees, which allocate even larger amounts of resources to support tissue to form sturdy trunks. So, like the herbaceous plants before them, a successful bush must be able to colonize new areas, reproduce, and then get out before they are overgrown by trees. Even different tree species play this trade-off of growth rate versus maximum height differently. You may have heard of different types of lumber being categorized as hardwoods or softwoods. If you have ever stacked firewood you have felt the difference with your muscles. Logs of the same size from different tree species can vary dramatically in weight. Softwoods are trees that grow relatively fast (for a tree) because in comparison to hardwoods they expend less building their woody support structure; but as a result, the wood is not as strong (or dense and heavy), so it cannot support as tall a tree. In the classic succession sequence, it is softer wood trees that first grow above bushy plants, and then harder wood trees eventually grow up above and shade out softer wood trees. Hardwood trees can potentially live for hundreds of years, but eventually they will fall over or burn down, and succession can start over again.

Two other trade-offs may also contribute to the occurrence of succession—disturbance in terrestrial plant communities: seed size versus dispersal ability and seed size versus competitive ability.

Early successional plants tend to have small seeds both because it is advantageous and they can get away with it. The advantage is that smaller seeds are better at dispersing to disturbance sites. Because smaller things take less force to move, wind or some other force-generating agent can more easily transport smaller seeds longer distances, so they are better at traveling the distances necessary to reach new disturbance sites. Furthermore, more small seeds can be produced per unit of resource than larger seeds, and the more seeds made the greater the probability that at least one will "win the lottery" by landing in a disturbance site. What they get away with is that by colonizing disturbance sites quickly, their seedlings avoid competition with other plants. Small seeds are small because they lack large amounts of food stores within the seeds. In other words, they are sent off to face the world by their parents with a very small sack lunch. With limited resources provided, they can only grow to a small size before they must begin to gather resources on their own. Being able to gather sufficient resources at a small size is more likely if there are no other plants around to block the sun, or use up the scarce water and minerals in the soil.

On the other hand, later successional plants tend to play this trade-off toward increased competitive ability. Seedlings of later succession plants must be able to survive and grow in places where earlier successional plants are already present. One means to increase a seedling's competitive ability is to make larger seeds. Larger seeds have the resources to produce larger seedlings that extend their leaves up higher and the roots down lower before having to care for themselves. As a consequence, these seedlings do better when faced with competition. However, larger seeds require more force to move and fewer can be made per unit of resource, so they are not as well suited for colonizing newly disturbed areas.

Two categories of plant succession:

• *Primary succession.* The starting point is bare rock. The first species that are able to colonize and grow (e.g., lichens) begin to break down the rock, and as they die they begin to add organic matter to the substrate. Slowly, a soil begins to form. More types of plants can colonize, which continue to break up the rock with their roots and add organic matter when they die. The soil continues to build.

• *Secondary succession.* Plant growth begins in an area after a disturbance that removes the preexisting plant community (i.e. fire, plowing). The soil is still intact. A typical secondary plant succession sequence: herbaceous annuals, herbaceous perennials, shrubs, shade-intolerant trees—need full sunlight (a relatively open area) to grow, and finally shade-tolerant trees—can grow without full sunlight.

Competition between generalists and specialists

The distinction between a generalist and a specialist may be familiar. What may not be as apparent, however, is recognition that the distinction is built around trade-offs. A generalist suffers the trade-off that by being good at more than one thing it cannot be great at anything. The idea is succinctly expressed in the common expression: "A jack of all trades but master of none." Alternatively, a specialist suffers the trade-off that by being great at one thing it cannot even be good at anything else.

The notion of a shape–performance trade-off easily incorporates the specialist–generalist dichotomy. Generalists, as redundant as this sounds, have a more general shape. In other words, the different dimensions of the shape tend to center around the average of the possibilities. Specialists, on the other hand, have shapes that appear more bizarre, more striking. This is because a specialist shape, in comparison to a generalist, is accentuated in some dimension (see Figure 5-18). A good way to verify this is to look at the tool shapes the next time you go to a hardware store. For instance, let's focus on pliers. The specialist pliers, which all have more specific names—such as needle-nose pliers—all deviate from the general pliers shape. For instance, needle-nose pliers are longer and narrower (see Figure 5-19). And anyone who works with tools knows this shape change makes them great at certain jobs, but not very good at many others. Other pliers become different types of specialists by accentuating some other aspect of shape.

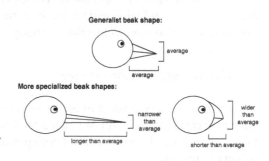

Figure 5-18. Beak shape in birds is used to illustrate the basic idea of a generalized versus a specialized shape.

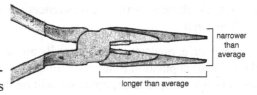

Figure 5-19. The shape of needle-nose pliers.

Given that a species can be more of a generalist or more of a specialist, the important question here is: Under what type of circumstance would a generalist be able to outcompete a specialist and vice versa. I would guess that you already have an intuitive feel for the answer, but to try to be more exact, consider a scenario with five ingredients: two environmental circumstances, two specialist species, and one generalist species. Each of the specialist species is specialized at dealing with one of the two environmental circumstances. That is, each specialist has a shape that makes it great at dealing with one of the two circumstances, but bad at dealing with the other. Alternatively, the one generalist is good, but not great, at dealing with both circumstances. The specific question is what would be expected to happen if all three species were thrown into the following two situations:

Situation 1: Both environmental circumstances continually exist within a locale. In other words, the locale is both stable and environmentally diverse.

Situation 2: Both environmental circumstances exist within a locale, but these two circumstances alternate back and forth in a somewhat unpredictable manner. In other words, the environment circumstance within the locale is variable.

In situation 1, the two specialist species are expected to persist while the generalist goes extinct. Each specialist should outcompete the other specialist and the generalist in the locale containing the environmental circumstance to which it is best suited.

In situation 2, the reverse may be true—the generalist persists while the two specialists go extinct. With the environment flipping back and forth, each specialist would at times have to compete under conditions that it is bad at dealing with. The generalist, on the other hand, is good at dealing with both sets of conditions. Whenever the overall good of the generalist is better than the mix of great and bad in each specialist, the generalist is expected to win the competition.

General conclusions: Specialists will tend to have the competitive advantage in stable environments, whereas generalists will tend to have the competitive advantage in variable environments. Specialists are also more vulnerable to change.

Coexistence of predator and prey

The issue: If a population of predators is able to consume all its potential prey, then its prey has gone extinct (at least locally). Without a food source, the extinction of the predator type will soon follow. Therefore, the persistence of both predator and prey depends on the predator not being too efficient of predator.

One factor that may help prevent predators from becoming too efficient is that predators always select for their own failure. Predators feed on those prey that they can catch. In so doing, they leave behind (to produce the next generation) those members of the prey population they did not catch. Now, if a performance difference contributed to why certain individuals ended up caught and others did not, and these performance differences are heritable, then the next generation should be more difficult to catch.

Of course, predators simultaneously are selecting for their own improvement. If those members of the predator population better at catching prey are more reproductively successful, and their abilities are heritable, the predator population will be shifting across generations toward better predators.

In total, predators and prey are caught in an evolutionary race—prey evolve to better escape their predators and predators evolve to better capture their prey. Coexistence depends on the outcome of that race. As long as the prey evolve fast enough to keep ahead, predator and prey should coexist. But if a predator continually gains on its prey, it may become such an effective predator that it wipes out its prey. If this prey is the predator's sole food source, the predator will follow its prey to extinction.

One factor that can affect the outcome of this race is relative generation times. Because evolution is a change in the composition of the population across generations, organisms with shorter generation times can potentially evolve at a faster rate. So, whenever prey (e.g., mice, rabbits) have shorter generation times than their predators (e.g., owls, coyotes), their faster evolutionary potential may make it possible for them to stay ahead in the race.

Another factor that can contribute to prey staying ahead in this evolutionary race is an asymmetry in the contest known as **the life/dinner principle**. The prey is running for its life, while the predator is only running for its dinner. A prey losing, thus, has a much greater influence on its relative reproductive success—in comparison to competing prey types—than a predator losing a contest. Prey are pushed to evolve faster than predators.

Some other factors that can contribute to the persistence of both predator and prey:

• *The existence of a refuge:* The structure of the environment is such that there exists a place for at least a relatively small number of prey to effectively hide from the predator. A refuge makes it impossible for the predators to ever be able to consume all members of the prey population.

• *Predators switching to feed more on the most abundant prey:* Consider a predator feeds on more than one prey type. If a predator generally concentrates its feeding on the prey type presently most abundant, presently rarer prey types will avoid persistence-threatening levels of predation.

• *A predator being kept in check by its predator.* If a predator itself has a predator, its predator may keep it from being able to overharvest its prey. A classic example of this is in the kelp→sea urchin→ sea otter food chain. Actually, this was uncovered when man entered the picture. Sea otters live along the Pacific Coast from Alaska to California. They manage to stay warm in the water, in large part, by having an exceptionally dense fur coat that creates a barrier between the water and the animal's skin. Their skin never gets wet. The problem, however, was that such a wondrous fur coat came to be prized by humans. Sea otters were almost hunted to extinction by the end of the nineteenth century. What was discovered with their removal, however, is that kelp—an exceptionally large growing algae, which grow in large stands called kelp forests—lacked the ability to defend itself from one of its predators—sea urchins. In essence, kelp depended on sea otters to keep the sea urchins in check. So, freed from its predators, sea urchins lunched with abandon. As their populations exploded, kelp forests were being decimated; large stretches of kelp forest disappeared. Other species depending on these kelp forests followed in their wake. Only efforts of conservationist to restore sea otter population kept this scenario from reaching its bleak conclusion. Now kelp forests and sea otters have returned to much of their original range.

Development of species richness

Based on the preceding discussion, one can conclude that the persistence of any species depends largely on four things:

• The *ability* of a species to be different than surrounding species. Differences in shape result in differences in performance ability.

• The *opportunity* for a species to be different than surrounding species. Environmental heterogeneity—which has both a physical and biological component—establishes such opportunity. Environmental differences make it possible for a species' performance differences to translate into a unique way of making a living. As a consequence, they cannot be competitively excluded by competing species.

• The species must, by some means, be held sufficiently in check so that it does not wipe out its resource supply.

• The species' predators and parasites must, by some means, be held sufficiently in check so that they do not wipe out the species.

The question of how species rich is any community depends, in part, on how many species can meet all four of these requirements. This depends, in turn, on other factors. Next I discuss four: energy, stability, piggybacking, and area.

Energy: The productivity of a community—that is, the amount of solar energy converted by photosynthetic organisms into high-energy molecules—depends on the interaction between the amount of solar energy and the amount of water available. For instance, throughout the course of a year regions near the equator receive the most solar radiation (in comparison to areas closer to either pole), so have the potential to have the greatest biological productivity. But this potential is only realized when water is also abundant. Equatorial areas without much rainfall are still low-productivity deserts. But when water is abundant, the lushest vegetation found anywhere grows. We know these areas as tropical rain forests.

The positive relationship between species richness and biological productivity that has been found in different studies makes sense in a very simple-minded way—the larger the overall productivity pie, the greater the number of species that would be able to get a sufficiently large slice to maintain a viable population. The overall trend of increasing species richness as one moves from either pole toward the equator may thus be at least partly explained by the accompanying trend (so long as water is not limiting) of increased biological productivity.

Stability: As mentioned earlier, the stability of the climate, or any other aspects of environmental circumstance—both from season to season and year to year—has an affect on whether generalist or specialist species are expected to win in competition. Generalists are favored in variable conditions; specialists are favored in stable conditions. This trend can subsequently affect species diversity. By their nature of being able to deal with different conditions, generalist species tend to have larger geographical ranges and fill more of the area within their range than specialists do. This means that more specialists should be able to be packed into an area than generalists should. Increasing stability thus creates the opportunity for increasing species richness—all else being equal.

Piggybacking: Environmental heterogeneity has two components: biological and physical. Biological heterogeneity increases as the number of species increases. The species richness of any area, thus, potentially feeds back on itself (see Figure 5-20). Each new species able to persist in an area creates a new opportunity for a parasite or predator to be different; they could specialize in the use of this new species. Furthermore, increasing species richness may also enhance physical heterogeneity. Different species may utilize the physical environment differently, creating a more and more patchy physical environment. And as argued earlier, increasing heterogeneity opens opportunities for even more species to be able to coexist within the area.

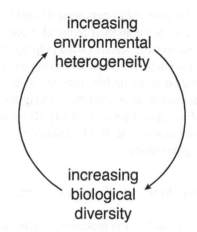

Figure 5-20. The positive feedback loop known as piggybacking.

Area. The basic suggestion is that more species can persist in a larger area. A quantitative rule of thumb has emerged from field research: The number of species doubles for every tenfold increase in area. Two reasons may contribute to this rule. First, a larger area will tend to have an increasingly diverse number of habitats—that is, more environmental heterogeneity. Second, larger areas, overall, can support larger population sizes, and larger average populations are less likely to go extinct via chance fluctuations. Or stated in reverse, in smaller average population sizes, chance population size fluctuations are more likely to fluctuate all the way down to zero.

The nature of community interactions (Question 3)

To begin to understand how the actions of one species affects the population size of another species, and vice versa, we need to understand the extent and the nature of interspecific interactions. This is not an easy task because both direct and indirect pathways of interaction may connect species to each other.

Direct interactions form when two species either share the same resource (e.g., competitors) or when one species is the resource for another species (e.g., predator–prey, parasite–host). Competitive interactions generate a mutual negative effect on each other's population size. On the other hand, the effects of predator–prey flip-flop. The population size of a prey species has a positive effect on the population size of the predator species, whereas the population size of the predator has a negative effect on the population size of the prey.

A chain, of any length, of direct interactions forges **indirect interactions** between two species. For example, in Figure 5-21, Herbivore A and Herbivore C are not direct competitors because they do not feed on the same species of plants. They

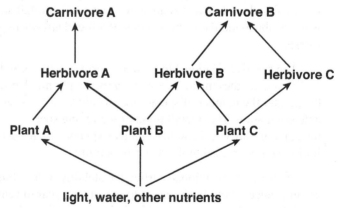

Figure 5-21. A simplified food web.

are, however, connected indirectly through the fact that each compete with Herbivore B. (Herbivore A competes with Herbivore B over Plant B, and Herbivore B competes with Herbivore C over Plant C.) Herbivore A can thus affect the population size of Herbivore C indirectly by directly influencing the population size of Herbivore B, and vice versa. Put in more general terms, the effect that one species' changing population size has on any other species' population size can be played out through effects on intermediaries.

What is striking about indirect effects is that every species within a biological community is connected to every other species by indirect pathways through food and waste webs. Look again at Figure 5-21 to prove this to yourself. Indirect pathways connect every species in this food web, even pairs of species with a direct connection. Moreover, even within this greatly simplified food web, species are *not* connected by just a single indirect pathway. Several indirect pathways connect each species. (To again prove this to yourself, see how many indirect pathways you can form between Herbivore B and Herbivore C.) Just think how many indirect pathways connect any two species in food and waste webs with hundreds or thousands (or maybe even millions) of species These connections are why a change in one species can affect any other species within a community, which, in turn, can feedback to itself. These indirect connections are also what make it extremely difficult, if not impossible, to predict how changes in one species will affect any other species. Consider a basic checklist of all the factors that would need to go into making such a prediction.

• Identify any and all direct and indirect pathways that connect these species. As two points in an entire tapestry of community interactions, the connecting pathways could be many.

• Identify whether the net effect along each pathway is positive or negative.

• Determine the time span between the actions of one species and the effects reaching the other species along each of these pathways.

• And finally, figure out how to integrate all the preceding considerations.

A scientific investigation illustrating the occurrence of both direct and indirect effects

Three common parts of a desert community are seed-eating ants, seed-eating rodents, and the annual plants whose seeds are eaten. In the Sonoran desert in southern Arizona, a group of biologists set out to study how, among many other things, the removal of ants or rodents would affect the other. Although seed-eating rodents tend to feed on slightly larger seeds than ants, the range in seed size fed on by each overlap considerably. Seed-eating rodents and seed-eating ants are thus competitors. So, in a sense, they were asking the question: Are things as simple as they first seem? The obvious expectation is that removal of competitors increases the resources available for those left. Their population size should increase, accordingly.

To try to answer this question (among others), they used a straightforward experiment design. They found a homogeneous region of desert, established plots of similar size and composition, and then either left the plots alone to establish a control or performed one of a variety of experimental manipulations. Three treatments were relevant to the preceding question: plots where they removed rodents, plots where they removed ants, and control plots where neither ants nor rodents were removed.

Short-term direct effects. Initially, populations tended to change as expected in the experimental plots. The number of ant colonies almost doubled in plots in which rodents were removed. Rodent population sizes also increased around 25% in plots where ants where removed.

Longer-term indirect effects. Here I focus on one specific result. In plots where rodents were removed, the number of ant colonies did initially increase, but in subsequent years the number of ant colonies did not stay at this higher level, as would be expected if the ant carrying capacity had increased. Instead, the number of ant colonies steadily declined. The reason had to do with an indirect interaction between ants and rodents. The first step of this pathway is the inability of ants to handle the largest seeds. So, without rodents present (who can feed on them) the population of larger-seeded annuals began to increase. Furthermore, in direct competition for sunlight from above or water or minerals in the ground, larger-seeded annuals tended to prevail over smaller-seeded ones. Larger seeds have the resources to produce larger seedlings that extend their leaves up higher and the roots down lower before having to care for themselves. So, in plots where rodents were removed, plants with relatively large seeds were able to increase dramatically and in time came to dominate the annual plant community. Subsequently, the supply of smaller seeds—which are better handled by ants—declined. With fewer resources available, the ant population followed along. So, although ants and rodents are competitors for intermediate-size seeds, by feeding on larger seeds, rodents are also a positive factor—a benefactor—to ants (see Figure 5-22). Conclusion: *In a complex world it is hard to distinguish between friends and enemies.* With many pathways of interaction connecting any two species, it is always possible that the effects along different pathways are inconsistent. Some may be positive, whereas others are negative.

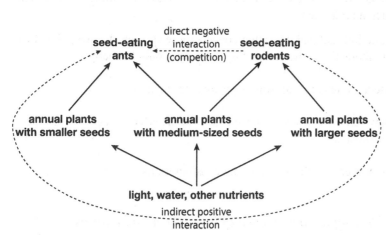

Figure 5-22. The food web showing how seed-eating rodents could have both a direct negative effect and an indirect positive effect on seed-eating ants.

In the words of Jim Brown and the other scientist performing this experiment: "A simple perturbation, such as the removal of rodents, sets in motion a complex series of changes that ripple through the community, affecting an increasing number of species. Eventually there must be a limit to these changes and the system should approach a new state, but it is a testimony to the importance of these indirect effects that we are still observing pronounced changes in plants and other organisms at least seven years after exclusion of rodents began."

Indirect interactions and human intervention: one example

In the early 1950s there was a severe malaria epidemic on the island of Borneo. (Actually, malaria is still the leading cause of death in the world.) Two hundred tribes, called the Dayak peoples, were threatened in Borneo's interior, so the World Health Organization (WHO) decided to help. Because mosquitoes carry malaria, how to control this outbreak seems all too obvious—kill mosquitoes. So, massive amounts of the insecticide DDT were sprayed in and around the villages. The operation was considered a success until the thatched roofs of the Dayak huts began to collapse. It turns out that the spraying did more than just (temporarily) reduce the mosquito population. For one, it also killed off a species of predatory wasps that preyed on a species of caterpillars that feed on dried vegetation. As a result, the caterpillar population increased to the point that they began to devour the thatched roofs on the villagers' houses. (Actually, these wasps did not use these caterpillars as a food source directly, but instead adult females would oviposit eggs inside a developing caterpillar, and then on hatching, the wasp larvae would use the caterpillar as a food source. Wasps that lay eggs on a still-living host are commonly called parasitic wasps.)

Cockroaches around the villages were also exposed to DDT, but many did not die. Instead, the DDT, which is fat soluble, accumulated in their fat stores. DDT levels began to accumulate to even higher levels within the fat stores of the gecko lizards that lived around the village because one lizard feeds on many cockroaches. DDT levels increased even further within the cats that lived in the villages for the same reason—one cat feeds on many lizards. The so-called biomagnification—accumulating levels as one moves up the food chain— of DDT reached lethal levels in these cats. Fewer cats lead to more rats, which now fed increasingly on the villagers' food stores. These rats also carried fleas, which were carriers for both bubonic plague and typhus.

In the end, an attempt to control malaria resulted in the loss of the two most basic commodities: food and shelter. In addition, a new disease threat emerged. In response to this dire situation, which was further complicated by the fact that Borneo's rough terrain makes it one of the least accessible places on earth, the WHO got the British Royal Air Force to parachute in 14,000 cats to these remote villages.

Moral of the story: When trying to manipulate nature, good intentions may not lead to good results. Or in the words of Garret Hardin: "We can never do merely one thing." This statement does not say exactly what to look for, but it does tell us to look hard at every proposed intervention in an existing system, to make sure we are not carrying out interactions that we may later regret.

What are side effects?

Although tales of ants and rodents and DDT use in Borneo may catch your attention, they are nothing more than trivial stories unless the point that they make truly sinks in. So let me state the general point loud and clear: All the results of any intervention in a complex system—that is, systems governed by many different types of interactions—are next to impossible to predict. You potentially experience this every time you take some type of medicine. Your body is a complex system, and any form of medication is an intervention attempting to alter your body's workings to achieve some effect. But you are probably aware that the medicine may do even more. A list of potential side effects accompanies every prescription. The only problem with this list is that there are really no such things as side effects. We use the expression *side effects* to designate unintended effects, but effects are effects, whether we want them to happen or not. Or put in terms of the preceding discussion, every effect is an effect regardless of whether it plays out through a direct or a very convoluted indirect pathway. The only difference is that one is easier to predict than the other.

Consider one last example. Myostatin is the name of a gene that (codes for a protein that) affects muscle growth. Specifically, it seems to play a role in stopping muscle growth once muscle mass has reached a "normal" amount. So what would happen if the myostatin gene was removed? It seems like the organism would develop bigger muscles. Speculation that being able to unleash muscle development may be useful in treating individuals with degenerative muscle diseases such as muscular dystrophy, or to produce meatier farm animals prodded scientists to do this experiment. They used a technique called genetic knockout to produce a strain of mice lacking myostatin. As expected, adult mice lacking myostatin grew two to three as much muscle as did normal mice. But there also was an unimagined effect on personality. The muscle-bound mice were very passive. So wimpy in fact that normal mice beat them up. So is this wimpiness a side effect? No it is an effect. Although the pathway to increased wimpiness may involve many more steps, myostatin appears to influence both the development of muscle mass and the personality component of the nervous system. Could it also affect other aspects of mice development?

The counterbalancing of nature

Historically the expression "the balance of nature" was used to convey the idea that interactions among species were harmoniously designed to ensure the stability of the overall community. That is, if the community was by any means disturbed from its present configuration—the types of species present and the population size of each—the interactions would act as a series of "checks and balances" to return the community to as it was before.

I prefer the expression "the counterbalancing of nature." This implies the present configuration of a community, if in any sort of balance at all, is a dynamic counterbalancing of contradictory interactions. A counterbalance that can be disrupted and once disrupted may undergo compositional changes—species population changing, some to the point of extinction—until these contradictory interactions come to a new balance point. Due to the complexity of the interactions, the new configuration will be difficult to predict.

The principle of contradiction

In our discussion of rationality in Chapter 1, we recognized that our mind is basically limited to viewing the world from one perspective at a time. So, to view the world more completely we need to continually switch perspectives. At times, however, such a switch can lead to something quite curious—how the world seems to work changes across perspectives.

For instance, when I view biological communities from one perspective I see that *living depends on death*. The continuance of any individual depends on the death of other individuals—either directly (e.g., eating all or a part of another organism) or indirectly (e.g., the recycling of materials necessary for plant growth and survival). Or as Charles Darwin put it ". . . we do not see, or we forget, that the birds which are idly singing around us mostly live on insects or seeds and are thus constantly destroying life." Yet, from a different perspective I see that *life depends on life*. Both through the release of wastes and the consumption of those resources available, all organisms foul their own nest. Each organism thus depends on the actions of other organisms to continually restore the immediate environment to one that is life sustaining.

So which perspective is right? Does life depend on life or does it depend on death? The answer, of course, is that it depends on both—both are part of the nature of biological communities. The appearance of contradiction, therefore, does not divide the world into right or wrong. Instead, contradiction indicates that one perspective does not capture it all.

In investigating the nature of light, physicists dealt with this same type of issue. Some experiments showed that light behaved like a wave (spread out over space), whereas other experiments showed that it behaved like a stream of particles called photons (each localized in space). So which is it, wave or particle stream? The simple fact that these two descriptions appear contradictory suggests that it is more than either one. In other words, light appears to be a more complex phenomenon than just being a simple wave or a simple beam of particles.

The physicist Neil Bohr summarized this more holistic view of light with his **principle of complementarity**. It basically states that to understand any given experiment we must use either the wave or photon view of light, but to understand light we must be aware of both its wave and particle nature. In other words, these two views of light complement each other. Because I think that this basic idea extends far beyond light, I extend Bohr's proposal with what I call the **principle of contradiction**. It states that instead of attempting to avoid contradictory (paradoxical) observations, we should embrace them. In other words, we should focus our attention whenever we find two or more tenets that each separately appear to be accurate (when viewed from a certain perspective of nature) but when considered together are contradictory. Why? Part of the reason is that struggling with the contradiction forces us to back away from a narrow perspective. We must take notice of all sides if we are to gain a better understanding of anything. This is basically Bohr's proposal. But I suspect that the reason goes deeper. I suggest that a common theme can be found in the dynamics that underlie the workings of Nature, and that theme is contradiction. In other words, the essence of Nature exists where the rational mind finds contradiction. (Does that sound a little too cosmic or what!). Clearly, this is at least part of the story in biological communities. Contradictory effects between species—such as seen in the ants and rodents example—contributes to the dynamics underlying communities. It forms the countering component of the counterbalancing described earlier. I suspect that light too is glued together by contradiction. Next I mention a few other examples that deserve our focus.

One more physics example:

Concerning the nature of matter and energy:

- Energy is a property of matter in motion.
- Matter is energy (or matter can be converted into energy).

Three social examples:

Concerning the first amendment:

- I should be able to say what I think is important to say.
- There are some things that others should not be allowed to say.

Concerning responsibility and opportunity:

- People should always be held responsible for their actions.
- Children should have the opportunity to develop their skills before they are held responsible for their actions.

Concerning the right to privacy and public leaders:

- We have a right to know what our elected leaders are doing, for we choose them to represent us.
- Every person has the right to keep parts of his or her life private.

Some key terms:

life history - an a organism's reproductive schedule—that is, how often it breeds, how many offspring it has per reproductive bout, and what proportion of its offspring make it to breed in the next generation.

trophic level - a species' position in an energy food chain. First trophic level, for example, are species able to use the sun as an energy source, second trophic level species acquire their needed supply of usable energy by feeding on first trophic level species, and so on.

gross production efficiency - the efficiency with which biomass consumed from one trophic level is converted into biomass at the next trophic level.

niche - the set of conditions (based on each species' set of requirements) under which a species can maintain a viable population.

carrying capacity - the maximum sustainable population size for each species within a community.

competitive exclusion principle - different species that share, hence compete for, the same limiting resource cannot sustainably coexist in the same area.

direct effect - whenever the actions of one species has an effect on another species' population size through a direct resource interaction. Two examples: two species competing for the same resource, or a predator-prey relationship where one species is the resource for the other.

indirect effect - whenever the actions of one species has an effect on another species' population size, and the effect is generated by a chain of two or more direct interactions with other species. A carnivore species, for example, can have an indirect effect on a plant species' population by eating the plant's herbivore.

Some study questions:

1. Explain how a biological species can be viewed as a process. Why does it make sense to divide the outputs into two types?

2. *Explain the concept of building and breaking in energetic terms.* Why are both building and breaking components of an organism building itself?

3. Explain the statement: Sun-using organisms can use sunlight to build molecules that are subsequently broken down to do other things, including building other molecules.

4. *Give two reasons that members of one species could benefit from feeding on members of another species.*

5. *Give three reasons that members of one species could benefit from inputting the waste of another species.*

6. *How do questions 4 and 5 relate to the formation of nutrient cycles. Why do nutrient cycles need a constant input of energy from the sun to keep running?*

7. In what sense are feeding connections and waste connections between species, regulatory connections?

8. *Explain how each of these factors, in general, affect any species' population size: the potential for exponential growth, a finite material world, a species' trophic level, a species' niche, the presence of competitors, the presence of predators, a change in the population size of some other species in the same community.*

9. (Question to think about) What kinds of information would you look for to try to determine whether humans are currently under or over their global carrying capacity?

10. *List the two general requirements for two competing species to coexist.* Use these two general requirements to discuss any examples presented in class.

11. What are some of the means by which predators are kept from eating all their prey?

12. Explain how productivity, stability, piggybacking, and area can each affect species richness. Which of these might help explain why tropical rain forests have higher species richness than other areas? Explain.

13. *What distinguishes a direct or indirect connection between two species within a community? How does the presence of both direct and indirect connections make it difficult to predict the consequences of some change to a community?*

Thinking about Biological Evolution

Simply stated, Life on this planet is amazing. Not only is there a mind-boggling diversity of living things, but also each species has somehow come to fit into an entangled web of relationships. Furthermore, as best as we can tell, all nearby planets are void of Life. These observations lead to what I call a big question: *How did the living world, which includes me, come to be as it is?* Big in that it is hard to imagine anyone (at some point in their life) not asking it, and big in that it is not easy to imagine how to try to go about answering it.

One means of explanation: deities and miracles

A common claim is that a **deity** assembled the living world. Accordingly, all living forms are examples of imposed organization. This claim is often backed up by a compelling argument. It seems *inconceivable* that the complexity woven throughout the present-day living world could have come to be without an external designer.

Moreover, it is generally assumed that the deity responsible for assembling Life on earth has **supernatural** powers—that is, the deity is not constrained to operate within the bounds of natural laws. Or stated differently, it can perform **miracles**. This is in stark contrast to you and me. We, for instance, cannot operate outside the natural law of gravity. If we choose to move a book from the floor to the table, levitation is not an option. We must grab the book and then apply the forces necessary to raise it to the table. The same cannot be said for a supernatural being because for it anything is possible; it can make anything happen in anyway that it wishes. Furthermore, the assumption is that this deity used these supernatural powers to assemble Life. In fact for some people, the very notion that Life has a supernatural origin is what makes it so special.

Staying within the realm of science

Because miracles by definition violate the natural laws, an explanation of how the living world came to be based on a deity performing miracles is by definition unscientific. *This does not mean that it's not the correct explanation.* It only means that it falls outside the scientific realm. As discussed in Chapter 1, the scientific enterprise is to attempt to establish basic patterns in the workings of the world—to discover natural laws—and then use these laws as a foundation with which to explain specific events of interest. Science attempts to explain phenomenon solely in **naturalistic terms.**

Furthermore, if a scientist interested in how Life's complexity came to be claims the intervention of a deity, he or she has only sidestepped the question. If we assume that which assembles highly organized arrangements must itself be highly organized, then we are left with the question: How did the deity come to be?

In our discussion of the becoming of Life we stay bounded by science. There is no claim that trying to understand the becoming of Life from the scientific perspective has or ever will yield all the answers. But it makes sense to see how far science can take us. The impetus behind such a quest is the possibility that on closer inspection, seemingly miraculous events may appear possible and even plausible.

The first step is to identify the aspects of Life itself that result in its continual change. This is the tool kit of evolutionary thinking. One cannot begin to go to work unless one understands the strengths and limits of the tools available. It is here that we spend most of our time.

A basic outline

The question of how anything came to be can be divided into two parts: How did it originate? And from the time of its origin, how did it persist? So the outline of this chapter seems obvious: First, discuss the origin of all the different life forms inhabiting this earth, and then discuss how they have persisted. But, such an approach fails to capture Life's ongoing dynamic nature. Consequently, I take a less obvious approach. First I develop the notion of what can persist. Next, I ask how could that which can persist ever originate. I then go on to discuss why that which originates tends not to persist. This may seem like I am ending with extinction of everything, instead of an incredible diversity of different life forms. But as you will see, an evolutionary explanation for what is here today depends on ongoing interplay between origin and extinction. It also suggests that what will be here tomorrow will not be exactly the same as what was here today. Recall that in Chapter 3 I pointed out that every organism currently living on this planet is connected to the past by a chain of reproductively successful ancestors. But that trend will not continue—every organism currently present will not continue to become a reproductively successful ancestor, and as a result, Life's composition will change.

Persistence: A First Look

As we know from Chapter 3, reproduction is the key to persistence. Here I discuss what can persist in the sense of staying exactly the same across generations. I call these units of organization **reproductive entities**. Strikingly, what constitutes a reproductive entity changes with different forms of reproduction.

When reproduction is asexual, a single organism is a reproductive entity. Not only can a single individual reproduce, but it can also produce offspring identical to itself. **Clones** are populations of genetically identical individuals formed by asexual reproduction.

The story changes when reproduction is sexual. First of all, single individuals (of a single gender) cannot reproduce on their own. Yet, even a mating pair may not qualify as a reproductive entity. As we discussed in Chapter 4, unless sexual partners are genetically identical, the mixing nature of sexual reproduction tends to result in offspring genetically distinct from either parent. When genetic variation exists among mating partners, the only thing that potentially stays the same across generations is the genetic constitution of an entire sexual population—what biologists term the population's **gene pool**. Here we run into a bit of a problem. This idea is too important to avoid any further discussion here. But the details are sufficiently complicated such that a full-blown discussion cannot happen without a much better understanding of genetics. So consider the following discussion as a primer. I want to begin to get you thinking about some topics that we will develop further later. I start by better explaining what is meant by genetic variation.

Genetic and phenotypic variation in sexual populations

Each organism within a sexual population has a genotype—that is, a specific set of genetic information. **Genetic variation** exists within a sexual population whenever all individuals do not have the same genotype.

Unfortunately, this definition is not as straightforward as it sounds. Here is where it gets more confusing: When organisms within the same sexual population have different genotypes, it is not because they have different genes, but because they have different forms of the same genes. To help visualize this, consider a simple analogy. Consider a single written driving instruction: turn when you get to 39th Street. This instruction is analogous to a gene because it codes for a specific activity. We could even call it the 39th-Street-gene. Notice, however, there is still room for different forms of this gene. The two most obvious alternatives would be turn right on 39th Street, or turn left on 39th Street. *Biological jargon*: Different versions of the same gene are called **alleles**.

A sexual population lacks genetic variation at the 39th-Street-gene when all members have the same alternative (same allele)—for instance, they could all have the turn-right alternative. On the other hand, population-level genetic variation exists (at this gene) when some members have the turn-right alternative, whereas others have the turn-left alternative. Extending this idea, a sexual population lacks genetic variation if all members have the same forms of every gene in their genomes. Alternatively, a sexual population has genetic variation if alternative forms exist in at least one of the many genes making a genome. The more genes that have alternative forms, the greater the sexual population's genetic variability.

Each variable gene within a sexual population can be quantified in terms of gene frequency. Every sexual population has a finite number of members, so there is also a finite number of copies of any gene. The copy number may be twice the population size because some sexual organisms are diploid—each individual has two genomes. The gene frequency is the proportion of these gene copies filled with each of the alternative forms. For example, a diploid sexual population made up of 500 individuals would have 1,000 copies of the 39th-Street-gene. If 200 copies were filled with the turn-left form and the remaining 800 were filled with the turn-right form, then the gene frequency would be 0.2 turn-left and 0.8 turn-right when expressed as proportions, or 20% turn-left and 80% turn-right when expressed as percentages.

Genetic variation within a sexual population can also translate into phenotypic variation. The existence of different gene-forms within a gene pool translates into different members of the same sexual population having different genotypes. Just as turning right or turning left will send you in different directions, these different gene forms may steer an organism's development in noticeably different directions. As a consequence, members of the same population may build noticeably different phenotypes.

A sexual population as a reproductive entity

Here is a brief overview of sexual reproduction in organisms like us—that is a genetically variable population of multicellular diploids containing males and females. (Note that every sexual reproducing organism does not fit into this category, but for the point I am trying to get across here that does not matter.) Start by envisioning a variable gene pool broken into many different genetic combinations. Each combination is the genetic information found within a single member of this population. In total, each individual's genetic information contains two complete genomes, having received one from each of its two parents. These two genomes may be variable in that they may contain different forms of the same gene. Prior to reproduction, germ-line cells within sexually mature members begin to form gametes, and in the process the two genomes are condensed into one. This means that for each variable gene, only one of the two alternatives (within the individual) makes it into a gamete. However, due to the constant shuffling, which alternative makes it can change with each gamete produced. Consequently, each gamete potentially has a unique combination of gene forms, especially when an individual has lots of variable genes. At some point before, during, or after gametes are formed, members of the opposite sex form mating pairs. Through some form of mating behavior, each pair attempts to get their gametes close together so that they can find each other and subsequently fuse to form a single cell called a zygote. All the zygotes formed by all the mating pairs are the start of the next generation. From here, these offspring try to successfully build themselves into a sexually mature form that can be a parent in the next generation.

With mixing of genetic information going on during both the forming and fusing of gametes it is difficult to see how a sexual population could stay the same across generations. Not only will offspring tend to be different than their parents, but even offspring sharing the same parents (full siblings) will tend to be different from each other. Consequently, the mixing alone would seem to result in each generation being different from the one before. And in one sense this is true: The exact genetic combinations found among the individuals that make up one generation will tend not to be repeated in the following generation. In another sense, however, it is not true: Mixing alone does not alter the gene frequencies in the gene pool as a whole. It is in this sense that a sexual population is a reproductive entity.

That the mixing of sexual reproduction, in and of itself, will not alter gene frequencies was independently proven by G.H. Hardy and W. Weinberg in the same year (1908). It is thus termed the **Hardy-Weinberg theorem**. The theorem mathematically demonstrates that when all other potentially gene-frequency-altering factors are removed from consideration, gene frequencies remain the same despite sexual mixing. The other factors eliminated are referred to as the assumptions of the Hardy-Weinberg theory because if violated—that is, if these conditions are not met—gene frequencies will change across generations. These assumptions are:

- No new gene-forms are introduced into the population.

- The population is effectively infinite, which means that the population is large enough that during gamete formation and gamete fusion no gene-forms will be disproportionately left behind by chance.

- Individuals randomly form mating pairs.

- All gene-forms (alleles) of all variable genes present in a sexual population are equally competent at getting copies of themselves into the next generation.

Origin of Reproductive Entities

There are three basic ways that a new reproductive entity could come into existence:

- **Spontaneous origin**—a new reproductive entity comes to be in one step. That is, with one sudden rearrangement a reproductive entity is formed from a set of materials that were not previously part of a reproductive entity.

- **Modified origin**—a new reproductive entity comes to be via the partial modification of a previously existing reproductive entity.

- **Symbiotic origin**—a new reproductive entity comes to be through the joining together of previously independent reproductive entities.

The idea of spontaneous origin has problems with complexity—the more complex an arrangement, the less chance that all the pieces will fall into place in one fell swoop. In fact, this is how we defined complexity earlier. All present-day reproductive entities, even the simplest asexually reproducing bacteria, are incredibly complex. This means that without the aid of an organizing deity, spontaneous origin of a currently existing reproductive entity, be it a single asexual organism or a sexual population, is so unlikely that it falls outside the domain of scientific explanation. The only place where spontaneous origin could play a role in a scientific discussion of the history of Life is at the very beginning. There may be a spontaneous element to how early forms of processors first came together to form an extremely rudimentary reproductive performance. However, the origin of reproductive loops, or what people more commonly referred to as the origin of Life, will not be discussed in this chapter. We do not yet have the background to discuss this issue meaningfully.

What we begin to address here is the origin of one type of reproductive entity from another. Although modified origin and symbiotic origin are both viable options, presently I focus solely on modified origin. Such a restriction makes it easier to build the conceptual foundation of evolutionary biology. Later (in Chapter 19) we explore the idea of symbiotic origin further in reference to the evolution of certain parts of eukaryotic cells.

Furthermore, we are interested only in heritable modifications. Only modifications that can be passed from parents to offspring have the potential to alter a reproductive entity in a lasting way. We, thus, need to distinguish between heritable and nonheritable modifications.

Heritable and nonheritable modifications

Whether the reproductive entity is a single asexual individual or an entire sexual population, modifications only happen within single organisms. Such modifications can be broken down into phenotypic or genotypic modifications. (Go back to Chapter 4 if you cannot remember this distinction.) So the question is: What forms of phenotypic or genotypic modifications are heritable?

Any form of body mutilation, such as having a limb cut off, would be a phenotypic modification. August Weismann, a famous biologist of the late 1800s, tested whether mutilations were heritable by chopping tails off mice for twenty generations. He then looked for any accompanying reduction in tail size in the sexual population across generations. What did he find? Nothing other than a population of mice still wearing full-length tails. There has never been any evidence that mutilations are passed directly to offspring—that is, directly influence how an offspring develops.

As discussed in Chapter 4, an organism's phenotype is also modified by how it uses its body. An organism's aerobic conditioning, for example, develops further with aerobic forms of exercise. Such modification would be directly heritable if traits that develop in parents, due to a particular pattern of body use, develop in offspring even though these offspring do not use their bodies in the same way. Parents that developed excellent aerobic condition through a diligent exercise program would produce offspring that develop the same level of aerobic conditioning even if the offspring did not train as intensely. Biologists have termed this idea the **inheritance of acquired characters**, or commonly called **Lamarckian inheritance**, named after Jean Baptiste Lamarck (1744–1829), who first championed this idea. This idea, however, has a major stumbling block—there is no evidence that it is true. Phenotypic modifications do not appear to be directly heritable—that is, directly intervene in how offspring develop.

There still is, however, an avenue that mutilations or patterns of body use and disuse could be heritable—we often call it parental influence. My wife, for example, chose to be mutilated. She had several holes bored through her earlobes. And my wife's decision may influence our daughter, at some point, to make the same choice. If so, parental influence acted as a means of heritability. (Of course, in this day and age, her peers may influence her to have holes bored in more places than just her earlobes.) Similarly, parents that use their bodies in certain ways could influence their children to participate in the same activities, which could steer their bodies to develop in similar ways.

The only way an offspring's development can be directly altered is for the information potentially passed from parents to offspring to undergo some form of error-based modification—that is, for some form of **mutation** to occur. Although this issue can be more complicated, think of a mutation as a modification of a gene—one of the individual instructions within an entire genome. Mutations thus alter one of an organism's developmental instructions. Because genetic information (whether it has been recently modified or not) can be copied and passed to the next generation, mutations are potentially heritable.

The path by which mutations are heritable is straightforward in most single-celled organisms. Single-celled organisms tend to reproduce by making an additional copy of their genotype followed by the single cell dividing into two. One genotype copy goes into each of the two cells. Genotypic modifications are passed on directly.

In contrast, all mutations are not potentially heritable in multicellular organisms. Every cell making up a multicellular organism's body has a complete set of genetic information, so mutations could occur within any cell. However, most of the cells that make up a multicellular organism's body—called **somatic cells**—are reproductive dead ends. Skin cells, intestine cells, kidney cells, and muscle cells are all examples of somatic cells found in most animals. Even though many forms of somatic cells continue to divide within an organism, they do not generate cells able to reproduce—that is, be a starting cell of the next generation. Consequently, **somatic mutations**—mutations in somatic cells—are not heritable. Access to the next generation is reserved for those cells, termed **germ cells** or **germ-line cells,** that retain the ability to start development over in the next generation. For example, gametes such as sperm (male) and eggs or ova (female) are formed from germ-line cells. So, only **germ-line mutations**—mutations occurring in germ cells—are potentially passed on to offspring.

Mutation is not replacement

A new gene form arising by mutation is a modification of a previously existing gene form. We discuss more of the details surrounding this fact in Chapter 12. Furthermore, in most cases, the previously existing gene form still exists even after such modification occurs. Remember that mutations occur within individuals. So, if more than one individual bears the same gene form—as would be true for both clones and other members of a sexual population—all individuals not experiencing such germ-line mutation will still pass to the offspring copies of the previously existing gene form.

From now on I refer to any newly arising type as the **modified type** and the type from which it arose as the **ancestral type**. Recognize any population in which both the modified type and the ancestral type exist is a genetically variable population.

Individual Performance and Persistence of Gene Forms

Genetic information potentially persists because it can be passed from one generation to the next by reproduction. There is, however, a big difference between the potential to be passed to the next generation and actually making it. As I imagine that you realize, especially those readers that have had offspring, reproduction does not just happen—certain tasks must be accomplished. Here I introduce the perspective that each of these tasks can be thought of as a **reproductive obstacle**. And obstacle is the right word; failure to negotiate any reproductive obstacle blocks reproduction from occurring.

As discussed in Chapter 4, genetic information is just encoded instructions. This means that genetic information itself cannot do the work needed to persist. An organism's phenotype, not its genotype, does the work of reproduction. So, gene forms are copied and passed to the next generation only if the phenotype in which they reside is able to do the work needed to negotiate all the reproductive obstacles.

So where does the phenotype come from? This was also discussed some in Chapter 4, but let's briefly review. All organisms start with both a genotype and a phenotype, but different than its genotype, an organism's phenotype changes across its lifetime. A larger and often more complex phenotype is built through a spiraling interplay between the genotype and the present phenotype. Consequently, the specific information within a specific genotype steers, within certain limits, the sequence of shapes through which a developing phenotype progresses. In other words, any organism's past, present, and future shapes are influenced by its genotype. Due to the shape–performance trade-off, shape influences performance ability, which in turn influences an organism's ability to negotiate reproductive obstacles. So, *whether genetic information encoded within a genotype makes it to the next generation is influenced by what sort of phenotype it helps to build.* Understand this last statement along with the flowchart shown in Figure 6-1, and you understand a lot.

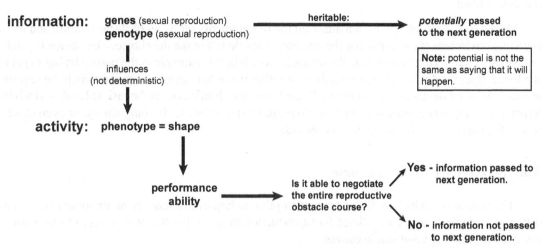

Figure 6-1. The flow chart that shows how genetic information can influence activity, which in turn can influence whether the information will be passed on to the next generation.

The conceptual basis of selection

The act of something attempting to negotiate an obstacle—whatever the obstacle, and whatever the reason something is trying to get over it—creates a selection process. Selection denotes a choice between alternatives, and there are always two alternatives associated with something attempting to negotiate an obstacle: *success* or *failure*. The choice is made by the performance of that attempting to negotiate the obstacle. It "selects" success if its efforts prove sufficient to negotiate the obstacle. Alternatively, it "selects" failure if its efforts prove insufficient to negotiate the obstacle.

Whether an individual's performance proves sufficient to negotiate an obstacle depends on an interaction of three factors:

• *The nature of the obstacle*—that is, what specifically needs to be accomplished.

• *Current environmental circumstance*—the present conditions under which the obstacle is to be negotiated.

• *The relevance of the individual's performance ability*—that is, how well do the skills of the organism attempting to negotiate the obstacle match the skills needed to negotiate the obstacle.

Consider a person attempting to get over a fence (see Figure 6-2). The fence is the obstacle. Its nature includes features such as its height and materials from which it is built. How difficult it is to get over a fence is clearly affected by its nature. Fences made from smooth concrete, for example, are harder to climb than ones made of chain link, and taller fences tend to be harder to get over than shorter ones. Environmental circumstance comes into play because it can further modify the demands of the task. Opposing gale force winds or a big mean dog on

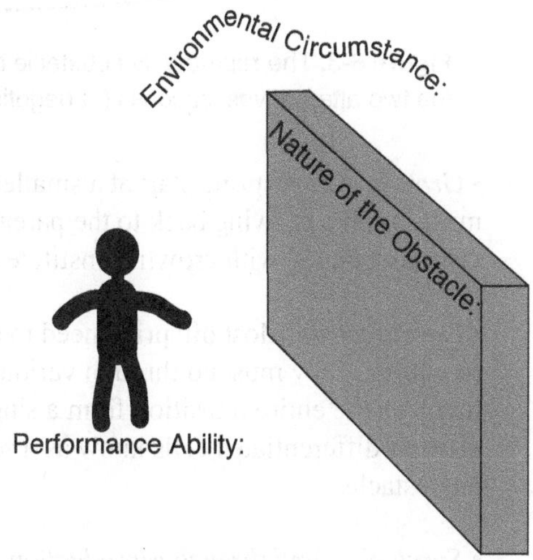

Figure 6-2. The different components of a selection process. (See text for further details).

the other side are two examples of environmental conditions that make getting over a fence even more difficult. The combination of an obstacle's nature and surrounding conditions set the requirements of the task at hand.

Maybe this is a subtle point, but although the requirements set by an obstacle's nature and its surrounding environment can influence the outcome, they do not make the choice. The choice is solely in the hands of that trying to negotiate the obstacle, which in this example is the person trying to get over the fence. Specifically, the choice is made by whether his or her performance can match the requirements. The more developed the individual's performance abilities are to the task at hand—which in terms of getting over a fence may include strength, jumping ability, climbing ability, or even cleverness—the more likely the choice will be success.

The reproductive obstacle course

The task of reproduction differs from attempting to hop over a fence in an important way—many different obstacles must be negotiated for reproduction to occur. In other words, reproduction always involves negotiating an **obstacle course**.

Although the details may vary, all obstacles along any organism's reproductive obstacle course fall into one of the following familiar categories: growth, development, survival, mating, fertility, and parental provisioning (see Figure 6-3). I quickly summarize the nature of each:

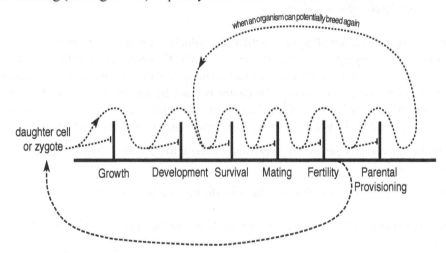

Figure 6-3. The reproductive obstacle course. The branch points prior to each obstacle represent the two alternatives: success (at negotiating the obstacle) or failure.

• *Growth.* All offspring start at a smaller size than their parents do, so part of the reproductive loop must involve growing back to the parental size. And because growth does not just happen, all the tasks associated with growth constitute reproductive obstacles.

• *Development.* Most offspring need to do more than just increase in size to reach their reproductive form. They must go through various phenotypic transitions. In multicellular organisms this involves the entire transition from a single undifferentiated cell to a spatially organized arrangement of differentiated cells know as a sexually mature adult. Each step along the way constitutes an obstacle.

• *Survival to and through reproduction.* All organisms must be alive to reproduce. Survival involves many different activities, such as acquiring sufficient resources, avoiding predators, combating disease, and repairing damage. Each of these constantly constitutes an obstacle.

• *Acquiring mates.* In sexually reproducing organisms, males and females must find a mate to reproduce. So, mate acquisition stands as an obstacle to reproduction for individuals of both sexes.

• *Fertility.* Even when a mate is acquired, gametes must still fuse. Again because this does not just happen, getting gametes together constitutes an obstacle. Furthermore, an obstacle is emplaced by the necessity that the two fusing gametes have sufficient complementary genetic information that they can work together to direct the development of a functional adult.

• *Provisioning offspring.* All offspring need at least some assistance from the parents to make it through the early stages of growth and development. These requirements of the offspring translate into obstacles for the parent(s).

For those into acronyms, the **reproductive obstacle course** can be shortened to ROC. Although it's nice to shorten long expressions, this acronym can also be used to make a point. Perhaps you have heard the expression caught between a rock and a hard place. All organisms, in contrast, are stuck in a slightly different dilemma. They are constantly caught between its ROC and death. To continue to live is to continue to successfully negotiate obstacles. The selection process faced by every organism is relentless. Death is the only escape.

Of course, all organisms do not encounter all these categories of obstacles. Asexual organisms, for example, do not encounter mating obstacles. At least in the same sense as multicellular organisms, single-celled organisms do not undergo development. Furthermore, how failure to negotiate an obstacle affects reproduction is different among the obstacles. Survival, for instance, is a one-chance obstacle. All organisms, including cats, have only one life, and dead things do not reproduce. On the other hand, mating is an example of an obstacle without such severe consequences. If one fails as a suitor once, damaged ego aside, one can still try again.

Each reproductive obstacle is also different than the fence example in that trying to reproduce is what emplaces reproductive obstacles. Mating is an obvious example. A sexual organism's need to acquire a mate is put in place by the nature of the organism, not by the nature of the environment. The same argument can be made for all other obstacles. Consider an organism living in a water-scarce environment such as a desert. Many discussions of how desert plants and animals deal with water scarcity make it sound like it is the environment that creates the problem (the obstacle) faced by these organisms. That is not the case. Water availability is an issue only because organisms need to have a certain amount of water to survive. An organism's constant need of a water supply is the obstacle. The relative abundance of water in the environment only adjusts what it takes for an organism to constantly negotiate this obstacle—which is to constantly maintain a sufficient water supply.

Biological Evolution

Biological evolution is often defined by the expression **descent with modification**. This expression, however, fails to make clear that a modified origin has an impact on the history of Life only if its introduction is followed by persistence across generations. I prefer the following definition: Biological evolution is the two-step process of descent with modification followed by persistence across generations.

Biological evolution has three main ingredients: modification, heritability, and reproductive success. The first is the ingredient of change; the last two are the ingredients of lasting change—that is, persistence across generations. Heritability makes persistence across generations possible, whereas reproductive success is needed to convert the possible into the actual. At minimum, at least one individual bearing a heritable modification must succeed in negotiating the entire reproductive obstacle course in each generation for that modification to potentially persist.

We have already discussed all the basic tools of biological evolution. Germ-line mutations are modifications that meet the first requirement of persistence—they are heritable. Through their potential to affect phenotypic development, newly arising gene forms can also influence their reproductive success. Specifically, the better a gene form helps to shape its associated phenotype's performance ability in relation to the obstacles to be negotiated and the environmental circumstance encountered, the better the chance that individuals carrying this gene form will be reproductively successful. Better reproductive success translates into a higher expectation that a newly arising gene form will persist (see Figure 6-4).

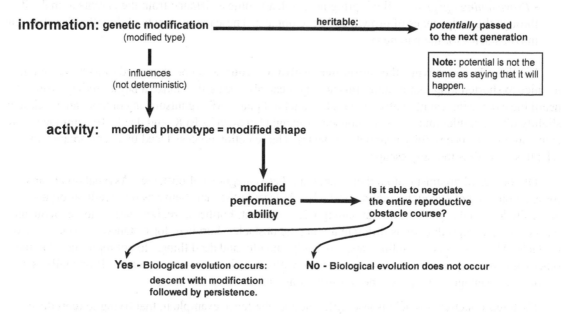

Figure 6-4. The flow chart that shows the basic ingredients of biological evolution—that is, how a genetic modification could persist.

Reproductive races

So far I have suggested that the key ingredient for a newly modified gene form to persist is to help produce phenotypes that are able to reproduce. In many cases there is an additional twist because modified gene forms are commonly caught in a reproductive race with their ancestral gene form. Such a reproductive race unfolds whenever the modified type and the ancestral types are caught competing for an exclusive resource. Recall from Chapter 5 that competitive exclusion is when each competitor can potentially drive the other to extinction by being able to take over the entire supply of some resource vital to both.

The potential for competitive exclusion between a modified gene form and an ancestral gene form is always there within a sexual population. Each gene resides at a specific location within a genome. Biologists refer to each gene's spot or location as its **locus**. The important point is that with one locus per genome, a finite population size with a finite number of genomes translates into a finite number of spaces for copies of every gene within a genome to fill. Alternative gene forms thus compete for an exclusive resource—the same space. Each genome filled with one of these alternative gene forms has no room for any others. If any one gene form comes to occupy all the genomes within a gene pool, all alternative gene forms have been excluded to the point of extinction. Whenever this happens the gene ceases to be a variable gene. Until another modification arises by mutation, only one gene form now exists within the sexual population.

Such competition between alternative gene forms is potentially tracked by how gene frequencies change across generations. Just the introduction of a modified gene form via germ-line mutation results in a change in gene frequency. In a previously nonvariable gene, for example, the gene frequency has changed from all the same gene form (expressed as proportion as 1.0 or as percentile as 100%), to some proportion of the modified gene form and some proportion of the ancestral gene form. Because germ-line mutations generally occur in only one individual out of an entire sexual population, the beginning proportion for any modified type tends to be rather small. Once present, however, a newly modified type could become increasingly common across generations—that is, its frequency could increase. If so, the frequency of the ancestral gene form correspondingly decreases. *Going to fixation* or *spreading to fixation* are phrases commonly used to refer to one gene form's frequency increasing to 1.0, hence ousting all competing gene forms. Whenever a modified gene form goes to fixation, it has completely replaced the ancestral gene form.

How gene frequencies change depends solely on the *relative* rate that competing gene forms are being copied and passed to offspring. This is what I meant by a reproductive race. It is a simple mathematical fact that any gene form's frequency will decrease if it is not as successful at getting copies of itself into the next generation in comparison to its competitors. Continue this trend for too many generations, and a gene form will become less common to the point of extinction.

When reproductive races are in place, biological evolution depends on the relative reproductive ability of modified gene forms. A modified gene form's persistence depends not just on getting into the next generation, but in doing so as fast as or faster than the ancestral gene form. Reproducing just as fast keeps it in the population. Reproducing faster allows the modified gene form not only to persist, but also to eventually replace the ancestral gene form. In both scenarios, biological evolution has occurred—modification has been followed by persistence across generations. Alternatively, the modified gene form will go extinct if it fails to reproductively keep up with the ancestral type. Accordingly, biological evolution has not occurred because there has been no lasting change in the gene pool's composition.

Some evolutionary biologists have gotten so caught up in the competition among alternative gene forms that they define biological evolution solely in terms of changing gene frequencies across generations. Although changing gene frequencies clearly captures much of the way change occurs within Life, biological evolution cannot be solely defined in these terms. Implicit in this definition is that biological evolution always involves replacement—one gene form becoming more common always at the expense of another becoming equally less common. The conditions of competitive exclusion among alternative gene forms, however, are not always met.

For example, when reproduction is asexual, a newly modified gene form and its ancestral gene form may or may not compete for a potentially exclusive resource. Without genetic mixing going on, the same type of competition for space in genomes does not exist. The potential for competitive exclusion depends on whether members of the newly modified clone and the ancestral clone compete for some ecological resource (e.g., some food type, shelter sites) in a potentially exclusive manner. Although this is possible, it is not guaranteed. If clones interact with their environment in sufficiently different ways, they may be able to coexist.

Natural selection

To repeat myself: Phenotypes do the work of reproduction, genotypes influence how a phenotype develops, and the gene forms making up genotypes are what can get passed across generations. Now add in the idea of a reproductive race, and an extremely important idea emerges. Whether a modified gene form is going to get passed to the next generation as fast as or faster than its ancestral gene form largely depends on how it affects phenotypic development in comparison to the ancestral gene form. Why? You already know. Modifying development means modifying the phenotype's shape, which, due to the shape–performance trade-off, modifies the phenotype's performance abilities. Modifying performance ability may then modify this phenotype's relative ability to negotiate the reproductive obstacle course. Stated simply, a performance-based reproductive race emerges (see Figure 6-5).

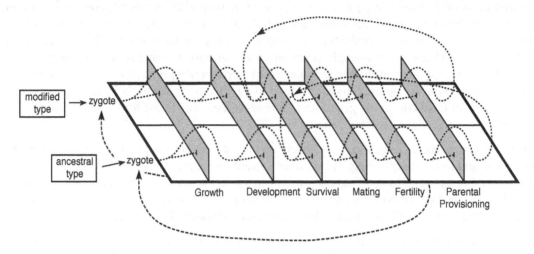

Figure 6-5. The performance-based reproductive race of natural selection.

Charles Darwin not only recognized that these performance-based reproductive races were taking place—what he termed the "struggle for existence"—but he also appreciated what effect such races could have on the entire structure of Life. He named this evolutionary mechanism **natural selection**. Any heritable change in shape and subsequent performance can be said to be "naturally selected" (in contrast to supernaturally selected) if this type becomes increasingly common within its population due to the simple fact that, in the context of current environmental circumstance, it is better at reproducing than competing types. *Biological jargon*: The gene form whose influence on phenotypes makes it the best reproductive competitor is said to have the highest **relative fitness**.

Natural selection when reproduction is asexual versus sexual

When reproduction is asexual, the contestants within any performance-based reproductive race are distinct units—they are distinct clones. When tied together by competitive exclusion, ancestral and modified clones are locked into a reproductive race for persistence. Genotypes are passed on intact, so each competing type remains the same across generations. Who replaces whom becomes a contest of which genotype, as a whole, generates a phenotype better able to reproduce.

Natural selection in a genetically variable sexual population has a distinctly different flavor. As already discussed, due to the mixing nature of sexual reproduction, most offspring produced have unique genotypes—that is, they have unique combinations of all the alternative gene forms. Each offspring with a unique genotype is thus a unique contestant entering this generation's reproductive race. Natural selection enters the picture when, due to genetic differences, phenotypic differences arise that have reproductive effects. Phenotypes that fail to grow, develop sexual maturity, survive, or find a sexually compatible mate are bumped from the race along with their genotypes. Even among those genotypes whose phenotypes do reproduce, all may not get an equal number of offspring into the next generation. So all in all, individuals bearing certain genotypes may contribute more to the next generation than others.

Because genotypes are scrambled in each generation, the best reproducing genotypes are not passed on intact. As a consequence, sexual mixing impedes the best performing genotypes from taking over the population in every straightforward way. Nonetheless, the gene pool as a whole is still changing. Those gene forms that tend to be a part of winning genotypes increase in frequency. And as a consequence, the scrambling nature of sexual reproduction will put together winning genetic combination with increasing frequency.

Genetic drift

It is important to note that what is expected to happen does not always happen. The expectation of natural selection is that types better at reproducing will replace their competitors. But chance events enter into every contest. The role that chance plays in the outcome in reproductive races is termed **genetic drift**. More specifically, genetic drift is the suite of uncontrollable factors that result in a deviation between an expected outcome in the relative reproductive success among competing types and the actual outcome. Like natural selection, genetic drift is an evolutionary mechanism. Chance events can lead to the genetic composition of a population changing across generations.

Genetic drift's role in evolution is most obvious when genetic differences do not lead to performance differences, such as when genetic differences do not affect the development of phenotypes, or when phenotypic differences are not relevant to the performance of reproduction. Without performance differences, the relative success of competing gene forms is solely in the hands of chance. Of course, one might argue that when genetic differences do not make performance differences, who cares? Whether chance deviations result in one gene form becoming increasingly common has no real effect on how Life works anyway. There are reasons that this argument is too simplistic, but none that I take up here.

The potential for chance events to affect outcomes does not disappear in the face of heritable performance differences. In a sports contest, for example, the most talented team does not always win; and chance occurrences such as lucky shots or bad bounces may have contributed to their demise. Similarly, the expectation of natural selection can go astray. In terms of reproduction, a less-talented gene form may drift to increased frequency against the current of natural selection.

Of course, the effect of chance events decreases as the number of trials increases. Suppose you were going to compete at tennis against a world-class tennis player. Which form of contest should you choose to maximize your chance at winning: play one point, play one game, play one set, play a best two-of-three set match, or play a best three-of-five set match? Your best shot would be to play just one point. If your skill cannot win the match, then you need to count on luck. The chance of getting lucky once is always greater than the chance of getting lucky enough times to win an entire match. Similarly, the smaller a population's size the more likely that chance events could result in gene forms involved in the assembly of poorer performing phenotypes increasing in the population. Or stated the other way, the larger a population's size, the less effect genetic drift is expected to have on its evolution.

A brief summary

Figure 6-6 summarizes all that has been said so far about biological evolution.

Selection Thinking

Natural selection is not just something that potentially happens once in a while; it is poised to happen always. Any heritable modification that affects any aspect of reproduction is subjected to natural selection. Which basically means that anything an organism does is potentially modified by natural selection because everything organisms do has something to do with reproduction.

How pervasively natural selection has structured the life forms we see at present depends to what degree useful heritable modifications have arisen at some point in the past. This is where time comes in. Given enough time, a large number of heritable modifications will arise. With 3.5 billion years of

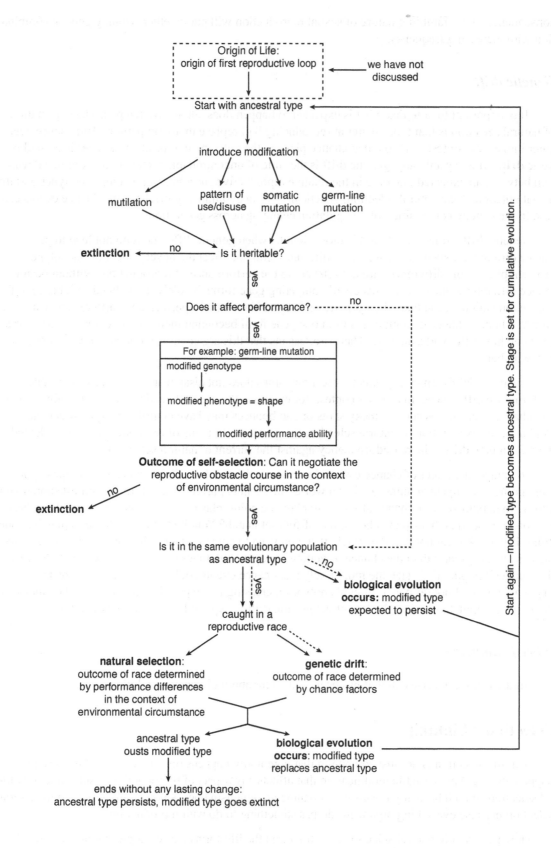

Figure 6-6. An overview of biological evolution.

reproduction, it takes little stretch of the imagination to assume that natural selection could have had a pervasive influence on all aspects of all living organisms.

If so, to understand Life one must get into the mind-set of reproductive races. To think in terms of natural selection one must consider alternative ways of doing things under different contexts, always asking the question: *Which alternative is expected to win?* As it turns out, this is not a trivial exercise. The many dimensions of reproduction and the many contexts in which reproduction takes place creates a plethora of alternatives and settings to be considered. Amid this diversity, the goal of **selection thinking** is to attempt to understand what can and cannot happen under its province.

Next I spend some time going through some of the ways that natural selection could have structured Life.

Why newly modified gene forms usually go extinct

Random motion occurs when objects are moving in all possible directions of motion with no direction being any more likely than any other. Motion becomes increasingly directional as objects move more in some possible directions than others. Completely directional motion is when all objects are moving in the same direction.

The same type of distinction can be made between directed and random occurrences in biological evolution. Change is random when each possibility is equally likely to occur. Change is directed when that is not true.

Natural selection is a *directed* or *nonrandom* occurrence. Each of the competing types does not have an equal chance of replacing the others. Instead, differences in performance ability direct change. Based on how they affect the phenotype, some gene forms are better at getting copied and passed on to the next generation than others.

What about the introduction of new types into a population? Are mutations directed or random? Germ-line mutations would be directed if those mutations that occur fall within a subset of the mutations that could possibly occur. Such directedness depends on some mechanism that either actively picks certain mutations or actively suppresses certain mutations. Alternatively, mutations would be random if no such mechanism existed—mutations would not be biased in any particular direction.

Biologists still clamor over the directedness or randomness of mutations. Directed mutation is an appealing notion. A mechanism that enables a parent to direct the mutations being sent to offspring is a means for parents to direct what new forms of genetic information its offspring would have. Now layer on another means by which organisms somehow perceive what genetic modifications would produce useful phenotypic modifications, and—abracadabra!—parents could use directed mutations to "improve" their offspring's performance abilities.

There is only one problem with this idea—there is no solid evidence of directed mutations. Mutations appear to be *random*.

Most random mutations will fail to persist. Any ancestral gene form is the ancestral gene form because it has worked. It has been part of genotypes whose resultant phenotypes have been able to reproduce. How likely is it that a random change will result in something that works as well or better? Envision a car running well enough to keep it on the road. Further envision making some random adjustment to the car. Say one opens the hood and randomly turns some screw on the carburetor. Is the car likely to run better? No. There may be adjustments that would improve the car's performance, but only rarely would random change make one of these "right" changes. And organisms are much more complex than cars, so randomly modifying them has even less chance of improving its performance. Only with rare exception would a mutation entering a population be expected to survive the scrutiny of selection.

Keep in mind that rare is not the same as never. Any improbable event will occur if given enough time.

Considering costs and benefits

Suppose that you knew that one of the competing types in a variable population was better than any of the others at surviving. Would that be sufficient information to expect this type to be the natural selection winner?

The answer is no. The reason hinges on the fact that survival is just one of the many obstacles associated with reproduction. Being the best at negotiating one obstacle such as survival or parental provisioning does not necessarily translate into being the best at negotiating the entire obstacle course. That would be true only if being better at negotiating any one obstacle makes one no worse at negotiating any other. The diverse nature of the different reproductive obstacles, in combination with shape–performance trade-offs, makes that unlikely.

To incorporate the notion of performance trade-offs, the expectation of natural selection can be discussed in terms of a **cost-benefit scenario**. *In fact, whether explicitly stated or not, all selection thinking involves a cost-benefit analysis.* Because natural selection is based on performance differences between competing types, a type's **benefits (B)** are all performance differences that make it better at negotiating reproductive obstacles relative to its competitors. Alternatively, a type's **costs (C)** are all performance differences that make it worse at negotiating obstacles relative to its competitors (see Figure 6-7). The type whose overall benefits exceed its overall costs (**B > C**) is the type expected to win in natural selection. Benefits exceeding costs states that it is better overall at negotiating the entire reproductive obstacle course because the ways it is better than its competitors exceeds the ways that it is worse. (Note: Assigning costs and benefits has a reciprocal nature—any performance difference between competing types that is a benefit to one type is an equal cost to the other type, and vice versa.

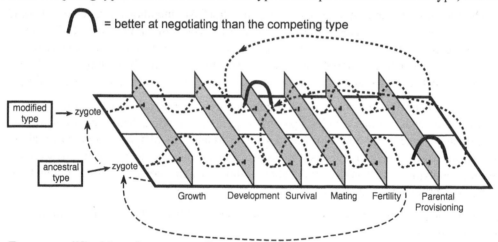

From modified type's perspective:

Benefits (B) - all the reproductive advantages associated with being better at surviving

Costs (C) - all the reproductive disadvantages associated with not being as good at parental provisioning

Modified type is expected to win the reproductive race if: **B > C**

Modified type is expected to lose the reproductive race if: **C > B**

Figure 6-7. An example of how the expectation of natural selection can be couched in cost-benefit terms.

As a consequence, whenever one type's benefits are greater than its costs, then in the exact opposite manner, its competitor's overall costs must exceed its overall benefits ($C > B$).)

Life history evolution

Back in Chapter 3 I introduced a fundamental trade-off in the workings of individual organisms—the trade-off between survival (which involves keeping things the same) and reproduction (which involves change). The trade-off evolved because, despite their opposing nature, both survival and reproduction are necessary components of persistence. An individual must be alive to reproduce and must reproduce to produce new individuals that can try to survive. This raises the question: How does each type of organism negotiate this trade-off? Here is where natural selection enters the fray. In the presence of variation, the ensuing reproductive race constantly shapes any **life history trait** (what biologists call traits caught in the intersection between survival and reproduction) toward a "strategy" that maximizes lifetime reproductive success. Such traits include the number of offspring initially produced in each reproductive bout, the amount and pattern of parental investment in each offspring, the size and/or age in which offspring become reproductively mature, and once reproductively competent, the time interval between reproductive attempts.

Just to set the stage, consider life history evolution in a world without trade-offs. All types of organisms would evolve toward producing an infinite number of offspring at each reproductive bout, each offspring would then mature at birth, and subsequently begin to reproduce continuously for a life span that extends forever. Reintroduce trade-offs—that is, return to the real world—and none of these components are possible. But envisioning the ideal is still instructive because it establishes a framework to consider life history evolution from a cost/benefit perspective. Any new heritable modification within a population that shifts individuals closer to some aspect of the life history ideal constitutes a benefit. But due to the inseparable but opposing nature of survival and reproduction, any change bearing benefits will also bear costs. Specifically, any modification that increases any aspect of reproductive output will decrease the probability of surviving through it, and vice versa.

Consider, for instance, the relationship between survival and parental provisioning. A universal aspect of parental provisioning is providing nutrients to offspring. Every egg or seed contains a pool of parentally supplied goodies. In some animals parental provisioning even continues after birth (or hatching). The link between providing nutrients and reproduction is straightforward. For an offspring to have any chance of becoming a sexual mature member of the next generation, parentally supplied nutrients must support an offspring's growth and development until it reaches the point that it can forage on its own. And support beyond this minimum level would increase an offspring's chance of reaching the next generation even further. So, how much should a parent provision each of its offspring? Just to the minimum, way beyond the minimum, or somewhere in between? And how many offspring should a parent try to raise at once? These are classic life history questions. Providing more nutrients (along with other aspects of parental care) to each offspring coupled with trying to raise more offspring at each reproductive bout are life history benefits—they potentially increase the current reproductive success. But increasing such effort will always be accompanied by survival costs. Any combination of provisioning each offspring more and increasing offspring number means a larger pool of resources need to be supplied. Consequently, a parent must either spend more time foraging or draw down further internally stored reserves, both of which can make it more vulnerable to predators or disease. The added weight and bulk associated with producing more and/or larger eggs prior to laying may also add to survival costs by further encumbering a female's locomotor performance. Decreasing speed and maneuverability will make prey capture or predator escape more difficult. Perhaps to an even greater degree, the same argument applies to female mammals that provision their young internally for extended periods of time. Consider, for instance, a human female in her last months of pregnancy. Running fast or jumping high is just not an option.

Age and size of sexual maturation can also get caught in the life-history crossfire. For example, in many insect species (as well as other types of animals) relatively larger females are able to produce more eggs in each reproductive bout. From a life-history perspective, a female growing to a larger size before becoming reproductively mature thus carries a benefit. But it also bears costs. To grow bigger requires more time (assuming the growth rate stays the same) or a relatively faster growth rate, and either incurs a survival detriment. The more time it takes to mature translates into a greater overall exposure to predators, parasites, accidents, or anything else that could kill or debilitate an individual prior to ever getting a chance to reproduce. In other words, increasing the time it takes to mature will decrease the probability of surviving to mature at all. Increasing growth rate has the same overall effect. Like all components of reproduction, the coacting nature of growth is disruptive to survival, and the faster any disruptive activity is performed the greater the potential risk (per unit time).

Two simple take-home messages are encased in the preceding scenarios. First, any change in reproductive effort entails change in either the *overall amount of time allocated* or the *intensity of the effort* within the allocated time (or some combination of both). But whatever the details, more is still always coupled with less—the greater the reproductive effort at any point in an organism's life, the less likely that it will survive to finish raising its current batch of offspring or survive to have offspring in the future. Second, due to the inescapable nature of life history trade-offs, any heritable modification within any organism that influences growth rate, maturation rate, egg size, offspring number, or any other life-history trait will be immediately and constantly subjected to selection. And once a heritable modified type enters into the life-history game, it is expected to spread in the population only if its benefits to lifetime reproductive success exceeds the costs.

Something to consider: Natural selection of life-history strategies is always a game of entangled risk and reward. And the nature of such games is that there is no one best way to play. Perhaps the increased probability of surviving associated with a decrease in reproductive effort at some life stage will lead to more than compensating gains in overall reproductive success due to an increased probability of surviving to reproduce in the future. Perhaps not. It all depends on the type of organism and nature of its environmental circumstance. Furthermore, the natural selection of risk and reward in the life history arena has an added twist. An overall riskier strategy may increase the average reproductive success per generation and still not be favored by natural selection. A riskier strategy increases the probability that all individuals of that type would suffer complete reproductive failure in the same generation. Which, of course, would result in the extinction of that type.

Elephants and mice

Evolutionary biologists, from theoreticians to field biologists, have had a lot of fun trying to understand the diversity of life-history strategies found in nature. Consider, for instance, the diversity found in two mammals: deer mice (*Peromyscus maniculatus*) and African elephants (*Loxodonta Africana*).

After spending only around 23 days developing inside mom, a deer mouse is born, along with typically three to five siblings. Each comes out tiny and helpless—hairless, eyes closed, and weighing only around 1.5 g (0.05 ounces). Yet 35 days later each has developed to the point that it can live independent of parental care—weaning usually occurs between 25 and 35 days. And within another two weeks or so, each is becoming sexually mature. In other words, in around 10 weeks after conception a deer mouse is ready to begin reproducing. At that point, it is usually around 15 to 20 cm (6 to 8 inches) in length (which includes a tail that can be as long as its body) and typically weighs somewhere around 15 g (a little greater than one-half ounce). Deer mice can breed year-round, and a single female can have multiple litters per year, although in the wild reproduction may not occur during winter or other unfavorable seasons. In captivity, deer mice can live as long as eight years. However, in the wild, life expectancy is much shorter, usually less than a year. (See Figure 16-8 for a summary.)

On the other hand, after conception, an African elephant develops inside mom for around 22 months (630 to 660 days) and weighs about 120 kg (264 lbs) at birth. All that time inside mom it is typically by itself, as twins are rare. After birth, it can nurse for several years and can continue to grow for 10 to 15 years. Females (cows) mature sexually at around 9 to 12 years old, when they weigh around 3,200 to 3,600 kg (7,000 to 8,000 lbs), and typically continue to reproduce every 3 to 4 years for the rest of their lives. Males (bulls), which can grow to twice the weight as females, reach sexual maturity around 12 to 15 years old. However, they often do not breed until they are about 30, when they become both strong and smart enough to compete successfully with other males for females. Elephants can live 50 to 60 years in the wild. (See Figure 16-8 for a summary.)

Ask anyone the difference between a mouse and an elephant, and size will likely be mentioned. An African elephant is the largest living land animal, whereas a deer mouse, at least in comparison to other mammals, is one of the smallest. So why do elephants grow so big? Is this a result of life-history evolution? Thinking along those lines makes no sense. Elephants do not grow bigger, in comparison to mice, so they can mature later, reproduce less frequently, and have fewer offspring each reproductive bout—all of which are moving away from the life-history ideal. (In fact, in comparison to the ideal,

life history	ideal	deer mouse	African elephant
gestation period	very short	23 days	22 months
size at birth	infinite?	1.5 g	120 kg
age at sexual maturity (females)	at birth	49 days	9 to 12 years
size at sexual maturity (females)	infinite?	15 g	3400 kg
number of offspring	infinity	3 to 6	typically 1
lifespan (in wild)	forever	less than a year	50 to 60 years

Figure 6-8. A summary of life history characters of a small mammal—deer mice (*Peromyscus maniculatus*), and a large mammal—African elephants (*Loxodonta Africana*), in comparison to life history ideals.

the only thing that elephants do better than mice is live longer.) Elephants have evolved to grow bigger because it has allowed them to interact with their environment in unique ways. For example, their size and strength, in conjunction with the dexterity of their trunk, has made it possible for then not only to forage on green vegetation from ground level to 20 or so feet, but also to feed outside their reach by breaking off branches and uprooting larger trees. But as size increased, the optimal life history strategy had to change as well. For example, it seems impossible that, like a deer mouse, an elephant would go from conception to sexual maturity in around 10 weeks. So although life history evolution did not make elephants, it did shape growth rate, patterns of parental investment, along with all other aspects of reproduction toward that which worked best for the elephant way of making a living.

Grouse and albatrosses

Although size clearly makes a difference, it alone cannot explain all life-history differences. For instance, blue whales (*Balaenoptera musculus*), which in terms of weight grow to 20 times the size of elephants, become sexually mature earlier—at around 6 to 10 years of age. Humans, who weigh around 60 times less than elephants, become sexually mature about the same age (or even a little later in females). So next let's consider two bird species—sage grouse (*Centrocercus urophasianus*) and laysan albatross (*Phoebastria immutabilis*)—that grow to roughly the same adult size (1.4 to 2.7

kg—3 to 6 lbs), but make a living in distinctly different ways. Here we see that difference in how organisms interact with their environment can also influence their life-history strategy.

After spending around 25 to 27 days inside an egg laid in a ground nest and incubated by mom (as dad does not participate in any parental care), around a 28 g (1 oz) sage grouse hatches out, typically joined by six of seven other siblings. After hatching sometime in May or June, the chicks leave the nest as a group as soon as they are dry and begin to forage for food. Although mom (the hen) spends considerable time keeping her chicks warm and guarding them for the first 4 to 5 weeks, the chicks feed themselves. Early on they feed mostly on insects such as grasshoppers, beetles, and ants, although plant material—including leaves, blossom pods, and buds—is also consumed. During this time they develop rapidly, as they can fly several yards by the end of their second week (around 6 weeks after conception) and several hundred yards by eight weeks. By four or five months (October) females have grown to upwards of 1.1 kg (2.5 lbs), and males are even heavier, weighing around 1.6 kg (3.5 lbs). As they get older their diet shifts more and more to plants, in particular to sagebrush. Due to colder temperatures, snow accumulation, and changes in vegetation, by winter they depend entirely on the soft evergreen leaves and shoots of sagebrush. Sexual maturity comes the next spring. At that time the females weigh about the same (1.1 to 1.4 kg—2.5 to 3 lbs), and the males have gotten even bigger (1.8 to 2.3 kg—4 to 5 lbs). Mating in sage grouse is fascinating. Mostly in March and April, large numbers of males (averages range from 14 to 70 birds, with peak counts in the hundreds) gather on display grounds known as **leks** early in the morning to perform a "strutting display" for gathering females. With their tail feathers and head plumes erect, males fill their pair of yellowish air sacs that, when inflated, protrude from their chest, and then with a forward strut shutter their wings and produce a guttural *woom-boom* sounding call. Females saunter through these displaying males, soliciting a copulation from the male that in some way strikes her fancy. On a given lek, most females prefer the same displaying males, meaning that a small number of males receive most of the mating opportunities in that area. Sage grouse, on average, only live for 1 to 1.5 years, although some may live for 3 to 4 years or more. (See Figure 16-9 for a summary.)

In contrast, a laysan albatross spends its first 65 days or so developing inside a 280 g (almost 10 oz) egg (which is about 12% of the female's body weight) in a shallow ground nest located on some small oceanic island. Both mom and dad take turns incubating. It hatches out as a large (around 200 g—7 oz) but only child, as only one egg is ever laid. For the first few days a parent remains with the chick, brooding it as it develops abilities, such as thermoregulation, that allows it to survive without constant parental care. After that both parents may leave the chick for days at a time to hunt for food in the open ocean. During each foraging trip a parent may travel hundreds to several thousand of miles in search of squid and flying fish eggs. Stored in the gut during flight, each parent feeds the chick a concentrated oily product by regurgitation on their return. This goes on for the next 5 to 6 months, during which the offspring's wings expand to adult length (around a 2 m—6.5 foot—wingspan), a

life history ideal		sage grouse	laysan albatross
incubation period	very short	25 to 27 days	65 days
size at birth	infinite?	28 g	200 g
age at sexual maturity (females)	at birth	1 year	6 to 8 years
size at sexual maturity (females)	infinite?	1.1 to 1.4 kg	1.4 to 2.7 kg
number of offspring	infinity	6 to 8	1
lifespan (in wild)	forever	1 to 4 years	12 to 40 years

Figure 6-9. A summary of life history characters of two birds of similar size, but different feeding strategies—sage grouse (*Centrocercus urophasianus*) and laysan albatross (*Phoebastria immutabilis*)—in comparison to life history ideals.

full plumage develops, and it grows to a weight that typically exceeds its parents. Upon fledging, the offspring heads out to sea and will not return to land for 3 to 5 years, when it is ready to try to find a mate. It then returns to its natal nesting site to enter a slow-moving dating scene. Courtship, which involves flight tests and elaborate courtship dances, can last a full two years. Yet, once a pairing is decided it becomes a monogamous partnership for life. First attempts at breeding do not start until 6 to 8 years of age, and from that point the pair will try to raise one offspring every year for the rest of their 12 to 40 year life span. (See Figure 16-9 for a summary.)

Despite their similar size, the life history of sage grouse and laysan albatrosses seems almost as disparate as the mouse/elephant comparison. But what has driven this difference? The most obvious answer is how they feed. Given that sagebrush is the most common shrub scattered around sage grouse habitat, feeding on sagebrush along with ground-dwelling insects seems "easier" than roaming long distances across the open ocean in search of squid and flying fish eggs. And their life histories support that notion. In sage grouse a single female can start off trying to raise 7 or 8 offspring in the first spring of her life, with at least some chance of success. In contrast, it takes 7 or so years of practice feeding on their own for a pair of laysan albatrosses to even attempt to raise a single offspring. And even that would be impossible if they did not nest on small tropical islands lacking predators. Otherwise a nearly immobile offspring in a ground nest could not be left alone for days at a time. The virtual absence of predators in the open ocean also contributes to making the needed long life span possible. Selection just had to shape other aspects of the growth/survival trade-off to make the details fit.

Natural selection and the environment

We have just seen that an organism's interaction with its environment can influence how its life history will be shaped by natural selection. Next let's consider how natural selection can shape an organism's interaction with its environment. From the outset, recognize that current environmental circumstance makes a difference because a performance difference beneficial in one environmental setting may not be beneficial in another.

Environmental circumstances get tangled up in reproduction in two basic ways: It is the *source* of what each organism needs *to get*, and the *source* of what each organism needs *to avoid*.

On the *get side* lie resources. All organisms need to get resources—both usable energy and materials—from their environment to build and maintain themselves and to produce and provide for their offspring.

So here is the easy conclusion: Any heritable modification that helps organisms extract resources from its environment will help that organism reproduce more successfully. But what sort of modifications would help an organism extract resources? Although the answer depends on the details of an organism's environmental circumstance—what types of resources in what forms are available—two general avenues of change could make a difference.

First, modifications could alter what an organism can use to meet its basic resource needs. For example, a common need for materials such as nitrogen or carbon does not constrain all organisms to get its carbon or its nitrogen in the same way. These needed elements are encased inside many different molecular forms. Modifications potentially change which of these molecular forms an organism can use, thus what they need to get from their environment. Similarly, all organisms are not constrained to acquire usable energy in the same way. (Note: Modifications that change what any organism can use to meet its basic resource needs becomes a means for one species to take advantage of another species' outputs, thus the means by which both food and waste connections among species could evolve. And, as I keep emphasizing, when every unique form of material output becomes the input of something else, output and inputs come full circle to form nutrient cycles.)

Second, modifications could alter an organism's ability to capture those specific forms of energy and materials it can use. For example, phenotypic modifications could affect how fast a predator runs or changes directions, which in turn could affect its ability to capture prey. Similarly, phenotypic modifications in a plant could influence how well its leaves can capture sunlight above ground, or how well its roots can capture water and minerals from the soil. And once again, environmental details make a difference. Whether a change in a predator helps it capture another type of animal present in the same environment depends, in part, on whether it helps the predator better counter the specific way that this species attempts to escape. Likewise, whether an alteration in a plant's roots helps it better capture water depends, in part, on how water tends to be distributed within the soil it is rooted in.

The *avoid side* of any organism's dealings with its environment stems from two facts: First, as organized things, organisms can potentially be disrupted. Second, environments are a source of disruptions. Changing climatic conditions, predators, and parasites, to name just a few, can make the task of maintaining organization difficult.

Once again we can come up with the easy conclusion: Any heritable modification that helps organisms avoid disruptive elements of its environment will help it reproduce more successfully. The important question is: What sort of modifications would help an organism avoid disruptions? Environmental circumstance again enters in. Every organism's environmental circumstance details exactly what it must contend with. So only modifications that help an organism deal with its particular set of problems leads to improvements. Two forms of change could make such a difference.

First, modification could alter what conditions are potentially disruptive. Consider temperature. Every organism functions best when its tissues are within a certain temperature range. It is the shape—performance trade-off coming into play again. Environmental temperatures that can cool or heat body temperatures beyond this optimal range are potentially disruptive. Yet, what constitutes disruptive environmental temperatures depends on an organism's optimal temperature. Humans for example have an optimal temperature around 37°C (98.6°F), so jumping into the nearly freezing waters around the North Pole is a life-threatening disruption. In contrast, the optimal body temperature of fish living in polar waters is near freezing, so the temperature of their environment poses no disruption.

Second, modifications could alter an organism's ability to avoid disruptive elements. Phenotypic modifications could affect how well a prey can escape a predator, or how well an organism can maintain its body temperature near its optimum, despite being surrounding by potentially disruptive temperatures. Again, environmental details make a difference in what types of change constitutes an improvement. For instance, whether change helps a prey avoid one of its predators depends in part on whether it helps the prey better counter the specific way that this predator attempts to capture it.

A brief philosophical discussion

Consider the following scenario: Bob and Bill repeatedly race each other in the 100-meter dash. Every time the weather is windy and they are running into the wind, Bill wins the race. Every time the weather is calm Bob wins the race. Wind conditions are thus a causal factor in determining the outcome. Changes in wind conditions are a difference that makes a difference.

Does it make sense to say that wind conditions selected the winner? In other words, did the wind cause Bill to run faster than Bob? Which, if true, also means that calm conditions caused Bob to run faster than Bill. Something seems wrong with both. The winner is not selected by the wind, but by how fast each can run in a given set of conditions. In other words, it is Bob's or Bill's performance ability that chooses whether they succeed (get to the finish line first) or fail (do not get to the finish line first). Hopefully, the shape–performance trade-off comes to mind when thinking about why Bob or Bill would be faster under one set of conditions and slower under another. Perhaps Bill has a more streamlined shape that makes him more effective at cutting through the wind, but slows his speed when air resistance is less of a factor.

Natural selection is conceptually no different than Bob and Bill racing each other. The performance of the contestants is what ultimately does the selecting. Yet natural selection is often discussed as if the environment does the selecting. Expressions like "predators select for this" and "cold temperatures select for that" are common. Environmental circumstance can influence the outcome of any contest, so to phrase its role as that which selects the winner may seem trivial. But I have seen so many people get so confused about the ways of natural selection that it seems important to be as clear and accurate as possible. Presenting the environment as doing the selecting is simply misleading. An organism's environment does not do the work of reproduction; in fact, it does not even set what tasks must be accomplished—the reproductive obstacles. Those are both properties of the organism itself. Current environmental circumstance simply sets the context in which the race takes place.

How one explains why the temperature drops when ice cubes are placed in a warm glass of lemonade is a conceptually similar example. The common form of explanation is to simply state that the ice cools down the lemonade. The other would be to say that the lemonade warms up the ice, melting it, and in doing so looses heat. The latter seems a bit more awkward, so why go to the extra effort? There is one good reason. The first implies that coolness somehow spreads toward warmness. Or stated differently, regions of slower motion spread into regions of faster motion. But diffusion does not work that way. Diffusion spreads from high to low. So although both ways of saying it lead to the same conclusion—the lemonade gets cooler as the temperatures equilibrate—only the latter is accurate. Being accurate is never trivial.

To what extent can environmental circumstance steer evolution?

The combination of random mutations and environmental influence on natural selection is a means by which environmental details can steer how a population evolves over time—toward phenotypes better able to contend with these details. Stated differently, this combination is a means by which organisms evolve **adaptations**—specific features or traits that, in terms of getting resources and avoiding disruptions, help organisms deal with the details of their environment.

But don't get carried away. Environmental circumstance influencing how populations evolve does mean that environmental details hold a tight leash on how each population can evolve. There is simply "more than one way to skin a cat"—an old adage that points out that there are many ways of accomplishing the same thing.

Consider an herbivorous insect species with a particular environmental detail—an insectivorous bird species that hunts by systematically searching the surfaces of plants for insects. What forms of modification could help this insect avoid this predator? Potentially lots of them. Some form of fleeing, fighting back, or hiding are the general options. And within each general category, there are myriad alternatives. Consider, for instance, the various ways an insect could hide. One can hide by getting behind something and staying out of the line of sight, or by camouflage, or what biologists commonly call **cryptic coloration**. Furthermore, there are many color and shape patterns that can be cryptic. The trick is to look like anything that this predator does *not* eat. Insectivorous birds do not eat leaves, twigs, bark, rocks, dirt, their own droppings, or many other things, so an insect looking like any of these can afford some protection. There are examples of insects looking like all these things. More on this later.

History can also make a difference

Maybe this is a strange way to put it, but organisms are also always adapting to themselves. Like environmental details, an organism's current features—its current shape and resulting performance abilities—can make a difference in what types of future modifications win or lose. Although there may be many ways to skin a cat, once a certain approach has been taken, future modifications will be evaluated in terms of whether they facilitate or debilitate this particular approach.

To better illustrate this point, let's return to the example of an insect species living amid an insectivorous bird. Although there are many ways that an insect could better avoid being eaten, once a certain approach begins to take shape—say looking like a twig—all further modifications will be evaluated in terms of helping or hurting this approach. Helping could happen in one of three ways: elaborate, coordinate, or compensate.

For an insect that begins to look like a twig, any modification of its external appearance will be evaluated in terms of whether it makes it look more or less twiglike. More twiglike is an *elaboration*. It is not a new disguise, just an improvement on the disguise already employed. Unless additional costs are created in some other way, elaborations should translate into greater reproductive success. They improve an organism's ability to do what it is already doing.

Fooling a bird into viewing an insect as a twig, hence passing it by, involves more than just appearance. An insect would not only need to look like a twig, but it would also need to act like one, and twigs do not move around a lot or bend in certain ways.,As we discuss much later, movement is under the control of the nervous system. So nervous system modifications that alter its movements to better simulate a twig may be more successful at reproducing than the ancestral type. The *coordination* between the workings of the nervous system and the external appearance has been improved.

Although looking and standing like a stick may help members of this insect species from getting nabbed by birds, it likely creates other problems. Maybe the combination of appearance and behavior increases this organism's tendency to lose water, raising the threat of death via dehydration. If so, the stage is now set for modification that helped block water loss to be favored by natural selection. Such change would help *compensate* for newly arising problems. For example, some form of circulatory system is found in every multicellular animal that grows beyond a certain size. But it is increasing size, not circulatory systems, that is a potential adaptation because becoming larger is one dimension by which animals can change their relationship with their environment. Yet becoming larger also causes problems, and one of the major ones is getting needed resources to and waste products away from all its cells. Circulatory systems are the way larger organisms have compensated for this problem.

Stating that natural selection evaluates each new heritable modification in terms of elaboration, coordination, and compensation means that along with the environment, the details of the organism being modified can make a difference in the outcome of every reproductive race. Every modification is evaluated in terms of whether it hurts or helps the cohesion with which an organism's different parts function.

This is where *history* enters the realm of biological evolution. Whenever a modification enters and persists within a population, it becomes part of the current organism's details that may make a difference in the fate of the next modification. Each newly arising modification is evaluated in terms of the modifications that came and persisted before, and those modifications were evaluated in terms of the modifications that came and persisted before that, and so on. The entire sequence in which modifications entered any population is the evolutionary history of each of this population's current members. This history, along with environmental circumstance, can make a difference in how the population evolves in the future.

Cumulative evolution

Earlier we dismissed the idea of the inheritance of acquired characters or Lamarckian inheritance. Nonetheless it is significant that in the early 1800s Lamarck used his conception of inheritance in attempt to explain how large differences between organisms could evolve through an accumulation of smaller changes. In doing so he introduced the notion of cumulative evolution. The classic Lamarckian evolutionary scenario concerns the development of long necks in giraffes. A brief synopsis: Ancestral giraffes with short necks fed on tree foliage. Due to competition with other ancestral giraffes, the foliage at the height that all could reach was in short supply. In response, some giraffes stretched to feed even higher. Stretching lengthened their necks, and this trait was then passed on to their offspring by Lamarckian inheritance. In subsequent generations individuals stretched their necks incrementally further to reach foliage that others could not reach, and each time this increased neck length was passed on. With time the necks reached the length found in present-day giraffes.

The modern version of this giraffe scenario still maintains that a longer neck could have a reproductive advantage as a result of decreased competition for food. What changes is the mechanism by which longer necks would have entered the population. Instead of ancestral giraffes stretching and then passing this increased neck length on, past individuals are thought to have experienced random mutations that on rare occasions prodded necks to grow at least a little longer. Of course, it is assumed that it could have also gone the other way. Due to their unplanned and undirected nature, mutations that acted to decrease neck growth would have also been expected to pop up in the population periodically. But this is where the nonrandom scrutiny of natural selection would have stepped in. Once any sort of heritable variation in neck length arose, it would have entered into a performance-based reproductive race. Only modifications in neck shape that further enhance reproductive success would have been expected to persist. Accordingly, any shorter-necked variant that arose would be expected to have lost and gone extinct. On the other hand, due to increased ability to gather food some early longer-necked variant would have been expected to enjoy increased reproductive success, and subsequently become increasingly common within the population. This in fact could be the end of the story if a single genetic changed caused neck growth to leap from a short-necked ancestor to as long as a modern giraffe. But that is a lot to ask for a single genetic change. So the alternative version is that the same scenario was replayed many times—that is, mutations that affected neck growth continued to be introduced, and selection continued to eliminate shorter-necked variants and favor longer-necked variants. As a consequence, increasing neck length continued to build on its past. And with time, relatively short beginnings reached the length found in present-day giraffes.

Of course, the preceding story cannot be the whole story. Necks getting longer created the need for other changes. For example, increasing neck length increases the distance between the heart and the head. As a consequence, the heart is also going to need to get stronger (hence larger) to compensate for the fact that getting an adequate blood supply to the brain entails pushing blood up a greater distance against gravity. Yet a stronger heart leads to higher blood pressure (a giraffe's normal blood pressure is around twice as high as a humans), which increases the risk of aneurysms, or other forms of blood vessel failures. So blood vessels are also going need to be modified. And the list goes on. Some of these changes may have needed to evolve through the combination of random mutations and natural selection. Others may have occurred simply by the developmental dynamics of use and disuse. Changing a body's shape in one way will change how connected parts are used during growth and development, which in turn will steer these connected parts to develop in ways better able to fit with the original change.

Nonetheless, we are now in a position to see that biological evolution (via the combination of random mutation and natural selection) is not just about change; it is about each change refining, adjusting, or building on past change. In other words, this combination is a means by which change can accumulate across generations—cumulative evolution. Despite the random nature of mutations, how such accumulation proceeds is anything but haphazard. Change tends to accumulate in ways that aids the task of reproduction in the context of the details of this population's history and environmental circumstance.

It is biological evolution's cumulative nature that potentially turns the seemingly impossible into the plausible. As we have mentioned, all present-day organisms are too complex of arrangements to have come about by chance. Not only are organisms complex, but they are also complex in extraordinary and marvelous ways. Each single organism has an incredible number of cohesively working parts. Even the simplest bacterium is a performance that quickly overloads the human mind with its array of details. And complexity builds from there: Nervous systems that coordinate a tremendous array of motor activities, immune systems able to recognize and remove bacteria and other invading organisms in a wide spectrum of ways, and eyes that focus across a broad range of distance are just a few examples. Layered on top of this comes the intricate ways organisms have come to contend with environmental details. To continue with a previous example, not only are there insects that sort of look like leaves, and rocks, and bird droppings, and other things that insectivorous birds do not eat, but there are also insects that look like these things down to an extraordinary level of detail. An evolutionary explanation thus demands that every organism found today started from simpler beginnings and then accumulated complexity over time. It also demands that each step toward increasing complexity, of whatever form, be relatively small, hence plausible, and that each step facilitated reproduction. Random mutation and natural selection, in the context of environmental circumstance and past evolutionary history, potentially meets these requirements. That is not to say that this is the means by which present organisms came to be, but it does form the framework of a plausible naturalistic explanation. To explore further how cumulative evolution can potentially explain the evolution of complexity, I highly recommend the first three chapters of a book entitled *The Blind Watchmaker* by Richard Dawkins.

An aside: Although cumulative evolution—via the repeated combination of natural selection working on sources of random heritable variation—can potentially generate complex and amazingly functional designs, it is not a designer that sets out to solve new problems with completely new sets of solutions. Instead, in the words of Francois Jacob, biological evolution is a tinkerer. It works by continually sifting through random mutations within, along with novel combinations between, existing genes. Keeping only those that generate interactions that work.

> The action of natural selection has often been compared to that of an engineer. This comparison, however, does not seem suitable. First . . . the engineer works according to a preconceived plan. Second, an engineer who prepares a new structure does not necessarily work from older ones. The electric bulb does not derive from the candle, nor does the jet engine descend from the internal combustion engine. . . . Finally, the objects thus produced de novo by the engineer, at least by the good engineer, reach the level of perfection made possible by the technology of the time.

> In contrast to the engineer, evolution does not produce innovations from scratch. It works on what already exists, either transforming a system to give it a new function or combining several systems to produce a more complex one. If one wanted to use a comparison, however, one would have to say that his process resembles not engineering but tinkering, bricolage we say in French. While the engineer's work relies on having the raw materials and the tools that exactly fit his project, the tinkerer manages with odds and ends. . . . He uses whatever he finds around him, old cardboards, pieces of string, fragments of wood or metal, to make some kind of workable object. The tinkerer picks up an object that happens to be in his stock and gives it an unexpected function. Out of an old car wheel, he will make a fan; from a broken table a parasol. (Francois Jacob, *The Possible and the Actual*, 1982)

Natural selection and sexual reproduction

As discussed in Chapter 4, reproducing sexually adds complications to the task of reproduction. Specifically, three more things need to be accomplished: (1) sexual organisms must get a mate, (2) the work of parental provisioning must somehow be divided among the two parents, and (3) offspring of two different types need to be produced—males and females. Because there are potentially different ways to try to get a mate, to divvy up the workload, or to invest in the production of males and females, and because some ways may be more successful than others may, sexual reproduction itself can make a difference in how organisms evolve. Here I spend a little time exploring how. Although it is number two on the preceding list, I start by discussing factors involved in how parents divvy up the task of caring for their offspring.

Who provides the needed care?

Although there are exceptions, across all species females tend to invest more than males in each offspring. Which raises an interesting question: How do males of different species get away with investing less?

The answer starts with the fact that females are by definition the gender that produces larger, more nutritionally laden gametes. Furthermore, in many species an offspring hatching from a fertilized egg has little or no chance of surviving without further care. So each parent's reproductive success (the success with which they produce offspring that survive to breed in the next generation) depends on at least one of the parents providing further assistance. But which parent should provide the care? The egalitarian view would be that each should parent cooperate with the other so that the work can be split equally between the two parents. But among the species providing postfertilization care, such equal division occurs only rarely.

The lack of cooperation stems from the fact that within a sexual population males are caught in a reproductive race with other males, and females are caught in a reproductive race with other females. This within-gender reproductive race—known as **sexual selection**—introduces an element of conflict between mates. For example, a male type that cooperates in the sense that it acts in a way that maximize the reproductive success of its female partner will not persist in the population if males acting in other less-cooperative ways are more reproductively successful. The cooperative male type would lose out in the reproductive race. The same is true for females. And cooperation will never be either gender's first choice. The best way for parents of either sex to maximize their reproductive success would be to abandon their current offspring and spend that time trying to find (and then reproduce with) a new mate, *so long as the other parent remains behind and supplies their current offspring with the needed care.* The problem is that all offspring will die if both parents leave. So the question of which gender within any species will supply more of the postnatal care boils down to which gender is more likely to be caught in a situation where their best reproductive option is to care for their offspring.

The answer depends on an interaction of several factors, including (1) which gender is caught in the position where they cannot be the first to abandon their offspring; (2) which gender has more to lose because it has already invested more in their current offspring; (3) which gender has poorer reproductive opportunities if it leaves; and (4) which gender has more confidence in the paternity or maternity of the current offspring. In most species, the answer to each of these questions leans toward females. For instance, consider species where fertilization occurs within the female (known as internal fertilization). A female cannot quickly abandon her developing offspring because the fertilized eggs are held within her body. In contrast, once a male deposits its sperm within a female, he is free to go. Furthermore, even after copulating with a female, a male can never be completely certain that all the offspring developing within the female's body are his. A female could mate with more than one male, which means another male's sperm may fertilize some portion of her eggs. So once a male has inseminated a female, it is the male that has both more options and more uncertainty. He could stay around and help care for the offspring after they come out of the female's body (as either eggs or live-born offspring). Alternatively, the male could abandon its current female partner to pursue other females, or he could just "hang out" and focus his efforts on trying to survive to the next breeding season. The fact that across all species with internal fertilization males rarely provide extensive parental care suggests that it is quite common for one of the latter two options to be the most reproductively successful male strategy. In such cases the females are clearly more involved in caretaking. It is, however, noteworthy that in a few species (even some with internal fertilization) the exact opposite takes place—the female deserts and the male assumes further care. Can you think of circumstances that could potentially lead to this reversal?

Sage grouse and laysan albatrosses where first introduced to make the point that feeding behavior could make a difference in life-history characters. But note that male parental behavior is also influenced. Given that in laysan albatrosses it is difficult for both parents working together to raise a single offspring, it would be impossible for a female to raise an offspring alone. Males deserting after copulation would never be a winning male strategy, as their reproductive success would always be zero. Instead, male laysan albatrosses are intensely involved in all aspects of postcopulation parental care (incubation and feeding). On the other hand, given that sage grouse offspring feed themselves after hatching, it is not obvious how much a male hanging around and helping could increase its reproductive success. Helping the female incubate eggs or brood and protect them after hatching may have little effect on how many offspring can be successfully raised. In fact it may even be a detriment. Predation is a constant threat for sage grouse, and a second parent hanging around is just one more thing to attract a predator's attention. So it makes sense that males forgo any attempt at helping raise offspring and spend their effort attempting to attract other mates.

Something to consider: Recall that sage grouse males gather in groups called leks, which are also found in other animals, to perform courtship displays. But why do the males gather together? Was the evolution of leks driven by females? If females that preferred to mate with males in groups were able to overall pick better males—because they could compare and contrast different males before deciding with whom to mate—the trait could spread in the population. And once it spreads, males would be, in essence, coerced to gather into groups to display. Otherwise they would have very little chance of mating. So although sage grouse males effectively desert females after copulation, females may still have manipulated male reproductive behavior.

Getting mates

The mating obstacle has a unique component—mutual consent. Within each sexual population every member, be it male or female, is simultaneously a judge and a contestant. The judge gives or denies consent; the contestant is given or is denied consent. Stated differently, members of one sex become the mating obstacle for members of the opposite sex.

This obstacle influences how the population as a whole evolves whenever a mating bias shows up in either sex. A **mating bias** is when variation exists within a sex, and some types are more successful at getting mates than others. Such bias could exist for one of two reasons. First, some types may be better at competing with other members of the same sex for mates. For example, during the rutting season, male elk (bulls) and male deer (bucks) fight with each other, and the better fighters tend to be able to gather and defend a larger harem of females. Second, individuals of one sex may have a mating preference, and consent is granted more readily to one type than another.

Here I focus on the evolution of, and the evolutionary effects of, mating biases. I concentrate, in particular, on mating biases that result from the females in a population having a mating preference. Although both sexes simultaneously act as judges and contestants, it is generally thought that females tend to be pickier than males because (as discussed earlier) females invest more than males in each offspring. As a consequence, they tend to have more to lose if they make a bad choice.

In species where males participate in parental care, a male can help a female produce offspring in two ways: it can be *good provider*, and/or it can contribute *good genes*. A good provider effectively helps with the chores of providing food and protection until offspring can care for themselves. Contributing good genes means that they contain genetic information that has positive effects on an off-

spring's ability to grow, develop, and survive to reproduction. In species where males do not participate in parental care, a male can only aid a female by providing *good genes*. In such species the only
contribution males make to their offspring is sperm, and sperm only contribute genetic information.

In either case, differences in male quality within a population set the stage for evolution of a
female mating preference. To start consider a sexual population where the females lack a mating preference—once a female is ready to mate it mates with the first male to come along. As a consequence,
females mate on average with males of average quality. Now let's introduce a mutation into this population that causes those females carrying this mutation to have a mating preference—that is, they use
criteria other than the first available male to pick a mate. All else being equal (that is, there is not extra
cost associated with being picky), when would this mutation be expected to increase in frequency
within the population? The simple answer is that if this mating preference tends to preferentially pick
males that are better-than-average providers and/or have better-than-average genes. By picking better-
than-average males the selective females should enjoy better-than-average reproductive success. As a
consequence, this mutation would be expected to win the reproductive race with its alternative—the
absence of a mating preference.

For example, females in some fish-eating birds called terns—of which there are several species—
seem to exhibit a mating preference concerned with picking a good provider. In terns, both males and
females are involved in provisioning. During courtship a male puts on an acrobatic flying display that
concludes with bringing the courted female a fish. By accepting the fish, the female lets the male know
that it has been accepted as a mate. The male's prior performance hints of being a tryout. Catching fish
depends on great aerial deftness, and demonstrations of flying skill, in addition to catching a fish, may
be good indicators of a male's future skill as a provider.

Although tryouts may be a way to assess a male's quality as a provider, such qualities are irrelevant when males do not participate in parental care. Here the evolution of a female mating preference seems to only make sense if a female can somehow pick males with better genes. The problem,
of course, is that a female cannot directly examine a male's genes. They can only look at a male's
phenotype, whose development was influenced by the male's genotype. But what aspect of a male's
phenotype would indicate the presence of genes relevant to the success of her offspring? The most
obvious would be looking healthy. A female attracted to healthy looking males is a female being attracted to a male that is physically capable of capturing adequate nutrition, avoiding predators, and
resisting disease (unless a male can somehow fake a healthy look). All of which are traits that would
be beneficial to a female's offspring. Perhaps genetic quality could also be accessed by the presence
of certain physical traits associated with being good at whatever a particular species tends to do. For
example, in a species where running is important, physical traits such as limb length or muscle tone
provide snapshots of running ability.

Although mating preferences for healthy physically capable males is known to occur, curiously
the evolution of mating preferences does not, however, seem to always be so straightforward. In many
species it seems that females prefer males whose contribution detracts from an offspring's ability to
negotiate the obstacles of growth, development, and survival to reproduction. Consider, for example,
female preference in guppies (*Poecilia reticulata*)—a fish species found in the wild in parts of the
Caribbean and South America, and in fish tanks. Guppies are strikingly sexually dimorphic. Males
are smaller but much more brightly colored than females. And females seem to prefer to mate with
males—which only contribute genes to their offspring—bearing the brightest coloration. Bright coloration, however, has the adverse effect of making males more conspicuous to predators. And because
male color pattern is somewhat heritable a female choosing to mate with the brightest colored male is
making a choice that decreases her son's survivability.

The obvious question raised is: How could such a mating preference ever evolve? Wouldn't any
alternative form of preference that picked males that did not negatively effect her son's survival be

expected to win the reproductive race? The answer is not always. Next I use a tale of tails to explain one way that this could happen.

Consider a population of birds where the males are basically all the same, and the females have no mating preference. Now let's introduce two new modified types (see Figure 6-10). One modification increases the tail length of male birds, which turns out to improve their flying ability so that they can better capture food and escape from predators. The other modification generates females who prefer to mate with longer-tailed males. Given that one modification improves male performance whereas the other increases the probability that a female will mate with a higher-quality male, both these modifications would be expected to increase in frequency in the population, and in this story they do. The population evolves toward longer-tailed males and females with a mating preference.

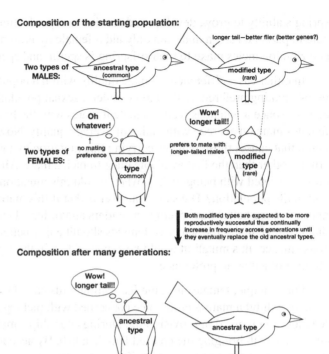

Figure 6-10. How the population described in the text would be expected to evolve across generations.

The story continues with the previously modified types taking over the population so that they are now the ancestral type. Now let's introduce another modification that leads to the development of males with even longer tails. The difference from before is that this further increase in tail length actually begins to encumber flight, so that these even-longer-tailed males are worse fliers. At first glance it seems that this new modified type would be expected to go extinct. How could they be more successful at reproducing than the better-flying ancestral type? But something new is brewing. These even-longer-tailed males are being introduced into a population where most, if not all, the females prefer to mate with males with the longest tails. In other words, the female mating preference is relative—the females prefer to mate with the males bearing the most exaggerated form of the preferred trait. So although these even-longer-tailed males will be worse than the ancestral male type at everything that involves flying, they will tend to be better at getting mates. This sets up an interesting form of cost-benefit scenario along the reproductive obstacle course. Whenever the mating benefit is

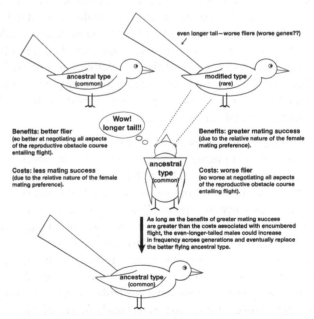

Figure 6-11. The conditions under which a newly modified male type could increase in frequency across generations despite the fact that its longer tail encumbers all aspects of flight-based performance.

greater than the costs associated with encumbered flight, then these even-longer-tailed males would be expected to increase in frequency and eventually replace the ancestral male type (see Figure 6-11).

In other words, once the longer-tailed male preference becomes common, the stage is set for male tail length to evolve even further. Genetic modifications resulting in males with even longer tails, tails that begin to encumber flight, will receive the benefits of female preference. And as long as costs associated with encumbered flight do not exceed the mating benefits, these longer-tailed but poorer-flying males are expected to reproduce relatively faster and eventually replace their shorter-tailed competitors. Each new mutation resulting in increasing tail length is evaluated similarly. The whole process will halt only when increased tail length becomes so encumbering that, in comparison to the previous tail length, the benefits of preference do not outweigh other costs.

Is there any evidence that relative mating preferences exist in nature? One of the best actually exists with birds and tail length. Recall the experiment discussed in Chapter 1 where tail length was manipulated in male long-tailed widowbirds, which normally have around a five-inch-long body and a twenty-inch-long tail. The fact more females chose to nest in the territories of the males with the longest tails (30-inch-long tails created by supergluing extra tail feathers on otherwise normal males) suggests that females in this species seem to have a relative preference for longer tails. But if this is the case, why haven't males evolved 30-inch-long tails or even longer? It could be that they are still in the process of evolving longer tails. But it is also possible that when tails increased beyond 20 or so inches, the costs of encumbered flight across the entire year begin to outweigh the mating benefits.

Putting this tale of tails in more general terms, the fact that potential mates are part of the same sexual population adds a new twist in terms of how history can make a difference. As more and more of the females prefer a male of a certain type, the reproductive success of male offspring depends more and more on whether they bear the specific features preferred by most females, regardless of whether that feature is longer tails, shorter tails, displaying a certain color pattern, producing some odor, having a specific type of call, or anything else. Furthermore, whenever the female mating prefer-

ence is *relative*, the benefit of being the most preferred male type in the population will always go to any males bearing a modification that further exaggerates the preferred trait. The cost of not being the most preferred is shifted to the previously most exaggerated, hence previously most preferred, male form. This shifting of benefits and costs sets the stage for increasingly exaggerated male types to repeatedly win the reproductive race against their less-exaggerated rivals, even when more-exaggerated forms are worse at surviving.

Furthermore, any form of mating preference becomes increasingly *self-reinforcing* as it becomes increasingly common. Any female who picks otherwise puts her sons at a reproductive disadvantage. Her sons will not develop the features preferred by most of the females in the population, so they will find it relatively more difficult to get a mate. As a consequence, once a

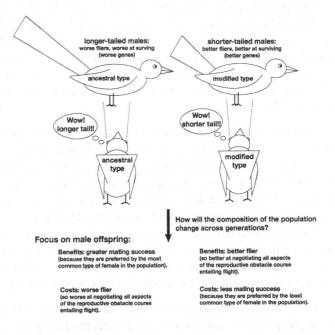

Figure 6-12. The self-reinforcing nature of any form of female choice once it becomes common.

form of mating preference becomes common, its commonness makes it more difficult for alternative forms of preference to replace it in the future—even if the new form of preference picks males that better contribute to offspring growth, development, and survival. The positive contribution to off-spring would need to be more than compensated for by the increased cost experienced during mating (see Figure 6-12). A common form of preference can thus maintain a trade-off between being good at getting mates and being good at some other aspect of reproduction, say survival.

The bottom line is that through the combination of a mating preference's self-reinforcing nature and the preference being relative, sexual populations can generate their own evolutionary momentum. As it does so, a sexual population becomes an evolutionary version of a runaway train. In fact, this snowballing process is commonly called **runaway selection**. Just as runaway trains do not stop at the place best for the passengers inside, sexual populations caught in runaway selection do not stop evolv-ing at the place best for the persistence of the population as a whole. They plow past the point where females prefer to mate with males that best contribute to their offspring's survival, instead creating a trade-off between mating and survival. Consider this scenario the next time you look at a male pea-cock. It is even possible that the internally generated momentum of runaway selection could carry a population to extinction.

Sex allocation

It takes resources to produce offspring. In sexual populations these resources must somehow be divided between male and female offspring—a topic termed sex allocation. The most basic natural selection question that accompanies sex allocation is what sort of proportional allocation between the sexes maximizes an individual's reproductive success. To consider the simplest case possible, let's assume that male and female offspring cost the same. The question then boils down to what sex ratio would maximize reproductive success.

One possible choice would be to produce more females than males. The seeming advantage to this is that it maximizes the reproductive potential of the population. Some males need to be around, but it is the female of any species that, in essence, produces offspring. Clearly in a population of 10, 9 females and 1 male can produce more offspring than 5 females and 5 males or 1 female and 9 males. But would this investment strategy be a natural selection winner against all potential competitors? Or put into evolutionary biology speak: Is investing more in females than males an **evolutionary stable strategy** (ESS)?

Because of the increased reproductive potential, one may be inclined to answer yes. The answer, however, is actually no. The no answer stems from a simple truth: Every sexual individual has both a mom and a dad. Within a population each sex always contributes an equal number of offspring to the next generation. (Of course, some males may be more successful at fathering offspring than other males, and likewise female reproductive success may vary. But the success of either sex, in total, is al-ways equal.) So, whenever a population's sex ratio is unequal, individuals of the rarer sex will tend to be more reproductively successful. The same number offspring divided by fewer individuals results in a larger number. In a population of fewer males, for example, each male must on average inseminate more than one female for all potentially reproductive females to reproduce. Males in this population would enjoy relatively more reproductive success than females.

Every offspring having a mom and a dad adds a new twist to the question of sex allocation. When-ever a population sex ratio is unequal, parents producing offspring of the rare gender will (on average) have reproductively more successful children. This is why producing mostly females is not an ESS. Introduce a heritable son-only producing variant into a population that produces mostly females, and until the population's sex ratio equalizes, offspring of the son-only producing variant would tend to re-alize greater reproductive success. Thus, when rare, the son-only producing variant would be expected to increase in the population. Reverse the situation, and a population that produces mostly sons could be invaded by a daughter-only producing variant. This symmetry points to the form of sex allocation that can beat all comers—produce, on average, equal numbers of males and females. In other words, sex-determining mechanisms that tend to produce a balance of males and females will be favored by natural selection. It is, thus, no surprise that the primary (at conception) sex ratio of most sexual organisms is near 50:50.

Frequency dependence

The two previous examples are both examples of **frequency dependent selection**—among the competing types, the type expected to win changes as the composition of the population changes. The self-reinforcing nature of mating preferences is an example of **positive frequency dependence**—the more common a type becomes, the greater the advantage it has over its competitors. Sex allocation, on the other hand, is an example of **negative frequency dependence**—the advantage enjoyed by one competing type diminishes as it increases in frequency.

Natural selection and helping behavior

Suppose that a heritable modification that affects behavior enters a population. Specifically, it results in an individual inclined to help another individual in the same population such as sharing food. How would such behavior fare in the reproductive races of natural selection? It is an intriguing question because it is asking whether self-sacrificing behaviors (commonly called altruistic behaviors) can win in a reproductive competition against the alternative of not acting altruistically. In other words, can we expect helping behavior to be a common feature among different species?

To consider this question, it helps to cast altruistic behaviors in cost-benefit terms. An altruistic act is where an individual gives up something at a cost to itself to benefit someone else. Stated differently, altruism is an interaction where the costs and benefits are split among individuals, with all the benefits going to the recipient of the help and all the costs going to the donor of the help (the altruist). To fit this into the realm of evolutionary biology, the costs and benefits must translate into effects on reproductive success, and the two interacting individuals are confined to being in the same population.

Acting altruistically will never spread through a population via natural selection if the costs of the altruistic act exceed the benefits. But what if benefits exceed costs? For example, suppose that a food-sharing individual only does so when it presently has an adequate food supply and gives food only to individuals currently in short supply. Giving away some of an already adequate food supply bears little costs to the donor, yet for an individual on the brink of starvation the benefits of some extra food would be high. Would such behavior be expected to spread via natural selection? Would this population be expected to become a population filled with small-cost, high-benefit food sharers? It seems so obvious that the answer should be yes. After all by maximizing potential benefits, the reproductive success of the entire population would go up, increasing the chance that the population as a whole would persist. Stated differently, such behavior would contribute to the survival of the species. There is only one problem—the answer is likely no.

Trying to understand how the answer could be no is a great exercise in selection thinking. It makes you come to grips with why reproductive competition within a population is not always expected to lead to the evolution of traits that would best help the population to persist. And the reason centers on a familiar notion: Persistence depends on loopiness, and helping behaviors may fail due to a lack of sufficient loopiness.

The degree of loopiness

To start, imagine a scenario where we have two teams engaged in a game of evolutionary basketball: the altruistic *Superiors* and the selfish *Inferiors*. The altruistic *Superiors* are much better, but for every two-point basket they score they give one-half their points (or one point) to the selfish *Inferiors* (who never give any of their points to the *Superiors*). If the altruistic *Superiors* score 50 baskets, how many baskets do the selfish *Inferiors* have to score to win the game? Answer: One. A team giving up half its points to its opponents can never come out ahead. An opponent who scores no points will still tie. An opponent that scores one or more points will win. So in a game where the *Superiors* score 100 points (50 baskets) and the *Inferiors* score only 2 points (1 basket) the final score will be: *Superiors* 50, *Inferiors* 52.

But what about scenarios where the altruists give up less than half of their benefits? In such cases which type (team) will win is not as easy to keep track of without

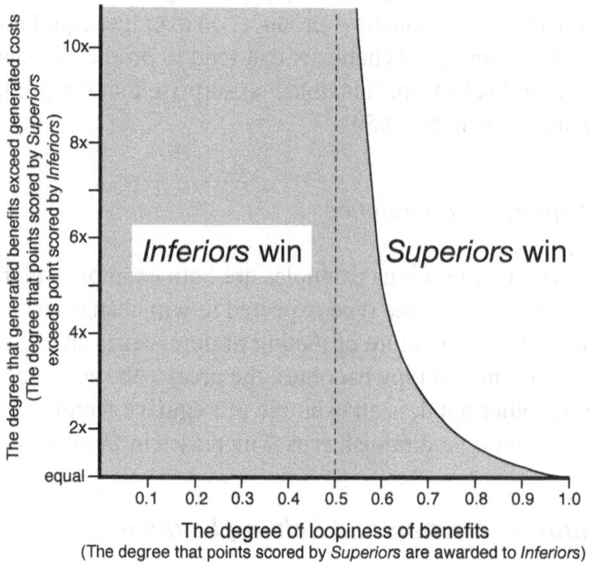

Figure 6-13. A graph that shows the how sharing benefits with a competitor gan greatly alter the outcome of the competition . As loopiness of benefits for one competitor decreases towards 0.5 the degree to which its must be better that its competitor to still win increases rapidly. Once the degree of loopiness decreases to 0.5 or beyond, winning is impossible.

developing the logic mathematically. The following equation (whose derivation is explained in Appendix I) does just that.

$$(2 \cdot L_b - 1) \cdot B_g > C_g \qquad (1)$$

Continuing with the basketball analogy, each team's **generated benefits** (B_g) are the points they score. Each team's **generated costs** (C_g) are the points it allowed the opposing team to score. The **degree of loopiness** (L_b) is the proportion of a team's points scored that loop back to their side of the scoreboard.

This equation reaffirms the obvious point made earlier. If the altruistic *Superiors* give half their points to their opponent ($L_b = 1/2$), they can never win. When $L_b = 1/2$ then $2L_b - 1 = 0$, and equation (1) reduces to $0 > C_g$, which is an expression that can never be satisfied.

L_b must exceed **1/2** for it to be even possible for the *Superiors* to win. Yet when L_b is greater than one-half but still less than one (that is, $1/2 \leq L_b < 1$), winning requires more than just the *Superiors* outscoring their opponents. For example, if $L_b = 3/4$ the *Superiors* need to score more than twice as many points as the *Inferiors* to win. (Substitute $L_b = 3/4$ into equations and it reduces to $B_g > 2C_g$.) And the needed point differential keeps increasing rapidly as L_b drops from there (see Figure 6-13). Just reducing L_b to **5/8** raises the winning differential to four times as many points. (Substitute $L_b = 5/8$ into equations, and it reduces to $B_g > 4C_g$.)

Indiscriminate altruism is never expected to evolve

To be an indiscriminate altruism is to come to the aid of any member of one's population in need (where need is defined as any instance where the benefits to recipient are greater than costs to the altruist). It is the complete opposite of selfish, self-centered behavior. A population of indiscriminate altruists would be a completely cooperative society. The only problem is that indiscriminate altruism is never expected to evolve via natural selection. In distributing the benefits of their actions equally among all members of the same population, indiscriminate altruists would help out their competitors (any individuals that do not act altruistically) as much as they would help out other individuals of the same type (other individuals that will act altruistically whenever the opportunity arises). From our earlier discussion, this means that $L_b = 1/2$, and as already mentioned, putting that value in Equation 1 yields $0 > C_g$—a condition that can never be satisfied. Indiscriminate altruism is always expected to lose the reproductive race of natural selection Figure 6-14(a) portrays this same notion in a different way.

Put in terms of the food-sharing example discussed earlier: Any nonaltruists in the population gain full advantage of the altruists' generosity when their food is in short supply, but because they never share food, they never share the costs of returning the favor. This gives the nonaltruists a competitive advantage. In essence, by helping their competitors as much as themselves, indiscriminate altruists help themselves to extinction.

A closer look

Although I just argued that indiscriminate altruism is not expected to evolve via natural selection, many seemingly altruistic acts have been observed among social interactions in many different species. Some of the well-known examples are

• One family member caring for another family member when it is young, sick, etc.

• One individual helping another individual find a mate.

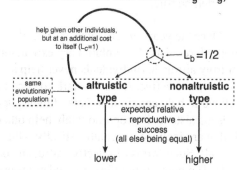

(a) indiscriminate altruism (where benefits to recipient of altruistic act exceed costs to donor—$B_g > C_g$)

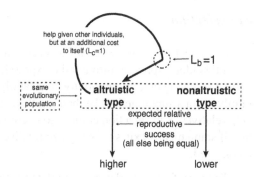

(b) perfectly selective altruism ($B_g > C_g$)

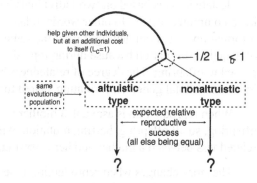

(c) partially selective altruism ($B_g > C_g$)

Figure 6-14. Three examples of how the degree to which altruistic acts are selective (extended toward other altruists) can effect the outcome of natural selection—that is, which type is expected to win the reproductive race. Indiscriminate altruism (a) is always expected to lose, completely selective altruism (b) is always expected to win, and whether partially selective altruism is expected to win or lose depends the interaction between the degree to which altruism is selective (L_b) and the degree to which the benefits to the recipients of altruist acts exceed the costs to the donor.

• One individual calling out to warn others of approaching predators. This act would be altruistic whenever the calling individual's risk of being captured by the predator is greater than if it had not made the warning call. Given that the call may also attract the predator's attention, this could often be true.

Over the years observations such as these have raised more than a few eyebrows among evolutionary biologists. An evolutionary explanation demanded that these observed interactions were either not truly altruistic (individuals never help another at a cost to themselves), or the altruism was at least somewhat selective. Altruism starts to become selective whenever altruistic individuals are more inclined to help certain members of their population more than others. If this ever occurs in a way that leads altruists to disproportionately help other individuals of the same type—that is, other individuals that are inclined to act altruistically—then the degree of loopiness of benefits would rise above one-half. Such forms of selective altruism could thus possibly evolve via natural selection (see Figure 6-14). The most straightforward and seemingly the most prevalent mechanism of selective altruism uncovered to date is referred to as **kin selection.**

Kin selection

Kin selection occurs when altruists confine their helping behavior to relatives. You may have heard this idea expressed through the expression: blood is thicker than water—that is, if you are going to help someone out, preferentially help family. Such selective altruism is easily orchestrated when family groups stay together. By helping those individuals that live in close proximity, one will tend to help relatives. Kin selection could also occur when family members disperse throughout the population if some means exists to recognize relatives. That way altruist acts can be reserved for only those recognized.

The very fact that relatives are related is the reason that kin selection increases the degree of loopiness of altruistic behaviors beyond one-half. Why this is so, however, requires some explanation.

Relatedness is based on two individuals having the same type of genetic information due to sharing a common ancestor. In other words, relatedness is not just about having the same type of genetic information, but about getting it from the same source. Common ancestry can be a common source of genetic information because during reproduction a parent's genetic information is copied and then passed to offspring. The degree of relatedness between any two individuals is the proportion of each individual's total genetic information shared through common descent. It ranges from 0 to 1

When reproduction is asexual, a mother will copy and pass all her genetic information to each offspring, so all offspring, barring mutation, will receive the same genetic information. The degree of relatedness between a mother and her offspring, or among her offspring, will thus be one.

The story changes when reproduction is sexual because sexual reproduction mixes genetic information (see Chapter 4). The simplest way to view relatedness in sexual populations starts with the realization that mom and dad each contribute one-half of an offspring's genetic makeup, so an offspring's degree of relatedness to either of its parents is always one-half. Each parent only copies and passes one-half of its genetic makeup to any offspring, so a parent's degree of relatedness to its offspring is also always one-half. But this degree of relatedness of one-half between parents and offspring also means there is the probability that any piece of genetic information in a parent has a 50% chance of being copied and passed to an offspring. Furthermore, it means that there is a 50% chance that any piece of genetic information copied and passed from a parent to one offspring will also be copied and passed to another offspring. So for full siblings (i.e., same parents), this translates into a 50% chance that any piece of genetic information can be traced back to a common source. The degree of relatedness for full siblings is thus one-half. In half-sibs (i.e., share one parent) there is still a 50% chance that they share a common source of genetic information from their common parent, but there is no chance of a common source for the half of each sib's genetic makeup contributed by the unshared parent. So, in total, the degree of related for half-sibs is one-fourth. Some other sexual population examples:

• The degree of relatedness between uncles and aunts and their nieces or nephews = 1/4

• The degree of relatedness between first cousins = 1/8

To incorporate how helping only relatives could facilitate the evolution of adaptive altruism suppose that there is some form of genetic information that makes a difference in the development of acting altruistically. If so, any altruist helping a relative *may be* helping a common-descent-based-copy of the same genetic information. The degree of relatedness is the probability that it is *actually* doing so.

Put in mathematical terms, the degree of relatedness (R) is the common descent based probability that an individual is helping another individual of the same type (i.e., $L_b = 1$). Alternatively, $(1 - R)$ is the probability that the individual did not receive the same genetic information through common descent, so it is the probability that helping a relative is no different than helping anyone in the population at large (i.e., $R = 1/2$). Put these two possibilities together, and the overall degree of loopiness associated with helping relatives is

$$L_b = R(1) + (1 - R)(1/2). \tag{2}$$

Note that L_b will be greater than 1/2 whenever R is greater than zero. For instance, $L_b = 3/4$ when helping a sexually produced sibling ($R = 1/2$). On the other hand, $L_b = 1$ when helping a sibling in an asexually reproducing population ($R = 1$).

To make interpretation of kin selection easier, equation (2) can be substituted into equation (1)—which was introduced earlier. After a little algebra, the resultant equation reduces to

$$RB_g > C_g. \tag{3}$$

This equation is known as Hamilton's rule; it is named after the person who first derived it (although he did it differently than I did it here). The key point of Hamilton's rule is that the more closely related an individual helped by an altruist is, the easier it is for this condition to be satisfied. For instance, Hamilton's rule becomes $1/2B_g > C_g$ (or $B_g > 2C_g$) if an altruist helps a full sibling. The benefits to the full sibling helped only need to be twice the costs to the helper for the condition to be satisfied and therefore expected to evolve via natural selection. Yet if an altruist helps its first cousin ($R = 1/8$), Hamilton's rule becomes $1/8B_g > C_g$ (or $B_g > 8C_g$). Only when benefits are over eight times as great as the costs would altruism among cousins be expected to evolve via natural selection. And when helping an unrelated individual, Hamilton's rule becomes $0 > C_g$, which again points out that indiscriminate altruism is not expected to evolve via natural selection.

The take-home message is that *the higher the degree of relatedness between an altruist and those it selectively helps, the more likely such altruism could evolve via natural selection.*

Some possible examples of kin selected altruism

Parental care. The most pervasive case of altruism in the living world is parental care. Each time a parent provides an offspring with any resources, acts to protect it from predators, provides shelter, or provides any other form of care, the behavior is an altruistic act. The benefit of the exchange goes to the offspring, and the cost goes to the parent. Furthermore, early in development when offspring are extremely vulnerable, benefits to offspring will readily exceed costs to parents by more than the two-to-one margin needed for sexually produced offspring ($R = 1/2$). The only strange part of using parental care as an example of kin-selected altruism is that it does not seem to need any special explanation. Parental care is an essential part of reproduction, and reproduction is an essential component of persistence, so for any type of organism to exist, parental care must be present. But such thinking misses the important point. Any capable adult in a population could provide members of the next generation with its needed care. Kin selection, however, adds the expectation that care will typically be provided by the closest capable relatives available, which generally is a parent. The observation than animals that provide postnatal care typically refuse to care for anyone other than their offspring backs up the idea that parental care has evolved to be selective.

Helpers at the nest. In some species, individuals other than parents have been found to be involved in offspring care. Yet, these examples have only reinforced the idea of kin selection because on closer examination the other care providers have been found to be relatives.

For example, in Florida scrub jays (*Aphelocoma coerulescens*) offspring typically do not disperse right after they fledge. Instead they remain in their parent's territory for at least one year and often several years and help raise other offspring (produced in subsequent years) by bringing food to nestlings, watching for predators, and helping defend their territory against neighboring family groups. From a kin-selection perspective helping to raise siblings is essentially equivalent to raising one's own offspring. Assuming that both parents remain the same, the degree of relatedness is one-half in both cases. Natural selection would thus favor older siblings to remain as so-called helpers at the nest as long as the average number of siblings the individual raises through helping its parents is greater than the number of offspring that it could raise if it ventured off on its own. Curiously, this same behavior is not found in the western scrub jay (*Aphelocoma californica*) and is only rarely found in birds overall. So what is different about Florida scrub jays? To reproduce, a pair of Florida scrub jays need to be able to set up a breeding territory within a habitat type known as scrub. Scrub is a unique vegetation community composed of plants that are adapted to well-drained, sandy, nutrient-poor soil. And in Florida this habitat is limited in area and typically filled up with territories staked out by different family groups. It is thus difficult for a young bird to go off and stake out a suitable territory. As a consequence, staying around for a few years and helping parents may commonly be the more productive option. Hanging out in the natal territory may also accrue other benefits—such as helping them learn parenting skills prior to attempting to raise their own young, increasing their chance of surviving longer due to group protection, and providing an opportunity to take over the parent territory in the advent of a parent's death.

In most insects, young are on their own from the time they hatch. The only parental provisioning is the nutrients supplied within the egg by mom. In contrast, many different species of ants, bees, and wasps—all members of the insect order Hymenoptera—provision their young, called larvae, after hatching. Curiously, among most larva-feeding insects neither mom nor dad are the major providers. Instead, dad typically does nothing, mom specializes in becoming an egg-laying machine—known as a queen—and the early produced daughters continue to hang around as adults and do all the work of feeding and protecting their younger siblings. In other words, in an ant colony or a beehive, older female siblings have become more than just nest helpers, they take over the role of primary caretakers. It is no wonder that they are called *workers*. And typically this is not a transitional role, where at first they are a worker and then later strike out on the own to become an egg-laying queen in another colony. Instead, workers are typically sterile. Thus their only option to contribute to reproduction is helping care for younger siblings. But as I mentioned earlier, caring for siblings can be the reproductive equivalent of caring for your own offspring. So from a kin-selection perspective, it makes sense that this form of caretaking arrangement could evolve under the right circumstances.

This theme of relatives other than parents getting involved in postnatal offspring care extends beyond social insects and a few bird species. In fact, among mammals humans are an interesting example. Among the many curious aspects of humans is that we are the only animal on this planet that develops sexual maturity before becoming independent of parental care. It seems so bizarre. A parent that cannot even take care of itself would never be up to the task of caring for an offspring. All early attempts of reproduction would thus be doomed to failure—that is, unless there was additional help. Although many signs still linger today, some anthropologists have suggested that humans have a long history of being a social breeder. That is, the reproductive unit extended beyond a single female, or even a female with the help of her mate, to a larger family unit. Grandparents, in particular, are thought to have played a particularly important role in helping out younger daughters raise their offspring. Ever thought of day-care providers as hired grandparents?

Cooperative mating. Some male wild turkeys (*Meleagris gallopavo*) do a most altruistic deed. They pair up with another more physically dominant male and then go courting for females. Of course, that alone is not the altruistic part. In fact pairing up with another male has actually been shown to substantially increase reproductive success, in that pairs of males are able to attract more females than males that go courting on their own. The altruist part is that within these pairs only the more dominant male ever copulates with the females. So in effect, the subordinate male is taking on all the costs of displaying for females just to help the other male get mates. But once again kin selection helps explain this behavior. A recent study looked closely at the relatedness of these male pairs. It was found that the pairs of males were either brothers or half-brothers. Subordinate males that pair up with a brother are thus still involved in the business of reproduction, but instead of doing so through their own offspring, they are assisting in the production of nieces and nephews. And taking the degree of relatedness into account ($R = 1/2$ for sibling sharing both parents), two nieces or nephews is equal to one offspring. Given that a subordinate male courting alone has little chance of interesting any females, the evolution of this behavior makes sense. Helping out a more dominant brother is currently the best reproductive choice.

An interesting question that arises from the preceding scenario is this: Why are female turkeys (hens) more inclined to mate with a male courting in a pair, than a male courting alone? Perhaps the answer is as simple as it allows comparison. In turkeys, the males do not participate in any parental care; so a preference for picking among males that can be compared side by side over any single male may have evolved because it helped females assess male quality. This same idea came up earlier when I speculated that females preferring to mate with a male displaying in close proximity to other males could have been a driving force in the evolution of leks, areas where many males gather to display for females. Yet from the male perspective, leks raise a curious issue. Generally, just a few males within a lek get most of the matings. So why would a subordinate male engage in the work and risk of displaying on a lek day after day if it has almost no chance of mating? Maybe kin selection is involved. If the more dominant males are relatives, a subordinate that comes and displays is adding one more male for females to compare, and thus helping the more dominant relatives look even better. This idea is supported by two studies that showed that in black grouse (*Tetrao terix*) and peacocks (*Pavo cristatus*) males were more closely related to males within the same lek than to males at other leks.

Acorn woodpeckers. Acorn woodpeckers (*Melanerpes formicivorus*) are singled out here because they display an intriguingly complicated kin-based social system that, in essence, is based around a dead tree called a granary. Let me explain. Like their name implies, acorns represent a significant part of their diet. To extend their availability, they store acorns in the fall by drilling holes in a dead tree and stuffing acorns in them. This is the granary tree. Of course, acorns stored in this way require constant defense because other acorn woodpeckers can easily steal them. The formation of a cooperative group would thus be favored, as a single individual cannot always be around. And as expected, the group formed is a family group that establishes a territory around the tree. Furthermore, once a hole is drilled it can be used again, so territories around established granary trees, which can have up to 50,000 holes in them, are increasingly valuable. And that is the key. The nature of the acorn woodpecker's complex family group reflects the intense competition created by the limited number of high-quality breeding territories. First off, like Florida scrub jays, young woodpeckers typically stay with their parents for several years and help them raise more young. But the family groups in these wood-

peckers are actually much more complicated than a single breeding pair surrounded by offspring helpers. Instead, there can be up to six breeding males and three breeding females within a single territory.
Moreover, breeding females all lay their eggs in the same nest cavity. Both genders thus show a form
of cooperative mating, and as expected by the kin-selection model the males are brothers or fathers
and their sons, and females are sisters or a mother and her daughter(s). (Note: Breeders of opposite
gender are unrelated and thus avoid reproductive problems associated with incest.) The advantage of
cooperation goes back to competition for limiting nesting sites. When breeders within a territory of
either gender die, nonbreeders from other territories attempt to move in. The competition, however,
can be so intense that a single nonbreeder would have little chance of success. So instead siblings form
coalitions that battle together against other sibling groups in wild affairs called *power struggles*. The
winners become the new group of cobreeders, whereas losers return to their natal territory and resume
being nonbreeding helpers. (Also after a new sibling group takes over, helpers of the opposite gender
are now not related to their potential breeding partners and become cobreeders. This is how parent and
offspring can become cobreeders.)

Cooperation and conflict

The evolution of helping or cooperative (reciprocal helping) arrangements among kin does not
remove the possibility of conflict or disagreement within the group. For instance, in cooperative mating it may benefit male siblings to join forces to gain access to females, but once access is granted, kin
selection cannot lead to the evolution of an agreement of which male should mate. Subordinate male
turkeys in brother pairs never mated, but that was because females did not pick them, not because it
was in their best interest to let their brother do all the mating. In other words, cooperation evolved
because helping produce nieces and nephews is better than not reproducing at all. But the potential
for conflict still remains because producing offspring is reproductively better than producing nieces
and nephews. And in acorn woodpeckers that room for conflict is apparent in the behavior of both
cobreeding males and females. Males have been observed to rush in and attempt to disrupt copulation between one of their brothers (or father or son) and a breeding female. And cobreeding sisters (or
mother or daughter) even destroy each other's eggs. Specifically, before having laid any eggs of her
own, a female will remove any eggs found in the nest despite the fact that inside is a developing niece
or nephew. It is obviously not a daughter or a son. The egg destruction stops only after all the breeding
females have laid one or more eggs. Whose eggs are whose is now not clear. Yet after the mating and
egg laying is done, things calm back into a more cooperative mode. Both males and females incubate
the eggs and, along with nonbreeding helpers, provision the young and guard the territory.

The potential for conflict or disagreement even exists among parents and offspring. Specifically,
because they are equally related to all offspring, a parent would be favored to treat each equally. Yet
from a genetic perspective offspring see it differently. Each offspring is completely related to itself,
yet half related to its parents and its siblings. So natural selection would actually favor the evolution of
means for offspring to bias the distribution of parental care in their favor. This potential for disagreement in how parental resources should be allocated is called the **parent–offspring conflict**. In many
cases, however, this potential disagreement is trivial because the offspring has no means to influence
the allocation. For instance, offspring whose only parental care is the nutrients sealed inside their egg
would have little means of influence. The parental allocation is made shortly after fertilization, so the
offspring have had little time to develop any means to influence allocation. But placental mammals
are different. Here the developing embryo builds a hookup between itself and mom, called a **placenta**,
that gathers needed nutrients. Mom allowing a placenta to invade and feed from her body is clearly
a cooperative arrangement. But the potential for disagreement in terms of how far that cooperation
should extend raises the question: Do placentas ever try to pull more resources out of mom than mom
would be favored to give? And if so, do moms employ means to counter these efforts and thus limit
the placenta's ability to gather resources beyond the maternal optimum? Someone looked at this in

humans and found evidence for both. They even found evidence that the cause of fairly common maladies during pregnancy, such as gestational diabetes, gestational hypertension, or preclampsia, occur when placental actions and maternal counteractions get out of balance. Evidence of parent–offspring conflict is also found in species with postnatal care, as parents are now interacting with larger, physically more capable individuals. Weaning conflict in mammals—that is, offspring continuing to attempt to nurse even after the female parent is shutting it down—is a classic example.

Speciation: Branching Evolution

Here is a quick review of what we have discussed so far: (1) Random mutations can introduce phenotypic modifications in a population. (2) Whether these genetic changes persist across generations depends on the relative reproductive success of the organisms bearing these phenotypic modifications. (3) The details of environmental circumstance can make a difference in the outcome of this reproductive race. (4) The details of the organisms being modified can make a difference in the outcome of this reproductive race. (5) The dynamics of a sexual population can make a difference in the outcome of this reproductive race. Allow these five components to unfold over and over again, and simple beginnings can be converted into a whole lot of complexity. In other words, these ingredients create the framework for naturalistic explanation of how any present-day species came to be. It is also why each species is never done evolving. What we will find tomorrow is somewhat different that what we find today. The very nature of Life makes constant change unavoidable. For example, bacteria types that have recently evolved resistance to some antibiotic are turning up all the time.

Something, though, is still missing. Unless we want to start out each new species with a unique origin of a simple reproductive performance, we need another part to our explanation: A way that an evolving population (species) can branch into two or more distinctly evolving populations. We need to discuss **speciation**—one species becoming two.

Classic view of how speciation in sexual populations occurs

Biological speciation involves two basic steps:

• The first step is isolation. That is, a population is subdivided into two or more isolated units (i.e., mating occurs only among members of the same isolated group).

• The next step is evolution. Through the actions of mutation, natural selection, and genetic drift, each of these isolated subunits evolves independent of each other. If evolution occurs to the point that members of each different subunit cannot or will not interbreed when in proximity to each other, then speciation has occurred.

The type of isolation that is most easy to envision is geographic isolation. Geographic isolation occurs when a species is broken into reproductively isolated populations by the formation of a geographic barrier (e.g., separating continents, rising mountain ranges, rivers changing their course, building a highway). What constitutes a barrier depends on the biology of the organism. What constitutes a barrier to a bird, for example, would be different that what constitutes a barrier to a soil-dwelling insect.

Several factors may contribute to isolated populations following different evolutionary paths. Chance, for instance, may play a role. When a population is split by chance, each subunit does not get the same set of genes in the same frequency. Starting with a somewhat different set of genes may enhance the probability the subunits will evolve along different courses through time. Separated populations also may experience different mutations. Or the separated populations may experience different environmental conditions.

What keeps newly formed species from interbreeding?

Premating isolation is when individuals of one species do not attempt to mate with individuals of the other species. Premating isolation may occur through several means:

• Ecogeographic—geographic barrier removed, but the two species remain geographically isolated because neither can survive in habitat occupied by the other.

• Habitat isolation—ranges of the two species overlap, but each resides in different microhabitats.

• Seasonal isolation—the two species breed at different times of the year.

• Behavioral isolation—some aspect of behavior associated with mating maintains isolation between the two species (e.g., different courting behavior).

• Mechanical isolation—some physical difference inhibits mating between individuals from the two species (e.g., body size difference, insects—different shapes of genitalia).

Postmating isolation is when individuals of different species will still mate with each other, but the mating does not produce viable offspring. The stage at which postmating isolation is realized may vary:

• Gametic isolation—upon mating, fertilization is in some way prevented.

• Developmental isolation—fertilization occurs, but early development cannot proceed normally.

• Hybrid inviability—birth occurs, but the offspring is generally malformed, and often dies before it reaches sexual maturity.

• Hybrid sterility—hybrids develop healthy, vigorous phenotypes, but they are also sterile.

• Selective hybrid elimination—hybrids are somewhat less talented (than nonhybrids of either type) at negotiating the reproductive obstacle course, therefore lose in competition with nonhybrids.

Here is a question to ponder that will test your general understanding of biological evolution: Why will postmating isolation favor the evolution of premating isolation?

Speciation creates common ancestors

When one species undergoes speciation, then two (or more) new species are formed. The original species is now ancestral to the two new ones. Or stated differently, the two new species share a common ancestor—the ancestral species.

Any two species that share a common ancestor are considered to be **related**. How closely related depends on how far back in time the two species branched from their common ancestor. With three species, for example, the two most closely related species are those with the most recent common ancestor. We discuss this idea more in the next chapter.

Appendix I

Put in cost-benefit terms, an altruistic individual generates benefits that are spread to other individuals. Some of those individuals could also be altruists, so the benefit is given to the same type. On the other, an altruist could also spread benefits to another type, hence a competing type, within a population. Here a mathematical expression is developed that keeps track of which of two competing types, specifically altruists and nonaltruists, will win, given the total benefits the actions of each type generates, and the proportion of those benefits that return to the type that generated them. In the parlance of the basketball analogy started in the text, this equation should keep track of which team will win (either *Superiors* or *Inferiors*), given the points that each team scores and the proportion of each team's points awarded to them on the scoreboard.

The first step is to separate both benefits and costs into two categories: those **generated** and those **received**. The two are connected by what I term the **degree of loopiness** (L). An individual's **generated benefits** (B_g) are all its performance differences that positively contribute to reproduction within the population in comparison to its competitors. The **received benefits** (B_r), on the other hand, are the proportion of those generated benefits that loop back to either the same individual that generated them or to any other individual of the same type. Stated mathematically, $B_r = L_b \cdot B_g$, where L_b is the degree of loopiness of benefits. L_b can range between **0** and **1**. When $L_b = 1$, all benefits generated by an individual return to the same individual or others of the same type ($B_r = B_g$). This ceases to be true when $L_b < 1$. This raises an important question: When benefits generated by an individual do not loop back to the same type, where do they go? The answer: They go to and therefore help out competing types within the same population. For example, when L_b is equal to **1/2**, the generated benefits are equally distributed between the type that generated them and competing types. When L_b is between **1** and **1/2**, the generated benefits preferentially go toward the type that generated them, but some still go to competitors. On the other hand, when L_b is less than **1/2** the benefits preferentially go to one's competitors. In fact when L_b is equal to **0**, all generated benefits go to one's competitors.

The same relationship holds for costs. An individual's **generated costs** (C_g) are all performance differences that negatively contribute to reproduction within the population in comparison to its competitors. And the **realized costs** (C_r) equal the proportion of C_g that loop back to either the same individual or other individuals of the same type. Stated mathematically $C_r = L_c \cdot C_g$, where L_c is the degree of loopiness of costs.

To apply these mathematical expressions to more familiar terrain, let's return to the basketball scenario to illustrate how the degree of loopiness can influence the outcome of competition. The **generated benefits** (B_g) for either team are the points scored during the game. Note that each member of a team can be thought of as different individuals of the same type. So helping teammates to score is functionally the same as scoring oneself. It is the team that wins or loses. On the other hand, each team's **generated costs** (C_g) are the points it allowed the other team to score. The team that wins the game is thus the team in which $B_g > C_g$. Or is it?

Here is where the distinction between *generated* costs and benefits and *realized* costs and benefits comes into play. A team's generated benefits are the points a team scores, whereas a team's realized benefits are the points awarded to it on the scoreboard. This distinction may at first seem puzzling because aren't they always the same? In many competitions they would be, but as illustrated by the example of the altruistic *Superiors,* they do not have to be. And if points are not awarded in a completely loopy fashion, the team that generates the most points may not end up with the most points on the scoreboard (which is what determines which team wins the game).

Whether the altruistic *Superiors* win depends on two factors: the degree to which they are altruistic (the degree to which their L_b is less than 1), and the degree to which they outscore their opponent (the degree to which B_g is greater than C_g). Because they are altruistic, a proportion of the *Superiors'* points are awarded (specifically $(1 - L_b) \cdot B_g$) to the selfish *Inferiors.* The *Superiors'* realized costs thus include not just the points scored by the *Inferiors*, but also the proportion of their points that they gave to their opponents. Or put mathematically, the *Superiors'* $C_r = C_g + (1 - L_b) \cdot B_g$. So under this scenario the *Superiors* will win ($B_r > C_r$) only if $L_b \cdot B_g > C_g + (1 - L_b) \cdot B_g$. Using a little algebra this equation can be rearranged to

$$(2 \cdot L_b - 1) \cdot B_g > C_g.$$

This is equation (1) in the text. The general idea is: Winning in competition depends on more than just which type generates the most benefits in comparison to its costs; it also depends on the loopiness of a type's generated benefits.

The preceding equation is, however, limited in the sense that it fails to account for the fact that costs as well as benefits may not always loop back to the type that generated them. So here I derive a more general expression that keeps track of the loopiness of both. To do so one must first recognize that the loopiness of generated costs has exactly the opposite affect on the outcome of competition as the loopiness of generated benefits. In other words, although spreading benefits to one's competitors hurts one's ability to win, spreading one's costs to one's competitors helps it win. Mathematically, this is written as $L_b B_g + (1 - L_c)C_g > L_c C_g + (1 - L_b)B_g$, which rearranges into

$$(2 \cdot L_b - 1) \cdot B_g > (2 \cdot L_c - 1) \cdot C_g. \qquad (2)$$

I call this equation the **loopiness equation**.

The loopiness equation makes it clear that competition only occurs on a "level playing field" when the loopiness of benefits equals the loopiness of costs ($L_b = L_c$). Only then does equation (2) reduce to $B_g > C_g$; competitors are expected to win or lose solely on their own competitive merits. Neither competitor is either differentially subsidized or penalized by the efforts of their competitors.

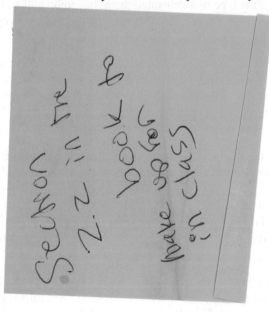

Some key terms:

naturalistic explanation - an explanation of some occurrence that stays within the realm of natural laws. (A naturalistic explanation stands in contrast to an explanation that employs supernatural events).

gene pool - the entire genetic constitution of a sexual population. (In other words, it is all the genetic information contained all the genotypes of the individuals that make up the population.)

mutation - a modification of the genotype within an individual cell. (In multicellular organisms such modification could occur in either a somatic cell—somatic mutation—or in its germ cells—germ-line mutation)

biological evolution - the two-step process of descent with modification followed by persistence across generations.

natural selection - whenever a modified type is caught in a reproductive race with an ancestral type, and the outcome of the race is affected by differences in performance ability.

genetic drift - whenever a modified type is caught in a reproductive race with an ancestral type, and the outcome of the race is affected by chance occurrences.

adaptation - a trait or feature of an organism that helps it deal with, in terms of getting resources or avoiding disruptions, the specific details of its environment

cumulative (biological) evolution - an accumulation of change that results from past modification (of a life-form) persisting and being further altered by more bouts of modification and persistence. (In other words, change accumulates through repeated episodes of biological evolution).

Some study questions:

1. Explain why a scientific explanation of how something happens cannot by definition include miracles.

2. *Explain the concept of gene frequency within a sexual population, and how it relates to the term genetic variability.* Explain this statement: The gene frequencies of all variable genes in a sexual population potentially remain the same across generations.

3. Spontaneous origin was dismissed as a possible avenue of origin for any present day life forms. Why?

4. *Explain how a germ-line mutation could alter an offspring's genotype. Next explain how such genetic change could alter the offspring's performance ability (in comparison to offspring receiving the ancestral gene form).*

5. Why is a modification being heritable necessary for it to persist, but not sufficient for it to persist?

6. Explain why reproduction was presented as being an obstacle course. Does every organism face all the same general obstacles? Explain. *Whether any performing entity is able to negotiate an obstacle depends on an interaction of three factors. What are these three factors?*

7. *In general, when is a newly modified type caught in a reproductive race with its ancestral type? When caught in such race, what must either type do to persist?*

8. *What does it mean to say that mutations are random and natural selection is directed? Explain the statement: Given that mutations are random, most mutations are expected to go extinct quickly.*

9. *How is genetic drift similar and how is it different than natural selection?*

10. Suppose a population contains two types and one type is better at surviving than the other type. *Is this sufficient information to know the expectation of natural selection? Explain.*

11. Finish this statemement: In the absence of tradeoffs, the life history of all types of organisms would evolve towards... What is the fundamental tradeoff underlying life history evolution?

12. *Understand how any population's environment can make a difference in what types of modifications are able to replace ancestral types.*

13. *Understand how a population has evolved in the past can make a difference in what types of modifications are able to replace ancestral types.*

14. *How could repeated rounds of mutation and natural selection lead to cumulative evolution?*

15. Why is it that the male and female parent do not typically contribute equally to postnatal care (in species where offspring are cared for after birth or hatching)?

16. How could a male battling with other males contribute to a male's reproductive success? How could a female mating preferentially with certain types of males contribute to her reproductive success? *Given your answer to the last question, why is it curious that in some species females seem to prefer to mate with "ornate" males. Explain what must be true for a heritable form of female preference for ornate males to win in competition with a heritable form of female preference for less ornate males.*

17. *Explain why individuals that on average produce male and female offspring in nearly equal proportions—that is, a 50:50 sex ratio—tend to have greater reproductive success than any other sex ratio.*

18. Explain why a heritable form altruism being adaptive (benefits to the receiver are greater than costs to the donor) is not sufficient for such behavior to spread in a population via natural selection. *Next explain how kin selection can increase the degree of loopiness to the point that certain forms of adaptive altruistic behaviors can evolve.* Name at least one example of an altruistic behavior that may have evolved via kin selection.

19. Explain how the evolution of cooperation via kin selection can still leave room for conflict or disagreement.

20. Explain the statement: Any aspect of any type of organism that in some way influences reproductive success is potentially changed across generations by the combination of mutation and natural selection.

21. *Explain how speciation via geographic isolation could work.*

The Theory of Evolution

Quite a few years ago I heard a couple of upper-level biology students talking outside my office. I know that it is not polite to eavesdrop, but the subject they were talking about was so intriguing that I set aside my manners and listened in. They were discussing evolution. During that discussion one of the students made a statement that has stuck in my head ever since. He said, "I do not want to take the evolution class (which was and still is a required class for all biology majors) because I do not believe in evolution."

To be frank, as a biology teacher, that statement disappointed me, but not in the way that you might think. I had no problem with a student expressing a belief concerning biological evolution. I was disappointed by the fact that this upper-level biology student's statement indicated that he did not understand the issues surrounding the topic. Specifically, he did not understand the difference between the *mechanisms of evolution* (e.g., mutation, natural selection, genetic drift, branching evolution) and the *theory of evolution*. Interpreted literally, the statement, "I do not believe in biology evolution," is a statement indicating the belief that Life on this planet is perfectly and completely static—that no life form has or will ever change in even the slightest of ways. Such a belief is roughly equivalent to not believing in gravity because like gravity, changes in the composition of populations over time can be easily observed. Some examples include New reports of a bacterial strain becoming resistant to a specific antibiotic are common, over 500 species of insects have become resistant to one or more insecticides in the last 50 years, and plant breeders have had a productive history of using selective breeding to generate many new types of plants such as new crop varieties and new varieties of roses. There are as many other examples as you care to take the time to find.

Yet if change within Life is readily observed, then where is there any potential controversy? Clearly controversy has followed evolutionary biology throughout its history. As discussed in Chapter 1, in science a theory is more than just an idea; it is an idea that effectively unifies, hence provides an explanation for, many and diverse phenomena of Nature. *The diverse phenomena in biology are all the different types organisms* that either presently live or used to live on this planet. The unifying idea is that the mechanisms of change inherent in biological (reproducing) systems *are sufficient* to explain the becoming of all past and present living forms.

Although the mechanisms of evolution are knowable, whether these mechanisms are sufficient is an *unknowable proposition* for a very simple reason. Without some form of time machine, evolutionary biologists cannot go back and directly observe the means by which Life first originated on this planet and subsequently how past life forms have been modified into extant (present-day) life forms. So it is impossible to know with certainty whether the mechanisms of evolution in and of themselves were sufficient to pull the whole thing off. Stated differently, it is impossible to rule out with certainty that something else was not involved. As a consequence, the potential for reasonable differences in opinion exists. This is where the potential for controversy exists. That said, recognize that as a biology teacher how you personally choose to answer the question of sufficiency, if you choose to take a stand at all, is not my concern. However, it is important to understand that your answer, whatever it might be, crosses the threshold of being a belief. My teacher-based concern is that you begin to understand evolutionary biology well enough to see the issues. This is why I would have felt much better if the biology student mentioned earlier had stated, "I do not believe that the mechanisms of evolution are sufficient to explain the becoming of all past and present life forms." I would have known that he understood where the uncertainty lies.

An important part of understanding the issues surrounding evolutionary biology is seeing that an unknowable component does not in any way detract from the theory of evolution's usefulness. In other words, an unknowable component does not mean that the theory of evolution is not a good theory. Quite the contrary, the theory of evolution has worked remarkably well. So well, in fact, that it is considered to be the one theory that unifies all biology. It has created an intellectual environment where both the observed similarities and observed differences among the different species inhabiting this planet fit together to build understandable patterns. Or in the words of a famous geneticist and evolutionary biologist Thomas Dobzhansky, "Seen in the light of evolution, biology is, perhaps, intellectually the most satisfying and inspiring science. Without that light it becomes a pile of sundry facts—some of them interesting or curious but making no meaningful picture as a whole."

The link between the theory of evolution and common ancestry

To state it again, the idea at the core of the theory of biological evolution is that the mechanisms of change inherent in biological (reproducing) systems *are sufficient* to explain the becoming of all past and present living forms—that is, they were sufficient to generate all the genotypic and phenotypic variation found in all the different life forms that have ever existed on this planet. The major mechanisms of change inherent in biological systems are modified origin via random mutations, differential persistence of modified and ancestral types via natural selection and genetic drift, and some form of isolating factor triggering the branching of one population into two or more separately evolving populations (speciation).

Although it may not be initially obvious, this idea carries with it a second proposal: That *all* species share a common ancestor (and some common evolutionary history) with every other species. The logic goes as follows: If the mechanisms of evolution are sufficient, then the past and present diversity of species have come to be by some combination of cumulative modification within ancestral populations, the branching of ancestral populations into two or more separately evolving species, and (although not yet discussed much) the occasional fusing of ancestral population into a single reproductive unit (symbiotic origin). This suggests that going back in time the evolutionary history of any two species converge at some branch point. At this point of convergence, the species share a common ancestor. Past this point of convergence, the species share a common evolutionary history (see Figure 7-1). Take this idea to its extreme, and the history of all species converges somewhere along Life's timeline—that is, all species share a common ancestor.

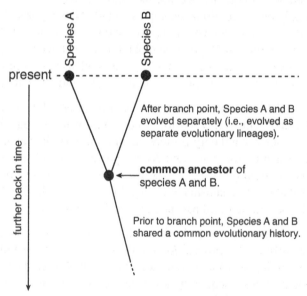

Figure 7-1. Two species sharing a common ancestor somewhere in the past means that they share a common evolutionary history prior to speciation, and separate evolutionary histories after speciation.

Why the theory of evolution is useful: Understanding the relationship between theory and facts.

It is no doubt that the theory of evolution is a mouthful. Not only does it contain an unknowable proposition, but also, at least at first glance, it is hard to imagine that it could be true. It is hard to imagine that such simple means of change such as random mutation and natural selection, combined on occasion with some means of isolation needed for branching evolution, could have generated the vast diversity of life forms that have and still do exist. It is hard to image that all species share a common ancestor because that means that a dog, the flea on the dog's back, the tree on which the dog commonly relieves itself, and the bacteria is the soil which is able to use nitrogen compounds in the dog's urine all share a common ancestor somewhere in their evolutionary past. And the same could be said for any other set of species that you care to consider. For example, your dog, your goldfish, and the tulip that you planted last fall would also share a common ancestor.

So if the theory of biological evolution is so hard to imagine, why do biologist consider it to be so useful? Why has it emerged as the organizing principle of all biological science? The reason has to do with how well the theory of evolution helps make sense of biological facts.

Collecting and comparing facts

In Chapter 1, we defined a scientific fact as any measured observation. So what kind of facts could a biologist collect about different organisms? The general answer is lots. Just think about what type of facts could be collected about you. To list just a few: Your height, your weight, how many arms you have, how many belly buttons you have, how many teeth you have, what is the chemical composition of your teeth, how many bones are in each of your arms, how many vertebrae make up your spinal column, what is the chemical composition of your bones, how many livers do you have, as you developed from a first cell into a multicellular adult when did you first have a liver, what part of your developing body was the precursor to the development of a liver, how has your liver changed over the course of your life, what nerve coming out of what part of your nervous system innervates each of your muscles, what are the different molecules found in each of your cells, do each of your cells have DNA, and how similarly is DNA arranged in different cells within your body. Of course, these same types of facts are potentially collected from me, or any other organism found on this planet. Some, but not all, of these same type of facts can even be collected from the fossil remains of organisms. The exact nature of the facts that can be collected from a fossil depends on what aspects of the organism were preserved. For example, fossil remains can commonly be used to determine the shape, size, and number of teeth and bones because skeletal material readily fossilizes. Facts about the geological strata that a fossil is found in and the fossil's material composition may also be collected, both of which can be used to date when in the past the organism lived. Aspects of cell composition, however, are much more difficult to ascertain from fossil organisms because cellular components are not readily preserved.

Collecting facts from different types of organisms helps us understand more about the organisms that we share this planet with, but it is hard to imagine stopping there. Whenever someone has a set of facts about two or more things, there is always the option of comparing them. By comparing facts we begin to ask how things are similar and how they are different. For example, after we measured some facts about you and me, we could ask in what ways are we similar and in what ways are we different. We could extend this comparison to other types of organisms. For example, we could sort through the facts and find out what other types of organisms have four limbs arranged in two pairs. In doing so, we delimit a group of organisms that share a particular similarity. Within this group we could then ask further questions about similarity and difference. For instance, which members of this group use bones to build each limb's support structure? And for those that use bones, how does the number, shape, and arrangement of the bones forming each limb's support structure compare with one another. Similarly, we could ask what other organisms are composed of cells, and in what ways the cells of these organisms are similar and in what way they are different. For example, one could ask: Is DNA found in the cells of different organisms? And then further ask: For those organisms containing DNA, how similarly is their DNA arranged?

It should come as no great surprise that biologists have collected and compared a lot of different types of facts from a lot of different types of organisms. And they continue to do so today at a rapid pace. One basic pattern that has emerged from all this work is that *all organisms on this planet share at least some similarities, but some organisms are more similar to each other than others are.* An example of a shared similarity is that *all* organisms observed to date are built of the same units of structure—cells, and the molecular processes that occur in cells share many similarities across organisms. All cells, for instance, contain DNA, and when we talk later about the process by which DNA is used to make more proteins, we will not go through separate discussions of how it occurs in bacteria, animal cells, plant cells, fungi cells, or any other cell type because all cells make proteins in basically the same way. That some organisms are more similar to each other than others are is so obvious that it never strikes many people as a curious observation. They see it as just the way the world is. Everyone knows, for example, that while cats and dogs share many similarities (e.g., have hair, teeth, and so on), different breeds of dogs are more similar to each other than they are to cats. And within different breeds of dogs, some breeds are more similar than others are. For example, a black lab is more similar to a golden lab than it is to a pekinese.

Using common ancestry to make sense of similarity

A major part of the reason that the theory of evolution has proved to be so useful is that it makes sense of both why all species share at least some similarities and why some species are more similar than others are. All species share at least some similarities because they all share the same starting point—a common ancestor. Furthermore, more similar species share a more recent common ancestor than more dissimilar species because they have had a shorter time to evolve differences. Stated in the opposite way, the further back in time that two species last shared a common ancestor, the more time (hence opportunity) they have had to evolve differences.

Although the idea of a common starting point through common ancestry can help explain observed similarity across all organisms (e.g., cellular processes common to all species), the same idea can also be used to make sense of similarity on a smaller scale. For example, it has been observed that among vertebrates with distinct forelimbs (amphibians, reptiles, birds, and mammals) the support structure appears to be modifications of the same basic arrangement of bones (see Figure 7-2). This fact is particularly striking given that the forelimbs of different birds and mammals are extremely diverse in both form and function. To mention just a few examples: The forelimbs of most birds are broad spread out wings used to fly; a mole's forelimbs are short squatty structures used to dig through soil; a deer's forelimbs are long slender structures used for running; a whale's forelimbs are flattened flippers used for swim-

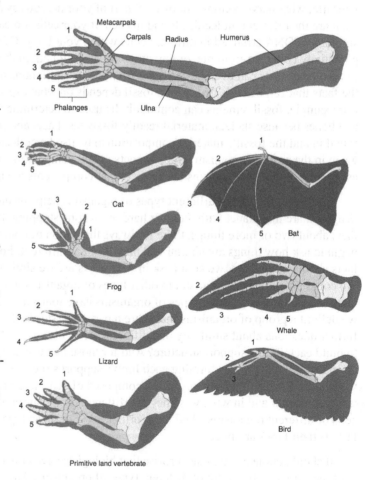

Figure 7-2. The similar bone arrangement found in the forelimbs of different vertebrates.

ming; and humans have hands perched at the end of their relatively long forelimbs that are capable of grabbing and manipulating all sorts of objects. If engineers set out to make a flipper, a wing, a digging apparatus, a running apparatus, and something able to grab and manipulate objects, it is rather doubtful that they would use modifications of the same basic support structure in each case. Different tasks would experience different types of forces that would best be countered by different types of structural design. In fact, they probably would not even build each of the support structures out of the same materials. For example, they may choose a strong but lightweight material to construct the support structure of a wing and some different material to build the support structure of a flipper. But in all these different forelimbs, both the structural material—bone, and the basic arrangement of bones are common throughout. Why does this unexpected similarity exist? The theory of evolution suggests that they are all **homologous structures**—that is, the similarity is based on common descent. Each more specialized forelimb found among different birds and mammals evolved through the modification of a forelimb pattern found in the common ancestor to both birds and mammals.

Using the idea of common ancestry to explain differing degrees of similarity among different species is expressed visually by building phylogenies. A **phylogeny** is a reconstruction of the evolutionary past that links a group of species (through common ancestry) into a proposed pattern of relatedness. All species connected by a common ancestor are considered to be related to each other, but species that share a more recent common ancestor are considered to be more closely related than other species. It is no different than why a sibling is considered to be more closely related than a cousin. You share a more recent common ancestor with a sibling (your parents) than with a cousin (one set of grandparents). Put in other terms, building a phylogeny can be seen as constructing a genealogy of species. Figure 7-3 provides an example of how measures of DNA similarity within a group of species can be organized into a phylogeny.

Suppose that using a technique called DNA hybridization, the percentage difference in DNA arrangement was measured among a group of of eight species (A-G). The results (the facts collected) are arranged below.

Using the idea that more similar species (in this case, a more similar DNA arrangement) share a more recent common ancestor, the above data set can be converted into a phylogeny—a proposed reconstruction of the evolutionary history that ties all eight species together.

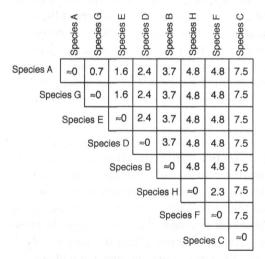

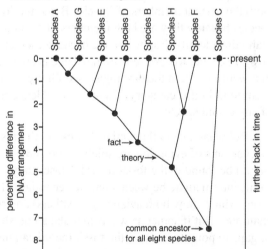

Figure 7-3. An example of how facts that in some way measure the degree of similarity between species can be used to construct a phylogeny. A phylogeny uses the notion of common ancestry and branching evolution to make sense of the facts (why some species are more similar to each other than others are, but all species share some degree of similarity). As an organizing idea, the phylogeny is theory.

Other types of facts

A theory continues to remain a good theory as along as it helps us make sense of all observations. So far we have seen that the common ancestry component of the theory of evolution can make sense of similarity to varying degrees observed among different species. But there is more to be observed about past and present organisms than just varying degrees of similarity. So does the theory of evolution help us make sense of those as well? Lets consider a few examples starting with some facts about the fossil record.

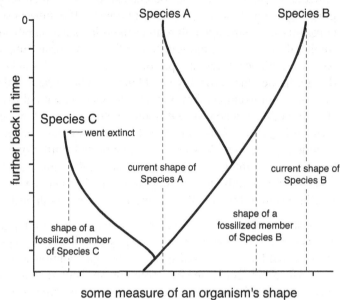

Figure 7-4. The two evolutionary reasons that organisms shaped differently than any extant species may show up in the fossil record. (See text for further discussion).

Strikingly, the fossil record reveals a whole suite of life forms that do not exist today. Dinosaurs are perhaps the most popularized example. With all the skeletons that have been dug up so far, there is little doubt that dinosaurs once inhabited this planet. And as well as we have explored this planet, there is little doubt that dinosaurs do not still exist today. It would be more than remarkable to find a report in tomorrow's newspaper about someone finding living dinosaurs in some isolated part of the planet. The theory of evolution makes sense of the observation in one of two ways. First, if present-day life forms evolved through modification of past life forms (by the mechanisms of evolution), then obviously, past life forms could be shaped differently. For example, Figure 7-4 show that fossil remains of an organism that was a member of Species B in the past would be shaped differently than any current member of species B. (Note: Both the current members of Species B and the fossil remains are all considered members of the same species because they are both members of a single evolutionary lineage. Any evolutionary lineage maintains identity despite change because each change is only a modification of what existed previously.) Second, a fossil remain may have been a member of a species (a distinct evolutionary lineage) that went extinct in the past (again see Figure 7-4). All the various species of dinosaurs discovered seem to fit in this category. There is no evidence that a *Tyrannosaurus Rex* was the direct descendant of any extant species.

But what about all the missing links in the fossil record? There is common claim that if the mechanisms of evolution are solely responsible for Life's evolution, then certain transitional life forms should be found in the fossil record. Close study of the fossil record actually does reveal many life forms intermediate between what we see today. The fossil remains of several individuals of *Archaeopteryx,* which show both avian (e.g., feathers) and reptilian (e.g., teeth) traits, is one of the more famous examples. But if someone wants to make a this-should-be-found argument, there will always be plenty of gaps to point to because the fossil record can never be a complete record of past life forms. Only rarely do dead organisms fossilize, so many if not most past life forms likely disappeared without leaving a fossil trace—that is, they disappeared without leaving any direct record of their existence. This will be particularly true for life forms composed entirely of soft tissues that tend not to fossilize. Furthermore, most fossil remains have yet to be found, and this will remain true even if search efforts intensify in the future. The earth is just too big to explore every place containing fossil remains. The fossil record is more like recording some event for posterity by shooting a snapshot here, a snapshot there, while most of the time forgetting to even take out the camera.

Whether the theory of evolution can help make sense of the fossil record, given its nature, is better evaluated by looking at what *has been found* both in terms of what should and what should *not* be found. For example, a striking observation about the fossil record is that the oldest fossils are simple in structure, and the discovery of increasingly complex life forms follows an orderly chronological sequence. In terms of complexity, the mechanisms of evolution can generate change in either direction. Through cumulative evolution, simpler organisms can change over time in ways that make them more complex, and complex organisms could evolve over time in ways that make them structurally simpler. There is only one trend that cannot happen via the mechanisms of evolution—organisms cannot start off complex. So the simple-to-complex trend found in the fossil record makes sense from the perspective of the theory of evolution because complex life forms should not be found early in the fossil record. Furthermore, using geological dating methods, the earliest fossil life forms (that have been found) date back 3.5 billion years or so, and major jumps in observed complexity happen slowly. For example, a major increase in larger multicellular animals is not found until 2.5 to 3 billion years later. Such observations again make sense in terms of the theory of evolution because large expanses of time would be required for cumulative change via the two-step process of selection and random modifications such as mutation to be solely responsible for this simple-to-complex trend.

Along a similar vein, I was once told that in a radio interview a famous evolutionary biologist named John Maynard-Smith responded to a question about what sort of observation would really shake up the theory of evolution by stating, "A Devonian rabbit." Huh? What is a Devonian rabbit? Basically it is a fossil remain that should not be found because it would be at odds with the rest of the fossil record. The Devonian period is a period in the geological time scale that dates from around 410 to 360 million years ago. Many fish fossils show up in the Devonian period, as well as evidence that some types of plants and animals were beginning to establish a terrestrial existence. But overall, the fossil record suggests that the prerequisites to the evolution of mammals were not yet in place. Stated differently, a Devonian rabbit would have a mammal showing up before the needed evolutionary stage had been set. So from the perspective of the theory of evolution, the fact that the earliest mammals do not show up in the fossil record until around 150 to 200 million years later makes sense. And that it was not until after the famed dinosaur extinction around 65 million years ago that the fossil record shows mammals diversifying into a large variety of forms. In other words, based on the rest of the fossil record, a Devonian rabbit would be around 300 to 350 million years too early.

The last observation raised is one discussed some in the previous chapter—that many organisms seem to possess physiological, morphological, and behavioral traits that appear well suited to living in their present environment. You will even hear people exclaim that some particular type of organism seems "perfectly" adapted to its environment. The species of preying mantis that looks just like an orchid is one of my favorite examples. The theory of evolution makes sense of such observations by the fact that the environment will always affect how any species evolves because the environment will always affect what it takes for organisms to continue to negotiate their reproductive obstacle course. So given enough time (and enough random mutations of the right kind) natural selection will always drive a species' phenotype to evolve in ways that help them contend with at least some of the particular environmental complications that they face.

Some key terms:

phylogeny - the pattern of relatedness among different species, where any two species relatedness depends on how recently they branched from a common ancestor. (For example, if among three species—A, B, and C—A and B share a more recent common ancestor than A and C or B and C, then A and B are the most closely related species among the three.)

Some study questions:

1. *What are the basic tenets of the theory of evolution?*

2. Explain how the mechanisms of evolution are a fundamental component of the theory of evolution, but are not equivalent to the theory of evolution. (A similar question) Change the statement: "I do not believe in evolution", to one that does not alter the belief but expresses a better understanding of the issues surrounding evolutionary biology.

3. *Be able to draw or interpret a phylogeny.* For example, suppose that using a technique call DNA hybridization, the DNA in members of five different species (A, B, C, D & E) was compared. Construct a phylogeny of these five species using the below data set.

• Species A and Species D differ by approximately 3%.
• Both Species A and Species D differ from the three remaining species by approximately 10%.
• Species B and Species C differ by approximately 2%.
• Both Species B and Species C differ from Species E by approximately 5%.

4. The degree of genetic differences I gave you in the above question are facts (measured observations). The phylogeny that you drew above is means to organize these facts around a unifying idea. Briefly explain what is this unifying idea.

5. We discussed several examples of how the theory of evolution is used to unify observations about different life forms on this planet. *In each of these examples, be able to distinguish between theory and fact, as well as understand the relationship between theory and fact.*

A Closer Look at Reproduction

Earlier I made the claim that reproduction is one of the two fundamental loops of life (nutrient cycling is, of course, the other). As we discussed the rudiments of biological evolution and biological communities, we began to uncover consequences associated with reproduction. But so far little has been said about how reproduction actually occurs. This is our next challenge. And challenge is the appropriate word. To understand the basic workings of reproduction, we must zoom in on territory unfamiliar by its very nature. Reproduction occurs at the molecular level. Although the actions and interactions of molecules form the basis of everything that we do and experience, it is easy to be completely oblivious to molecular ways. The reason is simple: They are too small to see. Even with the aid of our most powerful microscopes, the largest molecules appear as little more than shadowy outlines. We often pay little heed to parts of the world that slap us visually in the face every day, so for many it seems to be a stretch to take time to contemplate the ways of molecules.

But that is what we are going to try to do. For those of you who are wary, my underlying (and a bit optimistic) hope is that the loops of Life have so captured your imagination that you will twist your own arm to do the chemical exploration needed to understand the basic mechanics of reproduction. You may find that how reproduction emerges from molecules holds many treasures.

It would be easy to start this journey with a litany of chemical details. Of course, many of you would most likely get lost, then get frustrated, and eventually give up and go home. I start by trying to piece together the logic underlying a reproductive performance. In the process I outline in broad strokes the main interactions among the major groups of molecules involved. My goal here is to start to build a conceptual map that will help you navigate through the various details introduced in subsequent chapters.

Putting together a reproductive map

Recall the basic concept of reproduction introduced in Chapter 3: Reproduction is a collection of connected processors (a performance) acting to make more copies of the same processors with the same connections (e.g., jackrabbits making more jackrabbits, bacteria making more bacteria, or humans making more humans). It is this idea that we need to expand.

At the molecular level, most all of Life's processors are structurally similar. They fall into a class of molecules called **proteins.** All proteins are assembled from the same limited set of parts—20 in total. The 20 different protein parts are all different forms of **amino acids**. But until we discuss amino acids in detail, I refer to them as **protein parts** because it is more straightforward. Proteins are made by linking protein parts one after the other to form a chain. The most important feature of protein assembly is that each of the 20 different protein parts can be linked to any of the other protein parts. (This is true because all possible links form through the same type of chemical reaction.) Consequently, these 20 parts can be potentially linked in any conceivable sequence.

Linking two or more protein parts occurs most readily when something acts to facilitate the chemical reaction. Reproduction starts to come into focus with the realization that proteins themselves can perform this action—that is, certain proteins can act to facilitate the formation of a link between different protein parts. Whenever this happens *proteins would be acting as a processor to make more proteins* (see Figure 8-1).

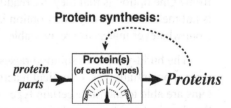

Figure 8-1. Proteins acting to make more proteins by facilitating the stringing together of protein parts. The dashed line indicates that the loopiness underlying a reproductive performance begins to emerge whenever some of the proteins made are the ones able to facilitate protein synthesis.

A major component of reproduction in all the various types of organisms known to exist is proteins acting to make more proteins, but that is not the whole story. Five basic aspects of a reproductive performance are still missing: different proteins do different things, getting parts, fuels, recipes, and containers. I discuss each in turn.

Different proteins do different things

Consider a fundamental question: If all proteins are assembled by stringing together protein parts, how can one protein be either the same or different from another protein? One possible difference is that proteins could be of different lengths—that is, the number of protein parts strung together could vary. But even more important is the fact that proteins are made up of *20 different types of interchangeable parts*. This means that the order in which the different types of parts are assembled into a chain can vary. So in total, proteins can vary in *sequence* and *length*. Two proteins of the same sequence and length are the same, whereas two proteins having a different sequence and/or a different length are different.

Why sequence makes a difference goes back to the shape–performance trade-off. Each of the 20 types of protein parts have different properties, thus each interacts with its watery surroundings and other protein parts in the same chain in unique ways. A protein's sequence thus specifies at what position in the chain each of these different interactions occurs. The position of each interaction, in turn, determines how the entire chain will fold into (self-assemble into) a three-dimensional shape. In other words, two proteins with the same sequence will tend to fold into the same shape, whereas two proteins with a different sequence will tend to fold into different shapes. Due to the shape–performance trade-off each protein's shape affects how it can perform as a processor. More specifically, a protein's shape affects what a protein can and cannot interact with and how the protein will alter that with which it interacts.

With 20 different parts, there are an almost unlimited number of different possible sequences that fold into correspondingly different shapes. This is what makes proteins so unique. Some protein would likely have the right shape to orchestrate almost any type of chemical interaction. Yet because of the shape–performance trade-off, each protein type will also tend to be the right shape to facilitate only a limited number (generally only one) type of chemical interaction. So if the number of different chemical interactions involved in reproduction increases, the number of different types of proteins that need to be involved will go up accordingly.

Getting parts

Proteins cannot be built unless protein parts are available. So where do the protein parts come from? One option is that they are readily available in the surrounding environment. But what if that is not the case? The only other option is for a reproductive performance to make its own protein parts from whatever materials are available.

The build-your-own solution raises an important question: Can proteins handle this task? The answer is potentially yes. Chemical reactions convert molecules from one type to another, and some proteins are able to facilitate certain types of chemical reactions. So, as long as the proteins that facilitate the chemical reactions needed to assemble protein parts from available molecules are present, proteins can handle the task. The assembly of biological molecules such as protein parts is termed **biosynthesis** or **synthesis metabolism** (see Figure 8-2).

There is an inescapable downside to proteins needing to make their own parts. More proteins would need to be involved. In addition to the proteins necessary to string together protein parts, others would be needed to assemble protein parts. So the reproductive performance, as a whole, needs to be more complex.

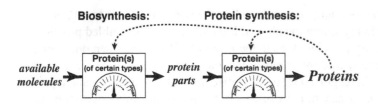

Figure 8-2. Proteins acting to make more proteins by first facilitating the assembly of protein parts and then stringing together protein parts to form new proteins. Again the loopiness underlying a reproductive performance (dashed lines) begins to emerge whenever some of the proteins made participate in either of these two steps.

Fuels

Assembling protein parts and stringing these parts together to build proteins requires usable energy, which poses some problems. The first law of thermodynamics states that proteins or anything else cannot create usable energy. The second law states that usable energy becomes unusable with use, so a new supply of usable energy must continually be brought in from elsewhere. And not just any form of usable energy will work. Like cars that need gasoline, reproductive performances run on two types of fuels: certain molecules containing **high redox potential** and certain molecules containing **high phosphorylation potential.**

The only thing that I want you to notice about these fancy-sounding chemical terms at the moment is that they are not sunshine. Although the sun is Life's basic supplier of usable energy, sunshine is not used directly to assemble proteins. Remember that although energy cannot be created or destroyed, it can be converted from one form to other. The option is thus to convert an available energy source—either sunshine or some other type of high-energy molecule available in the environment—into the required fuels. **Energy metabolism** is the name given to such energy conversions. This additional reproductive requirement, however, again raises the question: Can proteins also handle this task?

Once again the answer is yes (see Figure 8-3). Energy conversions can proceed through chemical reactions, and I have already stated that proteins are well suited to facilitate chemical reactions. Of course, this means even more types of proteins are needed to pull off reproduction, so the complexity of a reproductive performance continues to go up.

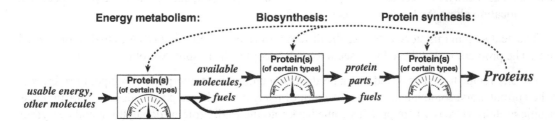

Figure 8-3. Proteins acting to make more proteins by facilitating three things: the assembly of protein parts, the stringing together of protein parts to form new proteins, and the conversion of some form of usable energy into a form that can act as a fuel source for the previous two steps. Again the loopiness underlying a reproductive performance (dashed lines) begins to emerge whenever some of the proteins made participate in any of these three steps.

Recipes

Reproduction is not just proteins acting to make more proteins. Reproduction is proteins acting to make more *of the same* proteins. This might seem like a small difference. It is not.

Given that each protein is a unique sequence of amino acids, making more of the same proteins requires more than just stringing protein parts together. The twenty different types of protein parts must be strung together *in the same sequence* as the proteins enacting the performance.

One way a reproductive performance might go about making the same proteins is to rely on chance. If the protein parts were randomly strung together, at least some of the assembled proteins would have the same sequence as the proteins involved in the assembly. However, when one starts looking at the numbers, random assembly fails miserably. Functional proteins tend to range between 50 and several thousand protein parts in length. Here, to maximize the odds, I consider a small protein that is 50 protein parts long and ask the question: How often would random assembly of 50 protein part chains come up with the same sequence? The answer is around once out of every 1×10^{65} attempts. One followed by 65 zeroes is more than a rather large number, which means that random assembly of even small proteins will not work because the chance of coming up with the same sequence again is just too small.

The remaining option is to use a **recipe**. A recipe can guide something's assembly by specifying how the parts should be put together. A protein recipe would thus be something that specifies the sequence in which the 20 protein parts are to be linked.

Because specific types of proteins can only be reliably assembled when a recipe is followed, recipes are a needed part of a reproductive performance. This observation raises the question: Can proteins serve as recipes for themselves? Here the answer is no. Proteins can be the actors in the reproductive process, but they cannot be the keepers of their own recipes. Instead, another class of molecules, called **nucleic acids**, has filled this role. One nucleic acid called **deoxyribonucleic acid** (although it most often goes by its acronym, **DNA**) has become the primary keeper. We have already used the name given to DNA-based protein recipes; they are called **genes**.

I once heard DNA described as a "fat cigar-smoking slob of a molecule." Such description conjures up the image of DNA as a large, lazy molecule that does not initiate doing much on its own. This is a fairly accurate description. Like chocolate-chip cookie recipes never make cookies and how-to-build-a-house books cannot build a house, the protein recipes encoded in DNA cannot assemble proteins. DNA's only reproductive role is to store protein recipes. In fact, to make the same proteins again the DNA incorporated into a reproductive performance must store a recipe for each of the many proteins involved. DNA is thus analogous to a recipe book; it holds an entire reproductive collection of protein recipes. As discussed in Chapter 4, this entire collection is called a **genome.** Like each recipe is located on a certain set of pages within a recipe book, each protein recipe is located at a specific location along the DNA molecules.

The next step in this story is to take the different roles of proteins and DNA to their loopy conclusions. The problem is that these loops seem to make people's head spin. So follow closely!

For any recipe to be converted into a product, something must interpret the recipe. In reference to the current story, something must do the work of using a protein recipe encoded in DNA to make a specific protein. Here is where proteins come back into the fold. Proteins do anything and everything that happens to DNA, including the interpretation of its recipes (with some minor but important exceptions that we discuss later). Interpretation is an active process, and proteins are the molecular actors. But if that is true, then where are the recipes for these interpretive proteins located? The answer: In the same recipe book. Interpretive proteins are part of the protein ensemble necessary for reproduction, so their recipes must be in the same genome as all other protein recipes. In other words, some protein recipes in a genome are recipes for proteins involved in interpreting recipes within the same genome.

But as we start to envision this loopy interaction, it is easy to get hung up on the seeming paradox of "which came first," commonly known as "the chicken and the egg" paradox. Interpretive proteins must be present to interpret any DNA-bound recipe, but the recipes of these interpretive proteins must be interpreted to build these interpretive proteins in the first place. We are confused by chicken and egg questions because our minds are most comfortable thinking linearly. We like it when (like the alphabet) there is a distinct starting point, and from that point A leads to B, and B leads to C, and so on. But the life-is-loopy paradigm points out that linear thinking often poorly emulates the way Life works. In fact within the ongoing continuity of Life, which came first is not a meaningful question. Any two events within Life are points on a loop, and loops do not have a definitive order. Each event comes before and after every other event. It all depends on how you look at it. (This still leaves the issue of how a reproductive performance involving DNA and proteins started in the first place. It a great question, but one best left alone until one better understands what needs to be explained.)

So let's look at this interactive loop from a specific starting point. If we start the loop at DNA and follow the production of new proteins, three sequential steps emerge: **genetic regulation, DNA transcription**, and **RNA translation** (see Figure 8-4). (Recognize that the loopy part is that interpretive proteins must have already been built for each of these steps to occur.)

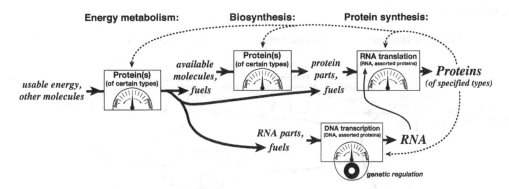

Figure 8-4. Proteins acting to make more proteins is now changed to proteins being directed to make proteins of specified types due to the incorporation of protein recipes (stored in DNA) into protein synthesis. The use of DNA encoded recipes (genes) in proteins synthesis involves three steps: genetic regulation, DNA transcription, and RNA translation (see text for further details). Again the loopiness underlying a reproductive performance (dashed lines) begins to emerge whenever the specific type of proteins produced are the same as the ones that facilitates some part of their synthesis.

To introduce the logic underlying these three steps, I introduce two constraints in the form of an analogy. Think of the DNA-made recipe book—the genome—as being held at the reserve desk of a library. Although it can be temporarily checked out, it cannot be removed from the library. The workplace where recipes are used to make proteins (I always envision a kitchen) is elsewhere. If the recipes and workplace are in two different locations, how can proteins be made?

Here is how you or I would likely do it. We would go to the library, pick out those recipes that we are interested in making, copy each recipe, take these copies back to our kitchen, and then cook them up. The whole process involves three major steps: picking recipes, making copies of the recipes, and then taking these copies to the kitchen, where they are used to make proteins. Proteins essentially follow the same steps. The main difference is that instead of one person doing all the steps, different proteins are involved at each step along the way.

Certain proteins first sort through the various protein recipes in the genome, choosing only certain ones at any particular time. This is **genetic regulation**. Regulation is about turning things on or off, or up or down, in response to some circumstance. Like with all aspects of regulation, sensors are involved. Picking a certain gene can be thought of as turning that gene on. Similarly, any gene that is not being used at any point in time is a gene that is currently turned off.

Working copies of a gene start to be made when a gene is turned from off to on. The process of making the working copy is **DNA transcription**. To transcribe literally means to write out a copy. Proteins again perform the actions involved. Like DNA, the working copy is a nucleic acid but of a slightly different form. It is a **ribonucleic acid** (or **RNA**) molecule.

The last step is **RNA translation**. To translate means to convert from one form to another. Here the RNA-based protein recipe—the working copy—is converted into the protein that it codes for. Although the idea is straightforward, RNA translation is the most confusing of the three steps. The hard part is that several things have to be put together simultaneously before it makes sense.

In addition to using protein recipes to build specific proteins within each generation, a reproductive performance must also include **DNA replication** (see Figure 8-5). Copies of the entire recipe book—the whole genome—must be made and passed to offspring. How else could the same proteins be made again in the next generation? As we will find out, while proteins do the work, a component of DNA structure makes replication possible. It is the same feature that makes it possible to store protein recipes. In other words, not only can DNA act as a sequence guide for proteins, but it can also act as a sequence guide for itself.

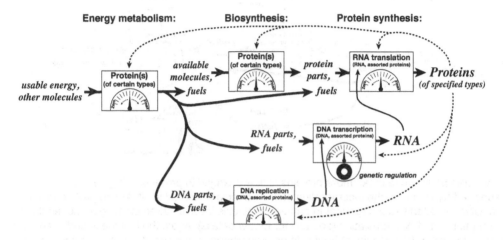

Figure 8-5. Adding DNA replication to the reproductive scheme being developed in this chapter.

A reproductive performance also needs to somehow address the fact that DNA is constantly being bombarded by change. Various aspects of a DNA molecule's environment (e.g., thermal agitation, ultraviolet radiation, interaction with free radicals) continually disrupt it. Copy errors also occur during DNA replication. Such changes can result in protein recipes being altered, or as biologists say, **mutations** can occur. And as we have already discussed, most mutations will be disruptive. So any protein that acts to minimize mutations would tend to benefit the persistence of the entire reproductive performance.

DNA caretaking proteins have been found that act to minimize DNA disruptions in one of two ways: prevention and repair. Prevention keeps errors from happening. For example, proteins involved in DNA replication also play a role in prevention because they act in ways that minimize replication errors. Repair is changing errors back to their original form after the error has occurred, but before the altered section of DNA is used as a protein recipe. Several forms of protein-based repair have been identified. Envision a collection of proteins that vigilantly patrol the DNA identifying recent changes and then restoring the DNA to its original form. Also note that the same structural feature of DNA that makes replication possible also makes repair possible.

Parts revisited: DNA parts and RNA parts

DNA and RNA are like proteins in that they are built by stringing more basic parts together. This is not to say that they are made from the same thing. DNA and RNA parts are called **nucleotides**, which are chemically quite distinct from protein parts. And with only four parts each, they are also fewer in number. Based on some slight chemical differences the nucleotides strung together to form

DNA are called **deoxyribonucleotides**, and those strung together to form RNA are called **ribonucleotides**.

Because more DNA is assembled during DNA replication, and new RNA is assembled every time DNA transcription occurs, a reproductive performance needs access to a continuous supply of DNA and RNA parts. So, like protein parts, DNA and RNA parts must either be present in the environment or they must be synthesized from available materials.

Biosynthesis of nucleotides is, in principle, no different than biosynthesis of protein parts (see Figure 8-6). Proteins do the work through facilitating chemical reactions. The difference is that different chemical reactions need to be facilitated, so different proteins need to be present to do so. And like all other proteins involved in a reproductive performance, the recipes for the proteins involved in the synthesis of nucleotides must be stored among the nucleotides that make up DNA.

Containers

For all the different proteins and nucleic acids involved in a single reproductive performance to interact they must remain close together. This raises the question: How are all these molecules kept together? The answer is that they are all enclosed within a container. It is a prison of sorts, and this is reflected in biological jargon. Containers that keep prisoners from escaping are called cells. To a biologist a **cell** is a membrane-bound enclosure that keeps the molecules of a single reproductive performance from escaping (see Figure 8-6).

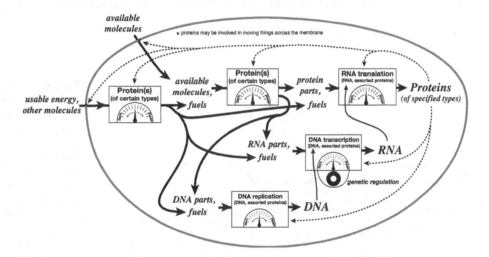

Figure 8-6. Adding two more things to the reproductive scheme being developed here: (1) the synthesis of RNA parts (ribonucleotides) and DNA parts (deoxyribonucleotides) from available molecules, and (2) a container that keeps the interacting molecules within a reproductive performance close together.

What are the membranes of biological containers made of? A first guess might be proteins, but that is not the correct answer. The molecules making up the container fall into another class of biological molecules called **lipids**. Fats are the most familiar type of lipid. Membranes are composed of a modified fat called a **phospholipid**.

Although containers must keep the reproductive molecules inside, they cannot completely seal off everything else because reproduction cannot occur in complete isolation. Resources need to be continually brought in, and waste products need to be expelled. Some of this movement occurs simply by the fact that what is a barrier to one thing may not be a barrier to something else. In other words, some molecules move freely across a cell membrane. But for a reproductive performance to successfully function inside a phospholipid membrane, passive movement alone will not suffice. A cell needs to be a dynamic container, one whose permeability to different substances changes with the needs of the reproductive performance going on inside. It is here that proteins come back into play. A cell's phospholipid membrane is embedded with proteins that are involved in the movement of molecules in and out of the membrane (see Figure 8-6).

Parts revisited: Container parts

Reproduction involves the generation of more containers, which means that for reproduction to occur, additional container parts must be available. As before, the options are the parts can be found in the environment, or the proteins needed for the biosynthesis of phospholipids from available materials must be present. Such biosynthesis again requires that the recipes for these proteins are stored in the DNA.

A Final Picture

Because it is always good to see something from more than one perspective, I use Figure 8-7 to summarize the image of a reproductive performance outlined in this chapter. Our next task is to use this framework to guide a more detailed discussion. In doing so we will further discuss proteins (Chapter 10), the interaction between proteins and nucleic acids (Chapter 11), containers (Chapter 12), biosynthesis (Chapter 13), and energy metabolism (Chapters 14 and 15). Before we delve in, however, I need to touch on a subject that underlies each of the various topics. That subject is chemistry (Chapter 9).

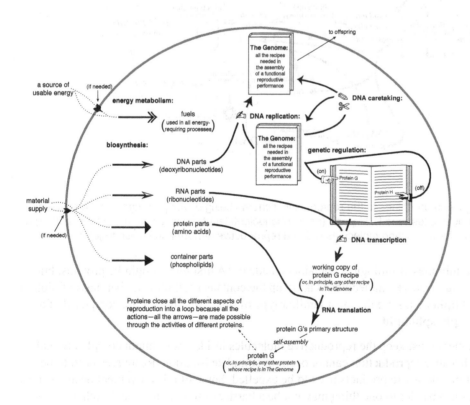

Figure 8-7. A figure that summarizes all the main aspects of a reproductive performance discussed in this chapter. I encourage you to spend some time connecting this picture with the text. I also suggest that as we delve further into the details in subsequent chapters that you continue to refer back to this figure to help you keep track of the big picture.

Some study questions:

1. *Define reproduction from a protein-perspective. Use this perspective to explain why both activity and information are needed components of reproduction.*

2. Some specific questions about information:
   • *Why do proteins need recipes to assemble more of the <u>same</u> proteins?*
   • What type of molecule stores protein recipes?
   • What do biologist call these stored form of these protein recipes?
   • What are the three basic steps involved in using a protein recipe to make a protein?

3. Some specific questions about activity:
   • *Proteins are the molecules in life that make things happen. Be able to explain what it is about proteins—in comparison to all other classes of biological molecules, specifically, nucleic acids (DNA and RNA), carbohydrates, and lipids—that makes proteins "so capable".*
   • In general, how are proteins involved in the two basic steps in building proteins: assembly of protein parts (amino acids), and stringing amino acids together to form proteins.
   • Why are fuels needed for both of these steps to take place?

4. *What basic role do containers play in reproduction?* What do biologist call these reproductive containers?

5. A general question for the future: To understand the patterns found in reproduction one must be able to distinguish, both functionally and structurally, the different parts involved. Below is a list of the most important molecules involved in a reproductive performance. Some were mentioned in this chapter. All will be discussed more extensively in the following seven chapters. Before we are finished with this section be sure you are comfortable with the similarities, differences and relationships among these different molecules.
   • amino acids
   • deoxyribonucleotides
   • ribonucleotides
   • fatty acids
   • simple sugars
   • proteins (polypeptides)
   • DNA
   • RNA
   • triglycerides
   • phospholipids
   • polysaccharides
   • nucleic acids
   • lipids
   • carbohydrates

Some Chemistry

As you look at this page you see paper and ink. Look at your hand and you see flesh and fingernails. A ring on your hand will be some type of metal with, perhaps, some type of rock set in it. Around you there may be plastic, glass, wood, and many other different types of matter. One does not have to look long or hard to realize that there are many different types of matter.

Each different type of matter has a unique set of physical properties such as a melting point, boiling point, density, viscosity, and hardness. Methyl alcohol and only methyl alcohol melts at minus 98 degrees C, boils at 65 degrees C, and has a density of 0.793 g/mL. Although having a similar name ethyl alcohol melts at minus 117 degrees C, boils at 78 degrees C, and has a density of 0.789 g/mL.

All this raises a most basic question: How is it that there are so many different types of matter? Or asked differently, what makes different types of matter different?

As it turns out this question can be answered simply. Different types of matter are different arrangements of only three parts: protons, neutrons, and electrons. Classically two features, their mass and their charge, distinguish these parts. Specifically:

- **Protons**—have a mass of approximately 1 atomic weight unit (awu) and bear one unit of positive charge (1+).

- **Neutrons**—have a mass of approximately 1 awu and lack a charge, or put differently, they are neutrally charged.

- **Electrons**—have a mass of 0.00055 awu and bear one unit of negative charge (1−).

Chemistry is all about emergent properties. Differences in the arrangement of protons, neutrons, and electrons make a difference in the associated physical properties. Perhaps this is part of what makes chemistry seem so hard to many. It may be difficult to imagine that so much is accomplished by so little. So what do we do? Often mistakenly we strive to make it harder! Let me make the opposite plea: Just don't do it.

This is not to say that much that falls under chemistry's cloak won't take your brain for a few laps around the track. Some of it is difficult. My plea is just that you not make it harder than it has to be. The way to do this, as always, is to look for basic patterns. I have already given you the most important one: Everything is made up of different arrangements of just three parts. The next step is to recognize that these arrangements come in two basic forms: atoms and molecules. So away we go.

Atomic Arrangements

An atom is a fundamental unit of organization of matter. It is the fundamental way that protons, neutrons, and electrons are arranged. All protons and neutrons within an atom are in close proximity and are central to the electrons. The region containing protons and neutrons is known as the **atomic nucleus**. Electrons roam about the nucleus at distances much greater than that separating protons and neutrons (see Figure 9-1).

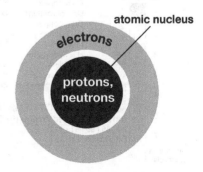

Figure 9-1. The basic atomic arrangement—that is, how protons, neutrons, and electrons are arranged relative to each other within an atom.

Atomic types

An atom's type is determined by one feature—the number of protons held within the nucleus. For example, any atom that has one proton is a hydrogen atom. Or stated differently, it is an atom of the **element** hydrogen, as is any other atom with one proton. An atom with six protons is a carbon atom, an atom with seven protons is a nitrogen atom, and an atom with eight protons is an oxygen atom. In total, there are 92 naturally occurring types of elements ranging from 1 to 92 protons. I mention these four, in particular, because these are the four most important elements in life's chemistry. Chemists refer to an atom's proton number as its **atomic number**.

One could just make a list of the names of these 92 elements, but that is not how chemists typically organize them. Instead they arrange them is a so-called **periodic table** (see Figure 9-2) to reflect a striking observation. As chemists started measuring properties of each element they found although no two elements were the same, plots of these measurements showed a periodic repetition in the patterns of change. Properties that display such periodicity include boiling points, melting points, ionization energy (the strength with which atoms hold on to their electrons), and the tendency for an element to enter into a particular type of chemical reaction.

The chemical details underlying this periodic behavior is not our focus here, but as you glance at the periodic table I would like you to notice just a few things. First, elements in the same column tend to display similar properties. In other words, carbon (C-6 protons) and silicon (Si-14 protons) share more similar properties than carbon shares with elements with a more similar number of protons, such as boron (B-5 protons) and nitrogen (N-7 protons). Second, the seven rows indicate that this periodic behavior starts over seven times. Don't let the fact that the number of elements found between the beginning and end of each period changes as the elements get larger confuse you too much at the moment (e.g. period 1 has 2 elements, periods 2 and 3 have 8 elements, periods 4 and 5 have 18 elements, and period 6 has 32 elements). This has to do with the patterns by which increasing numbers of electrons are arranged in an atom's outer shell. It is, however, curious that the 7th period is unfilled in nature, although additional elements in this 7th period have been created in laboratories. Third, note that it is the smaller elements that are predominately found in living organisms. In fact 21 of the first 30 elements are found in at least trace amounts in Life, whereas only 3 of the remaining 62 are found. And finally, note that it is curious that none of the elements in the last column, the so-called **noble gases**, are found in Life.

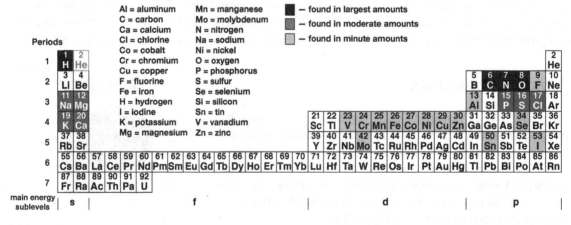

Figure 9-2. The 92 naturally occurring elements arranged in a periodic table. Each box contains the atomic number and the one or two letter abbreviation of each element's name. The elements found in Life are highlighted. (Note: Helium shows up twice in this table because in terms of periods it belongs in the last column, but both of its electrons reside in the s sublevel. The topic of sublevels is discussed more in the text.)

Some more on neutrons

Hydrogen atoms lack neutrons. No other element can make that claim. The difference stems from the fact that the nucleus of a hydrogen atom has one proton only. Without neutrons, more than one proton cannot be packed into a nucleus. As you know, like charges repel. Protons being of positive charge have a tendency to push away other protons. Neutrons, by generating some type of interaction, neutralize this tendency. All atomic arrangements with more than one proton have at least one neutron per proton. Most elements have more. The neutron excess tends to increase steadily as proton numbers increase past 20, suggesting that as proton number increases the number of neutrons per protons must increase to form a stable nucleus (see Figure 9-3).

In many, if not all, cases the number of neutrons present in an element varies. That is, atoms of the same element may not always have the same number of neutrons. **Isotope** is the name given to atoms with the same number of protons, but different number of neutrons. There are, for example, two naturally occurring forms of carbon isotopes: carbon-12 (nucleus contains 6 protons and 6 neutrons) and carbon-13 (nucleus contains 6 protons and 7 neutrons). Carbon-12 is the more common carbon isotope. Approximately 98.9% of naturally occurring carbon atoms are C-12 atoms. Because both organisms and biological researchers can distinguish isotopes, isotope analysis is a commonly used research tool. Such procedures, and the questions they can be used to address, however, are not the focus here. In fact, any further discussion of neutrons is not the focus here.

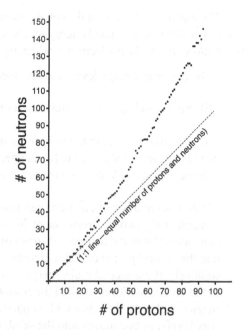

Figure 9-3. The most common number of neutrons found within an atomic arrangement is plotted against the number of protons.

Because neutrons and protons have nearly equal mass, whereas electron mass is considerably less, an atom's total mass—its so-called **atomic weight**—is nearly equal to its total number of protons and neutrons. The atomic weight of carbon, for example, is just that—12. The atomic weight of the most common isotope of gold (Au) is 197 (79 protons plus 118 neutrons).

Some more about electrons

Atomic arrangements tend to have the same number of electrons as protons. That way opposite charges (of equal strength) balance out, leaving the atom as a whole neutrally charged.

How tightly this balance is held, however, varies among different atomic types. Certain atomic types, in particular, easily lose or gain electrons. That is, they readily become **ions**. Ions are atoms that bear a charge due to having an unequal number of protons and electrons. Ions are not neutrally charged because the opposite charges on protons and electrons do not balance. More protons than electrons, and the charge is positive; more electrons than protons, and the charge is negative. The strength of the charge increases by one unit each time the difference between proton and electron number increases by one. Some examples of atoms that tend to form ions are sodium (Na^+—one more proton than electron), potassium (K^+—one more proton than electron), calcium (Ca^{++}—two more protons than electrons), and chlorine (Cl^-—one more electron than proton).

The electrons of an atom do not all "hang out" at the same place. Instead they roam about the nucleus at different so-called energy levels and sublevels. Although chemists and physicists have much more to say about electrons and energy levels, I need to make only four points:

• The closer an energy level is to the nucleus the lower the energy it has.

• Electrons tend to reside at the lowest energy level possible.

• An electron residing in the lowest possible energy level has reached equilibrium. It will stay in that energy level unless some force, specifically electromagnetic radiation, acts on it. Electromagnetic radiation can knock an electron to a higher energy level.

• Only a set number of electrons can reside within each main energy level and sublevel. For example, only two electrons can reside in the lowest or first main energy level. And it is not coincidental that the first period (row) of the periodic table contains only two elements. And recall that the second period contains elements and eight electrons in total, which can reside in the two sublevels of the second main energy level (two in the first sublevel—called the *s* sublevel, and six in the second sublevel—called the *p* sublevel). As you move onward, however, the story gets a bit fuzzier. Although there is a wide separation in energy values associated with the first two main energy levels, as one moves into the third, fourth, and fifth main energy levels there can be overlapping of energies. At first glance this does not make sense because why define a main energy level as third versus fourth or fourth versus fifth if they are not distinct? The confusion arises from the definition of sublevels within main energy levels. Each sublevel represents a switch in the basic way that electrons are arranged within an atom, and the number of these switches increases by one with each energy level. The first main energy level has one sublevel (the *s* sublevel), the second main energy level has two sublevels (the *s* and *p* sublevels), and the third main energy level has three sublevels (the *s*, *p*, and *d* sublevels), and so on. But when you mix this conception of energy levels with the actual pattern that increasing numbers of electrons follow in filling an electron shell, the patterns do not coincide. For example, electrons fill the beginning of the fourth main energy level—the *s* sublevel—before they begin to fill the *d* sublevel of the third main energy level. So by definition 4*s* electrons are lower energy than 3*d* electrons. Yikes!

Okay, so how are we going to make sense of this confusion? First, we are not going to worry about it a lot. But it is worth noting that each period (row) within the periodic table starts with electrons moving into the next *s* sublevel and ends with electrons completely filling the *p* sublevel (with the exception of the first energy level which does not have a *p* sublevel). This is why the third period (row) in the periodic table does not align perfectly with the third main energy level. Eighteen electrons in total can reside in the three sublevels of the third main energy level (2 in the *s* sublevel, 6 in the *p* sublevel, and 10 in the *d* sublevel), yet, like the second period, the third period only has eight elements. The next two electrons to be added (found in potassium (K) and calcium (Ca), respectively) tend to take up residence in the 4*s* sublevel before addition electrons begin to move into the 3*d* sublevel. And we will use this understanding when we say that the first energy level fills with 2 electrons, the second energy level fills with 8 electrons, and the third energy levels also fills with 8 electrons (see Figure 9-4), even though the third main energy level can hold 10 more electrons in the 3*d* sublevel.

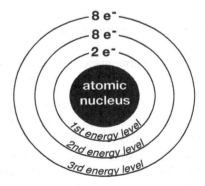

Figure 9-4. The number of electrons that can fill the first three energy levels of an atomic arrangement. (Note: See the text for further discussion.)

The size of atoms

Overall, atoms are extremely small. In fact, it is difficult to imagine just how small atoms are. Here are the numbers. Atoms range in size from about 1 to 5 angstroms in diameter. One angstrom equals 1×10^{-8} cm (1 times 10 to the minus 8 centimeters). There are 2.54 centimeters in an inch. This means that around a hundred million atoms 2.5 angstroms in diameter lined up end to end would span an inch. See, I told you that they are smaller than you can even imagine. Here is a size analogy, but it probably still will not help: If an orange was blown up to the size of the earth, the atoms making up the orange would still only be the size of cherries. The best part of this analogy is that I find myself wondering how a bunch of cherries can combine to form an orange. It is the type of question that gets one into the chemistry spirit.

The smallness of atoms can be unsettling. How can we know anything about atoms if they are too small to even see? Not being too familiar with the methods used by chemists and physicists to investigate atomic structure, I cannot fill you in on the technical details. Even if I could, attempting to do so would be way beyond our purpose here. But I do want you to think about something: Even though we tend to be visually oriented organisms, seeing is not everything. It would be interesting to try to convince a blind person that they cannot build a clear picture of the world. Like a blind person, chemists build their picture of the world through other, often indirect, means. The trick is in knowing how to exploit the tools available.

Atoms are dynamic entities

Now here is a bit of a puzzler: Atoms are mostly space. The elementary particles (protons, neutrons, and electrons) occupy only a very small portion of the space within an atom. Try this comparison on for size. If an atom was enlarged to the size of the dome of St. Peter's Cathedral—the largest dome in the world—the nucleus would be the size of a grain of salt and the electrons would be specks of dust whirling about.

I remember my brother telling me something about this in my younger days. He told me that when you place your hand against a doorknob there is a chance that the atoms could all line up such that one's hand will slip into the doorknob. This is actually a cruel thing to tell a young child. Curiously, I never did worry about my feet slipping into the floor or any other related issue, but for some time after I approached doorknobs with much caution. The worry, of course, evaporated with time. The solidity of doorknobs seemed to be too reliable a pattern to fret about for too long. But the whole issue does raise an interesting question: If atoms are mostly space, then how is it that matter, which is composed of atoms, appears solid? The answer relates to an observation that can be made about the propellers on a plane. When propellers are stationary the area about their rotation is mostly space. But when spinning at high speeds they present a solid appearance. Furthermore, you cannot stick your hand through it—at least, you cannot stick the same hand through it twice.

Similarly, the elementary particles making up atoms are not just standing around. They are dynamic entities. Particles that form the nucleus have been clocked at speeds around 40,000 miles per second (mps). Electrons appear to travel at speeds of around 600 mps. It is movement that creates the barrier that we call solid.

A last comment: What exactly these elementary particles actually are, at least to my head, is not at all clear. I, however, leave that question to you, with encouragement to explore the befuddling but fascinating world of quantum physics. But in this chapter, protons, neutrons, and electrons are simply parts that can be arranged into atoms and molecules.

Three classes of elements

Based on physical properties, all elements are divided into three classes:

• **Metals** are those elements that show a metallic luster when polished and are malleable, ductile, and good conductors of heat and electricity. They are found in the left-hand columns in the periodic table.

• **Nonmetals** are those elements that do not show the preceding properties to any considerable degree. They are found in the right-hand columns of the periodic table.

• **Metalloids** are the elements that fall in between both in terms of properties and their position within the periodic table.

Molecular arrangements

The basic difference between atomic arrangements and molecular arrangements is that atoms combine to form molecules. To me a more interesting way to see the difference between atoms and molecules is to focus on their spatial differences. In contrast to atoms, the protons and neutrons making up a molecule are not all located in close proximity. Instead they are separated into discrete packets—the different nuclei of the atoms that comprise the molecule. Correspondingly, nuclei are not central to electrons. Electrons instead roam in between the various nuclei. The fundamental difference between atoms and molecules is thus how protons, neutrons, and electrons are arranged in space (see Figure 9-5).

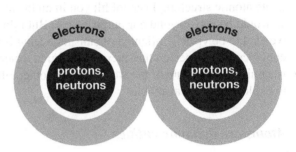

Figure 9-5. The basic molecular arrangement—that is, how protons, neutrons, and electrons are arranged relative to each other when two atoms combine to form a molecule.

Consider neon and water. They have very different physical properties. They, however, both consist of 10 protons and 10 electrons. How can two things made up of the same number of parts be different? The answer is, of course, that they are arranged differently. Neon is an atomic arrangement—all the protons are located centrally to the electrons. Water is a molecular arrangement with a familiar molecular formula—H_2O. Eight of the protons are in the oxygen nucleus, and one proton is in each of the two hydrogen nuclei. The 10 electrons weave between the three nuclei (see Figure 9-6). So not only can different types of matter emerge from different numbers of parts taking on the same fundamental arrangement—as with atoms of different elements—but also different types of matter can emerge from the same number of parts taking on different arrangements.

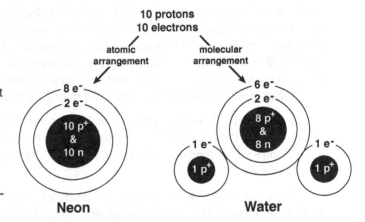

Figure 9-6. Neon and water have very different physical properties, yet they both contain the same number of proton and electrons. The difference stems from the fact that these parts are arranged differently. Neon is an atomic arrangement. Water is a molecular arrangement.

Combining these two possibilities generates a large number of possible matter types. Although there are only 92 naturally occurring elements, there are literally more than a million different ways that atoms combine to form molecules. Each molecule has its own characteristic set of physical properties. Most important, the physical properties of any molecular type do not reflect the properties of elements from which it is made. It is no wonder that chemistry was once known as the madman's science. Emergent properties have the look of madness. How else could one explain sticking together two things and ending up with something completely different? It is no wonder that Hollywood's mad scientists are commonly lurking about their chemical laboratories.

Consider this classic example. At room temperature sodium is a silvery solid metal that reacts explosively with water. Chlorine is a greenish poisonous gas. But on reacting they form table salt. Table salt, as I am sure that you are aware, neither explodes in contact with water nor is poisonous. It is something that we put on our french fries. Table salt, in essence, is not sodium and chlorine (NaCl). Although it can be formed from these elements and decomposed back into these elements, once combined it is table salt. Similarly, water is not really H_2O. It can be formed from hydrogen and oxygen and broken back into hydrogen and oxygen, but when these parts are combined it is water. Nothing about water reflects that of which it is composed. If you take one more step back, this is no different than the fact that the properties associated with any atomic arrangement does not reflect the properties of the protons, neutrons, and electrons of which it is composed.

The formation of molecules

The basic question about molecules is: Why do atoms ever combine to form them? In other words, why don't atoms just hang out by their lonesome? The answer has to do with the stability of arrangements. The atoms of some elements lack a stable electron arrangement. Such atoms are susceptible to change, especially if the change increases stability. Here is where molecules come to be. Atoms with unstable electron arrangements can combine with other unstable atoms in ways that increases the stability of all involved.

Whether or not an atom's electron configuration is stable depends on the number of electrons occupying its outermost energy level (or sublevel) in relation to the number that it can hold. Specifically, atoms with filled outer energy levels are stable and unreactive, and thus they tend to hang out alone as single atoms. Such elements are called **inert gases**, and they form the furthest right-hand column of the periodic table. Helium is the smallest inert gas. As we have already pointed out, the first main energy level fills with two electrons, and helium typically has two electrons (that accompany its two protons). Neon is the next member of this column. Neon's 10 electrons (accompanying its 10 protons) fill the first two main energy levels. After two of neon's 10 electrons fill the first energy level, 8 remain to fill the second. Argon, along with the other three inert gases, exist in the region of the periodic table where periods and main energy levels do not align perfectly, and we have already discussed that whole confusion enough. The only thing I add here is that a full outermost p sublevel is the feature that unifies these inert gases. (For more on sublevels and stability, you will need to consult a chemistry class or book.)

Given that filled outer energy levels form stable arrangements, what constitutes an unstable arrangement should come as no surprise—unfilled outer energy levels. Atoms with unfilled outer energy levels tend to gain, lose, or share electrons with other atoms until they achieve a stable configuration by filling their outer energy levels. The number of electrons required to fill the outer energy level depends on the element. Hydrogen with its one proton and one electron must associate with one more electron to fill the first energy level. (Remember the first energy level fills with two). Carbon must associate with four more electrons to reach a full outer orbital. Carbon has six electrons to match its six protons. Two electrons fill the first orbital leaving four to occupy the second level. The second level fills with eight, so it is four electrons short. Nitrogen with seven protons and electrons, and oxygen with eight protons and electrons, must associate with three and two more electrons, respectively, to fill the second energy level. (Make sure this last sentence makes sense!)

Electron affinity

Associations between different atoms form because atoms with unfilled energy levels can pull on another atom's electrons. The pulling force that any atom has is termed **electron affinity** or **electronegativity**. Electron affinity varies among elements. Such differences tend to follow two patterns:

• The closer the outer energy level is to being full, the higher the element's electron affinity.

• Except for the first energy level, the lower the energy level unfilled the higher the element's electron affinity.

Table 10-1 lists the electron affinities of some elements common in the chemistry of life. Note that electron affinity does not come in units of force, such as pounds per square inch (lbs/in²) because it is a relative measure. The element fluorine was assigned an electron affinity of 4.0, and everything else was compared to it. The larger the measure of electron affinity is the stronger the pull. Oxygen, therefore, has the highest electron affinity of the elements listed.

Table 9-1. Electron affinity of some biologically important atoms.

Element	electron affinity
O (oxygen)	3.5
N (nitrogen)	3.0
Cl (chlorine)	3.0
C (carbon)	2.5
S (sulfur)	2.5
P (phosphorus)	2.1
H (hydrogen)	2.1
Na (sodium)	0.9

A continuum of molecular bonds

Now we can begin to envision molecules. Two (or more) atoms interact when they get sufficiently close to pull on each other's electrons. Each is trying to pull the other's electrons to their side. If the electron affinity of two interacting atoms is equal, or nearly so, the pulling match comes to a draw. This has important implications. By continuing to pull, but never being able to win the electron tug-of-war, each continues to hold on to the other. They form a mutual embrace that chemists call a **covalent bond**. This embrace results in a so-called equal sharing of the contested electrons. The two atoms form a molecule by holding together.

Different elements can form different numbers of covalent bonds. The number depends on the number of electrons needed to fill an atom's outermost energy level. Accordingly, hydrogen will form one bond, carbon will form four bonds, nitrogen will form three bonds, and oxygen will form two bonds. Furthermore, any atom able to form two or more covalent bonds can do so in two distinct ways. One option is each covalent bond is linked to a different atom. Carbon, for instance, can form four covalent bonds with four different atoms. Alternatively, two atoms may share more than one electron. In molecular oxygen (O_2) the two oxygen atoms share two electrons, forming a **double bond**. The two nitrogen atoms in molecular nitrogen (N_2) share three electrons, forming a **triple bond**.

The bonding together of atoms with equal electron affinities is one end of a continuum of types of molecular bonds. The bonding of atoms with greatly different electron affinities forms the other end of the continuum. When the difference in electron affinity between two atoms approaches a value of two or more, an electron tug-of-war results in a winner and a loser. The higher-affinity atom is able to grab at least one electron from the other atom. Ironically, even with winners and losers, the atoms may still stay together. Due to the electron shift, each atom becomes an ion of opposite charge. The atom gaining electrons gets a full negative charge for each electron acquired. The atom losing electrons gets a full positive charge for each electron given up. The electromagnetic attraction between opposite charges may hold these two atoms together. If so, the resultant bond is termed an **ionic bond**. Compounds held together by ionic bonds are called **salts**.

In general, ionic bonds form when a metallic element interacts with a nonmetallic element. Electrons are lost from the metal atom, resulting in a positively charged ion, and gained by the nonmetal atom, resulting in a negatively charged ion. Such oppositely charged ions can arrange into layers of alternating charges forming a crystal. For example, the interaction between sodium and chlorine results in oppositely charged ions (Na^+ and Cl^-) that stack into a cube-shaped crystal known as table salt. The crystal is one big molecule.

The formation of **polar covalent bonds** lies between the two ends of the continuum. Here one atom has an advantage—significantly higher electron affinity—in the electron tug-of-war, but the force difference is not great enough to pull the contested electrons completely away. Instead the contested electrons are still shared between atoms, but unequally so. It is the electron sharing that makes it a covalent bond. It is the unequal sharing that makes it polar. To explain this, however, I need to first explain polar.

The terms **polar** and **charged** are commonly confused. Something is **charged**, or has a charge, whenever there is an unequal number of positive and negative charges. An ion, for example, is charged because there is an unequal number of protons and electrons. The term **polar** also has an inequality associated with charge. It is not, however, an unequal number of opposite charges. What is unequal is the *distribution* of charges. In other words, something is polar whenever there is an equal number of opposite charges distributed unequally. One region has an excess of one type of charge, but the adjacent region has a counterbalancing excess of the opposite charge. Sometimes polar is defined more succinctly as a separation of charge. The only problem with this definition is that many memorize it without having a clue what they are saying.

An unequal sharing of contested electrons generates polarity for the following reasons. At the start, each atom has an equal number of protons and electrons, and that never changes. But as the electron tug-of-war ensues, protons stay put in their respective nuclei, but the shared electrons are pulled more toward the higher electron affinity atom. It is this slight shift in electron distribution that generates polarity. More negative charges (electrons) gather at the high electron affinity end, leaving more positive charges (protons) at the other end. The high affinity end assumes a slight negative charge. The other end assumes positive charge of equal strength.

In terms of bond strength (which is measured by the force needed to pull the atoms apart), covalent bonds are the strongest, ionic bonds are the weakest, and polar covalent bonds lie in between the other two.

There are also metallic bonds—metals binding with metals—but we will not discuss them here.

The difference between a molecule and a compound

As implied earlier, a molecule is formed when two or more atoms are bonded together. This includes cases where the atoms bonded together are the same element. For example, molecular oxygen is the joining of two oxygen atoms (O_2).

A compound is also a molecule. But to qualify as a compound, the molecule must be made up of two or more different types of atoms. So whereas O_2 is a molecule, it is not a compound. Water, on the other hand, is a compound because it is composed of hydrogen and oxygen.

Chemical Reactions

One example of a chemical reaction is atoms joining together to form a molecule. Perhaps more commonly chemical reactions involve atoms within molecules rearranging to form new molecular arrangements. For example in Figure 9-7, methane (also known as natural gas) and molecular oxygen are rearranged to form carbon dioxide and water. And because chemical reactions are potentially reversible, Figure 9-7 also shows that carbon dioxide and water could be rearranged into methane and molecular oxygen.

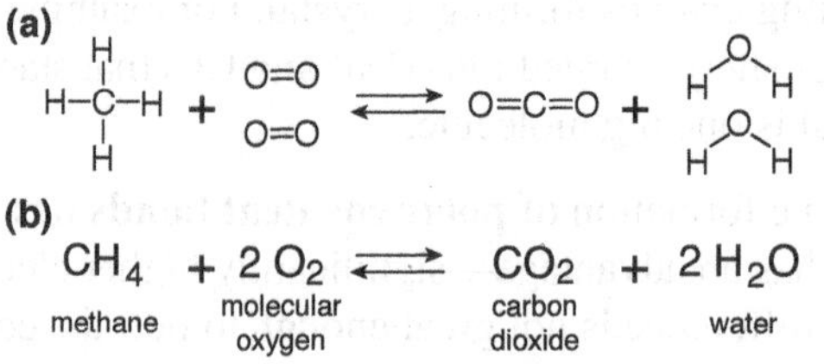

Chemical reactions do not just occur. Due to the presence of forces holding a molecule together, any molecular arrangement will persist unless some additional force intervenes. However, forces are always intervening. Unless the temperature is absolute zero, molecules are in constant motion and consequently are constantly colliding into each other. Each collision knocks each molecule out of its equilibrium configuration. To picture this, envision two tennis balls colliding. Their round shape is their equilibrium configuration and this round shape is distorted upon collision. Each tennis ball flattens in the direction of impact. Colliding molecules do something similar.

Figure 9-7. Two representations of the chemical reaction discussed in the text. (a) shows a structural representation of the reaction. Here it is easy to see the chemical reaction as a rearrangement of the atoms making up the molecules. (b) shows the same reaction in the short-hand notation used by chemists.

After each collision everything returns to an equilibrium configuration. The question is whether the equilibrium is as it was before, or if it is new. The postcollision equilibrium remains the same if the same molecules entering the collision are the ones that bounce away. Besides having their shape momentarily distorted by the collision, nothing changed. But with colliding molecules there is another option. In some cases what emerges from the collision is different than what entered. The collision so shuffles the molecular parts that the parts reconfigure into a new equilibrium arrangement. A **chemical reaction** has occurred. Because every molecular arrangement has unique physical properties, what exits after the collision is fundamentally different than what entered (see Figure 9-8). Here colliding tennis balls serve as a poor analogy. Colliding tennis balls do not emerge as something else.

$$A + B \rightleftharpoons C \quad \text{(not AB)}$$

Figure 9-8. The fact that chemical reactions produce new molecular arrangements with unique physical properties is illustrated in this generic representation of a chemical reaction. Molecule A and molecule B combine to form a completely new molecule called C. The fact that chemical reactions are reversible also means that C could separate back into A and B.

Chemical reactions, activation energy, and catalysts

Chemical reactions will not occur unless the collision packs sufficient punch to disrupt the stability of the present arrangements. This is why adding heat increases the rate of chemical reactions. Increasing the rate of random molecular motion means that molecules are zipping about, on average, at faster speeds. Molecules thus collide more often with the orientation and pace necessary to generate an instability. The level of thermal energy that must be present before a specific chemical reaction will occur (at some specified rate) is known as the reaction's **activation energy**. The concept of activation energy is a concept of control. If for some reason you were trying to get a certain reaction to proceed at a certain rate, then you would want to know the temperature necessary to do so.

A **catalyst** is anything that facilitates the occurrence of chemical reactions without undergoing a chemical reaction itself. Catalysts are important because they decrease the temperature needed to get a chemical reaction to occur (at some rate). In other words, catalysts reduce a chemical reaction's activation energy. Whether we are talking about controlling a chemical reaction that is a step in a commercial manufacturing process or controlling a chemical reaction within a living organism, there are always three basic advantages associated with using catalysts. First, catalysts can decrease the energy cost associated with controlling a chemical reaction. Less heat needs to be added, so less fuel needs to be burned to get a reaction to occur at the desired rate. Second, catalysts can decrease the associated thermal disruption because, as we learned in Chapter 2, the lower the temperature the slower thermal agitation will move any ordered arrangement toward disorder. In living organisms, which are amazingly organized and ordered, this advantage associated with using a catalyst is very important. And third, catalysts are reaction specific, so adding a catalyst to a certain setting can facilitate one type of reaction without concurrently facilitating other types of reactions. (This is in striking contrast to increasing temperature, which increases the rate of all potential reactions.) For any organism, this type of control is essential. A basic component of living is getting the right reaction to occur in the right place at the right time, while concurrently preventing the wrong reactions from occurring in the wrong place or at the wrong time. Consequently, we will spend a lot of time discussing the molecular catalysts of living systems. They are called **enzymes**.

Catalysts seemingly operate by being a shape that "grabs" certain types of molecules, each of which have unique shapes, and places them together in the orientation in which they most easily react. So when a catalyst is operating, a reactive meeting between molecules is much less dependent on chance collisions. This decreases the overall temperature dependence of a reaction because there does not need to be as many collisions per unit time to get a sufficient number of molecules together with the right orientation for the reaction to proceed at some rate. Furthermore, a single catalyst can facilitate the same reaction over and over. Whenever a catalyst-facilitated reaction takes place, the reaction product is freed because it is now a different shape and so does not fit the shape of the catalyst. The catalyst returns to its original shape and is ready to facilitate the same reaction again (see Figure 9-9(a)).

You may think of catalysts as a chemical matchmaker. In essence, they operate just like a person (the matchmaker) who selectively gets two people together in attempt to facilitate some "chemistry." The catalyst image that I will push, however, is to recognize *a catalyst as a processor* (see Figure 9-9(b)). Any time a catalyst-facilitated chemical reaction occurs, the outputs of the catalyst are different than the inputs.

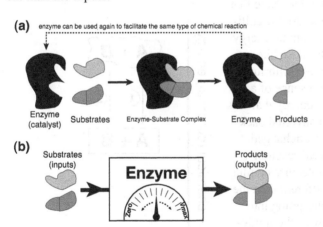

Figure 9-9. In (a) a catalyst (in this case an enzyme) facilitates a reaction by being the right shape to align potentially reactive molecules (substrates) in the right orientation to get the reaction to go. In (b) the same reaction is used to illustrate the idea that an enzyme can be seen as a processor—an agent of change that converts inputs into different outputs.

The rate of chemical reactions

How fast can chemical reactions take place? At first glance, it may seem like they would not occur very often. Consider, for instance, a chemical reaction facilitated by a catalyst such as an enzyme. For the reaction to occur, the enzyme and the substrates (the molecular inputs to the reaction) must all collide via random molecular motion. In other words, the reaction needs to wait until all the participants bump into each other by a chance encounter. Relying on chance seems to introduce an inherent slowness to the process. Winning a lottery just does not happen very often.

However, we have failed to consider the immense number of molecules present and how quickly random molecular motion sends molecules zipping around colliding into each other. Let me pull a rather impressive calculation somewhat out of thin air. ATP is a molecule that we will talk much more about in the future. A typical concentration of ATP within a cell is around 1 mM (millimolar), which means that even the smallest of cells, which are only around 1 mm (micrometer—millionth of a meter in diameter, would contain around 1×10^{13} ATP molecules. Add in the speed at which these molecules are moving around at 37°C (the temperature that you tend to keep your body at), and it has been calculated that each site on a protein molecule will continually be bombarded with around one million ATP molecules per second. Did you get that—one million per second! And this is not an extraordinary figure. Within a soup of random collisions, molecules of each and every type continually bump into each other at a rate that is hard to imagine. As a consequence, a typical enzyme has been estimated to catalyze somewhere around 1,000 reactions per second. And with some reactions the rates can even go significantly higher.

So as we proceed, always keep in the back of your mind that the chemistry occurring within living cells can happen fast, very fast.

Energetics

Any molecule, like any form of arrangement, can be viewed as containing two forms of energy. One form is the energy associated with the movement of the molecule—the molecule's **kinetic energy**. **Thermal energy** is the kinetic energy found within a randomly moving group of molecules. Stated differently, thermal energy is a collective measure of the motion of a group of molecules. The other form is the energy contained (or constrained) within the molecule's structure. This is a molecule's **chemical energy**, which is a form of potential energy.

Any chemical reaction begins with thermal (kinetic) energy being converted into chemical (potential) energy. Figure 9-10 shows the level of chemical energy found in two molecules (**A** and **B**) prior to colliding with each other and right after they collide. Note that the chemical energy is increased by the collision. As the collision distorts the arrangement of each molecule, kinetic energy is converted into chemical (potential) energy because like a spring that is being wound up, the distorted (nonequilibrium) arrangement has more potential energy. In the absence of a chemical reaction, the same amount of thermal energy that was converted to chemical energy will quickly be converted back to kinetic energy as the molecules bounce apart unchanged. However, that might not be the case if a chemical reaction takes place. The chemical energy within the molecules coming out of the reaction—the **products**— may be different than the amount of chemical energy within the molecules going into the reaction—the **substrates**. If so, the first law of thermodynamics comes into play. The increase or decrease in chemical energy must be compensated with an equal decrease or increase of kinetic energy. The energy account must balance. If so, the amount of potential (chemical) energy transformed into kinetic (thermal) energy at the end of the reaction will be different than the opposite transformation that started the reaction.

For example, for any reaction where the products have less chemical energy than the substrates, the amount of

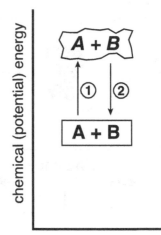

Figure 9-10. (1) The increase in chemical energy due to kinetic energy being converted into potential energy upon the two molecules (A and B) colliding. (2) The conversion of potential energy back into kinetic energy when the same two molecules bounce apart after the collision.

potential (chemical) energy transformed into kinetic (thermal) energy at the end of the reaction will be greater than the opposite transformation that started the reaction (see Figure 9-11). So overall there will be a net conversion from chemical energy into kinetic energy in the form of heat and/or radiation (e.g., light). This direction of conversion is known as an **energy-releasing reaction,** as energy is released from its stored form into its active form. Such reactions are also known as **exothermic, exergonic, catabolic**, and **breaking-down reactions**. The conversion of methane and molecular oxygen to carbon

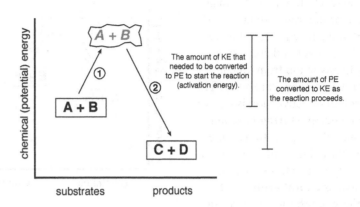

Figure 9-11. (1) A reaction occurs because a collision of the right orientation generates a sufficient increase in chemical energy to reach an instability. (Note this threshold plays a role in the setting a reaction's activation energy.) (2) Because the products have less chemical energy than the reaction substrates, the reaction results in a net conversion of chemical energy into kinetic energy.

dioxide and water is a well-known energy-releasing reaction (see Figure 9-12). We typically think of it as burning natural gas. A lighted match can provide a sufficient increase in thermal energy to get the reaction going, and during the course of the reaction more heat and light are released than the amount needed to start the reaction. That natural gas can be converted into heat and light is why we consider it to be a fuel.

Two things to note about exothermic reactions:

• Because they add heat to the system, their occurrence can accelerate the future rate of chemical reactions. For example, lighting a match in a room full of natural gas will lead to an explosion. The lighted match starts a reaction that releases enough heat to get more methane and oxygen to react. As long as the input of methane and oxygen is kept at a controlled rate, the burning just keeps itself going. But if natural gas and oxygen are in excess the amount reacting grows exponentially—or put in more common terms, it explodes.

• Overall, the reaction products tend to be structurally less complex than the molecules entering the reaction. This is the breaking-down component of exothermic reactions.

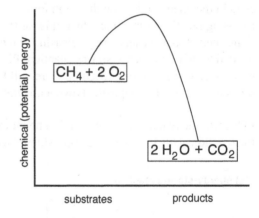

Figure 9-12. An energetic representation of methane and molecular oxygen being converted into water and carbon dioxide. The initial increase in chemical energy represents the reaction's activation energy. But because the chemical energy within the products is less than found in the substrates, the reaction overall is a energy-releasing reaction.

On the other hand, for any reaction where the products have more chemical energy than the substrates, the amount of potential (chemical) energy transformed into kinetic (thermal) energy at the end of the reaction will be less than the opposite transformation that started the reaction (see Figure 9-13). So overall there will be a net conversion from kinetic energy into chemical energy. This direction of conversion is known as an **energy-storing reaction**, as overall energy is transformed from its active form to its stored form. Such reactions are also known as **endothermic, end-ergonic, anabolic**, or **building reactions**.

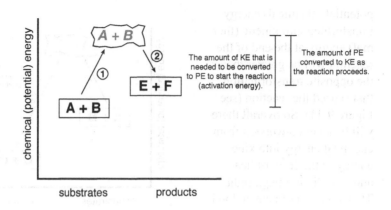

Figure 9-13. (1) A reaction occurs because a collision of the right orientation generates a sufficient increase in chemical energy to reach an instability. (2) Because the products have more chemical energy than the reaction substrates, the reaction results in a net conversion of kinetic energy into chemical energy.

Three things to note about energy-storing reactions:

• Because they take heat from the system, their occurrence can decrease the rate that chemical reactions occur in the system.

• If a reaction that proceeds in one direction is energy-storing, then the reverse reaction will be energy-releasing. Figure 9-14 shows this by contrasting the energy-storing reaction of converting carbon dioxide and water into natural gas and molecular oxygen with the energetic representation of the reverse reaction shown. Furthermore, this reversible reaction is much more likely to proceed in the energy-releasing direction for a simple reason—the activation energy for the energy-releasing reaction is much less than it is for the energy-storing reaction. Consequently, the conditions needed to drive an energy-releasing reaction are more likely to occur than the conditions needed to drive an energy-storing reaction. Plus, whenever there is sufficient activation energy to drive an energy-storing reaction, there will be more than enough activation energy to drive the reverse reaction. The opposite, however, is not true.

• Overall, the reaction products tend to be more structurally complex than the molecules entering the reaction. This is why they are considered to be building reactions.

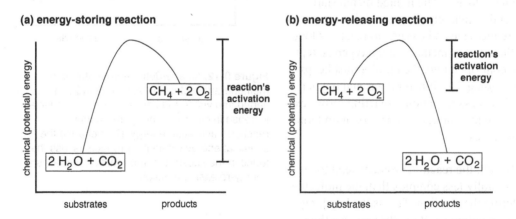

Figure 9-14. An energetic protrayal of the reaction shown in Figure 9-7. Two things, in particular, are noteworthy: (1) the reverse of an energy-storing reaction is an energy-releasing reaction, and (2) that the activation energy of an energy-storing reaction will always be greater than the activiation energy of the reverse energy-releasing reaction. As a consequence, the reaction is more likely to proceed in the energy-releasing direction, than the reverse.

Coupled reactions

A **coupled reaction** is defined as a set of reactions in which the energy released from an energy-releasing reaction is used to fuel an energy-storing reaction (see Figure 9-15). In other words, the energy released in breaking something apart is used to build something else. This is the basic means by which living organisms get the energy needed to assemble structures—building and breaking apart are inseparably intertwined.

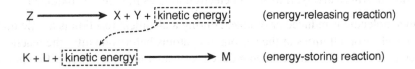

Figure 9-15. Basic structure of a coupled reaction. Each letter represents a distinct type of molecule

Redox (or Oxidation-Reduction) Reactions

Chemists love to fling the terms *oxidation* and *reduction* around. At times it seems they do so to keep the rest of us clueless. Although it can have that effect, I do not believe it is their intention. They are simply discussing an unveiled pattern. It is a pattern connecting energetics and electron affinity. Here we start to put this pattern together. The specifics of redox reactions are discussed further in Chapter 14.

The basics

Atoms, not molecules, are the units that can either be oxidized or reduced. The oxidation or reduction of a molecule depends on the oxidation and reduction of the atoms of which it is comprised.

The most general definition of **reduction** is an increase in an atom's association with electrons. The most clear-cut example is an atom (which may be part of a molecule) gaining another electron, although (as we discuss later) a more subtle change can constitute an increase in an atom's association with electrons. Keeping track of reduction is important for one reason: Reduction is always associated with an energetic gain. Reduction of an atom that is part of a molecule increases the amount of energy stored within the molecule as a whole. Reduction thus constitutes a building, energy-requiring chemical reaction.

A side note: One difficulty with the way chemists use the term *reduction* is that it seems to go against its meaning. Reduction means to become less. Yet chemists, at first glance, define it in terms of gain. It seems wrong. Frankly, that is how I commonly remember the definition—it is the opposite of what I think it should be. There is, however, some reasoning to this madness. Gain of electrons reduces the charge by adding more negative charge. Chemists also describe molecules generally by oxidation state numbers. Adding electrons reduces the value of a molecule's oxidation state number.

Oxidation is simply the opposite of reduction. Its most general definition is a decrease in an atom's association with electrons. Loss of an electron by an atom is thus the most clear-cut example, although like reduction, the change in electron association can be subtler. It is also opposite in an energetic sense. The oxidation of an atom within a molecule decreases the amount of energy stored within the resultant molecule. Oxidation constitutes a breaking-down, energy-releasing chemical reaction.

Finally, oxidation and reduction reactions go hand in hand. Whenever one atom is oxidized, then another atom must be reduced. One event never occurs in the absence of the other. Furthermore, as opposites, an atom reduced in a chemical reaction going in one direction is oxidized in the reverse chemical reaction.

Using electron affinity to determine oxidation or reduction

To determine when a single atom is oxidized or reduced is simple. It is simply of matter of whether the electron number changes. If an atom, for example, becomes negatively charged due to gaining an electron, then it is reduced. Alternatively, if losing an electron ionizes it, then it is oxidized.

Whether an atom in a molecule is reduced or oxidized during a chemical reaction is a little trickier. One must compare the electron affinities of the surrounding atoms before and after the reaction to determine what has been oxidized and what has been reduced. Consider atoms of three different types of elements that we label 3, 2, and 1. The numbers represent their relative electron affinity. Element 3 has the lowest electron affinity, 1 has the highest electron affinity, and 2 is in between. In all the following examples we consider whether a 2 atom is oxidized or reduced.

• If the molecule 2-2 undergoes a chemical reaction to 2-3—one of the 2 atoms is replaced with a 3 atom—then the remaining 2 atom is reduced. In replacing one atom of equal electron affinity with one of lower electron affinity, the remaining atom forms a stronger association with the shared electron. Similarly, a 2 atom is reduced if 2-1 becomes 2-2 or 2-3.

• Conversely, a 2 atom is oxidized if 2-3 becomes 2-2 or 2-1, or if 2-2 becomes 2-1. Replacing one atom of less or equal electron affinity with one of higher electron affinity means that the shared electron will be pulled more toward the new atom. The association of the shared electron with the remaining atom is less.

Oxidation and reduction reactions involving H, C, N, and O

The most prevalent elements in the chemistry of life are hydrogen, carbon, nitrogen, and oxygen. It is oxidation-reduction reactions involving these elements that need our focus. Most important, we need to know about hydrogen and oxygen. Remember that hydrogen has the lowest electron affinity of these four and oxygen has the highest. Consequently, whenever a bond with carbon, oxygen, or nitrogen is replaced with a bond to hydrogen, the atom to which the hydrogen bonds is reduced. An atom with higher electron affinity is replaced with one with lower electron affinity. Alternatively, because oxygen has the highest electron affinity of the four, an atom of any of the other three elements is oxidized whenever it forms a new association with oxygen.

For example:

• When CO_2 (carbon dioxide) undergoes a chemical reaction to form CH_2O (the general molecular formula for carbohydrates) the carbon atom is reduced. In the reverse reaction the carbon atom is oxidized (see Figure 9-16).

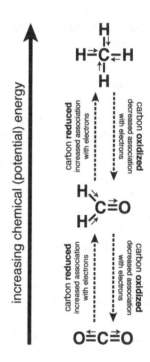

Figure 9-16. The basic scheme by which a carbon atom becomes increasingly reduced or increasingly oxidized as it moves through three molecular forms. The small arrows idicate in which direction the shared electrons are pulled most strongly (due to the atom having higher electron affinity).

• When CH_2O undergoes a chemical reaction to form CH_4 (the hydrocarbon methane) the carbon atom is further reduced. Again, in the reverse reaction the carbon atom is oxidized (see Figure 9-16).

• When N_2 (molecular nitrogen) undergoes a chemical reaction to NH_3 (ammonia) the nitrogen atom is reduced. In the reverse reaction the nitrogen atom is oxidized.

• The series of chemical reactions where N_2 is first converted to N_2O (nitrous oxide) then converted to NO_2^- (nitrite), and finally converted to NO_3^- (nitrate) is a continuing series of oxidation of the nitrogen atom. In any of the reverse reactions the nitrogen atom is reduced.

• When O_2 (molecular oxygen) undergoes a chemical reaction to form OH_2 (normally written H_2O) the oxygen atom is reduced. Water is the reduced form of oxygen.

• When H_2 undergoes a chemical reaction to form H_2O the hydrogen atoms are oxidized. This means that although water is the reduced form of oxygen, when viewed from the hydrogen perspective water is the oxidized form of hydrogen. Which of these two perspectives is correct? In one sense the answer is neither. Oxidation and reduction are features of chemical reactions, and how a molecule came in to existence is not necessarily known. In another sense it is both. In terms of oxidation and reduction, the state of water depends on which element's perspective is used to view water.

The most oxidized and most reduced forms of these four elements in combination with each other are

	Oxidized form	Reduced form
carbon	CO_2	CH_4
nitrogen	NO_3^-	NH_3
oxygen	O_2	OH_2 (normally written H_2O)
hydrogen	H_2O	H_2 (hydrogen gas)

Some Chemical Tidbits

Some properties of water

Perhaps water's most important biological feature, besides being a liquid at temperatures compatible with life, is that it is polar. Because of the differences in electron affinity, each of the hydrogen–oxygen bonds is a polar covalent bond. The presence of polar covalent bonds alone, however, is not what makes a water molecule polar. The second component is that the two hydrogen atoms are asymmetrically distributed about the oxygen atom. The angle formed between the hydrogen atoms coming off the oxygen atom is less than 180 degrees in one direction and greater than 180 degrees in the other. Given this asymmetric distribution, the hydrogen end of the molecule has a slight positive charge, and the oxygen end has a slight negative charge (see Figure 9-17).

Because they are polar, water molecules will tend to form hydrogen bonds with other water molecules (see Figure 9-17). A **hydrogen bond** is a weak electromagnetic bond between the hydrogen region of a molecule bearing a slight positive charge and a region of another molecule bearing a slight negative charged. In reference to water molecules, hydrogen bonds form between a hydrogen end of one water molecule and the oxygen end of another water molecule. Hydrogen bonds between water molecules tend to align water molecules in a somewhat structured arrangement. This structured arrangement results in:

• *Surface tension.* For something to break through the surface of any body of water, it must break hydrogen bonds. When something applies a force to a water surface, the surface will bend before it breaks. Surface tension is what makes it possible for an insect called a water strider to walk on water.

• *Water in a solid state—ice—being less dense than water in a liquid state.* When water freezes, more hydrogen bonds form between water molecules resulting in water molecules being spread further apart. This decreased density is observed easily—just watch ice cubes float in a glass of water.

• *Water being able to absorb thermal energy without its structure being greatly altered.* When water receives an input of energy, the increased motion of the molecules usually occurs along the hydrogen bonds. Only when the energy input exceeds a certain point—when the temperature approaches the boiling point—do water molecules move completely independent of each other.

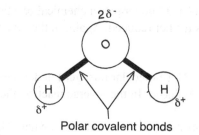

Polar covalent bonds

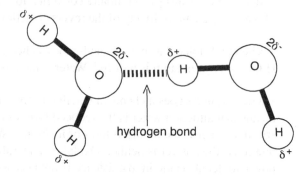

hydrogen bond

Figure 9-17. The polar nature of a single water molecule, and how water molecules will tend to align because of they are polar structures. The electromagnetic interaction between the slight positive charge of a hydrogen portion of a water molecule and the slight negative charge of the oxygen portion of a water molecule is known as a hydrogen bond.

Water is often called the solvent of life. The chemical reactions that, in essence, comprise the basis of life take place within a water medium. Humans, for example, are composed of about 70% water, with some tissues, such as your brain, being considerably higher (around 92% —no wonder it feels like your thoughts float around). Note that terrestrial organisms, such as humans, being largely composed of water suggests that an important component of transitions to land was the means to somehow carry their needed water within them. Life seemingly started immersed in water, which was made possible in part by its transparent nature—light can largely penetrate and is thus available to aquatic organisms.

Whether something dissolves in water depends on its electromagnetic properties. Charged or polar molecules tend to dissolve in water. Nonpolar molecules will not dissolve. Instead they tend to aggregate in a way that minimizes their contact with water. Water, in essence, squeezes such molecules out of the solution. Oil droplets are a good example of molecules that tend to minimize their contact with water.

Life is carbon based

Life on earth is often referred to as a carbon-based life form. It is an accurate description in that biological molecules tend to have a carbon backbone or skeleton. Carbon atoms linked together run through the molecule forming the framework for the entire molecule.

Carbon is well suited to form this framework in a wide variety of molecules because each carbon atom tends to form four covalent bonds with other atoms. Carbon atoms can thus bond with other carbon atoms in a wide array of branching and looping chains and still have room to form covalent links with other types of atoms.

Monomers and polymers

Both proteins and nucleic acids (DNA and RNA) are linear arrangements of their respective parts. To put this in chemical terms, small molecules of the same type are being joined together to form large molecules, often called **macromolecules**. **Monomer** is the general name given to these small molecules that can be linked to form macromolecules. **Polymers** are the molecules that result from linking like-monomers together. The joining of monomers into polymers is called **polymerization**. As a review I list the chemical names of the monomers for proteins, DNA, and RNA.

Monomer	Polymer
amino acids	protein
deoxyribo**nucleotides**	DNA
ribo**nucleotides**	RNA

Life, in large part, is found in the loopy interaction between DNA, RNA, and proteins. The basis of this loop is polymers acting in ways to string together the same types of polymers. Monomers are linked together by a **dehydration** reaction (or condensation reaction), so called because a water molecule is freed during the reaction. An input of usable energy is also required because polymerization is a building process. The form of chemical energy used to link together amino acids or nucleotides is the same—high phosphorylation potential.

The reverse reaction (the chemical reaction that occurs to break polymers formed by dehydration back into monomers) is called **hydrolysis**. A water molecule is used in breaking the covalent linkage between two linked monomers. Note that as the reverse to dehydration, hydrolytic reactions are energy releasing. This means that without a directed input of energy there is a tendency for the polymers to fall apart faster than being built up. Under such circumstance there is no Life.

Some key terms:

atomic arrangement - an arrangement of protons, neutrons, and electrons where all protons and neutrons are in close proximity—contained within the so-called atomic nucleus—and all electrons roam about the nucleus. (In other words, the protons and neutrons are positioned central to the electrons.)

ion - an atomic arrangement that has an unequal number of protons and electrons, hence as a whole bears a charge. (The charge is positive if there are more protons than electrons, and the charge is negative if there are more electrons than protons.)

molecular arrangement - the arrangement that forms when more than one atom interacts in a way that holds the atoms together. (Long version: an arrangement of protons, neutrons, and electrons where protons and neutrons are separated into discrete packets—the nuclei of the different atoms that comprise the molecule—and the electrons roam in between the different nuclei in a way that holds the different atoms together.)

electron affinity - the pulling force that an atom has on another atom's electrons.

covalent bond - two atoms holding on to each other (that is, bonding into a molecule) due to each atom pulling equally (or nearly so) on each other's electrons.

ionic bond - two ions of opposite charge held together by the fact that opposite charges attract.

polar - an arrangement where an equal number of opposite charges is distributed unequally, which results in one region of the arrangement being positively charged and a counterbalancing region being negatively charged. (Commonly referred to as a separation of charge.)

chemical reaction - when the arrangement of atoms within molecules emerging from a collision is different than the arrangement entering the collision.

activation energy - the speed with which certain molecules must collide before they can undergo a chemical reaction.

catalyst - anything that facilitates a chemical reaction by reducing the required activation energy, without undergoing a chemical reaction itself.

chemical energy - the potential energy contained within a molecular arrangement.

coupled reaction - a set of reactions where the kinetic energy released from an exothermic reaction (net change of PE to KE) is used to fuel an endothermic reaction (net change of KE to PE).

reduction - an increase in the number of electrons in close association with an atom.

oxidation - a decrease in the number of electrons in close association with an atom.

hydrogen bond - a weak electromagnetic attraction that forms between a slight positive charge located at a hydrogen region of one molecule and a slight negatively charged region of another molecule.

monomer - the generic name given to small molecules that can be linked together to form large molecules (macromolecules).

polymer - the generic name given to any molecule formed by linking together many small molecules (linking together many monomers).

Some study questions:

1. *Know the difference between: an atomic arrangement and a molecular arrangement, an ion and a neutral atom, a covalent bond and an ionic bond, a charged molecule and a polar molecule.* Rank the following in terms of relative size: an atom, an atomic nucleus, and a molecule. Approximately how many atoms would need to be lined up side by side to span one inch?

2. *Why does it make sense to say that chemistry is all about emergent properties?*

3. *What is wrong with the below molecule in terms of the arrangement of covalent bonds?* How could you fix it? Be able to explain why different elements tend to form different numbers of covalent bonds, including why helium and neon do not tend to form any covalent bonds with other atoms.

4. Explain the relationship between the tendency of two atoms to form a covalent bond and each atom's electronegativity.

5. What is the relationship between catalysts and activation energy? What are protein catalysts called?

6. *In which of the below pairs of molecules is (are) the carbon(s) overall more reduced? Which molecule in each pair has the most chemical energy?*

7. Consider just C, H, O, and N. *Molecular hydrogen and molecular oxygen can react to form water. Why does it make sense to say that the hydrogens in the water formed have been oxidized, while the oxygen has been reduced?* (In other words, why can water be termed the oxidized form of hydrogen and the reduced form of oxygen?) *What molecule is the most reduced form of hydrogen? of carbon? of nitrogen? What molecule is the most oxidized form of oxygen? of carbon?*

8. *Why is water a polar molecule? Be able to draw three or more water molecules held together by hydrogen bonds. Furthermore, be able to label the charged regions of each water molecules, the covalent bonds, and the hydrogen bonds.* What are some properties of water that result from its polarity?

Chemistry worksheet:

Three important ideas: *Arrangement, Rearrangement, and Emergent Properties*

Everything is made up of an arrangement of three "things"

"things"	weight or mass	charge
_____	_____	_____
_____	_____	_____
_____	_____	_____

Atomic arrangements (or atoms):

Size: _____ angstroms (Å), 1 angstrom = _____ cm, or _____ m

How many 2.5 angstrom atoms would need to be lined up to span 1 inch?

Basic arrangement:

What is this called?

What is found here?

What is found here? —

Dynamic entities:

Estimated speed that parts that make up the nucleus travel:
Estimated speed that electrons travel:

Different arrangements:

The element type of any atomic arrangement is determined by its number of _____ .

How many of these are found in: hydrogen _____, oxygen _____, carbon _____, nitrogen _____, helium _____, sodium _____, chlorine _____, potassium _____, magnesium _____, calcium _____.

What is the symbol used for each of the elements in the above list?

How has the idea of emergent properties just entered the discussion?

What is the only atomic arrangement that lacks any neutrons?

Why would neutrons be needed in all other atomic arrangements?

What is an isotope?

Atomic arrangements tend to have an equal number of what two "parts"?

When is an atomic arrangement also an ion? What is an important difference between nonionic arrangements and ionic arrangements?

Electrons and energy levels:

Within an atomic arrangement, electrons tend to reside in the _____ energy level possible.

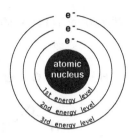

Fill in the number of electrons that can fit into the first three main energy levels:

Fill in the below diagrams for each of the elements listed: (Note: I did the first one as an example.)

hydrogen (H)

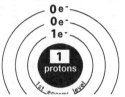

Number electrons needed to fill outer energy level? **1**

helium ( )

Number electrons needed to fill outer energy level? ____

carbon ( )

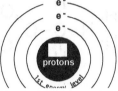

Number electrons needed to fill outer energy level? ____

nitrogen ( )

Number electrons needed to fill outer energy level? ____

oxygen ( )

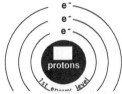

Number electrons needed to fill outer energy level? ____

neon ( )

Number electrons needed to fill outer energy level? ____

sodium ( )

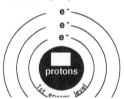

Number electrons needed to fill outer energy level? ____

chlorine ( )

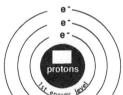

Number electrons needed to fill outer energy level? ____

argon ( )

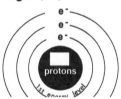

Number electrons needed to fill outer energy level? ____

Molecular arrangements:

Define electron affinity?

What is a covalent bond?

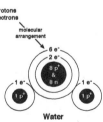

Why does the number of potential convalent bonds for each of these elements make sense?

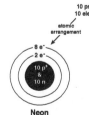

H—?   ?—O—?

Why do each of these structures make sense?

H—H   O=O   N≡N   O=C=O

Proteins: Structure and Function

Here is the image of proteins that I hope that you have gained so far. Proteins, more than any other class of molecules found in organisms, are the molecules that make things happen. Within every organism they are the processors operating at the molecular level. In fact in Chapter 8 I introduced the perspective that reproduction can be viewed as proteins acting to make more of all the same type of proteins.

The reason proteins can do so many different things is a simple one: Each protein tends to self-assemble into a unique shape and different proteins (different sequences of protein parts) take on a wide array of different shapes. So although any one type of protein is confined by the shape–performance trade-off to perform only a limited range of activities, proteins as a group can do a lot of different things.

Why proteins can take on so many shapes can also be answered simply. Proteins are made from a large number—20 to be exact—of variable parts. (The most we will see in any other class of biological molecules is four not-so-variable parts.) Just think if you had a set of Legos or some other form of building blocks with 20 distinctly shaped parts; the number of different shapes you could assemble is seemingly unlimited. Although this analogy is not strictly accurate, it illustrates the general point.

Some details of protein structure: Protein parts

All 20 different types of protein parts fall within a group of molecules called **amino acids**. (There are more than 20 different types of amino acids, but only 20 are found in the proteins made by bacteria, plants, animals, and all other types of organisms). The structure of an amino acid is organized around the fact that a carbon atom can form four covalent bonds. Any molecule is considered to be an amino acid when three of the four linkages around a central carbon atom are occupied by an amino group (—NH$_2$), a carboxyl (or acid) group (—COOH), and a single hydrogen atom. The type of amino acid is determined by what attaches to the central carbon atom at the remaining position. This last linkage group is the variable side chain or **R** group (**R** designates a variable group; see Figure 10-1).

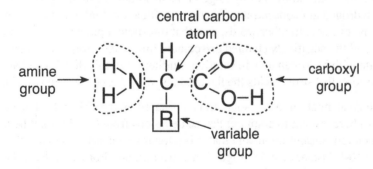

Figure 10-1. An amino acids basic structure.

A closer look at carboxyl groups and some brief comments on acids

Whenever a carbon atom is linked to one oxygen atom by a double covalent bond and another oxygen that is part of a hydroxyl group (an oxygen and a hydrogen—OH) by a single covalent bond, the entire arrangement is called a **carboxyl group** (see Figure 10-1). The focus here is why a carboxyl group is also known as an acid group. Compounds containing carboxyl groups are known as **carboxylic acids**.

An **acid** is defined as a molecule that acts as a hydrogen ion or proton donor. When an acid is dissolved in water at least one of the molecule's hydrogen atom tends to dissociate into its component parts—the single proton moves off into the solution, whereas the single electron stays with the rest of the molecule. Both parts are now ions. The extra electron adds a single negative charge to the remaining molecule, whereas the proton has a single positive charge and is called a hydrogen ion (H^+).

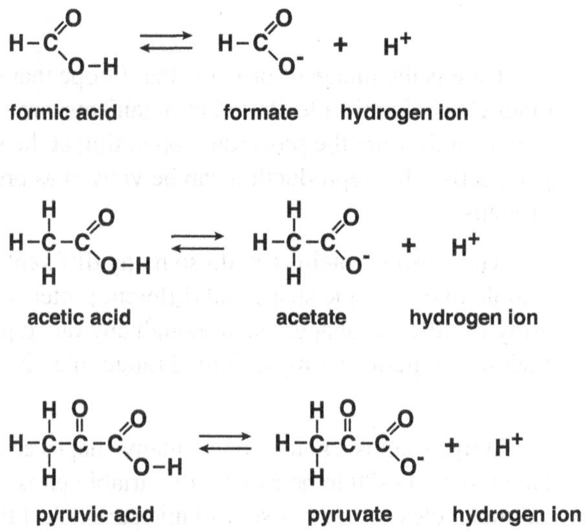

Carboxyl groups tend to act as acids because in water the hydrogen in the hydroxyl group tends to dissociate, with the electron remaining with the oxygen and the proton going into solution. Figure 10-2 shows this dissociation in the three of the simplest carboxylic acids: formic acid, acetic acid, and pyruvic acid. Note that when a carboxylic acid acids loses a hydrogen ion, the negatively charged ion remaining is designated by the suffix -*ate* (formate, acetate, and pyruvate in Figure 10-3). Formate, acetate, and pyruvate are not acids

Figure 10-2. Three molecules containing carboxyl groups in their associated (acid) and dissociated (ionized) form. (See text for further details.)

because none of the remaining hydrogen atoms tend to dissociate. They can, however, act as a **base** or proton acceptor. This means that potentially they can associate with a hydrogen ion in solution.

But if acetate or one of these other compounds acted as a base, wouldn't it become an acid again? And if it did become an acid again, wouldn't it donate the hydrogen ion back to solution? So how could any of these compounds ever really act as a base? This all sounds confusing because (in my opinion) chemists made a mistake by ever using the term *acid* in labeling compounds (e.g., acetic acid). Labeling a compound as an acid implies that it will always act as an acid—that is, that it will always donate hydrogen ions in solution. But that is not the case. Whether a potential acid acts as an acid depends on the concentration of hydrogen ions in solution. For any potential acid there is a threshold where hydrogen ion concentration becomes sufficiently high that the tendency for hydrogen ions to dissociate is reversed. In other words, past that threshold a potential acid tends to hold onto its hydrogen ion, and the negatively charged dissociated forms (e.g., formate or acetate) tend to act as bases and associate with hydrogen ions in solution. Furthermore, this threshold changes with different potential acids. In so-called strong acids the threshold is much higher than in so-called weak acids.

Hydrogen ion concentration in any solution is measured on the **pH scale**. The details of the scale are not my concern here, except to point out that scale ranges from 0 to 14, that the lower the value the higher the hydrogen ion concentration, and that it is a logarithmic scale so that a change in one unit actually represents a 10-fold change in hydrogen ion concentration. For example, if the pH of a solution decreases from 6 to 5, the hydrogen ion concentration has increased 10-fold. This also means that a change in pH from 6 to 3 represents a 10,000-fold (10x10x10) increase in hydrogen ion concentration. The threshold I spoke of in the preceding paragraph is known as a potential acids **pK**, which is defined as the pH where a solution contains an equal concentration of associated and dissociated forms. The pK of carboxylic acids tends to range between 2 and 5. So in solutions where the pH is greater than a specific carboxylic acid's pK, the molecule tends to dissociate into two ions. Conversely, in solutions of pH less than a carboxylic acid's pK the molecule tends to stay together (in their associated form). Because the range of pH found within cells is generally between 6 and 8, carboxylic acids located inside a cell tend to be in their dissociated or ionized form.

The amino group

Recall that nitrogen atoms tend to form three covalent bonds. In amino groups hydrogen atoms occupy two of these bonds, and the remaining one is used to connect the amino group to the rest of a molecule.

Even when the hydrogen ion concentration in solution is very low, the amino group tends to act as a base. Hydrogen ions are taken out of solution as they associate with the nitrogen atom's remaining unshared pair of electrons (the pair not involved in forming one of the three covalent bonds). In the process, the amino group is ionized with a single positive charge (see Figure 10-3). The pK of this potential association for different molecules containing amino groups typically ranges between a pH of 9 to 12. Noting again that the pH found within cells is generally between 6 and 8, amino groups located inside cells tend to be their associated or ionized form.

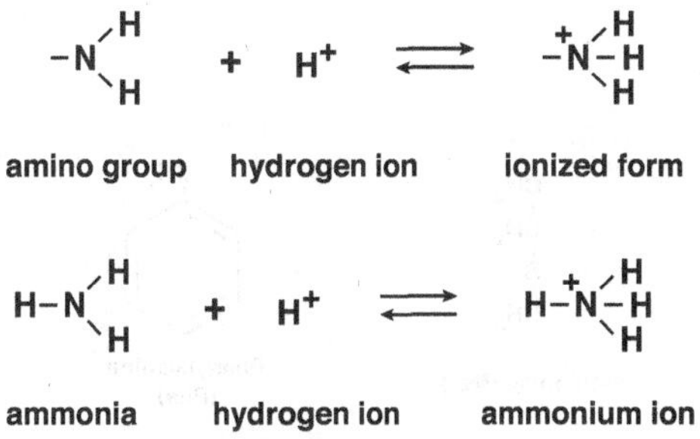

amino group   hydrogen ion   ionized form

ammonia   hydrogen ion   ammonium ion

Figure 10-3. An amino group and ammonia (the simplest molecule containing an amino group) in their dissociated (uncharged) and associated (ionized) forms. (See text for further details.)

Based on the discussion of both carboxylic groups and amino groups, Figure 10-4 shows the most common form of these two groups within an amino acid at three different pH values.

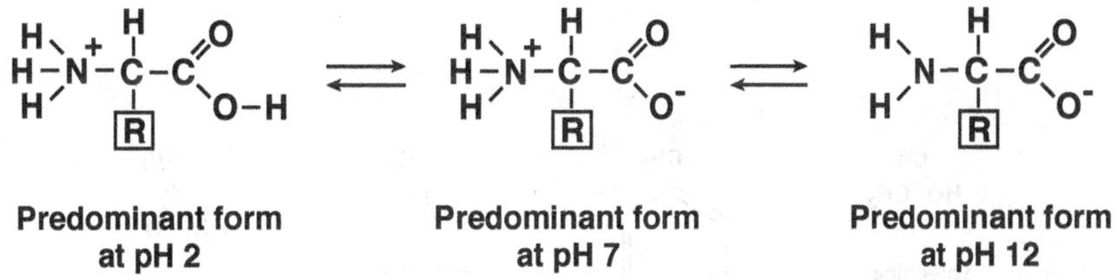

Predominant form at pH 2   Predominant form at pH 7   Predominant form at pH 12

Figure 10-4. The ionized states of an amino acid at different pH values.

The variable group

You already know how many variable side chains there are in biologically relevant amino acids. There are 20, one for each of the 20 different types of protein parts. In other words, each of the 20 different types of protein parts has a different **R** group attached to the central carbon atom. These 20 different side chains vary in terms of size, shape, charge, capacity to form hydrogen bonds, and tendency to participate in chemical reactions. Let us look at these different side chains.

The feature that unites the first group of biological amino acids shown in Figure 10-5 is that they are all nonpolar and consequently hydrophobic—that is, like fats they tend not to interact with water. This group starts with the simplest side chain, a single hydrogen atom, and generally continues with hydrocarbon arrangements of increasing size and varying shape. For example, the presence of a hydrocarbon ring dramatically changes the size and shape of the side chain in phenylalanine and tryptophan. The only two side chains in this group that contain elements other than hydrogen and carbon are methionine, which contains a single sulfur embedded within a hydrocarbon chain, and tryptophan, which contains a single nitrogen. Proline also differs by the fact that the hydrocarbon side chain forms covalent bonds with both the central carbon and the nitrogen from the amine group.

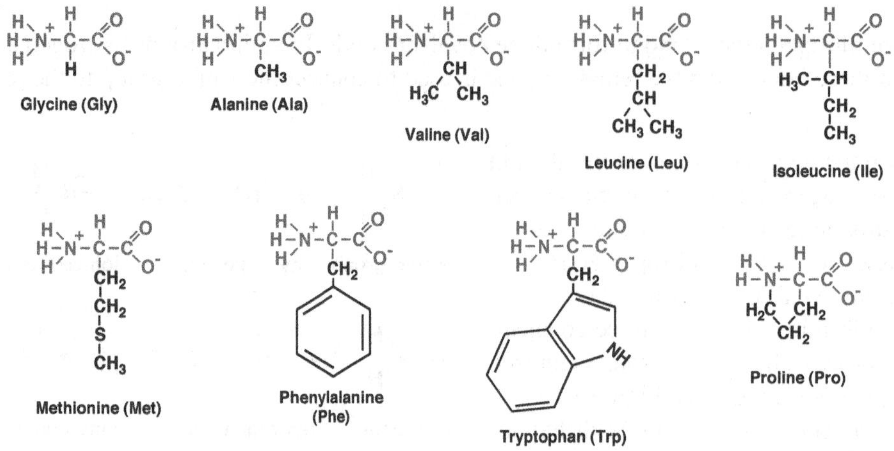

Figure 10-5. The nonpolar amino acids found in biological proteins.

Figure 10-6 displays the biological amino acids with polar side chains. The first three amino acids shown in this figure have similar side chains to three amino acids shown in the previous figure—alanine, valine, and phenylalanine. The difference is that the polar side chains include a hydroxyl group (—OH), which makes them more hydrophilic (more interactive with water) and increases their chemical reactivity. The sulfur and hydrogen group at the end of the side chain in cysteine is also highly reactive. The remaining two amino acids, asparagine and glutamine, bear side chains that are chemically interesting because both the NH group and CO group can participate in forming hydrogen bonds.

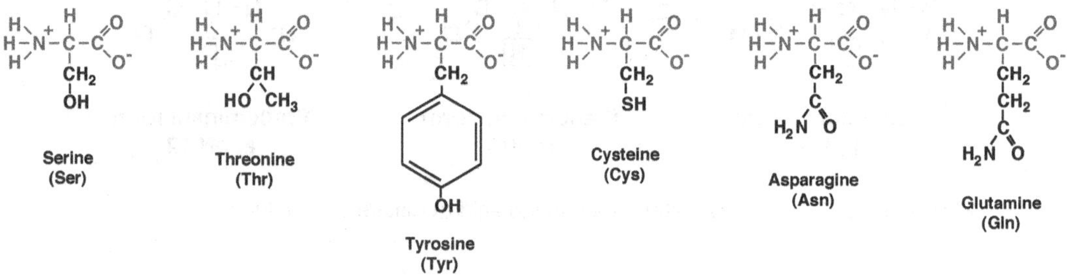

Figure 10-6. The polar amino acids found in biological proteins.

The remaining biological amino acids shown in Figure 10-7 are grouped because their side chains tend to be ionized at common cell pH values (between 6 and 8). The first two have side chains that contain a carboxyl group that (as discussed earlier) tends to donate a hydrogen ion to the solution at biological pH values and thus become a negative ion. These two amino acids—aspartic acid and glutamic acid—are commonly called aspartate and glutamate to emphasize that within cells they are generally in their ionized form. In contrast, lysine and arginine have a terminal amino group on their side chains that (as discussed earlier) tends to act as a base at biological pH values and become a positive ion by associating with a hydrogen ion. Although held within a ring structure, histidine also contains a nitrogen atom that can act as a base and ionize by associating with a hydrogen ion. However, it does not do so nearly as readily as lysine or arginine.

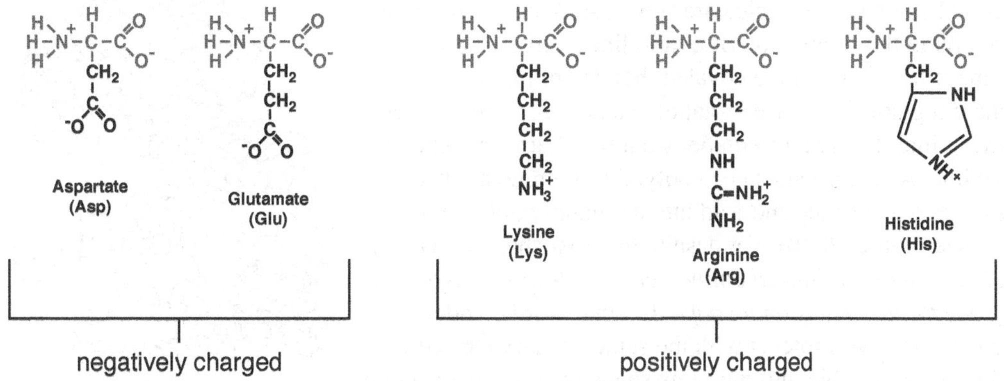

Figure 10-7. The charged amino acids found in biological proteins.

Some details of protein structure: Forming polymers and self-assembly

Amino acids are monomers because they can be linked to form polymers. Each is linked in the same way. The carbon in the acid group of one amino acid is covalently linked to the amine group's nitrogen in the next amino acid (see Figure 10-8). In the process a water molecule is freed, so this reaction is called a water-releasing or **dehydration reaction**. The resultant covalent bond is called a **peptide bond**. The formation of a peptide bond is an energy-storing reaction, which means an input of usable energy is needed to drive the reaction. As we discuss more in the next chapter and in Chapter 14, a molecule with high phosphorylation potential called ATP is the fuel used to supply this required energy.

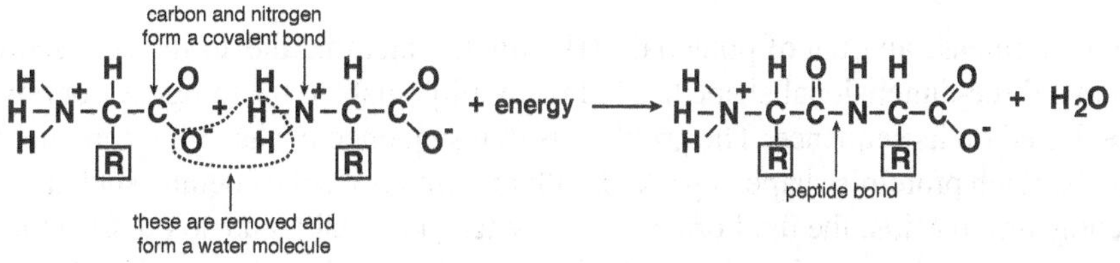

Figure 10-8. Amino acids become linked together when the carbon atom in the carboxyl group of one amino acid forms a covalent bond with the nitrogen atom in the amino group of another amino acid. The resultant covalent bond is called a peptide bond.

A **dipeptide** is two linked amino acids. A **polypeptide** is a polymer of three or more linked amino acids. **Proteins** are polypeptides somewhere between 50 and several thousand amino acids in length. The **primary structure** of any protein is simply its sequence of amino acids (see Figure 10-9).

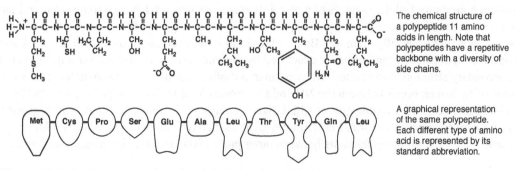

The chemical structure of a polypeptide 11 amino acids in length. Note that polypeptides have a repetitive backbone with a diversity of side chains.

A graphical representation of the same polypeptide. Each different type of amino acid is represented by its standard abbreviation.

Figure 10-9. A polypeptide in both its chemical and graphical form.

In the top part of Figure 10-9, the variable side chains on each of the 11 linked amino acids are shown sticking out in same direction, giving the impression of a rigid linear structure. This is far from the truth. Many of the covalent bonds linking the atoms of this chain together allow free rotation, so not only can the side chains swing into different orientations but the chain's backbone is also flexible. As a consequence, a polymer of amino acids can potentially bend and rotate and fold into an innumerable number of shapes (see Figure 10-10). Yet despite this vast shape potential, *any specific sequence of linked amino acids tends to self-assemble into only one three-dimensional shape*. In other words, under similar conditions two proteins with the same primary structure will tend to self-assemble into the same shape (or the same protein once unfolded will tend to fold back into the same shape), where-as two proteins with different primary structures will tend to fold into at least somewhat different shapes. The unique relationship between a protein's primary structure and its shape arises because the different variable side chains have different chemical and physical properties. As a consequence, each amino acid interacts somewhat differently with the surrounding water and with other amino acids.

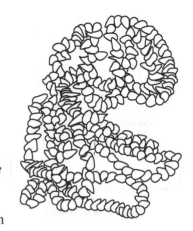

Figure 10-10. A chain of approximately 300 amino acids—each represented as a sphere—folded into a 3-dimensional shape.

Coupling the length of proteins—50 to thousands of amino acids in length, with an average length being somewhere around 300—along with a choice of 20 amino acids at each position leads to an astronomical number of different possible sequences. Just to get you thinking about this, consider the fact that there are 160,000 ways to arrange 20 different parts into a chain four parts long ($20^4 = 20 \times 20 \times 20 \times 20 = 160,0000$). And even more mind-boggling, there are 20^{300} ways to arrange the 20 different amino acids into a chain of 300. With each sequence folding into at least a slightly different shape, it is no wonder that proteins have a seemingly unlimited potential to take on different shapes.

Yet despite the immense amount of potential variation, the fact that the amino acid sequence specifies a protein's three-dimensional shape has led many biologists to try to figure out how to predict a protein's shape based on its sequence. The problem is that sequence to shape interpretation is not as simple as it sounds. Each protein's shape is packed with an immense set of details such as the distance between interacting amino acids, the final orientation of each side chain, and so on. One means of studying protein shape called x-ray crystallography has already discovered more than 100 different types of folds. So it is likely that each unique sequence has some to many subtle and potential unique nuances in how it folds that would need to be accounted for before its shape could be accurately pre-dicted. Proteins will not yield their folding secrets easily.

The self-assembly of a protein's shape is potentially affected by three levels of interactions

Although predicting all the nuances of a protein's shape has proved difficult, some structural pat-terns have been found to occur regularly. Two patterns, known as **alpha helixes** (α helixes) and **beta sheets** (β sheets) are especially common. Both of these fall into the category of protein folding known as **secondary structure**. Instead of being structured by the interactions among the variable side chains per se, secondary structure is characterized by regular and often repetitive shapes held together by the formation of hydrogen bonds between the NH and CO groups found within the polypeptide back-bone. The sequence of the variable groups still, however, plays a role because only certain sequences allow these hydrogen bonds to form. Furthermore, all alpha helixes and beta sheets are not identi-cally shaped. Variable group interactions between other parts of the amino acid chain as well as the surrounding medium can cause the basic cylindrical shape of an alpha helix and the planar shape of a beta sheet to become twisted or in some other way distorted.

An amino acid chain twists into an alpha helix whenever hydrogen bonds form repetitively between one amino acid and the forth amino acid ahead of it in the chain (see Figure 10-11). Overall this helical arrangement creates a rigid cylinder coated with the various R groups that protrude to the outside. Many proteins contain at least one or more regions of alpha helix interspersed among their length (see Figure 10-12). These helical regions thus contribute to the protein's final shape.

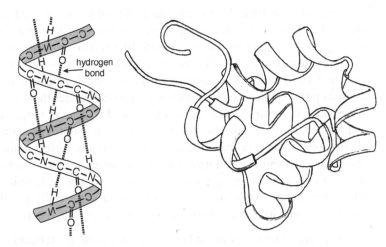

Figure 10-11. An alpha helix. Dotted lines represent the hydrogen bonds that form between amino acid within the chain. Variable groups are not shown, but protrude outside the cylinder.

Figure 10-12. Model of a protein that contains five sections of alpha helix separated by nonhelical regions.

Beta sheets form when hydrogen bonds form between NH and CO groups in distinct regions of an amino acid chain that lie adjacent to each other. Figure 10-13 illustrates some variations on this theme. Specifically beta sheets can be *antiparallel* (where the aligning sections of the chain run in opposite directions) or *parallel* (where the aligning sections of the chain run in the same direction). Furthermore, there is no set length of chain that lies between sections connecting into a beta sheet. In other words, beta sheets can form in regions where the chain quickly folds back on itself, or it can form between quite distant regions of the chain.

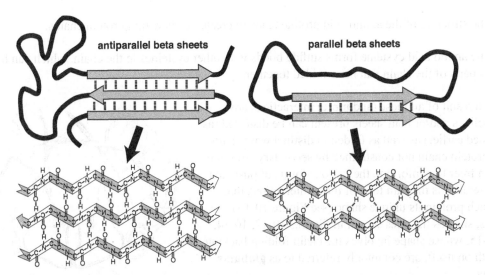

Figure 10-13. The left side shows a beta sheet formed by three portions—each designated as an arrow—of a single polypeptide chain held together by hydrogen bonds (dashed lines) in an antiparallel arrangement. A closer look at the hydrogen bonds forming between CO and NH groups within the backbone of the polypeptide chain is shown below. The R groups, which are not directly involved in the formation of beta sheets, have been left out. The right side shows the same thing, except the beta sheet is formed by two portions of the polypeptide chain arranged in the same orientation (parallel arrangement).

You will sometimes hear a beta sheet referred to as a **pleated beta sheet** because of the regular zigzag-bending pattern found within each participating region of protein (see Figure 10-13). Do not, however, let this pleated pattern create the illusion that beta sheets are easily stretched. Each amino acid chain within a beta sheet is extended about as far as possible. In fact, beta sheets form rigid structures that often serve as the framework around which the rest of a protein's shape is constructed. Furthermore, note that Figure 10-13 illustrates an antiparallel and a parallel beta sheet that are both structurally perfect in the sense that each amino acid forms a hydrogen bond with each neighboring amino acid. In reality most beta sheets are not perfect, which allows beta sheets to take on more twisted conformations. Figure 10-14 shows a protein with extensive regions of twisted beta sheets.

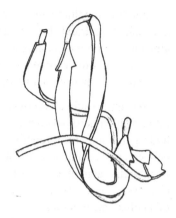

Figure 10-14. Model of a protein that contains a twisted antiparallel beta sheet formed by four different portions—each designated as a flattened arrow—of a single polypeptide chain.

The second level self-assembly, known as a protein's **tertiary structure**, involves all aspects of a protein's shape determined by interactions among the variable groups with each other and with the surrounding medium (which in all living organisms is water). Some of these different types of interactions are

• Amino acids with hydrophobic (nonpolar) side chains pull the chain inward when immersed in water, as they tend to cluster toward the interior. The different sizes and shapes of the nonpolar variable side chains make it possible to form clusters that exclude all water by packing tightly together.

• Amino acids with hydrophilic (polar or charged) side chains orient to face the surrounding water, tugging the chain outward in the process.

• Polar **R** groups can form hydrogen bonds with other polar **R** groups.

• Electrically charged **R** groups can form ionic bonds with oppositely charged **R** groups.

• The structure of the amino acid proline tends to create bends within protein chains.

• The amino acid cysteine forms sulfide bonds with other cysteines in the chain, which can hold in two parts of the chain that have folded together.

As a result of all these (and more) interactions any alpha helixes and/or beta sheets present can be distorted (as mentioned earlier) as well as folded in distinct ways. Parts of the protein chain not constrained by secondary structure are even freer to conform to the various forms of push and pull. Overall it is the sum total of these interactions that gives each protein its unique shape (see Figure 10-15). Proteins, such as the ones shown in Figures 10-12, 10-14, and 10-15, whose shape involves the chain folding backing and forth on itself, are commonly referred to as **globular proteins**.

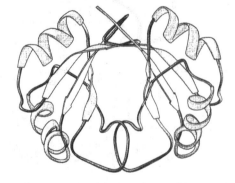

Figure 10-15. Model of a protein that contains a two twisted antiparallel beta sheets and four regions of alpha helix all folded into a distinct 3-dimensional shape.

The last recognized level of interaction occurs when amino acids from different polypeptide chains (different proteins) form chemical associations that join the two or more chains into a single structure. Both the shapes of the individual proteins and how they fit together determine the structure's overall shape. The aspect of a protein's shape that results from interactions between different polypeptide chains is known as its **quaternary structure**. Each chain within the structure is called a **subunit,** and the combination of subunits is sometimes called a **protein assembly** or a **protein complex**. The subunits can be identical or different (see Figure 10-16).

The basis of protein action

That shape affects performance is an idea that we first developed in organisms. Now we are seeing that it holds true at the molecular level. The shape–performance trade-off applies to proteins, and as a consequence, different tasks occurring within a cell likely requires the presence of a unique protein—that is, one with a distinct shape. Yet due to the huge diversity of potential shapes, it is still possible for proteins to perform a wide variety of tasks. But what is it, in particular, about this vast shape potential that makes proteins so capable of facilitating different activities? Such capacity boils down to two things: selective binding and shape changing.

Figure 10-16. Model of a protein called hemoglobin that shows secondary, tertiary, and quaternary structure. Four independent polypeptide chains (two of one type—alpha subunits—and two of another type—beta subunits), each of which has a globular conformation, interact with amino acids from different chains such that they self-assemble into a single structure. Each subunit binds a nonprotein group called heme.

With such a vast shape potential, some protein is going to have the right shape to bind with almost any molecule. In other words, whatever shape any molecule has, a protein with a complementary shape potentially exists. Being able to selectively bind to other molecules makes many things possible.

Enzymes

For one, *proteins can act as catalysts*. Through binding to molecules, proteins can position two or more molecules in a way that facilitates a chemical reaction (see Figure 10-17). Protein catalysts are called **enzymes,** and the region of an enzyme that binds with molecules is called the **active site**. Enzymes are an essential component of living because living depends on the constant but controlled occurrence of chemical reactions. The fundamental way to speed up the occurrence of any chemical reaction is to increase temperature—molecules moving faster tend to react more often. But increasing temperature poses two problems: living organisms are organized structures, and higher temperatures are increasingly disruptive to organization, and increasing temperature will speed up all potential

Figure 10-17. In (a) an enzyme faciliates a reaction by being the right shape to align potentially reactive molecules (substrates) in the right orientation to get the reaction to go. In (b) the same reactions is used to illustrate the idea that an enzyme can be seen as a processor—an agent of change that converts inputs into different outputs.

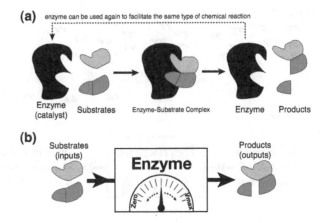

chemical reactions and not just the ones currently needed for living. Enzymes assist with both of these problems. First, enzymes allow chemical reactions to proceed at lower, less-disruptive temperatures. Furthermore, organisms can begin to control the type of chemical reactions that occur by controlling what enzymes are currently present. A chemical reaction will tend to occur only if the enzyme that facilitates that particular reaction is present.

A little more information: Although the chemistry of life (or metabolism) involves a vast array of chemical reactions, and thus a vast array of differently shaped enzymes, relatively few chemical structures are actually transferred between molecules during these reactions. In other words, in at least some ways metabolism is not as complex as it may first appear. The presence of a common set of protein **cofactors**—which are often divided into two broad groups: coenzymes or prosthetic groups—underscores this pattern. A cofactor is defined as a nonprotein molecule to which an enzyme must first bind to function as a catalyst. But the important thing to see is that the same cofactor is commonly used by more than one enzyme. For instance, a **coenzyme** (or cosubstrate) is a nonprotein organic molecule that associates with more than one type of enzyme, but in each case is able to either accept or donate the specific chemical group (e.g., electrons, phosphates, acetate) transferred during the enzyme-driven biochemical reaction. Coenzymes bind only loosely to an enzyme during the reaction and then are released afterward. A **prosthetic group**, in contrast, is a nonprotein chemical that becomes permanently affixed to an enzyme in a position that allows it to become a component of its active site. In other words, the enzyme permanently holds on to a chemical structure that can both accept and donate the functional group transferred in the chemical reaction that it facilitates. Different enzymes with the same prosthetic group thus facilitate the transfer of the same functional group between different molecules. Prosthetic groups can be organic molecules, inorganic chemicals such as certain types of metal ions (e.g., manganese, iron, cobalt, zinc), or a combination of an inorganic and organic chemical (e.g., heme, which consist an iron ion attached to a structure called a porphyrin ring).

Other forms of action

Other actions that a protein's binding ability can facilitate *include transport, regulation, and protection.*

Proteins used to facilitate transport operate at different scales. For example, **permeases** are proteins involved in selectively moving molecules into and out of cells (and between compartments within cells) by transporting the molecules across a membrane barrier (see Figure 10-18). Such transport is selective because a permease can only move those molecules that it can bind with, which will always be a limited number and in some cases will include only a single type of molecule. The binding of molecules with proteins can also be used in transport on a larger scale, such as transport through

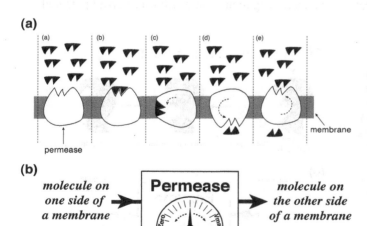

(a)

(b)

molecule on one side of a membrane → **Permease** → *molecule on the other side of a membrane*

Figure 10-18. Permeases are membrane bound proteins that transport molecules across a membrane by first selectively binding a molecule and then shuttling it across. Like an enzyme, a permease can be seen as a processor—an agent of change—with the change being a change in position.

a multicellular organism's circulatory system. Certain proteins facilitate transport through circulatory systems by binding to a molecule that would otherwise not dissolve well in blood. Hemoglobin (pictured in Figure 10-16) is a classic example. The ability of the heme group (which is a prosthetic group) within each subunit to bind with molecular oxygen increases the amount of oxygen that can be absorbed into the bloodstream and thus increases the amount of oxygen that can be transported throughout the organism.

The basic principle by which a protein's binding ability is used to regulate (turn on or off, up or down) certain activities is straightforward. Whenever a protein binds with another molecule, the overall shape of both molecules is changed. This shape change could prevent certain interactions from occurring and consequently turn off a specific activity. Alternatively, this shape change could convert a nonfunctional shape into a functional one and consequently turn on a specific activity. How this idea is actually put to use is discussed more in subsequent chapters.

The fact that a protein binding with another molecule creates an overall shape change is also used for protection. Although you have probably never thought about it in this way, a healthy organism is one that has all its needed proteins and each one is working properly. A toxic or otherwise harmful molecule is thus one that can impair health generally by binding with some functional protein in a way that gums up its workings. So how could an organism neutralize a toxin? One way would be to alter the toxin's shape in a way that keeps it from binding to the protein it disrupts, and that could be accomplished by producing a protein whose sole function is to bind with the toxin. This is one of the ways that proteins that you produce called antibodies help protect you.

The second aspect of proteins that allows them to orchestrate a wide range of activities is that some change shape when they bind with another molecule. These shape changers are called **allosteric proteins**. Shape changing opens the door to new forms of action. For example, changing shape on binding may be how a permease is able to move the molecule it binds with from one side of a membrane to the other. Organisms also generate directional motion by the actions of certain shape-changing proteins. As we discuss further in Chapter 14, a repeating cycle of shape change within a protein is harnessed to move something in a specific direction. It is analogous to a bicycle harnessing someone spinning its pedals to move forward. In fact, the contraction of your muscles used in pedaling your bicycle is based on a shape-changing protein called myosin. Even an enzyme's catalytic ability may be enhanced by shape change. The change in shape associated with binding may aid a chemical reaction by enclosing the bound molecules more tightly.

Proteins also play structural roles

Not all proteins contribute to a reproductive performance by orchestrating specific types of change. Some proteins play structural roles in that they hold things together (like a tendon linking a muscle to a bone). Collagen is a classic example. It is a protein whose shape is a combination of secondary structure and quaternary structure. Individual polypeptides coil into an alpha helix (secondary structure), and then three polypeptide chains coil together (quaternary structure) to form ropelike fibers (see Figure 10-19). This fibrous arrangement has extremely high tensile strength—it resists breaking when being pulled at each end. It thus makes sense that collagen is a major component of tendons. Collagen is in fact used to hold all the cells of a multicellular body together. Some other examples of proteins playing structural roles are

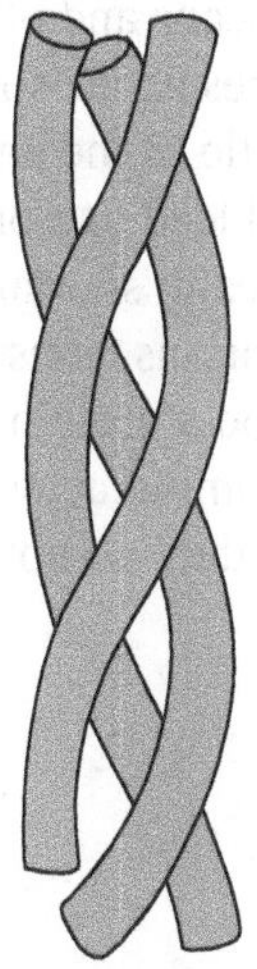

• Keratin is a helical fibrous protein found in fingernails, hooves, horns, and hair.

Figure 10-19. Model of a protein called collagen that shows secondary and quarternary structure. Three independent polypeptide chains, each of which has a helical conformation, interact with amino acids from dif-

• Silk, spider webs, scales, claws, and beaks are examples of structures built out of proteins that form extensive beta sheets.

Globular proteins can also act as structural proteins. One example is a group of DNA-binding proteins found in eukaryotic cells called **histones**. Eukaryotic cells have tremendous amounts of DNA. Histones help hold all this DNA together. The extensive DNA is completely coiled around the histones to form a tightly compacted structure.

Storage proteins

Storage is an important theme in the workings of Life. It makes sense whenever an organism faces a situation where a supply of something important is abundant now and potentially scarce later. Beyond that, various storage stories are in the details. For instance, both squirrels and bears store food in the fall to survive the winter, but they do it in different ways; squirrels hide nuts outside their bodies, whereas bears deposit fat inside their bodies. Much less dramatic, but equally important, we, and all other animals that feed periodically, store high-energy molecules and other nutrients after every meal so that we have the means to keep ourselves running until the next meal.

A protein could potentially be used to store amino acids. Excess amino acids at one time could be polymerized into a protein that instead of acting as an enzyme or orchestrating some other function, could simply "hang out" until an organism experienced an amino acid shortage. Storage protein could then be broken back down to provide the amino acids needed to build functionally important proteins.

Are there storage proteins? I suspect that nearly every organism makes them, but I only know of specific examples in plants. They make proteins with no enzymatic activity that are typically deposited within the cells of seeds, tubers, or other regions of a plant that would benefit from the ability to grow rapidly after a period of dormancy (such as after winter).

Dietary information: The amount of protein in the seeds of some legumes, such as soybeans, can be as high as 40 to 50% of their dry weight, with about 85% of those being storage proteins. This is why beans and other legume seeds are a good source of dietary protein, although attempting to use legumes as the sole or major protein source is problematic. The storage proteins of legumes have too little of the amino acid *methionine* to met human requirements. Any amino acid in short supply would lead to a production shortage of all proteins requiring that amino acid, which in turn would lead to a health shortage due to the disruption of whatever functions those proteins performed. For strict vegetarians, consuming cereal seeds (e.g., wheat, barley) along with legumes can help. They are not as good a protein source—10 to 15% of their dry weight—and their storage proteins have too little of three amino acids to met human requirements—*threonine*, *tryptophan*, and particularly *lysine*—but because they do not share the same amino acid deficiencies, consuming both is complementary.

Some key terms:

amino acid - one of the twenty monomers that are linked together to form proteins. In each of the twenty amino acids three of the four groups attached to a central carbon atom are the same— an amine group, an acid group, and a single hydrogen atom. It is differences in the fourth group that results in different amino acids.

peptide bond - the name of the covalent bond that links two amino acids together.

primary structure (of a protein) - a protein's specific sequence of linked amino acids.

secondary structure (of a protein) - the aspects of a protein's three-dimension shape that forms due to the formation of hydrogen bonds between the NH and CO groups found within the polypeptide. The shapes formed are often repetitive, such as seen in alpha helixes and beta sheets.

tertiary structure (of a protein) - the aspects of a protein's three-dimension shape determined by interactions among the variable groups in the same chain with each other and with the surrounding water medium.

quaternary structure - the three-dimension shape that results from more than one protein (polypeptide) binding together. The overall shape is determined both by the shape of the individual subunits (polypetides) and how the subunits fit together.

enzyme - any protein that acts as a catalyst for a specific chemical reaction.

permease - any protein that aids in the movement of a specific type of molecule across a cell membrane.

Some study questions:

1. *Understand well the relationship between a protein's amino acid sequence (its primary structure) and its shape.*

2. In general terms, explain how a protein could act to catalyze a specific chemical reaction, say a reaction between two molecules called **A** and **B**. Next explain why this particular enzyme could repeatedly facilitate a reaction between **A** and **B**. Finally, explain why such a protein probably cannot facilitate any other type of chemical reaction. (In answering the last question, be sure to discuss the shape-performance tradeoff in terms of proteins.)

3. Why does it make sense to call enzymes molecular-level processors?

4. Besides acting as enzymes, what other functional roles do different proteins play in organisms?

5. Explain the following: Every different task occurring with a cell likely requires the presence of a unique protein—that is, one with a distinct shape. For instance, catalyzing 2041 different chemical reactions likely requires 2041 unique enzymes. Or shuttling seven different types of molecules across a cell's membrane likely requires seven unique permeases.

234   Chapter 10

The Interaction between Proteins and Nucleic Acids

Due to their nearly unlimited variation in shape, proteins can perform a large variety of actions. Even so, proteins are unable to reproduce alone. Proteins bog down when it comes to making more *of the same* proteins. To do that, proteins need recipes to follow, but proteins are unable to store their own recipes. Recipe storage has become the province of another class of molecules known as nucleic acids. One type of nucleic acid in particular fills the bill. It is deoxyribonucleic acid, but it is better known by its acronym, DNA.

Proteins and DNA have become entangled in a reproductive loop. DNA plays the role of the golden tablet loaded with a genome—a set of all the protein recipes involved in a reproductive performance. Proteins interact with DNA in several important ways: They interpret the recipes encoded in the DNA. DNA must also be continually cared for or the information will be lost through copy errors and damage, and it is the actions of proteins that orchestrate this ongoing repair. Proteins also carry out the action of making copies of DNA that can be passed on to one's descendants. In other words, the relationship between DNA and proteins involves the three components mentioned in Chapter 8: DNA replication, DNA caretaking, and interpretation. Here we discuss each in more detail. To do so, we must first know more about DNA's basic structure.

DNA's Basic Structure

DNA is a polymer made from four different types of monomers. Earlier, I called the four monomers DNA parts. All four monomers fall within a group of molecules called **deoxyribonucleotides**. Every deoxyribonucleotide consists of three components: a five-carbon sugar called deoxyribose, a phosphate group, and one of four different **nitrogenous bases—adenine, guanine, cytosine**, or **thymine**. Two of the nitrogenous bases—adenine and guanine—are double-ringed structures called **purines**. The other two—cytosine and thymine—are single-ringed structures called **pyrimidines**. The occurrence of four different nitrogenous bases is why there are four different types of deoxyribonucleotides. These details are summarized visually in Figure 11-1.

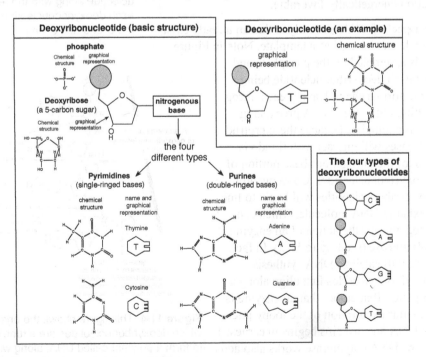

Figure 11-1. Basic features of deoxyribonucleotides.

As with the polymerization of amino acids, linking deoxyribonucleotides is an energy-requiring reaction fueled by high phosphorylation potential. Here, we get our first glimpse of high phosphorylation potential because in contrast to protein synthesis, this energy form is packaged within each deoxyribonucleotide. Before one deoxyribonucleotide can link to another, it must be "activated" by linking two more phosphates to the one already present. In other words, an **activated deoxyribonucleotide** is a deoxyribonucleotide **tri**phosphate, and the triphosphate arrangement has high phosphorylation potential. (What exactly is meant by high phosphorylation potential will be discussed in Chapter 14.) In Figure 11-2, the four different types of deoxyribonucleotides are pictured in their activated form.

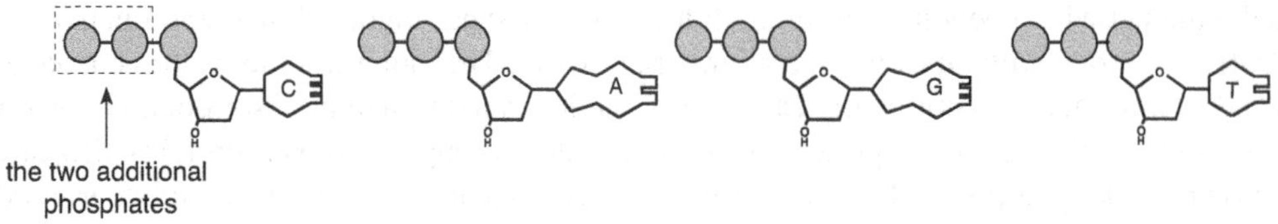

the two additional
phosphates

Figure 11-2. The four different types of deoxyribonucleotides each in their activated or triphosphate form.

Another important detail about deoxyribonucleotides has to do with fact that chemists number the five carbons in the 5-carbon sugar portion of a deoxyribonucleotide (see Figure 11-3). By this numbering system, the phosphate is attached to carbon number 5, so the phosphate portion of each deoxyribonucleotide is called the **5' end** (pronounced "5 prime end"). The region around carbon number 3 is called the **3' end** (pronounced "3 prime end"). These two regions have drawn focus because whenever deoxyribonucleotides are polymerized the 3' end of one nucleotide attaches to the 5' end of another (see Figure 11-4). Figure 11-4 also shows that each time an activated deoxyribonucleotide is added on to a growing DNA chain, it is the removal of the two additional phosphates that makes the reaction energetically favorable.

A striking aspect of DNA assembly is that an already existing DNA molecule can be used as a template. Note in Figure 11-4 that DNA is assembled by the phosphate and sugar portion of each deoxyribonucleotide being strung together to form a chain, leaving each nitrogenous base sticking out to the side. A preexisting DNA can serve as a template because these protruding nitrogenous bases will interact with (bind via hydrogen bonds to) the nitrogenous base portion of free-floating deoxyribonucleotides. Consequently, free-floating deoxyribonucleotides will begin to line up along a preexisting DNA molecule, which can then be strung together by the action of an enzyme called **DNA polymerase** (see Figure 11-5). In fact, DNA polymerase will catalyze DNA synthesis only when deoxyribonucleotides first align along a preexisting template. (Remember that an enzyme is a protein, so here our exploration of the loopy interaction between DNA and proteins begins in earnest.) The details of how DNA polymerase works also adds a directional constraint to stringing together deoxyri-

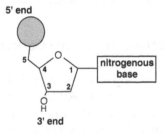

5' end

nitrogenous
base

3' end

Figure 11-3. The numbering system for the 5 carbon atoms in the deoxyribose portion of a deoxyribonucleotide along with the regions of each deoxyribonucleotide known as the 5' end and 3' end.

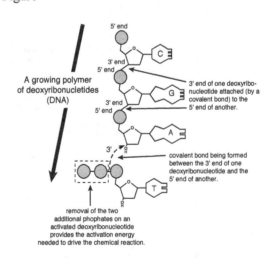

5' end

3' end
5' end

A growing polymer
of deoxyribonucletides
(DNA)

3' end of one deoxyribo-
nucleotide attached (by a
covalent bond) to the
5' end of another.

3' end
5' end

3'

covalent bond being formed
between the 3' end of one
deoxyribonucleotide and the
5' end of another.

removal of the two
additional phophates on an
activated deoxyribonucleotide
provides the activation energy
needed to drive the chemical reaction.

Figure 11-4. This figure shows the orientation by which deoxyribonucleotides are strung together to form a polymer called DNA, along with why deoxyribonucleotides need to be in their activated form to be polymerized.

bonucleotides—it can direct the attachment of the 5' end of a deoxyribonucleotide to the 3' end of a growing polymer (see Figure 11-5), but not vice versa. In other words, deoxyribonucleotides are only added on to the 3' end of a growing DNA molecule, so DNA only grows in the 5' to 3' direction.

Furthermore, interacting nitrogenous bases pair in a very specific pattern. First off, **purines** (double-ringed nitrogenous bases) only bond with **pyrimidines** (single-ringed nitrogenous bases; see Figure 11-1). This facilitates the lining up of incoming deoxyribonucleotides with those already part of the growing DNA molecule because the total width of each set of paired nitrogenous bases is three rings wide. Second, pyrimidines and purines pair in a specific fashion. **Adenine** (commonly abbreviated as **A**) only pairs with **thymine** (**T**), and guanine (**G**) only pairs with cytosine (**C**).

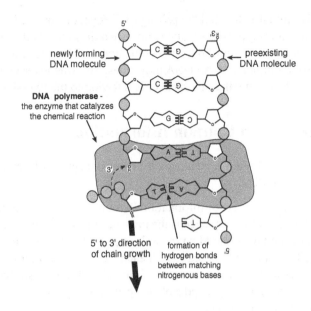

Figure 11-5. The use of a preexisting DNA molecule as a template in the assembly of a second DNA molecule.

An **A-T** pair is joined by two hydrogen bonds, whereas a **G-C** pair is joined by three hydrogen bonds. Overall, a new DNA molecule is built on the back of an old one based on these distinct coupling patterns. As a consequence *the preexisting DNA molecule guides the order in which deoxyribonucleotides of the newly assembled DNA are arranged* (see Figure 11-5). In other words, DNA can be used to make more DNA with a specific sequence.

This capacity for one DNA molecule to specify the sequence of a newly formed DNA molecule is the so-called magic of DNA—for it is this property that makes reproduction possible. Recognize, however, that these two resultant DNA molecules, the new and the old, are not identical copies of each other. They are **template copies**. Each is an exact pair-based match of the other side. I will refer to these two DNA molecules as *matching* or *complementary* DNA molecules.

Perhaps you noticed in Figure 11-5 that the two complementary DNA molecules run in opposite or *antiparallel* orientation to each other. The newly forming DNA molecule is growing in the 5' to 3' direction, but as it grows, the addition of matching deoxyribonucleotides is moving along the preexisting DNA molecule in the opposite or 3' to 5' direction. (Because the pairing of nitrogenous bases causes the two complementary DNA strands to face each other, the antiparallel orientation is the only arrangement that allows the two sides to fit together in a compatible way.) This antiparallel orientation is shown schematically in Figure 11-6. So, overall there are two elements of directionality in DNA synthesis: a newly forming DNA molecule grows in the 5' to 3' direction, and a preexisting DNA molecule is used as a template in the 3' to 5' direction.

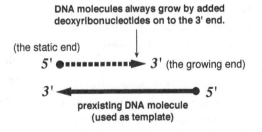

Figure 11-6. The antiparallel orientation of two DNA molecules when one is being used as a template to form the other.

A DNA molecule is a single polymer of deoxyribonucleotides. However, when one DNA molecule is used to assemble another, the two complementary DNA strands tend to remain together. The two antiparallel oriented strands are held together by the same hydrogen bonds that initially directed the pairing of nitrogenous bases. In fact, within living cells two matching DNA molecules typically separate only when they are pried apart by the actions of certain proteins. This brings up a point of potential confusion. DNA molecules usually exist in plural—the two-sided form is two (complementary) DNA molecules. Yet, whenever you hear the singular phrase *DNA*, it is probably safe to assume that the speaker is referring to the two-sided form.

DNA Can Contain Information

Recall that we began to discuss a concept of information in Chapter 4. Now it is time to discuss it a little further.

The concept of information introduced earlier is based on one idea—sequence. The basic feature of any form of sequence is the presence of "slots" that can be filled by more than one thing. Consider, for example, a line of a type written page. Each line contains a number of slots or spaces. A whole suite of different things can fill each space. These alternatives include all the letters of the alphabet, the different punctuation marks, any other different-shaped ink markings for which the typewriter (or keyboard) has keys, and a blank space. As a typewriter's keys are pushed, a corresponding sequence appears on the page.

Does every sequence of letters, punctuation marks, and spaces contain information? The answer is no. A sequence contains information only if it meets one simple criterion: *It can code for a specific activity.* In other words, the arrangement has the emergent properties of being able to be interpreted. For example, the arrangement of letters **quit studying biology now** contains a suggested course of action (that you may be inclined to take me up on) to anyone who can read English. Alternatively, a different arrangement of the same letters in each word—**ituq ditnygus loogiby won**—lacks information because it cannot be interpreted.

A DNA molecule potentially can contain information because of its structure. Each deoxyribonucleotide (monomer) along a DNA molecule is, in essence, a slot potentially filled by one of four things—one of four possible nitrogenous bases, which we abbreviated **A**, **T**, **G**, and **C**. Any sequence of nitrogenous bases is possible because deoxyribonucleotides with different nitrogenous bases can be polymerized in any order.

The four distinct nitrogenous bases found within DNA are sometimes referred to as a chemical or molecular alphabet. It is an okay analogy as long as you don't take it too far. These four bases are not arrangements of ink on paper; they are molecules with distinct shapes and consequently distinct tendencies to interact with certain other molecules. As a consequence, they can be part of a process where chemical reactions convert certain inputs into specific outputs. But here is the important point: *The effect that DNA has on how inputs are rearranged into biologically important outputs is based on its sequence.* In other words, DNA commonly plays an *information role* when it becomes part of a processor. The contrast, of course, is a molecule that plays an *activity role*. Here, the molecule's effect on how inputs are rearranged into outputs is based on its shape (see Figure 11-7). Proteins, as we have discussed, commonly take on this role.

Recognizing this shape-activity/sequence-information distinction leads us to a simple but important insight. Molecules that have shape-based effects, such as proteins, can qualify as a processor on their own (can convert inputs into different outputs), but the range of resultant outputs

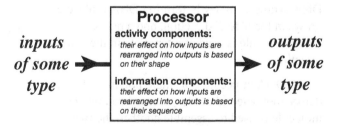

Figure 11-7. Here the distinction is made that any components within a processor can be thought of as taking on either an activity or information role.

is limited by how shape alone can rearrange available molecules. On the other hand, molecules that potentially have sequence-based effects cannot operate independently; they need to be accompanied by the right mix of shape-based molecules—ones able to orchestrate the activity needed to interpret the sequence. But what is striking is that when the effects of shape and sequence (activity and information) are combined, the range of potential outputs is extended to anything that is potentially coded for. I made that point in an earlier chapter, but it is definitely worth repeating.

Two final points:

• Single-sided RNA molecules (discussed later in this chapter) are of particular interest because they play on both sides of this information–activity coin. Certain RNA molecules have shape-based effects, whereas others have sequence-based effects.

• Potential and actual are not the same. As we will learn later, any sequence of nitrogenous bases along a DNA (or RNA) molecule can code for some form of molecular output. So, in a sense, any nitrogenous base sequence can play an information role. Yet, this is like saying that any arrangement of letters can code for an output because it can be pronounced. Although this is true, it reduces the concept of information to being trivial. The important idea is that information exists when the arrangement of letters or nitrogenous bases codes for some type of action. With letters, this is true when the arrangement describes some form of action. With nitrogenous bases, this is true when the arrangement codes for a molecule such as a protein, whose resultant shape enables it to catalyze a specific chemical reaction or perform some other type of activity. Once this criterion for information is met, the question that remains is: Is the information useful? It is a question that is worth keeping in mind.

The Importance of DNA Being Two Sided

If a specific sequence of DNA carries information crucial to an organism's ongoing survival and reproduction, then it is crucial that this information (i.e., the specific sequence) is preserved across time. The two-sided nature of DNA plays an important role in this preservation.

First off, because each side can serve as a template for the other, one two-sided form can be replicated into two identical two-sided forms. Recall that reproducing faster than falling apart is the key ingredient to persistence. Also, if only one side is altered or damaged in any way, the undamaged side can be used to restore the altered side to its original sequence. We discuss both DNA replication and DNA repair more later.

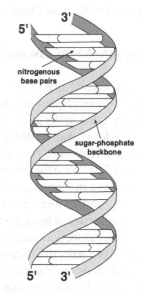

Furthermore, the two-sided arrangement may help prevent alterations from happening in the first place. If the goal is to preserve some idea, writing it down is better than relying on memory because an arrangement of ink on paper is an inert structure; it is not going to change. Memories, on the other hand, seem to be caught in the ongoing activity of the brain. As a result, memories tend to fade and/or change as more memories are added. Similarly, the best way to preserve information stored in a molecular sequence would be for the molecule to take on a relative inert shape—one that does not readily participate in chemical interactions. Two-sided DNA arrangements seem to fit the bill. Regardless of the **base pair** sequence—where a base pair is one pair of matching deoxyribonucleotides—two-sided DNA always self-assembles into the same basic shape; it coils into a helical shape commonly called the **double helix** (see Figure 11-8). In other words, in complete contrast to proteins, different sequences of two-sided DNA tend to arrange into the same shape. And this nonfolding, fairly regular helical arrangement is not a particularly active shape.

Figure 11-8. The double helix.

DNA Replication

The possibility of DNA replication is what makes genetic information potentially heritable. As the DNA making up a genome is copied and passed to an offspring, the offspring receives the same protein recipes.

A reasonable-sounding definition of DNA replication is proteins acting on one DNA molecule to make a second identical DNA molecule. Such a definition, however, has one problem. It is not clear whether one is referring to a single-sided DNA molecule or to a two-sided DNA molecule. If one pictures a single-sided DNA molecule, then the definition is wrong. DNA replication is proteins acting on a two-sided DNA molecule to form two identical two-sided DNA molecules. Identical means the nitrogenous base pair sequence is the same in both of the resultant two-sided molecules.

Overall DNA replication is a straightforward process with two basic steps: splitting or unzipping a two-sided DNA into two separate single-sided DNA molecules, followed by using each single-sided DNA molecule as a template to build new complementary DNA molecules. Next, I discuss each of these in a little more detail, as well as portraying them visually in Figure 11-9. Know, however, that I am leaving out as many details as I think I can get away with, while still giving you a solid introduction. Once a good framework is in place, the details can be easily added later.

Unzipping

A two-sided DNA molecule is first "unzipped" by a specific type of protein called **DNA helicase**, forming two single-sided DNA molecules (see Figure 11-9). By unzipping I mean the DNA helicase moves along a two-sided DNA molecule breaking the hydrogen bonds that hold the complementary nitrogenous base pairs together. As the nitrogenous base pairs separate, the two DNA molecules separate.

Actually, other types of proteins are involved in breaking apart a two-sided DNA molecule because there are additional tasks. Most important, the helical arrangement must first be unwound before the two sides can be pried apart. Proteins called **topoisomerases** are involved in the unwinding. For now, I leave how they might do so to your imagination. (Note: Topoisomerases are not pictured in Figure 11-9 because I have made no attempt to draw DNA in its helical arrangement in the first place.)

Template-based assembly

The second step in DNA replication is based on the fact that other proteins—**DNA polymerase** being a major player—can use a single-sided DNA molecule as a template to assemble a complementary DNA molecule. In addition to the proteins that do the work, a supply of activated deoxyribonucleotides is also needed. Consider, for instance, how many activated deoxyribonucleotides would be needed to replicate a two-sided DNA molecule 100 base pairs long. The answer is not 100, but a minimum of 200. Once the two sides unzip, 100 new deoxyribonucleotides must pair with each side. Two hundred is a minimum number because that many would be sufficient only if each of the four types (A, G, C, and T) were present in the exact proportion needed. When you apply this understanding to living cells (which replicate their DNA every time one cell divides into two) the number of activated deoxyribonucleotides needed becomes quite staggering. For example, a single bacterium with three million base pairs of DNA would require a minimum of six million activated deoxyribonucleotides each cell division. Your cells with three billion base pairs of DNA would need to come up with a minimum of *six billion* activated deoxyribonucleotides every time one of your cells divides (which is going on throughout your body right now).

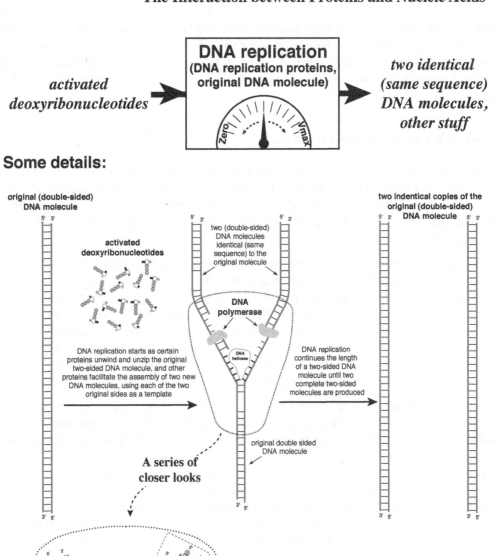

Figure 11-9. DNA replication first presented as a processor that converts one two-sided DNA into two indentical two-sided DNAs, followed by a closer look at the basic details of how DNA is replicated.

DNA replication is truly replication because one two-sided DNA molecule is converted, barring any mistakes in matching nitrogenous bases, into two new two-sided DNA molecules identical to both the original DNA molecule and to each other. By identical I mean that they have the same sequence of nitrogenous base pairs (i.e., the same order of A-T, T-A, G-C, and C-G pairs) as the original DNA molecule.

One complicating aspect of DNA replication

From what we have discussed so far it seems that DNA replication could be summarized as follows: First a two-sided DNA molecule begins to be unzipped. Next, as each of the two sides becomes free, both are used as templates to form new DNA molecules. Furthermore, the two newly forming DNA molecules each grow (along the preexisting DNA) in the *same* direction as the original two-sided molecule is being unzipped (see Figure 11-10(a)).

This scenario, however, encounters a problem. Due to the antiparallel nature of two-sided DNA, the two separating DNA molecules are not oriented in the same direction. One side, known as the **leading strand template,** or **leading side** for short, runs from the initial point of separation on down in the 3' to 5' direction. In contrast, the other separating side, known as the **lagging strand template,** or **lagging side** for short, is oriented along the same route in the 5' to 3' direction. As a consequence, newly forming DNA molecules growing in the same direction along both DNA strands would violate one of the directional growth constraints discussed earlier. Specifically, the newly forming DNA molecule on the lagging strand template would need to grow in the 3' to 5' direction (see Figure 11-10(a)).

It turns out that Life has come up with a way to replicate DNA along the lagging side without changing the 5' to 3' growth rule, but the mechanism carries a cost of increased complication. A good starting point for understanding the basics of what actually happens is to keep in mind an obvious fact: The formation of new DNA along an existing template must have a starting point. Because growth on the lagging side cannot take place in the same direction as the original two-sided DNA is being un-zipped, growth in the 5' to 3' direction could occur in one of two ways. For one, template-based assembly along the lagging side could wait to begin until the whole DNA molecule is unzipped. Then, a new DNA molecule could be assembled along the lagging side with only one starting point. Growth would start at the last-to-be-unzipped-end and then grow back along the entire length of the lagging side. Of course, DNA replication would take twice as long because the lagging side would not even start until after the leading side was finished. Alternatively, the lagging side could have multiple starting points (in contrast to the leading side, which has one). Periodically, a new start point could form as the two strands are being unzipped. Each start point could then grow backwards to the previous start point, and then the two pieces could be spliced together. Continue to repeat these steps along the entire length of the original DNA, and template-based assembly will occur along the entire lagging side at the same time that it is occurring along the leading side (see Figure 11-10(b)).

DNA replication follows this second scenario. Before they fuse, the separate pieces of DNA that form from each start point are called **Okazaki fragments**, named after the Japanese scientist Reiji Okazaki who discovered them. Another protein called **DNA ligase** catalyzes the linkage of each new Okazaki fragment with the previous ones.

A final piece of information

So far, we have characterized DNA polymerase as the enzyme that in conjunction with a preexist-ing DNA molecule catalyzes the polymerization of deoxyribonucleotides. The only correction to be added is that DNA polymerase cannot start the process; it can only add deoxyribonucleotides onto an already existing string of nucleotides, which is known as a **primer**. Furthermore, the nucleotides in the primer must be paired with a preexisting template.

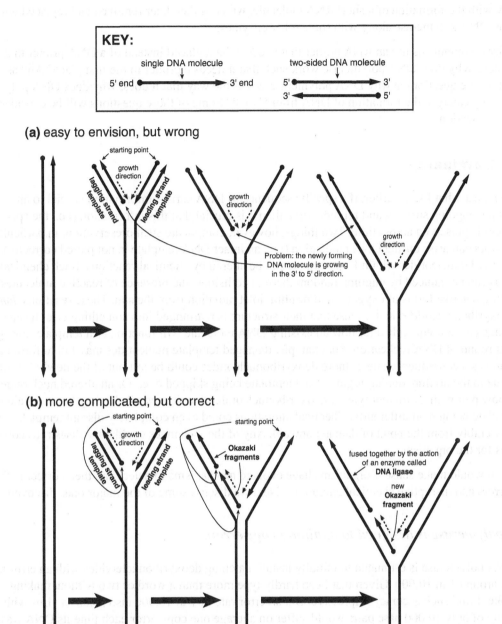

Figure 11-10. The top sequence illustrates that the 5' to 3' growth constraint would be violated on the lagging side if growth proceeds in the same direction that the DNA was being unzipped. The bottom sequence shows how the repeated formation of Okazaki fragments (along with the sealing of the fragments together by DNA ligase) can form a new DNA molecule along the lagging side at the same time as a DNA molecule is being formed along the leading side.

The necessity of a primer raises the question: Who builds the primer? The one start point on the leading side and the multiple start points on the lagging side must start (before DNA polymerase can take over) with the assembly of a primer. Curiously, the primer in DNA replication is a short string of matching **ribonucleotides**, instead of deoxyribonucleotides. An enzyme called DNA primase catalyzes the formation of the ribonucleotide string. In other words, template-based DNA assembly starts out initially with the formation of a short RNA molecule, which is then later removed and replaced with DNA by DNA polymerase along with some other enzymes.

Why do organisms use an RNA primer that needs to be replaced instead of a DNA primer that would not? Why does DNA polymerase work such that it needs a primer in the first place? And as long as we are questioning why DNA polymerase works the way that it does, why does DNA polymerase only catalyze the formation of DNA from 5' to 3'? Some of these questions will be considered in the next section.

DNA Caretaking

To repeat what I said earlier, if a specific sequence of DNA carries information crucial to an organism's ongoing survival and reproduction, then it is crucial that this information (i.e., the specific sequence) is preserved across time. Two things, however, complicate such preservation, in particular: Copy errors can arise during DNA replication (i.e., an intact DNA template is not paired correctly), and deoxyribonucleotides within DNA strands can be altered by chemical reactions. Such chemical reactions can be induced by ongoing random thermal collisions, the presence of reactive molecules (including reactive forms of oxygen), and/or ultraviolet radiation from the sun. These reactions *damage* deoxyribonucleotides in the sense that their structure is rearranged into something else. Instances of damage can subsequently alter how an existing DNA molecule will function as a template during the next round of DNA replication. For example, damaged template nucleotides may fail to form base pairs, and as a consequence one or more deoxyribonucleotides could be left out of the newly forming DNA due to the nonfunctioning region of the template being skipped over. Or an altered nucleotide could now pair with a different type of deoxyribonucleotide (than it used to), leading to places along the template being read differently. Chemical alterations could even completely disrupt template-based DNA assembly from the point of damage onward. Any of these changes could have disastrous consequences for the organism.

So, it would make sense if organisms have evolved mechanisms to detect and then correct both copy errors and disruptive chemical alterations. Next we discuss some of the major ones discovered.

DNA polymerase is designed to minimize copy errors

DNA polymerase is estimated to initially install matching deoxyribonucleotides with an error rate of only around 1 in 10,000. Given that I can hardly type more than a word or two without making a mistake, I find such accuracy impressive. But an error rate of 1 in 10,000 also means a virus with a genome of only 10,000 base pairs would suffer on average one copy error each time its DNA was replicated. It may be difficult for such a virus to persist by reproducing faster than it falls apart when nearly every offspring suffers at least one copy error. And for a bacteria type with a genome size of 3 million base pairs, persistence would be virtually impossible. Each offspring would suffer around 300 copy errors on average. It is hard to imagine any offspring with that many copy errors being functional. And the problem would only get worse in organisms with larger genomes.

In other words, I have just argued that a 1 in 10,000 error is way too high for any present-day organism to persist. The question then is how the incidence of copy errors has been reduced even further. It turns out that at least some of this needed improvement was incorporated into DNA polymerase itself. DNA polymerase has its own proofreading mechanism.

The fact that DNA polymerase cannot start DNA synthesis along a template from scratch, but instead requires a primer, is best explained as a first step in a means to reduce copy errors. The primer requirement is really a requirement that a matched set of nucleotides (between the DNA serving as a template and the newly forming polymer) must be in place before DNA polymerase can catalyze the addition of a new deoxyribonucleotide. The last pairing is particularly important. DNA polymerase does not work well whenever a primer has a terminal mismatch—that is, when the nitrogenous base on the last (3' end) nucleotide does not pair with the nitrogenous base on the other side. Given this trait, consider a DNA polymerase moving along a template catalyzing the addition of deoxyribonucleotides to a growing DNA molecule. Suppose, however, that the last deoxyribonucleotide added to the growing chain was a mismatch; its nitrogenous base does not match the corresponding one on the template. A copy error will be made if DNA polymerase proceeds despite this mismatch. But proceeding is made difficult by the fact that DNA polymerase does not work well with a mismatched last pair. In fact, in the presence of a terminal mismatch DNA polymerase typically stops, and a catalytic unit called an **exonuclease** (which is attached to DNA polymerase) begins to work backward and clip off the unmatched nucleotide(s). Then, once a matching end is restored, DNA polymerase begins again to add deoxyribonucleotides. The correct deoxyribonucleotide will most likely be added the next time around. So overall the effect of halting when errors are made in combination with exonuclease activity has built a self-correcting proofreading mechanism into the function of DNA polymerase (see Figure 11-11).

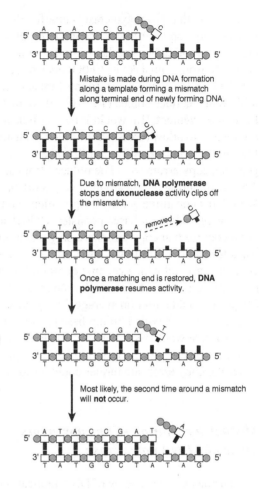

Figure 11-11. The scheme by which the DNA polymerase proofreading mechanism works.

The importance of this proofreading mechanism may explain why DNA polymerase only catalyzes DNA synthesis in the 5' to 3' direction. There is no underlying chemical constraint that prevents 3' to 5' growth. And recall that the ability to grow in both directions would make certain aspects of DNA replication less complicated. So the fact that DNA replication has constrained itself to a single growth direction (5' to 3') despite the added complications argues for a good biological reason underlying this directional growth constraint. That DNA polymerase's proofreading mechanism could not operate if growth went from 3' to 5' may be that reason. The absence of proofreading in one direction of growth would lead to copy errors occurring more frequently on the lagging side than the leading side during every replication event.

Figure 11-12 illustrates why DNA polymerase's proofreading mechanism cannot accompany 3' to 5' growth. The problem boils down to the fact that if a chain growing 3' to 5' is shortened to remove a mismatched nucleotide, there will not be an activating triphosphate available to power the addition of the next deoxyribonucleotide. So the first step in the proofreading process—removal of a mismatched nucleotide—would have the unfortunate result of terminating further DNA synthesis. (Note that when growth occurs in the 5' to 3' direction the activating triphosphate is always located on the incoming free deoxyribonucleotides (see Figure 11-11), while with growth in the opposite (3' to 5') direction the activating triphosphate is located on the last nucleotide in the growing chain. This is why pruning off the end to remove a mismatched nucleotide would also remove the needed activating triphosphate.)

Even with DNA polymerase's proofreading mechanism, copy errors still occur. DNA polymerase's proofreading mechanism may reduce the error rate from 1 mistake in 10,000 nucleotides copied (1 in 10^4) to somewhere around 1 mistake in 10 million nucleotides copied (1 in 10^7). If so, that is a huge improvement. But would it be a sufficient improvement to allow reproduction-based persistence? For the bacteria type with a 3 million base pair genome, copy errors would be reduced from around 300 per offspring to 1 in around every 3 offspring. Would that constitute getting it right often enough to allow reproduction-based persistence? Perhaps, but recognize that copy errors are only one of many ways for an organism to fall apart. And once you get to a yeast cell with a genome of 50 million base pairs, this error rate still seems far too great. Each offspring would suffer on average 5 copy errors. And in your cells with 3 billion base pairs of DNA the error rate would rise to around 300 copy errors each time one of your cells divided. So, a means to lower the copy error rate further could be advantageous.

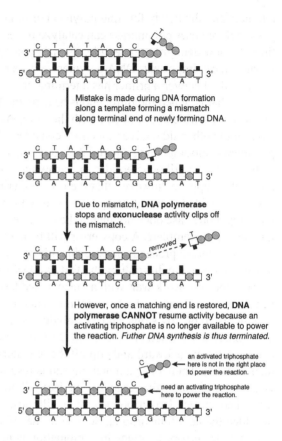

Figure 11-12. The reason that the DNA polymerase proofreading mechanism will not work if DNA polymerase catalyzes polymerization in the 3' to 5' direction.

Mismatch repair picks up copy errors missed by DNA polymerase

The measured accuracy of DNA replication in different organisms falls somewhere in the mind-boggling range of 1 mistake in 1 billion nucleotides copied (1 in 10^9) to 1 error in 100 billion nucleotides copied (1 in 10^{11}). DNA polymerase's proofreading mechanism does not, however, achieve this level of accuracy alone. A second mechanism to fix copy errors, called **mismatch repair**, has been discovered.

The key feature of mismatch repair is that it works after DNA polymerase has completed DNA synthesis. In other words, it picks up copy errors that were missed by DNA polymerase's proofreading mechanism. Mismatch repair is brought about by several proteins (which will remain nameless) working in sequence. First, a type of protein binds specifically to conformational changes in the DNA double helix that result from the presence of a mismatched pair of deoxyribonucleotides. Think of this protein as detecting a slight bulge that results from the mismatched nucleotides not fitting well together.

Once detected, the next step involves other proteins removing a mismatched nucleotide (some nucleotides adjacent to the mismatch may also be removed) from one side of the double helix, and then letting the DNA replication machinery (i.e., DNA polymerase and DNA ligase) accurately replace this missing piece by using the remaining side as a template (see Figure 11-13). An additional feature of this mechanism deals with the fact that which side is removed makes a difference. Copy errors are a mismatch of the existing template, so it is the newly replicated side that bears the error. As a consequence the only way to fix the copy error is to selectively remove and subsequently replace a piece of the newly replicated side. (Note: Randomly selecting between the two sides will not reduce copy errors. Although random selection would pick the correct side half the time, picking the wrong side would suffer the penalty of doubling the error rate because the copy error spreads to both sides.)

But how can a cell "know" which side was the original template and which side is newly replicated? Isn't newly synthesized DNA exactly the same as DNA that was synthesized a while ago? Perhaps the most common recognition mechanism centers around the fact that the DNA of many organisms undergoes some minor chemical modifications after it has been formed (specifically, a methyl group (—CH$_3$) is added to certain type of deoxyribonucleotides embedded in specific sequences), but the modification takes a while to occur. Due to this time lag, these modifications will not be present on the newly formed side for a while after replication. And proteins involved in mismatch repair use this chemical difference to selectively remove a portion of the newly formed side (after a mismatch has been identified).

Something to think about: Suppose the copy error rate in humans is the incredibly low rate of 1 mistake per 100 billion nucleotides. As mentioned earlier, the human genome is 3 billion base pairs in length, and the entire genome is found in each of the approximately 75 trillion cells that make up a human body. So to build you from your first starting cell, your 3 billion base-pair genome has been copied at least 75 trillion times. (Many cells are continually replaced, so that copy number would actually be much higher). Given these numbers, how many copy errors would you estimate to have suffered throughout your development? The answer is 2.25 trillion. Which raises another question: With that many errors, how are you

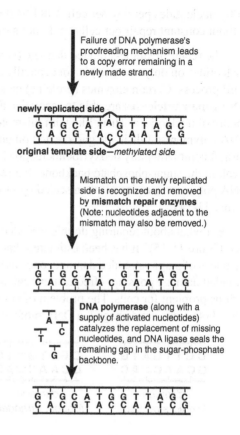

Figure 11-13. Scheme by which mismatch repair works.

still alive? For the moment consider three things: Some copy errors do not make a difference, selection is going on within cell lines during development so faulty cells can be replaced with functioning one, and you are also diploid. The diploid part of the answer will be discussed further in Chapter 19.

DNA repair deals with damage

Damage differs from copy errors in that the chemical structure of nucleotides is altered. Damage includes any form of chemical conversion that converts any of the four normal or natural deoxyribonucleotides into "abnormal" or "unnatural" nucleotides. Also unlike copy errors, damage does not just occur during replication. Environmental agents such as ultraviolet radiation, certain chemicals, and thermal fluctuation that can facilitate nucleotide damage constantly bombard cells. Furthermore, the constant hum of metabolism within any cell can generate potentially DNA damaging molecules—especially when electrons hook up with O$_2$ to form highly reactive products such as superoxide radicals and hydroxyl radicals.

And evidence suggests that in the absence of repair, damage could quickly accumulate to lethal levels. For example, within each human cell's DNA it has been estimated that around 5,000 purine bases (guanine and adenine) are broken off the sugar-phosphate backbone per day by thermal fluctuations, and 320 thymines are modified to a chemical form called thymine glycol per day. So, by just considering two of the many forms of potential damage, one comes up with a damage rate of over

5,000 nucleotides per day per cell. YIKES! It seems that without constant repair our cells could not survive long.

The repair of single-stranded damage (damage to nucleotides on only one side) is conceptually a straightforward process. Certain enzymes (proteins) generically called **DNA repair nucleases** are able to recognize and remove abnormal nucleotides. Then, like with mismatch repair, DNA polymerase fills in the gap created on one side with normal complementary deoxyribonucleotides, and the final break in the sugar-phosphate backbone that remains once DNA polymerase is done is then sealed by DNA ligase (see Figure 11-14).

But what about repairing double-stranded damage (see Figure 11-15)? It has been estimated that for every 60 instances of single-stranded damage, one case of double-stranded damage pops up—frequent enough to pose a serious problem for cells. The problem of course is that when both sides are damaged, a DNA molecule has lost

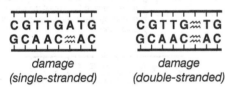

damage
(single-stranded)

damage
(double-stranded)

Figure 11-15. The difference between single-stranded and double-stranded damage.

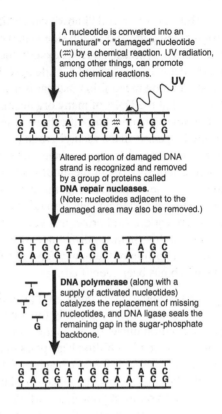

A nucleotide is converted into an "unnatural" or "damaged" nucleotide (≈) by a chemical reaction. UV radiation, among other things, can promote such chemical reactions. **UV**

Altered portion of damaged DNA strand is recognized and removed by a group of proteins called **DNA repair nucleases**. (Note: nucleotides adjacent to the damaged area may also be removed.)

DNA polymerase (along with a supply of activated nucleotides) catalyzes the replacement of missing nucleotides, and DNA ligase seals the remaining gap in the sugar-phosphate backbone.

Figure 11-14. The scheme by which DNA replair (of damaged nucleotides) works.

any record of what was formerly there. And relying on chance to restore the original sequence will not work well—four different types of nucleotides means there is only a 25% chance at each position of getting it right. Despite this, cells have come up with a means to repair double-stranded damage, but we are going to delay that discussion until Chapter 19.

Mutations cannot be repaired

The notion introduced so far is that a mutation is an alteration or modification of information. Now we are ready to add to this notion. Because information is stored within nitrogenous base sequences along a DNA molecule, a mutation would be any form of sequence change. This could occur by one type of base at any specific position being changed to another type (what is known as a **point mutation**), the insertion of one or more new nucleotides into an existing sequence (what is known as an **addition mutation**), or the

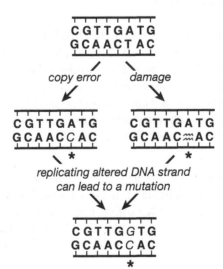

copy error   damage

replicating altered DNA strand
can lead to a mutation

Figure 11-16. Using a DNA molecule that has suffered a copy error or nucleotide damage as a template during DNA replication can result in a mutation. (Note: Although a specific form of mutation as a result of damage is implied in this figure, what exactly will happen during replication of any damaged region is uncertain because damaged nucleotides will not pair or pair properly.)

removal of one or more nucleotides from an existing sequence (what is known as a **deletion muta-tion**).

The problem with both copy errors and damage is that if they are not corrected, they can result in a mutation (see Figure 11-16), and mutations have two fundamental problems. First, they are most likely bad. Rarely do random changes to information result in a beneficial change. Second, once a mutation has occurred, it cannot be repaired to the former sequence. Once a change has been encoded on both sides of a two-sided DNA, no telltale indicator remains to know where the change occurred and what type of change it was. Furthermore, an altered nucleotide sequence does not disrupt the ability of any chunk of DNA from being replicated (so it is heritable) or from being used as a protein recipe (i.e., a mutation will not disrupt transcription—which is discussed later in this chapter—of any gene). As a consequence, the only means for a bad mutation to be removed is for all the cells/organisms that contain this mutation to go extinct—which will tend to occur by selection whenever a mutation negatively affects the reproductive success of those cells/organisms that contain it.

Gene to Protein: Genetic Interpretation

As mentioned in Chapter 8, there are three basic steps involved in using a gene to assemble a pro-tein: genetic regulation, DNA transcription, and RNA translation. To try to reinforce a general frame-work, I briefly discuss each again. More detail comes afterward.

The issue of genetic regulation can be introduced with an observation. Within any organism there are thousands of different protein recipes—different genes—within a genome, but not all of these genes are being used to make proteins at any particular time. Instead, the different genes are being regulated in that they are being turned on and off (as well as up or down) across time. The basis of this regulation is that certain genes are equipped with a type of sensor, so whether any gene is currently turned on or off depends on the current status of the conditions detected by its sensor.

Turning on a gene is to initiate DNA transcription. Transcription of any gene involves the action of certain proteins using a DNA template to make a working copy of a particular gene. This working copy is not made of DNA, but instead is made of a slightly different nucleic acid called RNA (ribo-nucleic acid).

The final and most involved step in protein synthesis is RNA translation. Here an RNA-based working copy of a protein recipe is used to assemble a polymer of amino acids with a specified se-quence—the primary structure of a protein. Based on the primary structure, the amino acid polymer then self-assembles into the protein's three-dimensional shape.

Although it may seem reasonable to do so, I am not going to discuss these three steps in order. It is easier to explain genetic regulation if one first understands DNA transcription because genes are regulated by controlling transcription. So the order of discussion will be step 2, step 1, and then step 3.

DNA transcription (step 2)

In the most basic sense, **DNA transcription** is the process by which DNA is used to make RNA. Like DNA, a **ribonucleic acid** or **RNA** is a polymer of nucleotides, but the nucleotides are ribonucle-otides instead of deoxyribonucleotides. Figure 11-17 illustrates the similarities of and the differences between the two. In contrast to DNA replication, only relatively small portions of a two-sided DNA molecule are transcribed at any one time. Each of these independent units of transcription is called a **gene**. In other words, an entire two-sided DNA molecule is not a gene but there are many genes—*transcription units*—located within a single two-sided DNA molecule. That each gene only occupies a small portion of the entire DNA molecule at a distinct location is analogous to a single recipe occupy-ing a small portion on a certain page of a recipe book.

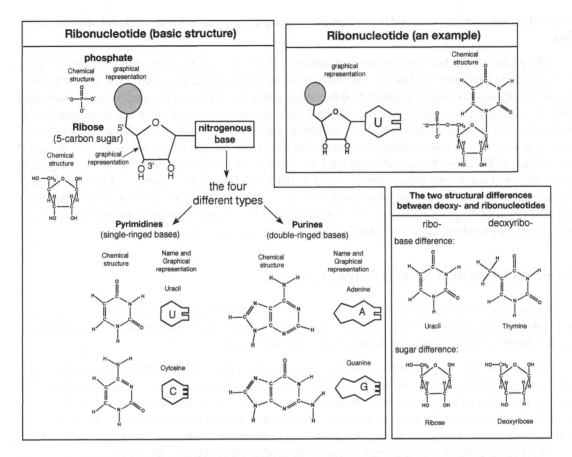

Figure 11-17. Ribonucleotides are similar to deoxyribonucleotides in that they are composed of the same three types of parts: a 5-carbon sugar, a phosphate, and one of four types of nitrogenous bases. There are, however, two differences. The 5-carbon sugar contains an additional oxygen, and so is termed ribose instead of deoxyribose. One of the four nitrogenous bases associated with deoxyribose is also different. Uracil (U), which like thymine (T) pairs with adenine (A), takes the place of thymine (T). Adenine (A), guanine (G), and cytosine (C) are found in both ribo- and deoxyribonucleotides.

To turn on a gene is thus to initiate transcription along a particular transcription unit. The process starts with the two-sided DNA beginning to be unzipped by protein action (that breaks the hydrogen bonds that hold the complementary sides together). Once the two-sided DNA is opened up both sides could conceivably be used as templates to guide the assembly of a polymer of ribonucleotides. However, within a gene's location only one of the two sides is used. So, in essence only one side actually encodes a recipe. I think of the recipe-storing side of a two-sided DNA as the **gene side**, although technically it is termed the **sense side** with the complementary side being called **antisense side**. What specifies which of the two sides is used is determined by which direction along the gene that transcription occurs. Recall that DNA can be used as a template only in the opposite direction that DNA (and RNA) grows, and both grow in the 5' to 3' direction. So, in relation to the direction of transcription the gene side is the one oriented in the 3' to 5' direction.

The actions of many proteins are involved in making DNA transcription happen. The most prominent one is **RNA polymerase**. In fact, the location and length of genes are determined by how DNA and RNA polymerase interact. The basic idea is that every gene along a DNA molecule is delimited by two special deoxyribonucleotide sequences. One designates the start of the gene and is called the **promoter**. The other designates the end of the gene and is called the **termination signal**. Functionally, a promoter is any DNA sequence to which RNA polymerase can bind tightly. Once it binds, RNA polymerase locally pries open a small piece of double helix, making the nitrogenous bases available to form complementary pairs with available ribonucleotides (which are bouncing around due to random molecular motion). Due to the fact that ribonucleotides share three out of four nitrogenous bases with deoxyribonucleotides, they form pairs along a DNA in much the same way. For example, adenine-containing ribonucleotides pair with thymine-containing deoxyribonucleotides—that is, **A** still pairs with **T**. The one difference is that everywhere the nitrogenous base adenosine (**A**) is found on a gene-side DNA sequence, the matching RNA base is not thymine (**T**), but uracil (**U**). Once these matching pairs form at the start of the gene side, and the ribonucleotides are in their activated or triphosphate form (so the energy needed to drive the reaction is available), RNA polymerase can catalyze the reaction that joins or strings the first two ribonucleotides together. RNA synthesis has begun. Transcription continues as RNA polymerase literally moves along the DNA continually repeating the steps of opening up the DNA and catalyzing the joining of ribonucleotides that align along the gene-side template. The farther RNA polymerase moves along the DNA the longer the RNA strand gets. And it does so at an impressive rate, adding around 30 ribonucleotides per second to the growing RNA chain. This repeated process continues until the RNA polymerase encounters a termination signal—a DNA sequence that alters the contour of the double helix in a way that dislodges RNA polymerase. The newly formed RNA is also forced off the DNA as the more stable DNA–DNA helix arrangement comes back together. So, in total DNA transcription leaves much unchanged. As it zips back together the stretch of DNA used returns to its original form. Barring any damage, the dislodged RNA polymerase is once again free to bind with another promoter (of the same gene or a different one) and start another round of transcription. What is new is an RNA molecule whose nucleotide sequence has been specified by the gene-side sequence of the DNA stretch used. Figure 11-18 visually summarizes this whole process, starting with the now-familiar notion of seeing RNA polymerase in conjunction with a gene as the processor that converts activated ribonucleotides (the inputs) into an RNA molecule of a specified sequence (the outputs).

An important aside: The presence of a promoter and termination signal along a two-sided DNA molecule seems out of line with something I said earlier—that two-sided DNA, regardless of the nitrogenous base pair sequence, coils into a regular helical arrangement. If this is true, it seems that a protein of the right shape to bind with one region of the double helix would be of the right shape to bind all along the double helix because the same shape is repeated throughout. Earlier I used a fudge phrase that I rather doubt you noticed. I said the double helix, regardless of the base pair sequence, has the same basic shape. Although every sequence arranges into a helical arrangement, different sequences generate slight modifications. These slight differences in shape are enough for proteins to notice. Any DNA-binding protein will be of the right shape to bind only to regions of the double helix with a certain nitrogenous base pair sequence. So, the promoter is a region along the double helix with the nitrogenous base pair sequence that contours the double helix to the shape recognized by RNA polymerase. This idea will come up again in the discussion of genetic regulation.

So far, we have characterized the RNA produced by DNA transcription in one way—it is a working copy of a protein recipe stored within an organism's DNA. One problem with this characterization is that the RNA sequence is not a copy per se of the gene-side DNA sequence—it is a template copy. The more important problem with this characterization is that it is not true. Not all genes code for proteins. Transcription of some genes result in RNA molecules that are still involved in protein synthesis, but these RNA molecules play quite different roles. So, to try to avoid confusion I will refer to any stretch of DNA that encodes a protein recipe as a **protein gene**. (Later in this chapter we discuss two other types of genes: tRNA genes and rRNA genes.) The RNA molecule produced by transcription of any protein gene is called **messenger RNA** or **mRNA** for short.

A summary of some differences between DNA replication and transcription

Because both DNA transcription and DNA replication use an existing DNA molecule as a template to form a new polymer of nucleotides, the distinction between the two is easily muddled. To help keep them straight I highlight a few key differences.

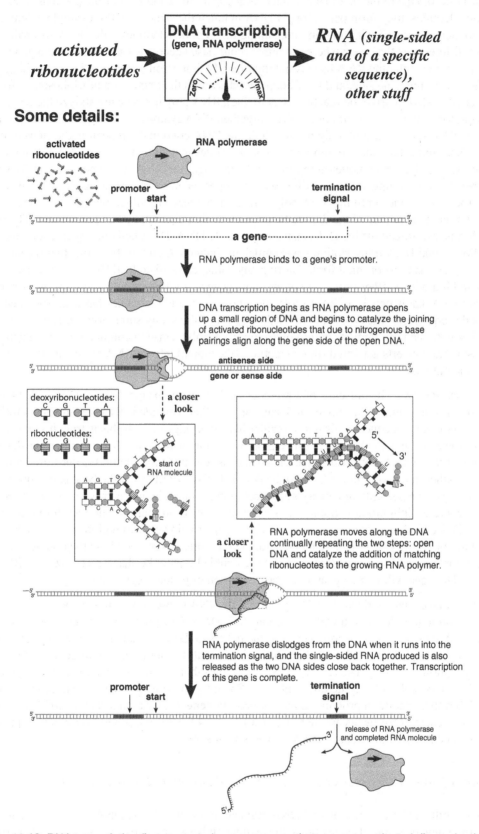

Figure 11-18. DNA transcription first presented as a processor that converts activated ribonucleotides into a RNA molecule of a specific sequence, followed by a closer look at the basic details of how DNA is transcribed.

The amount of DNA molecule involved. Whenever DNA is replicated the entire two-sided molecule is involved. That is, one two-sided molecule becomes two identical two-sided molecules. They are identical in that they both have the same sequence of deoxyribonucleotides. Alternatively, in DNA transcription only portions of the DNA molecule are transcribed, specifically those regions bounded by a promoter and termination signal. Regions of DNA bounded in this way are called genes.

The number of sides involved. In replication, both sides of the DNA molecule are used as a template. In contrast, only one side—the gene or sense side—is used as a template in DNA transcription. The antisense side is not involved.

The types of nucleotides. The polymers formed in DNA replication are made from deoxyribonucleotides forming new DNA molecules. In transcription, ribonucleotides are used, and that is why the polymer formed is called RNA.

Staying or not staying attached. In DNA replication the two new polymers formed each stay attached to their respective template side. Two new two-sided DNA molecules are formed in this way. In transcription the two DNA sides come back together knocking off the newly formed RNA molecule.

Genetic regulation (step 1)

Genetic regulation is to control the rate at which a gene is transcribed—that is, the rate at which a gene is used to make RNA. In the simplest sense, regulated genes are either turned off (transcription rate is zero) or on (transcription rate is Vmax), and our discussion is mostly confined to this scenario. Be aware, however, that more subtle regulation also occurs, regulation where transcription rates are turned up or down (and not just on and off).

In both prokaryotic and eukaryotic cells the same type of RNA polymerase transcribes all protein genes, and any functional cell has an enormous number of copies lurking around in constant "search of" available promoters. Genetic regulation is accomplished by controlling the rate at which these RNA polymerases can bind to a particular gene's promoter. In other words, a gene is turned off whenever something prevents any of the available RNA polymerases from binding with its promoter, and it is turned on when binding is made possible. The question remaining is how can this change back and forth?

Whether RNA polymerase can bind with a gene's promoter depends on whether they have complementary shapes. So, regulation's obvious avenue is to change the shape of either RNA polymerase or the promoter. Furthermore, we know such shape changes can occur through the binding of some other molecule.

For example, genetic regulation could potentially occur by the presence or absence of some molecule, call it molecule-X, that binds with RNA polymerase. So when molecule-X is present, RNA polymerase takes on one shape; when molecule-X is absent, RNA polymerase takes on another shape, and only one of these two shapes can bind to a gene's promoter. So, a gene's transcription rate would change in response to the presence or absence of molecule-X. Further assume that RNA polymerase binds to the promoter when it is in its unbound or molecule-X-absent shape (although choosing the alternative only makes a difference in the details).

This regulatory scenario, however, *has a serious problem*—it would not allow different genes to be regulated differently. As I mentioned earlier, the same type of RNA polymerase transcribes all the different protein genes. So, think about what would happen whenever molecule-X becomes increasingly abundant. More and more copies of this RNA polymerase would be converted to its nonfunctional shape, which would turn down the transcription rate of all the protein genes simultaneously. It would be analogous to putting all the lights in your house or apartment on the same switch. Not a very effective way to allocate resources or generate flexible responses. All the lights would have to be turned on whenever you needed light in just one place (like your bedroom). Similarly, the production

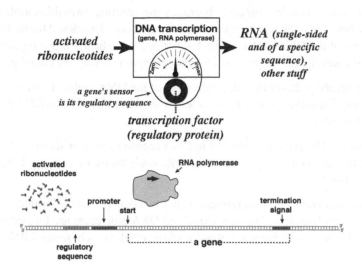

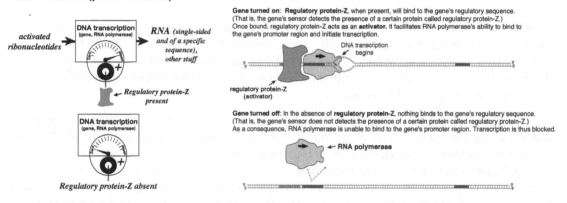

Positive Control (positive sensor):

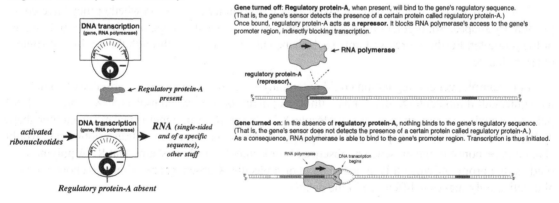

Negative Control (negative sensor):

Figure 11-19. Genetic regulation is first presented as the addition of a sensor onto the processor that performs DNA transcription. That is followed by a closer look at the most basic way that a protein binding to a gene's regulatory sequence could form either a positive or negative sensor.

rate of all the proteins a cell has the recipes to make would need to increase (or decrease) whenever a cell needed more (or less) of any one type of protein.

The secret to different genes being regulated independently lies in *each gene having their own sensor* (each of which potentially detects different things). Such a gene-level sensor would operate by changing whether RNA polymerase's could bind by changing the shape of a particular gene's promoter. In other words, a sensor for a gene would respond to certain types of change by altering the promoter's shape to one that is either open (RNA polymerase can bind) or closed (RNA polymerase cannot bind). Control at the individual gene level makes possible almost any pattern of gene expression (which genes are turned on and off across time).

The key component of any gene-level sensor is a stretch of DNA (usually somewhere in the proximity of a gene's promoter) called a **regulatory sequence**. Like with the promoter, the order of base pairs in the regulatory sequence results in a distinct shape that is the right shape to be bound by a specific protein (other than RNA polymerase). This is the detection part of story. A gene's sensor detects the presence or absence of the protein with the correct shape to bind with a gene's regulatory sequence. Any protein that binds to a regulatory sequence is generically called a **regulatory protein**. The regulatory part of the story is that the binding of a regulatory protein to a regulatory sequence affects the associated gene's transcription rate. It does so in the way mentioned earlier; somehow the binding alters the promoter's shape, which in turn affects the ability of RNA polymerase to bind with the promoter and initiate transcription. How such binding affects transcription rate has been found to go both ways—that is, both positive and negative gene-level sensors have been found. A gene has a *negative sensor* if such binding results in a shape change that blocks RNA polymerase's access to its promoter. Alternatively, a gene has a *positive sensor* if such binding results in a shape change that facilitates RNA polymerase's ability to bind to the promoter. See Figure 11-19 for more clarification.

Now let's take the idea of genetic regulation back one step. If a regulated gene's (a gene with a sensor) transcription rate is controlled by the presence or absence of a specific type of regulatory protein, the next step back is to understand what controls the presence or absence of any specific regulatory protein. As absurd as it might first sound, the answer is genetic regulation. Regulatory proteins are synthesized in the cell in the same way that any other protein is. So, for any specific regulatory protein to be present, its recipe—its gene—must first be turned on, resulting in the transcription of a working copy of the recipe, which in turn is translated into a protein. **Regulatory gene** is the generic name given to any protein recipe that codes for a regulatory protein.

Genetic regulation and reproduction

The preceding description of genetic regulation points to an underlying structure—a sequence exists because one event must precede another. Here the production of one protein—specifically a regulatory protein—must precede the regulation of another protein. But what regulated the production of the regulatory protein? Regulatory proteins by definition cannot always be produced, otherwise the genes that they regulate would always be turned on or off, which is not regulation. So the regulatory gene must also have a sensor that detects the presence or absence of another regulatory protein that regulates it, and so on *ad infinitum*. Of course, the idea of a sequence quickly runs into trouble if one insists on linear thinking. One then needs to ask where this sequence begins and where it ends. Not so, however, if this sequence is pulled into a loop—specifically the loop of reproduction.

Offspring do not come out ready to reproduce. Instead, each new generation of individuals must first go through a series of changes before they are ready to reproduce. And it makes sense that within this reproductive cycle, each generation would start at the same place as the previous generation. That way each newly produced offspring could make the transition to reproductive maturity by going through the same series of changes (as the previous generation). Using a very simplistic model, let me explain how the sequential component of genetic regulation could be used to generate such a cycle.

Consider a cell that reproduces by splitting into two. Assume that this cell's genome has just four regulatory genes—**A, B, C,** and **D**. Further assume that due to the presence of gene-level sensors, each regulatory protein orchestrates three effects: (1) it stimulates the production of one of the other regulatory proteins, (2) it inhibits the production of one other regulatory protein, and (3) it stimulates the production of a whole suite of other proteins that manifest a specific suite of changes within the cell. Figure 11-20(a) shows how these three effects can form a regulatory loop that forms a cycle of protein action. Figure 11-20(b) shows how this cycle could be incorporated into a reproductive cycle that starts off each generation at the same place.

(a)   **(b)**

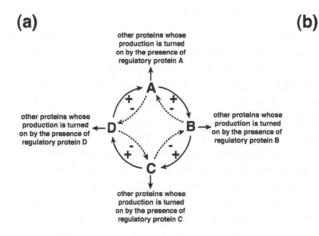
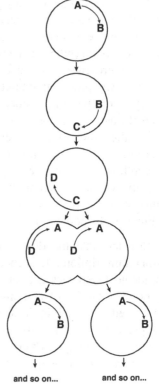

Figure 11-20. In (a), four regulatory proteins form a loopy pattern of protein production. The basis of the loop is that the gene for each regulatory protein has two sensors, a positive sensor that detects the presence of one of the other three regulatory proteins, and a negative sensor that detects the presence of one of the two remaining regulatory proteins. For example, the gene for regulatory protein A has a positive sensor to regulatory protein D and a negative sensor to regulatory protein B. As a consequence, the production of A will be turned on by the presence of D, while the presence of B will have the opposite effect. The loop forms because of the specific arrangement of these types of regulatory effects. In (b), this regulatory loop is tied into a reproductive performance. Starting with A, envision that the sequential actions of each set of proteins whose production is triggered by each regulatory protein carries out a necessary step in preparing a cell for cell division. As the cell divides, the presence of D again stimulates the production of A, so the next generation starts over at the same place.

A hint about what has been left out

The details of genetic regulation are currently a hot topic. More is being learned every day, and much of what is being discovered makes my discussion too simplistic. I have at most captured the basic features of genetic regulation. To begin to add just a little more depth, I mention three more issues:

• Sometimes nonprotein molecules (such as steroid hormones or sugars) play a role in gene regulation. They do not bind to regulatory sequences directly—that is still is the province of regulatory proteins. Instead, they bind to a regulatory protein and in so doing change the protein's shape. The shape change alters the regulatory protein's ability to bind to its associated regulatory sequence in either a positive or negative way.

• Much of genetic regulation is combinatorial. This means that more than one regulatory protein must be present to turn on or off a gene. In such cases, a gene's sensor is constructed from more than one regulatory sequence. The advantage of combinatorial regulation comes from the fact that patterns of presence or absence of relatively few regulatory proteins can form many different combinations. So, as long as the sensors on different genes are set up to detect different patterns, just a few regulatory proteins can differentially regulate many genes.

• Certain regulatory genes are termed **master genes**. A master gene codes for a regulatory protein that regulates a whole suite of other genes. This is a beneficial setup whenever certain components of a reproductive performance involve turning on (or off) many different genes simultaneously. Note that the four regulatory proteins in Figure 11-20 have the flavor of being master proteins—regulatory proteins coded for by master genes.

Regulatory proteins are chemical signals

Regulatory proteins provide our first introduction to the various forms of communication going on in Life. Biological communication always requires two parts: a **signal** and a **receptor**. In other words, to qualify as a biological signal, be it visual, auditory, or chemical, two conditions must be met. First it must be generated by—is an output of—some processor within an organism. Second, any output cannot act as a signal unless there is a corresponding receptor (which is also sometimes called a receiver). A receptor is a processor whose sensor is sensitive to the signal.

Regulatory proteins qualify as signals. They fall within a group of molecules produced by living organisms called **signal molecules** or **chemical signals**. Regulatory sequences are the associated sensors found on regulated genes—the receptors. Specifically, regulatory proteins are **intracellular** signal molecules. They remain within the cell in which they are produced and consequently can only affect transcription of genes within that cell. As we will discuss in later chapters, **intercellular** signal molecules also exist. They are released from the cells that produce them and somehow travel—often simply by diffusion—to other cells whose activity they can affect. These can be cells within the same multicellular body (e.g., hormones and neurotransmitters) or cells within the body of another organism (e.g., pheromones).

RNA translation (step 3)

RNA translation is one of the most fundamentally important feats in all of Life—it is the means by which a working copy of a protein recipe—an mRNA—is used to assemble a protein (with a specified amino acid sequence). Although the idea of following a set of instructions to build something is familiar, the details of how a protein recipe is interpreted can seem a bit complicated. Hopefully, an analogy will help set the stage.

Interpreting a bracelet recipe

Consider a recipe that specifies the color sequence of a beaded bracelet. The recipe uses symbols, English words in this case, that code for each of the different colored beads. The arrangement of different colored beads is specified by the left to right sequence of the different words that code for the different colors. A left to right arrangement is used because we read from left to right. Here is an one possible example: green - red - yellow - yellow - blue - purple - blue - blue - yellow . . .

Two things must be in place before such a recipe could be translated: a supply of colored beads and some type of **translator**. A translator is what can translate a code—such as the word *green*—into the act specified by the code, such as placing a green bead in the first position.

One translator could translate the entire recipe as long as the translator could recognize all the different codes. For example, if you are not color-blind and can read English, you could act as a single translator. In response to seeing *green,* you would pick up a green bead and place it in the first position. Proceeding, your attention would turn to the next word. On seeing *red,* you would pick out a red bead and place it in the second position, and so on.

Protein recipes, however, are not translated in this familiar manner. Instead, translation occurs by what I call the **tRNA way** of recipe translation. Rather than *one* translator interpreting *many* different codes as in the preceding example, the tRNA way involves *many* translators, each of which are able to interpret only **one** code within the recipe.

Consider a beaded bracelet recipe translated in the tRNA way. To create a bracelet, translators for all the different codes must be present, and each translator must have the following characteristics:

• It picks up one and only one color of bead.

• It responds to one and only one of the different codes in the recipe by placing its bead on the bracelet chain.

• The color of bead that it picks up must match the code to which the translator responds. For example, translators that pick up green beads must respond only to the letter arrangement green. Translators that pick up blue beads must respond only to the letter arrangement blue.

Bracelet assembly would proceed one translator at a time, each translator placing a single bead in the growing sequence of beads whenever the code they respond to comes up in the recipe. Multiple copies of the same color code in one recipe would be handled by having multiple copies of each distinct type of translator. Furthermore, each individual translator could be used more than once. After dumping off a bead, a translator could go back and fetch another so that it is loaded and ready to be used again.

Some details: The gene language

Like the preceding bracelet recipe, protein recipes are organized in a straightforward fashion. There are different symbols that code for each of the 20 different amino acids used in protein assembly. Plus, there are two more codes in addition to these 20: one that specifies where along the mRNA the protein recipe begins, and one that specifies where it ends. Furthermore, the protein recipe contains an inherent reading sequence, from 5' to 3', so the arrangement of the amino acid codes within the reading sequence specifies the sequence in which the different types of amino acids should be strung together.

To make it more familiar, I refer to each of these different symbols as **gene words**. Different gene words, like written words, are made through different combinations of characters. But, as mentioned earlier, the characters are not really analogous to letters found in a written language; they are a set of distinctly shaped molecules. In DNA, the four different molecules are the four different nitrogenous bases—**A, G, C,** and **T**—found in deoxyribonucleotides. In RNA, the four different molecules are the four different nitrogenous bases —**A, G, C,** and **U**—found in ribonucleotides. Because it is the working copy of a gene—a mRNA—that is actually translated, I base my discussion of the nature of gene words using the RNA set of molecules.

In the English language, and I assume any written language, different words are made of different numbers of characters. Some words, like the word *a*, have only 1 characters, whereas other words, like *deoxyribonucleotides*, have 20. Most words range somewhere in between. This, however, is not the case for the chemical language of nucleotides. All gene words are made up of the same number of nucleotides. The reason may have something to do with simplicity. By keeping all words the same length, the translation machinery would not need to adjust for words of different lengths. It also may have something to do with blank spaces. Written languages punctuate the beginning and end of each word with a blank space. Framed by black spaces, it is easy to tell where a word begins and ends, regardless of its length. The gene language, on the other hand, has no blank spaces. Soifwordswereofdifferentlengthstherewouldbenowaytodeterminewhichletterswerepartofwhichwords.

The constraint of a standard word length does raise an obvious question: How long are gene words? The underlying issue is that there needs to be at least 22 words because there are 22 things that need to be said.

Words of one ribonucleotide in length can be ruled out. In a four-letter chemical alphabet, only four different words are possible, and four words are not enough.

What if words were two ribonucleotides in length, and order mades a difference—for example, CU and UC are not the same thing? To see if this would work, I wrote out all the possibilities:

$$
\begin{array}{llll}
AA & GA & CA & UA \\
AG & GG & CG & UG \\
AC & GC & CC & UC \\
AU & GU & CU & UU \\
\end{array}
$$

There are 16 different arrangements and 16 is still not enough.

What if words were three ribonucleotides in length? One could continue to explore the possible number of distinct combinations by writing down all the possibilities and then counting them. If you did that, you would find that 4 different characters taken three at a time could be arranged into 64 unique combinations. Increase the word length to 4, and the number of unique combination increases to 256. There is, however, a quicker way to figure out all the possible combinations. Because the number of unique combinations changes with both the number of characters and the word length in a regular way, the pattern can be expressed as a simple mathematical formula. The number of unique combinations equals the number of different items to be arranged—4 in this case— raised to the power equaling the length of the arrangement. For example, 4 characters taken one at a time is $4^1 = 4$, four characters taken two at a time is $4^2 = 16$, four characters taken three at a time is $4^3 = 64$, four characters taken four at a time is $4^4 = 256$, and so on.

Gene words must be at least three ribonucleotides in length. Sixty-four is greater than 22. But by the same criteria, gene words could also be of length four, five, or more. So which length is it? Life, not unexpectedly, "chose" the simplest possibility. Gene words are all **triplets**—words of length three. Because 64 is closest to 22, triplets get the job done with the least amount of slop. Each triplet or gene word within an mRNA (that is part of the protein recipe) is called a **codon**.

A particularly striking feature of gene words is that all 64 possible words have meaning. There are no nonsense combinations. This stands in sharp contrast to written languages, where recognized words are only a small subset of possible letter combinations. But how is that possible if there are only 22 meanings? It is actually quite simple; some of the different words mean the same thing. Figure 11-21 shows the **genetic code**—that is, it shows which of the 64 triplets code for start, stop, and each of the 20 amino acids. There are several things worth noting.

• There is considerable variation in the number of triplets that code for any amino acid, ranging from one to six. Why do some amino acids have more codons than others? It may have at least something to do with the commonness of use, as the two amino acids coded for by only one triplet, methionine and tryptophan, are the least commonly used amino acids in protein construction. But there is more to this story.

• For those amino acids represented by more than one triplet, generally the first two nitrogenous bases are the same. In other words, most of the codon variation within an amino acid occurs at the last or third position.

Ala	Arg	Asp	Asn	Cys	Glu	Gln	Gly	His	Ile	Leu	Lys	Met (start)	Phe	Pro	Ser	Thr	Trp	Tyr	Val	stop
	AGA									UUA					AGC					
	AGG									UUG					AGU					
GCA	CGA						GGA			CUA				CCA	UCA	ACA			GUA	
GCC	CGC						GGC		AUA	CUC				CCC	UCC	ACC			GUC	
GCG	CGG	GAC	AAC	UGC	GAA	CAA	GGG	CAC	AUC	CUG	AAA		UUC	CCG	UCG	ACG		UAC	GUG	UAA
GCU	CGU	GAU	AAU	UGU	GAG	CAG	GGU	CAU	AUU	CUU	AAG	AUG	UUU	CCU	UCU	ACU	UGG	UAU	GUU	UAG UGA

Ala=Alanine, Arg=Arginine, Asn=Asparagine, Asp=Aspartic Acid, Cys=Cysteine, Glu=Glutamic Acid, Gln=Glutamine, Gly=Glycine, His=Histidine, Ile=Isoleucine, Leu=Leucine, Lys=Lysine, Met=Methionine, Phe=Phenylalanine, Pro=Proline, Ser=Serine, Thr=Threonine, Trp=Tryptophan, Tyr=Tyrosine, Val=Valine.

Figure 11-21. The genetic code—that is, which of the 64 possible ribonucleotide triplets or codons on a mRNA code for the 20 amino acids used to assemble proteins, plus what codon signals where along an mRNA protein assembly should start (the start codon) and where it should stop (the three stop codons).

The mRNA to amino acid decoder

1st base in codon	2nd base in codon U	amino acid	2nd base in codon C	amino acid	2nd base in codon A	amino acid	2nd base in codon G	amino acid
U	UUU	Phe	UCU	Ser	UAU	Tyr	UGU	Cys
	UUC	Phe	UCC	Ser	UAC	Tyr	UGC	Cys
	UUA	Leu	UCA	Ser	UAA	Stop	UGA	Stop
	UUG	Leu	UCG	Ser	UAG	Stop	UGG	Trp
C	CUU	Leu	CCU	Pro	CAU	His	CGU	Arg
	CUC	Leu	CCC	Pro	CAC	His	CGC	Arg
	CUA	Leu	CCA	Pro	CAA	Gln	CGA	Arg
	CUG	Leu	CCG	Pro	CAG	Gln	CGG	Arg
A	AUU	Ile	ACU	Thr	AAU	Asn	AGU	Ser
	AUC	Ile	ACC	Thr	AAC	Asn	AGC	Ser
	AUA	Ile	ACA	Thr	AAA	Lys	AGA	Arg
	AUG	Met(start)	ACG	Thr	AAG	Lys	AGG	Arg
G	GUU	Val	GCU	Ala	GAU	Asp	GGU	Gly
	GUC	Val	GCC	Ala	GAC	Asp	GGC	Gly
	GUA	Val	GCA	Ala	GAA	Glu	GGA	Gly
	GUG	Val	GCG	Ala	GAG	Glu	GGG	Gly

Figure 11-22. A genetic decoder. The genetic code is set up in a way that makes it easy to look up what is coded for by any of the 64 possibly codons (mRNA triplets).

Ala=Alanine, Arg=Arginine, Asn=Asparagine, Asp=Aspartic Acid, Cys=Cysteine, Glu=Glutamic Acid, Gln=Glutamine, Gly=Glycine, His=Histidine, Ile=Isoleucine, Leu=Leucine, Lys=Lysine, Met=Methionine, Phe=Phenylalanine, Pro=Proline, Ser=Serine, Thr=Threonine, Trp=Tryptophan, Tyr=Tyrosine, Val=Valine.

• Three triplets act only as stop codons, so only 61 of the 64 possible codons actually code for an amino acid. In contrast, the start codon (AUG) also specifies the amino methionine; so all proteins synthesized start with the amino acid methionine.

Figure 11-21 displays the genetic code in a way that makes it is easy to look up what codons code for any particular amino acid. The amino acids are listed in alphabetical order, so any one is easy to find. But to go the other way is more difficult. If you start with a codon and want to know what amino acid it codes for, your only option is to scan along all the codons. To make going from codon to amino acid easier, the genetic code is often organized in the form of an easily used decoder (see Figure 11-22).

Perhaps the most striking feature of the genetic code is its seeming universal nature. Basically, all organisms appear to use the same code, as only some minor variation has been found so far. In other words, you may not be able to speak directly to a goldfish or an oak tree or a tiny soil-swelling nematode, but when it comes to making proteins, we all speak the same language.

Although we know that gene words are triplets, there still is a question of how they are read. Specifically, are gene words read overlappingly or nonoverlappingly? Overlapping means that some of the letters from the last word are used in the next word. In contrast, nonoverlapping means that each letter is part of one word only.

In one sense, reading overlappingly is more efficient. Overlapping reading yields more triplets per total number of ribonucleotides. Consider, for instance, an RNA sequence nine ribonucleotides long: 5'-UGAACAUUG-3'. One way this sequence could be read overlappingly would be to read the first triplet, then skip one letter and then read the second triplet, and so on. Reading this sequence in this manner yields a total of seven triplets: UGA GAA AAC ACA CAU AUU UUG. Alternatively, reading the same sequence nonoverlappingly yields only three triplets—UGA ACA UUG.

The problem with overlapping, however, is that it is hard to say what one wants to say. Consider writing an English sentence in the same nonoverlapping manner described earlier. If you started a sentence with the word *the*, then the next word would have to start with *he*. Okay so you choose *hen*. Now the next word has to start with *en*. Perhaps it could be *end*. By now the point should be obvious, once you start any sentence, the first word severely limits what you can say. Start with the word *the*, and you end up with *the hen end*, or some other limited set of options. The same would be true if an mRNA sequence was read overlappingly. So, it should not be surprising that just as with written language, mRNA is read nonoverlappingly.

There is one more point to be made about the gene language. The absence of spaces separating words and the presence of meaning in each of the 64 possible triplets results in an interesting outcome. Any sequence of ribonucleotides contains not one, but three protein recipes. It all depends on where the reading starts. Consider, for instance, the following portion of ribonucleotide sequence:

$$\ldots 5'\text{-UUGCUAGUAGCUUAAGA-3}'\ldots$$

The recipe it encodes depends on whether one starts reading at the first, second, or third nucleotide.

$$\ldots\text{UUG CUA GUA GCU UAA GA}\ldots$$
$$\ldots\text{U UGC UAG UAG CUU AAG A}\ldots$$
$$\ldots\text{UU GCU AGU AGC UUA AGA}\ldots$$

The starting point sets what is called the **reading frame**. As we will discuss more later, the position of the start codon within a mRNA sets the reading frame, hence sets which of the three possible recipes the mRNA encodes.

Let's summarize what we know about how mRNA sequences form recipes:

• There is an inherent reading sequence from 5' to 3'.

• Each gene word is a ribonucleotide triplet read nonoverlappingly.

• There are no spaces between words.

• All 64 possible triplets encode an action, but with only 22 total actions sometimes different triplets mean the same thing.

• The recipe that an RNA sequence encodes depends on the reading frame.

Some more details: There is more than one type of RNA molecule

Earlier I stated that the problem with characterizing every RNA molecule as a working copy of a protein recipe is that it is not true. Now it is time to elaborate. Many, if not most, RNA molecules produced (by DNA transcription) play an information role in that based on their sequence they carry a protein recipe—that is they act as messenger RNA or mRNA. Yet other RNA molecules (which are still formed by DNA transcription) play a shape-based activity role—they serve as parts of the translation machinery. So, although its is easy to create the simple dichotomy that nucleic acids (DNA and RNA) store information and proteins generate activity, it is not a completely accurate dichotomy.

And for you to really understand the interaction between genes and proteins, it is essential for you to understand where and how this dichotomy breaks down. (Note: For people interested in the origin of reproduction, the fact that RNA has been found to play both sequence- and shape-based roles is a source of glee. By having the capacity to both generate activity and store their recipes, the possibility arises that early reproductive loops were solely RNA based—a much simpler scenario. Only later were these two jobs partitioned between two types of molecules—proteins and DNA—because each could do one of the two jobs better. It is during this transition that RNA assumed its present role—serving as the intermediary between the two.)

The RNA molecules that are part of the translation machinery fall into two general categories: translators and mediators.

A language translator is able to hear a word in one language and then match it to a word with the same meaning in another language. The essence of such translation is pairing together dissimilar sounds. The issues in RNA translation are similar except that the translation is chemical in nature. Instead of dissimilar sounds, dissimilar molecules are paired. Specific gene words—the three nitrogenous bases extending from a triplet of ribonucleotides—are paired with specific amino acids—a protein monomer. Here certain RNA molecules play the role of translator. They are termed transfer (or translator) RNAs, or **tRNAs** for short.

The role of mediator is to get the message and the translators together. Structures called **ribosomes** play this role. They bring the mRNA and the various tRNAs together. RNA is involved in that a ribosome is made up of both proteins and RNA molecules. These RNA molecules are called ribosomal RNAs, or **rRNAs** for short.

We already know where mRNAs come from; they are produced through the transcription of a protein gene—a segment of DNA that encodes a protein recipe. But where do tRNAs and rRNAs come from? The answer is the same. They are also products of DNA transcription. And because **gene** is the name given to any transcribed segment of DNA, all genes cannot be protein genes. In addition to protein genes, there are **tRNA genes**—segments of DNA that when transcribed produce tRNA molecules—and **rRNA genes**—segments of DNA that when transcribed produce RNA molecules used in the assembly of ribosomes. So, in total, there are three classes of genes: protein genes, tRNA genes, and rRNA genes.

Single-sided RNA molecules can take on different shapes

Recall that DNA transcription produces single-sided RNAs. The absence of a complementary strand has important shape implications. Two-sided nucleic acids, whether they are DNA or RNA, will self-assemble into a double helix. As I pointed out with DNA, this is basically an inert shape. Single-sided RNA molecules (or DNA molecules), on the other hand, are not so mundane. They can take on a variety of shapes, and like proteins, the sequence of its parts affects the shape that a single-sided RNA will self-assemble into.

We already know that complementary nitrogenous bases tend to form hydrogen bond – based associations. This is how two-sided nucleic acids stay together. Now add in the fact that the phosphate-sugar backbone within a single-sided nucleic acid is flexible enough to fold back on itself, so coupling between nitrogenous bases within the same molecule is possible. Such coupling between regions with matching sequences can hold a single-sided nucleic acid in a particular shape (see Figure 11-23). Furthermore, this shape is affected by sequence because where the loop and stem regions (shown in Figure 11-23) form is affected by the molecule's nitrogenous base sequence. This capacity to take on different shapes is what makes its possible for different RNAs—specifically tRNAs and rRNAs—to play activity roles within the translation machinery.

Note, however, that the potential diversity of shapes is not nearly as great as proteins. The basic reason is straightforward: The nucleic acid building set has fewer distinct parts (four instead of 20), and in terms of chemical and physical properties the four different nucleotides are more similar to each other than the 20 amino acids used to assemble proteins. Back to analogy used earlier, the RNA lego set has fewer less-diverse-shaped pieces. As a consequence, the range of activities that RNAs can potentially facilitate is much less than proteins.

Some more information on tRNA molecules

Earlier I called the use of many translators, each able to interpret only one code within the recipe, the tRNA way of translation. Why? Because this is the way that tRNA molecules translate an mRNA into a protein. Cells produce different types of tRNAs, and each is responsible for the positioning of only one of the 20 types of amino acids within a growing protein.

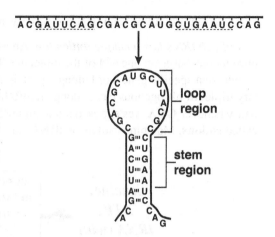

Figure 11-23. How pairing matching regions of nitrogenous bases could transform a single-sided RNA into a polymer with a distinct shape. Shown is the folding of an RNA into one stem region and one loop region, but depending on the sequence this type of folding could occur repeatedly throughout an RNA, leading to much more complex shapes.

How many different types of tRNAs does a cell produce? One might first suspect that there are 20, one unique type for each of the 20 different amino acids. But there is another consideration—the genetic code is redundant. Recall that that the 20 amino acids are coded for by 61 unique codons (triplets on mRNA). So you might also suspect that there are 61, one that recognizes each of the 61 codons. So which is it? Are there 20, which means that a single type of tRNA would have to be able to recognize more than one codon, or are there 61, which means that more than one type of tRNA would associate with the same type of amino acid? The answer turns out to be somewhere in between. Some amino acids associate with more than one type of tRNA, and some tRNAs are able to recognize more than one codon. And the exact mix is not always the same, as all cells do not produce the exact same number of tRNA types.

Each different type of tRNA is a variation on a theme. They are all relatively small polymers—only around 70 to 90 ribonucleotides in length—that due to their sequence, fold into three distinct stem and loop regions. As a consequence, all the different types of tRNA have a similar shape. Similar, however, is not the same. The sequence differences among the different types of tRNA still orchestrate sufficient folding differences to create unique aspects to their shape (see Figure 11-24).

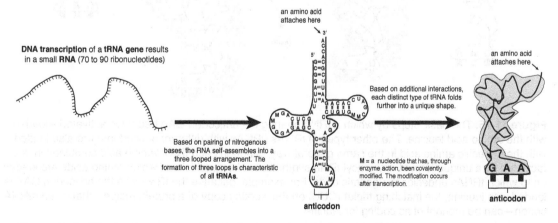

Figure 11-24. The basic steps involved in the formation of a functional tRNA.

Two features allow each tRNA to serve as a translator in protein synthesis.

• *Each tRNA has a unique* ***anticodon***. An aspect of each tRNA's shape is the exposure of three nitrogenous bases on one end of the molecule. This nitrogenous base triplet is how a tRNA is able to recognize a specific gene word along a protein recipe—the tRNA triplet can pair with the complementary triplet of nitrogenous bases along an mRNA. For instance, if a tRNA's triplet was **CAU**, it would pair whenever **GUA** was exposed along an mRNA. As you may recall, triplets along an mRNA are called **codons**. Matching triplets on tRNAs are termed **anticodons**.

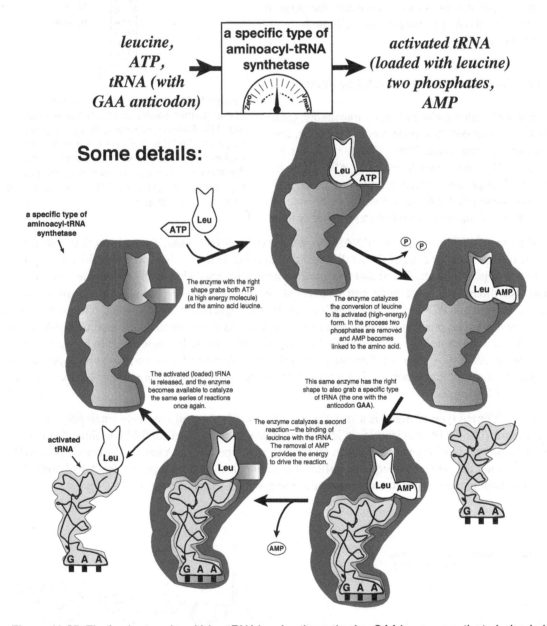

Figure 11-25. The basic steps by which a tRNA bearing the anticodon GAA becomes activated—loaded with the amino acid leucine. The other types of tRNAs (tRNAs with different anticodons) are also loaded with their specific amino acid in the same general way, although each tRNA/amino acid combination is faciliated by a unique form of aminoacyl tRNA synthetase. The specificity of which amino acids are loaded on to which tRNAs underlies the genetic code. For example, because the tRNA with the anticodon GAA is loaded with leucine, the matching triplet (CUU) on the working copy of a protein recipe—that is, an mRNA codon—can be thought of as coding for leucine.

An important aside: The reason that cells can get away with having less than 61 different types of tRNA is that some tRNAs can bind with more than one codon. This means that some codon – anticodon pairings can occur despite the presence of a mismatch. Interestingly, such tolerable mismatches always occur in the third position. In other words, as long as accurate pairing occurs with the first two bases, some tRNAs can still bind with a codon despite a third-position mismatch (of at least some types). Biologists call these third-position mismatches **wobbles**. The general pattern of tolerable third position mismatches is a single-ringed nitrogenous base pairing with the nonmatching double-ringed base (i.e., C with A or U with G), or vice versa. A few other types of mismatches are also known to occur. The existence of these third-position wobbles helps explain a pattern we mentioned earlier: When an amino acid has more than one codon, the variation generally occurs at the third position.

• *Each tRNA can be loaded with only one type of amino acid*. Enzymes (known as **aminoacyl-tRNA synthetases**) exist that can facilitate the attachment of an amino acid on to the 3' end of a tRNA. Because both tRNAs and amino acids have unique shapes, a specific type of amino acid can be attached to a specific type of tRNA only if an enzyme with the right shape to facilitate this pairing exists within a cell. It turns out that cells only produce one type of enzyme for each tRNA, so each tRNA is typically paired with the same type of amino acid (see Figure 11-25).

A tRNA with an amino acid attached is said to be an **activated tRNA** (although I prefer to call them **loaded tRNAs** because the term loaded emphasizes that something has been attached). Attaching an amino acid to a tRNA is an energy-requiring reaction. The molecule that contributes the needed energy to drive this loading reaction turns out to be an activated ribonucleotide known as ATP. The basic scheme of how ATP is used as an energy source to drive this reaction is shown in Figure 11-25, but as I have mentioned before, do not worry about the details here because we will discuss ATP and how it can be used as an energy source much more in Chapter 14. Later on in protein synthesis, the energy captured in each activated tRNA can be used to drive the polymerization of amino acids through the formation of peptide bonds.

Some information about ribosomes

Ribosomes (see Figure 11-26) are the sites of protein synthesis. They mediate the translation process by bringing an mRNA in contact with the loaded tRNAs whose anticodons match each codon along the protein recipe. They accomplish this by having three RNA binding sites. One that binds to an mRNA and in doing so exposes two adjacent codons along the mRNA. The remaining two binding sites hold tRNAs whose anticodons match the exposed codons. For reasons that would be hard to explain at this moment, one of these two tRNA binding sites is called the **P-site** (peptidyl-tRNA binding site), and the other is called the **A-site** (aminoacyl-tRNA binding site). In addition to getting

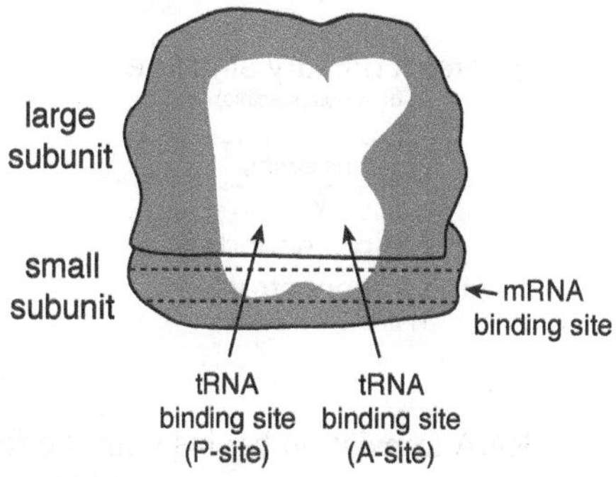

Figure 11-26. A simple cartoon of a ribosome.

tRNAs together with an mRNA, ribosomes also contain the machinery to catalyze the reaction that strings the incoming amino acids together into a growing polypeptide. Furthermore, it is important to note that ribosomes are unspecified devices; any ribosome can facilitate the translation of any protein recipe. This is true because the mRNA binding site can bind to any mRNA, and it can facilitate pairing of any tRNA whose anticodon matches any codon found along the bound mRNA.

Each ribosome comes in two pieces, one about twice the size of the other. The larger subunit is called, amazingly enough, the large subunit (or large ribosomal subunit). The smaller is called (any guesses?) the small subunit (or small ribosomal subunit). Both of these subunits are made of a mixture of ribosomal RNA and proteins. In total, a ribosome consists of several different RNA molecules, ranging from 120 to 5,000 ribonucleotides, and upwards of 70 different proteins. RNA and proteins each make up around half of a ribosome's total weight. Interestingly, its is the RNA component that seems to form the core of ribosome function; for it is not the proteins but the RNA component that seem to play a central role in a ribosome's catalytic activities. Furthermore, some of the proteins present have been shown to not be essential for ribosomal function.

Putting translation together

RNA translation strings together amino acids in a specified sequence through the interaction of three functionally different types of RNA molecules (mRNA, tRNA, and rRNA) along with a host of associated proteins (see Figure 11-27).

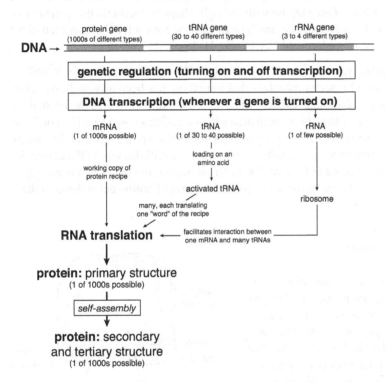

Figure 11-27. A overview of the link between DNA and proteins. RNA translation sits at the crossroad, as an interaction between many different types of proteins (which are not shown in this figure) and three functionally distinct types of RNA—each formed by DNA transcription—results in the formation of proteins with specified sequences and lengths.

RNA translation begins with the formation of an **initiation complex** (whose assembly and subsequent attachment to an mRNA is orchestrated by the action of several proteins called initiation factors). This complex forms when an activated start tRNA binds with a small ribosomal subunit (see Figure 11-28(a)). In other words, not any tRNA can participate, only the tRNA whose anticodon is UAC and thus matches the start codon (AUG). As you can look up on your handy genetic decoder (Figure 11-22), this tRNA is also loaded with the amino acid methionine, which brings up an interesting point. The first amino acid in every protein is methionine (although this first methionine is sometimes cleaved off later).

Translation proceeds when the initiation complex binds with an mRNA and then propels itself along the mRNA until it finds a start codon. This first pairing between a tRNA and the mRNA sets the reading frame (see Figure 11-28(b)). At this point, several attached initiation factors detach, which makes room for a large ribosomal subunit to bind. Once this binding occurs, the translation stage is set: A complete ribosome is attached to both an mRNA and the start tRNA (in the P-site), and the start tRNA is positioned at the mRNA's start codon (see Figure 11-28(c)).

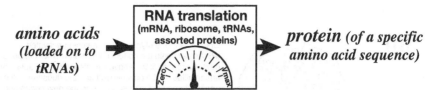

Some details:

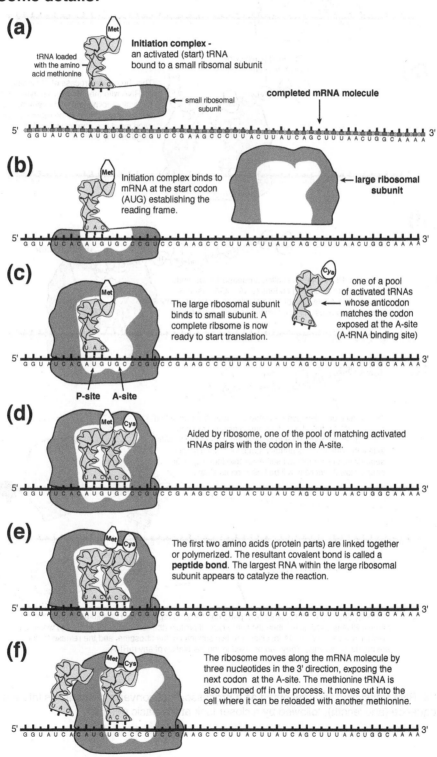

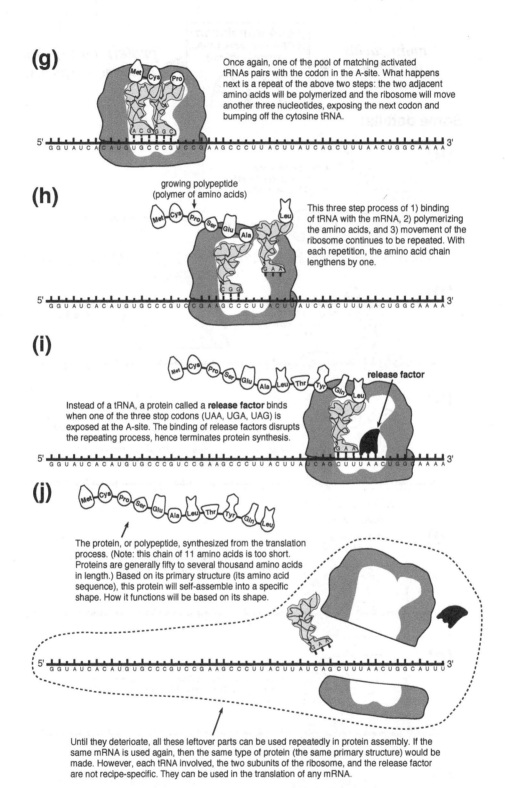

(g) Once again, one of the pool of matching activated tRNAs pairs with the codon in the A-site. What happens next is a repeat of the above two steps: the two adjacent amino acids will be polymerized and the ribosome will move another three nucleotides, exposing the next codon and bumping off the cytosine tRNA.

5' GGUAUCACAUGUGCCCGUCCGAAGCCCUUACUUAUCAGCUUUAACUGGCAAAA 3'

(h)

growing polypeptide
(polymer of amino acids)

This three step process of 1) binding of tRNA with the mRNA, 2) polymerizing the amino acids, and 3) movement of the ribosome continues to be repeated. With each repetition, the amino acid chain lengthens by one.

5' GGUAUCACAUGUGCCCGUCCGAAGCCCUUACUUAUCAGCUUUAACUGGCAAAA 3'

(i)

release factor

Instead of a tRNA, a protein called a **release factor** binds when one of the three stop codons (UAA, UGA, UAG) is exposed at the A-site. The binding of release factors disrupts the repeating process, hence terminates protein synthesis.

5' GGUAUCACAUGUGCCCGUCCGAAGCCCUUACUUAUCAGCUUUAACUGGCAAAA 3'

(j)

The protein, or polypeptide, synthesized from the translation process. (Note: this chain of 11 amino acids is too short. Proteins are generally fifty to several thousand amino acids in length.) Based on its primary structure (its amino acid sequence), this protein will self-assemble into a specific shape. How it functions will be based on its shape.

5' GGUAUCACAUGUGCCCGUCCGAAGCCCUUACUUAUCAGCUUUAACUGGCAUUU 3'

Until they deterioate, all these leftover parts can be used repeatedly in protein assembly. If the same mRNA is used again, then the same type of protein (the same primary structure) would be made. However, each tRNA involved, the two subunits of the ribosome, and the release factor are not recipe-specific. They can be used in the translation of any mRNA.

Figure 11-28. RNA translation first presented as a processor that converts amino acids into a protein of a specified sequence (and length), followed by a closer look at the basic details.

RNA translation then proceeds as a series of repeating steps: (1) Of the numerous activated tRNAs present within a cell, only one whose anticodon recognizes (matches) the codon exposed at the remaining tRNA binding site (the A-site) will readily attach (see Figure 11-28(d)). (2) Once activated, tRNAs are in both binding sites, the two amino acids they carry are in close proximity. The largest RNA within the large ribosomal subunit then catalyzes the formation of a covalent bond (called a peptide bond) that links these two amino acids together (see Figure 11-28(e)). In the process, the bond between the tRNA in the P-site and its amino acid is broken. (3) After the peptide bond is formed, the ribosome physically moves exactly three nucleotides along the mRNA (see Figure 11-28(f)). The move results from a shape change (which like many other things in this chapter is somehow powered by high phosphorylation potential) in one of the ribosomal proteins. Several important things happen as the ribosome moves: (a) The tRNA (now in its nonactivated form) in the P-site is bumped off and is thus added to the pool of nonactivated tRNAs within the cell. So, it can be used again in protein synthesis, but only after it has been reloaded (activated again) with its specific type of amino acid. (b) The tRNA that was positioned in the A-site is now in the P-site. And (c), once again the A-site is available to bind with an activated tRNA whose anticodon matches the newly exposed codon. The same three steps can then start again. The only difference is that each time the cycle happens, the growing amino acid chain is lengthened by one (see Figure 11-28 (g and h)).

This repeating three-step process continues until one of the three stop codons shows up in A-site. There are no tRNAs that bind with stop codons. Instead, one of the proteins called a **released factor** binds to and subsequently changes the catalytic properties of the ribosome so that a water molecule is added on to the end of the growing amino acid chain. Once this happens, there is nothing left for the ribosome to hold on to, so the newly formed protein (polypeptide) is released. It is now free to complete its folding into its characteristic three-dimensional shape. In the process, the ribosome also releases the mRNA as it dissociates back into its two subunits (see Figure 11-28(i and j)). RNA translation is complete.

A brief review

A good way to see if the complex interaction of RNA translation is beginning to make sense is to ask a series of basic questions about each of the three main parts involved—mRNA, ribosomes, and tRNAs:

- How many were involved in the synthesis of one protein?

- Once each one is used, could it be used again in the synthesis of another protein?

- If it can be used repeatedly in protein synthesis, is the protein formed each time the same type (same amino acid sequence)?

mRNA. The synthesis of each and every protein involves just one mRNA. Recall that an mRNA is produced by transcription of a protein gene, and consequently, it carries a complete copy of a protein recipe. Although each mRNA is a single copy of a protein recipe, it can be used to make more than one protein. It is no different than one copy of a chocolate chip cookie recipe being used to make more than one batch of cookies. All that is required is that before an mRNA degenerates (which will happen eventually), more than one ribosome hops on the mRNA and carries out translation. In fact, oftentimes, a new ribosome hops on an mRNA and starts RNA translation before the last ribosome to do so is finished. This can happen as soon as the first ribosome moves far enough down the mRNA that another can fit into the start location. Whenever an mRNA is used to make more than one protein, all the proteins will be the same (barring any translation errors). The same protein recipe is being used over and over.

ribosome. Like mRNA, the synthesis of each protein involves just one ribosome. The large subunit binds with the small subunit to form a single ribosome that moves down the mRNA from the start codon to one of the three stop codons, and in the process, a single amino acid string is formed. After a ribosome dissociates into its two parts at the termination of protein synthesis, these parts can be used again. That is, they can hop onto another mRNA and initiate translation. But because a ribosome can bind to any mRNA formed within a cell, and cells tend to always be making more than one type of mRNA, the next protein formed may not be the same as the last.

tRNAs. Whenever a protein is assembled, the number of tRNAs involved is the same as the number of amino acids that were linked together. This one-to-one ratio is a result of each tRNA being loaded with only one amino acid. Once an activated tRNA adds its attached amino acid to a growing polypeptide, the tRNA can be reloaded with another amino acid (of the same type) and then reused in protein synthesis. Because each tRNA is specific only to the codon type that it recognizes (pairs with), any activated tRNA can be used in the synthesis of any protein whose recipe contains one or more copies of this codon. So any one tRNA may play a role in the synthesis of many different types of proteins.

A Second Look at Mutations

So far, we know two basic things about mutation. First, a mutation is a change in some aspect of the information stored within a cell's DNA due to a sequence change. Second, mutations generally fall into one of three basic categories: *Point mutations*, where the overall length of the DNA stays the same but there has been a base substitution—one type of nitrogenous base at any a specific position is changed to another type. *Addition mutations*, where one or more new nucleotides are inserted into an existing sequence. Or *deletion mutations*, where one or more nucleotides are removed from an existing sequence.

Mutations potentially alter a cell's function in several ways. For instance, a mutation within a regulatory sequence could alter when a gene is turned on or off. Alternatively, a mutation within a gene's promoter could stop transcription of this DNA region altogether by disrupting the ability of RNA polymerase to bind and initiate transcription. In essence, a gene is converted into a nongene. Mutations could also occur within a tRNA, rRNA, or protein gene. And the list goes on.

What I discuss further here is the effect that each of these three types of mutations have when they occur within a protein gene—that is, when a sequence change occurs between a protein gene's promoter and termination signal. Overall, the basic effect of any type of mutation within a protein gene is the same—mutations can alter a protein's shape. A change in the recipe can change the amino acid sequence that the recipe codes for, and a different amino acid sequence may self-assemble into a different shape. If the shape change is not too great, then the protein may still act as the same type of processor. For example, the altered protein may still catalyze the same reaction, but it may do so either better or worse. Alternatively, the shape change could be so significant that that altered protein either functions as a different type of processor (e.g., catalyzes a different reaction), or it may not perform any function at all. Because actions of individual processors collectively shape the performance of the organism as a whole, such changes could significantly affect the organism as a whole.

Different types of mutations alter the protein recipe in different ways. A single point mutation (a single base substitution) will change only one triplet within a recipe (see Figure 11-29). So, at most, the meaning of one gene word (the amino acid specified by the triplet) within a recipe is altered. In other words, a base substitution within a protein gene can lead to an amino acid substitution within the protein. For example, the second triplet in Figure 11-29 initially coded for the amino acid valine, but after the point mutation, it codes for alanine. Depending on what type of amino acid is swapped for what, and where in the protein this amino acid substitution occurs, the effect of an amino acid altering point mutation on a protein's shape and consequent function can range from completely insignificant

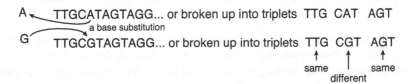

Figure 11-29. On the left side, a DNA sequence (shown as only a one-sided sequence of nitrogenous bases) that suffers a point mutation (a G replaces an A on the side shown, so a C replaces a T on the complementary side). The right side shows how a point mutation could change one gene word within a protein recipe.

to having a dramatic impact. Effects on the small side can occur because in comparison to the amino acid it replaced, the substitute amino acid has sufficiently similar chemical properties to not significantly alter the protein's resultant shape. A small effect can also result from the amino acid substitution being located (along the protein) in a place where a resultant shape change does not greatly affect function. For example, the shape change could occur in a place far away from a protein's active site. Any sequence alteration within a protein gene structure that does not alter the workings of the protein that it codes for is called a **neutral mutation**.

Due to the fact that many amino acids are coded for by more than one codon, some point mutations do not even lead to amino acid substitutions. Because codon variation usually occurs at the third position (look again at Figure 11-21), third-position mutations, in particular, can change the sequence without changing the recipe. Just to get you to look at the genetic code even more closely: What three types of first-position point mutation would not lead to an amino acid substitution?

A deletion mutation will tend to have a much greater impact on a protein recipe than a point mutation. Remember that there are no spaces or anything else that designates where each gene word starts and stops. So, the reading frames determine which triplets along a sequence code for amino acids. Anything that changes the reading frame (what biologist call a **frame shift**) would thus dramatically change the recipe. Deletion mutations cause a frame shift from the point of the deletion mutation onward (see Figure 11-30). As a consequence, from the point of the deletion onward a single deletion can change every amino acid coded for within a protein recipe. This is why deletion mutations are said to have a **positional effect**. The earlier in the protein gene the deletion occurs, the more significantly the recipe is affected (see Figure 11-30).

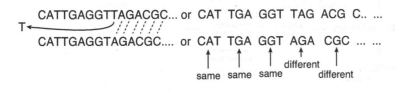

Figure 11-30. On the left side, two identical DNA sequences suffer a deletion mutation at two different locations. The right side shows that a single deletion within a protein recipe can change the gene words from the point of the deletion onwards due to a shift in the reading frame. A position effect is illustrated by comparing the two differently positioned deletions; the deletion earlier in the sequence (bottom) changes more gene words than the later deletion (top).

As odd as it might first sound, a deletion of three nucleotides in a row (or multiples of three) actually disrupts a protein recipe less than a deletion of one or two. Because gene words are triplets, knocking out three does not change the reading frame. So except for the loss of one amino acid (and potentially the alteration of one more—think about it), the amino acid sequence coded for will remain the same.

In comparison to deletion mutations, addition mutations can have similar effects because they can also cause a frame shift and thus greatly alter a protein recipe. Only if the number of nucleotides added is some multiple of three will the reading frame remain intact. And because they can cause a frame shift, addition mutations also display a positional effect.

A Final Summary

I started this chapter by stating that a loopy interaction exists between DNA and proteins. I end this chapter with two figures that are worth staring at and contemplating.

Figure 11-31 summarizes how as the keeper of the recipes for proteins as well as for the various types of tRNAs and rRNAs, DNA plays a role in the formation of every protein. On the other hand, the activity facilitated by proteins (as well as certain RNAs) plays a role in every thing that happens to DNA both directly and indirectly. Direct interactions would include orchestrating replication and transcription. Indirect interactions would include orchestrating all the actions of the cell in which the DNA resides. Note that we have yet to cover some of things mentioned in Figure 11-31, such as metabolic pathways. That is our task in the next couple of chapters.

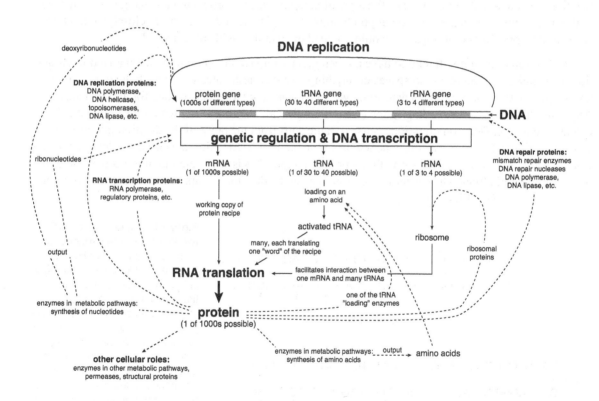

Figure 11-31. A summary of the loopy interaction between DNA and proteins.

Figure 11-32 starts with a basic definition of reproduction and then outlines how reproduction involves as loopy interaction between activity and information. Here, both the division of labor and the constant interaction between DNA and proteins is made evident. The intermediary nature of RNA molecules in this whole process is also made apparent, as only RNA molecules straddle both sides of the activity/information dichotomy. Specifically, messenger RNA molecules (mRNA) play on the information side of the interaction, whereas transfer or translator RNA (tRNA) and ribosomal RNA (rRNA) play on the activity side.

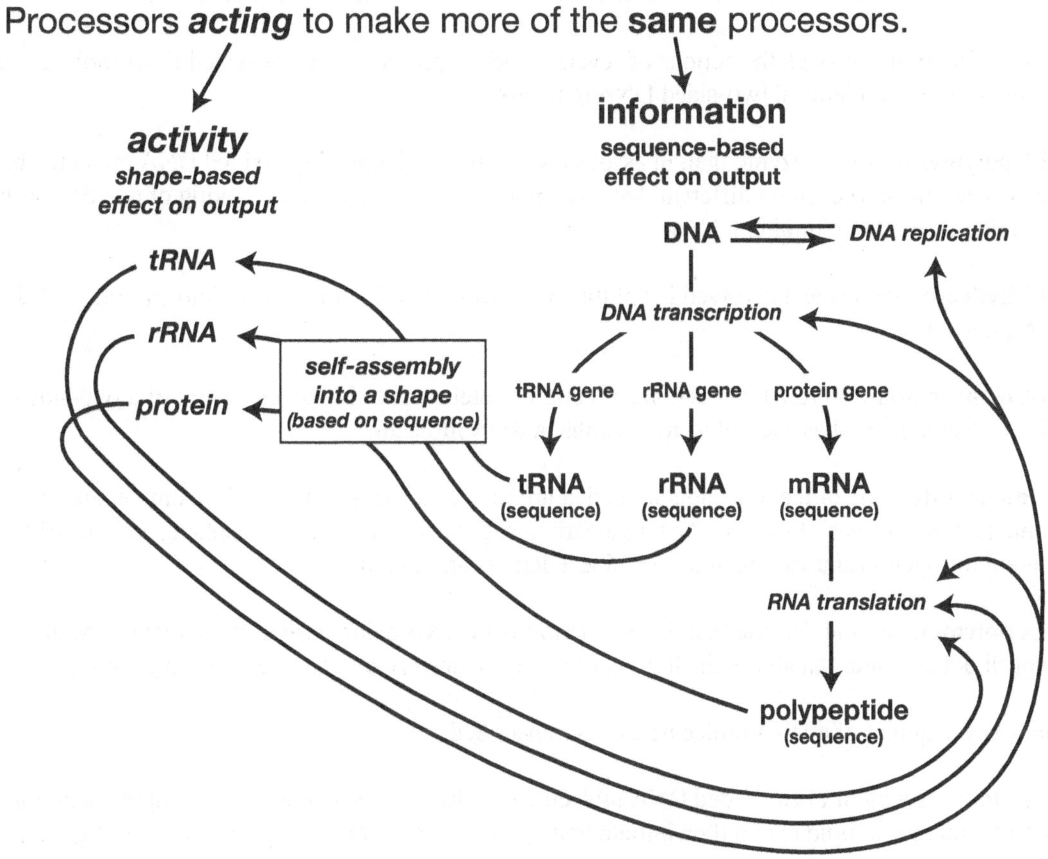

Figure 11-32. A summary of the loopy interaction between activity and information that underlies reproductive performances.

Some key terms:

deoxyribonucleotide - one of the four monomers that are linked together to form a DNA molecule. Each deoxyribonucleotide consists of three parts: a five-carbon sugar called deoxyribose, a phosphate, and one of four different nitrogenous bases (guanine, cytosine, adenine, and thymine).

DNA replication - through the actions of several types of proteins, one two-sided DNA molecule is converted into two identical two-sided DNA molecules.

DNA polymerase - the enzyme that, in association with an existing single-sided DNA molecule being used as a template to position different deoxyribonucleotides, catalyzes the linking of one deoxyribonucleotide to another (forming DNA).

DNA helicase - the protein involved in splitting one two-sided DNA molecule into two one-sided DNA molecules.

DNA transcription - through the actions of certain proteins, one side of a segment of a two-sided DNA molecule is used as a template to assemble a RNA molecule.

ribonucleotide - one of the four monomers that are linked together to form a RNA molecule. Each ribonucleotide consists of three parts: a five-carbon sugar called ribose, a phosphate, and one of four different nitrogenous bases (guanine, cytosine, adenine, and uracil).

RNA polymerase - the enzyme that, in association with DNA being used as a template to position different ribonucleotides, catalyzes the linking of one ribonucleotide to another (forming RNA).

gene - any segment of a DNA molecule that is transcribed.

promoter - a segment of two-sided DNA molecule that due to its sequence has the right shape for RNA polymerase to bind to and then initiate transcription. Promoters designate the start of genes.

terminal sequence - the DNA sequence that designates the end of a gene—that is, where transcription stops.

protein gene - any segment of DNA that codes for a functional protein (is a protein recipe).

messenger RNA (mRNA) - the generic name given to the RNA molecule that results from the transcription of a protein gene. (The mRNA formed is, in essence, the working copy of the protein recipe.)

genetic regulation - the turning on or off of transcription of any gene within a genome. (The "choosing" of which gene to transcribe.)

regulatory protein - the generic name given to any protein that can bind to DNA (at a regulatory sequence) and influence (either positively or negatively) RNA polymerase's ability to bind to a gene's promoter (and subsequently initiate transcription).

regulatory gene - the generic name given to any protein gene that codes for a regulatory protein.

RNA translation - the means by which a mRNA molecule is used to assemble a protein.

codon - a string of three ribonucleotides, with a specific sequence of nitrogenous bases, on a mRNA molecule that codes for a particular amino acid.

tRNAs - RNA molecules (made up of around 70 to 90 ribonucleotides) that play the role of translators during RNA translation. Each tRNA can be loaded with only one type of amino acid and has a unique anticodon.

anticodon - a string of three riboncleotides positioned at one end of a tRNA molecule in a way that the three nitrogenous bases can pair with three matching nitrogenous bases (a codon) on an mRNA molecule.

tRNA gene - any segment of DNA that codes for a functional tRNA.

ribosome - a structure made out of both RNA and proteins that get the message (a mRNA) and the translators of this message (the tRNAs that match each codon along the mRNA) together.

point mutation - a change in a cell's DNA sequence due to the substitution of one deoxyribonucleotide with another deoxyribonucleotide having a different nitrogenous base. (A base substitution.)

deletion mutation - a change in a cell's DNA sequence due to the loss of one or more of the deoxyribonucleotides.

addition mutation - a change in a cell's DNA sequence due to the gain of one or more deoxyribonucleotides.

Some study questions:

1. What is the relationship between nucleotides and nucleic acids? Be able to recognize each. *Explain what aspects of the molecular structure of DNA make it possible for a DNA molecule: to be replicated, to "store" information.*

2. Be able to explain how DNA is replicated. How is the fact that different types of proteins orchestrate DNA replication an example of Life's loopiness? What are some of the proteins involved?

3. *Earlier I defined reproduction as: Proteins acting to make more copies of the same proteins. Explain how DNA replication plays an important role in offspring making the same proteins as their parents.*

4. How does the fact that DNA polymerase only works in the 5' to 3' direction complicate DNA replication? In general terms, explain how complication is resolved.

5. How does the fact that DNA polymerase only works in the 5' to 3' direction help minimize the occurrence of copy errors during DNA replication.

6. How does mismatch repair "know" which side of a two-sided DNA the copy error occurred? Why is "knowing" the error side important?

7. Why is two-sided damage more difficult to repair than one-sided damage? Why can't a mutation be repaired?

8. (A repeat of a chapter 9 study question.) What are the three basic steps in a gene being used to assemble a protein? Be able to explain in general what happens in each of these steps.

9. *Be able to walk through the mechanics of DNA transcription from the point that RNA polymerase binds to the promoter.*

10. Why is it more accurate to call the working copy of a protein gene (a mRNA) a template copy instead of just a copy?

11. *What are some similarities and some differences between DNA replication and DNA transcription?*

12. Explain the statement: The secret to genetic regulation lies in the fact that RNA polymerase's access—ability to bind—to each gene's promoter can be controlled. *How are regulatory sequences and regulatory proteins involved in genetic regulation?*

13. Explain the following statement: RNA translation involves many translators each able to do only one thing.

14. *Explain why a codon length of three (read nonoverlappingly) works "best" in terms of translating mRNA to an amino acid sequence.* (In other words, explain why a codon length of 1, 2, 4, 5, etc. would not work as well as three).

15. What are differences and similarities between protein genes, tRNA genes, and rRNA genes?

16. How many different roles do RNA molecules play in RNA translation? What are these different roles?

17. *Explain how each of the different types of tRNA come to have different shapes, and how that shape is related to what type of amino acid they are "loaded" with.* What happens to a tRNA molecule after is it "unloaded"?

18. *Explain this statement: Each tRNA being able to be loaded with more than one type of amino acid would make it impossible for a particular DNA sequence to code for a particular amino acid sequence.*

19. Overall, describe how translation (interpretation) of an mRNA sequence to an amino acid sequence takes place. Specifically, what are the roles played by tRNAs and ribosomes?

20. What is the primary structure of a protein coded for by the DNA sequence TGGC-TACCCATTTTCACATAG...? What are the codons and anticodons of the above DNA sequence? On what structures are these codons and anticodons found?

21. *Explain why a deletion or addition mutation may result in a larger alteration of a protein's primary structure than a point mutation.* Why does the position along a gene of a deletion or addition mutation, but not a point mutation, affect the degree of alteration that will result? Explain how three deletion (or addition) mutations may result in less of an alteration of the protein's primary structure than one deletion (or addition) mutation.

Containers

So far we have seen that proteins and nucleic acids can form a loopy interaction. For this interaction to occur, however, these molecules must stay in close proximity. Diffusion is thus a nemesis to reproduction. The tendency for molecules to move from high to low concentration will result in molecules wandering apart.

A container impermeable to proteins and nucleic acids may be of service to reproduction by separating the world into an inside and outside. Molecules trapped together on the inside are confined to interact together and cannot escape the consequences of themselves. Each molecule's actions, be they positive or negative, will affect the reproductive success of the very performance that assembled them. Due to the effects of each molecule coming full circle, each molecule becomes part of a larger unit, called an individual, by creating a region where the degree of loopiness equals one.

This chapter would be brief if the containers that enclose proteins and nucleic acids were also impermeable to everything else—that is, whatever started inside stayed on the inside, and whatever started outside stayed on the outside. After a discussion of container structure, there would be little more to say, *except that it would not work*! To be part of a reproductive performance, a container must selectively allow some substances to pass, as resources need to be continually brought in, and waste products may need to be expelled.

Some selective exchange can occur simply by the fact that what is a barrier to one thing is not necessarily a barrier to everything else. A chain link fence, for example, is a barrier to dogs but not to mice. The structure of cellular membranes—commonly a membrane lipid bilayer—has similar properties. It is freely permeable to some things, somewhat permeable to others, and almost completely impermeable to yet others. But that is still not good enough. Some molecules needed cannot pass through a membrane lipid layer or cannot pass through fast enough. Furthermore, permeability to different substances needs to change in concert with the needs of the reproductive performance inside. It is here that proteins come back into the thick of things. A cell's membrane is embedded with proteins that help ferry molecules from one side to the other. What moves in and out is largely affected by what membrane-bound proteins are present and in what abundance.

Before we go into more detail about membrane-bound proteins and other associated issues, we need to back up. It is critical to understand how containers come together in the first place. To address this we need to know more about membrane structure. This creates the opportunity to introduce another class of biological molecules called lipids.

Lipids

Lipids, although structurally diverse, are lumped together by the fact that the entire, or at least a majority, of each structure is neutrally charged and thus insoluble in water.

Some more information: Recall that water molecules are "friendly" with each other. Due to their polar nature, water molecules form hydrogen bonds with other water molecules by aligning opposite charges. Charge-bearing molecules can mix in with a water crowd. They intermingle by aligning with the opposite charges found on polar water molecules. Some chemists, obviously with a romantic bent, have gone so far as to call these molecules water loving, or **hydrophilic**. Neutral molecules, on the other hand, are not accepted by water. They have no opposite charge with which to form a relationship. Neutral molecules are thus sometimes termed water fearing, or **hydrophobic**.

Fatty acids are used in the assembly of all lipids except steroids. They are a single hydrocarbon chain with a carboxyl or acid group attached to one end (see Figure 12-1). Although the hydroxyl group (–OH) is polar, the much larger hydrocarbon chain is not. The hydrocarbon chain usually contains an even number of carbon atoms and is typically 14 to 24 carbon atoms long. They can either be

saturated or **unsaturated**. Each carbon in a saturated fatty acid, as the name implies, is covalently linked with as many hydrogen atoms as possible. In contrast, all carbons in unsaturated fatty acids are not connected to as many hydrogen atoms as possible, and thus one or more double bonds form

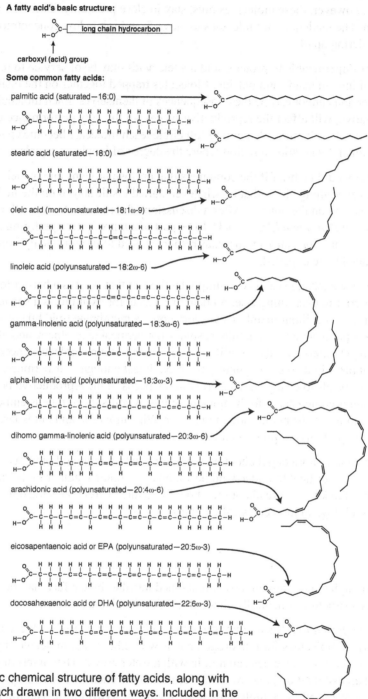

Figure 12-1. The basic chemical structure of fatty acids, along with several examples—each drawn in two different ways. Included in the second (right side) structural representation is a bend in the chain (arbitrarily chosen to be 18 degrees) at each double bond. This is not meant to be an accurate two-dimensional representation, but to illustrate that increasing the number of double bonds causes the structure to be less and less linear. Each fatty acid has an associated set of numbers (e.g., 18:3ω-3). The first number indicates the number of carbon atoms in the hydrocarbon chain. The second indicates the number of double bonds in the chain. The third, where ω (or omega) is the last letter in the greek alphabet, indicates the position of the first double bond from the terminal end. For instance, in an omega-3 (ω-3) fatty acid the first double bond comes after the third carbon from the end.

between pairs of carbon atoms in the chain. The presence of double bonds creates a structural difference. Saturated fatty acids are straight, whereas the hydrocarbon chain bends or kinks at every double bond in unsaturated fatty acids. (We discuss implications of this difference later.) Although fatty acids are used in the construction of larger molecules, they are not polymerized—that is, unlike amino acids and nucleotides, they are not monomers that are repeatedly linked together.

Triacylglycerols or triglycerides are composed of three fatty acids that are joined (via dehydration reaction) to a three-carbon molecule called glycerol (see Figure 12-2). These three fatty acids can all be the same type, or they can be two or three different types. This fatty acid arrangement is an efficient means of energy storage for two reasons. First, the carbons in each fatty acid are highly reduced (they are covalently linked to either a hydrogen atom or another carbon atom) and thus entrap a lot of chemical energy. Second, the entire structure is neutrally charged—the bonding of three fatty acids to glycerol eliminates all the polar hydroxyl groups (–OH)—so instead of mixing with, and being diluted by, surrounding water molecules, it will naturally form into clumps composed solely of triacylglycerols (or other fat-soluble molecules). The neutral charge is why you will hear triacylglycerols sometimes referred to as neutral fats. In addition, triacylglycerols are used to form protective cushions for various parts of multicellular bodies, and fat layers just below the skin provide insulation.

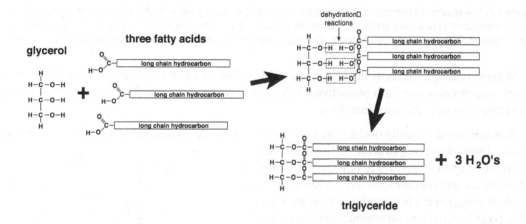

Figure 12-2. The basic steps involved in the synthesis of a triglyceride (a neutral fat).

Membrane lipids are the most "confused" about their interactions with water. They are typically composed of a relatively larger polar structure—called the **polar head region** or polar head group— hooked to two long, fatty acid–derived, hydrocarbon chains. The most common arrangement, called a **polar glycerolipid**, is similar in structure to triacylglycerols in that fatty acids are hooked to a glycerol molecule. The difference is that fatty acids are hooked to only two of the three "attachment sites," and the remaining is connected to a polar chemical structure. The term **phospholipid** is used for any polar glycerolipid in which a negatively charged phosphate attaches to the glycerol and makes up part of the polar head group. Molecules such as choline (see Figure 12-3(a)), serine, glycerol, and inositol are then commonly found attached to the phosphate. Phospholipids of some form have been found in the membranes of all types of organisms. **Galactolipids** are also a major membrane lipid in some photosynthetic groups (e.g., cyanobacteria, plants). They are still polar glycerolipids, but instead of some phosphate-based structure, a galactose (a six-carbon sugar) arrangement makes up the polar head group. Given that photosynthetic organisms can make sugars, the advantage of this switch may lie in reducing its dependence on acquiring phosphorus—which is needed to make phosphates—to grow. In certain environments (like some soils), phosphorus can be a scarce, thus limiting, resource. Finally, the last major group of membrane lipids, called **sphingolipids**, lack glycerol altogether. One or two fatty acids are attached to the polar head group formed by the amino acid serine, along with other added structures. Although sometimes ignored, sphingolipids are mentioned here because their role in membrane structure is becoming increasingly understood. We will bring them up again later.

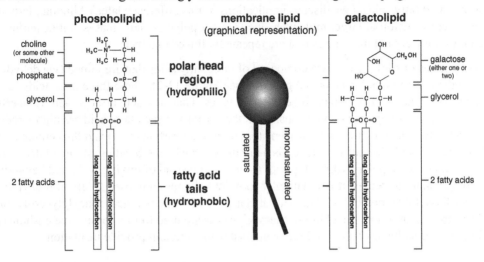

Figure 12-3. A graphical representation of a membrane lipid is aligned with the chemical structure of two common forms of membrane lipids: a phospholipid (specifically phosphatidyl choline) and a galactolipid (specifically monoglactosyldiacylglycerol). Because glycerol is present in each, they are both glycerolipids.

Waxes are long-chain fatty acids attached to long-chained alcohols or carbon rings. They are used as structural molecules to form protective coatings on leaves, stems, and skin. Such coatings, among other things, act as barriers to water loss.

Steroids are structurally distinct from any other lipid group mentioned in that they lack fatty acids entirely. Their identifying structure is four interconnecting rings of carbon atoms. Three of these rings contain six carbon atoms, one ring contains five carbon atoms, and the whole arrangement is nonpolar. Sterols are steroids with a polar hydroxyl group attached to the number 3 labeled carbon. Cholesterol is the most common animal sterol. Phytosterols are a diverse group of similar, but not identical, compounds found in plants. Bacteria lack sterols, but some have structurally similar compounds called hopanoids, which have five, instead of four, carbon rings. Animal and plant sterols, along with hopanoids, all seem to play similar roles—to modulate the fluidity of membranes. The arrangement of carbon rings forms a rigid, planar structure, that can increase the stiffness of lipid membrane arrangements (discussed more later). Sterols, such as cholesterol, are also further modified to form other steroids, such as vitamin D, and many hormones, such as testosterone and estradiol (an estrogen; see Figure 12-4).

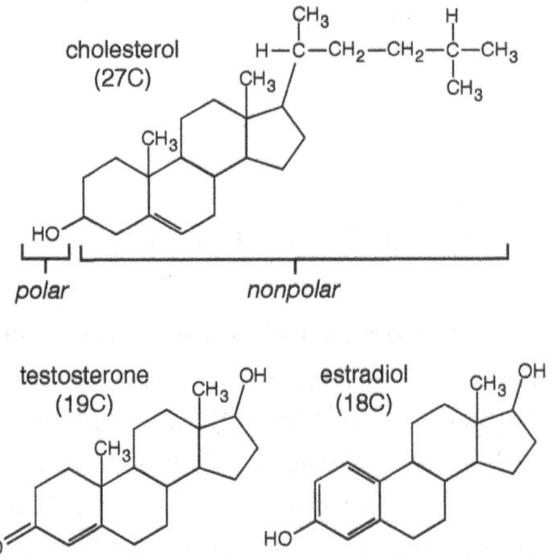

Figure 12-4. The chemical structure of cholesterol and two steroid hormones—the sex steroids testosterone and estradiol (an estrogen).

Membrane lipids tend to self-assemble into containers

The fact that all membrane lipids have a split personality when it comes to interacting with water—the polar head region is hydrophilic, whereas fatty acid tail region is hydrophobic—raises the question: How will a bunch of membrane lipids arrange in water? In other words, into what shape will they self-assemble? If the two ends were separated, they would do quite different things. The polar ends would disperse throughout water or dissolve. The fatty acid ends would huddle together. The actual arrangement must then be some sort of compromise between these two tendencies.

One compromise shape is where the fatty acid tails stick inward, away from the water, and the heads stick outward, toward the water. However, such an arrangement—called a **micelle**—is possible only if the two tails are short or the number of tails is reduced to one. Two long tails make it difficult to pack the polar head regions tightly together without running out of room to fit the tails (see Figure 12-5).

But what alternative arrangement would have the head regions face water and the tail regions hide from water? It starts with a bilayer where the head regions face outward in opposite directions, and the two abutting tail regions are sandwiched in between. The head

Micelles can form if membrane lipids have short tails or have single tails.

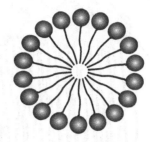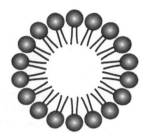

Membrane lipids with two long tails cannot self-assemble into micelles. The tails cannot all fit in the middle.

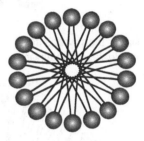

Figure 12-5. Why some membrane lipids (or similar molecules) will self-assemble into micelles and others will not.

regions face the surrounding water on each side of the bilayer, and the lipid tails are tucked away. Self-assembly further favors the structure to take on an edgeless arrangement, such as a sphere. And a spherical membrane lipid bilayer is a container because it separates the world into an inside and an outside (see Figure 12-6). Furthermore, the bilayer is impermeable to proteins and nucleic acids.

The fact that membrane lipid bilayers initially self-assemble into edgeless containers also means that the container will self-repair. Any tears through a container create edges, and edges will, if possible, reseal back into an edgeless arrangement.

Temperature and fluidity

In Figure 12-1 we saw that increasing the number of double bonds increased the kinks and contortions in a fatty acid's hydrocarbon chain. Now it is time to discuss why that is important. The backdrop is that every time an organism synthesizes a fatty acid it starts out saturated. Double bonds are only added afterward at two costs: the extra resources used in their formation (resources used to build the enzymes—called desaturases, in conjunction with the energy sources needed to drive the chemical reactions), and the decrease in chemical energy stored as the removal of hydrogen atoms decreases the level that carbons in the chain are reduced. So why would any organism ever go to the trouble?

The answer has to do with two related terms: fluidity and melting point. Whether fatty acids are part of triacylglycerols (energy storage) or membrane lipids, the nature of fatty acids within the mix influences how they will arrange. Put quite simply, the greater the proportion of saturated fatty acids, the more ordered the arrangement will be, given that their straight hydrocarbon can be packed together in a tighter, more orderly fashion (see Figure 12-7(a)). Stated the other way, increasing the proportion of unsaturated fatty acids, as well as the degree that each is unsaturated (the number of double bonds),

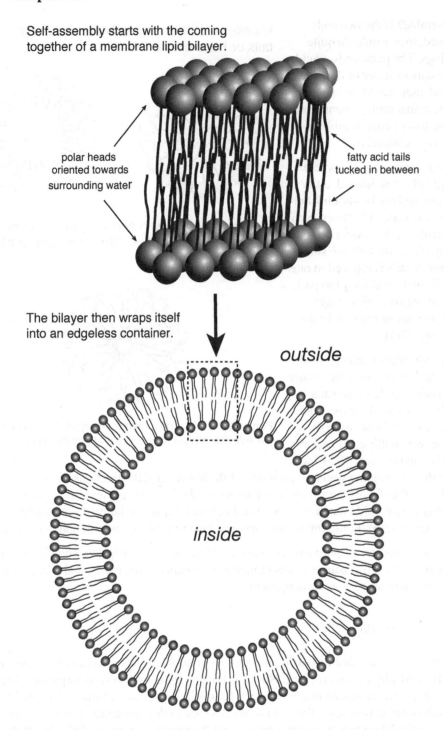

Self-assembly starts with the coming together of a membrane lipid bilayer.

polar heads oriented towards surrounding water

fatty acid tails tucked in between

The bilayer then wraps itself into an edgeless container.

outside

inside

Figure 12-6. The self-assembly of long-tailed membrane lipids into a lipid bilayer that forms into a container.

increases the degree of disorder (see Figure 12-7(b)). Kinked and crooked hydrocarbon chains get in each others' way, prohibiting tight, orderly packing. The degree of order (or disorder) influences a measurable property called **melting point**—the temperature at which a solid changes into a liquid. More ordered arrangements have a greater tendency to stay together and thus can remain a solid at higher (more disruptive) temperatures. You have observed this many times. Butter is composed of mostly saturated fatty acids and is a solid at room temperature, whereas so-called oils (such as olive oil) are composed of more unsaturated fatty acids and are liquid at room temperature. Table 12-1 shows what a pronounced effect increasing the number of double bonds can have on decreasing the melting point. Yet, whereas scientist can readily measure melting point, the biologically relevant issue is the fluidity of membranes or storage fats at temperatures relevant to the organism. The two are, however, connected in that the lower the melting point, the more fluid the arrangement will be at any given temperature.

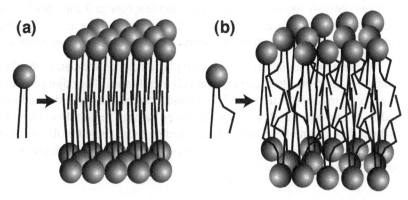

Figure 12-7. How the nature of fatty acid tails could influence the arrangement of membrane lipids into a bilayer. In (a) both fatty acid tails are saturated (straight), and thus the membrane lipids can be packed into a tight, ordered arrangement. On the other hand, in (b) one of the two fatty acid tails is unsaturated with three double bonds (three kinks in the tail), which prevents the membrane lipids from packing so tightly, and thus creates a more disordered arrangement.

This sets the issue: An organism should go to the trouble of adding more and more double bonds to their fatty acids whenever they need to compensate for the decreasing fluidity caused by lower temperatures. Here are a few examples: Different than animals, adult plants do not store energy as fats, but due to the higher energy content per unit weight, many plants add triacylglycerols to their seeds as an energy store for emerging seedlings. Yet, fat stores need to

Table 12-1. Influence of the number of double bonds on the melting point of four fatty acids, each with 18 carbons in the hydrocarbon chain.

Fatty acid	# of double bonds	Melting point
Stearic acid	0	70°C
Oleic acid	1	13°C
Linoleic acid	2	-5°C
Linolenic acid	3	-11°C

be fluid to be used, so plant species that germinate at colder temperatures have been found to add more double bonds to these fat stores. Membranes also need to be fluid to function, and plants growing at colder temperatures have also been found to incorporate more highly unsaturated fatty acids into their membrane lipids. Similarly, in artic Svalbard reindeer (*Rangifer tarandus platyrhynchus*), fats deposits closer to the surface—and thus more likely to experience colder temperatures—were found to have higher levels of unsaturation.

An aside: Most animals, including humans, cannot synthesize either omega-6 or omega-3 fatty acids. That is, they lack the enzymes needed to add double bonds either six carbons or three carbons from the hydrocarbon end of a fatty acid. The degree to which animals have highly unsaturated (or polyunsaturated) fatty acids available is dependent on their diet. Plants can make both types. Interestingly, the availability of these more highly unsaturated fatty acids has been found to influence the behavior of several species of hibernating mammals. Most significant was the finding that body temperature of animals fed a diet rich in saturated fatty acids did not drop as low during hibernation, and thus these animals maintained higher, more expensive metabolic rates. The higher temperatures were likely a result of hibernation relying on fat stores as the energy source and saturated fats not being as fluid—thus as available—at colder temperatures. This effect was further manifested by these same animals entering hibernation later and staying in the hibernating state for a shorter duration.

Another aside: The relative proportion of omega-6 and omega-3 fatty acids available is also dependent on diet. This has become an important health issue in humans, as our "modern" diet tends to have relatively too many omega-6 and too few omega-3 fatty acids. The inability to properly adjust membrane fluidity appears to be part of the issue, and there are likely other components that we are not ready to discuss; nonetheless I strongly encourage paying attention to your own diet choices.

Bacterial hopanoids and sterols also play a role in modulating the fluidity of membranes. These molecules are typically found in outer cell membranes. The adjoining rings form a planar, rigid structure that spans about half of the bilayer and interacts with membrane lipids on each side. The polar hydroxyl group in sterols extends into the polar head region. In contrast to adding double bonds to the hydrocarbon chain of membrane lipids, adding these ringed molecules increases the order or rigidity of the membrane. Thus, adjusting the amount present becomes another avenue for organisms to adjust their membrane properties.

Lipid rafts

The cell membrane was initially envisioned as a fluid, relatively homogeneous structure, due to the constant and random mixing of its parts—the different types of membrane lipids and membrane-bound proteins. This view was known as the **fluid-mosaic model**, where a "mosaic" of proteins float around in a "fluid" lipid bilayer.

At least in some cell types, a different view of membrane organization is emerging. Instead of a rather simple homogeneous layer of proteins and lipids, many biological membranes seem to be organized into discrete regions with distinct lipid and protein content. This organization appears to start with patches of more ordered and more disordered arrangements of lipid membranes forming (and coexisting) within the same membrane. In other words, regions with different fluidity form within the same membrane. The more ordered, less fluid, patches are called **lipid rafts** due to the fact that they will tend to "float" around in more fluid surroundings. Next, distinct types of membrane proteins sort differentially into raft and nonraft areas, and their ability to function depends on them doing so. The advantage to these occurrences unfolds via a common theme: Partitioning discrete functions into separate areas better eliminates interference and thus allows more things to happen at once.

The formation of raft and nonraft areas may have started with the behavior of membrane lipids with contrasting levels of double bonds along their fatty acids. Specifically, sphingolipids—whose fatty acids are largely saturated—along with some phospholipids composed of mostly saturated fatty acids, appear to have some tendency to hang together. But the addition of sterols seems to be the key ingredient, as only membranes that include cholesterol or other sterols have been observed to form lipid rafts. Sterols have a strong affinity for sphingolipids, and this coupling appears to hold rafts together. As will be mentioned again in a later chapter, the evolution of sterol synthesis is at least correlated with the evolution of a new cell type characterized by a host of novel membrane-associated cellular processes. It is also interesting to note that well-functioning brain cells have high levels of cholesterol and high levels of long polyunsaturated fatty acids within their membranes. The former is needed to form rafts, and the later is needed to form the most fluid nonraft areas. Brain cell membranes are incredibly dynamic, and it makes sense that dynamic membranes would require regions of dynamic contrast.

Trans fats

Given that you have likely heard nutritional advice suggesting you avoid trans fats, it makes sense to briefly mention what they are. Most of the time when an organism adds double bonds to a fatty acid, the two hydrogen atoms still attached end up on the same side of the double bond. Chemists call this a *cis* configuration. On rare occasions, however, the two hydrogen atoms are twisted such that they end up on different sides of the chain, forming a *trans* configuration (see Figure 12-8).

In many processed foods, polyunsaturated oils are partially hydrogenated to produce fats that do not go rancid (spoil) as readily and thus can last on a shelf longer in the absence of refrigeration. Although the obvious effect of partial hydrogenation is to remove some double bonds via the addition of hydrogen atoms, it also has been found to reconfigure many (up to 45%) of the remaining double bonds into a *trans* configuration. In other words, partial hydrogenation creates increasing levels of trans fats. A *trans* configuration increasingly straightens the kinks out of double bonds and thus increases the melting point in comparison to fats with the same number of double bonds in the *cis* configuration. Therefore, the problem with consuming high levels of trans fats may be as simple as reducing one's ability to generate the needed fluidity of fat stores or membranes, or perhaps even reducing the ability to generate effective lipid rafts, due to having an insufficient supply of the highly fluid membrane lipids needed to make the nonraft regions.

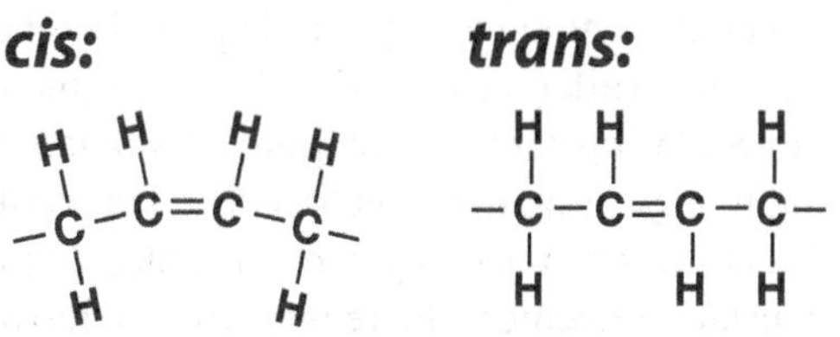

Figure 12-8. The difference between a *cis* and *trans* configuration.

There could also be all sorts of other complications. For instance, in one six-year-long study with male African green monkeys (*Chlorocebus aethiops*), two groups were fed identical diets, except that 8% of their calories were from trans fats in one group, whereas the other group was given equivalent amounts of olive oil. Not only did the trans fat group gain more weight (7.2% versus 1.8% increase), but also they increased their deposition of belly or abdominal fat. Increasing levels of abdominal fat has been found to be associated with all sorts of health problems.

Movement across Membranes

Any type of molecule can move across a membrane if the membrane is permeable to it at least to some extent. That, I hope, is obvious. What may not be so obvious is that discussion of molecular movement is in reality a discussion of **net movement**. Given permeability, individual molecules can pass across the membrane in either direction. The question is: Are more molecules passing in one direction than the other direction? If so, there is a net movement.

The way of diffusion: High to low

The striking aspect of diffusion is that net movement takes place within a backdrop of no overall movement. To be more explicit, diffusion generates a net movement of a specific type of molecule, even though collectively the entire mixture of molecules is not moving in a particular direction. Let me take a moment to explain.

As we know, molecules are in constant motion when temperature is above absolute zero molecules. Within this buzz of activity, molecules are constantly changing directions as they collide with other molecules. Suppose, amid these constant collisions, we followed an individual molecule for some duration of time. At the end, would the molecule be expected to be in the same place as it was when we started watching? The answer is no. By chance, collisions will bounce a molecule more in some directions than others. So the molecule will travel about

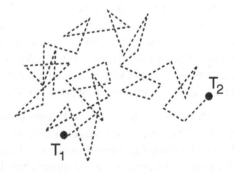

Figure 12-9. The type of path along which any molecule (represented as a solid circle) could move between two points in time (starting at T1 and ending at T2). Each change in direction results from a collision with another molecule. The overall movement is known as a random walk.

the mixture along a very erratic path. In other words, it will move about by what has been termed a **random walk** (see Figure 12-9). The same is true for every other molecule in the mix. Each and every molecule constantly embarking on a random walk does not, however, result in the entire group moving in any particular direction. Random walks balance out on average. One molecule moving in one direction is balanced by another molecule moving in the opposite direction. So even though there is constant movement, there is no overall movement.

Net movement can still occur in absence of overall movement as long as there is a **concentration gradient**. A gradient is a slope. But how can concentration have a slope? The answer is the same way that a hill has a slope. Something changes across distance. With hills it is elevation that changes. As one moves up or down a hill the elevation changes from either higher to lower or lower to higher. Replace elevation with concentration, and you now have a concentration gradient. A concentration gradient exists whenever the concentration of a particular type of molecule within the overall mix changes across distance. A concentration gradient across a membrane simply means that one side of a membrane has a higher concentration of some molecule than the other side (see Figure 12-10). (Note: A molecular concentration gradient is sometimes termed a **chemical gradient**. I will stick to using concentration gradient.)

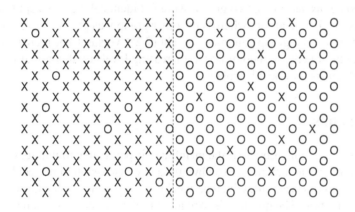

Figure 12-10. Two concentration gradients exist as one moves from one side of the dashed line to the other. Move from left to right and the concentration of **X**'s changes from higher to lower. Alternatively, move from right to left and the concentration of **O**'s changes from higher to lower.

The combination of random walks and concentration gradients is what generates diffusion. Due to ongoing random walks, all the molecules of the same type (call them type **X**) within a molecular mixture move equally (on average) in all directions. But what if we add a concentration gradient on top of random motion? As **X**s move every which way, some **X**s located in the region of high concentration will move toward the region of low concentration. Similarly, **X**s from the region of low concentration will move toward the region of high concentration. The movement in both these directions will not be equal simply because there are more **X**s to move from the higher concentration area to the lower concentration area than vice versa. A high to low net movement of **X**s will take place. Unless something else intervenes, this cannot work any other way.

Diffusion cannot continue forever because as diffusion continues, the concentration in both regions shifts toward the middle. Higher gets lower and lower gets higher until the concentrations equilibrate. Diffusion literally diffuses the very gradient on which it depends. At equilibrium, movement of **X** between the two regions continues, but the rate of movement tends to be equal in both directions.

Before we are done, another form of gradient will come into play—an **electrical gradient**. An electrical gradient is an unequal distribution of positive and negative charges in the form of ions. Like concentration gradients, electric gradients can power diffusion. Because opposite charges attract, ions of one charge tend to move toward regions bearing excess of the opposite charge.

The three basic modes of movement across membranes

To consider how different molecules move across cell membranes, we need to keep two things in mind: permeability and concentration gradients. There are three basic modes of movement.

The first is called **simple diffusion**. Because it depends on a concentration gradient to power the movement, simple diffusion can only occur if a concentration gradient across a membrane exists. The simple part is that it is restricted to substances able to pass directly through the phospholipid bilayer (see Figure 12-11). All lipid-soluble substances such as O_2, CO_2, and other electrically neutral molecules fit into this category. Small polar molecules such as water also seem to pass through phospholipid membranes somewhat readily. This to me is puzzling. We all know that lipids and water do not mix, so one would think that a phospholipid bilayer's lipid interior would effectively block small polar molecules from passing through. Permeability does, however, slow considerably as polar molecules get larger. Phospholipid membranes form the strongest barrier to anything bearing a charge, including small single atom ions such as Na^+, K^+, and Cl^-.

Simple diffusion:

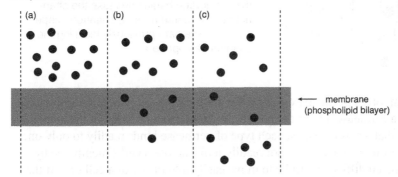

Figure 12-11. In (a) a concentration gradient exists across a membrane. Because this type of molecule (solid circle) is able to pass directly through the membrane, in (b) diffusion begins to move these molecules with the concentration gradient (from high to low). Although movement of these molecules across the membrane will still occur, in (c) net movement by diffusion will stop because the concentration on each side of the membrane is equal.

Movement across a membrane is in many cases helped along by a protein or protein complex. When such movement is powered by diffusion, the protein's sole role is to increase permeability. When a protein helps in this type of movement across a membrane, it is termed **facilitated diffusion**. Recognize that when proteins are involved, the genes within a cell's genome indirectly influence what can get into or out of a cell. Any protein able to facilitate transport can only be assembled within a cell if the protein's recipe (gene) is present in the cell's genome. Facilitated diffusion comes in two forms: channel-mediated diffusion and carrier-mediated diffusion.

Channel-mediated diffusion involves proteins with a hollow interior that go all the way through the membrane. They thus create a transmembrane opening or a channel. What can pass through these transmembrane channels is clearly affected by size. Just as one cannot eat anything bigger than one's

Facilitated diffusion: channel-mediated

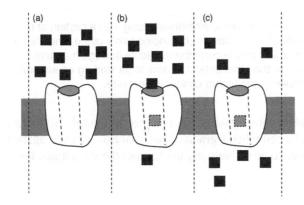

Figure 12-12. In **(a)** a concentration gradient exists across a membrane. Even though the membrane forms an effective barrier to these molecules (solid squares), in **(b)** diffusion begins to move the molecule with the concentration gradient (from high to low) because a protein-formed channel exists that this molecule can fit through. Although movement of these molecules through the channel will still occur, in **(c)** net movement by diffusion will stop because the concentration on each side of the membrane is equal.

mouth, no substance larger than the protein's opening can pass through. These protein channels can be even more selective. Because like charges repel, positively or negatively charged amino acids positioned along the channel's interior will impede like-charged molecules from passing through. Using both channel size and charge distribution, some protein channels are so selective that basically only one type of ion can pass through (see Figure 12-12). Many of these protein channels (especially ion channels) have an added feature. The channel can be opened and closed. The opening of these so-called **gated channels** regulates when diffusion of those things able to pass through the channel is possible (see Figure 12-13). (Gated ion channels will be explored more fully when we discuss the nervous system.)

Facilitated diffusion: gated channels

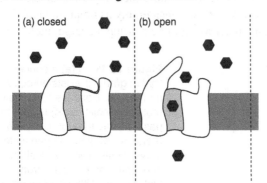

Figure 12-13. In (a) a concentration gradient exists across a membrane, but diffusion is prevented because the membrane forms an effective barrier to these molecules (solid hexagons) and the protein-formed channel that they can fit through is closed. In (b) diffusion across the membrane begins because the channel has (for some reason) changed shape such that the gate previously blocking the channel has opened.

Carrier-mediated transport involves **permeases**. Permeases are membrane-bound proteins that bind to substances. On binding, a permease moves the bound substance from one side of the membrane to the other. Like proteins that act as enzymes, each type of permease binds readily to only one (or few) substances. So, any ion or molecule that cannot readily move across a cell's membrane by simple diffusion or channel-mediated diffusion will be to move easily into or out of a cell only if the cell has built a permease that specifically binds to that ion or molecule (see Figure 12-14).

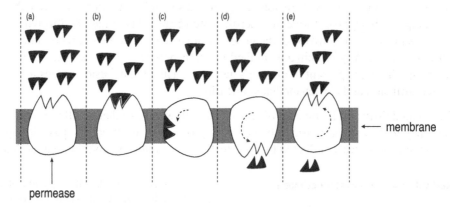

Figure 12-14. In (a) a concentration gradient exists across a membrane along with a protein of the right shape to bind with one of these "bat-shaped" molecules. In (b) binding takes place, and then in (c) and (d) the bind protein changes shape in a way that escorts the molecule through the membrane. Finally, in (e) once it loses the molecule to the other side, it returns to its starting orientation where it can potentially bind to another molecule on the higher concentration side.

Diffusion alone, whether simple or facilitated, cannot totally meet the needs of a cell. Sometimes substances will need to be moved into or out of a cell when a gradient does not exist or even against a concentration gradient. If so, the substance needs to be actively pumped across the membrane. Permeases are involved, but a permease acting as a pump has an additional requirement: Pumps require a power source.

Some permeases are able to use phosphate bond energy (from a molecule called ATP) to pump a substance against a concentration gradient. **Active transport** is the name given in that case (see Figure 12-15). Directly using ATP to drive a pump, however, is not the only way that cells move substances against a concentration gradient. Sometimes movement of a molecule, call it **Y**, against a concentration gradient is powered by an ion moving with a concentration gradient. The two things required are the presence of a favorable concentration for the ion and a permease that can move the ion across the membrane with the concentration gradient *only if it is simultaneously bound to* **Y**. So as the ion is moved across the membrane from high to low concentration, **Y** is dragged along even if such movement is against a concentration gradient. Active transport can still play an indirect role in this type of cotransport because often active transport of the ion is how the ionic concentration gradient needed is established in the first place. Due to active transport's indirect role, the whole process tends to be called **secondary active transport**. Other terms have been added to describe whether the cotransport of the ion and the other substance occurs in the same or opposite direction. **Symport** is when the ion and cotransported substance move in the same direction. **Antiport** is when they move in opposite directions.

Active transport:

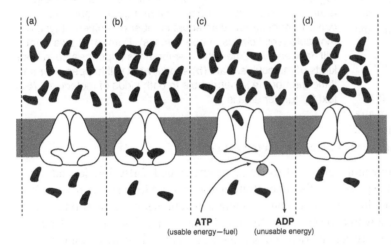

(a)   (b)   (c)   (d)

ATP
(usable energy—fuel)

ADP
(unusable energy)

Figure 12-15. In **(a)** a concentration gradient exists across a membrane along with a protein of the right shape to bind with two of these "horn-shaped" molecules on the lower concentration side of the membrane. In **(b)** binding takes place, and then in **(c)** the transfer of a phosphate from ATP to the permease cause it to change shape in a way that moves the molecules to the high concentration side. In **(d)** the phosphate is removed and as a result the permease returns to the shape that can potentially bind two more molecules on the low concentration side. Overall molecules are "pumped" against the concentration gradient (from lower concentration to higher concentration).

Semipermeable membranes can create pressure differences

In Figure 12-16 a container is separated into two equal-sized compartments by a membrane. One type of molecule fills one of these two compartments, and an equal number of a different kind of molecule fills the other compartment.

What happens next depends on the membrane's permeability. If the membrane is either impermeable or permeable to both molecular types, the results are straightforward. In the impermeable case nothing happens; the distribution of both molecules stays as it was (Figure 12-16, path (a)). On the other hand, the distribution will change when the membrane is permeable. Because a concentration gradient exists across the membrane for both molecular types, each type diffuses across the membrane until reaching concentration-based equilibrium. At this equilibrium, the total number of molecules and the concentration of each molecular type in each compartment is the same (or nearly so; Figure 12-16, path (b)). Once reached, this equilibrium tends to persist, not because the movement of molecules across the membrane stops, but because the net rate that each molecular type moves across the membrane in each direction tends to be equal.

Things become more interesting when the membrane separating the two compartments is **semipermeable**. The general definition of a **semipermeable membrane** is one in which some things can pass through whereas others cannot. In our example, semipermeable means that the membrane is permeable to one of the two molecular types but not to the other.

In Figure 12-17 we start with two compartments separated by a semi-permeable membrane each filled with an equal number of a different type of molecule. Because by definition diffusion cannot occur through an impermeable membrane, the distribution of the molecular type to which the membrane is impermeable remains the same over time. But what happens to the distribution of the permeable molecule? The crux of this question is: Can the restricted movement of one type in any way alter the movement of the other?

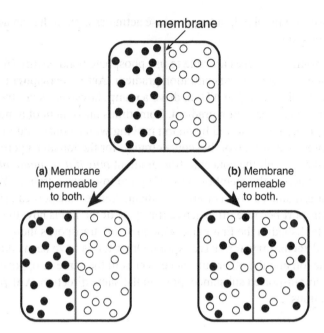

Figure 12-16. The starting configuration is a container separated into two compartments by a membrane, and each compartment contains an equal number of a different type of molecule (solid circles or open circles). Path **(a)** shows what will happen over time if the membrane is impermeable to both kinds of molecules. Path **(b)** shows what will happen over time if the membrane is permeable to both kinds of molecules. (See text for further details.)

The answer is yes, but why the answer is yes requires some explanation.

The tendency for the permeable molecule to diffuse remains unchanged. Diffusion depends on one factor and one factor only—the presence of a concentration gradient. As long as a concentration gradient exists, the net movement will be from the compartment with a higher concentration of permeable molecules to the compartment with a lower concentration of these molecules. Other molecules, no matter how they are distributed between the two compartments, cannot change that. But in this case, as the permeable molecules begin to diffuse from one compartment to the other, more things change than just the lessening of the concentration gradient. More molecules are moving in one direction through the membrane than the other direction, and as a consequence, what started out as an equal number of molecules in each compartment shifts to an increasingly unequal number of molecules between the two compartments. More molecules means more pressure, so the pressure in each compartment is also becoming unequal.

Pressure is a collective force generated by molecular movement. Gases and liquids are good at exerting pressure because molecules in both these states are basically free to move about randomly. In so doing they collide constantly with any surrounding surface, and the pressure that any surrounding surface experiences at any slice of time is the sum of the force of the individual collisions. Two factors can thus increase the pressure exerted on the surfaces of any container: increasing the number of molecules, and raising the temperature. Adding molecules to a container can increase pressure because (as long as the temperature remains the same) the more molecules present, the more often a molecule will collide into the container's surface. On the other hand, increasing temperature increases pressure because faster-moving molecules collide into a surface more often and with more force.

The important point so far is that we have identified a situation where the movement of one thing toward a balance pushes something else out of balance. Because the membrane is semipermeable, diffusion pushing toward an even distribution of the permeable molecule between the two compartments results in an uneven distribution of pressure. So what will happen? Like any self-respecting imbalance, it begins to push back, picking up steam as the imbalance becomes greater. Despite the continued presence of a concentration gradient, the more pressure-packed the one side becomes, the more difficult it becomes for permeable molecules to realize a net movement. The increasing rate of molecular collisions associated with increasing pressure increasingly knocks permeable molecules the other way. Eventually it settles into what could be called a **compromise equilibrium**. Neither pressure nor concentration reaches the point where they are equal between the two compartments. Instead somewhere along the continuum of the pressure gradient building as the concentration gradient lessens, these two opposing forces will be equal and opposite (see Figure 12-17, path (a)). At that point net change stops

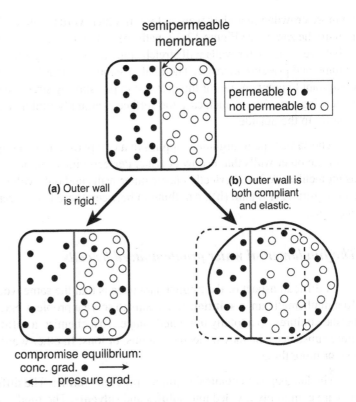

Figure 12-17. Like Figure 12-16, the starting configuration is a container separated into two compartments by a membrane, and each compartment contains an equal number of a different type of molecule (solid circles or open circles). The difference is that the membrane is semipermeable (permeable to the smaller filled in circles and impermeable to the larger open circles). Path **(a)** shows what will happen over time if the outer walls of the container are rigid. Path **(b)** shows what will happen over time if the outer walls of the container are both compliant and elastic. (See

because even though neither component is in equilibrium, the two imbalances are in balance with each other. Conceptually it is no different than two people taking on a tilted, unbalanced stance, but staying upright by leaning against each other. Although alone each person would fall over, a balance arrangement is formed when each person tips to the point that they exert an equal and opposite force on the other.

So far I have implicitly assumed that the surfaces surrounding each compartment were absolutely rigid so that only concentration and pressure could change. But the volume of each compartment could also potentially change. If the outer surfaces of each compartment are at least somewhat **compliant**, they will stretch as pressure increases. On the other hand, if the outer surfaces are at least somewhat **elastic**, they will shrink as pressure decreases. Making the outer wall of our container both compliant and elastic changes the nature of the equilibrium. For example, adding molecules to one compartment will increase the pressure, but the increased pressure causes the outer walls to stretch further, which in turn will decrease pressure. (The number of molecules per unit volume affects pressure, so as volume increases pressure decreases.) Whether the compartment's pressure after adding molecules is greater than it was before depends on how compliant the outer walls are. If they don't stretch at all, then we return to the preceding scenario, where pressure increases but volume stays the same. On the other end of the continuum, the outer walls could be so stretchy that molecules filling the container end up no more crowded than they were before. In other words, volume increases sufficiently for pressure to remain the same (see Figure 12-17, path (b)). In many cases, the end result will come out somewhere in between. The outer walls will stretch some but not enough for the pressure to stay the same, so both volume and pressure increase. The final possibility is that the outer membrane is neither sufficiently compliant to compensate for the increase in pressure by stretching nor strong enough to hold in the increasing pressure. In such case the surface eventually ruptures. The built-up pressure subsequently escapes to the outside.

The same type of argument applies to a compartment losing molecules, except it is the elasticity of the outer walls that is now at issue. Perfectly inelastic outer walls and only pressure decreases as molecules are lost. Perfectly elastic outer walls and only volume decreases as molecules are lost (see Figure 12-17, path (b)). Anything in between these two extremes, and both pressure and volume decrease.

The fundamental water problem faced by cells

A difficult aspect of the English language is that the same word can have more than one meaning. To a mathematician, a **solution** is a means to solve a problem. Say the same word to a chemist, and he/she conjures up a totally unrelated image. To a chemist, a **solution** is a uniform mixture of two or more substances, be they molecules, atoms, or ions. In other words, a solution is a random mixture of two or more things.

The language of chemical solutions proceeds further. The different substances within a solution are commonly divided into **solutes** and **solvents**. The fundamental distinction is that the solute is the part of the solution that dissolves into (is suspended within) the solvent. If water and table salt are mixed together, a solution known as salt water is formed. Water is a liquid at room temperature, whereas table salt is a solid. Salt water is, however, a liquid. It is salt that changes states of matter. So it is salt that dissolves in water and not vice versa. The ions that separate and become suspended in water—Cl^- and Na^+—as table salt dissolves are the solutes, and water is the solvent.

Water is the solvent of Life. Due to water's polar nature, polar and charged substances can become suspended or held up by the attraction between opposite charges within a water medium. All of Life's chemical interactions, such as between proteins and nucleic acids, play out as molecules drift through water. Furthermore, every living cell on this planet needs to be immersed in water to survive. It is thus easy to see why the lack of water (dehydration) is a potential threat to all life forms, especially those living on dry land. But curiously, every living cell's **most fundamental water problem** is not having too little water; it is having *too much* water. A cell's basic setup is such that more water molecules tend to move into a cell than move out, and a cell's outer membrane will eventually burst if too much water enters. To better explain why water tends to move inside cells, I need to first develop some language to talk about water concentrations.

Osmolarity, osmosis, and tonicity

As more solutes dissolve into water, the concentration of water within the solution goes down. Water is being increasingly displaced by solutes. Solute concentration is commonly measured in terms of the number of dissolved molecules per unit volume of solution (technically, the number of osmoles of solute per liter of solution). This measure is termed the osmotic concentration or **osmolarity** of a solution. The higher a solution's osmolarity, the greater proportion of the solution that is solutes, and the less that is water.

Note that as measured, the size of a solute makes no difference in a solution's osmolarity. A dissolved sodium ion or a dissolved protein many times larger counts as one molecule of solute dissolved within a set volume of solution. In other words, one dissolved thing is one dissolved thing. Solute particle size is often ignored because whether there will be a net movement of water by diffusion is best predicted by an **osmolarity gradient** (or **osmotic gradient**), and when water will diffuse across a membrane is the important issue.

Osmosis is the diffusion of any solvent toward regions lower solvent concentration. The semipermeable nature of cell membranes set up the possibility of osmosis. Water molecules generally move readily through cell membranes, whereas many solutes do not. Water thus moves from the high water side of the membrane to the low water side, and the solutes remain behind. Water will continue to diffuse until the osmolarity of each side is equal.

The only potentially confusing aspect of osmosis is when the direction of net movement is discussed in terms of osmolarity or osmotic gradients. It can sound like water is moving the wrong way because water tends to move from a region of lower osmolarity to a region of higher osmolarity. It is not because a solution with higher osmolarity has a lower water concentration than a solution with lower osmolarity. Remember that osmolarity is a measure of the number of solutes per unit volume, and the more solutes there are per unit volume, the less space that remains for water molecules to occupy.

The term **tonicity** describes the relative osmolarity of the solution surrounding a cell in comparison to the solution inside the cell. Because this relationship affects whether a cell is gaining water, losing water, or staying the same, tonicity also describes what will happen to cell volume. **Isotonic** is when the osmolarity of the two solutions are the same. In such a case, a cell will remain the same size. With water moving equally in both directions, a cell is neither gaining nor losing volume (see Figure 12-18, path (a)). That is not true when a cell finds itself in either hypotonic or hypertonic conditions. **Hypertonic** is when the osmolarity outside the cell is higher (so water concentration is lower) than the osmolarity inside the cell. The higher water concentration inside a cell results in a net outflow of water causing the cell to shrink (see Figure 12-18, path (b)). **Hypotonic** is when the osmolarity outside the cell is lower (so water concentration is higher) than the osmolarity inside the cell. Here, the net flow of water is into the cell causing the cell to expand, perhaps to the point that it ruptures (see Figure 12-18, path (c)). Volume changes in either direction are disruptive to the performance inside. Just imagine

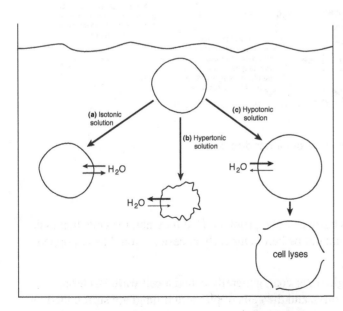

Figure 12-18. Because a cell's outer membrane is more permeable to water than to solutes, the net flow of water (osmosis) depends on the relative concentration of water between the inside and outside of the cell, which in turn affects a cell's volume. In (a) the osmotic concentration of the solution outside the cell (the solution in which the cell is immersed) is equal to that inside the cell (isotonic solution), so water moves in and out at the same rate keeping cell volume the same. In (b) the osmotic concentration of the outside solution is greater than that inside the cell (hypertonic solution), which means that the relative concentration of water is higher inside the cell in comparison to that outside the cell. Consequently, more water moves out than in causing the cell to lose volume and shrink. In (c) the osmotic concentration of the outside solution is less than that inside the cell (hypotonic solution), which means that the relative concentration of water is lower inside the cell in comparison to that outside the cell. Consequently, more water moves in than out causing the cell to swell perhaps to the point that it lyses.

walking along when all the sudden your cells began to shrink or to expand to the point that they begin to rupture. It is not a pretty thought.

Why cells tend to have too much water

Cells tend to have too much water for the very reason that containers were useful to reproduction in the first place. All else being equal, a container that keeps reproductive molecules on the inside will have more solutes on the inside than the outside. As a consequence, cells tend to be hypotonic. Water wants in, and cell membranes cannot stop it.

Let me explain this hypotonic tendency further. All evidence points to reproductive performances held within a container starting in the ocean. Seawater, as you know if you have ever swallowed any, is salty. A fair concentration of salts such as sodium chloride (NaCl) and magnesium chloride (MgCl$_2$) are dissolved in seawater. Salts dissolve by breaking into ions—some positively charged and others negatively charged—that become suspended in the water. A container that forms in seawater will have an equal concentration of ions on the inside and the outside, making it isotonic with its surroundings. But let's now start to add reproductive macromolecules—such as proteins, DNA and RNA—to the inside. Alone, their impact is small. They are few in number in comparison to ions within a cell, and remember that in terms of osmolarity it is the number not the size of the dissolved particles that counts. But their osmotic impact goes further. These large biological molecules are highly charged. These macromolecules thus attract large numbers of ions of opposite charge—counterions. As a consequence, more ions are pulled inside the container. Furthermore, to assemble new macromolecules, their monomers—amino acids for proteins, nucleotides for nucleic acids—must be in solution inside the cell. These further increase the osmolarity inside a cell. Many of these monomers are also charged so they too attract counterions. The overall picture is one of disaster. The outside is a solution of ions, whereas the inside is an equal concentration of ions, plus the reproductive monomers and polymers, plus all the additional ions attracted by charges on these monomers and polymers. Water, which can freely move across cell membranes, will freely follow this osmotic gradient and, unless something interferes, cause the cell to rupture (see Figure 12-19).

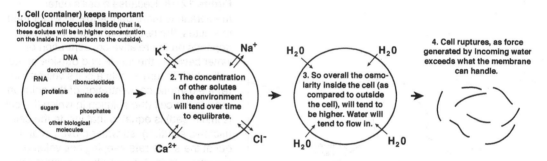

Figure 12-19. A cell's basic water problem. See text for further discussion.

Some solutions

Cells have come up with solutions to this basic osmotic problem. Had they not, the cells that make up you and every other cell on this planet would not be here. Our early ancestors would have popped long ago.

The most basic solution was to build a rigid outer coat, generally called a **cell wall**. Bacteria, some protists (single-celled eukaryotic organisms), and the cells of plants and fungi are surrounded by cell walls. Although a cell wall's chemical makeup varies between cell types, the idea stays the same. Once a cell membrane swells to its wall, the cell wall's rigidity begins *to push back*. The osmotic gradient still exists, but as long as the cell wall is sufficiently rigid, cell membranes are prevented from expanding to the point of rupture (see Figure 12-20).

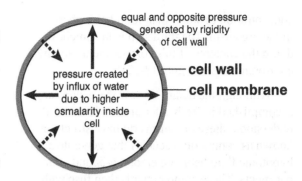

Figure 12-20. How a cell wall can prevent rupture of a cell's membrane.

Many protists, along with all animal cells, lack cell walls. Consequently, they must contend with the osmotic problem in a different way. Animal cells and (to at least some extent) protists living in seawater do so by *diffusing the osmotic gradient*. The relatively higher osmolarity inside the cell is countered by pumping solutes out of the cell by active transport, constantly tossing out enough to create an isotonic situation. Of course, the molecules directly involved in the reproductive performance are not the ones pumped out. Instead ions, in particular sodium ions (Na^+)—the most common positive ion in seawater—are actively removed from the cell (see Figure 12-21). Pumping out calcium ions (Ca^{++}), another fairly common ion in seawater, may also play a role. Both sodium and calcium pumps are common features of these cell types.

A fun fact: You (or more correctly, the cells that make up you) spend a considerable amount of energy—about one-third of resting energy use—continually pumping out Na^+. Considering that the alternative is your cells swelling until they burst, it seems like a good use of energy.

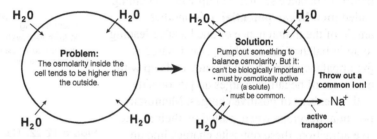

Figure 12-21. The problem of higher osmolarity inside a cell is potentially countered by actively pumping out enough of a common ion to balance the solute concentration on both sides of the cell membrane.

On the other hand, freshwater protists lacking cell walls live in an environment where pumping out ions to generate an osmotic balance with their surroundings could never work. Solutes are just too scarce (the osmolarity is too low) in freshwater for a cell to be able to pump out a sufficient amount of ions to generate an isotonic situation. The only potential solution is to have some means to get rid of water as fast as it is coming in. For small protists, this may involve removing a volume of water equal to their body volume every few minutes. (Note: To decrease the severity of the problem, freshwater protists commonly have evolved means to reduce the rate that water is moving into cells. Such means include decreasing the permeability of their outer membrane to water and minimizing their internal osmolarity to reduce the osmotic gradient between them and their environment.)

What makes removing excess water tricky is that there are no known means to pump water against a concentration gradient. In other words, active transport of water does not occur. A more indirect means must be used instead. Although the details may vary in different organisms, the three basic steps are the following: First, a solution isotonic to the organism must somehow be trapped behind a membrane-bound compartment. Second, the combination of this compartment's membrane having ion pumps and being impermeable to water is used to generate a solution more dilute (lower osmolarity or hypotonic) than the organism. Specifically, ions are pumped out of this compartment (and back into the organism), and because the membrane is impermeable to water, water cannot follow the developing osmotic gradient. The result is a compartment containing a solution with a relatively higher concentration of water than found elsewhere in the organism. The third step is to somehow dump the contents of this compartment into the environment (see Figure 12-22).

Although the details of how these steps are accomplished in freshwater protists is not well understood, these organisms do have structures known as contractile vacuoles that generate a hypotonic fluid behind membrane-bound compartments. These compartments then fuse with the outer membrane, releasing excess water to the outside.

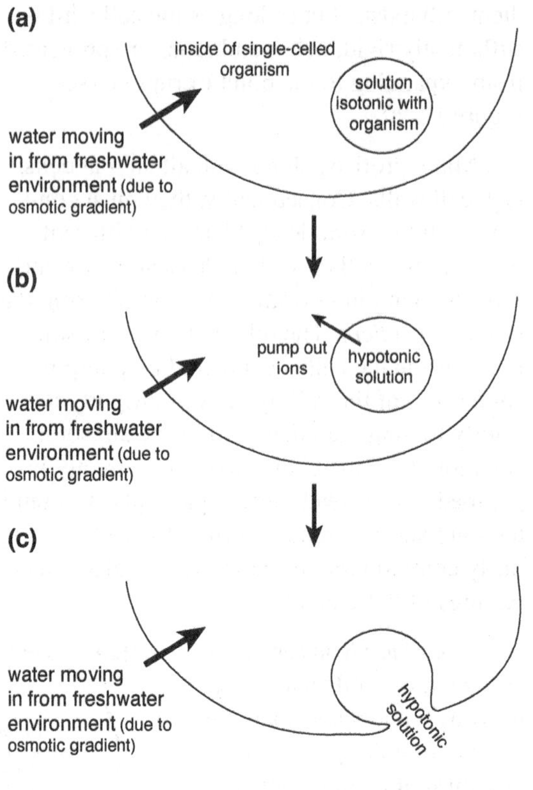

Sodium pumps create membrane potential

All cells that use sodium (or calcium) pumps to balance solutes end up with something called **membrane potential**. It is another example of the maintenance of one balance leading to an imbalance in something else. Charge is the imbalance here. A cell's inside ends up with an excess of negative charges and its outside with an excess of positive charges. Membrane potential develops when, pulled by their respective attraction, these opposite charges line up along the two sides of the membrane. In this way, a cell's membrane is lined in its entirety by a charge imbalance.

Membrane potential's importance as a biological topic comes from one thing leading to another. Certain cells now use membrane potential to respond to changes in surrounding conditions. All the cells that make up your nervous system and muscles, for example, use membrane potential in this way. The details of how they do so come later. The present task is to better establish why membrane potential happens in the first place.

(a) inside of single-celled organism / solution (isotonic with) organism / water moving in from freshwater environment (due to osmotic gradient)

(b) pump out ions / hypotonic solution / water moving in from freshwater environment (due to osmotic gradient)

(c) water moving in from freshwater environment (due to osmotic gradient) / hypotonic solution

Figure 12-22. The three basic steps by which some freshwater single-celled eukaryotic organisms (freshwater protists) maintain water balance. Due to living in a hypotonic environment, water always tends to move into the cell. This excess water is moved back to the environment by actively pumping out ions from membrane bound vesicles formed within the cells, and then dumping this hypotonic solution outside the cell.

Cells employing a sodium ion (Na^+) pump are constantly tossing out positive charges. On the other hand, the molecules that are being selectively kept inside the cell—that is the molecules involved in the reproductive performance, such as proteins and nucleic acids—tend to have an excess of negative charges. So overall, cells are selectively removing positive charges and selectively retaining negative charges. The result, as seems obvious, would be the creation of a charge imbalance across the cell membrane. There is, however, more to the story. There are other ions of both positive and negative charge floating in solution (chlorine ions (Cl^-), and potassium ions (K^+) are particularly common), so one must consider why these other ions don't take on a distribution that neutralizes the charge imbalance.

The negatively charged interior, due to negatively charged biological molecules, attracts K^+ and repels Cl^-. The positively charged outside, due to the excess of Na^+, does just the opposite. As stated earlier, phospholipid membranes are good barriers to ions, but they are not leak proof. So K^+ will begin to accumulate on the inside of cells, and Cl^- will begin to accumulate on the outside. As this happens the charge gradient across the membrane lessens. In fact, membrane potential would disappear completely if such charge-driven diffusion proceeded until reaching an electrical equilibrium. The excess of K^+ on the inside and the excess of Cl^- on the outside, as well as the distribution of rarer ions, would perfectly balance the initial charge imbalance caused by pumping out Na^+ and restricting movement of negatively charged biological molecules.

Such electrical equilibrium, however, is never reached because two types of gradients influence diffusion of these ions, and these two gradients pull in opposite directions. The second gradient is a concentration gradient. As already implied, as K^+ is pulled inward and Cl^- is pulled outward by electrical gradients, a concentration gradient forms for each of these ions. The concentration of K^+ becomes higher on the inside, and Cl^- becomes higher on the outside. So at the same time that the electrical gradient is pulling K^+ to the inside, an ever-increasing concentration gradient is pulling these ions back out. The same is true for Cl^- except that the directions are reversed. Two diffusional gradients pulling in opposite directions always means that neither will win. Instead, they will reach another example of a compromise equilibrium at the point where the pull of the charge gradient and the opposite pull of concentration gradient becomes equal. A cell's membrane potential is the electric gradient that remains (see Figure 12-23).

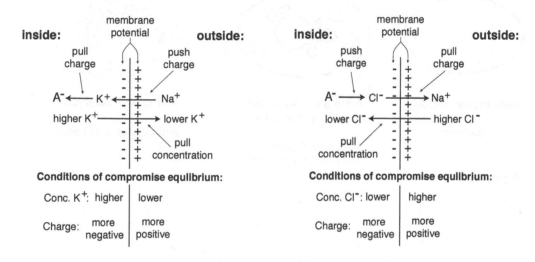

Figure 12-23. A summary of the forces acting on potassium ions (K^+) and chloride ions (Cl^-), along with the conditions of the compromise equilibrium for each ion. (See text for more details).

A final note: In many cells with sodium pumps, permeability to K^+ and Cl^- is further increased by the presence of ion channels called leak channels. The movement of K^+ inward may also be facilitated by the fact that sodium pumps are commonly sodium-potassium pumps. For every three sodium ions pumped out, two potassium ions hitch a ride inward. Neither leak channels nor linking potassium ions to the sodium pump, however, changes the equilibrium distribution. What they change is the rate at which equilibrium is reached after disruption.

What about more than one container?

Would a reproductive loop ever be served by having more than one container? The answer is yes because the performance could add new dimensions with each additional container. More containers make increasingly complex performances possible.

With only one container, an entire reproductive performance must occur within its confines. Yet the actions of any protein within a reproductive performance is more closely linked to some proteins than to others. Keeping functionally linked proteins close together may help the performance to run more efficiently than keeping all proteins together, no matter how they interact or do not interact. Additional containers make such partitioning possible. The more containers, the more differentiated the containers and the performances within could become.

Additional containers also make it possible for incompatible proteins to be part of the same reproductive performance. Incompatible proteins could be separated into different containers. Different processors could be incompatible in either of two ways. They may require different conditions to function or one could act in a way that impedes the function of the other.

There are two ways to increase the number of containers: place containers within containers or group containers together. Figure 12-24 illustrates these possibilities in relation to different cell and organism types. In this illustration, the possible complexity of a reproductive performance increases as one goes from left to right.

single container   containers within containers   containers adjacent to containers
(and containers within containers)

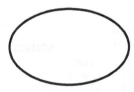

some prokaryotic cells   some prokaryotic cells   multicelluar eukaryotic
all eukaryotic cells

bacteria   multicellular organisms

bacteria & protists
(single-celled organisms)

Figure 12-24.

Some key terms:

fatty acid - any of a group of molecules that consists of an acid (carboxyl) group attached to a long hydrocarbon chain.

triglyceride - a molecule that consists of three fatty acids covalently attached to a three-carbon molecule called glycerol. Often used as a storage form of fatty acids.

phospholipids - the major structural component of cell membranes. They are structurally similar to triglyceride molecules, except one of the three fatty acids is replaced with a polar group containing a phosphate.

concentration gradient - a change in concentration across distance (In biology the term concentration gradient is used mostly to discuss a change in concentration across a membrane).

electric gradient - an unequal distribution of positive and negative charges, in the form of ions, across distance. (In biology the term electric gradient is used mostly to discuss an unequal distribution of charge across a membrane).

simple diffusion - net directional movement of some type of molecule across a membrane, where the movement is powered by the presence of a concentration gradient (movement from high to low), and the molecules cross simply because the membrane is permeable to this type of molecule.

facilitated diffusion - net directional movement of some type of molecule across a membrane, where the movement is powered by the presence of a concentration gradient (movement from high to low), and the molecules cross the membrane with the aid of a channel protein or a permease.

active transport - net directional movement of some type of molecule across a membrane, where the movement goes against a concentration gradient so the movement is powered by some usable energy source supplied by the cell, and the molecules cross the membrane with the aid of a permease.

semipermeable membrane - a membrane that is permeable to some type or types of molecules but not others.

osmotic concentration - the ratio of the number of molecules dissolved in water (the solutes) to the number of water molecules (the solvent). (The higher the ratio the higher the osmotic concentration.)

osmosis - the diffusion of solvent molecules (water molecules) towards regions of higher osmotic concentration (hence regions of lower water concentration).

isotonic - the osmotic concentration inside a cell is the same as the osmotic concentration surrounding the cell.

Some study questions:

1. (A repeat of a chapter 9 study question). Why is a container an important component of reproduction?

2. Explain why membrane lipids in water self-assemble into a bilayered container.

3. What is the relationship between the average number of double bonds in membrane lipids or triacyl-glycerols, and the melting point and fluidity of the membranes or storage fats of which they are a part? In general, when would it benefit an organism to alter the fluidity of its cell membranes or storage fats.

4. What is a lipid raft?

5. *What are the various means by which matter can move into or out of a cell? What are the distinguishing features of each of these different means of transport? Why is the transport of matter across cell membranes important?*

6. *How can keeping certain molecules enclosed within a container create an osmotic problem? How have cells dealt with this problem?*

Biosynthesis and the Metabolic Performance

Containers seem to bring out the curious child in all of us. We want to know what is inside. We tantalize this curiosity whenever we wrap a gift. For some, this beguiling question has been directed to tiny containers that biologists call cells. The issue of size, however, makes this quest more difficult. Cells are tiny, and the molecules inside, as we learned in our earlier discussion of chemistry, are unimaginably smaller. One cannot peer directly into a cell and sort through its various contents. But if we could—or more conceivably, if we learned the various techniques employed by biochemists to identify that which we cannot see—we would find various types of molecules, some of whose names are hopefully becoming familiar. Molecules such as DNA, RNA, proteins, deoxyribonucleotides, ribonucleotides, amino acids, as well as enough other molecules to fill an entire biochemistry text. More will surely be found as people continue to look.

Once a container's inside is unveiled, another question pops up: How did that which is inside get inside? Or put in cellular terms: How do the molecules found inside cells come to be there?

Molecules get inside cells in one of two ways, both of which should have a familiar ring. First, a molecule may be inside a cell because by simple diffusion, facilitated diffusion, or active transport it moved into the cell from the outside. Second, the molecule was formed by a chemical reaction that took place within the cell. Here the fundamental notion of a chemical reaction returns. When a molecule or molecules undergo a chemical reaction, they become something else. The atoms making up the molecule or molecules entering the reaction are neither lost nor transformed into different elements, but the same atoms are rearranged, and each new atomic arrangement is a new type of molecule. In essence, a molecule or molecules entering a chemical reaction disappear—that is, the specific arrangements are lost—and new molecules appear.

Chemical reactions occurring within a cell is not a new notion. In Chapter 11 we talked about how more DNA molecules could be made within a cell (DNA replication), how RNA molecules are assembled in a cell (DNA transcription), and how protein molecules are made within a cell (RNA translation or protein synthesis). The common theme underlying all these transformations is that certain types of molecules—deoxyribonucleotides for DNA, ribonucleotides for RNA, and amino acids for proteins—are strung together (polymerized) to form long chainlike molecules. A chemical reaction takes place whenever a link (a monomer) is added to the chain. Consequently, each time a monomer is added—such as an amino acid added to a growing protein—the monomer, in essence, disappears from the cell. So, for synthesis of DNA, RNA, and proteins to continue, a supply of their respective parts must continually be replenished.

The focus of this chapter is to explain a bit more about how cells continually replenish their supply of these monomers—as well as other molecules—especially when such molecules are not readily available from the environment. The theme is to bring in molecules present in the environment and then use chemical reactions to rearrange the atoms in these molecules into molecular forms needed by the cell.

Although performing such rearrangements sounds easy enough, two issues, in particular, complicate this task. First, chemical reactions must be somehow controlled within the cell so that only the "right" chemical reactions occur, where "right" means a chemical reaction leading to rearrangement that is useful to the cell. Here is where proteins again come into play. Certain proteins, generically called enzymes, have shapes such that they "grab" certain molecules in a way that promotes certain chemical reactions. Cells thus exercise control over what chemical reactions take place within their confines by controlling what enzymes are present. And if you understood the discussion of genetic regulation in Chapter 11, you understand the basic means by which this is accomplished. In brief review: Any specific enzyme will be found in a cell only if the gene (recipe) for that enzyme is encoded in the cell's DNA—the cell's genome—and that gene is currently turned on—the recipe is currently being used to make this specific protein.

Second, the molecules available in the environment often have quite different arrangements than those needed by the cell. Extensive rearrangement is thus needed. Yet, wholesale atomic rearrangements cannot be made in a single chemical reaction. Extensive rearrangements are only possible through a series of smaller stepwise transformations.

Metabolic Pathways

A metabolic pathway is a stepwise series of chemical transformations within a cell, where an enzyme facilitates each step. This means that any metabolic pathway can take place within a cell only if the cell assembles each of the enzymes specific to each step along the way.

To put metabolic pathways in more general terms, realize that an enzyme meets my definition of a processor. Each time an enzyme grabs molecules and then facilitates a chemical reaction, inputs (to the enzyme) are different than outputs. Metabolic pathways form whenever two or more enzymes are produced in a cell in which an output of one enzyme is an input to the next.

Through metabolic pathways, cells can take molecules available in the environment and then, through an orchestrated series of chemical reactions, rearrange the atoms into other molecules. This is illustrated in Figure 13-1. In this figure, molecule A—which is available in the environment— is brought into the cell, and then through the actions of three enzymes—enzyme AB, enzyme BC, and enzyme CD—it undergoes a stepwise series of chemical reactions until it has now been rearranged into a molecule D. Why would the cell want molecule D? It depends, of course, on what molecule D is. Suppose molecule D is one of the 20 amino acids. Cells making these three enzymes would now have a means to produce a continuous supply of this amino acid—which can be used to build proteins—so long as molecule A is available. This cell can exist in an environment that lacks this amino acid because it can build it itself. In biology speak: The cell acquires a supply of this amino acid through **biosynthesis**. Biosynthesis is the use of metabolic pathways to rearrange atoms in molecules available to the cell into biologically useful molecules.

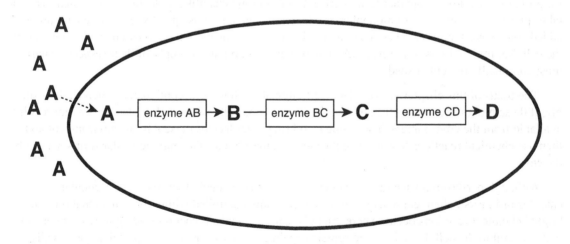

Figure 13-1. Molecule A is brought into a cell from its environment and then rearranged through a three-step metabolic pathway into molecule D.

Using carbon dioxide as a carbon source to build G3P

Carbon is an atom found in essentially every biological molecule. So an important component of biosynthesis is to be able to take a carbon-containing molecule available in the environment, bring it into the cell, and use the carbon atoms to build biologically useful molecules. The carbon-containing molecule that fills this bill is one that I suspect you have heard of. It is called **carbon dioxide** (CO_2).

As one begins to explore biology, a few metabolic pathways are so significant that their names are worth remembering. The first that I highlight is called either the **Calvin–Benson cycle** (named after its discoverers), or the **carbon reduction cycle** (which tells you that carbon gets reduced in the process).

The Calvin–Benson cycle's bottom line is that it takes the carbon atom and one of the two oxygen atoms from each of three carbon dioxides and combines it with six hydrogen atoms from a molecule called NADPH plus a phosphate group from a molecule called ATP—both of which we discuss much more in the future—to form a three-carbon molecule called **glyceraldehyde 3-phosphate**, which can be abbreviated by the acronym **G3P** (see Figure 13-2). (Note: Two other acronyms sometimes used are **GAP** and **PGAL**, with the latter coming from **phosphoglyceraldehyde**— another name for the same molecule.) The reduction component of this metabolic pathway is, if you remember our discussion of oxidation and reduction in Chapter 9, the replacement of the some of the carbon–oxygen bonds found in carbon dioxide with the carbon–hydrogen and carbon–carbon found in G3P (see Figure 13-2).

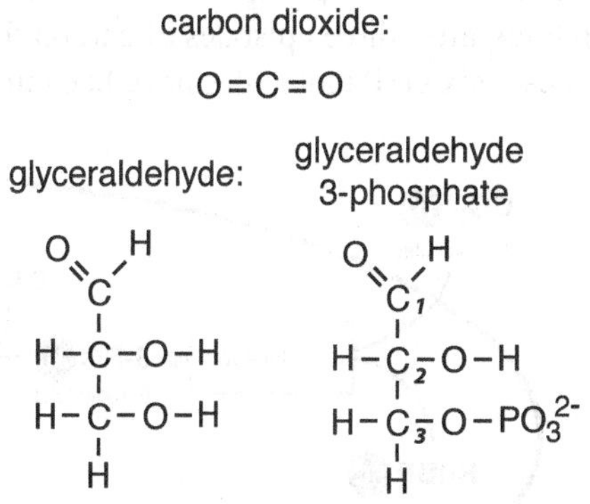

I imagine that the name glyceraldehyde 3-phosphate, or G3P, does not does not strike up any distinctive image in your head—perhaps other than nerdy chemists labeling molecules with impossible names. But this fact should help put G3P into at least somewhat familiar framework. Glyceraldehyde is a sugar. In other words, glyceraldehyde structure places it with a class of molecules known as **sugars** or **carbohydrates**. Furthermore, the addition of the phosphate makes G3P a **sugar phosphate**. As a preview to further discussion in the next chapter, let me mention that adding a phosphate to any type of molecule is significant. Most important, it makes molecules more reactive, hence more readily rearranged into other molecules. Plus, it helps trap molecules inside a cell. Movement through membranes is impeded by the phosphate's negative charge.

carbon dioxide:

$$O = C = O$$

glyceraldehyde: glyceraldehyde 3-phosphate

Figure 13-2. Structural representations of three molecules mentioned in the text. Note: Chemists keep track of the carbons in organic (carbon-bearing) molecules by numbering them—as shown in glyceraldehyde 3-phosphate (G3P). The 3 in G3P refers to the phosphate being attached to the number 3-labeled carbon. (Recall that 5' and 3' used with nucleotides was also based on numbering the carbons in the sugar component.)

A closer look at the Calvin–Benson cycle

The first step of the Calvin–Benson cycle is the attachment of a single CO_2 molecule with a 5-carbon molecule called ribulose 1,5-biphosphate (RuBP) to form an unstable 6-carbon compound. This 6-carbon compound splits quickly to form two molecules of 3-phosphoglycerate (3-PG or PGA), a 3-carbon compound. A protein called **RuBP carboxylase,** or **RuBisCo,** catalyzes the attachment of CO_2 to RuBP. The attachment of CO_2 to RuBP is known as **carbon fixation**.

An aside: In the world of enzyme kinetics—that is, the rate that enzymes catalyze chemical reactions—RuBisCo is very slow, being able to convert only around three molecules of CO_2 and RuBP to 3-PG per second. In contrast, the next two enzymes discussed have reaction rates in the order of 1,000 to 100,000 per second, respectively. So, the only way for RuBisCo to keep up is for a cell to make lots. In fact, due to this relative increase in production needed to compensation for its slow rate, and given that within Life there is a whole lot of Calvin–Benson cycling going on, RuBisCo is thought to be the most abundant protein on planet Earth.

Next, another enzyme called **3-PG kinase** (or PGA kinase) grabs a 3-PG, plus a molecule generally designated by its acronym **ATP**, and facilitates the transfer of a phosphate group from ATP to 3-PG. The resulting molecule now has two phosphates; hence it is called 1,3-**bis**phosphoglycerate (1,3-BPG) or **di**phosphoglycerate (DPGA). In the loss of the phosphate, ATP (adenosine **tri**phosphate) becomes ADP (adenosine **di**phosphate). The third enzyme in the metabolic pathway is named **G3P dehydrogenase**. It grabs 1,3-BPG and another molecule that goes by its acronym, **NADPH**. This enzyme promotes the exchange of a phosphate group attached to 1,3-BPG with a hydrogen atom from NADPH to form G3P. This is the step where reduction of a carbon atom coming from carbon dioxide takes place. $NADP^+$ (NADPH with, in essence, a hydrogen removed) is also left over from the reaction. In addition, the removed phosphate attaches to water to form orthophosphate (commonly designated as P_i). In total, after three episodes of carbon fixation—after this metabolic pathway has been repeated three times—six G3P molecules have been made (see Figure 13-3).

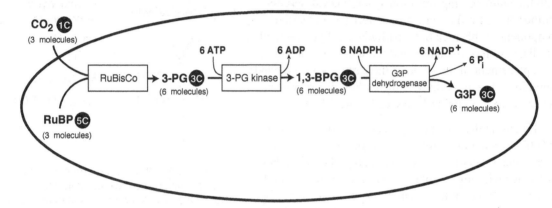

Figure 13-3. The metabolic pathway by which 3 CO_2 molecules brought into the cell from the environment and 3 RuBP molecules are converted into 6 molecules of G3P. See text for more details.

An aside: Although all the acronyms for molecule and enzyme names may seem, at first glance, a little overwhelming, remember that chemistry is just rearrangement. So far we have: added a CO_2, split a 6-carbon molecule into two 3-carbon molecules, added a phosphate, and exchanged a phosphate for a hydrogen. Although there are a lot of details within these reactions, the basic idea is not overwhelming. Some enzyme names also start to make a little sense when you pay attention to patterns. For instance, kinase is always the name used for an enzyme involved in transferring a phosphate from ATP to something else. 3-PG kinase is thus the enzyme that catalyzes the transfer of a phosphate to 3-PG (to form 1,3-BPG). But if we follow that same logic, G3P dehydrogenase seems backwards. By its name, a dehydrogenase would seemingly catalyze hydrogen removal. But in the reaction described, hydrogen is added (in exchange for a phosphate). But also notice, in contrast to 3-PG kinase, that the end product (G3P) instead of the starting molecule (1,3-BPG) is included in the name. When everything seems backward, it likely is. In a couple of chapters, this reaction will be emphasized again, although the focus will be on the reverse direction—hydrogen is removed from G3P (in exchange for a phosphate)—and the same enzyme catalyzes the reaction. The name is thus based on historical order. The reverse reaction was discovered first, hence called G3P dehydrogenase. In terms of the direction discussed here, the better name might be 1,3-BPG hydrogenase.

A cell-level nutrient cycle

Before going on with all that a cell can do with G3P molecules, you need to look close enough at this metabolic pathway to realize one thing. For this pathway to be repeated over and over, a cell needs more than just a continual supply of CO_2 from the environment. The cell also needs a continual supply of RuBP (the molecule that initially binds with CO_2), as well as ATP and NADPH.

Let's focus for the moment on RuBP. Here the notion of nutrient cycling again comes into play. Whereas CO_2 must continually be supplied from outside the cell, RuBP is continually made available by a nutrient cycle taking place entirely within the cell. The cycle is, in essence, a metabolic pathway—a stepwise series of enzyme-facilitated chemical rearrangements—that comes full circle. Although RuBP is continually lost in one part of the cycle—when RuBP along with CO_2 is converted to two 3-PGs—its supply is continually restored elsewhere.

I mentioned earlier that for every three CO_2 (and three RuBP) entering this pathway, six G3P molecules were formed. The maintenance of a constant RuBP supply requires five of these six G3P molecules being converted back, through a complex series of enzyme-facilitated reactions, to three molecules of RuBP. If so, the loss and gain of RuBP within the cell remains balanced. The three RuBPs lost have been fully replaced so that the cycle can start anew (see Figure 13-4).

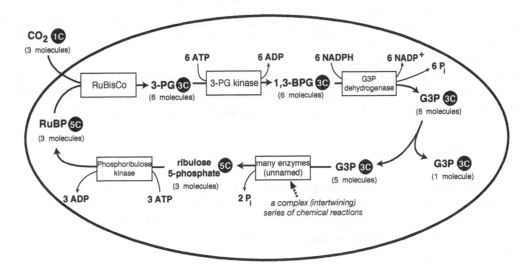

Figure 13-4. Overview of Calvin-Benson cycle—the cycle by which a supply of RuBP is continually replenished within a cell.

The sixth G3P molecule is the output from the cycle. For every three spins of the Calvin–Benson cycle, the cell increases its supply of G3P by one. The carbon atoms in the newly created G3P come from the three carbon atoms in the three fixed CO_2 molecules.

An aside: Although it is the ideas, not the chemical details, being emphasized here, in Figure 13-5 I show the maze of molecules (without enzyme names) involved in the entire Calvin–Benson cycle. It is worth looking at for at least three reasons: (1) you may recognize a few molecules, such as ribose 5-phosphate and fructose 6-phosphate; (2) most of the reactions will show up again, starting with the next figure; and (3) the whole flow is an interesting little mathematical puzzle of how five 3-carbon molecules can be converted back into three 5-carbon molecules. The seemingly simplest solution—combine five 3-carbon molecules into a 15-carbon molecule that is then split into three 5-carbon molecules—is not seen. Instead, two forms of changes are seen: First, three-carbon molecules are joined with another molecule, although the largest resultant molecule is seven-carbons; and second, two-carbon pieces are split off one molecule and transferred to another. I challenge everyone to use these rules to figure out the arrangement of reactions seen, and you can even explore whether there is another possible solution.

Like the supply of RuBP within a cell, the environmental supply of CO_2 would eventually run out without a functioning nutrient cycle. However, the cycle of which CO_2 is a part, commonly called the **carbon cycle**, tends to operate on a much larger scale—specifically at the ecosystem level, where both different species and geological events are the processors making up the cycle. The two key biological steps are (1) cells able to use Calvin–Benson cycle to input CO_2 and rearrange the carbon into G3P, as well as many other types of molecules (discussed more later), and (2) cells that can convert the carbon atoms in these synthesized molecules back into CO_2. Your cells, for example, can do the latter. You take many of the carbon atoms in your food and rearrange them back into CO_2. You then release this CO_2 back into the atmosphere with each exhalation.

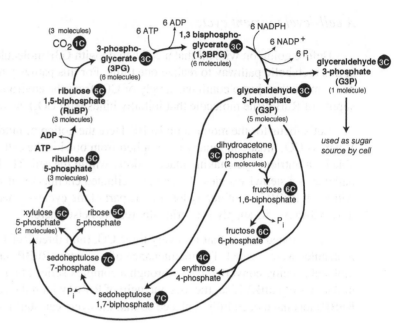

Figure 13-5. All the molecules involved in the Calvin-Benson cycle. The molecules also found in Figure 13-4 are in bold letters.

What about ATP and NADPH?

ATP and NADPH are often called the two cellular fuels. Their input at various steps in the Calvin–Benson cycle, in essence, provides the usable energy that keeps the cycle spinning. In fact, if you do some counting in Figure 13-4, you will find a cell expends nine ATP and six NADPH just to assemble a single G3P molecule while maintaining a supply of RuBP. The conversion of CO_2 to G3P is energetically expensive.

Further discussion of these two fuels is the focus of the next two chapters

Some More about Carbohydrates

Sugars, or carbohydrates, are familiar molecules. We probably talk about them, or at least hear some one talk about them, almost daily. And amid this extensive carbohydrate prattle, I am sure that you have realized one reason that carbohydrates are biologically important: They are a source of usable energy. (Actually, sugars serve as an energy source for organisms only indirectly. Sugars are systematically broken apart, and the energy released is then used to build one of the two cellular fuels: ATP or NADPH. These, in turn, are what powers the cell's workings.)

Carbohydrates, however, are not only used as a source of usable chemical energy. The next time that you fail to pay attention and run into a tree, for instance, just what do you think you are running into? It is not bone, concrete, or steel—you are running into largely sugar. A major structural component of plants are polymers of sugars such as cellulose—which are cell wall components. Bacterial cell walls are also largely composed of sugar polymers. Even the exoskeleton of an insect—the insect's rigid exterior—is made mostly of sugar polymers. Sugar also forms one part of deoxyribonucleotides (deoxyribose) and ribonucleotides (ribose), the monomers of DNA and RNA, respectively. Furthermore, much of the rest of this chapter will discuss how sugars can be used as **metabolic intermediates**, which is just a fancy way of saying that metabolic pathways exist within cells that can fashion sugars into other biological molecules. And if we were to delve even further into the biological role of carbohydrates, a few more items would be added to this list.

As stated earlier, glyceraldehyde is a sugar. But what is it about glyceraldehyde that makes it a sugar? Chemists classify any molecule whose structure meets the following requirement as a **simple sugar**. First, simple sugars are composed of atoms of only three elements—carbon (C), hydrogen (H), and oxygen (O). Second, the ratio of these elements is always two hydrogen atoms for every one carbon and one oxygen—CH_2O. Third, the number of carbons per molecule ranges from three to seven. A common way of summarizing all three of these requirements is that simple sugars are molecules with the generic formula $(CH_2O)_n$, where n ranges from 3 to 7. A final sugar requirement is that the hydrogens and oxygens are attached to a chain of carbon atoms in equal proportions.

By looking closely at Figure 13-2 of a glyceraldehyde molecule, you can see for yourself that it meets all these requirements. More specifically, glyceraldehyde is a three-carbon sugar.

Final note: Sugars within the chemistry of life are commonly phosphorylated—a phosphate is added in exchange for a hydrogen. Sugar phosphates will thus have one less hydrogen than the generic sugar formula would suggest for each of the one or two phosphates added.

G3P can be further rearranged into a variety of carbohydrates

Most, if not all, cells produce the enzymes needed to rearrange G3P into many different simple sugars, or to be more accurate, simple sugar phosphates. Figure 13-6 illustrates some common pathways by which this is accomplished. Every molecule included is a simple sugar phosphate, but the number of carbons spread across the entire possible range (from 3 to 7 carbon atoms).

It is worth noting that all but one sugar, and almost all the reactions shown, are part of the maze of Calvin–Benson cycle reactions involved in converting five molecules of G3P (a 3-carbon sugar phosphate) back into three molecules of ribulose 5-phosphate (a 5-carbon sugar phosphate). In other words, within the chemistry of the Calvin–Benson cycle, we have already found the ability to convert G3P into a variety of other sugars.

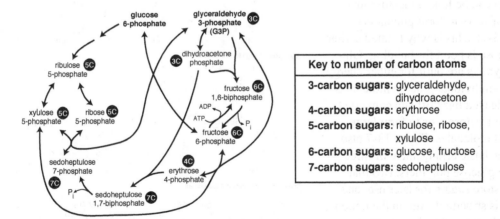

Figure 13-6. Summary of the metabolic pathways by which G3P can be converted into other sugar phosphates. Enzymes are not named here, but specific enzymes must be present to facilitate each chemical reaction. Although not mentioned in the text, note that not only can G3P be converted into other sugar phosphates, but other sugar phosphates can be converted to G3P. Lines with arrowheads at both ends signify that the same enzyme can facilitate the reaction in either direction. Two separate arrows means different enzymes are needed to move the reaction in opposite directions.

What is the one sugar (or more accurately, sugar phosphate) unique to Figure 13-6? The one that you have most likely already heard of—glucose (or glucose 6-phosphate)! When two 3-carbon sugars (actually sugar phosphates) first combine, they form the six-carbon sugar known as fructose (actually fructose 1,6 biphosphate), which can then lose a phosphate to form fructose 6-phosphate. Both of those reactions are part of the Calvin–Benson cycle. The conversion of fructose 6-phosphate into glucose 6-phosphate is, however, an additional step. Which raises the question: Why do sugar-producing organisms ever go to the trouble of rearranging fructose into glucose? Why not stop at producing fructose? The general answer is: Different molecules have different shapes and properties, which can be utilized in different ways. Fructose is particularly good at being split back into two three-carbon sugars. In other words, it is ready for chemical action. In contrast, glucose's structure is more chemically stable, which makes it better for storage and building. I explain further later.

An aside: Although the significance has yet to be discussed, Figure 13-6 also shows something else—a path by which glucose 6-phosphate can be converted into 5-carbon sugar phosphates (e.g., ribose, xylose, and ribulose). It will come up again in a couple of chapters.

Rings and polymers

I would bet that if asked to name a simple sugar—prior to reading the last few pages—you would have not come up with glyceraldehyde. In fact, I would suppose that most of you have never even heard of glyceraldehyde before (at least consciously). Yet, sugar molecules like glucose and fructose are mentioned all the time. Why these, and not the central sugar in biology? The answer has to do with rings.

Let's start with glucose. More so than any other sugar, six-carbon glucose molecules form into a ringed arrangement that can be linked together in a variety of ways to form polymers (see Figure 13-7). This is why I stated earlier that glucose is good for building. Glucose polymers are built for either energy storage—individual glucose molecules can be cleaved back off and converted back into fructose—or to form large structural molecules. Figure 13-7 also shows the basic arrangement of three common glucose polymers: two that serve to store sugars for later use, and one that is structural. Add in the notion of food chains, and it should now be clear why glucose is the most available dietary source of sugar. When an animal eats a plant, or another animal, the potentially most available form of carbohydrate will be the large polymers put

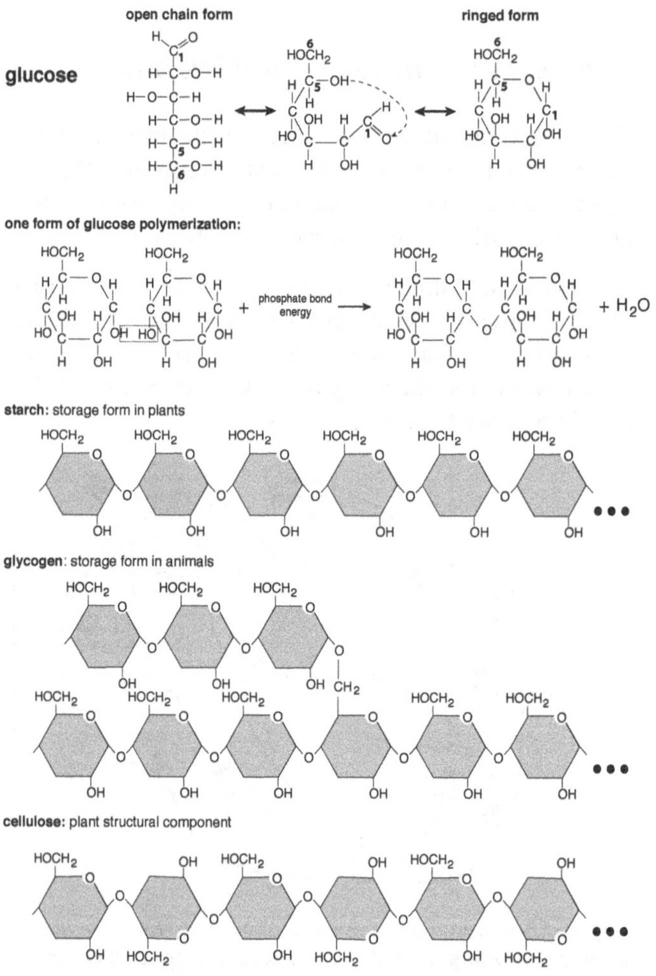

Figure 13-7. Glucose folding from a linear form to a ringed form, along with three biologically important polymers of glucose.

into storage or structure. The digestion of any of those polymers—breaking the polymers back into monomers—results in glucose being the most common sugar to first enter the body.

Other six-carbon sugars (e.g., fructose, galactose), as well as five-carbon sugars (e.g., ribose, xylose), can also fold into ringed structures (see Figure 13-8) that are used in the assembly of larger molecules. For instance, in the last chapter, we saw ringed forms of ribose and deoxyribose being used in the assembly of nucleotides. And many other examples exist within Life's chemistry. Both five- and six-carbon ringed sugars are also included in a wide variety, both in terms of length and arrangement, of sugar polymers. Figure 13-9 shows two molecules made up of a mixture of two 6-carbon sugars. Sucrose—glucose linked with fructose—is typically produced in relatively small quantities by many plants and thus is generally consumed in small amounts higher up in food chains. Humans, however, have employed a mixture of agriculture and technology to make much more

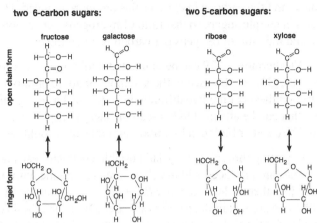

Figure 13-8. Two six- and five-carbon in both linear and ringed forms.

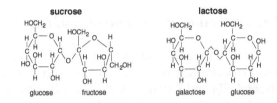

Figure 13-9. Two common disaccharides.

sucrose available. You know it as table sugar and may have put on your cereal this morning. Lactose—glucose combined with galactose—is commonly called milk sugar, as it the carbohydrate source found in mammalian milk. It is thus an important part of every mammal's diet prior to weaning. Here again, humans are unusual as certain agricultural practices have made milk available for postweaning consumption. Interestingly, some humans, especially those with a long history of maintaining domesticated animal herds, have a mutation (in gene SNP C/T13910 on the second chromosome) that encodes lactase persistence—that is, it maintains the production of lactose-digesting enzymes after weaning. Humans not bearing this mutation are sometimes referred to as being lactose intolerant, which is a strange term, given that the inability to digest lactose after weaning is the ancestral condition.

Some terminology: Five- and six-carbons sugars are commonly referred to as **pentoses** and **hexoses**, respectively. Ringed forms of pentoses and hexoses that can be polymerized are often called **monosaccharides**. **Disaccharides**, as their name implies, are molecules formed by linking two monosaccharides (see Figure 13-9). **Polysaccharides** are polymers of many monosaccharides.

G3P Can Be Arranged into Noncarbohydrate Molecules

Have you ever had a thought like: I am going to get fatter if I eat another cookie or candy bar (or any other sugary food)? If so, you have an important piece of biochemical knowledge: Within cells, sugar molecules can be converted into fat molecules. Or to be more long-winded, not only do cells generally produce the enzymes needed to rearrange G3P into different sugars, but they also produce enzymes needed to rearrange the atoms in G3P into molecules that are not carbohydrates. Fats are not carbohydrates because they do not meet the carbohydrate guidelines listed earlier. Go back and look at the illustrations of fats found in Chapter 12. Although fats are still arrangements of the same elements as carbohydrates—carbon, oxygen, and hydrogen—the actual arrangement is strikingly different. The core of both molecules are chains of carbon atoms, but the chains in fatty acid molecules can be much longer, and the carbons in these chains are more reduced. Hydrogens replace many of the oxygens found in simple sugars so that ratio of hydrogens per carbon in fatty acids is much higher than in sugars, and the ratio of oxygens per carbon is much lower.

Furthermore, G3P can be converted into more noncarbohydrate molecules than just fats. For instance, G3P can be used in the assembly of all 20 amino acids. Certain amino acids can then be used in the synthesis of the five different nitrogenous bases—guanine, cytosine, adenine, thymine, and uracil—that can be attached to five-carbon sugar phosphates to form nucleotides—the monomers of DNA and RNA. Other biologically important molecules could be added to this list if we were to dig deeper.

In sorting through the myriad possible chemical rearrangements, a big picture point emerges: Enzymes are produced within cells that can guide the rearrangement of the atoms in G3P, in combination with other molecules, into *all* the biologically important molecules. Stated differently, starting at G3P, there are metabolic pathways that end in the synthesis of all biologically important molecules. This is why the Calvin–Benson cycle is the carbon entry pathway in biosynthesis. Entering through this pathway, carbon atoms originally in carbon dioxide can end up in all different types of biological molecules.

The conversion of G3P into neutral fats

Recall that neutral fats or triglycerides are three fatty acids attached to a three-carbon molecule called glycerol. Figure 13-10 highlights some of the major chemical transitions involved in the conversion of G3P into glycerol phosphate and the conversion of G3P into fatty acids. Once sufficient supplies of both of these molecules are formed, the two can be combined to form neutral fats.

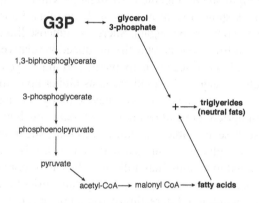

Figure 13-10. Summary of the metabolic pathways by which G3P can be converted into fatty acids and glycerol 3-phosphate. These two molecules can then be combined to form molecules of neutral fat.

Using G3P and molecular nitrogen to synthesize the 20 amino acids

The use of G3P in the synthesis of amino acids has a slightly different flavor than using G3P to assemble fats. In addition to being an arrangement of carbon, hydrogen, and oxygen atoms, all amino acids also have nitrogen atoms. So, although G3P molecules can be rearranged to form the carbon-based component of the different amino acids—or in the words of biochemist, G3P can be used to form carbon precursors—the nitrogen must come from elsewhere. Figure 13-11 shows the various carbon precursors used in the formation of different amino acids and the metabolic pathways by which G3P could be converted into each of these.

The most abundant source of nitrogen in the environment is molecular nitrogen (N_2). At everyday temperatures, molecular nitrogen exists as a gas. It is, in fact, the most abundant molecule in our present atmosphere. About 80% of atmospheric molecules are molecular nitrogen. Despite its abundance, however, no cell can directly use molecular nitrogen to build amino acids or any other biologically important molecules containing nitrogen. The nitrogen in molecular nitrogen—like the carbon in carbon dioxide—must first be reduced. The resulting molecule is likely familiar—it is ammonia (NH_3). This conversion of N_2 to NH_3 is known as **nitrogen fixation**. At conditions normally found within cells, most ammonia molecules pick up another hydrogen ion (H^+) and become an ammonium ion (NH_4^+).

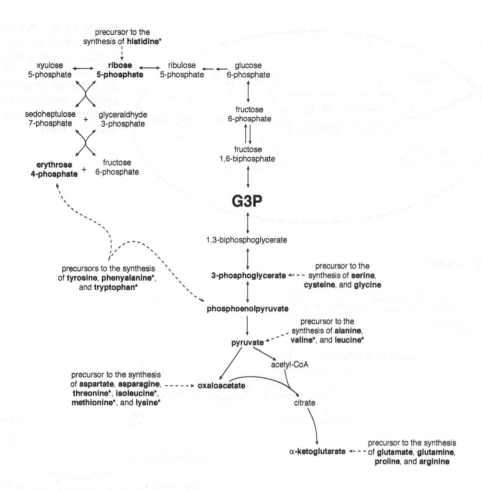

precursor to the
synthesis of **histidine***

xyulose ← **ribose** ← ribulose ← glucose
5-phosphate   **5-phosphate**   5-phosphate   6-phosphate

sedoheptulose + glyceraldhyde
7-phosphate   3-phosphate

fructose
6-phosphate

fructose
1,6-biphosphate

erythrose + fructose
4-phosphate   6-phosphate

G3P

1,3-biphosphoglycerate

precursors to the synthesis   precursor to the
of **tyrosine, phenylalanine***,   **3-phosphoglycerate** ← --- synthesis of **serine,
and **tryptophan***   cysteine**, and **glycine**

phosphoenolpyruvate

precursor to the
synthesis of **alanine,
valine***, and **leucine***

pyruvate

acetyl-CoA

precursor to the synthesis
of **aspartate, asparagine**, ------→ oxaloacetate
threonine*, isoleucine*,
methionine*, and **lysine***

citrate

precursor to the synthesis
α-ketoglutarate ← --- of **glutamate, glutamine,
proline**, and **arginine**

Figure 13-11. Summary of the metabolic pathways by which G3P can be converted into precursor molecules used in the synthesis of the 20 amino acids. The precursor for each different amino acid is indicated. Asterisks (*) indicate amino acids that humans cannot synthesize (discussed in text).

Like the Calvin–Benson cycle is for carbon, nitrogen fixation is the nitrogen entry pathway of biosynthesis. It takes a form of nitrogen readily available in the environment and reduces it to a form that can be used to build biologically important molecules. Although the details of nitrogen fixation are beyond our present scope, two aspects are noteworthy. First of all, nitrogen fixation is energetically expensive. The triple covalent bond that holds the two nitrogen atoms of molecular nitrogen together is difficult to pry apart and subsequently replace with hydrogen atoms. Twelve ATP are expended in the synthesis of just two ammonia molecules. Plus several molecules with even higher reducing power than NADPH—the molecule used in the Calvin–Benson cycle—are needed to donate the six hydrogens. Commonly, a molecule called **ferrodoxin** serves this role (see Figure 13-12). Second, nitrogen fixation can occur only in the complete absence of oxygen.

Once a cell has a supply of ammonia, it can be incorporated into a biological important molecule—a process called **direct amination**—in very few places (see Figure 13-13). Arguably, the most important is the combination of ammonia with a molecule called α-ketoglutarate to form glutamate—one of the 20 amino acids. During their synthesis, most other amino acids then get their amine group (–NH$_2$) from glutamate. **Transamination** is the name given to this transfer of the amine group from glutamate to amino acid precursors other than α-ketoglutarate to form the other amino acids (see Figure 13-13). During transamination, glutamate gives up its amine group and is converted back into α-ketoglutarate. The α-ketoglutarate can then be reused to incorporate another ammonia.

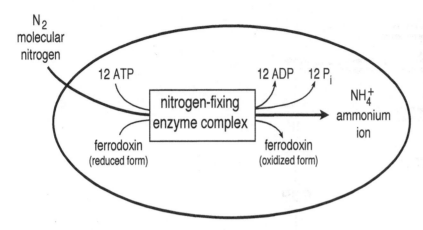

Figure 13-12. Overview of nitrogen fixation—how molecular nitrogen is brought into a cell and converted into ammonia, which under most cellular conditions picks up another proton to become ammonium ion.

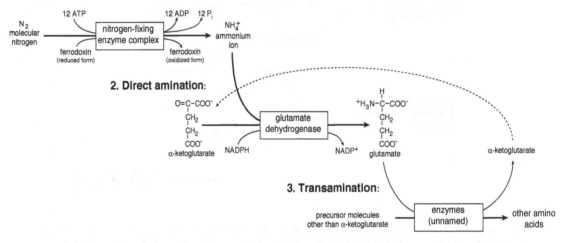

Figure 13-13. The three steps by which molecular nitrogen is incorporated into amino acids.

G3P and amino acids can be used to synthesize nucleotides

Assembling nucleotides involves synthesizing five-carbon sugar phosphates (either ribose-phosphate or deoxyribose-phosphate) and the five different nitrogenous bases (adenine, guanine, cytosine, thymine, and uracil) and then sticking these together. G3P, as we discussed earlier, can be converted into five-carbon sugar phosphates. G3P and ammonia can be used to build amino acids. Nitrogenous bases, for the most part, are derived from the amino acids glutamine, aspartic acid, and glycine.

A summary of biosynthesis

Figure 13-14 summarizes how the carbon in carbon dioxide and the nitrogen in molecular nitrogen—both atmospheric gases—can be used in the synthesis of the four major classes of biological molecules.

Major Pathways of Biosynthesis

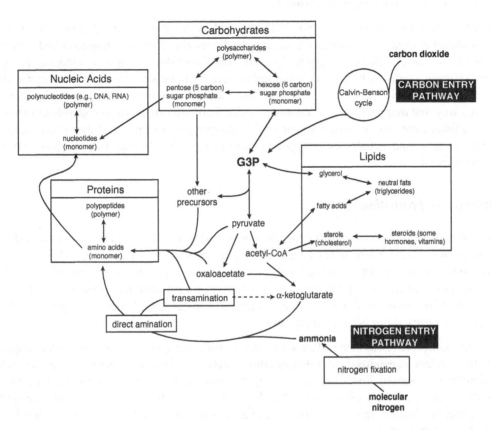

Figure 13-14. Overview of how the carbon in carbon dioxide and the nitrogen in molecular nitrogen—both atmospheric gases—can be used in the synthesis of all the major classes of biological molecules.

Autotrophs, Heterotrophs, and Food Chains

Although every cell needs a supply of G3P as a carbon source for biosynthesis, not all cells produce the enzymes needed to take CO_2 from the atmosphere and reduce it into this three-carbon sugar-phosphate. In other words, not all cells can perform the Calvin–Benson cycle.

How do cells that cannot synthesize G3P from CO_2, get their needed supply? We answered this question in Chapter 5 when we discussed food chains. There I pointed out that every cell comes to have each of its biological molecules by one of two means. They can either assemble them from other molecules (biosynthesis), or they can get them from some other organism that can assemble them. **Autotrophs**—cells able to reduce CO_2 to sugars—thus form the base of the carbon food chain. All additional links are **heterotrophs**—cells unable to do the Calvin–Benson cycle. Heterotrophs thus must either barter for or somehow steal—most commonly by feeding on—simple sugars from autotrophic cells (or other heterotrophs that feed on autotrophs, and so on). Without autotrophs, heterotrophs could not persist.

The terms *autotroph* and *heterotroph* are typically reserved to describe how different cells get their supply of simple sugars. But the idea can be extended to other elements, especially nitrogen. Just like carbon, all cells need a supply of reduced nitrogen (ammonia) to be able to synthesize amino acids and other nitrogen-containing biological molecules. But like the Calvin–Benson cycle, not all cells are able to perform nitrogen fixation. In fact, of all the life forms on this planet, only certain bacteria, called nitrogen-fixing bacteria, are up to the task. These nitrogen-fixing bacteria thus form the base of the nitrogen food chain—they are the **nitrogen-autotrophs**. All other cells, including the cells making up your body, are thus **nitrogen-heterotrophs**.

Dividing cells into nitrogen-autotrophs and nitrogen-heterotrophs is complicated by a few facts. For one, some other organisms, such as plants, can reduce another form of nitrogen called nitrate (NO_3^-) into ammonia. But from a certain perspective, this ability does not qualify plants as nitrogen-autotrophs. Nitrate would not be present in the soil (where it can be absorbed by plants) in the absence of nitrogen-fixing bacteria. Certain bacteria forms use the ammonia made available by nitrogen-fixing bacteria in a way that outputs nitrate as a waste product. Furthermore, many nitrogen-heterotrophs, such as all animals, are more than one step up in the nitrogen food chain in that they prefer to get their nitrogen not as ammonia, but already incorporated into amino acids. In fact, high levels of ammonia are toxic to animals.

Biosynthesis and nutrition

Is CO_2 a nutrient? The answer is: It depends. A **nutrient** is any molecule or element that if brought in from an organism's environment is useful to the organism. So, for an autotroph, CO_2 is a nutrient. It can be used to make G3P. On the other hand, because of its inability to use it in biosynthesis, CO_2 is not a nutrient for a heterotroph. Similarly, N_2 is a nutrient for nitrogen-fixing bacteria, but not for any other type of organism. And this is a common theme. The nutritional status for a whole suite of molecules or elements varies between organisms.

Once any molecule or element is deemed a nutrient for some type of organism, a second question arises: Is the nutrient an **essential** (or **indispensable**) **nutrient**? The combination of two factors leads to a nutrient being essential. First, a cellular supply of the nutrient is needed for normal function—that is, no other molecule can be used as a substitute. Second, within cells this nutrient cannot be synthesized from other molecules. In other words, the organism must get it in its diet because it needs it and cannot make it on its own.

As with nutrients, what is an essential nutrient varies across species. Consider, for instance, you and your dog (if you have one) sitting down to breakfast—you with a bowl of cereal and a glass of orange juice, and your dog with a bowl of dog chow. While musing over a swallow of orange juice a question pops into your head: Why am I not also giving some orange juice to my dog? Doesn't she also need some Vitamin C? Humans lacking a dietary supply of Vitamin C eventually develop a disease called scurvy. Dog food lacks Vitamin C, so why doesn't your dog get scurvy?

The answer to this nutritional puzzle has to do with synthesis. The dog does need a supply of ascorbic acid—the chemical name of Vitamin C—to function normally, but she does not need to get her supply from her diet. She can synthesize ascorbic acid by rearranging other molecules present in her diet. So, although ascorbic acid is a nutrient for your dog, it is not an essential nutrient. On the other hand, it is an essential nutrient for you because you need it, but in contrast to your dog, you cannot make it.

To make a semantic point, ascorbic acid would not be called vitamin C when speaking of dogs. The word **vitamin** is reserved for essential nutrients needed in only trace amounts. But I just said that for a dog, ascorbic acid is not an essential nutrient, so it is not a vitamin.

Another semantic point concerns the term *essential nutrient*. Humans, at least early in their life, have nine essential amino acids (see the amino acids marked by asterisks in Figure 13-10). What does that say about the other 11 of the 20 amino acids? Should they be called **nonessential** (or **dispensable**) **amino acids?** Although this term is used, it can be misleading. One must not make *the mistake of concluding that nonessential means unnecessary.* Designating an amino acid, or any other biological molecule, as nonessential does not in any way, shape, or form mean that the organism does not need a supply. In the case of amino acids, humans need a supply of all 20 amino acids to build proteins.

Nonessential is just another way of indicating that because the organism can synthesize it from other molecules acquired in the diet, it does not need a dietary supply. It would thus be correct to say that ascorbic acid is a nonessential nutrient for your dog.

The evolution of biological molecules as essential nutrients

Suppose a mutation occurs in a gene that codes for an enzyme needed to assemble some biological molecule. Further suppose that this mutation disrupts the enzyme's catalytic ability. The organism bearing the mutation has thus lost the ability to synthesize this biological molecule. What will be the evolutionary fate of such a mutation?

The answer to this question, like so many others, is: It depends. Any individual bearing this mutation can grow and develop normally so long as it acquires sufficient amounts of this biological molecule in its diet. This may happen if this organism feeds on other organisms capable of making this biological molecule. If so, any individual bearing this mutation could survive and reproduce, potentially passing this modification on to its offspring. Relying on other organisms to make one's biological molecules can even have benefits. Any energy or other resources required to make the molecule can now be expended elsewhere. I find it intriguing that the essential amino acids in humans are those with complex pathways of synthesis, whereas the pathways to nonessential amino acids involve fewer, simpler chemical reactions. Not only can more go wrong in complex pathways, but also the amount of resources saved by avoiding such synthesis will be greater.

Taking into account that mutations are random, different species have different diets, and once branching from their common ancestor, different species have separate evolutionary histories. The preceding scenario predicts that at least some variation should exist among what types of biological molecules constitute essential nutrients for different species. Although our information is limited, this prediction seems to be upheld. Ascorbic acid, discussed earlier, is one example. It is a vitamin in humans, whereas dogs can synthesize their own. Furthermore, variation among species in the ability to synthesize other vitamins as well as amino acids is known. (Due to their tedious nature, experiments to determine what biological molecules are essential nutrients have been performed on very few types of organisms. As to be expected, we know most about the dietary requirements of humans and domestic animals.)

Curiously, there is one group of biological molecules that all cells on this planet have seemed to retain the ability to synthesize. *There are no known cases of essential nucleotides.* In other words, no cells require an input of nucleotides to build DNA and RNA. Every cell has the ability to synthesize what they need.

Regulating the Metabolic Performance

We have seen that the same molecule, such as G3P, can be used in the synthesis of many different molecules. The different options arise from the fact that metabolic pathways within cells are like roadways with intersections. Intersections make it possible for a car to travel more than one route. Similarly, metabolic pathways with intersections make it possible for a molecule to be rearranged in more than one way. The difference is that enzymes instead of asphalt establish the layout of these "metabolic roadways."

Metabolic intersections form whenever the output of one enzyme can be used as an input by more than one type of enzyme. Each of these different enzymes takes the common input off in a different chemical direction. Figure 13-15 shows just a small portion of the intersecting metabolic pathways found commonly in many cells.

The observation of metabolic intersections raises a basic question: What is steering the metabolic traffic? Or more basically, if a cell has a supply of a certain molecule able to be used in the synthesis of many different molecules, how should the cell choose which molecules to make? And how does a cell make such choices?

Common sense provides us with a good answer to the "how should" question. The cell should divert resources toward the synthesis of biomolecules that are currently in short supply and away from the synthesis of biomolecules that are currently in abundance. That way, the resources available will be used in the most efficient manner to maintain an adequate supply of all the needed biomolecules. Natural selection thinking reinforces this notion. All else being equal, cells able to use resources more efficiently will do better in a reproductive race than those that do not.

The general answer to how a cell can use resources efficiently is to set up a counteracting response. Attempting to maintain an adequate supply of all the needed biomolecules is to try to respond to change in a way that attempts to keep things the same. Furthermore, the means to set up this type of counteracting response has a common theme. Available molecules are blocked from moving down metabolic pathways that synthesize biomolecules currently in sufficient supply. Consequently, the pathways open will be the ones that synthesize biomolecules currently in short supply. Classic negative feedback loops can be used to open and close these metabolic roadblocks at the appropriate time. All that is required is for biomolecules in sufficient supply to

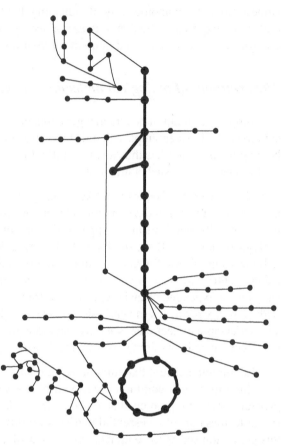

Figure 13-15. A very incomplete map of the metabolic roadways common to many cells. Each dot represents a specific type of molecule. A line connecting two dots represents a possible enzyme facilitated chemical transition. The larger dots and heavier lines represent a very commonly used pathway of chemical reactions. Each intersection represents a place where a cell has to make a "choice", as it could use the molecule in more than one way.

loop back and block molecules from moving down the metabolic pathway that produced them. Most important, such feedback loops can potentially respond appropriately to fluctuations in the supplies of different biomolecules. Products in short supply are being synthesized and hence are headed toward a sufficient supply status. As this happens, negative feedback slows down these pathways. On the other hand, any product currently in sufficient supply is continually being used and hence is always headed toward being in short supply. For example, the supply of any specific amino acid synthesized in a cell is always being used up as proteins are being made. Once in short supply, however, negative feedback releases its stranglehold on the metabolic pathway that produces it. More of this amino acid will start to be produced.

What remains is to better explain how these negative feedback loops work in cells. Complicating this task is the fact that such feedback loops have been found to operate at two distinct levels: gene-level and enzyme-level. Before taking on either, however, I need to first discuss rate-limiting steps and how a protein can have a sensor.

Rate-limiting steps

The rate that metabolic traffic flows along any metabolic pathway is controlled by its most rate-limiting step—that is, the step where inputs are converted into outputs most slowly. The rate-limiting step is the pathway's bottleneck. Speeding up the traffic upstream—the reactions preceding the rate-limiting step—will not widen the bottleneck. Once available enzymes are working as fast as they can, increasing the input supply further will not speed things up. And past the bottleneck, all downstream steps will be slowed by input limitation. Inputs will become available slower than the available enzymes can process them.

Rate-limiting steps mean that controlling a single step can control an entire metabolic pathway. Consequently, slowing enzyme activity at any one step to the point that it becomes the rate-limiting step can slow the rate that any metabolic pathway produces its final product.

Proteins can have sensors

All proteins function by having the shape to bind with something else in a way that orchestrates some change. The particular region of a protein's surface configuration directly involved in such binding is known as the **active site**. For instance, an enzyme's active site is the region shaped in a way that it can hold potential reactive substances in a manner that facilitates a chemical reaction.

Any protein can be said to have a sensor if its active site can be changed to a nonfunctional shape by certain conditions. In other words, the protein responds to the presence of certain conditions by *turning off*, and conversely, it responds to the absence of certain conditions by *turning on*. For example, the active site of certain **allosteric proteins** (shape-changing proteins) are known to be modulated (switched on or off) by the presence of a **ligand**—the name given to any molecule able to bind with a certain protein. Protein function being controlled by ligand-induced shape changes is called **allosteric modulation**.

Allosteric modulation can be either negative or positive (see Figure 13-16). The modulation is *negative*—the protein has a negative sensor—when the presence of the ligand turns off the protein and the absence of the ligand turns on the protein. In other words, the protein's active site is in its functional configuration (i.e., it is turned on) only when the

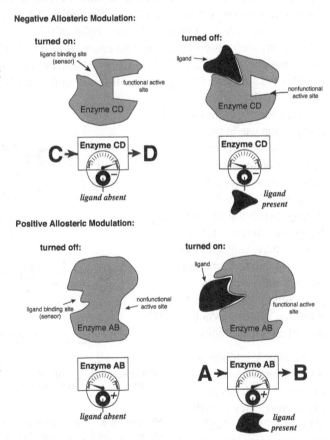

Figure 13-16. Both negative and positive regulation—turning an enzyme off or on—by shape-changes induced by the binding of another molecule, which is generically called a ligand. Whether an enzyme is on or off is determined by whether its active site (the region of the enzyme that binds with the substrates of the reaction it catalyzes) is in its functional form or shape. Each state is also represented as a processor with a sensor (that detects the presence or absence of a specific ligand).

ligand is absent. The modulation is *positive*—the protein has a positive sensor—whenever the reverse is true. The active site is in its functional configuration (is turned on) only when the ligand is present and bound. It is turned off otherwise.

Enzyme-level regulation: feedback inhibition

Feedback inhibition is the simplest means of establishing negative feedback loops in biosynthetic pathways. The basic design was first discussed in Chapter 3 (see Figure 3-30). It has only one requirement: One of the enzymes making up the metabolic pathway must have a negative sensor that detects the pathway's end product. Stated differently, one of the enzymes must be negatively allosterically modulated by the pathway's end product. Put in terms of Figure 13-17, *molecule F* is *enzyme CD*'s ligand, so whenever the supply of *molecule F* increases, more and more of the available copies of *enzyme CD* will be bound by *molecule F*. Each ligand-bound copy of *enzyme CD* is turned off by negative allosteric modulation, which increasingly slows this step of the metabolic pathway. As this step slows to the point that it is the pathway's rate-limiting step, *molecule F* production slows. Consequently, increasing supplies of *molecule F* is counteracted by decreasing the rate at which *molecule F* is produced. Alternatively, decreasing supplies of *molecule F* are counteracted by increasing *molecule F*'s production rate. Whenever *molecule F* supplies fall, fewer and fewer copies of *enzyme CD* will be bound by *molecule F*, so more and more copies of this enzyme will be turned on. As long as this is the rate-limiting step, speeding up the conversion of *molecule C* to *molecule D* will speed up the production of *molecule F*. Figure 13-17(c) shows a biological example of feedback inhibition. The pathway involves the synthesis of proline, one of the 20 amino acids used in protein synthesis. Feedback inhibition will thus act to balance proline synthesis with proline use in protein synthesis. Decreasing supplies due to increased use in protein synthesis will lead to less inhibition, thereby increasing the rate of proline production. Conversely, increasing supplies of proline due to decreased use in protein synthesis will result in a slower rate of proline synthesis via increased enzyme inhibition.

Feedback inhibition can do more than balance the rate of synthesis of certain molecules with the rate of use; it can also be used to regulate the efficient flow of resources through metabolic intersections. To do so, however, the feedback enzyme—the enzyme bound by the pathway's end product—must be the first enzyme past the intersec-

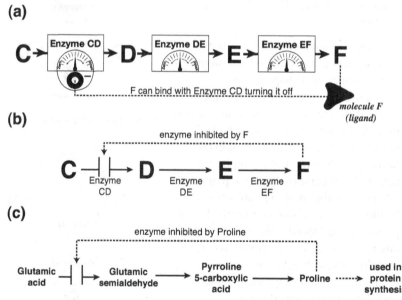

Figure 13-17. Feedback inhibition within a metabolic pathway. The end product molecule F is a ligand to enzyme CD. When F builds up, it binds with more and more of the available copies of enzyme CD. Through negative allosteric modulation, these copies of enzyme CD are turned off, increasingly slowing the conversion of molecule C to molecule D. This, in turn, slows the entire pathway (through input limitation), hence slows the production of molecule F. In (a), enzymes are shown as processors, and enzyme CD has a negative sensor that slows this processor as levels of molecule F increase. In (b), the same scenario is illustrated in a much simpler way. In (c), a biological example is provided. Although the names of each enzyme have been omitted, each solid arrow represents a chemical reaction catalyzed by a different enzyme.

tion. Let me explain why. At any metabolic intersection, the various pathways compete for their common input. For example, in Figure 13-18 whenever a copy of *enzyme CD* grabs a *molecule C* (converting it into *molecule D*), one less *molecule C* is available to go down the other metabolic pathway—the pathway involved in the synthesis of *molecule N*. To be useful, feedback inhibition must skew this competition in ways that prevent a cell's available resources (such as the available supply of *molecule C* in Figure 13-18) from moving into pathways where they are not currently needed. Inhibiting any other enzyme besides the first past an intersection would fail to do that. In Figure 13-18(b), the feedback enzyme in the pathway leading to the synthesis of *molecule F* is the second past the intersection—*molecule F* binds to *enzyme DE* (instead of *enzyme CD* as shown in Figure 13-18(a)). Even when *molecule F* is abundant, functional copies of *enzyme CD* would still be around to convert *molecule C* into *molecule D*. Consequently, some of the available supply of *molecule C* will be used to make a molecule currently not needed—*molecule D*; and as a consequence this portion of the *molecule C* supply becomes unavailable to be used in a more useful way. Clearly this would be a less than optimal way to allocate resources.

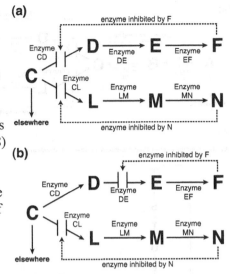

Figure 13-18. Feedback inhibition combined with a metabolic intersection. (a) works much better than (b) in allocating the available supply of molecule C toward the production of the end product (either molecule F or molecule N) currently in the shortest supply (see text for further explanation).

Is there any evidence that this type of design shows up in living organisms? Perhaps not surprisingly, the answer is yes. Although, unlike an engineer, natural selection cannot plan ahead to come up with the most efficient design, any design that comes about by random modification that improves resource use efficiency should aid reproduction. So, over time, metabolic regulation would be expected to evolve toward an efficient design. Figure 13-19 shows a biological example.

Usually, the synthesis of any biologically important molecule passes through more than one sequentially arranged branch point. Efficient resource use depends on each branch point being regulated. Figure 13-20(a) illustrates one way, called **sequential feedback control**, that feedback inhibition loops can regulate flow through a series of intersections. When *molecule F* and *molecule N* are both abundant, each blocks the first metabolic step unique to their synthesis. When this happens, there is also no need to build more *molecule C*. The addition of another feedback inhibition loop that blocks

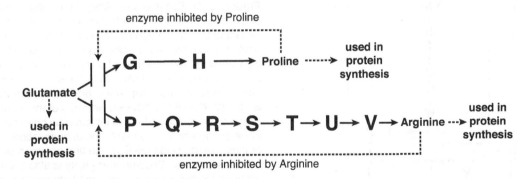

Figure 13-19. Glutamate, one of the 20 amino acids used in protein synthesis, can be further modified by two different metabolic pathways into two other amino acids. These two pathways are regulated in an efficient manner—each pathways displays feedback inhibition and the feedback enzyme in both pathways is the first past the intersection.

(a)

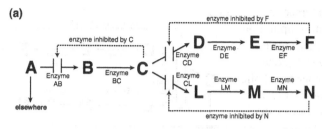

(b)

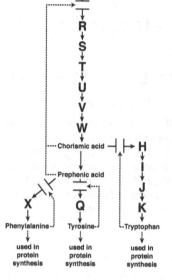

Figure 13-20. Sequential feedback control. In (a), three feed-back inhibition loops not only direct the available supply of molecule toward the production of the end product in shortest supply, but prevent the overproduction of molecule C when-ever both molecule F and molecule N are in adequate supply. In (b), a biological example of the sequential use of feedback control is shown. In the bacteria *Bacillus subtilis*, each of the three amino acids inhibits the first enzyme in their divergent metabolic pathway, while the two metabolic intermediates prior to branch points—chorismic and prephenic acid—inhibit the first common step in the overall pathway.

(a)

(b)

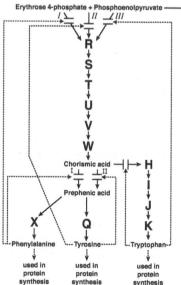

Figure 13-21. Enzyme multiplicity. In (a), the excess conversion of molecule A into molecule B and then molecule C is prevented by each end product—mol-ecule F and molecule N—binding with and inhibit-ing one of the two isoforms of enzyme AB. In (b), a biological example is shown. In the bacteria *Escheria coli* the first common step in this branching pathway is catalyzed by three different isoforms of the same enzyme, and each isoform is inhibited by one of the three amino acids. As a result, the accumulation of any of these amino acids will slow the first common step in their synthesis. Enzyme multiplicity is also used to regulate the excessive conversion of chorismic acid to prephenic acid. One isoform of the enzyme catalyzing this reaction is inhibited by tyrosine and the other is inhibited by phenylalanine.

the production of *molecule C* (at the metabolic intersection involving *molecule A*) solves the problem. As the supply of *molecule C* builds up, the supply of *molecule A* is diverted to where it is needed. Figure 13-20(b) provides a biological example. The bacteria *Bacillus subtilis* uses sequential feedback control in the branching synthesis of the three aromatic amino acids (the variable group of each of these amino acids contains a carbon ring).

If there is more than one way to accomplish the same thing, then it is always possible for alternatives to evolve in different organisms. This has proved true in metabolic regulation. One of the alternatives to sequential feedback control found is called **enzyme multiplicity**. This scheme involves the first common step in the synthesis of more than one biologically important end product catalyzed by more than one form of the same enzyme. In biology, different forms of the same thing are called **isoforms** in general and **isozymes** when referring to an enzyme. These different isozymes catalyze the same reaction (so they have the same shaped active site) but are each inhibited by only one of the biologically important end products. Figure 13-21(a) illustrates this. Whenever the supply of *molecule F* or *molecule N* builds up, not only do they inhibit the first metabolic step unique to their synthesis, but they also inhibit one of the isozymes catalyzing the first step common to both end products. So a buildup of either will slow the conversion of *molecule A* to *molecule B*, freeing more of *molecule A* to be used elsewhere. A buildup of both *molecule F* and *molecule N* could completely block the first common step. Figure 13-21(b) not only shows a biological example of enzyme multiplicity, but also shows that not every organism regulates the same pathways the same ways. Some of the steps in the synthesis of the three aromatic amino acids, which are regulated by sequentially feedback control in the bacteria *Bacillus subtilis* (as shown in Figure 13-20(b)), are regulated by enzyme multiplicity in the bacteria *Escherichia coli* (*E. coli*).

Figure 13-22 punctuates this section. It illustrates the pattern of enzyme-level regulation found in at least some bacteria in the synthesis of four amino acids used in protein synthesis—lysine, methionine, isoleucine, and threonine. There are two reasons I show this figure: First, it again illustrates all the aspects of regulation discussed earlier. But second, the regulatory network does not appear to be perfect. For instance, if you were the engineer laying out the regulatory design, would you have threonine inhibit the formation of homoserine? Or would you have the synthesis of isoleucine exist within the same branch as threonine synthesis? If you did, I am not sure you would graduate from engineering school. But evolution is not expected to produce perfection. It is historical, so it can only work through random modification of what has evolved in the past. As a consequence, not every option can be or will be considered. The only issue is whether it works well enough to reproduce faster than any competitors that it faces. So, although this regulatory design must work to persist, other possible designs may work even better.

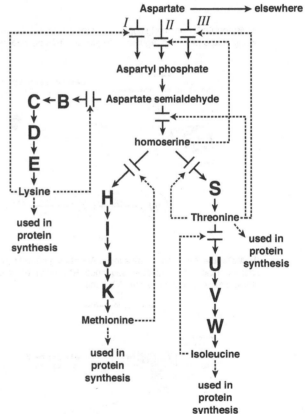

Figure 13-22. A regulatory design found in the branching metabolic pathway involved in the synthesis of four amino acids—lysine, methionine, threonine, and isoleucine. (Note: The first molecule, aspartate, is also an amino acid used in protein synthesis.) See text for further discussion.

Gene-level regulation

As we have seen, enzyme-level regulation turns on and off the catalytic capacity of enzymes already assembled. In contrast, gene-level regulation turns on and off the production of enzymes making up a metabolic pathway.

Gene-level regulation can still involve allosteric modulation of a protein. But instead of an enzyme, a regulatory protein is allosterically modulated. The basic scheme is as follows. An end product of a metabolic pathway binds with a regulatory protein whenever it is abundant, changing the regulatory protein's shape. The new shape somehow stops production of at least one of the enzymes making up this metabolic pathway. With no new enzyme(s) being produced, the metabolic pathway slows as the present enzyme supply starts to fall apart. Active degradation of these enzymes within the cell would speed up this response. So, in total, the response to a sufficient supply of some synthesized biomolecule is to turn off the production of one or more of the enzymes involved in this molecule's synthesis. And like with feedback inhibition, the counteracting response reverses as this molecule becomes scarce. Due to its scarcity, a copy of the molecule cannot continue to bind with the regulatory protein. Once freed of its ligand, the regulatory protein returns to the shape that can turn on enzyme production, which in turn will increase the rate that this biomolecule is synthesized.

The details of any gene-level feedback lie in filling the details of how binding of an end product with a regulatory protein turns off enzyme production. There are two distinct possibilities. In Figure 13-23, I explain one of these. The key to understanding this figure is remembering the details of ge-

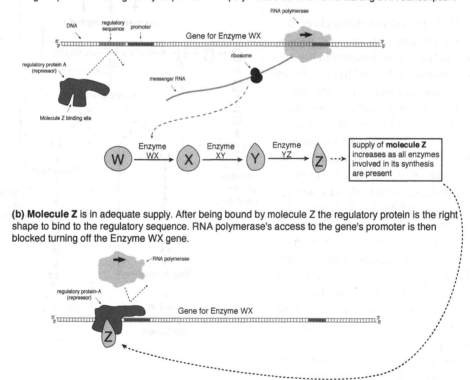

(a) **Molecule Z** is in short supply. Gene for Enzyme WX is turned on because regulatory protein is of wrong shape to bind to regulatory sequence. RNA polymerase can then bind starting DNA transcription.

(b) **Molecule Z** is in adequate supply. After being bound by molecule Z the regulatory protein is the right shape to bind to the regulatory sequence. RNA polymerase's access to the gene's promoter is then blocked turning off the Enzyme WX gene.

Figure 13-23. Gene-level regulation of a metabolic pathway. An abundance of the end product Z feeds back to turn off the production of one of the enzymes forming the metabolic pathway producing molecule Z.

netic regulation discussed in Chapter 11. This is a case of negative genetic regulation. Binding of the regulatory protein blocks RNA polymerase's access to the gene's promoter, turning off DNA transcription. The only thing new is allosteric modulation of the regulatory protein. It is of the right shape to bind to the gene's regulatory sequence (and subsequently block DNA transcription) only when first bound to the end product. Figure 13-24 highlights the workings of the negative sensor that underlies this negative genetic regulation in the way first developed in Chapter 3 (see Figure 3-31).

The second possibility revolves around positive genetic regulation—DNA transcription can take place only if the regulatory protein first binds to the regulatory sequence. If you wish to test your understanding, combine allosteric modulation of the regulatory protein with positive genetic regulation to come up with a negative feedback loop. However, I am not going to press this idea any further.

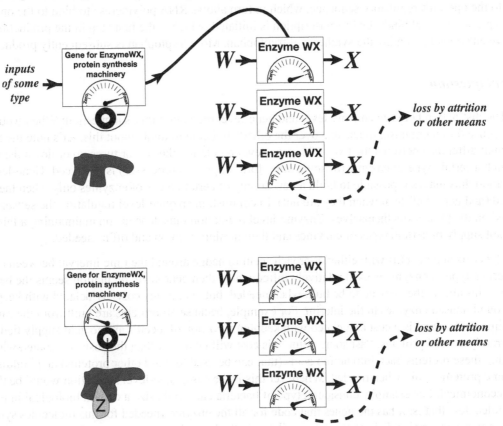

Figure 13-24. The workings of the negative sensor that controls the production of Enzyme WX. It does not detect the presence of regulatory protein-A unless molecule Z first binds with it, and when this happens production of Enzyme WX is shutdown. As a consequence, the supply of Enzyme WX will become less and less as the previously produced copies of this enzyme either fall apart or are actively degraded. Overall, this is part of a counteracting response because molecule X is a precursor in the metabolic pathway that forms molecule Z, so slowing the rate of molecule X production will subsequently slow the rate of molecule Z production.

A classic example of gene-level regulation

In prokaryotic cells (but not eukaryotic cells) genes that code for proteins involved in the same metabolic pathway often lie next to each other along the DNA. They are also regulated as a unit—that is, they are turned on or off together. This unit of genes and its associated regulatory genes is called an **operon**. In the bacteria *E. coli* one such operon found is the tryptophan operon. The tryptophan operon is five adjacent genes all involved in the biosynthesis of the amino acid tryptophan. When the operon turns on, all five genes within the operon are transcribed. So, in the end, the five different enzymes catalyzing subsequent steps in the synthesis of tryptophan are all produced.

The details of turning on and off the production of these five enzymes coded for in the tryptophan operon is the same as shown in Figure 13-23. The regulatory protein associated with the tryptophan operon acts as a **repressor**—binding of the regulatory protein to the regulatory sequence turns off enzyme production by turning off DNA transcription. The regulatory protein is of the right shape to bind to the regulatory sequence, however, only when it first binds with tryptophan. Abundant tryptophan thus curtails tryptophan production. The tryptophan operon remains shut down until the supply of tryptophan is again depleted by tryptophan use in protein synthesis. At that point, tryptophan releases from the repressor molecule. Due to the associated shape change, the repressor cannot continue to bind to the operon's regulatory sequence, which in turn allows RNA polymerase to bind to the operon's promoter. As it binds, DNA transcription is initiated, which is the first step in the production of the five enzymes facilitating the synthesis of tryptophan. More tryptophan is subsequently produced.

A final question

The distinction between enzyme-level and gene-level regulation raises a question: When would it make sense for an organism to use one over the other? To begin to think about this, let's note the fundamental difference between the two. With gene-level regulation the sensor turns up or down the rate at which a certain type of enzyme (or some other form of protein processor) is produced. Gene-level regulation thus makes it possible to build a new supply of certain types of enzymes only when they are needed (and get rid of them when they are not). In contrast, in enzyme-level regulation the sensors are located on the processors themselves. Enzyme-level regulation thus depends on maintaining a fairly constant supply of certain types of enzymes and then turning them on and off as needed.

The costs and benefits with either approach seem to hedge around the time interval between uses. If a certain type of enzyme is used relatively infrequently, then gene-level regulation seems the best option. This allows the enzyme to be built when needed, but avoids any costs associated with keeping around unused enzymes in the interim. For example, because all proteins are built from the same 20 amino acids, there is a cost associated with keeping a portion of a cell's amino acid supply tied up in currently unused proteins. Past some point, this cost will be higher than the costs associated with breaking these proteins back into amino acids (that can be used to build other proteins) and building the same proteins again when needed. Whenever this is the case, gene-level regulation would be the most economical. For example, consider a type of bacteria can synthesize a certain biological important molecule—that is, it has the genes that code for all the enzymes needed for this molecules synthesis—yet this same molecule is commonly available in the bacteria's environment. As a consequence, it only needs to synthesize this molecule when it cannot get it from the environment. Gene-level regulation would allow the organism to build this set of enzymes only at these times. Can you think of other scenarios where gene-level regulation would make sense?

In contrast, enzyme-level regulation seems the best way to make moment-by-moment adjustments in rate at which metabolic pathways are making products constantly needed by the cell. Here pathways are never being turned off for any extended period of time, but an efficient flow of resources depends on each branch in this ongoing buzz of metabolism being constantly fine-tuned. A little excess is building here, so the pathway needs to be momentarily slowed down—just until the excess disappears. A little shortage developing over there, so the pathway needs to be momentarily speeded up—just until the shortage disappears. The constant monitoring of enzyme-level feedback inhibition makes this fine-tuning possible. The enzymes to catalyze each step along the way are always in place, but some of the copies are turned on or off as needed. And ligands can bind and unbind quickly. In contrast, breaking down enzymes and then building them again takes time, so gene-level regulation cannot adjust rates as quickly or as accurately.

Some key terms:

metabolic pathway - a step-wise series of chemical reactions (outputs of one become inputs to the next), where each reaction is facilitated by a different enzyme.

biosynthesis - the use of metabolic pathways to rearrange atoms in molecules available to the cell into biologically useful molecules.

polysaccharides - polymers formed by stringing together many simple sugars (in their ringed form).

nitrogen fixation - the process where molecular nitrogen (N_2) is reduced to form ammonia (NH_3)

autotroph - a cell able to reduce carbon dioxide (CO_2) to a three-carbon sugar (called glyceraldehyde). (A cell able to perform the Calvin cycle.)

heterotroph - a cell unable to reduce carbon dioxide (CO_2) to a three-carbon sugar, thus, must get their needed supply of simple sugars from autotrophic cells (via barter or theft).

nutrient - any molecule or element which if included in an organism's diet is (in someway) useful to the organism.

essential (indispensable) nutrient - any nutrient that must be included in an organism's diet if normal function is to continue, typically because the molecule is both a needed component of metabolism and cannot be synthesized (from other available molecules) by the organism.

allosteric protein - a protein that changes shape when it binds with (or is covalently linked to) another molecule.

ligand - any molecule that can bind with a specific site on a protein and in so doing alters the protein's shape.

allosteric modulation - whenever a protein's function (whether it is turned on or off) is controlled by ligand-induced shape changes.

Some study questions:

1. *How do different types of enzymes form metabolic pathways? Explain, in general, how molecules found in a cell's environment can be brought into a cell and then (the atoms making up these molecules) rearranged into biologically useful molecules (e.g., one of the 20 amino acids).*

2. Trace, in general, how a carbon atom in a carbon dioxide molecule can end up as a carbon atom in a GAP molecule, a glucose molecule (or any of the other sugar molecules), any one of the 20 different types of amino acids, a fat molecule, or a nucleotide.

3. *Why is it important that the Calvin-Benson cycle (carbon reduction cycle) is a cycle?*

4. What is it about five-carbon and six-carbon sugars that have made it possible for them to be used in organisms such as plants as a structural material?

5. Trace, in general, how a nitrogen atom in molecular nitrogen could end up as a nitrogen atom in any one of the 20 amino acids, or any of the nucleotides.

6. Explain the connection between essential biological molecules, such as essential amino acids, and food chains.

7. Explain the idea of a metabolic intersection.

8. *Explain how certain enzymes have sensors.*

9. Explain how counter-acting responses (negative feedback loops) can be set up at the enzyme level?

10. *Explain this statement:* Metabolic traffic within a cell is commonly regulated at the enzyme level by preventing available molecules from moving into metabolic pathways whose end products are currently in sufficient supply, instead of actively directing molecules toward metabolic pathways whose end products are currently scarce. (Note: To explain this statement, one must consider how negative feedback loops can be used to efficiently allocate resources through metabolic intersections.)

11. Explain the difference between enzyme-level and gene-level regulation of biosynthesis. Understand how gene-level regulation could work.

Basic Principles of Energy Metabolism

All life forms require a constant and sufficient flow of energy to accomplish the ongoing work of living. I would bet that most readers buzzed through this last sentence without much pause. It sounds so correct, and it is. It is no different than saying that your car cannot run without gasoline. This smooth truth, however, gets increasingly bumpy when one begins to focus on how all this happens. But **energy metabolism**—the means by which cells maintain a constant supply of usable energy—is the major piece left of the reproductive puzzle outlined in Chapter 8, so the time left to avoid it has run out. I start the discussion by first summarizing what we already know.

First and foremost, Life runs on sunlight. Unlike materials, usable energy—because it becomes unusable with use—cannot be recycled. A constant input of usable energy is thus needed for life to persist on this planet. The sun supplies this constant input of usable energy.

Two reasons why all life forms need a continual supply of usable energy have been identified in the last few chapters. First, reproduction involves building more of all the molecules that make up a cell, and building molecules require energy. Building amino acids from carbon dioxide and molecule nitrogen, for example, requires a usable energy source, as does stringing together these amino acids to form proteins. Second, for a cell to move molecules in and out as needed, cells at times need to transport molecules in the absence of a favorable concentration gradient. Active transport can occur, however, only if the cell supplies energy. There also are a couple of other energy-requiring activities commonly performed by cells. You are already aware of one of these. Living things commonly move, which means that cells must be able to generate motion. Cells move internal parts around and move themselves in relation to the environment.

Combine the last two paragraphs and a conclusion unfolds: All cells on this planet use sunlight to power biosynthesis, active transport, and movement. The problem is that this statement is both true and misleading at the same time. The misleading part is that one could get the impression that cells **directly** use sunlight to power these three activities. That is not the case. Instead, all cells use two forms of chemical energy to directly power these activities: **high phosphorylation potential** and **high redox potential** (also called **reductive power** or **reducing power**). Remember that chemical energy is potential energy (PE) stored within the bonded arrangement of atoms composing molecules. Stating that cells use these two forms of chemical energy is saying that cells have the means to release these forms of chemical energy contained in certain molecules in a way that can be used to power their activities. Although the details are quite different, it is no different than saying that most cars are set up to release the PE in gasoline molecules in a way that can be used to spin their wheels.

In cells, these two usable forms of chemical energy are most commonly encapsulated in two molecules that mostly go by their acronyms: **ATP** (**a**denosine **t**riphosphate) and **NADPH** (the reduced form of **n**icotinamide **a**denine **d**inucleotide **p**hosphate). I tend to call these two molecules the two cellular fuels. **High phosphorylation potential**, the form of chemical energy found in **ATP**, is functionally the more diverse of the two fuels. It is used to power biosynthesis, active transport, and motion, as well as turning on and off certain enzymes. Alternatively, **high redox potential**, the form of chemical energy found in **NADPH**, is used by cells to perform reductive biosynthesis (discussed further later).

Hopefully you are beginning to wonder: Did the sun suddenly go down in this discussion? One moment I was saying that sunlight powers all biological activities, and the next I was discussing different types of chemical energy held in molecules with such long confusing names that they go by their initials. What is the connection?

The connection enters with a fact: No cell gets either of these two cellular fuels from outside the cell. Instead, every cell uses an external energy source to generate its own supplies of ATP and NADPH. Sunlight enters the picture because some cells can use it as the external energy source. Other cells use high-energy molecules picked from their environment as their external energy source. Sunlight, however, is still indirectly involved whenever the high-energy molecule is one initially built by a sunlight-using cell.

Although it sounds so simple, the details underlying the flow of energy through life tends to give people fits. To try to make this discussion more manageable, I break the topic into two chapters. The focus of this chapter is to establish the basics. Specifically, we discuss two things: (1) the basic means that an external energy source can be used to generate ATP or NADPH, and (2) the basic means that ATP and NADPH can be used to power the various types of work involved in living. In other words, we discuss the general means by which these two fuels are made and how they are used. This, in turn, sets the stage for the next chapter, where we discuss the details of how cells use sunlight or high-energy molecules as the external energy source.

To start we need to go back and learn a bit more chemistry. In particular, we need to learn how to think about group-transfer chemical reactions because they form the chemical basis of all energy metabolism.

Group-Transfer Chemical Reactions

For some molecules it makes sense to divide them into a **base-group** and a **transfer-group**. The distinction is that the transfer-group is the portion of the molecule moved from one molecule to another during a chemical reaction. The base-group is then the rest of the molecule, or stated differently, the portion remaining after the transfer group moves elsewhere. This description alone, however, fails to capture the entire notion of a base-group. To call something a base-group, it must be able to accept the transfer-group from one source and then donate to another, and it must be able to do this over and over.

This distinction becomes particularly useful when many molecules have the same transfer-group. This is another way of saying that the same transfer-group can move among more than one base-group. A group-transfer chemical reaction is thus nothing more than the movement of a transfer-group from one base-group to another (see Figure 14-1).

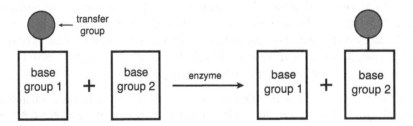

Figure 14-1. A group-transfer reaction. Facilitated by an enzyme, the transfer-group is moved from base-group 1 to base-group 2.

Coenzyme is the name given to biologically significant base-groups. The term *coenzyme* is used because the transfer can occur only in close association with specific enzymes. Particular important coenzymes in the workings of life are not limited to being used by a single enzyme. As a consequence, the transfer-group attached to some coenzymes can be moved to a variety of different molecules. In other words, such coenzymes can serve a variety of different reactions where the same transfer-group is required.

Group-transfer potential

An important question concerning group-transfer reactions is, What other molecules can a transfer-group loaded onto a specific base-group be moved to?

In the realm of biology, part of the answer was stated by the use of the term *coenzyme*. The movement of a transfer-group from one base-group to a specific other can take place only if the enzyme specific to this reaction is present.

The second part of the answer has to do with energetics. The transfer has to be energetically favorable—that is, the transfer must result in a net loss of chemical (potential) energy. This requirement is met only when the transfer-group is held in a higher energetic position by the donating base-group than by the potentially accepting base-group. Or in chemical speak: The base-group donating the transfer-group must have **higher group-transfer potential** than the molecule accepting the transfer-group.

Because the notion of group-transfer potential is an important one, let's use a strength-based analogy to put it into a familiar perspective. Consider the movement of a book (the transfer-group) from your hand (a base-group) to my hand (a different base-group). Such a transfer is energetically favorable under one condition: My hand is stronger and hence can grasp the book tighter than your hand. Only then is the book "falling" into a more stable (more tightly held) arrangement.

Keeping track of the energetics of potential book-transfers when there are more than two hands is done most easily by creating some means to measure the relative strength of each hand and then arranging each hand on a common scale. In somewhat of a curious twist, let's arrange this scale in terms of each hand's relative **book-transfer potential**—that is, in comparison to other hands, how readily any particular hand gives up a held book. The curious aspect of such a scale is the flip-flop in its nature. The relatively *weakest* hand has the relatively *highest* book-transfer potential because it is most likely to encounter an empty hand with a stronger grip and hence is most likely to give up its held book. Conversely, the relatively *strongest* hand has the relatively *lowest* book-transfer potential. Once it grabs a book, no other hands can pull it away. All other hands range somewhere in between.

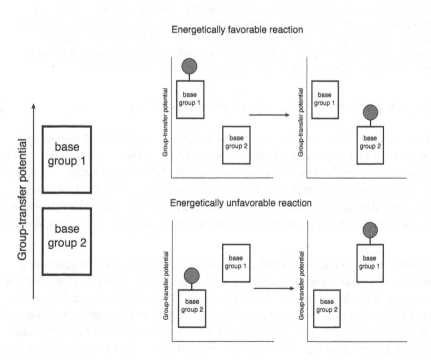

Figure 14-2. Base-group 1 has higher group-transfer potential than base-group 2. As a consequence, the movement of a transfer-group from base-group 1 to base-group 2 is energetically favorable, and the reverse is not.

In principle, a scale of the same sort could be created to measure relative group-transfer potential of all base-groups sharing the same transfer-group. Once each base-group is measured on the same scale, it is straightforward about whether the movement of the transfer-group from one base-group to the other is energetically favorable. Only if the donating base-group is higher on the common group-transfer potential scale than the accepting base-group would the movement of the transfer group between the two be energetically favorable (see Figure 14-2).

The other advantage of creating such a scale is that one can easily figure the energy released—the amount of PE converted to kinetic energy (KE)—in any group-transfer reaction. The amount of energy released is simply the measured difference in group-transfer potential between the donor base-group and the accepting base-group. This fact leads to an important point: The amount of energy released is not determined by the starting height, but by how far something falls. A rock starting at 10 feet above the ground has more PE than one starting 5 feet up. But a rock starting at 10 feet falling into a hand 9 feet up, releases less energy than a rock starting at 5 feet and falling to 3 feet. The first falls 1 foot during the transition, whereas the latter falls 2 feet (see Figure 14-3).

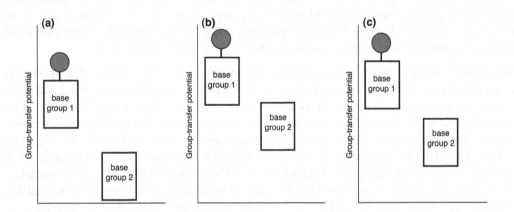

Figure 14-3. Which of these group-transfer reactions would release the most energy—that is, the most potential energy converted to kinetic energy? The answer is (a). Although the base-group with transfer-groups starts with less total potential energy than in (b) or (c)—not as high on the group-transfer potential scale—the difference in group-transfer potential between base-group 1 and base-group 2 is the greatest. The transfer-group, in essence, has the greatest distance to fall.

Differences in group-transfer potential is a source of usable energy

In Chapter 2, I welded the connection between something moving in a coherent direction and usable energy. Here, I emphasize that any source of usable energy acts as a **fuel**—is put to use—whenever that direction is used to influence the direction of something else. Wind, for example, is a source of usable energy. Air molecules are moving across space with a coherent direction. And this usable energy source can be put to use through collisions. Windmills are fueled in this way. The fan-shaped structure is shaped such that it spins when the coherently moving air molecules known as wind collide into its blades.

Group-transfer reactions can also generate a source of usable energy. They too can generate a coherent direction of movement. To see how, let's return to the book-transfer example. If my hand is stronger than yours is—that is, it has lower book-transfer potential—the book can move from me to you, but not the reverse. The movement is thus directional and hence potentially usable. As it turns out, such directional movement—a transfer-group being passed from a base-group with high group-transfer potential to one with lower group-transfer potential—is used as a fuel in a much different way than wind powers a windmill. Transfer-groups, as they move from one molecule to the next, are not colliding into things along their way. I wait, however, to say more because the means by which group-transfer reactions are used to power certain activities is best explained through the specific examples developed later.

Oxidation-Reduction Reactions as Group-Transfer Reactions

In many chemical reactions, electrons are lost from a molecule. Recall from Chapter 9 that an atom is **oxidized** if it undergoes a decreased association with an electron, and losing an electron certainly qualifies as a decreased electron association. The term *oxidation* applies to the molecule as a whole if the oxidized atom is part of a molecule and the rest of the molecule is unchanged. But that is only half the story. Electrons do not just fly off into space. They can be lost from a molecule only if they move to an atom in a different molecule. The molecule picking up the electron is **reduced**; it has an increased association with an electron. An oxidation reaction is, thus, always accompanied by a reduction reaction. Stated differently, when one molecule is oxidized another must be reduced. I encourage you to remember that fact.

This one-can't-happen-without-the-other coupling has lead to a combined and abbreviated name. Oxidation-reduction reactions go by the name **redox reactions**.

The important point here is that redox reactions certainly qualify as group-transfer reactions. Electrons are the transfer-group; they are transferred from one molecule to the next. The molecules donating or accepting electrons are the base-groups. The only sticky point in this representation is that the transfer-group in some redox reactions includes more than just electrons. Due to their opposite charge, a positively charged proton often accompanies a transferred electron. The transfer-group in such cases is a hydrogen atom. Why? One electron and one proton, in total, is one hydrogen atom.

The terms *reduced* and *oxidized* may even make more sense from a group-transfer perspective. They signify whether a base-group does or does not have a transfer-group attached. A base-group with transferable electrons (and perhaps accompanying protons) attached is said to be the **reduced form**, or just **reduced**. On the other hand, a base-group lacking transferable electrons is said to be in its **oxidized form**, or just **oxidized**.

Getting redox reactions to go

Whether a base-group is in its reduced or oxidized form affects the role it can play in a redox reaction. This makes sense. A molecule cannot give up a transfer-group unless it has one, and it cannot accept a transfer-group once it already has one. Reduced base-groups thus can serve as an electron donor, but not as an electron acceptor. Oxidized base-groups, alternatively, can only serve in the opposite role. It can accept electrons, but it cannot donate them.

The role a base-group can play in redox reactions is also affected by its redox potential. Like the previous hand-strength book-transfer potential example, different redox base-groups hold potentially transferred electrons more or less tightly and thus have different potentials to transfer or to accept electrons. **Redox potential**, **reducing power**, or **reductive power** are the names used to discuss the relative strength with which these different base-groups grab onto transferable electrons. And like with book-transfers, a redox reaction is energetically favorable only if the base-group donating electrons has a higher redox potential than the base-group accepting electrons. Only then are the electrons "falling" from a less stable (more energy) to a more stable (less energy) arrangement.

Redox reactions can, thus, unfold only if the base-group with the higher redox potential starts out reduced and the other base-group starts out oxidized. The reduced molecule has electrons to donate, whereas the oxidized molecule has a place to accept them, and the transfer would be energetically favorable. Note that as the transfer occurs, the state of each molecule switches. As it gives up its transferable electrons, the reduced molecule becomes oxidized. The oxidized molecule, as it accepts electrons, becomes reduced (see Figure 14-4).

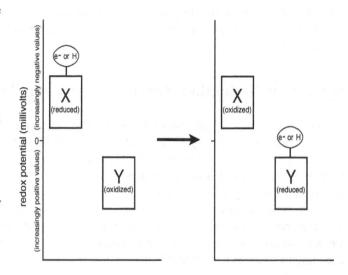

Overall, the higher a base-group's redox potential, the better it can act as an electron donor, but the worse it is as an electron acceptor. Base-groups (in the reduced state) with higher redox potential can better act as the donor in an energetically favorable electron transfer because there will be relatively more base-groups with a lower redox potential. This is also why base-groups higher on the redox scale are worse electron acceptors. When oxidized, they can potentially accept electrons only from the increasingly scarce number of base groups with even higher redox potential.

Figure 14-4. An energetically favorable redox reaction. In the course of the reaction base-group X, which starts out reduced, is oxidized, and base-group Y, which starts out oxidized, is reduced.

The flip side is that the lower a base-group's redox potential, the worse an electron donor it is—fewer base-groups have even lower redox potential—and the better it is as an electron acceptor—more base-groups have higher redox potential.

Figure 14-5 provides a check of your understanding of redox reactions. None of the setups depicted will result in a redox reaction. Make sure you understand why.

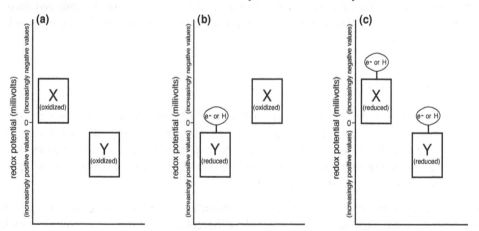

Figure 14-5. Three settings that will not lead to a redox reaction. In (a), there is no transfer-group to be transferred. In (b), the transfer is energetically unfavorable. In (c), both base-groups are reduced—contains a transfer-group—so base-group Y has no room to accept the transfer-group from base-group X.

A familiar example

Have you ever wondered why oxygen needs to be present for wood, gasoline, natural gas, or any other of our commonly used fuels to burn?

Burning, to a chemist, is a redox reaction. Electrons are donated from molecules with higher redox potential to molecules with lower redox potential. So only if both molecules are in place—a high redox potential molecule in the reduced form and a low redox potential molecule in the oxidized form—can burning happen. The PE released during such transfer is converted into heat and light—the warm flicker of a fire.

Wood, gasoline, and natural gas fill one of these roles. They are the molecules able to burn. That is, they are all molecules in the reduced form with high redox potential. Molecular oxygen, on the other hand, fills the other role. It is a molecule in the oxidized form with very low redox potential. In fact, on the redox scale, molecular oxygen is about as low as it goes. Energetically, electrons can thus fall a long way as they are transferred from one of the aforementioned fuel molecules. With such a far drop, the reaction, as you know, can be potentially explosive.

When molecular oxygen accepts electrons, protons tend to follow along. In other words, hydrogens are added on to oxygen. What is the resulting molecule? What is the reduced form of oxygen? What is the molecule formed when a couple of hydrogens are added to an oxygen atom? Water. Water is an end product of fire. This raises a question that I will leave you to ponder: Why does a molecule formed during fire also put out fire?

The other major output formed during a fire burning any of the aforementioned fuels is carbon dioxide. Wood is mostly made up of cellulose—a polymer of glucose. So wood is mostly sugar, and sugars are composed of carbon, hydrogen, and oxygen. Natural gas and gasoline are hydrocarbons, which are molecules made up of carbon and hydrogen. During a burning reaction, the hydrogens are transferred to molecular oxygen to form water molecules. In essence, the carbon atoms in sugars or hydrocarbons are being oxidized. In the process, oxygen begins to replace transferred hydrogens, which, if the oxidation is complete, results in the formation of carbon dioxide.

Some details on the measurement of redox potential

The topic of redox reactions is often put under the heading of electrochemistry because electricity is the movement of electrons. So it should, at least intuitively, make sense when I say that redox potential is measured in terms of **electric potential**—the potential for movement of electrons—or **volts**. The volts generated in any redox reaction is the amount of PE converted to KE, which is the difference in redox potential between the two molecules involved in the reaction. Because the amount of energy released in individual reactions is so small, the released voltage is usually expressed in millivolts (one thousand of a volt).

Although the redox potential scale works like any other—the higher a molecule is on the scale, the higher its redox potential—closer examination reveals a few potentially confusing features. In an attempt to prevent some later puzzling when this scale shows up in graphs, I will try to explain these quirky features.

The first problem is the location of the zero. We tend to think of zero resting at the bottom of a scale. Here the zero often shows up in the middle. The reason is that redox potential of any base-group is measured relative to a reference level. To measure redox potential of different molecules, one molecule is assigned the redox potential of zero under some standardized set of conditions. This molecule is the benchmark against which the redox potential of all other molecules is measured. And because molecules fall both above and below this reference molecule, zero is in the middle of the scale.

A familiar example of measurement by reference level is elevation. The reference level is sea level. That is, sea level is assigned the elevation of zero. Some other landmark could have been chosen, but the sea for many good reasons was picked. All other elevations on planet Earth are measured in terms of their deviation from sea level.

Measuring all elevations in reference to sea level makes it easy to compare the elevations of different geographic locations. For example, Mt. Everest is the tallest mountain not because it is the mountain with the greatest distance between its base and its top—the volcano that rises out of the sea to form the Hawaiian island known as Hawaii holds that distinction—but because its sticks up farther past sea level than any other mountain in the world. Using this reference measurement, it is easy to figure out how much taller Mt. Everest is than any other mountain of interest. It is simply the difference in the heights above sea level.

The second quirky feature of the redox scale is that it appears to be numbered backward. We tend to expect that as you go up any scale, the numbers become increasingly positive. That is not the case with the redox scale. Molecules with higher redox potential than the reference molecule are assigned an increasing negative value, whereas molecules with lower redox potential than the reference molecule are assigned an increasing positive value.

Only by knowing what is being measured do these backward-seeming values make sense. It is the change in chemical (potential) energy during a redox reaction with the reference molecule that is being measured. Energy-releasing reactions—ones where the molecule in question has a higher redox potential than the reference molecule—will thus have a negative value because there is a net loss in PE. And the size of the negative value increases as the difference in each molecule's PE increases. Alternatively, if a redox reaction with the reference molecule requires a net input of energy, then there is a net gain in PE, hence a positive value. Overall, a negative value means that the reaction is energetically favorable, whereas a positive value means that it is **not** energetically favorable.

Another way to remember these seemingly backward values is to think of the positive and negative poles of a battery. A battery uses redox reactions to create a flow of electrons. When connected by an electron conductor such as a wire, electrons flow from the negative pole to the positive pole. That is, the pole with the higher redox potential is the negative pole. Just as electrons tend to flow from the negative pole of batteries, they tend to flow from the molecules with the more negative redox potential.

The Fuel of Reductive Biosynthesis—NADPH

Commonly in biosynthesis, the starting molecules are more oxidized than the biomolecules to be built. Further reduction, through the addition of electrons or more generally hydrogen atoms, thus must take place along the way—a process called reductive biosynthesis. We already saw such an addition of hydrogens in both the Calvin–Benson cycle and nitrogen fixation. The hydrogens added to molecules, however, must come from somewhere. This is where NADPH enters the picture. When reductive biosynthesis takes place in cells, it is the most commonly used hydrogen source. Its usefulness in such a role stems from the fact that it holds potentially donated hydrogens in a high enough energy state that hydrogens readily move from NADPH to the molecule being reduced and not vice versa. In other words, NADPH is a base-group ($NADP^+$) loaded with a readily transferable hydrogen (plus an additional electron—discussed further later). (Note: NADPH was the source of reductive power used in the Calvin–Benson cycle but not in nitrogen fixation. In nitrogen fixation, a molecule with even higher reductive power was needed.)

Stating that NADPH is the fuel used in reductive biosynthesis has a particular meaning. The reductive part of this description simply states that the transfer-group is electrons. But why is it called a fuel? As mentioned earlier, fuels can influence direction of an occurrence. Because NADPH has relatively high redox potential, the flow of its transfer-group will move away from NADPH and onto other molecules (except in those rare cases where molecules have even higher redox potential than NADPH). Stated differently, a reductive fuel is a good hydrogen source, not only because it has a hydrogen (plus an additional electron) to give up, but also the movement of hydrogens away from the source will be energetically favorable. If this seems too simple, then . . . good!

The reason that NADPH is considered the major fuel of reductive biosynthesis goes further. Hydrogen atoms are added onto many different molecules in many different metabolic pathways within a cell. Each of these redox reactions requires not only a sufficiently energetic hydrogen source, but also an enzyme able to catalyze the reaction. To work, the enzyme must have the right shape to grab both the hydrogen source and the molecule to which hydrogen is added. A unique hydrogen source could be grabbed in each of the different redox reactions. It would, however, be a complex way of doing things. The cell would have to come up with many different reductive fuels, all performing, in essence, the same job. A much simpler scenario would be each of the different enzymes using the same hydrogen source. As you might expect, life evolved along the simpler pathway. NADPH is the hydrogen source used by nearly all the different enzymes catalyzing redox reactions within cells. It is, thus, the major reductive fuel.

A closer look at NADPH

Structurally, the core of this molecule is the NAD$^+$. NAD$^+$ is made from joining two ribonucleotides as indicated by the D in the acronym. D stands for **di**nucleotide. This fuel molecule being made from nucleotides—which we first discussed as monomers of DNA and RNA—point to the fact that in biology, molecules are often used in more than one way. It is another example of complexity arising from simpler beginnings. NA of NAD names the nitrogenous base component of these two ribonucleotides. The letter A stands for adenine, so one ribonucleotide contains adenine. The N, on the other hand, stands for a nitrogen-containing compound that has not come up before—**nicotinamide**, which is also called **niacin**. The other ribonucleotide thus contains nicotinamide. (You may have noticed niacin listed on a vitamin tablet label, on the side of a cereal box, or other nutritional labels. Labeling it a vitamin is a misnomer in that it is not an essential nutrient because you can synthesize it from the amino acid tryptophan, but a dietary supply is useful, especially if one's tryptophan supply is low. Why do you need it? So you can make NAD.)

NAD is a base-group, or to be more accurate NAD$^+$ is a base-group. The transfer group is two electrons followed by a proton—or stated differently, a hydrogen atom (one electron and one proton) plus an additional electron, or what chemists call a **hydride ion** (H$^-$). We are thus talking about redox reactions here. Add a hydride ion to NAD$^+$ and one gets NADH. The positive charge—due to an imbalance of one extra proton—disappears because the extra electron in the transfer group now balances it. The H added to the end of NADH represents the hydrogen in the transfer group. NADH is thus a reduced molecule (base-group with transfer group attached), whereas NAD$^+$ is the oxidized form (just the base-group; see Figure 14-6).

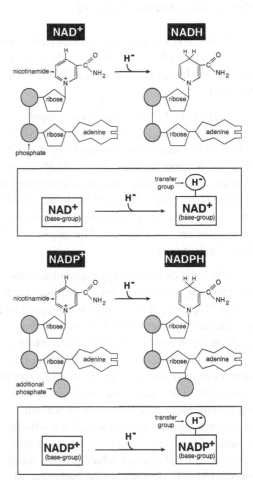

Figure 14-6. Structural representation of NAD$^+$ being converted to NADH, and NADP$^+$ being converted to NADPH, and vice versa. Inside boxes, these same two transitions are shown in terms of base-groups and transfer-groups.

What about the P? NADH and NADPH are the same except for the additional phosphate stuck on NADPH (see Figure 14-6). Although the addition of this phosphate represents a minor structural change, the change has biological significance. Both NADH and NADPH are used in cells as electron (hydrogen) donors. They are good at this role due to their relatively high redox potential. But many cells use these donated electrons in more than one way. The extra phosphate thus serves as a tag. Enzymes that grab NADH will not grab NADPH, and vice versa. NADH with an extra phosphate (NADPH or what I call NAD with a P) is used mostly in one way—that is, as a fuel in reductive biosynthesis. NADH without an extra phosphate (or NAD without a P) is used mainly in another way that we have yet to discuss. Tagging the same molecule for different uses creates a means to regulate these different pathways. Control the relative production of NADPH and NADH and you control the pathways that use one form or the other.

How cells generate NADPH

If NADPH is major fuel in reductive biosynthesis, then cells must have some means to maintain a continual supply. In broad terms, there are two steps involved in putting together NADPH. The first is the assembly of the base-group NADP⁺. The second is adding on a hydride ion to reduce NADP⁺ to NADPH.

Cells make NADP⁺ through a complex metabolic pathway involving many steps. It involves making certain nucleotides and then putting these together with the right modifications to end up with NADP⁺. But beyond recognizing that it happens, the synthesis of the base-group is not a focus here—with good reason. A new NADP⁺ is not built every time a new NADPH molecule is assembled. Instead, the base-group portion of this molecule is used over and over. The cycle is as follows: A hydride ion is attached to NADP⁺ to become NADPH. NADPH is then grabbed by one of the many enzymes that catalyze redox reactions and used as a hydrogen source. After donating its hydride ion it once again becomes NADP⁺. The sequence of events is then repeated. It is another example of a cell-level nutrient cycle.

The logic of why energy metabolism must involve material cycles is easy to understand. As we have already stated, to maintain function a cell cannot just maintain a flow of usable energy through it some of the time; it must maintain a supply of usable energy all the time. Consequently, the supply of material arrangements involved in capturing, storing, and releasing energy must keep up. In contrast to the alternative of using each arrangement of matter involved once and then replacing it, the fastest and most efficient way of maintaining this supply of needed material arrangements is to use the same ones over and over. Compare, for example, the alternatives in terms of NADP⁺. In contrast to using an NADP⁺ many times after first building it, building a new NADP⁺ from scratch every time one was needed would not only be a waste of the energy and materials used in its construction, but also the whole process would be considerably slower because gathering all the energy and materials needed to build it would take time. Continue to watch for the many more examples of cell-level material (nutrient) cycles that pop up throughout the discussion of energy metabolism

To reduce NADP⁺ to NADPH, a cell needs two things. Most significant, the cell must come up with a reduced molecule with even higher redox potential than NADP⁺. Only

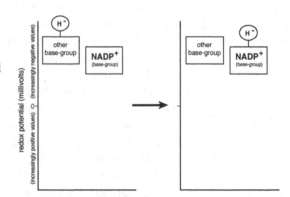

Figure 14-7. The generation of NADPH. A base-group with even higher redox potential transfers a hydride ion (H⁻) to NADP⁺.

then would the needed electron transfer be energetically favorable (see Figure 14-7). Plus an enzyme capable of facilitating the reaction must be present.

Although the details are not laid out until the next chapter, the two general ways that cells come up with reduced molecules with higher redox potential than $NADP^+$ are worth mentioning now. First, and in a sense foremost, light energy can boost the redox potential of certain molecules. Some cells use this fact to generate a reduced molecule with sufficient redox potential to power the reduction of $NADP^+$. Second, a cell can get some molecule from its environment with sufficient redox potential to power the reduction of $NADP^+$. Certain reduced carbon molecules such as sugars or fatty acids can play this role, as can hydrogen gas (H_2), which may be present in anaerobic (without oxygen) environments.

Phosphate-Transfer Reactions

Besides electrons, there is another important transfer-group in the workings of life. It is known as a phosphate. In total, a phosphate consists of three oxygen atoms surrounding a central phosphorus atom (PO_3^{2-}). The two negative charges result from an excess of two electrons in the arrangement.

As the transfer-group changes (from electrons to phosphates) so do the terms describing the transfer. As a redox reaction refers to the transfer of electrons, a **phosphorylation reaction** (or just phosphorylation) refers to the transfer of phosphate from one molecule to another. To say a molecule has been **phosphorylated** is equivalent in a redox reaction to say a molecule has been reduced. Both refer to a molecule (a base-group) that has just been passed a transfer-group. Similarly, **phosphorylation potential** is the conceptual equivalent of redox potential. Both refer to the group-transfer potential of the different molecules (base-groups). The important point thus remains the same. A transfer of a phosphate from one molecule to another is energetically favorable only if the phosphorylation potential of the molecule donating the phosphate is higher than the molecule accepting the phosphate. Furthermore, the greater the difference in phosphorylation potential between two molecules, the greater the amount of chemical (potential) energy that is converted to KE during the transfer.

To continue our discussion of energy metabolism, it is important to understand the conceptual similarities between electron-transfer and phosphate-transfer reactions outlined earlier. It is equally important to understand that conceptual similarity does not make them the same thing. When the transfer-group changes, so does the very nature of the reaction. A molecule loaded with a phosphate with high phosphorylation potential is a different form of chemical energy than a reduced molecule with high redox potential. And the big topic here is how the directional movement of phosphates along molecules with increasingly lower phosphorylation potential is used as an energy source.

Orthophosphate

Sometimes a good place to start is at the bottom. Here we find a molecule termed orthophosphate ($HOPO_3^{2-}$)—which, because it is also known as inorganic phosphate, commonly goes by the shorthand designation $\mathbf{P_i}$ (pronounced P sub i, where the *i* stands for inorganic). It is the phosphate-containing molecule with the lowest phosphorylation potential. Transferring a phosphate from orthophosphate to any other molecule is thus energetically **unfavorable**. Due to the reciprocal nature of energetics, this also means that the transfer of a phosphate from any other molecule to the precursor of orthophosphate is energetically favorable.

In chemistry speak: Orthophosphate is a product of hydrolysis of a phosphate-containing molecule. Hydrolysis (water breaking) is any chemical reaction where a covalent bond is cleaved with the accompanying addition of water, —H being added to one product of the cleavage and —OH to the other. Hydrolysis of a phosphate-containing molecule breaks the covalent bond holding the phosphate to the rest of the molecule. The phosphate then joins with the OH group from water (plus an additional electron) to form orthophosphate (Figure 14-8).

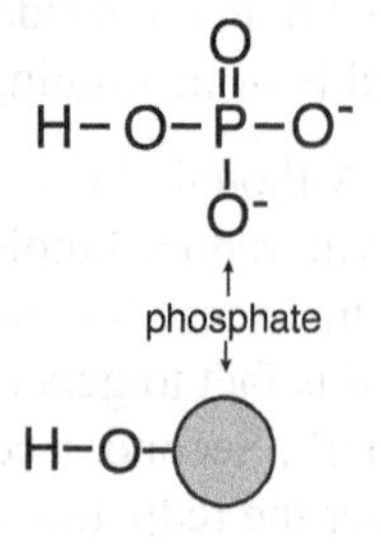

There is a problem with the previous description of orthophosphate formation, however. It fails to keep your eye on the ball. When speaking of hydrolysis, it is easy to lose sight of the phosphate-transfer part of the reaction. Orthophosphate is formed by the transfer of a phosphate from some other molecule to water. So know that water is being phosphorylated whenever you read or hear someone speaking about the hydrolysis of ATP (or any other phosphorylated molecule). Also know that the reaction is energetically favorable because in terms of phosphorylation potential, water sits at the bottom of the scale.

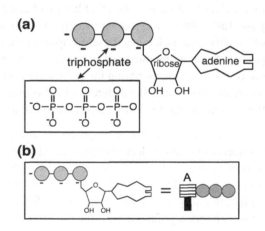

Figure 14-8. Two representations of orthophosphate (P_i).

ATP

Like with electrons discussed earlier, it is the directional movement of phosphates from molecules with higher phosphorylation potential to ones with lower phosphorylation potential that cells use as an energy source. Similarly, the phosphorylated molecule identified as a common fuel must have the following two properties: (1) It must have relatively high phosphorylation potential, and (2) many different enzymes catalyzing phosphate-transfer reactions must be able to use it as a phosphate source. The molecule that best fits this bill is known as ATP (adenosine triphosphate).

Although not highlighted specifically, ATP's basic structure was discussed in Chapter 11. All ribonucleotides and deoxyribonucleotides were said to be activated when two more phosphates—leading to a total of three—were stuck on the molecule. Only activated nucleotides contain enough PE to make their polymerization into RNA or DNA energetically favorable. ATP is one of eight different forms of activated nucleotides. Specifically, it is the ribonucleotide triphosphate containing the nitrogenous base adenine (Figure 14-9).

How to divide ATP into a base-group and a transfer-group is not completely straightforward. The transfer-group is clear—it is phosphate. The problem is what to do with the second phosphate in the three-phosphate string. In many phosphate-transfer reactions involving ATP, only one phosphate is transferred. Two phosphates are thus left behind; hence ADP (adenosine **di**phosphate) qualifies as a base-group. But in other reactions, the second phosphate is transferred as well, leaving behind AMP (adenosine **mono**phosphate). It too then qualifies as a base-group. Conceptually, this poses no problem other than needing to recognize that the base-group of ATP varies with the reaction. Here we concentrate on only single phosphate transfers. ADP will thus be our designated base-group.

Figure 14-9. (a) A simplied structural representation of ATP. Note that we have seen ATP before—it is an activated ribonocleotide. (b) The cartoon form of ATP, first seen in chapter 11, used in other figures in this chapter.

A nice thing about ATP is that understanding the finer points of chemistry, such as resonance stability, is not needed to have some sense of why ATP has relatively high phosphorylation potential. High phosphorylation potential results when it is easier to remove a phosphate than add a phosphate back on. If so, donating a transfer-group is favored over accepting a transfer-group. Why would this be true for ATP? Each phosphate has at least one negative charge, and like charges create a repulsive force (which is not the same as a revoltingly gross force). Two forces are thus acting on the outer two phosphates in an ATP triphosphate string. Covalent bonds hold the phosphates together. Charge repulsion is acting to pry the phosphates apart. Due to these opposing forces, the terminal phosphates are not held as tightly. They can be pulled off easier than they can be put back on. In a sense, the triphosphate string is like a wound-up spring held together by a latch. The spring pushes out, and the latch pulls in. The stored tension generated is PE. And if the latch ever breaks, the spring will spring forth, converting this PE into KE.

An interesting aside: Activated ribonucleotides other than ATP, such as GTP or UTP, have also been found to fuel certain cellular activities. ATP receives most of the attention solely because it is the most prominent one used. Interestingly, however, use of activated deoxyribonucleotides as fuels is conspicuously absent. Evolutionary history may well explain this fact. Many argue that reproduction first revolved around RNA, with the involvement of DNA and proteins coming later. If so, activated ribonucleotides would have been available at the start. And this availability would have set the stage for the evolution of processes fueled by phosphate-transfer from an activated ribonucleotide. This scenario, of course, does not answer why ATP is used more than any other activated ribonucleotide. And I know of no answer. Perhaps ATP has properties that make it more conducive to this role than other ribonucleotides, although I am not aware of them. Maybe chance had a lot to do with it. ATP is no better or no worse, but in the history of Life it just happened to be in the right place at the right time.

How ATP Is Used as a Fuel

ATP powers every move that you have ever made, every thought you have ever had, as well as other activities going on inside you that you may have never even thought to think about. And your cells are no exception; ATP seems to be the major power source for all cells on this planet. No doubt about it, ATP is a big topic.

The directional movement of phosphates from ATP to molecules with increasingly lower phosphate-transfer potential is known specifically to power four main activities: protein regulation (turning certain proteins on and off), active transport, biosynthesis, and the generation of movement. Here, I try to give you at least a sense of how ATP fuels each of these processes.

ATP can power the turning on and off of proteins

Usable energy may be needed to turn something on or off. Just think of a light switch in the off position. A directional force is needed to turn the switch on. A force in the opposite

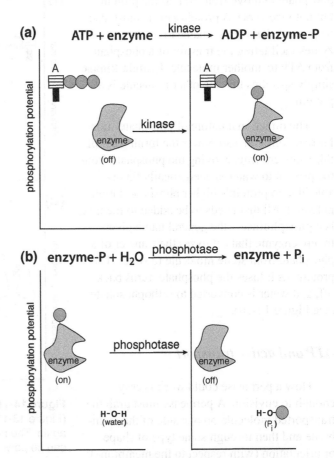

Figure 14-10. The turning on and then turning off of an enzyme is accomplished by two energetically favorable phosphate-transfer reactions. In (a), phosphate is transferred from ATP to an enzyme turning it on. In (b), the phosphate is transferred from the enzyme to water (forming orthophosphate) turning it back off.

direction is needed to turn it back off. Similarly, directional phosphate-transfer is used commonly to turn on and off proteins.

We know from the last chapter that a protein's functional capacity can be turned on or off by changing the protein's shape. There, noncovalent binding of a ligand induced the shape change. Due to the two negative charges, covalently linking a phosphate to one of a protein's amino acids can also affect a protein's overall shape. Most important, introducing a pull on surrounding positively charged regions of the protein and a push on surrounding negatively charged regions, the newly positioned charges could result in a protein's active site being bent into or out of a functional shape (turning it on or off, respectively).

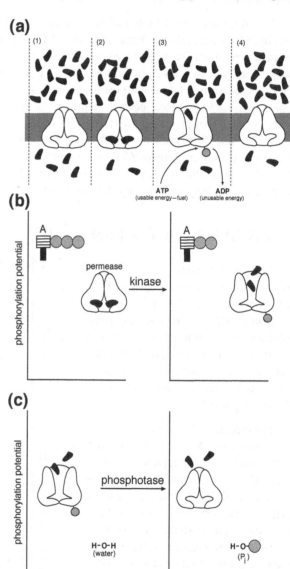

Consider, for instance, an enzyme that is turned on when a phosphate is attached and turned off otherwise. So long as ATP has higher phosphorylation potential than the protein, it can then power the turning on of this protein. It is energetically favorable for a phosphate to move from ATP to the protein, but not vice versa. A protein kinase must also be present. **Kinase** is a name given to any enzymes facilitating the transfer of a phosphate from ATP to another molecule. **Protein kinase** simply specifies that the other molecule is a protein.

The directional nature of phosphate-transfer reactions can also power the turning off of this same enzyme. Moving the phosphate from the protein to water is energetically favorable, due to protein's higher phosphorylation potential. All that needs to be added to the mix is a **phosphotase**—the general name given to any enzyme that catalyzes the transfer of a phosphate from some molecule to water. The protein, as it loses the phosphate, turns back off, and water is converted to orthophosphate (see Figure 14-10).

ATP and active transport

How a permease could work is easy enough to envision. A permease must grab the transported molecule on one side of the membrane and then through some type of shape or orientation (with respect to the membrane) change, escort the molecule to the other side. For this transport to be directional, it must grab molecules on one side of the membrane more often than on the other. The presence of a concentration gradient across this membrane

Figure 14-11. In (a), the illustration used in Chapter 13 (Figure 13-13) to first introduce active transport is shown again. The next two panels illustrate how active transport can be powered by two energetically favorable phosphate-transfer reactions. In (b), a phosphate is transferred from ATP to a permease, changing its shape such that it squeezes the specific molecules picked up on a membrane's low concentration side to the high concentration side. In (c), the phosphate is transferred from the enzyme to water, resulting in the permease returning to the shape able to pick up more molecules on the low concentration side.

is enough to make this happen because the permease will be exposed to the molecule it transports more often on one side of the membrane than the other. As a consequence, the permease will generate a net direction of flow—more molecules will be transported from the higher concentration side to the lower concentration side than vice versa. I just described the concept of facilitated diffusion that was introduced in Chapter 12.

Active transport introduces a dilemma. The permease must somehow continue to grab molecules on the low concentration side and move them across the membrane, while avoiding grabbing (and transporting) molecules from the high concentration side. In other words, the permease must interact with the transportable molecules on the low concentration side differently than it interacts with them on the high concentration side. How could a protein do that? One option is for the permease to take on different shapes on the two sides of the membrane. Specifically, it could take on a shape that tends to grab molecules on the low concentration side and a shape that tends to release molecules on the high concentration side. Furthermore, if this shape change continued to oscillate back and forth, the permease would act as a molecular pump. It would continually transport molecules against the concentration gradient. But such shape oscillations are not possible unless something else intervenes. With active transport, that something else is the directional movement of phosphates from ATP to the permease and then from the permease to water.

Here is the general idea. A permease's shape is altered by the initial transfer of a phosphate from ATP in a way that the permease facilitates the movement of some molecule from the low concentration side to the high concentration side. Then, before the reverse movement could also happen, the added phosphate is transferred to water. The permease returns to its original shape, which is unable to transfer molecules across the membrane in either direction. As long as an ATP supply is available, the same series of shape change could start again and again. The net result is the pumping of molecules from the low concentration side of the membrane to the high concentration side. Figure 14-11 illustrates a specific example of this general idea.

ATP and biosynthesis

The chemical reactions of biosynthesis have a fundamental problem: They tend to go the wrong way. Because they are energetically unfavorable, these reactions tend to go the other way, in the energetically favorable direction. A usable energy source is thus needed to push these reactions in the biologically important direction. And once again, the movement of phosphate from ATP to an intermediate molecule and then to water is the directional movement commonly tapped to make this happen.

How can a usable energy source turn a reaction around? By converting an energetically unfavorable reaction into an energetically favorable one. A reaction is energetically unfavorable when the molecules entering the reaction have less PE than the products of the reactions. So the basic means to

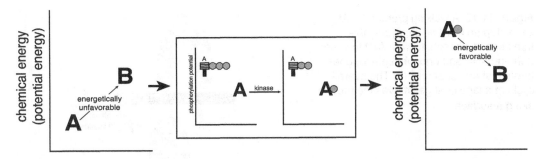

Figure 14-12. The chemical reaction A to B would not tend to happen because it is energetically unfavorable. The phosphorylation of A, however, increases its chemical energy to the point that the reaction is now energetically favorable.

convert an energetically unfavorable reaction to an energetically favorable one is to increase the potential (chemical) energy of the molecules entering the reaction enough to tip the energy scale so that what constitutes "downhill" is reversed. Phosphorylating molecules can help do just that (see Figure 14-12). The addition of a phosphate from ATP "juices up" a molecule by increasing its chemical energy. And in cases where adding one phosphate is not enough, a second or even a third phosphate can be added, which further increases a molecule's chemical energy.

The next step is to remove any newly added phosphates as the reaction proceeds by transferring them to water. Then much of the added PE is secondarily lost (converted to KE) because orthophosphate has the least PE of any phosphorylated molecule.

The basic means by which ATP can fuel motion

Think for a moment about how you walk. First a change in shape is involved. Right? At one step your right leg is in front and your left leg is behind. At the next step, the opposite is true—your left leg is in front and your right leg is behind. Next, the transition between the different shapes cannot involve reverses. For example, you are not going anywhere if a continual change in the relative position of your two front legs occurs by just moving your right leg back and forth—that is, continually reversing the movement direction of your right leg. Movement depends on a cyclic course of shape changes. The right leg must move forward, followed by the left leg moving forward, followed again by the right leg moving forward, and so on. And finally, you must be connected to the ground by gravity. Only then do you have a surface to move along. Someone generating a walking motion while hoisted up in the air goes nowhere.

(a)

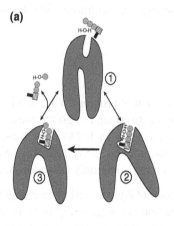

(b)

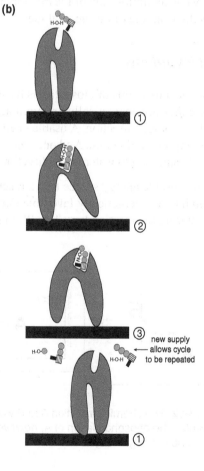

Figure 14-13. A walking protein. (a) At each step an enzyme catalyzing the transfer of a phosphate from ATP to water (forming ADP and orthophosphate) goes through shape changes. (b) The overall cycle of shape changes moves the protein along a surface.

I bring up walking because at the cellular level, getting a protein, in essence, to walk commonly generates motion. And these so-called **walking proteins** or **protein motors** work by the same rules. They move along some substrate by undergoing a cyclic transition between shapes. A fuel is needed to keep the protein's shape changes cyclic—that is, to prevent shape-changes from just reversing back and forth.

ATP is the fuel used. In comparison to the previous three scenarios, however, how ATP is used has a slightly different twist. Instead of a phosphate being passed from ATP to an intermediate molecule and then to water, here a phosphate moves directly from ATP to water. The cycle of shape-change is thus not a result of continually phosphorylating and then dephosphorylating the walking protein.

How does a walking protein work? Walking proteins are all enzymes that change shape during the course of catalyzing the hydrolysis of ATP—the transfer of a phosphate from ATP to water. Figure 14-13(a), for example, illustrates a protein changing shape at each of the three major steps in such an enzyme's action: when it first binds with the reactants (ATP and water), when the chemical reaction takes place (phosphate transfer), and when the final products (ADP and orthophosphate) are released. Put these three steps into a continually cycling sequence and this protein performs a walking motion. Add a surface that it will bind to and release from during the course of this cycle, and it will move (see Figure 14-13(b)).

The last thing to add is how ATP keeps these steps moving forward—that is, in a continually cycling sequence. Of these three steps, only one has a specific direction—the chemical reaction. Due to the large difference in phosphorylation potential, a phosphate will move from ATP to water (resulting in ADP and orthophosphate), but not the reverse. The other two steps—the enzyme binding with (step 1) or releasing (step 3) molecules—have no distinct direction. They go back and forth with equal probability. But one directional step is all that is needed to generate a directional cycle. Just think about it. To keep the cycle from moving forward, the other two steps would have to go backward as fast as the directional step went forward. But that would mean the other steps also have a distinct direction—the reverse direction—and I already stated that these other steps are direction neutral.

How Cells Generate ATP

Consider the following fact: It is estimated that an average adult human male breaks down about 150,000 grams—over 300 pounds—of ATP every day (every 24 hours). Such a fact tends to raise people's eyebrows. Average human males do not weigh 300 pounds. They surely do not eat (and output) 300 pounds every day. So how could they ever use 300 pounds of ATP every day of every month of every year? To help you think about this, let me add one more fact: At any one moment, spread throughout the cells making up its body, an average human male has only around 5 grams of ATP in total.

Did I hear someone bring up the nutrient cycling idea again? If I didn't, I should have. In all the previous descriptions of ATP fueling activities, phosphates removed from ATP were eventually transferred to water. Because these remaining pieces—ADP and the phosphate in orthophosphate—are not lost from cells, they are available to be built into an ATP once again. And that is what happens. An ATP molecule is commonly broken into ADP and P_i within a minute of its formation. Shortly thereafter, the cell pulls the phosphate off water and sticks it back on ADP to form a new ATP (see Figure 14-14). Run this cycle quickly and continually, and a mind-boggling amount of ATP can be used and correspondingly put back together within a day.

To run this ATP cycle, a cell must overcome a distinct obstacle—one-half of the cycle (the transfer of a phosphate from water back to ADP to form ATP again) is not energetically favorable. So to make it work, the phosphate on water must somehow be lifted to a higher phosphorylation potential than ATP. Only then would it be energetically favorable for the phosphate to move from P_i to ADP to form

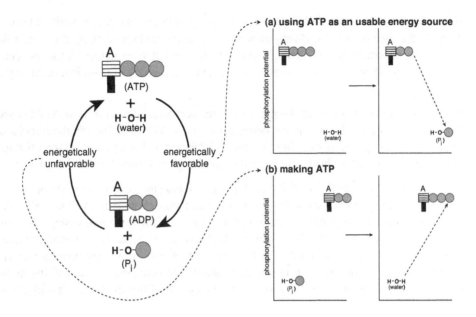

Figure 14-14. The ATP-ADP cycle.

another ATP. (A note: Just like the discussion of NADPH synthesis did not focus on the synthesis of the base-group NADP$^+$, discussion of ATP synthesis does not focus on the synthesis of the base-group ADP. It focuses solely on the reloading of a phosphate on to ADP.)

Cells power the loading of a phosphate back on an ADP to form an ATP by two general means: **substrate-level phosphorylation** and **oxidative phosphorylation**. An important similarity is that the same type of energy source drives both processes. Both use high redox potential, or more specifically, the directional flow of electrons due to differences in redox potential. In other words, in each process the redox potential is converted into phosphorylation potential.

Now take notice because the next point is more important than you might at first realize. As stated earlier, redox potential and phosphorylation potential are distinct forms of chemical energy. So, one cannot be directly converted into the other. Specifically, a molecule with high redox potential cannot, through a group-transfer reaction, result in a molecule with high phosphorylation potential. The transfer-groups are not the same. Consequently, *substrate-level phosphorylation and oxidative phosphorylation must make this chemical energy transformation through indirect means*. Another way to put it, the transformation cannot happen in a single step. Both the multiple steps and the chemistry underlying the types of steps involved add to the difficulty of understanding these processes. Next, however, I lay down only a broad view of what is going on without getting hung up in the chemical details.

Substrate-level phosphorylation

The first cells to generate ATP likely did so by some form of substrate-level phosphorylation. Basically, it involves two steps, with the first one being the key.

The first step involves a transfer-group swap. By passing electrons elsewhere a molecule is able to pick up a phosphate from orthophosphate. Stated more completely, the oxidation of a molecule—a molecule donating electrons to one with lower redox potential—is coupled with the transfer of a phosphate from orthophosphate to the oxidized molecule. The significance of this swap stems from the fact that the newly phosphorylated molecule has high phosphorylation potential, higher than even ATP. So, somehow the energetically favorable flow of electrons away from this molecule is used to hoist the phosphate to a higher energy level. In other words, this is where high redox potential is used to indirectly generate high phosphorylation potential. (Note: The chemical details underlying this swap are beyond my present grasp.)

The second step is much easier to envision. Once a phosphate-containing molecule with higher phosphorylation potential than ATP exists, the transfer of that phosphate to ADP (to form ATP) is energetically favorable.

In the next chapter, I point out a few places where substrate-level phosphorylation occurs, but I will not focus on any details.

Oxidative phosphorylation

Although all cells can generate at least some of their ATP by substrate-level phosphorylation, the evolution of oxidative phosphorylation was a major innovation because it greatly increased the efficiency in which high redox potential could be converted to high phosphorylation potential.

Like substrate-level phosphorylation, the transfer of electrons among molecules with decreasing redox potential is the energy source that indirectly fuels the phosphorylation of ADP. But here the workings are more indirect. Oxidative phosphorylation involves two distinct energy transformations. The first energy transformation uses an electron flow to establish a concentration gradient on opposite sides of a membrane. Hydrogen ions (H^+)—which in essence are simply protons—are moved against the concentration gradient by a pump driven by differences in redox potential. This hydrogen ion pump (or proton pump) is called an **electron transport chain (ETC;** see Figure 14-15). The second energy transformation occurs by a process termed **chemiosmosis**. Here, the hydrogen ion concentration gradient (sometimes called the proton motive force) is converted into high phosphorylation potential. Moving from high to low, a directional flow of hydrogen moves through a membrane-bound protein complex called **ATP synthetase**. ATP synthetase then somehow uses this directional flow to power the transfer of a phosphate from water to ADP to form ATP.

Next I further discuss each of these two distinct energy transformations.

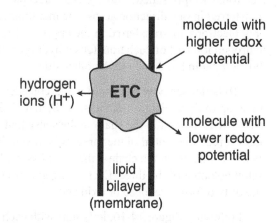

Figure 14-15. An electron transport chain (ETC) uses differences in redox potential to pump hydrogen ions (H^+) across a membrane.

Electron transport chains

Electron transport chains are composed of several different types of molecules embedded in a membrane. These molecules include flavoproteins, iron-sulfur proteins, cytochromes (iron containing porphyrin rings), and quinones. The structural details of these molecules, however, are not the focus here. Yet, some features of their chemical nature are relevant:

• Each is a base-group with either hydrogens (protons and electrons) or solely electrons being their transfer-group. Because the movement of electrons is the unifying theme, I will genericly refer to them as *electron carriers*.

• The redox potential of each electron carriers gradually decreases along the chain. Consequently, a series of energetically favorable redox reactions—a stepwise chain of electron transfers—is possible. The name electron transport chain is thus a good one because it describes what happens.

Electrons entering an ETC are passed from one electron carrier to the next and so on down the line.

Next I develop a general model by which the movement of electrons along a chain of molecules could be used to directly power the movement of protons across a membrane. As we shall see, such a direct mechanism will move one proton for every electron passed along. Because evidence suggests that somewhere around 1.5 to 2 protons are pumped across a membrane per electron, the following discussion is not the whole story. That, however, does not concern me because although it is nice to explain everything, it is more important to begin to understand something. The model allows you to begin to think about how electron transport chains could work.

The general idea is that a series of electron carriers can be converted into a hydrogen ion pump by coupling the orientation of the molecules within a membrane with the fact that some of these electron carriers transfer both electrons and protons (i.e., hydrogens), whereas others transfer only electrons. Simply stated, hydrogens are accepted and then transferred in one direction across the membrane, whereas only electrons are transferred in the opposite direction. The hydrogen ion part of each transferred hydrogen atom is thus left behind to come out the other side.

To better see how this could work, consider an ETC made up of three electron carriers: **A**, **B**, and **C**. Electron carrier **A** is the first in the chain in the sense that it has the highest redox potential of the three. **B** is next in line, and then **C** is the last in the chain—that is, it has the lowest redox potential of the three. Each electron carrier can be in one of two forms: reduced or oxidized.

Following Figure 14-16, let's start with each of these three electron carriers being in an oxidized state. The chain is not initially poised to run. There are no transfer-groups present to pass along. The importance of starting here is that it forces us to ask: From where do electron transport chains get their transfer-group to pass along? The answer is that they get it from some molecule, generically termed an **initial donor**, which is not part of the chain. To act as an initial donor, a molecule must have the following properties:

• It must be in its reduced form so that it has something to transfer.

• It must have higher redox potential than the first electron carrier in the chain so that such transfer is energetically favorable.

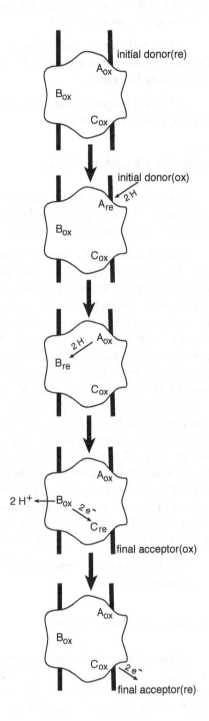

Figure 14-16. The basic model by which a series of redox reactions could be used to directly move hydrogen ions across a membrane. (See text for further explanation.)

• Finally, an enzyme must be present that can catalyze the transfer. That is, it must have the right shape to grab the initial donor.

The chain begins operation when the initial donor reduces electron carrier **A**, leaving the initial donor oxidized. During this redox reaction, two hydrogens are loaded onto electron carrier **A**. The stepwise transfer continues as the two hydrogens are transferred from **A** to **B**. Electron carrier **B** is now reduced, and because it has a higher redox potential than electron carrier **C**, the transfer can continue. The difference is that in the transfer between electron carrier B and electron carrier C, only two electrons are passed. Two hydrogen ions are thus left behind. It is here that the chain acts as a hydrogen ion pump. Due to the orientation of the three electron carriers, these leftover hydrogen ions come out the other side of the membrane. By other side, I mean the side opposite of where they first became incorporated into the chain. Hydrogen ions are pumped across the membrane using the stepwise oxidation of molecules as an energy source. In other words, a directional electron flow is used to move hydrogen ions across a membrane.

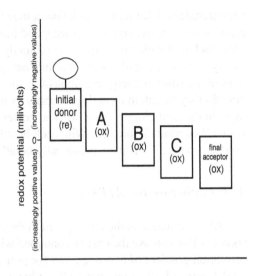

Figure 14-17. The type of arrangement along the redox scale needed for the flow of electrons from the initial donor through the electron transport chain and then on to the final acceptor to be energetically favorable.

We are still, however, not quite done. One more type of molecule, generically called a **final acceptor**, is needed to keep electron transport chains running. Here, in a roundabout way I explain why. When we last left electron carrier **C**, it was still in its reduced form. Suppose for the moment that it stayed that way. What would happen to the continual operation of the ETC? The answer is that it would stop. The whole thing would gum up. In its reduced state, electron carrier **C** could not accept transfer-groups from electron carrier **B**. So once reduced, electron carrier **B** would stay reduced. This only leads to this transfer-group traffic jam to back up even further. Electron carrier **A** is now unable to transfer anything to electron carrier **B**. Once electron carrier **A** becomes reduced, it will also stay reduced, making it unable to accept anything from the initial donor. The flow of electrons along the entire chain would be blocked. And without an electron flow, the pumping of hydrogen ions will also terminate.

For an ETC to continue to operate, the last electron carrier in the chain, which in this case is electron carrier **C**, must be able to transfer its newly accepted electrons on to some other molecule—a **final acceptor**. To work, the final acceptor must be an oxidized nonchain molecule with even lower redox potential than the last electron carrier. To continue to sound like a broken record, only then would the transfer be energetically favorable (see Figure 14-17).

The importance of a continual supply of initial donors and final acceptors to the continual function of the ETC cannot be overemphasized. Each time an initial donor is used, it is used up. Its transfer-group has

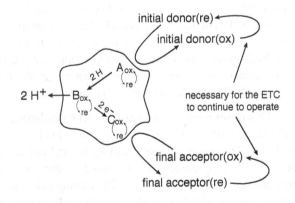

Figure 14-18. An electron transport chain can run repeatedly so long as a supply of reduced initial donors and oxidized final acceptors is maintained.

been transferred. Similarly, each time a transfer group is passed to a final acceptor, it is used up. In its reduced form, it has no room to accept additional transfer-groups. So, to keep the chain running—to keep each of the electron carriers continually oscillating between their oxidized and reduced states—a steady stream of initial donors and final acceptors must continue to come (see Figure 14-18). An important question in energy metabolism is thus: For cells generating ATP by oxidative phosphorylation, how do they maintain a continual supply of initial donors and final acceptors? This will be a major topic in the next chapter. As a preface, however, I suggest that you pause for moment here and feel yourself continually breathe. With each breath you are bringing in a new supply of the final acceptors used by your cells. You are continually breathing in molecular oxygen.

ATP synthetase (or ATPase)

ATP synthetase is the name given to the protein complex that can use the energy contained within a concentration gradient of hydrogen ions (or protons) to build ATP. Figure 14-19 shows that ATP synthetase is composed of two sections known as F_1 (F sub 1) and F_0 (F sub o—the letter, not the number zero). F_1 is sometimes called the head region; it extends out from the membrane. F_0 is sometimes called the tail region; it spans the membrane.

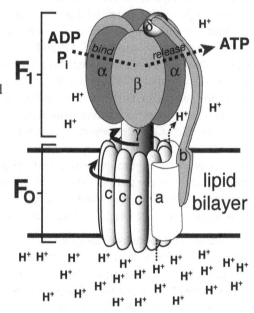

F_1 is composed of nine subunits of five different types: three *betas*, three *alphas*, one *gamma*, one *delta* and one *epsilon* (which is not pictured in Figure 14-19). We are not going to keep track of all these parts, but do notice in Figure 14-19 that the three *betas* and three *alphas* assemble in an alternating fashion into a somewhat cylindrical arrangement. The *beta* subunit is where ATP synthesis actually occurs. It is an interesting enzyme. Like a walking protein, it can catalyze the hydrolysis of ATP—the movement of a phosphate from ATP to water—while undergoing a series of shape or conformational changes in the process. ATP synthetase, on the other hand, uses the fact that through the intervention of an outside force, each of its *beta* subunits can be made to work in the other direction—that is, to make ATP. The force causes each *beta* subunit to reverse the series of shape changes that occur during

Figure 14-19. A simple drawing of ATP synthetase. A proton gradient is used to rotate the membrane-spanning cylindrical arrangement of c subunits in a certain direction, which in turn induces conformation changes in an ATPase enzyme (the beta subunits) in a way that reverses the inherent direction of the reaction—that is, phosphates are transfered from orthophosphate to ADP to form ATP. (See text for more details.)

ATP hydrolysis. This series of conformation changes first facilitates the binding of ADP and P_i, next it positions these molecules in a way that makes the transfer of a phosphate from P_i back to ADP to make an ATP possible, and finally it expels the newly produced ATP.

This raises a question: How does ATP synthetase generate the force that causes each of its *beta* subunits to work in the reverse direction? This is where the membrane-spanning F_0 region comes into play. The major component of F_0 is a cylindrical arrangement of 9 to 12 identical protein subunits—that go by the single letter name **c**—that can rotate within the membrane (while the **a** subunit remains stationary). This potentially rotating cylinder of **c**s is hooked to another F_1 protein subunit called *gamma*, which protrudes up into the F_1 cluster of *alphas* and *betas*. So, whenever the **c**-cylinder rotates, *gamma* also spins and pushes and pulls on each *beta* subunit along the way. The key twist in the story is that spinning *gamma* in one direction leads the *beta* subunits to undergo the series of conformation changes needed to make ATP. On the other hand, spinning it in the other direction only facilitates ATP use.

Next question: What can drive the **c**-cylinder to spin in the direction needed to make ATP? The simplest answer is a concentration gradient of hydrogen ions, where the higher concentration is on the membrane side opposite the F_1 or head region of ATP synthetase (see Figure 14-19). Figure 14-20 sets up the basic idea of how such a concentration gradient can cause the **c**-cylinder to rotate in the ATP-making direction. The subtle but key point is that the overall spin direction is determined by the probability with which protons bind or unbind to **c** subunits in regions 1 and 3. Both binding and unbinding will always be occurring, but when they are in relatively higher concentration on **Side A**, protons will be more likely to bind in region 1 and more likely to unbind in region 3. As a consequence, the **c**-cylinder will tend to rotate in the direction shown in the figure. Think about it! The relatively higher binding rate of protons in region 1 allows the **c** subunits to spin through region 2 more often than region 4, whereas the relatively higher unbinding rate in region 3 allows the **c** subunits to move through region 4 more often than region 2.

To check your understanding, consider how the **c**-cylinder would tend to rotate if the concentration gradient was reversed (higher on **Side B** than **Side A**). The goal is to be able to explain why it would tend to rotate in the opposite direction.

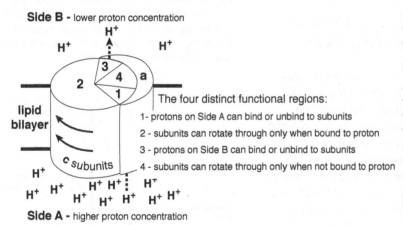

Figure 14-20. The different functional regions within the the membrane-spanning portion of ATP synthetase. The relative position of these different regions causes the cylinder of **c** subunits to tend to rotate in the direction shown when protons are in higher concentration on **Side A,** and to rotate in the opposite direction when the proton concentration gradient is reversed. (See text for more details.)

The evolution of ATP synthetase

The evolution of ATP synthetase may be an example of modular evolution, where two subunits with their own functions came together to perform in a new way. The F_1 region shows considerable structural similarity to a protein complex mentioned in Chapter 11, DNA helicase. They also can function in similar ways. DNA helicases use ATP to drive their spinning movement along the centrally enclosed helically shaped DNA. The F_1 region can use ATP to spin the central *gamma* subunit. On the other hand, the F_0 region displays similarity to the rotary motor used to spin prokaryotic flagella (which we will discuss more in Chapter 16). Both contain a ring of protein subunits that rotate relative to nearby stationary proteins using a hydrogen ion concentration gradient as the energy source. The flagellar motors are, however, structurally much more complex than the F_0 region.

The initial advantage of teaming up a DNA helicase-like arrangement with a membrane-spanning rotary motor may not have been to generate ATP from a hydrogen ion concentration gradient. More likely, its presence first proved beneficial to cells because it could do just the opposite. Using ATP as a fuel, the F_1 region can spin *gamma* and thus power the rotation of the **c**-cylinder in a way that will pump hydrogen ions in the opposite direction—from the head side to the tail side against a concentration gradient (Figure 14-21). Such a pump could help a cell from ever becoming too acidic by pumping out hydrogen ions whenever their concentration was becoming too high. Recall that acidity, which is measured on the pH scale, is a measure of the hydrogen ion concentration in solution. Hydrogen ion concentration greatly effects protein shape, hence protein function.

If ATP synthetase was first used as a proton pump, its design made it possible to subsequently get involved in ATP production. It was set up such that it was completely reversible. That is, it could use ATP to pump protons against a concentration gradient, or it could use the flow of protons along a concentration gradient to make ATP. If cars could do the same, they would not only be able to use gasoline to power uphill, but they could generate gasoline when going downhill. Wouldn't that be nice! (Although not completely analogous, hybrids use the motion of going downhill to charge batteries that power an electric engine that assists the gas-powered engine to go uphill.)

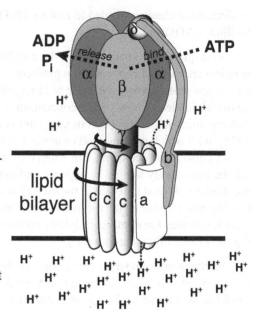

Figure 14-21. ATP synthetase can operate in the opposite direction. It can use the transfer of a phosphate from ATP to water to power the pumping of hydrogen ions across a membrane. (See text for more details.)

Oxidative phosphorylation is nothing more than the coupling of ETCs and ATP synthetase.

ATP synthetase's reciprocal nature set the stage for oxidative phosphorylation. To employ the ATP synthesizing ability of ATP synthetase, a cell only needed some other type of hydrogen ion pump—one powered by some energy source other than ATP. Here is where electron transport chains came into play. They could use differences in redox potential to pump hydrogen ions. So, once a cell had both ETCs and ATP synthetases embedded in the same membrane in the right orientation, it gained a new way to use a source of molecules with high redox potential to make ATP (a source of high phosphorylation potential). ETCs could generate an increased concentration of hydrogen ions on the ATP synthetase tail side of a membrane. The concentration gradient could then generate the needed flow through ATP synthetase for it to synthesize ATP (see Figure 14-22).

Figure 14-23 adds the final component of oxidative phosphorylation—a bound membrane. For ETCs to build a concentration gradient, the hydrogen ions that they pump across a membrane must not have a

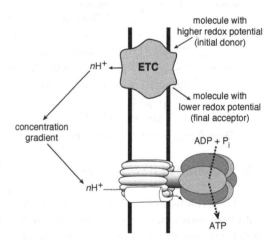

Figure 14-22. The two energy conversions making up oxidative phosphorylation. In total, differences in redox potential are used to generate a molecule with high phosphorylation potential (ATP).

route to move back in. Although it may first appear odd, Figure 14-23(a) represents the arrangement within cells that initially employed oxidative phosphorylation. (And this arrangement is still found in many cells today.) ETCs pumped hydrogen ions out across the outer membrane into the environment, and then ATP synthetase used the movement of hydrogen ions back into cell to make ATP. Although some hydrogen ions pumped out of a cell could be lost to the environment, this orientation of ETCs and ATP synthetases made sense for two reasons: (1) the molecules used as initial donors and as final acceptors would be supplied from inside the cell, and (2) ATP synthetase was in the orientation needed to be first used as a hydrogen ion pump. The arrangement found in Figure 14-23(b) is found in some cells, but not until cells began to evolve internal compartments. Only when one container was inside another could the source of initial donors be made within a cell, but still outside a bound compartment.

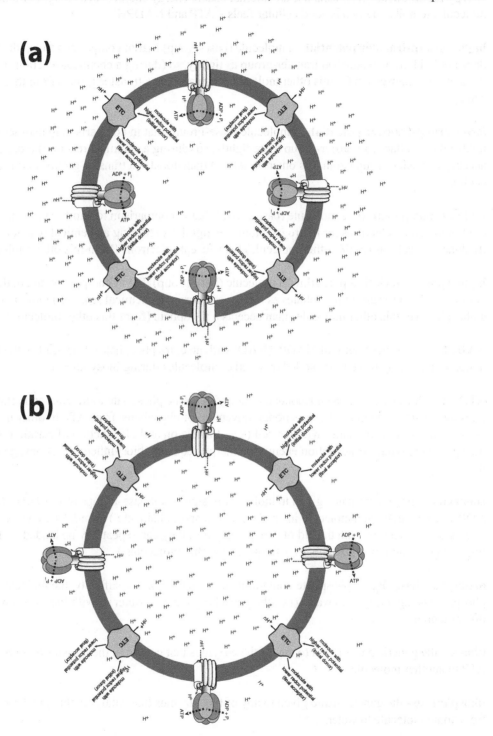

Figure 14-23. A summary of oxidative phosphorylation. Both electron transport chains (ETC) and ATP synthetases are embedded in a bound membrane. In (a), ETCs pump hydrogen ions out of the membrane bound enclosure, which can then flow back in through ATP synthetase powering the production of ATP. This was likely the first arrangement found in cells. The orientation of both ETCs and ATP synthetase is reversed in (b). This would only work in cells with internal comparments. (See text for further details.)

Some key terms:

energy metabolism - how cells use an external usable energy source, such as light or a high energy molecule, to make the two needed cellular fuels—ATP and NADPH.

higher group-transfer potential - a molecule (base-group) that in comparison to another molecule does not hold onto an attached transfer-group as tightly, so (during a chemical reaction) more readily donates a transfer-group (to this other molecule) than accepts a transfer-group (from this other molecule).

lower group-transfer potential - a molecule (base-group) that in comparison to another molecule holds onto an attached transfer-group more tightly, so (during a chemical reaction) more readily accepts a transfer-group (from this other molecule) than donates a transfer-group (to this other molecule).

higher redox potential - a molecule (base-group) that in comparison to another molecule does not hold onto certain electrons (or hydrogen atoms) as tightly, so (during a chemical reaction) more readily donates electrons (to this other molecule) than accepts electrons (from this other molecule).

higher phosphorylation potential - a molecule (base-group) that in comparison to another molecule does not hold onto certain phosphates as tightly, so (during a chemical reaction) more readily donates a phosphate (to this other molecule) than accepts a phosphate (from this other molecule).

NADPH - the reduced form of $NADP^+$ (NAD^+ with an extra phosphate). It is used as the hydrogen donor whenever hydrogens are added on to other molecules during biosynthesis.

ATP - a molecule (an activated ribonucleotide) with both a phosphate to transfer and relatively high phosphorylation potential. The directional movement of phosphates from ATP to other molecules is used to power many activities within a cell (e.g., turning on and off function of certain proteins, active transport, supplying the activation energy for energy-requiring biosynthetic reactions, generating motion).

coenzyme - the generic name given to biologically significant base-groups (e.g., NAD^+, $NADP^+$, ADP, coenzyme A, each molecule in an electron transport chain, etc.) (Note: Coenzymes can be used over and over. That is, with the aid of certain enzymes, they can repeatedly be loaded with a specific transfer-group and then pass this transfer-group to other molecules.)

orthophosphate (P_i) - a phosphate-containing molecule—more specifically, the molecule formed by a phosphate being attached to water (i.e., the phosphorylation of water)—with the lowest phosphorylation potential.

kinase - the generic name given to any of the enzymes that catalyzes the transfer of a phosphate from ATP to another molecule.

phosphatase - the generic name given to any of the enzymes that catalyzes the transfer of a phosphate from some molecule to water.

chemiosmosis - the processes by which ATP synthetase uses a flow of hydrogen ion (H^+) along a concentration gradient to power the transfer of a phosphate from orthophosphate to ADP to make ATP.

initial donor - the generic name for any molecule able to (because it has sufficiently high redox potential and the needed enzymes are present) donate electrons (hydrogens) to the first molecule (coenzyme) making up an electron transport chain.

final acceptor - the generic name for any molecule able to (because it has sufficiently low redox potential and the needed enzymes are present) accept electrons from the last molecule (coenzyme) making up an electron transport chain.

photoautotrophic cell - any cell that can use light to generate sufficiently high redox potential to generate the two fuels, and then use a portion of these two fuels to convert carbon dioxide into GAP.

Some study questions:

1. Know that energy metabolism is broken into two main topics: (1) how external energy sources (such as light or higher-energy molecules) are converted into the two main cellular fuels (ATP and NADPH), and (2) within cells, how ATP and NADPH are used as fuels.

2. *What is the basic idea behind a group-transfer chemical reaction? Be able to explain how differences in group-transfer potential (a property of different base-groups) can lead to certain group-transfer chemical reactions being energetically favorable and others energetically unfavorable.*

3. *Compare and contrast the terms redox potential and phosphorylation potential.*

4. NADPH is referred to as the fuel of reductive biosynthesis. In a nutshell, what does this fancy-sounding statement mean?

5. The directional flow of phosphates from ATP to water is used to power each of the following activities: turning on and off function of certain proteins, active transport, supplying the activation energy for energy-requiring biosynthetic reactions, and generating motion. Explain the basic idea behind how this phosphate flow is used to power each of these activities.

6. *Two types of molecules must be present for the base-group $NADP^+$ to be converted into its reduced form (NADPH). One is an enzyme that can catalyze the reaction. What are the general characteristics of the other molecule?*

7. Explain oxidative phosphorylation. That is, outline the basic steps by which a molecule with high redox potential in the reduced form can be used to power the phosphorylation of ADP to ATP. Include in the explanation the role of electron transport chains, bound membranes, concentration gradients, and ATP synthetase.

8. Be able to explain the basic ideas underlying the simplistic model of how electron transport chains might be able to use molecules with high redox potential to pump hydrogen ions across a membrane.

9. Be able to explain the basic ideas as to how ATP synthetase can use a concentration gradient of hydrogen ions to make ATP.

Different Themes in Energy Metabolism

Cells on this planet need a continual supply of ATP and NADPH, but details vary in terms of how they generate these two fuel molecules. We have already made quick mention of some key differences. Some cells can use sunlight as the external energy source needed to build ATP and NADPH. Of course, the sun does not always shine, so these same cells must either store enough ATP and NADPH made during the day to last the night, or they must store some other form of high-energy molecule during the day that can be converted into ATP and NADPH at night. It turns out that they do the latter, with sugars and fats being the major forms of energy storage. Other cells, in essence, employ the nighttime energy strategy of light-using cells, except they use high-energy molecules picked up from their environment. A two-step energy food chain forms whenever the high-energy molecule is one initially built by a sunlight-using cell. Any additional links are, in essence, repeats of the second link. Carnivores, for example, still use high-energy molecules taken from another organism to make the two fuels. Their source of high-energy molecules, however, is not sun-using organisms, such as plants, but is at least one step removed. In the simplest case, they get their high-energy molecules from herbivores—which in turn eat plants.

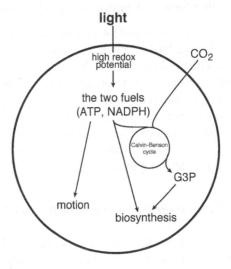

Figure 15-1. A photoautotrophic cell.

The task now is to dig deeper. I start by mentioning an important connection: The distinction between a cell being autotrophic or heterotrophic (see Chapter 13) and a cell's position in the energy food chain are not independent of each other.

Light-using cells, for example, are generally autotrophic cells. And this coupling makes sense. The Calvin–Benson cycle requires inputs of both ATP and NADPH. Sunlight is used to generate these two fuels, and then some is used to build G3P (a three-carbon sugar phosphate) via the Calvin–Benson cycle. G3P in turn can be used to build sugars, fats, amino acids, nucleotides, or other biologically important molecules used in organism construction or energy storage. The remaining ATP and NADPH are used to run all other cellular activities (see Figure 15-1).

In fact, the term **photosynthesis** refers to the coupling between using light to make fuels and then using a portion of the fuels to make G3P. *Photo-* implies light use. The *-synthesis* part refers to a particular aspect of biosynthesis—the ability to reduce carbon dioxide to sugars. So, a photosynthetic cell can also be termed a **photoautotrophic** cell.

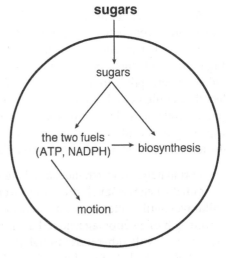

Of course, there is still the night problem, which prevents any cell from being a full-time photoautotroph. At night, they essentially run the whole thing backward. Stored sugars (or other molecules built during the day) can be used as a carbon source for biosynthesis or as an energy source to build the two cellular fuels. This form of energy metabolism is termed **heterotrophic** (see Figure 15-2). Photoautotrophs are thus nighttime heterotrophs. In contrast, your cells, (along with all other nonphotoautotrophic cells) are

Figure 15-2. A heterotrophic cell.

full-time heterotrophs. In other words, we run around day and night employing the energy metabolism of a nighttime plant. Animals are always on the "dark side"!

Production of the Two Fuels in Light-Using Cells

In the previous chapter, we introduced the basic ways cells build NADPH and ATP. Here, I bring one aspect of that discussion to the forefront—the assembly of both molecules has a common starting point. Each starts with a molecule bearing high redox potential. For NADPH, this made sense. To build a molecule with high redox potential, start with a molecule with even higher redox potential. But the same cannot be said for starting with high redox potential to build ATP. Now the conversion is complicated by the fact that one form of chemical energy (redox potential) has to be converted into another form of chemical energy (phosphorylation potential).

This observation raises a question: Why start with redox potential in both cases? The answer likely goes back to sunlight. Light can be life's primary energy source because it can be converted into chemical energy. But this conversion path is narrow. Light can only be converted into higher redox potential due to the fact that light energy (or photons) exerts a force solely on electrons. In essence, photons can knock electrons to higher energy states, being absorbed, instead of reflected, in the process. At higher energy states, electrons are held less tightly, hence a light-excited compound can transfer electrons to base-groups that they could not have otherwise. In other words, light excitation can turn an energetically unfavorable redox reaction into an energetically favorable one. Everything else unfolds from there.

Electromagnetic waves and pigments

Given that I stated back in Chapter 1 that I really do not understand field forces, such as gravity, it makes sense that the nature of electromagnetic radiation would also be fuzzy. Now we are talking about a field force (not composed of matter) that both oscillates (between an electric and magnetic component) and travels (always at the speed of light in a vacuum). The distance traveled between each oscillation is called its wavelength, and the shorter the wavelength, the more force or energy it contains. This concept is even further complicated by the fact that electromagnetic radiation exhibits both wave properties and particle properties at the same time—although, the one that reveals itself at any moment depends on how it is viewed.

Note: The length of waves potentially generated goes from very low energy radio waves— which range from hundreds of meters to tens of centimeters in length—to the highest energy gamma waves— which are shorter than 0.03 nanometers (nm), where a nanometer is one-billionth of a meter. Light, or visible light, is the small range of wavelengths—around 400 to 700 nm—of electromagnetic radiation perceptible to the human eye. This small range means that we perceive difference in wavelength, as little as 50 billionths of a meter, as a different color. Nearby wavelengths are ultraviolet (below 400 nm) and infrared (above 700 nm). The expression "ultraviolet light" uses the term *light* for wavelengths outside the range visible to humans, which can be confusing. It seems better to restrict the term *light* to the visible range and refer to all else as radiation, such as ultraviolet radiation.

Fortunately, however, the main thing we need to understand here is that electromagnetic radiation is emitted whenever an electron drops from a higher-energy to a lower-energy state, and once released will travel until it interacts with another electron somewhere else. More specifically, whenever any wavelength of electromagnetic radiation encounters some form of matter—which always contains electrons—it will either pass through (transmitted), be captured only long enough to be spit back out (reflected), or be held for a little while (absorbed). Here we are most interested in absorption, with the key idea being that each atom or molecule has certain energy levels—that is, certain wavelengths— with which it resonates and thus can absorb. Absorbed energy can then be either converted into increased motion (heat) or drive chemical reactions, as happens in light-assisted energy metabolism. After traveling around 93 million miles from the sun, the wavelengths used are primarily collected by a class of molecules called **chlorophylls**, although some other pigments are involved.

Note: A pigment is any chemical compound that differentially absorbs and reflects wavelengths within the visible range. For example, some common forms of chlorophylls absorb light below 480 nm and between 550 and 700 nm. So when white sunlight—wavelengths that span the visible range—intercepts these chlorophyll molecules, wavelengths between 480 and 550 are reflected back, a range that we perceive as greenish. In contrast, a different-colored pigment would absorb and reflect wavelengths in a different pattern.

More on chlorophylls

Clearly, something about chlorophylls works well at converting light into higher redox potential, as the basic structure appears to have remained remarkably constant through the history of Life. What is seen, however, are minor changes around the central structure that influence the pattern of wavelength absorption. Consider, for instance, two forms know as *chlorophyll a* and *bacteriochlorophyll a* (see Figure 15-3). The first is the major chlorophyll found in cyanobacteria (discussed later), photosynthetic algae, and plants, whereas the latter is found mostly in a group of photosynthetic bacteria known as purple bacteria. These lineages may have diverged up to several billion years ago, yet the chlorophylls differ only by one altered side chain and one double bond. Yet functionally, these differences make a difference. In contrast to *chlorophyll a*, *bacteriochlorophyll a* reflects a broader region of visible light and extends its absorption of wavelengths into the infrared range, allowing purple bacteria to utilize these lower-energy wavelengths. All other chlorophyll forms found in nature also have minor differences in side-chain groups around the central ringed structure.

Although structural details are not the focus here, a few aspects are worth highlighting. Let's start with the long, lipid-soluble, hydrocarbon tail that tends to keep chlorophyll molecules connected with membranes. In the previous chapter, we introduced membrane-bound electron transport chains (ETCs), and soon we will be hooking chlorophylls into their workings, so it makes sense that they too would need to be associated with membranes.

The **conjugated arrangement**—alternating single and double bonds—around the ringed structure, called a **porphyrin ring**, is also worth noticing. For one, each additional double bond lengthens the wavelength of electromagnetic radiation absorbed, and past eight double bonds (*chlorophyll*

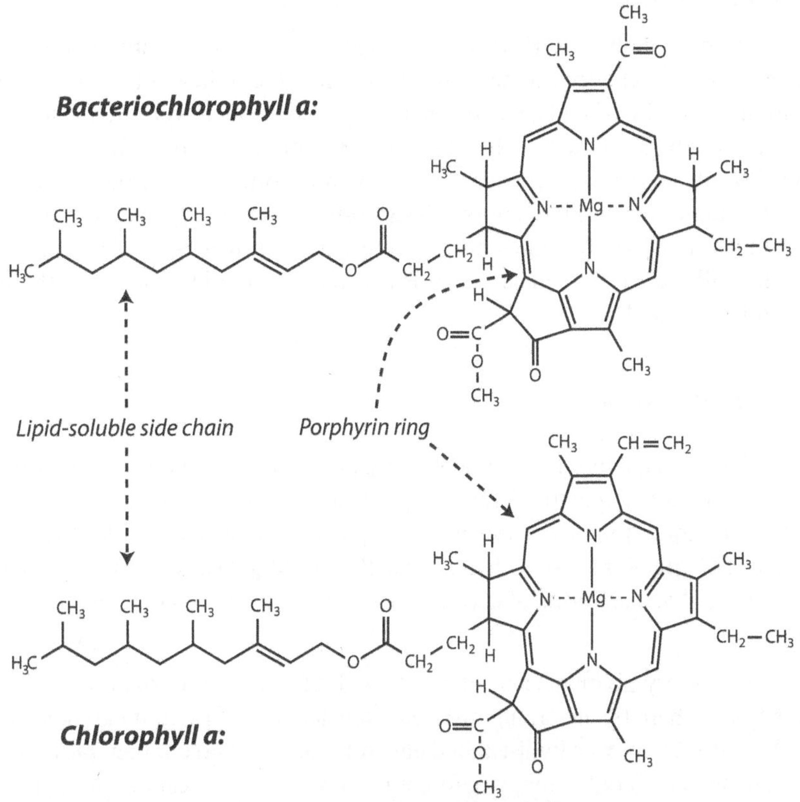

Figure 15-3. The chemical structure of two chlorophylls.

a has 10), the wavelengths absorbed move beyond ultraviolet—which are higher in energy and more dangerous—into the visible range. Furthermore, conjugated arrangements allow electrons to be delocalized in that they do not belong to a specific bond, but rather may move around the whole system. When free-ranging electrons absorb photons of light of the right wavelength, they are moved into the type of higher energy state more conducive to electron transfer. Therefore, conjugated arrangements greater than eight double bonds set the stage for electromagnetic radiation within the visible range to increase a molecule's redox potential. Encircling a conjugated arrangement into a ringed structure, as found in chlorophyll, allows electrons to roam freely around the entire structure, which may even further accentuate the potential to donate energized electrons to other molecules. The central metal ion, specifically Mg^{2+}, that anchors the ring may further enhance this ability.

The good and the bad

Several things can happen whenever a chlorophyll electron is excited to a higher energy level by light. Here, I focus on two that are useful and two that are potentially harmful.

One positive is a chlorophyll molecule transferring an excited electron to an electron acceptor, leaving the chlorophyll in an oxidized state. This is the redox reaction that starts all forms of light-based energy metabolism. Second, the return of one light-excited pigment to a lower energy state can be coupled with the excitation of a neighboring pigment molecule. This allows complexes of pigments to work together to gather the light energy needed to initiate electron transfer. Although not a major focus here, extant photosynthetic organisms have large numbers of pigment molecules arranged— often by being bound in a certain way by proteins—into a light-harvesting complex known as an *antenna*. Given the slight probability at any moment that a photon with the right energy signature hits a chlorophyll molecule in the needed location to initiate electron transfer, antenna complexes increase the odds by funneling light energy toward a *reaction center* —those chlorophylls involved in electron-transfer reactions.

Unfortunately, absorbed energy can also be channeled into disruptive pathways. For instance, the absorbed light energy can be completely converted to heat—that is, the electron initiates a series of rotational and vibrational changes on its way back to its lower-energy state. Although converting light to heat could help warm a colder photosynthetic organism to its thermal optima, basking in sunlight often leads to the generation of excess heat. Too much molecular motion is disruptive to the organization of any living organism. In addition, the absorbed light energy can be used to convert molecular oxygen from less reactive to a much more reactive state known as *singlet oxygen*. Although singlet oxygen is technically not a free radical, its effects can be similar by reacting with, hence damaging, important cellular molecules.

Accessory pigments

Obviously, every photosynthetic organism must have a least one form of light-absorbing pigment. What is interesting is that having more than one is the norm (if not universal). For instance, organisms that commonly produce *chlorophyll a* typically also produce *chlorophyll b* or some form or forms of phycobilin pigments—which are basically the ringed structure in chlorophyll chopped into a linear molecule. Various forms of carotenoids—typically red, orange, or yellow pigments—are also common.

Accessory pigments appear to be involved in two important roles: (1) they are part of the antenna complex where by absorbing different wavelengths of light, it extends the range of wavelengths that can be used to power light-excited electron transfer, and (2) they play a protective role by helping to dissipate excess light energy before it is converted into heat or singlet oxygen and/or by helping to dissipate heat or neutralize singlet oxygen once formed. Carotenoids, in particular, are major players in photoprotection. (Note: Evidence suggests that carotenoids can also play a protective role in animals, which is one of the reasons that nutritional advice tends to include a fairly large intake of plants.)

A little more about porphyrin rings

A common theme in Life is that some piece or part that initially was kept around—and further modified—because of its usefulness in one functional role, subsequently got put to use doing other things. For example, ATP is an activated ribonucleotide used to build RNA and to power many different forms of biological activities. Porphyrin rings, which were first introduced in Figure 15-3 as a major constituent of chlorophyll, are another example. Consider the following list: Replace the central magnesium ion (Mg^{2+}) with an iron (Fe) ion, and the basic structure is now known as a heme. On one hand, hemes are a major component of cytochromes, a group of molecules continually undergoing redox reactions in ETCs. On the other hand, hemes are part of hemoglobin molecules used to transport oxygen through the circulatory system of many animals (including us). Replace the central iron atom with cobalt (Co)—the next element over in the periodic table—and now it is part of molecule called cobalamin (or vitamin B_{12}). Cobalamin, which is only synthesized by certain forms of bacteria, plays an essential role as a protein cofactor—where it assists in chemical reactions involved in the exchange of hydrogen atoms or methyl groups (CH_3). Finally, replace the central cobalt atom with nickel (Ni)—the next element over in the periodic table—and it becomes part of a molecule involved in the formation of methane by certain bacteria.

Using light to make ATP

A warning: The way that light is used to make ATP can be understood only if one first understands oxidative phosphorylation—the process that coupled the actions of ETCs and ATP synthetase to make ATP. If you do not understand this process, go back to the previous chapter or seek out any other helpful source available to you. Pay particularly close attention to the role played by initial donors and final acceptors in the workings of ETCs. How cells come up with a continual supply of initial donors and final acceptors is a major focus in this chapter. The first example of such discussion starts next.

Remember this phrase: *Up to donate and down to accept*. We will put it to use shortly.

Light plays one role in making ATP. It makes it possible for the same molecule to be used repeatedly as an initial donor (for an ETC).

To act as an initial donor, a molecule must have two traits: (1) it must be reduced—that is, it must have electrons to donate, and (2) it must have higher redox potential than the first electron carrier making up the ETC. Only then is the movement of electrons from the initial donor into the ETC energetically favorable. These requirements put a snag in using the same molecule over and over. Once a molecule is used as an initial donor, it is oxidized—it gives up its potentially transferable electron. So, before it can be used again it needs to be reduced again—resupplied with transferable electrons. Here is where the problem lies. It can gain new electrons only from another reduced molecule with even higher redox potential. And because the initial donor needs to have higher redox than the first electron carrier in the ETC, the molecule it gets its electrons from must have an even higher redox potential. A constant influx of reduced molecules with sufficiently high redox potential would solve this problem. But what if such molecules were not available in the environment? The answer is to let the light shine in!

Light, as stated earlier, can boost the redox potential of a reduced (reaction center) chlorophyll molecule. A zap of light could change a chlorophyll with too low a redox potential to act as an initial donor, into one with sufficiently high redox potential. This is the *up to donate* part of the initially introduced phrase (see Figure 15-4).

The lift up is as important as the fall afterward. The fall moves the molecule *down* (to be in better position) *to accept* new electrons. Once a light-excited chlorophyll acts as an initial donor, it is not only now oxidized (it has given up electrons), but it has also dropped back down to its lower position on the redox scale. To reload an oxidized chlorophyll, a cell needs to come up with a reduced molecule with higher redox potential (see Figure 15-4). Next we discuss a clever—that is cyclic—way that this is done.

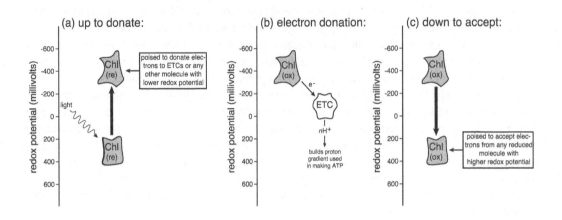

Figure 15-4. (a) A reduced chlorophyll molecule (Chl) moves up the redox scale when excited by light. (b) Once boosted up the redox scale, it donates its transferable electrons to the first coenzyme in an electron transport chain (ETC). The chlorophyll molecule is oxidized in the process. (c) In its oxidized form the chlorophyll falls back down the redox scale.

An electron nutrient cycle: Cyclic photophosphorylation

Two important questions were not answered in the preceding scenario: What molecule acts as a final acceptor in the ETC? What molecule transfers electrons to the oxidized form of the initial donor?

Two groups of phototrophic bacteria—specifically, purple and green bacteria—have answered these questions in the simplest way. They use an electron cycle. The final acceptor is the oxidized form of the initial donor. Stated differently, the electrons passing out of the ETC are the ones used again to reduce the initial donor.

Let me explain better. These groups of bacteria use some form of bacteriochlorophyll (either a, c, d, or e) as both the initial donor and the final acceptor. In its reduced form, light (which is partially a misstatement as bacteriochlorophyll absorb wavelengths of electromagnetic radiation up in the infrared, thus nonvisible, region) cranks up its redox potential so that electrons can be donated into its ETC. As these electrons enter the chain two things happen. The electrons are transferred from one electron carrier to the next until they reach the final electron carrier making up the chain. The oxidized chlorophyll returns to its low redox potential state. An electron loop forms—that is, the electrons end up back where they started—when the oxidized chlorophyll acts as a final acceptor. Electrons move out of the chain and back onto the chlorophyll. The chlorophyll is now reduced, so the cycle can start anew (see Figure 15-5).

As bad as it may sound, this process is appropriately called **cyclic photophosphorylation**. It is cyclic in that electrons, as they pass through the ETC, continually return to where they started. The prefix *photo-* indicates that light is involved. And phosphorylation designates that in the final step of oxidative phosphorylation, ADP is phosphorylated to form ATP.

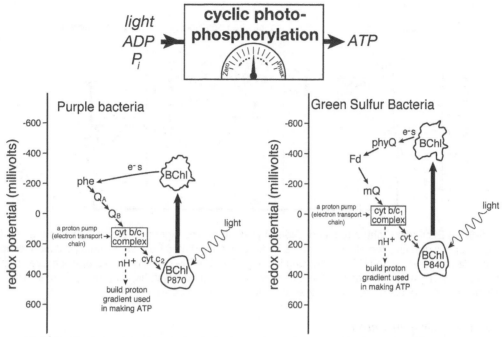

Figure 15-5. Cyclic photophosphorylation in both purple and green sulfur bacteria. BChl = a form of bacteriochlorophyll in the reaction center. P870 and P840 indicate the electromagnetic wavelength of maximal absorption. Other molecules are electron carriers: phe = pheophytin, a chlorophyll molecule lacking a central Mg^{2+} ion; Q (Q_A, Q_B, phyQ, mQ) = various forms of quinones; cyt (b, c, c_1,c_2) = various forms of cytochromes, which contain a porphyrin ring with a central iron ion; Fd = ferrodoxin, a protein containing an iron-sulfur complex.

Using light to make NADPH

Hopefully by now, it has been hammered into your head that to assemble NADPH—to reduce $NADP^+$ to NADPH—cells need a reduced molecule with even higher redox potential than $NADP^+$. The up-to-donate property of photoexcitable pigments is once again suited to power the assembly of NADPH. Light energy could be converted into the needed redox potential.

Using light to generate NADPH by this means, however, raises a new issue. A cell-level electron cycle is not possible. There is no path for the electrons leaving an excited photoexcitable pigment—bound for $NADP^+$—to return. Instead, they move onto $NADP^+$ (forming NADPH), and from there are transferred to some other molecule during reductive biosynthesis (in which case NADPH is oxidized back to $NADP^+$). Consequently, building NADPH requires more than just sunlight to keep replacing the electrons used. The cell must continually input an electron (hydrogen) source (see Figure 15-6). That is, it needs to keep bringing in from the environment some molecule from which it can pull off electrons (with protons following).

A good hydrogen source would meet two criteria. First, it would be plentiful in the environment. Each time an electron-donating molecule is used, it is used up—its transferable electrons are removed. NADPH assembly can continue only if a steady stream of electron-donating molecules flows into the cell. (On the flip side, the used-up oxidized form must be continually removed.) Maintaining such a replacement stream would be impossible if the molecule was too rare. Second, it would have higher redox potential than the oxidized form of the photoexcitable pigment used to make NADPH. The down-to-accept property of photoexcitable molecules, of course, lightens this requirement. The redox potential of the electron-donating molecule can be considerably lower than the redox potential needed to generate NADPH. But still there are limits. A photoexcitable molecule, with high enough redox potential in its light-excited state to reduce $NADP^+$, can drop down the redox scale only so far in its oxidized (unexcited) state.

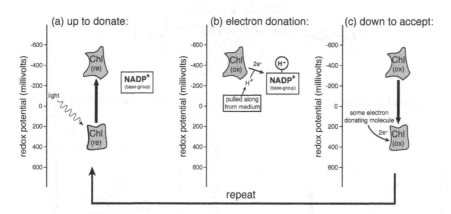

(a) up to donate: (b) electron donation: (c) down to accept:

Figure 15-6. (a) Excited by light, a reduced chlorophyll (Chl) moves higher on the redox scale than NADP+. (b) The chlorophyll donates two electrons, and a hydrogen ion is pulled from surrounding solution, so in total a hydride ion moves onto NADP+, reducing it to NADPH. (c) The oxidizided chlorophyll moves back down the redox scale where it excepts electrons from some molecule with higher redox potential. The chlorophyll is once again reduced, making it possible for the process to be repeated.

Two different hydrogen sources

The problem with ideals is that reality has a difficult time keeping up. Molecules used as hydrogen sources seem to pass one of the two criteria with flying colors, but come up short in the other. I discuss two hydrogen sources in particular: hydrogen sulfide (H_2S) and water (H_2O).

In terms of redox potential, hydrogen sulfide works well as a hydrogen source. Chlorophyll molecules exist whose redox potential in its light-excited state is higher than NADP+, but in its oxidized (unexcited) state it has lower redox potential than hydrogen sulfide. One example is the reaction center chlorophyll molecules of green sulfur bacteria.

With a supply of hydrogen sulfide, these bacteria can thus generate NADPH in a straightforward manner. First, electrons (with protons following) move from hydrogen sulfide to this bacteriochlorophyll. Elemental sulfur is left behind and, hence, is a by-product of this step in the process. Light then enters the picture. Zapped by light, the chlorophyll's redox potential then elevates to the point that electrons can favorably pass—through some intermediary molecules—to NADP+ (Figure 15-7).

Hydrogen sulfides' downside is that it is relatively scarce. Your nose knows that. A sulfury smell, often described as smelling like rotten eggs, permeates areas where hydrogen sulfide is present and being used as a hydrogen source. You may have noticed this smell around some hot springs, where it is formed geochemically, but it is not common. And in all those places where hydrogen sulfide is not available, hydrogen sulfide using green sulfur bacteria cannot exist.

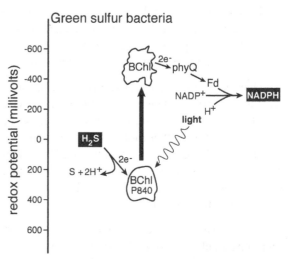

Green sulfur bacteria

Figure 15-7. The pathway by which green sulfur bacteria uses light to drive the energetically unfavorable movement of electrons from hydrogen sulfide (H_2S) to NADP+ to form NADPH. BChl = a form of reaction center bacteriochlorophyll. P840 indicate the electromagnetic wavelength of maximal absorption. Other molecules are electron carriers: phyQ = a form of quinone known as phylloquinone;Fd = ferrodoxin, a protein containing an iron-sulfur complex.

Water, in essence, is the flip side of hydrogen sulfide. It is abundant, but stingy with its electrons. If you have any doubts about its abundance on this planet, I recommend a trip to an ocean. You will see a lot of water. Oceans cover most of the Earth's surface. And even on "dry" land, water periodically rains down from the sky.

The zest with which water holds onto its electrons (hydrogen atoms) introduces a considerable downside to its use as an electron source. Water sits very low on the redox scale. Using it as an electron source would, thus, require a superman-like photoexcitable molecule—one able to leap large spans of the redox scale in a single, light-zapped bound. Only then could the photoexcitable molecule be both lower on the redox scale than water in its oxidized form and higher than $NADP^+$ in its light-excited reduced form. So what is this superman of a photoexcitable compound? It does not exist.

Does that mean that water cannot be used as a hydrogen source? For most cells on this planet, that is true. Its electrons are just held too tightly to be pried loose. But a certain group of cells, called cyanobacteria, came up with a way around this obstacle. In doing so, they revolutionized life on this planet. Their secret—use two steps when one will not do. Let's look closer.

The Z-scheme

Cyanobacteria lug electrons (with protons following) up the redox scale from water and on to $NADP^+$ by combining the workings of two different forms of reaction centers (along with all the accompanying antenna complex molecules). In essence, one pulls electrons up part of the way, and the second finishes the job.

Looking at the details of the two reaction centers, known as **photosystem I** and **photosystem II**, yields some interesting finds. For one, the electron carriers surrounding each reaction center—that is, the molecules that electrons are passed to—are very similar to the photosynthetic bacteria already discussed. Specifically, photosystem I resembles green sulfur bacteria, and photosystem II resembles purple bacteria, suggesting that cyanobacteria used already existing parts to assemble this tandem arrangement. An important difference, however, is that each reaction center chlorophyll was altered from a bacteriochlorophyll to *chlorophyll a*, which absorbs shorter, more energetic wavelengths. The absorption peak of photosystem I is around 700 nm, and in arranging *chlorophyll a* in a different geometry, photosystem II shifts the absorption peak to even shorter wavelengths (around 680 nm). Even more significant, this different arrangement (with the help of some manganese ions) shifts the strength in which oxidized *chlorophyll a* molecules can pull on electrons—that is, its redox potential—to even lower than water. The transfer of electrons from water to the photosystem II reaction center is thus energetically favorable.

The electron journey starts when two electrons leave a water molecule (the water molecule is split) and are transferred to, and thus reduce, a pair of *chlorophyll a* molecules in photosystem II. Each time two water molecules are split, one molecular oxygen (O_2) can form from the two freed oxygen atoms. (Note: Although molecular oxygen is the most common by-product here, freed oxygen atoms can also form oxygen radicals, which can have destructive effects on biomolecules such as lipids and proteins.) Light excitation then moves the reaction center chlorophylls up the redox scale, but not high enough to generate NADPH. The light-excited electrons then leave photosystem II, passing through a series of molecules with lowering redox potential until they eventually move on to a second pair of chlorophyll molecules in photosystem I. These reaction center chlorophyll molecules start off higher on the redox scale (which is why they could not accept electrons from water in the first place) and correspondingly move even higher up the redox scale when excited by light. At this point, the electrons that were originally part of a water molecule are poised to be passed to $NADP^+$. They are held high enough on the redox scale. After passing through a series of electron carriers, they are eventually transferred to $NADP^+$, reducing it to NADPH.

Figure 15-8 summarizes this whole process. Looking at this figure, you can see why this movement of electrons is often referred to as the **Z-scheme**—electrons move up and down the redox scale in the shape of the letter Z. The Z-scheme is a noncyclic pathway. Water must be split continually to keep the pathway running.

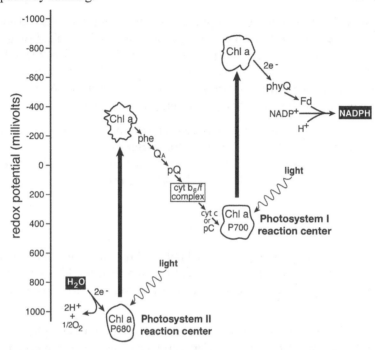

Figure 15-8. The Z-scheme. How cyanobacteria uses light excitation of two different reaction centers, each containing *chlorophyll a*, to drive the extremely energetically unfavorable movement of electrons from water (H_2O) to $NADP^+$ to form NADPH. P680 and P700 indicate the peak wavelength absorption of each reaction center. Other molecules are electron carriers: phe = pheophytin, a chlorophyll molecule lacking a central Mg^{2+} ion; Q (Q_A, pQ, phyQ, mQ) = various forms of quinones; cyt (b_6, f, c) = various forms of cytochromes, which contain a porphyrin ring with a central iron ion; pC = plastocyanin, a protein containing a copper ion; Fd = ferrodoxin, a protein containing an iron-sulfur complex.

Putting it together: Using light to make ATP and NADPH

So far we have mentioned three general types of bacteria: green sulfur bacteria, purple bacteria, and cyanobacteria. Each uses light to make both ATP and NADPH, but each does so in unique ways.

Green sulfur bacteria makes ATP by cyclic photophosphorylation, and NADPH is made by the light-induced transfer of electrons (hydrogen atoms) from hydrogen sulfide to $NADP^+$. There is an either/or component to the production of these two fuels (see Figure 15-9). Each time a chlorophyll is excited by light, this high redox potential can be used either to make ATP or to make NADPH. ATP is made when the electrons move into the ETC (and then eventually back to the chlorophyll that first donated them). Alternatively, NADPH is made when electrons head down the path leading to $NADP^+$. The electrons lost are then replaced by oxidizing hydrogen sulfide. Presumably, this "choice" is somehow regulated—electrons being somehow steered toward the ETC when ATP is in short supply, or steered the other way when NADPH is scarce.

Like green sulfur bacteria, purple bacteria uses a light-excited chlorophyll molecule to make either ATP by cyclic photophosphorylation or to make NADPH. The specifics of NADPH production, however, are somewhat different. It is a noncyclic process where excitation of a chlorophyll is involved, but the excited chlorophyll in purple bacteria lacks sufficient redox potential to reduce $NADP^+$. An additional boost is needed. Without becoming bogged down in details, where this additional boost comes from is worth mentioning. ETCs, as you know, generate a concentration gradient by pumping hydrogen ions across a membrane. Typically, this concentration gradient is then used solely to generate ATP. In purple bacteria, however, a portion of this concentration gradient is diverted toward making NADPH. By a process called reverse electron transport, a flow of hydrogen ions somehow provides the needed boost in redox potential.

For Z-schemers—that is the cyanobacteria—making ATP and NADPH is all wrapped up in the same process, a fact that I left out earlier. The initial focus was on how the Z-scheme takes on the challenging task of using light energy to drive the otherwise extremely energetically unfavorable noncyclic movement of electrons from H_2O to $NADP^+$ (resulting in the production of NADPH and molecular oxygen). What I failed to mention was as electrons pass between the two reaction centers—from a light-excited photosystem II to an oxidized photosystem I—they move through a

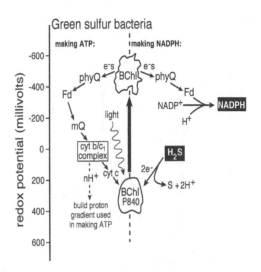

Figure 15-9. In green sulfur bacteria, light-excited reaction center bacteriochlorophyll can be used either to make ATP by cyclic photophosphorylation or to make NADPH. When NADPH is made, the electrons are replaced by splitting hydrogen sulfide (H_2S).

membrane-bound ETC (see Figure 15-10 (a, b)), which is structurally similar to a proton pump found in other photosynthetic bacteria. The concentration gradient of hydrogen ions generated by the ETC is then used by ATP synthetase to drive the phosphorylation of ADP to ATP. Furthermore, like we saw in green sulfur bacteria, in situations where ATP is scarce and NADPH is not, excited electrons out of photosystem I can follow a cyclic pathway and continue to run back through an ETC and thus produce ATP by oxidative phosphorylation (see Figure 15-10(a)). Final note: The Z-scheme is also known as **noncyclic photophosphorylation**.

The light and dark phases of photosynthesis

Using light and the Z-scheme to generate ATP and NADPH is often referred to as the light phase of photosynthesis. Light must be present for these reactions to take place. In photosynthetic cells (photoautotrophs) a portion of the light-generated fuel supply is then used to reduce carbon dioxide to sugars. This is known as the dark phase of photosynthesis. Dark means that once ATP and NADPH is formed, Calvin–Benson cycle reactions can happen in the absence of light.

Cyanobacteria, as well as purple bacteria, are classic photoautotrophs (see Figure 15-10(c, d)). Both use light to make the two fuels and can reduce carbon dioxide by the Calvin–Benson cycle. Green sulfur bacteria, however, are a bit more complicated. Although they can use light to make the two fuels, they cannot do the Calvin–Benson cycle. Some use another metabolic pathway to reduce carbon dioxide to sugars. So they are still photoautotrophs, in that they can still use light-generated fuels to synthesize their own sugar supply. Others are photoheterotrophs. They use light to make their fuel supply, but they depend on reduced carbon molecules from the environment to be their carbon source for biosynthesis.

The evolution of cyanobacteria and the "oxygen holocaust"

Currently, the major constituents of our atmosphere are molecular nitrogen (N_2—78% of atmospheric molecule), molecular oxygen (O_2—21%), argon (1%), and carbon dioxide (CO_2—0.03%).

(a)

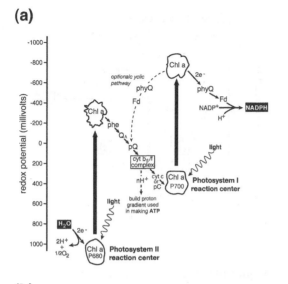

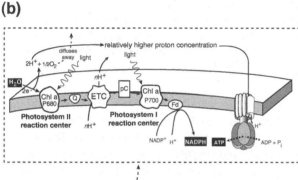

(b)

Figure 15-10. Photosynthesis in cyanobacteria. (a) The same as Figure 15-8 except that the cytochrome b6/f complex is now shown to be an electron transport chain (ETC). This creates an avenue for electrons moving from water to NADP+ to also be used to make ATP. A cyclic option is also shown. When a cell needs ATP more than NADPH, electrons can be cycled back through the ETC. (b) The molecules and movement of electrons and hydrogens ions in (a), plus ATP synthetase, are embedded in a membrane. This shows better the simultaneous production of ATP by oxidative phosphorylation (ETCs and ATP synthetase) and NADPH. (c) Presumably, the initial membrane of cyanobacteria photosynthesis was the plasma (cell) membrane, as is still found in one genus (Gloeobacter). Some of the NADPH and ATP produced is then used to drive the Calvin-Benson cycle—the dark phase of photosynthesis. (d) Most modern cyanobacteria have an internal system of membranes where the electron transfer reactions of photosynthesis occur called thylakoids, which presumably form compartments that facilitate the formation of a proton gradient. A long-standing controversy (thus, the question mark) surrounds how they form (e.g., are they invaginations of the plasma membrane?), and whether the thylakoid membranes exist inside the cell as separate compartments, or if they have physical continuity with the plasma membrane. (e) Summarizing the two stages of photosynthesis as two processors linked by output-input connections.

(c)   **(d)**

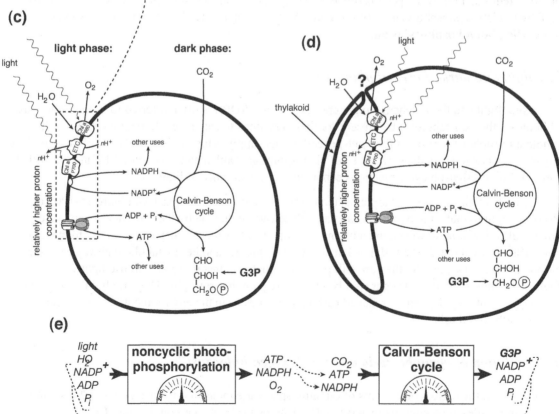

(e)

This atmospheric composition is an oxidizing atmosphere. The high level of molecular oxygen sets the stage for atoms in a more reduced state to react with oxygen and be oxidized. And given that an oxidized state has lower energy than a reduced state, such a shift is energetically favorable. In fact, oxidative reactions would, in essence, run rampant if the atmospheric composition of oxygen increased to just 25%. At that level, even damp vegetation would continue to burn once combustion (oxidation) started, and combustion would continue until all the combustible (reduced) material was burned.

Until around 2,000 million (2 billion) years ago, however, molecular oxygen was lacking in the atmosphere. The first 1.5 billion years or so of Life's history (remember the earliest fossilized life forms found date back around 3.5 billion years) took place in a more reducing environment, where more reduced forms of molecules (e.g., H_2, CH_2O, NH_3) were likely to be available. These molecules could have served as a source of redox potential for energy metabolism.

But as life began to multiply, competition for these high redox potential molecules likely began to increase. The different life forms, in essence, were locked in a scramble for the necessary but limiting usable forms of hydrogen. Light-using bacteria were, however, able to avoid this competitive scramble. They were able to pull hydrogen atoms off molecules with much lower redox potential. Cyanobacteria, in particular, came up with a way of pulling hydrogen atoms off water, leaving molecular oxygen as a by-product. Given the abundance of water, cyanobacteria proliferated. Concomitant with this spread was the increasing release of molecular oxygen.

At first, this newly released oxygen combined to oxidize the oceanic supply of dissolved molecules. Large amounts of dissolved ferrous iron, especially, were oxidized, resulting in large deposits of iron oxide.

After a billion years or so the supply of ferrous iron (and other dissolved reduced molecules) was used up. Oxygen began to spread into the atmosphere. And levels continued to increase because an oxygen ecosystem did not exist. Although cyanobacteria were releasing oxygen from water, other types of organisms were not converting oxygen back into water. Consequently, the atmospheric oxygen concentration began to increase. Many of the other types of bacteria present were unable to persist in an oxidizing environment. They, therefore, either perished, retreated to the few regions where oxygen didn't build up, or adapted. It was, in essence, the largest release of pollution in the history of life on Earth—an event that has been called the "oxygen holocaust."

It was in the evolutionary response to the increasing oxygen supply that an oxygen cycle began to take form. Specifically, a now widespread metabolic pathway (which will be discussed later) came to be, converting oxygen back to water. So, as oxygen became more common, the organisms using this pathway became more common. And eventually, the release and conversion of oxygen began to equilibrate, reaching present-day levels between 1.5 and 0.5 billion years ago and holding steady ever since.

Glucose Use in Heterotrophic Cells (and Photosynthetic Cells at Night)

Because heterotrophic cells cannot reduce carbon dioxide to sugars, they must get them in their diet. Structural and storage polymers are the most readily available supply, but can be used only if they can be digested back into individual sugar molecules. As the sugar most commonly polymerized, glucose is the most common sugar available to heterotrophs. Some other hexoses—such as galactose or fructose—along with some five-carbon sugars are also found in some food sources, but in relatively much smaller amounts. (Note: Humans consuming large amounts of high fructose corn syrup (found in soft drinks and other products) and/or sucrose (also known as table sugar, which is a disaccharide composed of equal amounts of glucose and fructose) introduce an odd twist in their diet—glucose is not necessarily the major sugar consumed. Evidence is accumulating that such a sugar shift can lead to a variety of problems. We are set up to consume mostly glucose.)

The nighttime problem—the fact that light needed to perform photosynthesis goes away for long stretches every night—is why photosynthetic cells are also included in this section. The need for metabolic activity does not similarly disappear, so each night photosynthetic cells use sugar molecules pulled out of storage polymers (e.g., starch) in much the same way as heterotrophic cells use sugar molecules acquired in their diet. The same story also holds for nonphotosythetic cells within a photosynthetic organism, such as plant cells that make up underground roots.

The question we address here is, What do heterotrophic cells (along with photosynthetic cells at night) do with these acquired sugar molecules?

Biosynthesis or energy metabolism or both

Think of a glucose as a string of six partially reduced carbons. Using glucose means that a cell does something with each of these six carbons. What can they do? One of two things: A carbon may end up in some other biologically important molecule, such as an amino acid. In that case, the carbon is used as a carbon source in biosynthesis. Alternatively, it may be used in energy metabolism. It is oxidized in a way that the energy released is used to build one of the two fuels. And once any carbon is oxidized completely—that is, it is converted to carbon dioxide—it is of no further use in either role. Biosynthesis is out because by definition heterotrophic cells are unable to convert carbon dioxide into sugars. Energy metabolism is also out because there is no more chemical energy (redox potential) to harvest. The only thing left is to get rid of it. It is a waste product. Your body is getting rid of carbon dioxide with each exhalation.

Filling out the details of how glucose is used in energy metabolism would be simpler if each glucose molecule entering was used either in biosynthesis or energy metabolism. In other words, right away glucose encountered a clear fork in the metabolic road. All glucose molecules entering one fork are used exclusively to make ATP and NADPH. In the process, all carbons are oxidized completely to carbon dioxide and then removed from the cell. All glucose molecules entering the other fork, in contrast, are used exclusively for biosynthesis. All six carbons end up as part of other biologically important molecules.

No such luck! The core pathway that glucose enters into to be used in energy metabolism is also a core pathway for use of glucose in biosynthesis. As the six carbons, originally part of a glucose molecule, are moved along through these series of chemical transitions, some may end up being used to build molecules, whereas others may be oxidized completely. Even the roles played by individual carbon atoms are not always one or the other. Carbons can be partially oxidized—with the energy released used in energy metabolism—and still be used to build other molecules. Only when a carbon is oxidized all the way to carbon dioxide has the point of no biosynthetic usefulness been reached.

Despite these options, next we center our focus more on one aspect of glucose use: How glucose molecules are used in the production of the two cellular fuels—ATP and NADPH.

A common first step

As you may have noticed, whenever sugars are rearranged during biosynthesis or energy metabolism, they are in a phosphorylated form. Yet, when sugars, such as glucose, are polymerized, they lose their phosphate in the process. To get back into the metabolic mix, after being cleaved back off a polymer, a glucose must first be phosphorylated (see Figure 15-11). ATP is used as the phosphate donor, and hexokinase or glucokinase are two enzymes that catalyze the reaction. In other words, in addition to the cost of producing any enzymes involved, it always cost an organism one ATP per glucose to return a glucose from a polymer to a metabolically ready state.

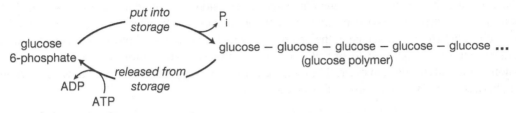

Figure 15-11. The cycle in which a glucose in a metabolically active state—that is, phosphorylated—is polymerized, and a glucose is removed from a polymer and returned to a metabolically active state.

Using glucose to make NADPH

A major way that glucose is used to make NADPH illustrates the tangled nature of biosynthesis and energy metabolism.

Glucose can be sent down the **pentose phosphate pathway** (Figure 15-12). This metabolic pathway converts glucose into ribose phosphate (a five-carbon sugar phosphate). Ribose 5-phosphate can then be used in building ribonucleotides, synthesis of an amino acid (histidine), as well as converted to other forms of sugars (see following). This pathway seems biosynthetic in nature. But that is true for only five of the six carbons. The carbon lost in the conversion is oxidized completely to carbon dioxide. The stripped electrons (hydrogen atoms) are transferred directly to $NADP^+$ to form NADPH. Two NADPH are formed for every ribose 5-phosphate produced. Glucose (or more correctly, the carbons making up glucose) has higher redox potential than $NADP^+$, making this transfer energetically favorable.

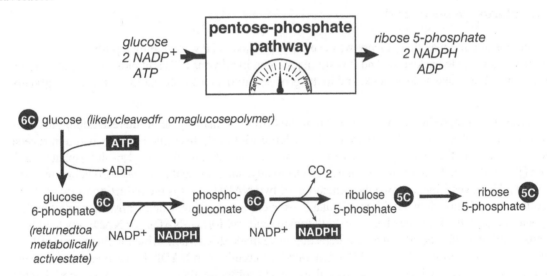

Figure 15-12. The pentose phosphate pathway first presented as a processor, followed by a closer look at the chemical reactions involved.

So, how should we view the pentose phosphate pathway? Is it a biosynthetic pathway that has an accompanying production of a fuel? Is it a fuel-producing pathway that also yields a molecule used in biosynthesis? I simply see it as a pathway that converts glucose into useful products, although, there is still the issue that a cell may not always need these products in the ratio produced. At times, for example, NADPH may be needed more than ribose 5-phosphate, or vice versa. Here, I leave the details as to how cells have come up with means to make such adjustments to biochemistry texts.

Just to add some context, note that the pentose phosphate pathway is part of the network of sugar conversions introduced in Chapter 13. Figure 15-13, shows part of Figure 13-6 again with the pentose-phosphate pathway highlighted. The remaining sugar conversions are found in the portion of the Calvin–Benson cycle where three-carbon sugars are converted back into five carbon sugars. In fact, add one more phosphate to one molecule in the pentose phosphate pathway—ribulose 5-phosphate—and it becomes ribulose 1,5-biphosphate, or RuBP, which was the five-carbon molecule that started our discussion of the Calvin–Benson cycle. The enzyme RuBisCo catalyzed a reaction, known as carbon fixation, between a RuBP and a carbon dioxide molecule.

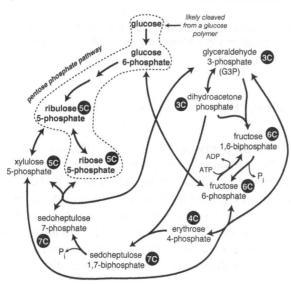

Figure 15-13. The pentose phosphate pathway is highlighted among the various possible arrangements of sugar phosphates.

Using glucose to make ATP

Perhaps the first way that glucose was ever used to make ATP was running a portion of the Calvin–Benson cycle backward. And it is still happening in all your cells and most other cells on the planet today. Let's take a closer look, and in the process build a metabolic pathway known as **glycolysis**.

Figure 15-14 (a, b) highlights the portion of the Calvin–Benson cycle of interest. Along this pathway, two ATP and two NADPH are used. In Figure 15-14 (c), this same pathway is run in reverse. One ATP is used in the first step (to convert fructose 6-phosphate into fructose 1,6-biphosphate), and two ATP are produced—a net gain of one ATP. Originally, such reversal probably also generated two NADPHs. However, I have shown the generation of two NADHs, that is the reduction of two NAD^+ (nicotinamide adenine dinucleotide) without a P—the extra phosphate. Chemically, the transition is very similar, and the difference has to do with which oxidized form—$NADP^+$ or NAD^+—is held by the enzyme involved. The advantage for cells that have made this switch, which include your cells, stems from the opportunity to use NADH generated differently than NADPH. The presence or absence of the extra phosphate will change the overall shape and subsequently change the enzymes with which they will interact. How cells use NADH differently than NADPH is discussed further later.

The two chemical steps where NADH and ATP are produced may have been the first and are still the most prevalent example of **substrate-level phosphorylation** (discussed briefly in the previous chapter). Here the process starts with a familiar molecule—G3P. Specifically, the oxidation of one of the carbons making up G3P is somehow coupled with the transfer of a phosphate from orthophosphate onto the same carbon oxidized. This coupling of electron removal and phosphate addition converts G3P into a molecule called biphosphoglycerate. This newly added phosphate has high enough phosphorylation potential to be transferred to ADP, forming one ATP. Because one fructose 1,6-biphosphate can be converted into two G3Ps, this step can be repeated, resulting in the generation of a total of two ATP. What is still left out is that G3P, or any other molecule, can be oxidized only if another molecule is reduced. Here is where NAD^+ (or $NADP^+$) comes into play. Two electrons and a proton are transferred from G3P to NAD^+ (oxidized form), forming NADH (reduced form).

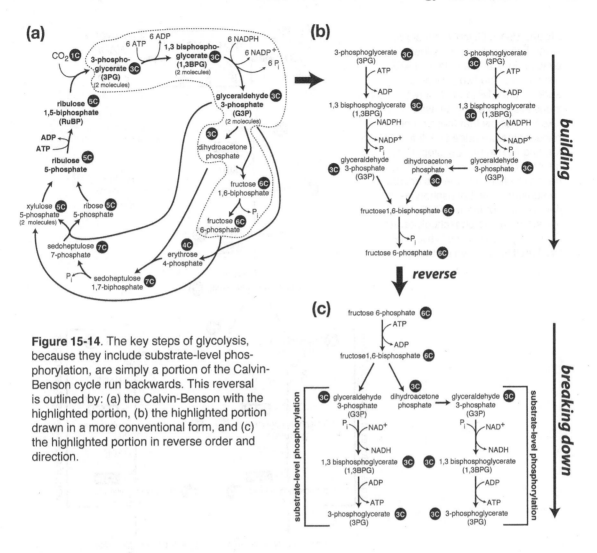

Figure 15-14. The key steps of glycolysis, because they include substrate-level phosphorylation, are simply a portion of the Calvin-Benson cycle run backwards. This reversal is outlined by: (a) the Calvin-Benson with the highlighted portion, (b) the highlighted portion drawn in a more conventional form, and (c) the highlighted portion in reverse order and direction.

Adding the finishing touches to glycolysis

We need to add something to both ends of Figure 15-14(c) to finish building glycolysis. Let's start at the front end.

The starting molecule, so far, is fructose 6-phosphate. A heterotrophic cell can continue to run this pathway to produce ATP only if it can maintain a supply of this molecule. But, from where is it going to get it? Obviously, the answer has to eventually go back to photosynthesis, but here we start with glucose polymers. Glycolysis is usually represented as starting with glucose in an unphosphorylated form—that is, a glucose that has just been cleaved off a polymer (see Figure 15-15). The glucose is then first converted back into its metabolically active state by adding a phosphate. An ATP is used in the process. Next, glucose 6-phosphate is rearranged into fructose 6-phosphate.

Adding these two steps, however, muddies the idea of glycolysis yielding ATP. Although two ATPs can be produced by substrate-level phosphorylation, it takes two ATPs to convert glucose into the two G3P molecules needed. Two minus two equals zero. Only through the addition of two more steps at the end does glycolysis yield an ATP profit. The two rounds of substrate-level phosphorylation end with two phosphoglycerates—a three-carbon molecule with a phosphate attached. The first added step is a rearrangement that increases the phosphate transfer potential of each, and the second step uses this increased phosphorylation potential to transfer a phosphate onto ADP to form ATP. A

Figure 15-15. Glycolysis first presented as a processor, followed by a closer look at the details of ATP production. The two phosphates added from ATP in the first two steps are marked by an asterisks (*) to show that these same phosphates are added back to ADP forming ATP in the last step. In total, no ATPs are lost or gained. The net production of two ATPs occurs by substrate-level phosphorylation as each of the two G3Ps are transformed into phosphoglycerate. Overall, glycolysis yields two ATPs, two NADHs, and two pyruvates.

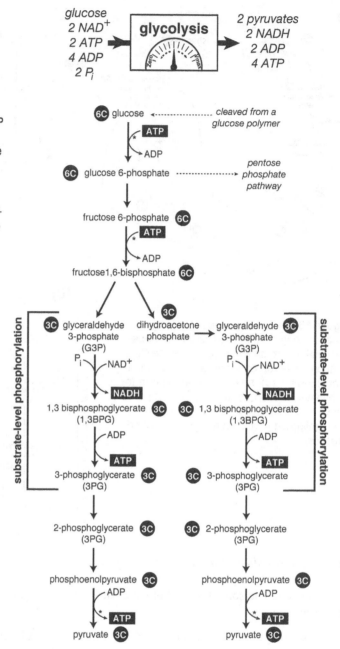

three-carbon molecule called pyruvate is left over. So, in total, two more ATPs are produced. (In fact, the phosphates transferred in this last step are the phosphates added in the first few steps when glucose is converted to fructose 1,6-biphosphate.) Starting with a single glucose, glycolysis thus has a net production of two ATPs, along with two NADHs and two pyruvates.

The rest of the story

The rest of the how-cells-use-glucose-to-make-ATP story deals with what happens to the two pyruvates and two NADHs per glucose coming out of glycolysis. Here the story splits into two forks: fermentation or respiration.

Fermentation

Fermentation is a means by which cells can keep glycolysis and its subsequent production of two ATPs per glucose running despite the output NADH. The quandary is a familiar-sounding one. How can the supply of a needed input be maintained when the process keeps converting this input into an unusable output? As stated earlier, NAD^+ is the molecule that accepts electrons from G3P in the first of the two substrate-level phosphorylation steps. In the process, NAD^+ is converted to NADH. Once a cell converts its entire supply of NAD^+ into NADH, this step cannot happen. No NAD^+s are left to accept the electrons. Block one step, and the entire pathway shuts down. Stop production of ATP, and the cell dies.

As should come as no surprise, the only feasible way to maintain a supply of NAD^+ is recycling. As fast as NAD^+ is being reduced to NADH in glycolysis, NADH needs to be oxidized back to NAD^+. How can this happen? The best answer is to oxidize NADH (back to NAD^+) in some useful way. Although we emphasized in the previous chapter that NADPH (NAD with a P) is the major reductive fuel, in some cells, at least in certain metabolic pathways, NADH (NAD without a P) can be used in a similar role. Next we discuss another useful way that NADH can be oxidized.

Fermentation comes into play when glycolytic production of ATP is needed and useful options to oxidize NADH either cannot keep up or are not available. In fermentation, pyruvate—the other output of glycolysis—acts as the electron acceptor for NADH. In other words, NADH passes its electrons to pyruvate, resulting in NAD^+ and some chemical modification of pyruvate. NAD^+ can then be used again in glycolysis.

The advantage of passing electrons to pyruvate is that a cell can generate ATP with only one input. Because the electron donor (G3P) and the electron acceptor (pyruvate) are both derived from glucose, a fermenting cell needs only a continual input of glucose to maintain oxidation-reduction balance.

Fermentation's downside is that this output—what pyruvate is converted into—generally needs to be discarded from the cell. To keep up with the ATP demand, a fermenting cell will likely produce more of this output than it could possibly use. All excess is a metabolic waste product.

Fermentation varies among different organisms—especially among bacteria—in the sense that the waste product generated is not always the same. The chemical details underlying pyruvate's acceptance of electrons from NADH differ, resulting in pyruvate being converted into different molecules. The two most familiar examples are probably ethanol and lactic acid (see Figure 15-16). Yeast, as well as certain bacteria, convert pyruvate into ethanol (and carbon dioxide) when they ferment. We use this type of fermentation to make wine and other alcoholic

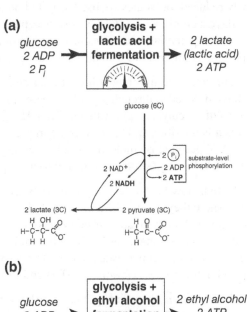

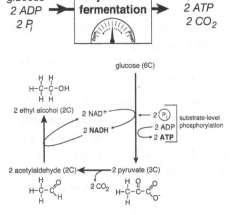

Figure 15-16. The two types of fermentation mentioned in text first presented as processors, followed by a closer look at the key chemical reactions involved.

beverages. Certain bacteria reduce pyruvate to lactic acid (or lactate). But that is probably not why you have heard of it. Whenever any of your cells ferment, which is most common after a period of intense exercise, pyruvate is reduced to lactic acid. Most other end products found in different bacteria are also organic acids (carbon compounds that carry a COOH group). Formic, acetic, propionic, butyric, and succinic acids are among the examples.

Respiration

Before we get into any details, let me summarize the overall logic of respiration. To start, consider a cell with a supply of high-energy molecules or, more specifically, molecules with high redox potential. A sugar molecule fits the bill, but so do fatty acids and amino acids. So, although our present discussion focuses on glucose, keep in the back of your mind that fatty acids and amino acids can also be respired. Respiration begins when any one of these molecules proceeds down a metabolic path that results in the complete oxidation of each of the carbons present—that is, each carbon is converted into carbon dioxide. Whenever something is oxidized, something else is reduced, and in respiration these newly reduced molecules are used as initial donors in an ETC. To keep the ETC running, a cell must also have a continuous supply of final acceptors. In respiration, the final acceptors used are low-energy (low redox potential) molecules brought in from the outside environment. Molecular oxygen is an important example. And with an ETC running, a cell can make ATP by oxidative phosphorylation.

Currently, we are in the middle of our discussion of how a glucose molecule is oxidized. So far, we have proceeded through glycolysis. How respiration differs from fermentation is that the two outputs of glycolysis—pyruvate and NADH—are used to make more ATP. Oxidative phosphorylation makes this possible, and the results are impressive. A respiring cell may produce as much as 19 times more ATP per glucose molecule as a fermenting cell. Stated differently, respiring cells potentially generate 38 ATP per glucose as compared to the 2 per glucose yield of a fermenting cell. Not bad!

Here is how the two glycolytic outputs are used. The two NADH are used as initial donors in an ETC (where they are oxidized back to NAD^+). Recall that ETCs are the first step in oxidative phosphorylation. And pyruvate is used to make more initial donors—that is, make more NADHs as well as a similar molecule that goes by the acronym $FADH_2$ (the reduced form of flavin adenine nucleotide). The three carbons in pyruvate are completely oxidized to carbon dioxide, and NAD^+s and FADs are reduced in the process (forming NADH and $FADH_2$, respectively).

An important note: Finally, I can finish the NADPH (reduced NAD with a P) versus NADH (reduced NAD without a P) story started in the previous chapter. In respiring cells, the presence or absence of this phosphate tag directs these otherwise identical molecules to be used in distinctive roles. When the extra phosphate is missing (NADH), the molecule is used as an initial donor, which in the larger picture means that it is used to make ATP. When the extra phosphate is present (NADPH), the molecule is used in reductive biosynthesis.

Although all respiring cells use NADH and $FADH_2$ as initial donors, the molecules used as final acceptors vary considerably between cells. Breathe in here. Your cells can only use molecular oxygen as a final acceptor. You breathe continually to supply your cells continually with their needed final acceptor. In fact, all eukaryotic cells can only use molecular oxygen as a final acceptor. The great diversity of final acceptors exists among different types of bacteria. Some, like us, use oxygen. Nitrate, nitrite, sulfate, carbon dioxide, bicarbonate, fumarate are among the other molecules used by different bacteria as final acceptors.

Respiration using oxygen as a final acceptor is known as **aerobic respiration**. **Anaerobic respiration** is when any molecule other than oxygen serves as the final acceptor.

Converting pyruvate into initial donors

Converting pyruvate into initial donors starts with the **oxidative decarboxylation** of pyruvate (a three-carbon compound) to acetate (a two-carbon compound). Oxidative decarboxylation means, in general, that a carbon compound is oxidized, and in the process, one of the carbon atoms is converted to carbon dioxide. Like always, when something is oxidized, something must be reduced. Here one NAD^+ is correspondingly reduced to NADH. The first initial donor is on the books.

The other thing going on during the oxidative decarboxylation of pyruvate to acetate is that acetate is loaded onto a base-group called **coenzyme A** (CoA) forming a compound termed **acetyl-CoA**. In other words, coenzyme A's transfer-group—acetate or also called an acetyl group—is added on. In the next step, the acetyl group will be passed to another molecule (called **oxaloacetate**). Joining with coenzyme A makes this step possible, due to its high acetyl transfer potential. Like all types of base-groups, once passing the acetyl group, coenzyme A is ready to be used again.

When acetate is passed from acetyl CoA to oxaloacetate (to form citrate) another cell-level nutrient cycle enters the picture. It is known as the **Krebs cycle**, the **citric acid cycle**, or the **tricarboxylic acid cycle**, but none of these names really indicate what it does. A functional name would be something like the **acetate oxidation cycle**, because that is what happens. In one spin of the cycle, the two carbons entering as acetate are completely oxidized to carbon dioxide. What is the benefit of breaking acetate all apart? Coupled with acetate's demise is the production of four more initial donors—the reduction of three NAD^+ and one FAD—plus the powering of one instance of substrate-level phosphorylation (see Figure 15-17).

Why cyclic? The logic is the same as in the Calvin–Benson cycle, where carbon dioxide is reduced to sugar without using up the supply of the molecule—RuBP—needed to get this process started. Similarly, the Krebs cycle wrings the energy out of acetate—to produce more initial donors—without using up the supply of the molecule—oxaloacetate—needed to get it started. In humans it has been calculated that if the oxaloacetate molecules assisting in ATP production were not regenerated, we would need to synthesize over two pounds of it per day. Not only would that require taking in a sufficient supply of materials, but also the energetic cost of synthesis would far exceed the energy derived.

Let's walk through the Krebs cycle's major steps (see Figure 15-17).

As mentioned earlier, two-carbon acetate enters the cycle when acetyl-CoA transfers it to oxaloacetate (a four-carbon compound) to form a six-carbon tricarboxylic acid called citrate or citric acid. Citrate then undergoes oxidative decarboxylation twice. Each time, the release of a CO_2 is coupled with the reduction of NAD^+ to NADH. Two more initial donors are thus formed. The two carbons that joined oxaloacetate have now left as carbon dioxide. Succinate is the four-carbon compound remaining.

The cyclic or regenerative part of the Krebs cycle occurs as succinate—which like the acetate entering the cycle is loaded on coenzyme A to form succinyl-CoA—goes through a series of reactions that convert it back into oxaloacetate. This conversion is still moving energetically downhill, and the energy released is captured in three events:

• The substrate-level phosphorylation of one GDP to GTP (guanine triphosphate). GTP, like ATP, is an activated ribonucleotide. The only difference is that the double-ringed nitrogenous base guanine is present instead of the double-ringed nitrogenous base adenine. The GTP formed is, in certain cases, used directly as a source of phosphorylation potential. Otherwise, GTP transfers a phosphate to ADP to form ATP.

• The reduction of one FAD to $FADH_2$.

• The reduction of three NAD^+ to three NADH.

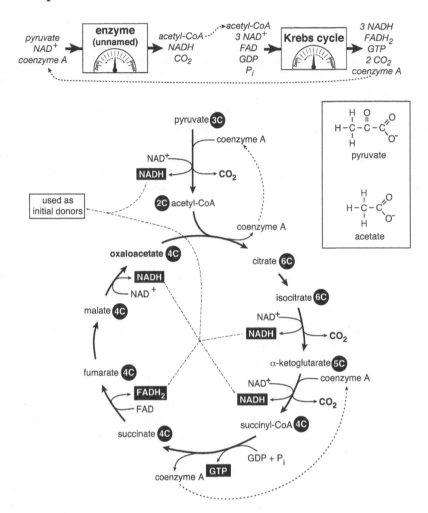

Figure 15-17. The conversion of pyruvate into initial donors first presented as two processors linked by output-input connections, followed by a closer look at the chemical reactions involved. The cyclic portion of the metabolic pathway shown—the cyclic regeneration of oxaloacetate—is known as the Krebs cycle (see text for further discussion). The box shows the structures of pyruvate and acetate.

A brief pause

In terms of making ATP, what is left is using these initial donors generated to start oxidative phosphorylation—that is, to use them (one at a time) to run an ETC. Before going on, however, it seems a good time to step back, rub one's chin, and reflect on all that has been going on.

First, starting with a single glucose, let's tally the outputs of glycolysis and the Krebs cycle combined. The only tricky part is remembering that during glycolysis one glucose becomes two pyruvates. So, the transition from pyruvate to acetate and then spinning acetate through the Krebs cycle can happen twice per glucose molecule (see Figure 15-18).

• In total, four activated ribonucleotides are formed by substrate-level phosphorylation—two ATPs in glycolysis, and one GTP in each of the two spins of the Krebs cycle. Because GTP can be converted to ATP, this is generally expressed, for convenience, as the production of four ATPs.

• Ten NAD+ are reduced to NADH. One as single pyruvate is converted to acetate, and three more as acetate are oxidized in the Krebs cycle, for a total of four per pyruvate. Double this to account for two pyruvates, and the total reaches eight. Add the two more produced in glycolysis, and the total reaches ten.

• Two FADs are reduced to FADH$_2$, one in each of the two turns of the Krebs cycle.

• Six carbon dioxides are formed as all six carbons in the glucose molecule are oxidized complete- ly, two as the two pyruvates are converted to acetate and four in the two turns of the Krebs cycle.

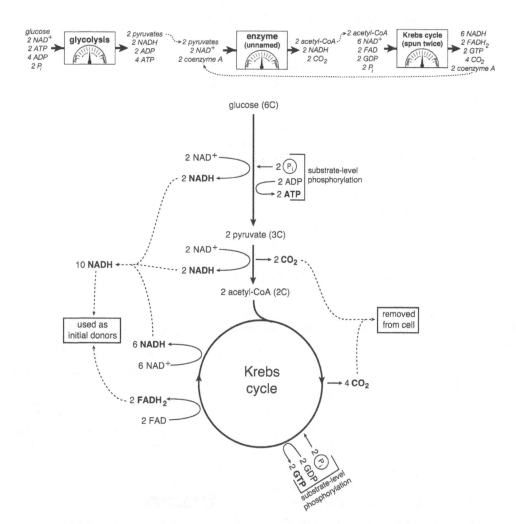

Figure 15-18. An overview of the complete oxidation of the carbons in a glucose molecule first presented as three processors linked by output-input connections, followed by a more standard overview of the metabolic pathways involved.

Next, let's remind ourselves again that discussing biosynthesis and energy metabolism in different chapters is a false division. They are both ongoing in a cell at all times. Furthermore, there is extensive overlap in the types of molecules involved in these different activities. Go back to Chapter 13, and you will find that many of the molecules of glycolysis and the Krebs cycle (e.g., pyruvate, acetate, and oxaloacetate) are identified there as precursors used in the assembly of amino acids or other biological molecules. How can a single pyruvate molecule be used to build an amino acid, and at the same times proceed on to the Krebs cycle where all its carbons are completely oxidized to carbon dioxide and initial donors are made in the process? How can an acetate (loaded on coenzyme A) be used to make fatty acids, and at the same time be oxidized in the Krebs cycle? How can an oxaloacetate be used to build an amino acid and at the same time be available to combine with acetate to start the Krebs cycle? The answer to all these similar-sounding questions is the same: They cannot. Like anything else a single molecule cannot be used in two ways at once. Cells must constantly be making choices between how to allocate their available supply of these molecules. Including energy metabolism to the mix simply adds one more option. Adding another option, however, does not change the manner that such moment-by-moment allocation decisions are made. Feedback inhibition is still the tool of choice. Figure 15-19 shows all the places where a buildup of ATP supplies feeds back to block enzymes along glycolysis and the Krebs cycle, which in turn slows the production of ATP by slowing the production of initial donors. At such times, molecules along these pathways will be diverted more toward biosynthesis.

Finally, let's place this fact—when used to make ATP, each of a pyruvate's three carbons are oxidized completely to carbon dioxide—into a larger perspective. Carbon dioxide, as I mentioned earlier, is a useless carbon source for heterotrophic cells. All carbon dioxide formed is thus released back into the atmosphere (or into water in aquatic organisms). There it floats around, prevented from escaping into outer space by the Earth's gravity, until an autotrophic cell takes it in. There the carbon is reduced to G3P. Through branching metabolic pathways, each of the carbons in G3P will then find its way into one of many possible biological molecules. Through the food chain, some of these same biological molecules may find their way back into another heterotrophic cell. There they may be used in biosynthesis. But eventually, somewhere along the food chain, the need for energy will catch up. The carbons will once again be oxidized completely to carbon dioxide (to make more ATP by making more initial donors for an ETC). The carbon dioxide will float back into the atmosphere. The ecosystem level carbon cycle has spun once.

Something to contemplate: As a carbon atom journeys repeatedly through the ecosystem-level carbon cycle, the living portion of this journey is punctuated at both ends by cell-level nutrient cycles. It is brought into life's fold by the Calvin–Benson cycle. It leaves life in the Krebs cycle. So overall, there are cycles within cycles (see Figure 15-20).

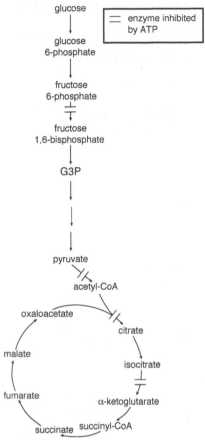

Figure 15-19. The steps along glycolysis and the Krebs cycle where the enzymes are inhibited, via negative allosteric modulation, by ATP. High concentrations of ATP within the cell will thus feedback and block these steps.

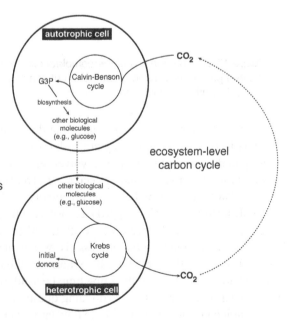

Figure 15-20. Cycles within cycles. Two major steps in the ecosystem-level carbon cycle are performed by cell-level nutrient cycles. In autotrophic cells, the Calvin-Benson cycle converts carbon dioxide from the atmosphere into GAP, which can then be used to make other biological molecules. Carbon dioxide mostly returns to the atmosphere as heterotrophic cells oxidize carbon-containing biological molecules in the Krebs cycle to generate initial donors.

A closer look at electron transport chains

So far, we encountered an ETC in light using cells. These are one-pump chains. Each time electrons pass down the chain, hydrogen ions are pumped across the membrane in one location. Respiratory ETCs, in contrast, have been found to be up to three pump chains. Whenever electrons pass the entire length of such a chain, hydrogen ions are pumped across a membrane in three distinct locations. Recall (from the previous chapter) that although two electrons at a time enter into an ETC, it is not yet known exactly how many protons are moved across the membrane at each pump. It seems to be somewhere around three to four, and the number may vary somewhat between pumps.

Each of the three pumps is a complex of membrane-bound electron carriers. Their technical names are NADH-Q reductase, cytochrome reductase, and cytochrome oxidase. I am going to just call them pump-1, pump-2, and pump-3, respectively. (A side note: Pump-2, cytochrome reductase, is chemically similar to the pump found in the ETC of light-using cells.)

The same electrons can pass sequentially through all three pumps because the redox potential of the electron carriers making up each pump decreases from one pump to the next. Specifically, electrons passing through pump-1 are donated to an electron carrier (called ubiquinone) with sufficient redox potential to transfer the electrons into pump-2. Ubiquinone acts, in essence, as an electron shuttle between pump-1 and pump-2. Similarly, the electrons leaving pump-2 are donated to an electron carrier (called cytochrome c) with sufficient redox potential to transfer the electrons into pump-3 (see Figure 15-21).

With three pumps each moving 3 to 4 hydrogen ions, a total of 9 to 12 hydrogen ions are moved across the membrane by this three-pump chain Where do all these hydrogen ions come from? Two hydrogen ions accompany the two electrons that move into the ETC from the initial donor. These two are pumped out of pump-1. The rest are pulled from the solution surrounding the membrane (see Figure 15-21).

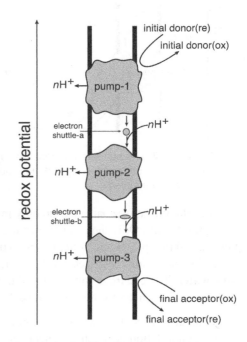

Figure 15-21. The three-pump respiratory electron transport chain. As electrons move through the chain—from the initial donor to the final acceptor—hydrogen ions are pumped across the membrane in three distinct locations.

The NADHs and $FADH_2$s generated in glycolysis and the Krebs cycle are the (molecules used as) initial donors (of the respiratory ETC). They are not, however, equally good initial donors. Where these two molecules donate electrons into the chains differs. Only NADH has high enough redox potential to transfer electrons into pump-1. $FADH_2$ is limited to donating electrons into pump-2. Use of $FADH_2$ as an initial donor thus shortens the ETC from the top—pump-1 is bypassed, so it cannot operate (see Figure 15-22).

As mentioned earlier, the list of molecules used as final acceptors by different types of bacteria is much more diverse. Within this list, however, molecular oxygen stands out. It is the only final acceptor low enough on the redox scale to accept electrons out of pump-3. So, pump-3 can operate only when molecular oxygen is the final acceptor. Final acceptors other than oxygen shorten the ETC from the bottom. Some, like nitrate, can accept electrons out of pump-2, so only pump-3 is bypassed (see Figure 15-22). Others accept electrons out of pump-1, meaning that both pump-2 and pump-3 cannot operate.

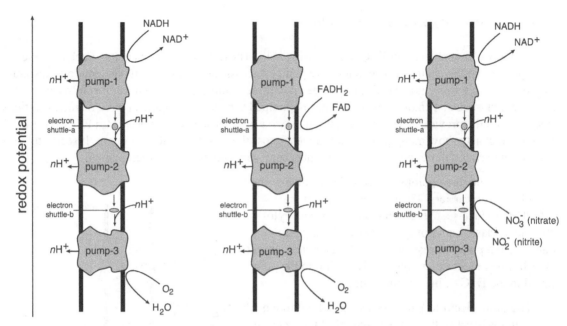

Figure 15-22. The number of pumps that operate in a standard respiratory electron transport chain depends on both the initial donor and the final acceptor. The three examples discussed in the text are presented.

All told, the entire chain can run only in the joint presence of NADH and molecular oxygen (O_2; see Figure 15-22). Only then can electrons enter at the first pump and journey down through both pump-2 and pump-3 before being taken up by molecular oxygen. What does molecular oxygen become after accepting these electrons? Water, which to distinguish where it came from is called **metabolic water**. The electrons coming out of the chain are joined by some hydrogen ions in solution, so in total two hydrogen atoms are added to each oxygen atom.

What difference does how many pumps operate make? The amount of ATP generated by oxidative phosphorylation is affected. Whenever a pump does not operate, fewer hydrogen ions are pumped across by the ETC, so there are less hydrogen ions to pass back through ATP synthetase to form ATP. To make this point clear, let's do some calculating.

Calculating ATP yield

Calculating the number of ATP that could be produced via oxidative phosphorylation requires knowing three things: (1) the number of hydrogen ions pumped across the membrane each time a pump operates, (2) the proportion of the hydrogen ions pumped across that will flow back through ATP synthetase, and (3) how many hydrogen ions need to flow through ATP synthetase for it to make one ATP. Let's briefly discuss each. The first has already been addressed, as I mentioned earlier that three to four hydrogen ions are estimated to be pumped across the membrane each time a pump within an ETC operates. (Although that figure may change with further investigation.) But what about the other two? The proportion of hydrogen ions pumped one way that return back through ATP synthetase is somewhat unknown. In a perfectly closed system, the answer would be all of them. But as shown in Figure 15-23, the first ETCs were thought to pump hydrogen ions out of the cell, where some will be lost. Yet for the moment, let's assume that most that are pumped out come back in. The final piece—the number of protons it takes for ATP synthetase to make ATP—will be affected by the aspects of its structure, such as the number of c subunits (return to Figure 14-19) or the size of the different function regions around the c-cylinder (return to Figure 14-20); but given that three ATPs can be made each time the c-cylinder rotates once (there are three beta subunits in each ATP synthetase), it will take the passage of at least two, and maybe as many as three or more hydrogen ions to make one ATP.

Given the range of uncertainty surrounding each of these figures, as well as the rough similarity between the number of protons pumped and the number needed to make an ATP, let's make it simple and just assume that every time a pump within an ETC operates, close to one ATP can be produced. Calculating potential ATP yield then is as easy as totaling the number of pumps that can operate. One NADH and one O_2 can, for example, yield around three ATPs. When NADH is the initial donor and O_2 is the final acceptor, all three pumps in the ETC can run. One $FADH_2$ and one O_2, on the other hand, potentially generate only around two ATPs—only two pumps (pump-2 and pump-3) can run with this combination of initial donor and final acceptor. Just to test yourself, why would one $FADH_2$ and one nitrate be able to generate only around one ATP?

One glucose respired aerobically

Using the one-pump-to-one-ATP conversion, it is estimated that around 38 ATPs can be gener-ated each time one glucose molecule undergoes aerobic respiration. How does one come up with this figure?

First, tally all the NADH and $FADH_2$ generated through the complete oxidation of one glucose. We did that earlier and found the total to be 10 NADHs and 2 $FADH_2$. With a ready supply of O_2 to act as final acceptors, each of these 10 NADHs can yield around 3 ATPs (30 ATPs total) and each of the 2 $FADH_2$ can yield around 2 ATPs (4 ATPs total). The total oxidative phosphorylation ATP yield per glucose is thus around 34 ATPs.

What about the missing 4 ATPs? Along the path of glucose being completely oxidized, 4 ATPs are generated by substrate-level phosphorylation—2 during glycolysis and 2 during the Krebs cycle. The grand total thus comes to approximately 38 ATPs (see Figure 15-23).

One glucose respired anaerobically

In anaerobic respiration—when substances other than oxygen act as final acceptors—ATP yield drops substantially. **Nitrate-reducing bacteria** are an example. They use nitrate (NO_3^-) as a final ac-ceptor—which is converted into more reduced forms of nitrogen such as nitrite (NO_2^-) in the process. As mentioned previously, nitrate accepts electrons before pump-3. When pump-3 cannot be used, the ATP yield from each NADH drops from around 3 to 2, and it drops from around 2 to 1 for each $FADH_2$. Correspondingly, the total ATP yield from one molecule of glucose drops from around 38 to 26—4 by substrate-level phosphorylation, 20 from the 10 NADHs, and 2 from the 2 $FADH_2$. Most nitrate-reducing bacteria, however, seem to be **facultative anaerobes**. They use molecular oxygen whenever it is present and switch to nitrate when molecular oxygen is absent. Why does this make energetic sense?

Sulfate-reducing bacteria, as their name implies, use sulfate (SO_4^{-2}) as a final acceptor. It is reduced to hydrogen sulfide (H_2S) in the process. Sulfate has a higher redox potential than nitrate and therefore can accept electrons only prior to pump-2. The ATP yield with sulfate, consequently, drops even further. When both pump-2 and pump-3 cannot be used, the ATP yield from each NADH drops to 1, and $FADH_2$ is of no use. It donates electrons at the same place that sulfate pulls them out. Overall, the ATP yield per glucose would drop to around 14—4 by substrate-level phosphorylation and 10 from the 10 NADHs. Also different from nitrate-reducing bacteria, sulfate-reducing bacteria are **obligate anaerobes**. Not only are they unable to switch to using O_2 as a final acceptor when available, but also they generally cannot live in an oxygen-containing environment. Molecular oxygen is toxic to these organisms.

In either case, anaerobic respiration is still much more energy efficient than fermentation with its yield of 2 ATPs per glucose.

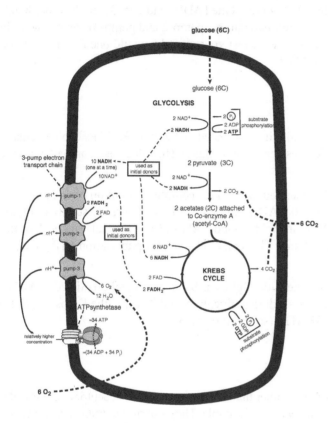

Figure 15-23. An overview of the respiration of one glucose molecule in an aerobically respiring bacteria. Through glycolysis and the Krebs cycle, the carbons in glucose molecules brought into the cell are oxidized completely to make initial donors. These initial donors are then fed into a respiratory electron transport chain, which is the first step in ATP production via oxidative phosphorylation. Four ATPs are also made by substrate-level phosphorylation along the way.

Respiring molecules other than glucose

Glucose can be respired because cells can couple the oxidization of its carbons (to carbon dioxide) with the generation of initial donors—the reduction of NAD^+ and FAD to NADH and $FADH_2$. But glucose is not the only molecule that can be subjected to such conversion. Fatty acids and amino acids are two important examples.

Fatty acids

Many cells use fatty acids as an energy source—that is, they respire fatty acids. The starting point is, however, different than glucose. Glycolysis is not involved. Instead, the oxidation of a fatty acid begins with a process called **beta-oxidation** or **fatty acid oxidation**. Remember that fatty acids contain carbon chains upward of 20 carbons in length. Beta-oxidation begins with the linking of coenzyme A with a fatty acid. Coenzyme A plus two carbons from the fatty acid then break back off, shortening the fatty acid's carbon chain by two. The energy released in this split is coupled with the production of two initial donors. One NAD^+ is reduced to NADH, and one FAD is reduced to $FADH_2$. The two-carbon molecule split from the fatty acid is acetate, and when joined to coenzyme A is called acetyl-

CoA. I am hoping that this name rings a bell. Previously, we discussed pyruvate losing a carbon to become acetate and in the process joining with coenzyme A to become acetyl-CoA. So, in total, one round of beta-oxidation yields a fatty acid shorter by two carbons, one acetyl-CoA, one $FADH_2$, and one NADH (see Figure 15-24).

The fatty acid remaining can continue to go through another round of beta-oxidation until the entire molecule is chopped into acetyl-CoAs. For instance, palmitic acid—a 16-carbon fatty acid—could be split into eight acetyl-CoAs by seven rounds of beta-oxidation. (At first glance one might think that it would take eight rounds of beta-oxidation to break up a 16-carbon chain into eight 2-carbon molecules. But it only takes seven. After six rounds of beta-oxidation, the carbon chain is reduced to four. Only one more round is needed because one split of a 4-carbon chain yields 2-carbon molecules.)

The acetate in the acetyl-CoAs coming out of beta-oxidation can then be used to make even more initial donors. Like we discussed earlier, it can be fed into the Krebs cycle where it is completely oxidized. Three NADH and one $FADH_2$ result (see Figure 15-24).

Counting them all up, the complete oxidation of one palmitic acid—involving seven rounds of beta-oxidation and eight spins of the Krebs cycle—would result in the generation of 31 NADHs and 15

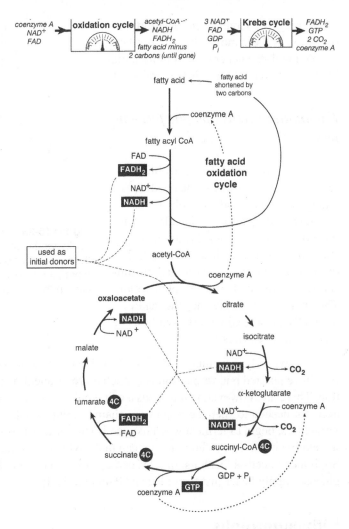

Figure 15-24. The conversion of fatty acids into initial donors first presented as two processors linked by output-input connections, followed by a closer look at the chemical reactions involved. Fatty acid oxidation breaks a fatty acid into two carbon acetates. Attached to coenzyme A, the acetates can then be fed into the Krebs cycle to finish the oxidation.

$FADH_2$. Using molecular oxygen as the final acceptor, these initial donors could then generate around 123 ATPs. Add on the eight GTPs made by substrate phosphorylation during the eight spins of the Krebs cycle, and the total is upped to around 131 ATPs. The grand total actually drops 2 to around 129 ATPs because 2 ATPs are expended in the initial activation of a fatty acid.

Amino acids

In Chapter 13, we learned that molecules along glycolysis and the Krebs cycle could also be used as precursors in the synthesis of amino acids. This can also work in reverse. After cleaving off the amine group—which subsequently becomes ammonia—the carbon skeleton of all amino acids can be converted back to pyruvate, acetate, or one of the molecules in the Krebs cycle (see Figure 15-25). These molecules can thus be oxidized further. The last part is then to enter somewhere along the glycolysis—Krebs cycle. The further oxidation of these molecules can thus be coupled with the generation of more initial donors—the reduction of NAD^+ and FAD.

Facultative versus obligate fermenters

Many types of bacteria are obligate fermenters. Regardless of the conditions under which they find themselves, they generate ATP by fermentation alone. The most obvious reason for this fermenting stick-to-itness is that these bacteria lack the ability to produce the cellular machinery needed for oxidative phosphorylation. They may, for example, lack the genes indirectly associated with the synthesis of ETC electron carriers.

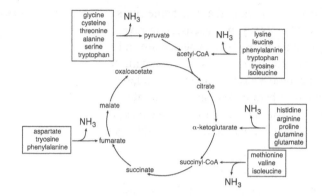

Figure 15-25. The molecules the carbon skeletons of amino acids can be converted into. Each of these molecules can then be further oxidized to generate initial donors, and in most cases power the substrate phosphorylation that occurs in the Krebs cycle.

Alternatively, a facultative fermenter is able to generate ATP both by respiration and fermentation. As I have pointed out, respiration is a much more efficient means of generating ATP than fermentation. There are, however, two reasons a cell would ferment instead of respiring. For one, the final acceptor needed to keep the respiratory chain running is not available. Your cells, which are facultative fermenters, begin to ferment when oxygen is temporarily not available. The other reason is that despite its relative inefficiency, fermentation can make ATP around 2.5 times faster than aerobic respiration. So, if a cell needs a fast burst of ATP, perhaps to dash quickly away from a predator, it may use up its glucose supply faster just to produce ATP more quickly.

Lithoautotrophs

Lithoautotrophs are discussed briefly here to make you aware that not all autotrophs are photoautotrophs. Like respiring heterotrophic cells, lithoautotrophic bacteria use an external source of oxidation-reduction energy to generate the two fuels. The difference is that they use inorganic (i.e., not a reduced carbon) compounds as the energy source. This makes them unique because they can use energy sources unavailable to other organisms. They then plug some of the generated supply of the two fuels into the Calvin–Benson cycle to synthesize reduced carbon compounds such as sugars.

The redox potential, however, of many of the inorganic compounds used as an energy source is not very high. When an inorganic compound is the initial donor, even with oxygen as the final acceptor, only one or two pumps on the ETC can operate. So, most lithoautotrophic bacteria generate ATP at a relatively slow rate. Also, these low redox potential inorganic compounds lack sufficient redox potential to generate NADPH. In these bacteria, sufficient redox potential is likely generated by some form of reversed electron transport (mentioned briefly earlier during discussion of purple bacteria). The persistence of most lithoautotrophic bacteria, however, does not hinge on their ability to grow at a fast rate. Instead, it is based on their ability to use unique energy sources.

A brief survey of different types of lithoautotrophic bacteria

Some bacteria use molecular hydrogen (H_2) as an energy source. Molecular hydrogen has the highest redox potential of any inorganic molecule used. In fact, it is the only inorganic molecule used with sufficiently high redox potential to power the reduction of $NADP^+$ to NADPH. When H_2 is used to generate ATP, its electrons are transferred first to NAD^+ to form NADH. NADH then becomes the initial donor in the ETC.

All bacteria that couple the use of hydrogen and oxygen to generate ATP can also use certain organic compounds as an energy source. The ability to use an alternative fuel is important because H_2 tends to be a rare commodity in aerobic environments.

A strictly anaerobic group of bacteria called methanogens also use H_2 as an energy source. The final acceptor, however, is CO_2 instead of O_2. In acting as the final acceptor, CO_2 is reduced to CH_4, which is known also as methane or natural gas. Methane is thus a by-product of this form of energy metabolism, hence the name methanogens. Some methanogenic bacteria live in the anaerobic portion of your gut. They feed off hydrogen gas generated as a by-product of a fermentation pathway used by other types of gut bacteria. Consequently, one constituent of your "unmentionables" is methane.

Given that CO_2 has considerably higher redox potential than O_2, electrons from H_2 can pass through only one pump before being accepted by CO_2. Therefore, the ATP yield in methanogens is not very high. This also means that the methane formed still has considerably high redox potential. In yet another example of output-turned-input, certain bacteria can use methane as an energy source. As you know, humans now pull this same trick. We burn natural gas to generate heat for activities such as cooking meals, heating houses, and producing electricity.

Some bacteria use nitrogen compounds as an energy source (nitrifying bacteria). The most common inorganic nitrogen compounds used as energy sources are ammonia (NH_3) and nitrite (NO_2^-). The completely oxidized form of nitrogen is nitrate (NO_3^-). The bacteria able to use ammonia as an initial donor only oxidize it to nitrite. A different set of bacteria can use nitrite as an initial donor, completely oxidizing it to nitrate. Thus, the complete oxidation of ammonia occurs through the actions of two groups of bacteria acting in sequence. Oxygen is the final acceptor in both cases. As mentioned in Chapter 3, these bacteria form important links in the ecosystem-level nitrogen cycle.

Some bacteria use sulfur compounds as an energy source (colorless sulfur bacteria). The most common inorganic sulfur compounds used are hydrogen sulfide (H_2S), elemental sulfur ($S°$), and thiosulfate. In one case, sulfur-oxidizing autotrophic bacteria constitute the base of the food chain for an entire biological community. In the late 1970s, a complex community of organisms were found to inhabit regions of the deep sea surrounding hydrothermal vents. Light does not reach the deep ocean, so the existence of photoautotrophic cells is not possible. Correspondingly, most of the deep ocean is void of much life. However, the hot waters that pour out of these vents are rich in hydrogen sulfide. Sulfur-oxidizing bacteria use hydrogen sulfide to generate the two fuels and subsequently to reduce carbon. The presence of reduced carbon molecules sets the stage for heterotrophic organisms to persist, hence the development of a food chain.

Most interestingly, the sulfur-oxidizing bacteria in these vent communities reside inside the cells of many vent-dwelling animals. In other words, it is an **endosymbiotic** relationship. "Symbiotic" refers to the idea that both organisms are intimately connected to the other. "Endo" indicates that this intimate relationship is formed by one organism living inside the other. The animals get their needed source of reduced carbon molecules from these endosymbiotic bacteria. If the bacteria also benefit from being housed inside these cells, perhaps by being protected from certain vagaries of the environment, then this endosymbiotic relationship is also mutualistic—both organisms benefiting from the relationship. In essence, these animal-bacteria combinations are the "plants" of the deep-sea community. They form the base of the food chain.

A Summary of Terms

There are two fundamental nutritional requirements for any organism to synthesize biological molecules and to generate motion. These are

• *Their source of high redox potential*. That is, how they generate or acquire high-energy **hydrogen-donating** molecules. High redox potential is an organism's most basic **energy source**. It can be used directly, and it is a prerequisite for an organism to synthesize molecules with high phosphorylation potential. It is also an organism's material source of hydrogen.

• *Their source of carbon*. Although organisms need a variety of materials, the most basic material required is carbon. Carbon forms the backbone of most biologically important molecules. Thus, particular attention is often paid to the form in which an organism gets its carbon for biosynthesis (i.e., its carbon source).

The source of redox potential for different types of organisms falls into two general categories:

• **Phototrophs**—can use sunlight as an energy source to generate high redox potential from low redox potential molecular arrangements.

• **Chemotrophs**—must get molecules that already have high redox potential from their environment. Chemotrophs can further be divided into two categories:

• **Organotrophs**—require organic molecules—reduced carbon compounds—as a source of redox potential. In general, organic molecules are biosynthetic products of other organisms.

• **Lithotrophs**—can use inorganic molecules with high redox potential. In general, such molecular arrangements will not be biosynthetic products.

The carbon source for different types of organisms also falls into two general categories:

• **Autotrophs**—can obtain the carbon they need for cellular biosynthesis from carbon dioxide (CO_2).

• **Heterotrophs**—must obtain the carbon they need for cellular biosynthesis from organic molecules.

Putting sources of redox potential and carbon sources together:

• **Photoautotrophs** or **photosynthetic organisms**—can use light to generate redox potential and carbon dioxide as their carbon source.

• **Lithoautotrophs**—can use inorganic molecules as their source of redox potential and carbon dioxide as their carbon source.

• **Photoheterotrophs**—can use light to generate redox potential and organic molecules as their carbon source (and probably also as a source of redox potential).

• **Heterotrophs** (or one could more accurately call them organoheterotrophs, but no one does)—can use organic molecules as their source of redox potential and carbon.

Some key terms:

photoautotrophic cell - any cell that can use light to generate sufficiently high redox potential to generate the two fuels, and then use a portion of these two fuels to convert carbon dioxide into GAP.

glycolysis - the metabolic pathway that converts one glucose molecule into two pyruvate molecules, with the subsequent production of two ATP.

Krebs cycle - a cyclic metabolic pathways where a two-carbon molecule (called acetate) enters and the complete oxidation of these two carbons to carbon dioxide is coupled with the reduction of four initial donors and production of one GTP.

NADH - the reduced form of NAD^+. It is used as an initial donor in respiring cells. (In fact, it is the initial donor that can donate electrons into the first pump of the three-pump respiratory electron transport chain.)

metabolic water - the name given to water molecules formed whenever molecular oxygen acts as a final acceptor in a respiratory electron transport chain.

Some study questions:

1. Know that light energy can be directly converted into only one form of chemical energy—redox potential, because light is only able to excite electrons.

2. Explain how the statement: *up to donate and down to accept*, can help describe how certain bacteria use a cyclic flow of electrons to generate ATP.

3. *Some bacteria (cyanobacteria) are able to take the electrons from H_2O—oxidizing water to O_2—and transfer them to $NADP^+$, reducing $NADP^+$ to NADPH. What makes this a difficult task? How are these bacteria able to get around these difficulties? How is oxidative phosphorylation incorporated into this process?*

4. *Know the major inputs and outputs in both the light phase and the dark phase of photosynthesis.*

5. (A question that ties Chapter 14 and Chapter 16 together) In a respiring heterotrophic cell, each of the carbons in an entering glucose molecule can either be used in biosynthesis or energy metabolism. What is different about the fate of a carbon atom between these two possible uses?

6. Why does a cell that just uses glycolysis to make ATP potentially face a shortage of NAD^+s? How will such shortage influence future ATP production? How does fermentation deal with this NAD^+ shortage?

7. *Explain, in general terms, how cells able to do the Krebs cycle convert acetate into initial donors and GTP. Summarize these events by listing the major inputs and outputs of this whole process. Furthermore, explain why it is important that the Krebs cycle is a cycle.*

8. Be able to see how a single glucose molecule can be used by a certain cells to make 12 initial donors (reduce 10 NAD^+s to 10 NADH and 2 FADs to 2 $FADH_2$) and generate 2 ATP and 2 GTP.

9. What is the major difference between the electron transport chains found in photosynthetic cells and those found in respiring cells.

10. *Explain how each of the following molecules are used in the production of ATP (via oxidative phosphorylation) in an aerobically respiring bacteria: NADH, FADH$_2$, and O$_2$.*

11. Be able to calculate the number of ATPs that could be made from a single glucose molecule in an aerobically respiring bacteria.

12. Certain bacteria can use either molecular oxygen or nitrate as a final acceptor. More specifically, they use oxygen as the final acceptor when it is present, and switch to NO$_3^-$ (nitrate)—which is then reduced to NO$_2^-$ (nitrite)—when oxygen is absent. Explain why the use of nitrate results in a lower ATP yield. Be able to calculate how many fewer ATP could be produced from a single glucose molecule.

13. *Is glucose the only molecule that an aerobically respiring bacteria can respire? Explain.*

14. *(Overview question) Compare and contrast fermentation, aerobic respiration, and anaerobic respiration along the following lines: ATP yield per glucose, involvement of glycolysis, involvement of Krebs cycle, involvement of oxidative phosphorylation, involvement of substrate-level phosphorylation.*

15. *(Overview question) Explain the role that chemical cycles play in energy metabolism. What are some molecular types that are recycled (or regenerated) within the cell?*

16. (Overview question) Trace the basic means by which an aerobically respiring cell can use a supply of acetate and molecular oxygen (O$_2$) to produce ATP. Briefly explain two ways that an aerobically respiring cell could generate a supply of acetate.

Prokaryotes

If you could take a ride in a time machine back a couple of billion years ago, the world you step into would be strikingly different. First, you would quickly die from lack of oxygen (see Chapter 15), but before you blacked out you may be struck by the seeming absence of living things. But it is not as though they were not there. Organisms appear to have had a continuous run on this planet for the last 3.5 billion years or so. It is just that organisms present were either too small to see or had the appearance of what we might call "scum."

The metabolizing, reproducing cells at this time fall into a group termed prokaryotic cells or prokaryotes. Prokaryotes are generally the smallest and overall simplest organisms found on this planet. Their cell structure is the most basic, and prokaryotic cells often exist as single-celled organisms. Even when prokaryotic cells remain attached to other prokaryotic cells, which is not uncommon, each cell within the group commonly retains the ability to reproduce independently. As such, groups of prokaryotic cells are often better described as a colonial arrangement of single-celled organisms, instead of a single, labor-dividing, coherently functioning, multicellular organism.

Given their relative simplicity, it is not surprising that prokaryotic organisms seem to have the longest history. There is no clear evidence that the eukaryotes (the other major group of organisms) came onto the scene until about the last 1.5 billion years ago, suggesting that the first couple billion years of Life's history was strictly prokaryotic. This means that Life in its complete form—that is two loops and one sun—is a prokaryotic phenomenon. One loop, reproduction, started the ball rolling. The sun entered the picture as soon as some prokaryotes came to use light as an energy source. The second loop—nutrient cycles—formed via the hallmark of prokaryotes, taking advantage of new opportunities through metabolic diversification. Not only did some they come up with ways to make a living in wide ranging habitats and environmental conditions, but also effectively every output of one type of prokaryote eventually became an input for another. In the process prokaryotes diverged into a seemingly large, but still unknown (and perhaps unknowable) number of different species (if that term is actually meaningful), each with population sizes that typically make trillions seem like an incredibly tiny number. (Recall the earlier discussion—in Chapter 5—of the population sizes and type diversity of single-celled prokaryotic organisms.) Even today, the nutrient cycles of Life would keep chugging along through the collective action of prokaryotes. However, as was discussed with the nitrogen cycle in Chapter 3, the reverse is not true. Remove all prokaryotes, and all the eukaryotes will quickly go extinct due to running out of needed material inputs. In other words, Life is a prokaryotic phenomenon, whereas eukaryotes (although quite fascinating) are an embellishment.

So why don't we pay closer attention to prokaryotes? Basically because they are invisible. It is not that we can see right through them, but that they are far too small to see. Objects must be around 200 μm (micrometers, where a micrometer is one millionth or 0.000001 meters) or bigger before they break into our visual range. Individual prokaryotic cells do not even come close. They are spherical to rod-shaped cells commonly ranging between 1 and 10 μm in length, so even the larger prokaryotes are 20 times smaller than what we can see without some form of microscope. Only when bacteria form large colonies do they break into our visual range.

The purpose of this chapter is to give you a basic feel for the nature of this huge, but invisible, component of Life. We will start by addressing why prokaryotic cells are so small.

Why Are Prokaryotic Cells So Little?

Physical realities keep prokaryotic cells so tiny. Two factors in particular limit cell size. First, prokaryotic cells rely on diffusion to move materials in, out, and around cells, and diffusion is slow, especially as distances increase. As a consequence, diffusion becomes an increasingly inadequate means to move stuff around as cells get larger. Second, the movement of materials into and out of any cell via diffusion occurs through the cell's surface. It turns out, however, that as a cell gets larger (without changing shape) the amount of surface unit volume decreases. This trend makes it more difficult for larger cells to get enough materials in and out to meet their metabolic demands. Next I discuss each in more depth.

A mathematical preface

To discuss issues surrounding size, it would be helpful if you were comfortable with a little math—specifically expressions such as: $y \propto x^z$. Let's read this out: The value of y is proportional to the value of x raised to the exponent z.

As you know, at times details can get in the way of seeing the bigger picture. The same holds true when using math. Calculating exact answers can, at times, add a mind-numbing and often intimidating-looking level of detail. Clarity is served by focusing on only those factors that have the most pronounced effects on any relationship. To a mathematician this often means focusing in on those parts of a calculation raised to an exponent because exponents have the greatest effect on an answer. For instance, multiply 10 by two different numbers, say 2 and 3, and then compare the difference between these answers and the values obtained by raising 10 to the 2nd or 3rd power. Multiplying 10 by 3 instead of 2 surely makes a difference in the answer—30 is bigger than 20. But compared to changing the exponent from 2 to 3, the effect is minimal. Here switching exponents results in a 10-fold change: $10^2 = 100$, whereas $10^3 = 1000$.

Next we focus on how an object's surface area—the amount of space that wraps the outside of any object—changes as objects become bigger. We could make such comparisons by calculating the exact surface area of every object. Yet except for simple shaped objects such as cubes or spheres, the task of calculating exact surface areas is difficult. That turns out, however, not to pose a problem because the relationship we need to uncover can be illustrated without exact calculations. We just need to know generally how surface area changes as similarly shaped objects get bigger. It turns out that the surface area of an object is proportional to the object's length raised to the second power (surface area $\propto$ length^2, or abbreviated as $SA \propto L^2$). Squaring the length of any object will not exactly calculate its surface area, but it will put you in the ballpark.

Diffusion is slow

Diffusion is one way that materials such as certain types of molecules can be moved from one place to another. Overall, molecules tend to move from regions of high concentration to regions of low concentration than vice versa. (Diffusion is discussed in more detail in Chapter 12). But now, I add another consideration: How fast can diffusion move materials across a distance?

Suppose someone walks 10 meters in 5 seconds at comfortable pace. How long would take them to walk 20 meters? Twenty meters is twice as far, so it would take twice as long, or 10 seconds. To put it in mathematical speak, when it comes to walking—at least until tiredness enters the picture—time is directly proportional to the distance traveled (time $\propto$ distance). Twice the distance takes twice as long, three times the distance takes three times as long, and so on.

Does diffusion work similarly? Does the time it takes to move materials via diffusion increase in direct proportion to distance? Although intuitively it may seem like it should, it does not. With diffusion, materials move in all directions from the source (the high concentration area). Materials spreading out over an increasingly large area with increasing distance results in it taking more than twice as long to get a fixed quantity of materials twice as far. Roughly, time goes up in proportion to the square of distance (time $\propto$ distance^2). To move the same amount of materials twice as far takes 4 times as long, 10 times as far takes 100 times as long, and so on.

Because of this, diffusion may be an excellent way to move materials in, out, and around organisms for very short distances, but not for longer distances. For example, consider the movement of oxygen from the environment to inside an organism. A fixed amount of oxygen diffuses extremely short distances quite rapidly. It has been estimated that oxygen can diffuse 10 micrometers (μm; the diameter of a large prokaryotic cell) in just 1/100th of a second. But what about longer distances? Consider oxygen traveling via diffusion what still seems like a very small distance—one millimeter (1 mm or one thousandth of a meter). One millimeter (which is approximately 0.04 inches) is a 100 times greater distance, so it takes approximately 100 x 100 ($100^2 = 10,000$) times longer for diffusion to move the same quantity of oxygen. Multiplying 10,000 times 1/100th second comes to 100 seconds. It is now closing in on 2 minutes for diffusion to move the same amount of oxygen just 1 mm. It is not clear that any oxygen-using cell could wait that long. Yet recognize what this means. Any part of a cell cannot be as far as 1 millimeter away from an oxygen-yielding surface. Yikes!

Just to really get into the swing of this problem, let's extend the distance to a meter. A meter is 1,000 millimeters, and so it takes a fixed amount of oxygen around $1,000^2$ times longer to diffuse a meter in comparison to a millimeter. Thus $1,000^2$ times 100 seconds (the time it takes to move a millimeter) comes to 100 million seconds, or over 3 years! It should be abundantly clear that diffusion through an exterior surface alone could not keep meter-sized cells adequately supplied with oxygen.

Conclusion: One reason that cells are small is that they depend on diffusion to move materials in, out, and around the cell. But due to diffusion's slowness, diffusion distances must remain small.

Surface area to volume ratio changes with size

The second reason that prokaryotic cells are so small has to do with how the surface area to volume ratio (*SA/V*) changes with size.

The amount of area that encloses any cell (its surface area) is the amount of area that a cell has to get molecules in and out. So the larger the total surface area, the faster a cell can exchange molecules with its environment—a realization that at first glance seems to argue in favor of larger cells. Larger objects obviously have more total surface area, so the larger a cell is, the faster such an exchange can take place. It is too bad that stories are not always so simple.

The other aspect to this story is that increasing size changes the total amount of molecules that a cell needs to exchange. This amount depends on how fast a cell, through chemical reactions, converts molecules into unusable forms; which in turn depends on the overall metabolic demand of the organism. Because metabolism occurs within the volume of a cell (volume being the amount of stuff wrapped up inside its surface area), metabolic demands should go up at least roughly as fast as a cell's total volume increases. And like surface area, a cell's volume increases with increasing size.

Now let's get to the heart of the matter. We have two things increasing as a cell gets bigger: the rate it can exchange molecules with its environment, and the rate that it can process (hence needs to exchange) molecules. The rate of exchange increases with increasing surface area, and the rate of processing increases with increasing volume. Yet because both surface area and volume increase with increasing size, it may seem that size makes no difference because both would cancel each other out. Wrong! Although both volume and surface area increase with increasing size, they do not increase at the same rate. Volume increases faster than surface area. So demand for resources increases faster than the ability to get resources in. This is not a healthy trend. In fact, if cells grow past a very small size, they will starve to death because supply cannot keep up with demand. That bigger cells will die of starvation is clearly another reason that cells tend to be quite small.

Figure 16-1 shows the exact relationship between surface area to volume ratios for some simple-shaped objects—cubes and spheres—over a series of sizes. In particular notice that in both cubes and spheres, volume increases with increasing size faster than surface area. Specifically, as the side length of a cube or the diameter of a sphere increases fourfold, volume increases 64-fold, whereas surface area increases only 16-fold. This means that the surface area to volume ratio (SA/V) decreases with increasing size. Larger objects (of the same shape) have less surface area per unit volume as do smaller objects—always!

By just paying attention to the exponents one can see that volume always goes up faster than surface area. Calculating the surface area of either a cube or a sphere involves squaring (raising to the second power) something, whereas calculating the volume for either shape involves cubing (raising to the third power) something. Cubing increases the size of any number faster than just squaring it. In general terms, the surface area of any shaped object (not just cubes and spheres) is roughly proportional to the length of that object squared ($SA \propto L^2$), whereas the volume is roughly proportional to the length of the object ($V \propto L^3$).

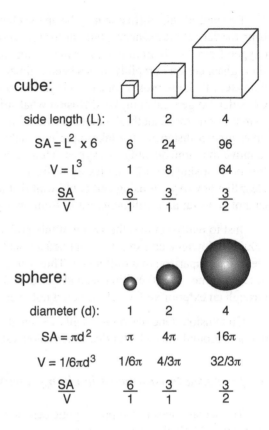

Figure 16-1. The exact calculations for how surface area to volume ratio (SA/V) changes for both cubes and spheres as a linear dimension (side length in cubes and diameter in spheres) doubles twice (from 1 to 2, then from 2 to 4). The unit of length is arbitrary, meaning that it could be centimeters, inches, meters, miles, or anything else.

Basic Features of Prokaryotic Cells

The basic structure of a prokaryotic cell is, for the most part, the generalized version of a cell I started building in Chapter 8. Proteins are the molecules that do the work, and a single circular molecule of two-sided DNA called the **bacterial chromosome** or **prokaryotic chromosome** stores recipes of the needed proteins. (By circular I am not implying that the DNA is arranged in a circle, but that the deoxyribonucleotide polymer connects back on itself, so that, like a circle, the double-side polymer has no ends.) Ribosomes and tRNAs are involved in protein synthesis. Basic metabolic pathways such as glycolysis are used to build ATP (energy metabolism). Metabolic pathways branching off glycolysis are used to build needed molecules (biosynthesis). A phospholipid membrane forms a container that keeps all the reproductive parts (e.g., DNA, RNA, and proteins) inside, and various molecules move in and out via simple diffusion, facilitated diffusion, or active transport. Finally, prokaryotic cells usually deal with the general osmotic problem (discussed in Chapter 12) by surrounding the cell with a rigid cell wall composed of familiar parts—amino acids and sugars.

Reproduction

Here is a riddle: How can reproduction take place when no parents remain and nothing has died? Answer: A single-celled organism pulls itself apart to form two new cells. Biologists call these two new cells **daughter cells**. The parent cell is in essence gone, but it has not died. The process of one cell becoming two is commonly termed **cell division** or **binary fission**.

Cell division cannot be as simple as dividing the cell in half. In particular, splitting a cell's DNA in half will just not do because when it comes to genomes, half of one is nothing. For each daughter cell to potentially grow up and reproduce, it must start with an entire genome (as well as a full complement of any other cell parts needed to get it on its way), which means that a cell's DNA must be duplicated prior to cell division. These two genomes must then be distributed so that each daughter cell receives at least one of each duplicated part.

An intriguing question concerning DNA duplication is, How fast can it occur? In other words, how fast can a single circular chromosome be made into two identical chromosomes? The answer depends on the interplay between three factors: (1) how much DNA there is to be replicated; (2) how fast deoxyribonucleotides can be polymerized along each template side; and (3) how many places along the chromosome replication is initiated. Our discussion of Okazaki fragments and DNA synthesis showed that the machinery to fuse pieces of DNA together is present. And simultaneous initiation of replication at more than one spot along the circular chromosome would clearly speed up the time it takes to replicate the whole chromosome.

Among different types of prokaryotic cells, chromosome size appears to range between 6 hundred thousand and 13 million base pairs with 3 to 4 million base pairs being a fairly typical size. A chromosome of 3 to 4 million base pairs has somewhere around 4,000 genes present and stretched out from end to end is somewhere around 1,000 times the diameter of a typical prokaryotic cell. To fit inside the cell the chromosome is twisted and coiled into a more compact arrangement. So the bottom line is that there is a fair amount of DNA to be replicated with each cell division.

The polymerization rate in prokaryotic cells is another reminder that it is hard to envision how fast chemical reactions can proceed within a cell. The estimated rate is around 500 deoxyribonucleotides per second. Yet although this rate seems remarkable, it would still take over two hours to replicate a chromosome of 4 million base pairs if replication started in one place and proceeded in one direction. What is puzzling about this two-hour figure is that under favorable conditions prokaryotic cells with a 4 million base-pair chromosome have been observed to replicate every 20 to 30 minutes. How is this possible? Part of the answer is that replication proceeds in both directions whenever it is initiated, which effectively doubles the 500 nucleotide per second polymerization rate. But even at 1,000 nucleotides per second, a 4 million base-pair chromosome would still take over an hour to replicate, so something else must be going on. The seemingly obvious addition would be to initiate replication at more than one place along the chromosome. In prokaryotic cells replication is initiated at specific sites along the chromosome known as **replication origins**, which can be as long as 300 base pairs and contain characteristic DNA sequences. Two replication origins on opposite sides of the chromosome would cut the replication time in half, three replication origins spaced equidistantly along the chromosome would cut the replication time by a third, and so on. The only problem with this solution is that prokaryotic chromosomes seem to have only one replication origin. Sometimes the obvious answer may not be the correct one. What seems to be going on is that under favorable conditions a cell begins a new round of DNA replication (at the same replication origin) before the last round is completed. As a consequence, daughter cells emerge from each round of cell division with a head start—they have already begun to replicate their DNA.

Correctly distributing chromosome copies between daughter cells is complicated by the fact that DNA does not do anything. Something must effectively latch on and pull a whole genome's worth of DNA into each daughter cell. In prokaryotic cells, this distribution system is based on a protein-based arrangement that connects the circular chromosome to the cell's plasma membrane. This protein anchor divides as the chromosome duplicates. The force needed to pull one chromosome copy into each daughter cell is actually a pushing force generated by growth of the cell membrane (and cell wall) in between the two anchors. As the membrane grows, the anchor points are pushed apart, which in turn pulls one copy of the chromosome into each daughter cell (see Figure 16-2).

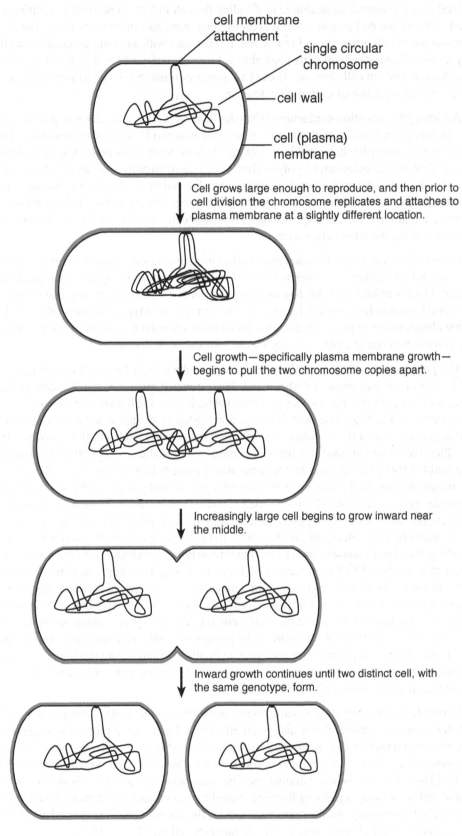

cell membrane
attachment

single circular
chromosome

cell wall

cell (plasma)
membrane

Cell grows large enough to reproduce, and then prior to
cell division the chromosome replicates and attaches to
plasma membrane at a slightly different location.

Cell growth—specifically plasma membrane growth—
begins to pull the two chromosome copies apart.

Increasingly large cell begins to grow inward near
the middle.

Inward growth continues until two distinct cell, with
the same genotype, form.

Figure 16-2. A generalized view of prokaryotic cell division.

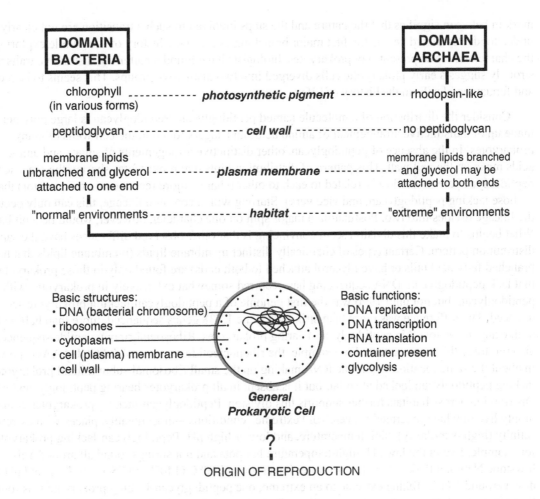

Figure 16-3. A phylogeny summarizing the split of prokaryotes into two distinct groups.

This distribution system may explain why prokaryotic cells house their entire genome within a single chromosome. Effective distribution depends on membrane growth occurring between the duplicated anchors. With only one chromosome, this seems possible to coordinate. But envision a prokaryotic cell whose genome was broken up into more than one chunk of DNA (more than one chromosome). Each chromosome would have a separate anchor that duplicates as the chromosome duplicates. But now effective distribution depends on membrane growth occurring between each set of duplicated anchors. How is this supposed to happen? Either each anchor set would have to perfectly straddle a single line of growth, or membrane growth would need to occur at a number of locations. Implementing either sounds complicated. With more than one chromosome to keep track of, there are simply more things to go wrong.

A future note: The genome in eukaryotic cells is typically broken up into more than one chromosome. For example, the human genome is broken up into 23 chromosomes. But as we will discuss much more in the next chapter, it seems likely that this was made possible by the evolution of a different type of distribution system.

Phylogeny and diversity

Figure 16-3 places the general prokaryotic cell in an evolutionary perspective. In this phylogeny, the first reproductive entities evolve eventually into a generalized prokaryotic cell. The question mark in between signifies that the nature and the steps involved in such a transition are not clearly understood. Postulated next is the first major branching event in the history of life. While exploring the characteristics of present-day prokaryotes, biologists have found a pattern of distinctive traits that strongly suggests early prokaryotic cells diverged into two distinctive groups. This seems to be a deep and fundamental split in the history of Life.

Consider the distribution of a molecule named peptidoglycan. Peptidoglycan is large polymer made up of a distinctive arrangement of amino acids and sugars found in the cell walls of many prokaryotes. In the absence of peptidoglycan, other distinctive arrangements of sugars and amino acids make up the cell wall. This pattern of distribution hints that prokaryotes sharing the presence of peptidoglycan are more closely related to each to other (share a more recent common ancestor) than to those lacking peptidoglycan, and vice versa. Starting with a common lineage, this can only occur if the lineage divides into two. Postulating a major split on one character, however, would be a bit hasty. What begins to make this division seem convincing is that other observed differences have the same distribution pattern. Certain types of chemically distinct membrane lipids (membrane lipids that have branched fatty acid tails or have glycerol attached to both ends) are found only in those prokaryotes that lack peptidoglycan. DNA sequencing has occurred somewhat extensively in prokaryotes with peptidoglycan, but not until 1996 was the first genome of a peptidoglycan-lacking prokaryote sequenced. The difference was more than striking. Of the 1,738 genes sequenced, more than half were unlike any genes found in peptidoglycan-bearing prokaryotes. Ribosomal ribonucleotide sequences also reinforce this same pattern. For example, the ribonucleotide sequence AAACUUAAAG shows up in about the same location within the RNA making up the small ribosomal subunit in all prokaryotes lacking peptidoglycan looked at so far, but it is absent in all prokaryotes bearing peptidoglycan tested. Distribution across habitats further supports this division. Peptidoglycan-lacking prokaryotes commonly live in what are termed "severe" or "extreme" conditions—most notably, places with extreme salinity (high osmolarity), high temperature, and low or high pH. Peptidoglycan-lacking prokaryotes, for example, live in the low pH, high-temperature hot pots and hot springs found all around Yellowstone National Park, where temperatures hover around 60°C (140°F) to 75°C (167°F), and pH is down around 1 or 2. Taking extreme to an extreme, one peptidoglycan-lacking prokaryote was found living near a volcanic vent on the ocean floor. Tests showed that not only could it survive in temperatures up to 110°C (230°F), but it also functioned best when temperatures were around 98°C (208°F). Finally, some members of both groups are able to use light as an energy source, but the nature of their photoexcitable molecules (pigments) is quite different. All peptidoglycan-bearing prokaryotes use some form of chlorophyll, whereas the other group uses a pigment similar to the light-receptor protein **rhodopsin** found in the rod cells of vertebrate eyes.

These groups of peptidoglycan-lacking prokaryotes are classified as the domain **Archaea,** which contains one kingdom, the **Archaeabacteria**. Alternatively, peptidoglycan-bearing prokaryotes are classified as the domain **Bacteria**, which contains one kingdom, the **Eubacteria**. This division changes the way we must think and speak about prokaryotic cells. In the past, all prokaryotic cells were referred to as bacteria as though all prokaryotes fit neatly into one group. That view does not fit anymore. To add some perspective to how fundamental this split within the prokaryotes seems to be, all the Life falls within only one more domain, **Eukarya**, which is commonly split into four kingdoms: **Protista**, **Plantae**, **Fungi**, and **Animalia**.

Despite having a similar basic structure, prokaryotic cells in each of these two domains are not all the same. The basic prokaryote plan has diverged into a wide variety of different types of organisms that, due to shape–performance trade-offs, display an equal wide range of performance differences. They all persist by taking advantage of different opportunities. To give you some sense of how bacteria have diversified, Figure 16-4 points out six of the major avenues of modification that have occurred within the Eubacteria. Just imagine all the different types of organisms that could be put together through permutations of these six variables. Lots! (Note: To delve further into prokaryotic diversity one could focus more closely on the different types of prokaryotic organisms and try to understand

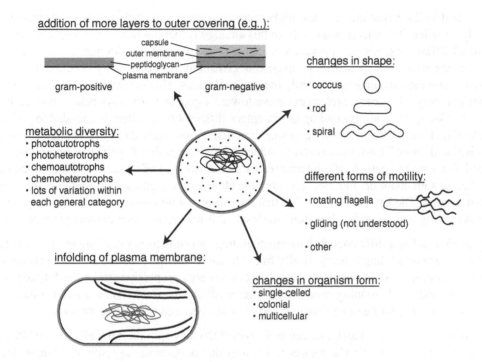

Figure 16-4. Six of the major themes along which Eubacteria diversified into different types.

how each of these differences allows them to make a living. But doing so is beyond the general scope of this discussion.)

Motility and the effects of size

Being able to move is advantageous for organisms, especially when combined with some form of sensory system. Combining motility with the ability to detect the presence of certain things in the environment creates the possibility for an organism to move away from danger of different forms or move toward food sources or other positive environmental settings.

Many prokaryotic cells use structures called flagella to move through water. Each flagellum is a stiff structure composed of protein subunits that sticks out from the cell (like a tail on a dog) and is connected to a rotating motor located on the cell's surface. When the motor rotates, the flagellum rotates as well, literally propelling the bacteria through water. The motor, like ATP synthesis, uses a proton motive force (a hydrogen ion gradient) as a fuel source and has been shown to spin as fast as 54,000 rotations per minute (rpm). Not too bad, considering your car's engine may get up to around 5,000 to 6,000 rpm. How fast can they propel themselves along? In terms of absolute speed, they move quite slowly—somewhere between 20 and 80 micrometers per second. Just to get some perspective, at 50 micrometers per second a cell could move a meter in little over 5.5 hours. But in terms of how many body lengths per second they can move, they are impressive. A four-foot-long cheetah moving at 70 mph is moving at around 25 body lengths per second. In contrast, some flagella-driven bacteria have been clocked at more than 30 body lengths per second. Furthermore, flagella-driven movement is used in biologically important ways. With the aid of chemical sensors, flagella-driven prokaryotes demonstrate **chemotaxis**—where positive chemotaxis is moving toward the source (toward higher concentrations) of favorable chemicals, and negative chemotaxis is moving away from (toward lower concentrations of) harmful chemicals.

So far flagella-driven prokaryotes might seem analogous to propeller-driven submarines, only a whole lot smaller. But what is missing from this analogy is that the tiny size of prokaryotes introduces additional differences. For one, prokaryotes cannot propel themselves through the water in a straight line. They are small enough that they can be knocked about, thus constantly knocked off course, by collisions with the surrounding randomly moving molecules. This fact adds a complication to the chemotaxis story: How can a prokaryote move toward a goal if it is always being knocked in different directions? Wouldn't it always end up in someplace different from where it intended to go? To compensate, flagella-driven prokaryotes generate directional movement through a strange combination of "tumbles" and "runs." Each run involves counterclockwise-rotating flagella that propel the prokaryote forward. But runs are periodically interrupted by a brief reversal of flagella rotation, which causes the bacterium to spin about or "tumble." Each tumble changes the organism's orientation in a seemingly random manner. The key to chemotaxis is that the runs last a bit longer when the prokaryote senses that it is moving in a favorable direction. So slowly this bias results in movement in a net direction.

Size also makes a difference in how much gliding can be incorporated into movement. This is significant because gliding is energetically free. The more an organism can glide, the cheaper that it can travel. You, for instance, glide through air between each propulsive stroke (each time you push off from the ground) while running. Even in a thicker medium like water, fish use a thrust-and-glide motion, in some cases gliding more than five body lengths between propulsive strokes.

Is the same true for a flagella-driven prokaryote? Do they spin their flagella for a while and then glide for a while, and so on? The answer is that they do not because they cannot. At their size the inertial forces that underlie gliding are quite small in comparison to the opposing viscous (frictional) forces of the medium (which in their case is water). Physicists express this relationship by saying that these tiny prokaryotes live at a low **Reynolds number**. Reynolds number is the ratio between the inertial forces (which are determined by the mass times the velocity of the organism) and the viscous forces of the medium (the more viscous the medium the greater the viscous forces, e.g., molasses is more viscous than water, whereas water is more viscous than air). (An additional note: Reynolds number is a dimensionless value or number because all the dimensions like distance per unit time (e.g., feet/sec) attached to the components of the Reynolds number equation cancel out, leaving behind an absence of any dimensions). An organism's Reynolds number gives you an idea of how far the organism will glide after turning off its propulsive machinery (called the **stopping distance**). In low Reynolds numbers the stopping distance can be very small. A two-micrometer-long bacterium operates at a Reynolds number of around 0.000001 (1×10^{-6}), which translates into a stopping distance of around 10^{-17} micrometers—a distance much less than the diameter of a single atom. So for all practical purposes, prokaryotes cannot glide. Consequently, prokaryotes must keep their flagella rotating constantly if they want to move. Just for comparison, a swimming human experiences a Reynolds number of around 1,000,000 (10^6, or a million). This means that a human-sized animal's capacity to glide in water is around 1,000,000,000,000 times greater than that of a prokaryotic cell.

Waiting instead of moving

Environmental conditions experienced by any organism constantly change. In part, the organism itself facilitates this change as it brings in inputs from the environment and dumps back out different outputs. Environmental conditions also change as a result of weather changes, daily cycles, seasonal cycles, and so on. At any location, conditions currently favorable for some organism will often not remain that way, and an organism needs to respond when conditions turn from good to bad. The most obvious response is to move to a better location (e.g., positive chemotaxis in flagella-driven prokaryotes). But due to their small size, prokaryotes are never going to be able to move very far. Previously we calculated that to move just a meter could take 5.5 hours, and that assumed that the prokaryote could move in a straight line.

But if moving is not always a potential solution, how do prokaryotes persist in the face of fluctuating environments? Some do something that I find to be both very clever and somewhat hard to imagine. Instead of dealing with input scarcity by doing something to increase the supply, like moving, they reduce their need for inputs—that is, they reduce their demand. They respond to nutrient scarcity (and perhaps other forms of environmental change) by differentiating into a dormant form. Depending on the details of how the conversion occurs, the dormant form is called an **endospore**, an **exospore**, or a **cyst**. The common feature of each is that some portion of a metabolically active cell is encased in extra thick layers of cell wall–like material. The biological significance of a dormant stage is clear; instead of needing to move whenever local conditions turn bad, the organism can stay put and wait for good conditions to return. With the return of good conditions, it often takes only a matter of minutes for a spore to convert back to an active cell—a process known as spore germination.

An intriguing question is, How long can a spore (or other dormant form) wait around? The presence of any metabolism within the dormant forms would set a limit because eventually a spore or cyst would use up its supply of stored nutrients. Yet, this may not be a factor as mature spores have no detectable metabolism. Still, DNA within spores would be expected to degrade with time, given the absence of DNA repair enzymes, and the ongoing presence of background radiation, as well as other things capable of initiating chemical reactions. Yet, at least in short-term tests, spores tend to be highly resistant to environmental stresses such as high temperature, irradiation, and strong acids. That spores can last months to even years seems quite clear. But what about even longer than that? It is a hard question to address because prokarotes are so pervasive that it is difficult to find settings where spores were deposited years before and subsequently sealed off in a way that prevents more recent contamination. Archeological digs through lake sediments have found viable endospores that may be thousands of years old. If true, this is remarkable. In the early 1990s spores were isolated from the stomach of a bee that had been sealed in amber around 25 to 40 million years ago, and they germinated—that is, they were still viable. Perhaps, somehow contamination occurred, and these were faulty findings, but if true, then it was much more than remarkable. It begins to suggest the absence of any clear upper limit to spore "survival"—an idea bolstered in the late 1990s when viable spores were found embedded in salt crystals thought to be deposited around 250 million years ago. Is this really possible?

Prokaryotic ecosystems

As mentioned earlier, the nutrient cycles of Life formed as metabolic diversification within prokaryotes continued to take advantage of new opportunities, and every output of one type of prokaryote eventually became an input for another. What warrants further discussion is how certain types of output/input connections actually formed in prokaryotic ecosystems. Waste connections seem the most straightforward, as any molecule that somehow can be released through the cell membrane (and cell wall) of one type of prokaryotic cell could be brought back through the cell membrane of a different type of prokaryotic cell. But feeding connections are more puzzling. How would one prokaryotic cell gain access to a biological molecule inside another prokaryotic cell? Cells encased in a rigid cell wall cannot rearrange their shape in a way that allows them to engulf another organism (and subsequently "steal" their molecules). Furthermore, many of the molecules worth harvesting (that is, stealing) from another organism are polymers (e.g., proteins, DNA, RNA, polysaccharides), which means these molecules would need to be digested—that is, use enzymes to break the polymers back into their monomer form—before they could be utilized. Yet, if a cell somehow brings in a biological polymer built by another, and then subjects it to enzymatic degradation, wouldn't it also digest itself? For instance, enzymes that break up proteins into amino acids are going to digest self-proteins as well as any protein brought into the cell. However, the only other option is to digest harvested biological polymers outside the cell (and then bring the monomers across the cell membrane), but how is a cell supposed to build and deliver digestive enzymes to the outside? In Chapter 12, we spent some time on how cells build proteins, but the underlying presumption was that the proteins were built inside the cell. Next, we discuss each of these issues (biomolecular theft and digestion) in turn.

Biomolecular theft

A common theme by which one organism feeds on (steals biomolecules from) another is in someway engulfing either all or a part of the "prey." Furthermore, in the part of the living world most familiar (i.e., visible) to us, predators—which by definition kill their prey in the process of engulfing them—are typically larger than their prey. Yet, as mentioned earlier, single-celled organisms encased in a rigid cell wall (the typical prokaryote) do not have the option of engulfing anything. This suggests that predator–prey type feeding connections may not exist in the prokaryotic world. That is, instead of prokaryotes higher on a food chain killing others to gain access to their inner molecules, they must either live off molecules secreted from others or play the role of a decomposer by waiting for other prokaryotes to die and spill their contents.

It turns out, however, that although more patient food chain connections may be common features of prokaryotic ecosystems, predatory prokaryotes do exist. Furthermore, they are phylogenetically diverse (i.e., evolved multiple times from different lineages) and ubiquitous in both terrestrial and aquatic environments. They just do their killing differently. To start, they tend to be smaller than their prey because in lieu of swallowing them, they either adhere to their outside or penetrate inside. For example, a predatory bacteria known as *Vampirococcus* attaches to the outer surface of its prey, where it remains and multiplies while somehow feeding off the cytoplasm. Essentially, only the prey's cell wall and the outer membrane remain after they finish. In contrast, *Daptobacter* are rod-shaped, gram-negative bacteria that after attaching to a prey cell, somehow bore into its interior and degrade its prey's cytoplasmic molecules, using these resources to grow and undergo cell division while still inside its prey. The third known predatory strategy is exemplified by a prokaryote called *Bdellovibrio*. These small bacteria invade the periplasmic space—the space between the outer and plasma membrane—of certain gram-negative bacteria. They then proceed to feed off the cytoplasmic contents by making the plasma membrane very leaky, which as a result kills the cell.

Digestion

Let's build a simple, but seemingly universal, digestion scenario. Digestion is an essential part of biomolecular theft whenever the consumed organism has biological polymers (that it made), but the monomers are the theft's (commonly known as consumers) true target, as they can be used by consumers to build their own polymer arrangements or rearranged further in their own metabolic pathways. Proteins are a common example. They are universal components of cells, thus readily available to be stolen, but typically are not of much value unless first broken down into amino acids for use by a consumer to make its own protein arrangements, or metabolized in some other useful way. Similarly, polysaccharides commonly need to be cleaved into simple sugars before a cell can use them in energy metabolism or some other metabolic pathway. The question that remains: Where should digestion occur? Given that the prokaryotic world is, in essence, divided into two spaces—inside and outside a cell—there are two possibilities. Each, however, poses its own complications.

For digestion to occur within the cytoplasm of a thieving cell, two events would need to take place. First, mechanisms able to transport all forms of polymers with useful monomers across the cell membrane would need to be present. The large molecular size of polymers, along with their potential variety of shapes (especially among proteins) would seemingly make such a task immensely complicated. This may help explain why there is no evidence of its occurrence. But even if it did, the second needed step would also be complicated to pull off. Any cell making polymers similar to those being brought would need a means for digestive enzymes—the enzymes needed to cleave polymers into monomers—to break up foreign polymers, while leaving functional self-made forms alone. Otherwise, a cell would literally digest itself. Mechanisms have been discovered by which self-made proteins that are damaged or currently unneeded are tagged within a cell and subsequently targeted for destruction (digestion). But given that the first needed step does not occur, a mechanism to only target foreign polymers for digestion has not been needed, so presumably has never evolved. Could it have evolved? Possibly, but the bottom line is the cytoplasmic digestion of foreign polymers, for whatever reason or reasons, has not become part of Life's story.

This means that the other alternative—prokaryotic cells coming up with a means to produce and dump digestive enzymes into the surrounding environment—is part of Life's story. What follows is a very brief sketch of how this seems to happen.

All ribosomes remain in a cell's cytoplasm after being synthesized in a ready position to attach to any newly formed mRNA. On the other hand, all mRNAs are *not* the same. First, when they are transcribed from different genes, they contain different protein recipes. But there can be another significant difference. The beginning of certain mRNAs also code for a specific amino acid sequence known as a **signal peptide**. In such cases, the initial string of amino acids formed by RNA translation—typically 5 to 30 amino acids long—is not part of the protein coded for by the mRNA, but acts as a signal that designates the site of protein synthesis. When the signal peptide is absent, the ribosome–mRNA complex remains freely floating within the cell's cytoplasm, and consequently any newly synthesized protein is released into the same space. In contrast, when an mRNA that intially codes for a signal peptide attaches with a ribosome, the story, via some added complexity, changes. First, structures made within the cell from several proteins and a single RNA molecule (or a ribonucleoprotein complex) known as **signal recognition particles (SRPs)** have the right shape to bind with (recognize) signal peptides. In effect, this means that they can bind with any ribosome–mRNA complex currently engaged in protein synthesis that starts out producing a signal peptide. Furthermore, this binding inhibits mRNA translation and hence typically stops the continual addition of amino acids prior to translating the protein-coding portion of the mRNA. This work stoppage, however, tends to be temporary. Bound to the plasma membrane of prokaryotic cells are structures made from two polypeptides called **SRP receptors**. One of the two subunits anchors this structure to the membrane. The other subunit plays two important roles: (1) It has a region that can bind with an SRP molecule attached via a signal peptide to a mRNA-ribosome complex, and (2) it attaches with—and thus keeps nearby—a membrane-embedded protein complex called the **translocon** or **translocation channel**. Now comes the punch line! When an SRP molecule bound to a signal peptide–ribosome–mRNA complex also binds with a membrane-bound SRP receptor, a shape change (driven in part by the hydrolysis of a GTP molecule) frees the SRP molecule, allowing the signal peptide to switch and now bind with the adjacent translocon. With the SRP molecule out of the way, mRNA translation can start up again and proceed into the protein coding region. Due to signal peptide–translocon connection, the emerging polypeptide subsequently moves into the membrane-embedded channel as an unfolded string of amino acids. Finally, after translation is finished, an enzymatic region cleaves off the signal peptide, and the remaining protein is free to slip through the channel to the other side—that is, to the outside of the cell—and fold into its functional shape. (All the steps discussed here are illustrated in Figure 16-5.) If that shape acts as a digestive enzyme, it would then begin cleaving apart any polymers of the right type that it comes in contact with. Resultant monomers could then potentially move into the cell by facilitated diffusion or active transport.

Couple this ability to produce digestive enzymes outside the cell with the predatory scenarios described earlier, and it becomes clear how each type was able to degrade the prey cell's cytoplasm. But the ability to produce external digestive enzymes would not only be useful to prokaryotic predators. Cells that die for reasons other than being killed by a predator tend to lyse and spill their contents into the environment, including polymers made up of valuable monomers. Prokaryotes making a living as scavengers or decomposers would, thus, also benefit from being able to secrete digestive enzymes into the environment.

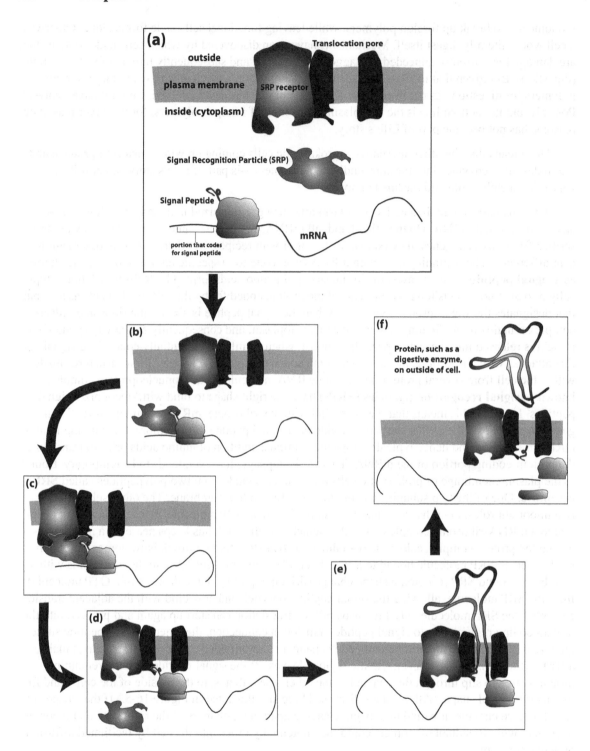

Figure 16-5. The major steps in the protein secretory pathway. (a) All the main components are labelled, and the portion of an mRNA that codes for a signal peptide has been translated. (b) The signal recognition particle (SRP) binds with the signal peptide emerging from the ribosome engaged in translation, stopping further translation. (c) Still bound to the signal peptide-ribosome-mRNA complex, the SRP binds with the membrane bound SRP receptor. (d) Due to conformation changes, the SRP is released and the signal peptide attaches to a binding site on the translocation channel. (e) Released from SRP inhibition, translation continues, with the newly formed polypeptide slipping through the translocation channel. (f) Protein synthesis is completed, the signal peptide is cleaved from the rest of the polypeptide, freeing it to move into the space outside the cell and fold into the 3-dimensional shape dictated by its primary structure. See text for further details.

Furthermore, although the ability to release digestive enzymes into the environment has potential benefits, what was described earlier is a general protein secretory pathway. There is no reason that secreted proteins other than digestive enzymes could accrue benefits. For instance, certain proteins released could be harmful to other prokaryotes competing for similar resources. If so, the extra cost associated with their production could be more than made up for by the benefits of decreased competition. Also, recall that prokaryotic flagella are composed of protein subunits positioned outside the cells and thus need to be secreted. The same would be true for any other external protein structure. In fact, the same seems to be true for proteins embedded in membranes—such as those discussed in topics like facilitated diffusion or electron transport chains. Hopefully, it is clear by now that for a protein to remain in a membrane, the embedded regions would need to be lipid soluble. But how did it get there? Perhaps whenever a cell produces a protein with lipid soluble regions, eventually it would come to embed in a membrane, as that would be the most stable arrangement. That could be how the first membrane-bound proteins took up their arrangement, and it could still happen in modern cells. But, curiously, in modern cells membrane-bound proteins commonly use the signal-peptide-based-secretory-pathway to take up their position. Here is the twist! As any newly formed protein threads its way through the translocation channel it still associates with hydrophobic regions of the lipid bilayer. As a consequence, proteins with lipid soluble regions can remain embedded in the membrane instead of passing through. In contrast, proteins that are largely water soluble will not be held up and thus can be secreted to the outside.

An aside: Once the signal-peptide-based-secretory-pathway evolved in prokaryotic cells, which of the proteins made were destined to be synthesized in a translocation channel (and thus either secreted——water soluble, or embedded—lipid soluble regions) was determined by one simple factor—whether the beginning of the gene coded for a signal peptide. Although not discussed here, there are mechanisms by which pieces and parts of DNA can be copied and rearranged or inserted into new regions. So, once a signal-peptide-based-signal-pathway existed, DNA regions coding for signal peptides could potentially be inserted at the start of any protein gene in the genome. Of course, any time such a switch occurs, it will be immediately scrutinized by the reproductive race of natural selection. Only those changes that overall prove useful would be expected to persist across generations.

Bring on phage

The next chapter focuses on the evolution of eukaryotic cells, and it is likely that their initial success was largely driven by their ability to come up with a new way to prey on prokaryotes. But for some reason the evolution of eukaryotic cells took a long time—perhaps as much as a couple of billion years after the advent of prokaryotes. But long before, perhaps even before the divergence of the two prokaryotic domains, another type of nonprokaryotic reproductive "thing" came along with the ability to get inside and utilize, even to the point of killing, prokaryotic cells. We call them viruses. Biologists refer to viruses that infect prokaryotes as **bacteriophages**, or just **phages**.

Phages, like anything else, need to reproduce to persist. But the way they do so is strikingly different. The difference is made evident by all the things that they *lack*, yet still need to reproduce. The three most striking omissions are (1) a cell membrane, so they do not form a distinct container (in other words, they are acellular), (2) the ability to make ATP by some form of energy metabolism, and (3) the machinery to perform protein synthesis. They get these things from the prokaryotic cells that they invade. Once inside, phages use the prokaryote's metabolic machinery to make more viruses, at times killing the prokaryote in the process.

Perhaps the best way to begin to envision the workings of a phage is to first consider a chunk of DNA inside a prokaryotic cell that is not part of the prokaryotic chromosome (see Figure 16-6(a)). Specifically, consider the expected fate of this chunk of DNA. There are a couple of reasons that it will likely go extinct. For one, even if it is replicated when the prokaryote's chromosome replicates, there is no means to distribute duplicate parts into each daughter cell during each round of cell division. Recall that it is through a membrane attachment that one copy of the chromosome is pulled into each daughter cell. Incorporation into the chromosome by some means (see Figure 16-6(b)), would solve the distribution problem, but raises the issue of what effect this DNA chunk has on the cell. If it does not code for anything, it is just extra DNA for the cell to copy before each round of cell division, which wastes both time and energy. So all else being equal, cells with this extra DNA would be expected to come out losers if caught in the reproductive race of natural selection with cells absent this extra burden. The only scenario with a reasonable expectation of persistence is if the extra DNA codes for proteins, and the effect of these proteins on the cell as a whole is sufficiently positive to outweigh the extra costs of replicating this extra DNA before each cell division.

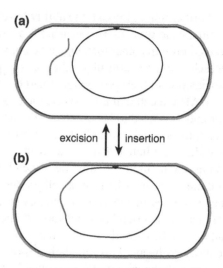

Figure 16-6. A chunk of DNA inside a prokaryotic cell that is either: (a) separate from the cell's chromosome, or (b) incorporated into the cell's chromosome. The possibility of a DNA chunk moving between these two states (insertion or excision) is an important component of the life cycle of a bacteriophage.

Now let's explore another path to persistence. Suppose this chunk of DNA codes for proteins whose effects do *not* help the cell as a whole reproduce better, but instead help the chunk of DNA that coded for them persist at the expense of the cell. If this occurs, then the DNA chunk has become what we now call a virus.

Figure 16-6 outlines a typical life cycle of a phage, showing the two means they use to persist: the lysogenic cycle and the lytic cycle. The lysogenic cycle was described earlier—incorporate into the chromosome and be replicated and distributed with each bout of cell division. The lytic cycle introduces a means for this phage to reproduce independent of the prokaryotic cell. Reproduction here includes not only making more copies of phage DNA, but also creating a means to get these copies into other prokaryotic cells. In some ways, the lytic cycle is the phage becoming a predator that consumes its prey. The science fiction sounding difference between phage and what we think of as a typical predator (e.g., a coyote preying on a rabbit) is that the phage not only uses its prey for resources, but it also uses its prey's metabolic machinery to do the work of making more phage.

The relationship between phage and prokaryotic cells is not typically characterized as predator and prey, but as parasite and host. The common notion of a parasite is that it lives within (upon) its host and does not kill it outright. Moreover, a parasite is so dependent on its host that it will die if its host dies. During the lysogenic cycle, phage clearly meets all these criteria. So what does the lytic cycle have to do with being a parasite? It is a solution to the dilemma that every parasite faces: A parasite cannot persist by just staying put within one host. For phage, the lysogenic cycle is not a reliable path to persistence for the reasons discussed—added replication costs without any added benefits. For parasites of multicellular organisms, the host will eventually die. Hosts may also be able to turn on defenses against a parasite after infection (such as an immune response) that renders the host to be only temporarily a suitable place to live. Consequently, part of the life cycle of a persistent parasite must include attempts to spread to (to infect) new hosts, even if such attempts harm the current host in the process. And because parasites typically increase transmission efficiency to new hosts by manipulating their current host to act in parasite-spreading ways, increased harm to the host will be a common feature. Acting in the best interest of the parasite means the host is being diverted from acting in the best interest of itself.

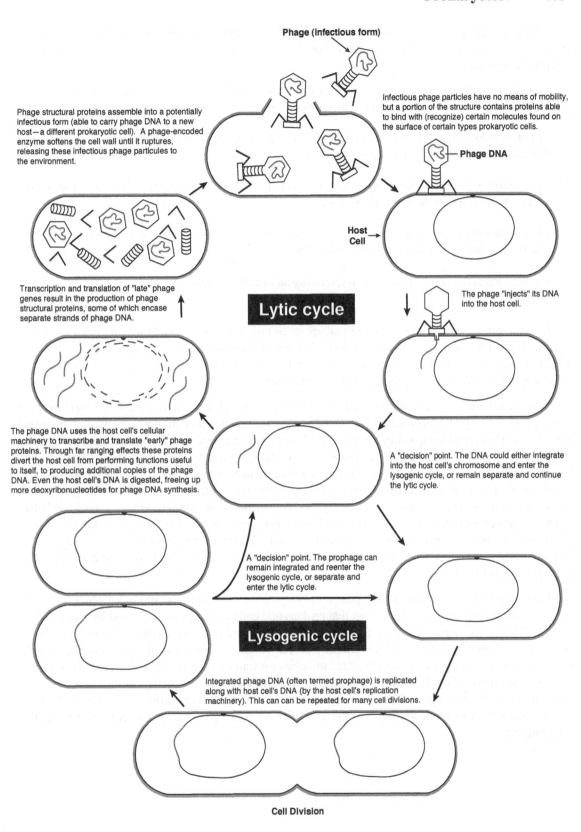

Phage (infectious form)

Phage structural proteins assemble into a potentially infectious form (able to carry phage DNA to a new host—a different prokaryotic cell). A phage-encoded enzyme softens the cell wall until it ruptures, releasing these infectious phage particules to the environment.

Infectious phage particles have no means of mobility, but a portion of the structure contains proteins able to bind with (recognize) certain molecules found on the surface of certain types prokaryotic cells.

Phage DNA

Host Cell

Transcription and translation of "late" phage genes result in the production of phage structural proteins, some of which encase separate strands of phage DNA.

Lytic cycle

The phage "injects" its DNA into the host cell.

The phage DNA uses the host cell's cellular machinery to transcribe and translate "early" phage proteins. Through far ranging effects these proteins divert the host cell from performing functions useful to itself, to producing additional copies of the phage DNA. Even the host cell's DNA is digested, freeing up more deoxyribonucleotides for phage DNA synthesis.

A "decision" point. The DNA could either integrate into the host cell's chromosome and enter the lysogenic cycle, or remain separate and continue the lytic cycle.

A "decision" point. The prophage can remain integrated and reenter the lysogenic cycle, or separate and enter the lytic cycle.

Lysogenic cycle

Integrated phage DNA (often termed prophage) is replicated along with host cell's DNA (by the host cell's replication machinery). This can can be repeated for many cell divisions.

Cell Division

Figure 16-6. The basic components of a bacteriophage life cycle.

This perspective sheds light on a familiar topic. Many of symptoms of diseases represent ways that some clever parasite modifies its current host to facilitate its spread. Following is a list of some potentially familiar examples:

• Influenza, common cold, and whooping cough (pertussis) induce the host to cough or sneeze, thereby broadcasting the parasites toward perspective new hosts.

• Cholera induces massive diarrhea that makes it easier for the parasite to get into and then spread through a water supply shared by potential hosts.

• For parasites that catch rides from host to host on biting insects, the lethargy of feeling ill may make it more difficult for the host to fend off insect bites.

• The open genital sores caused by venereal diseases such as syphilis or the skin lesions caused by smallpox create contact-based transmission pathways.

• Rabies drives a dog into a biting frenzy, creating an infection avenue.

In other words, making a host sick or perhaps even killing the host may be a by-product of promoting efficient transmission. From the parasite's point of view, as long as killing a host increases infection rate over not killing a host, the parasite's interest is best served by manipulating its host in lethal ways. The lytic cycle of phage is a classic example.

What is still very interesting about the phage life cycle is that it can switch back and forth between being a somewhat innocuous parasite (the lysogenic cycle) to being an extremely virulent parasite (the lytic cycle). This raises the question: When would switching from one to the other best promote persistence? One obvious situation where switching from the lysogenic cycle to the lytic cycle would be favored is when the host cell has suffered some form of damage. In other words, if one's current ship is sinking, it makes sense to get out and try to find another ship. Notably, exposure to damaging UV radiation promotes phage to switch from the lysogenic to lytic cycle. Although I know of no evidence, I suspect high population densities would also favor a lysogenic-to-lytic switch. Given the infectious phage particles have no means to actively search for and move toward new hosts, the only way for infectious phage particles to reliably come in contact with other potential hosts is if there are lots of other potential hosts around.

Let me end this brief interlude into phage–prokaryotic cell interactions (and more generally, host–parasite interaction) by pointing out that prokaryotic cells do not passively stand by as a phage invades. Prokaryotes have evolved defenses. For example, some prokaryotes defend themselves by producing enzymes, called **restriction endonucleases**, which will bind to viral DNA entering the cell at specific sequences (called restriction sites) and cleave it into smaller, noninfectious pieces. Their own DNA is protected by the concurrent production of enzymes that add methyl groups (—CH_3) to certain bases located within these same restriction sites during the replication of their own DNA. These methyl groups change the shape of the restriction site, thus preventing restriction endonucleases from binding.

Some key terms:

prokaryotic (bacterial) chromosome - a single circular two-side DNA molecule attached to the cell membrane that contains a prokaryote's entire genome.

peptidoglycan - a large polymer made up of a distinctive arrangement of amino acids and sugars found in the cell walls of prokaryotes in the domain Bacteria.

bacteriophage - a virus that infects a certain type of prokaryotic cell.

lysogenic cycle - when the phage DNA inserts into its host's chromosome and is replicated along with the rest of the chromosome during cell division.

lytic cycle - when the phage DNA uses its host's machinery to make more copies of a phage's infectious form. The host is killed in the process.

chemotaxis - an organism being able to use changes in concentration to move either away or towards the source of a diffusible chemical.

Some study questions:

1. Explain how the rate that materials can move by diffusion is involved in limiting the size of prokaryotic cells.

2. Explain how surface area to volume ratio (SA/V) changes as objects of the same shape get bigger. (Note: keep in mind that volume goes up as a cube of some linear dimension of size (such as length), while surface area goes up as a square of some linear dimension of size.) Next explain how this relationship is involved in limiting the size of prokaryotic cells.

3. What is the basic means by which prokaryotic cells distribute their DNA across cell division.

4. Why can't flagella-driven bacteria glide?

5. Why would it ever make sense for a prokaryote to convert into a dormant endospore?

6. Trace the basic steps by which a prokaryotic cell could produce digestive enzymes that end up outside the cell (starting with the transcription of a gene for a digestive enzyme, and including the role of signal sequences, SRPs, SRP receptors, and translocons).

7. Why would it ever make sense for a parasite such as a bacteriophage, to harm its host?

The Becoming of Eukaryotic Cells

I mentioned in the previous chapter that cells on this planet fall into two broad categories: prokaryotic and eukaryotic. Yet the fossil record does not suggest that they originated simultaneously. The structurally simpler prokaryotes appear to have preceded eukaryotes by as much as two billion years, which means that if eukaryotic cells were derived from previously existing life forms, then they arose from prokaryotic cells. How they may have done so is the focus of the next two chapters.

We have already discussed evolution as a result of cumulative bouts of modification and persistence within a single evolutionary lineage. We continue this theme to discuss how a prokaryotic cell may have evolved the standard features of a eukaryotic cell, such as flexible membranes that formed internal compartments that, among other things, wrapped around a cell's DNA forming a nucleus. The presence of a nucleus is often considered the defining feature of a eukaryotic cell.

This standard form of evolutionary explanation, however, may not be sufficient to explain the becoming of certain features found in many eukaryotic cells. The new proposed twist discussed in the next chapter is symbiotic origin. The basic argument is this: Free-living prokaryotes came to reside inside members of the eukaryote lineage—something termed **endosymbiosis**. Once inside, the prokaryotes subsequently evolved to the point that only remnants of their bacterial heritage remain. Mitochondria and chloroplasts seem to be the clearest examples of structures whose evolution started through endosymbiosis, but some have speculated that the evolution of other eukaryotic cell parts started this same way.

The Evolution of Basic Eukaryotic Features

Due to the presence of a cell wall, the standard prokaryotic cell is a rigid container. The evolution of eukaryotic cells likely started with a prokaryote evolving a flexible outer container, and so the flexibility must have started with the loss of the cell wall. Even though it sounds so simple, casting off a cell wall is no trivial change. We will discuss shortly why the loss of a cell wall is such an important step, but first let's mention potential disadvantages that must be countered.

In Chapter 12, we discussed how cell walls are used to solve a cell's basic osmotic problem. Their rigidity can prevent a cell from bursting from too much water pouring in due to the inherent inward osmotic gradient. So, for a cell to get away with losing its wall, it must have some other means in place to deal with this osmotic problem. Present-day wall-less cells in seawater (the likely setting where eukaryotic cells first evolved) actively pump out inorganic ions, such as Na^+, to diffuse the osmotic gradient. Presumably, such ion pumps were present in initially wall-less cells.

Furthermore, the membranes in prokaryotes are typically reinforced by a cell wall. Consequently, removal of cell wall support must be accompanied by some means to maintain the integrity of the outer membrane without this outer enclosure. Two factors may have played a role. Perhaps most important was evolution of structural elements positioned inside the membrane. Eukaryotic cells have a so-called internal skeleton or **cytoskeleton** that helps hold the outer membrane in place, and precursors to these structural elements have been found in prokaryotes. Furthermore, the nature of the membrane may have also changed. One membrane component unique, with rare exceptions, to eukaryotic cells is sterols (which were introduced in Chapter 12). Their addition increases the degree of order or stiffness of membranes, so altering sterol levels can be used to adjust fluidity and flexibility in a way that stabilizes outer membranes over a wide range of conditions. Some eukaryotic membranes have as many cholesterol molecules as membrane lipids. Sterols are also the key ingredient to formation of dynamic, heterogenous membranes composed of raft and nonraft areas. And this membrane differentiation is thought to play an important role in membrane-associated processes that characterize eukaryotic cells, such as endo- and exocytosis (discussed later). So don't be fooled by all the bad press about the animal sterol, cholesterol. Although excess of anything can cause problems, as an organism made up of eukaryotic cells, cholesterol plays extremely important roles in maintaining your health.

Further recognize that a cytoskeleton, in addition to an increasingly dynamic membrane, would have not only helped a cell cope with the loss of a cell wall, but would also have set the stage for a cell to be able to change its shape. A dynamic cytoskeleton—that is, one that can be rearranged into different shapes—can push and pull the outer membrane (plus the rest of the cell) along with it. And a dynamic membrane would seemingly be more capable of adjusting its properties such that it can follow the cytoskeleton's lead without breaking.

Why would it be advantageous for a cell to be able to take on a variety of shapes? In general, it may be able to conform more readily to the nuances of its environment. For instance, it could better flatten against a surface on which it is feeding, tuck into some nook that offers better protection, or acquire food in new ways—perhaps by even becoming a predator.

Controlling shape via a cytoskeleton

The concept of a dynamic internal skeleton within a cell is no different than your body's internal skeleton. Your arrangement of bones holds your shape (just imagine the shape you would take on if your skeleton was somehow removed), and the fact that your skeleton is articulating (has joints), in combination with muscles, makes it dynamic. Your skeleton is constantly changing its shape and in so doing pushes and pulls the rest of your body along with it.

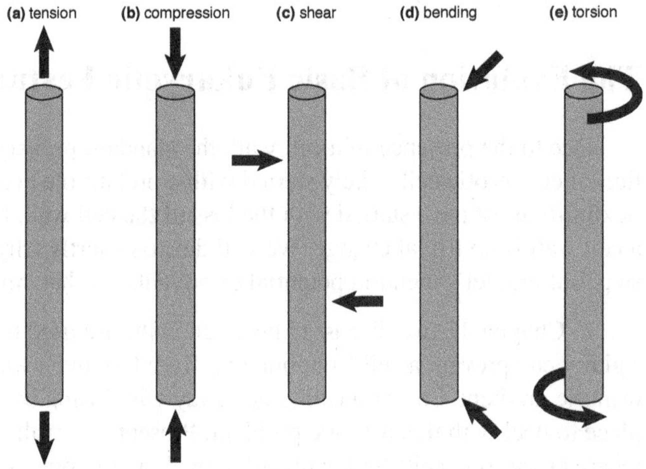

To hold a particular shape, a skeleton must be able to resist deforming forces. Sounds simple enough. But deforming or loading forces come in a variety of forms, such as tension, compression, shear, bending, and torsion (see Figure 17-1 to clarify the differences between these different types of loading forces). And what is required to resist them is different for different types of deforming forces. Ropes, for instance, are good at resisting tension, but are completely incapable at resisting compression. So, ropelike structures alone could only form a somewhat limited skeleton.

Figure 17-1. Some different arrangements of two forces acting on an object. Each of these force arrangements is called a deforming force because each will act to change the shape of the object.

A composite structure with different elements resisting different forces is a better means to assemble a broadly capable skeleton. Bone, for example, is a composite of collagen fibers (consisting of three helically arranged polypeptides coiled around each other to form a rope-like structure) and a hard-mineralized material called hydroxyapatite. The collagen fibers resist deformation caused by tension or shear, whereas the hard-mineralized component resists compression. This arrangement is analogous to reinforced concrete (concrete containing steel rods). The steel rods resist tension and shear, and the hard concrete resists compression.

Cytoskeletons (in wall-less cells) also commonly contain different elements, each of which is better at resisting different forces. The two main components are actin filaments, which resist pulling forces (tension), and microtubules, which are better at resisting all the rest. I discuss each in turn.

Actin filaments

Actin filaments take the idea of polymerization to a new level. Proteins are polymers formed by linking amino acids. Actin is a protein composed of 375 amino acids, which self-assemble into a globular three-dimensional shape. In other words, actin itself does not look like a filament. With actin, however, polymerization does not just stop there. Actin molecules have a tendency under certain conditions to link to form a helically shaped chain of actin molecules. (ATP can help speed up this polymerization, but it is not essential for actin molecules to bind together.) Typically, two helical chains form alongside each other in an intertwined arrangement to form a thin, flexible, ropelike structure known as an **actin filament** (see Figure 17-2). In other words, the protein polymer actin acts as a monomer in building actin filaments.

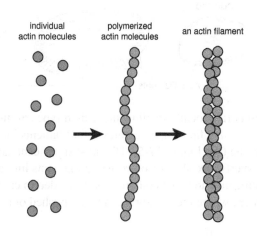

Figure 17-2. Individual actin molecules forming an actin filament.

The first striking thing to note about actin filaments concerns their distribution. Although they are present throughout the cell, they are most concentrated just beneath, and often attached to, the plasma membrane—a region known as the **actin cortex**. Furthermore, each filament within the actin cortex does not typically exist in isolation, but instead is attached to other filaments by a variety of proteins (known generically as actin filament cross-linking proteins). Cross-linking more than one actin filament into aggregates and bundles forms a structure much stronger than could be formed by individual filaments. So, an obvious function of this actin layer is to add mechanical strength to the outermost portion of the cell.

But adding mechanical strength is not the extent of its function, for this network of actin filaments is not assembled into a set arrangement. Quite the contrary, it is a dynamic assemblage. It is constantly undergoing different forms of shape changes at different locations, which, in total, enables a wall-less cell to power a variety of surface movements. Three aspects of actin filaments, in particular, contribute to this dynamic nature.

First, and perhaps foremost, actin filaments themselves are not static entities. At any moment, any actin filament is potentially getting longer (by the addition—one at a time—of more actin molecules), or getting shorter (by the depolymerization of actin molecules), or staying the same length (either through the absence of both polymerization and depolymerization, or both of these occurring at the same rate—a phenomenon known as treadmilling). As individual actin filaments change length, the shape of the actin framework as a whole also changes, which in turn may change the shape of the plasma membrane. In fact, it has been suggested that the act of lengthening or shortening actin filaments itself is used to generate shape-changing forces. (A side note: The two ends of any actin filament are not the same. One end, called the **plus end**, adds or subtracts actin molecules at a much faster rate than the other end, called the **minus end**.)

Second, the arrangement of existing actin filaments may change. Different cross-linking proteins hold actin filaments in different orientations, and different orientations play a role in changing the shape of the cell (see Figure 17-3). For example, a protein named filamin cross-links actin filaments into a three-dimensional net arrangement referred to as gel (see Figure 17-4), which likely holds the cytoplasm, and subsequently the surrounding membrane, in place by greatly increasing its viscosity. On the other hand, another protein named gelsolin acts in reverse. When activated by binding with calcium ions, gelsolin breaks up this cross-linked network, which may serve to loosen or liquefy the

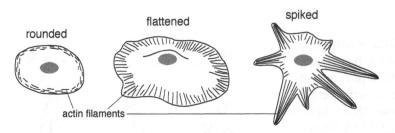

Figure 17-3. Three examples of how change in length and orientation of actin filaments can change cell shape.

cell cortex locally to allow more fluid types of movements. In contrast, a different actin-binding protein, called fimbrin, assembles actin filaments into a very tightly packed arrangement called a parallel bundle (see Figure 17-5). The most significant aspect of this three-dimensional bundle may be that it converts flexible tension-resisting filaments into a stiffer better-at-resisting-compression arrangement. Being able to resist compression is needed to create pushing forces, and parallel bundles are found in places where the membrane is being pushed out.

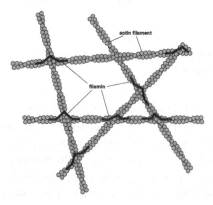

Figure 17-4. Individual actin filaments are cross-linked by a protein named filamin to form a three-dimensional net-like structure.

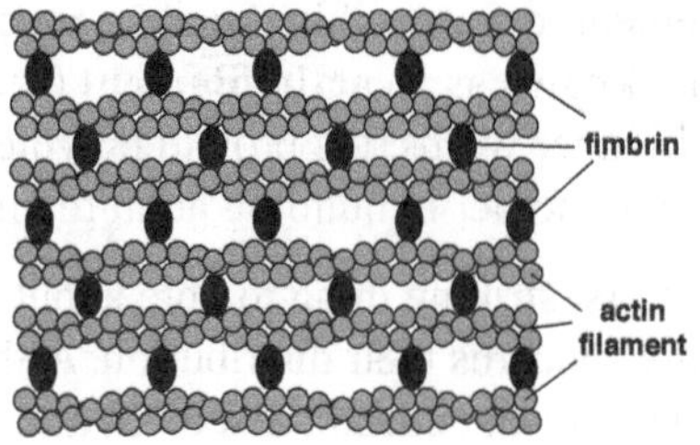

Figure 17-5. Individual actin filaments are cross-linked by a protein named fimbrin to form a three-dimensional parallel bundle.

And finally, a class of walking proteins (protein motors) called **myosin** is also involved in the shape-changing act. (If needed, return to Chapter 14 to review the workings of a walking protein.) One end of myosin molecules uses the hydrolysis of ATP to walk along actin filaments. The nonmotor end, on the other hand, binds to something else, such as another actin filament or the plasma membrane (see Figure 17-6). So as the motor end moves along, the relative arrangement of actin filaments to each other and to the plasma membrane changes. In other words, as myosin generates forces, it is able to change the relative arrangement of actin filaments with each other and with the membrane. By changing the relative arrangement, myosin movement is potentially translated into membrane movement.

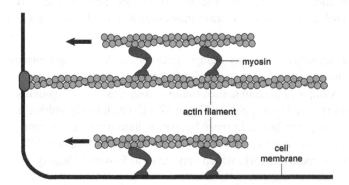

Figure 17-6. Myosin molecules are "walking proteins" that attach to one structure (a cell membrane and an actin filament are shown) and then walk along an actin filament. In doing so, the position of the actin filament is changed relative to that to which the actin molecules are attached.

Microtubules

In many ways, microtubules are like actin filaments. First, they are both polymers of a globular protein. In microtubules, the globular protein is called tubulin, which is composed of two tightly linked polypeptides called alpha-tubulin and beta-tubulin. Second, they are also both very labile structures that are not the same at both ends. They mostly grow or shrink from one end, called the plus end. The opposite or minus end is more stable. A third similarity is that they both form associations with other proteins that can cross-link individual fibers into a larger structure. And finally, they both have associated walking proteins. In microtubules, these walking proteins come in two basic forms: dyneins and kinesins. The striking difference between these two groups is that they walk along microtubules in opposite directions. Kinesins move toward the plus end, whereas dyneins move toward the minus end. (A side note: All the proteins associated with microtubules—both cross-linking and protein motors—are generically called microtubule-associated proteins, or MAPs.)

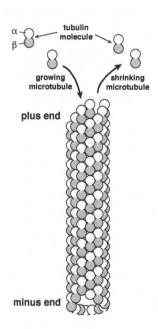

The key difference is that microtubules (as the name implies) are arranged as very small tubes. Tubulin molecules polymerize into 13 linear filaments that bundle together to form a hollow, cylindrical structure (see Figure 17-7) about 25 nm in diameter (where a nanometer is one-billionth of meter). This is around three times thicker than actin filaments, which are only around 8 nm in width.

Figure 17-7. The basic structure of a microtubule.

The reason a tubular arrangement is so significant is that tubes resist loading forces differently than filaments. Per unit weight, tubes are stiffer (better able to resist compression, shear, and bending) than any solid arrangement. This is because all the structural materials are located on the outer edge where loading forces concentrate.

Consider, for example, something undergoing compression. Unless the compressive forces are perfectly aligned, which is unlikely to happen, compression also generates bending forces. Bending forces can cause the structure to buckle. Any bending force, however, is really just a composite compression and tension. Compression forms on the side that the bending is toward, whereas tension develops on the opposite side (see Figure 17-8). But midway between these two opposite

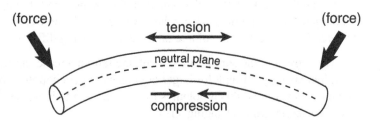

Figure 17-8. A diagram that shows how bending forces create a composite of tension and compression. The side being lengthened by bending experiences tension, while the side being shortened by bending experiences compression. In between lies the neutral plane which experiences neither of these two forces.

forces cancel out, leaving a region (identified in Figure 17-8 as the neutral plane) that experiences no force. With no forces present, structural materials at or near this neutral plane are wasted (because there is nothing to resist). Given that bending forces can happen in any orientation, the middle will be the one place that is always part of the neutral plane. This leads us to the structural logic of a tube. In a tube, structural materials are absent from the area that experiences the least amount of forces (the middle) and concentrated along the edges where the largest loading forces are experienced.

Due to their greater stiffness than microfilaments, microtubules are able to influence cell shape in different ways. For example, parallel bundles of microfilaments seem to be sufficient to reinforce small projections of plasma membrane, but microtubules make much longer projections possible. And wall-less cells have exploited this capacity. Microtubule-reinforced projections extending outward up to many body lengths (cell lengths) are found in many types of organisms. Furthermore, due to the dynamic nature of microtubules, these projections are not static. They can be retracted once formed and then formed again. One type of microtubule-reinforced projections, known as eukaryotic flagella, will be discussed further later.

Microtubules are also used to hold a cell in a particular shape. Recall that a wall-less cell has the tendency to take on a spherical shape. Some single-celled organisms, how-ever, have a corset-like arrangement of microtubules just beneath the plasma membrane that holds the cell in a more oblong shape (see Figure 17-9). One of the more important uses of a more rigid oblong shape is that it makes the cell easier to propel through water (discussed more later).

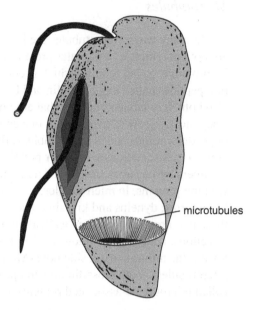

Figure 17-9. A single-celled eukaryotic organism (known as Retormonas) that shows the corset-like arrangement of microtubules used to maintain cell shape.

Getting bigger

Size makes a difference. In reference to the task of persisting, organisms of different sizes can do things such as avoid different hazards or utilize different resources. As we discussed in Chapter 5, the ability to be different is an essential ingredient for each type of organism to carve out its own unique niche within a biological community.

Given that prokaryotic cells capitalized on being small, the only way left for changing size is to get bigger. A cell cannot get larger, however, unless it can overcome the two factors limiting cell size: decreasing surface area to volume ratios and increasing diffusion distances.

We know that the surface area to volume ratio decreases as similar-shaped objects get larger, mak-ing it increasingly difficult for larger organisms to get enough resources in and out to keep them going. The only way around this problem is for surface area to increase as fast as volume with increasing size. The secret lies in changing shape.

Have you ever wondered why soap bubbles are spherical? The answer has to do with surface area to volume ratios. The soap film takes on a spherical shape because such a shape minimizes the contact between it and the surrounding air. In other words, spheres minimize the surface area to volume ratio.

The way to increase the surface area to volume ratio for any set volume is then to make the shape increasingly *less* spherical. Envision, for instance, a lump of clay that can be molded into different shapes. Regardless of the shape, the amount or volume of clay does not change. But the clay's surface area increases, hence its surface area to volume ratio increases, as its takes on nonspherical shapes. For example, roll a round ball of clay into a "snake," and its surface area to volume ratio (SA/V) increases. The longer and skinnier the snake becomes, the more the SA/V increases. Flattening the ball of clay or folding its outer surface will accomplish the same thing. Overall, the more any set volume of material is elongated, flattened, and/or folded, the greater the surface area to volume ratio becomes. The flattened and spiked shapes of the cell in Figure 17-1, for example, have higher surface area to volume ratios that the rounded shape.

The capacity for a cell to change its outer shape opens the door to increasing size. Cells can overcome the problem of having insufficient absorptive surface area by making their absorptive surfaces increasingly convoluted. Such shape changes make it possible for surface area increases to keep pace with volume increases, as organisms get larger (see Figure 17-10).

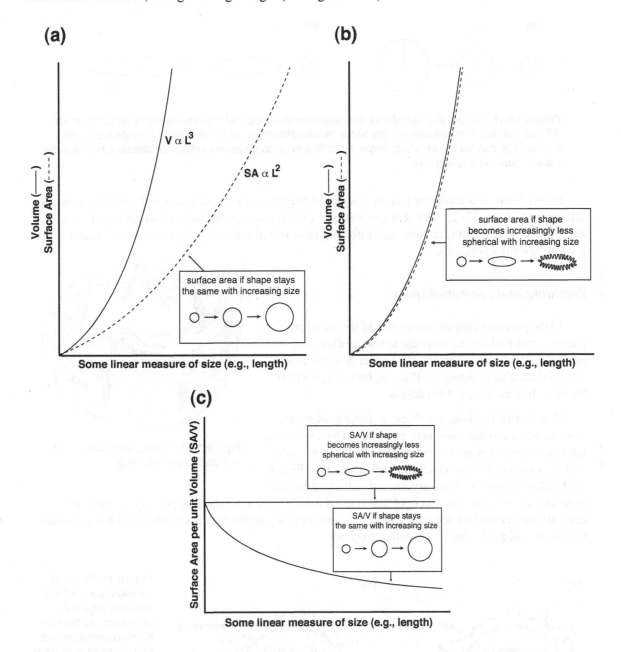

Figure 17-10. All three graphs show an aspect of how surface area and volume change as a function of increasing object length (or some other linear measure of size). In (a) the shape of the object remains the same as length increases, so volume—which increases as a cube of length—goes up significantly faster than surface area—which increases as a square of length. In contrast, (b) shows that if an object's shape becomes increasing convoluted as length increases, surface area potentially goes as fast as volume. In (c) the relationships shown in (a) and (b) are shown in terms of how surface area to volume ratio changes as a function of increasing length.

In addition to increasing surface area, changing shape can simultaneously help to counter the diffusion problem. Not only do such shape changes increase the amount of surface area through which diffusion can occur, but they also get around the slowness of diffusion by decreasing the distance that diffusion must carry materials (see Figure 17-11).

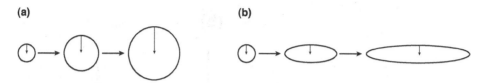

(a)   **(b)**

Figure 17-11. The small arrow shows the maximum distance that material would need to move via diffusion when (a) shape remains the same as size increases, or (b) the object's shape becomes increasingly convoluted as it gets larger. Note that in (b) the maximum diffusion distance remains the same despite increasing size.

Here I focus on a particular pattern of shape change that would increase a cell's surface area—infolding (see Figure 17-12). Not only can this type of shape change allow a cell to get larger overall, but it is also easy to envision how such infolding gave rise to some other crucial features found in present-day eukaryotic cells.

Infolding and controlled space

In the previous chapter, we discussed the secretory pathway that prokaryotic cells use to release digestive enzymes into the environment. We further discussed the potential benefits of doing so. There is, however, a part of the story that we have yet to address.

Figure 17-12. Cross-section of a cell with pockets of infolding.

Due to their rigid outside shape, a single prokaryotic cell can never use digestion very efficiently. Once released, both the digestive enzymes and the digested food particles will disperse in all directions through diffusion (see Figure 17-13). Consequently, a prokaryotic cell will never be able to absorb all, or even very much, of the digested food particles. Competing prokaryotic cells may even absorb some of what escapes. If so, the competitors gain the benefits of digestion without bearing the cost of producing the digestive enzymes.

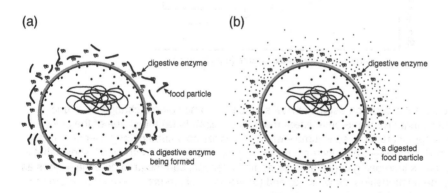

(a)   **(b)**

digestive enzyme

food particle

a digestive enzyme being formed

digestive enzyme

a digested food particle

Figure 17-13. In (a), a prokaryotic cell has released digestive enzymes into the surrounding environment that contains food particles too large to absorb. Yet in (b), the scattering effects of diffusion make it impossible for the cell to absorb all that it digested.

Infolding of outer membranes potentially increases digestive efficiency. Although not completely sealed, infolded areas would better contain both digestive enzymes and digested food particles. As a consequence, fewer digestive food particles escape through the random movement of diffusion (see Figure 17-14). In essence, infolding creates a means for an organism to gain better control over its outside environment.

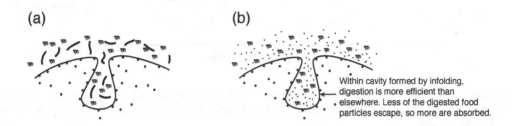

(a) (b)

Within cavity formed by infolding, digestion is more efficient than elsewhere. Less of the digested food particles escape, so more are absorbed.

Figure 17-14. The same scenario as Figure 18-13, except that now the cell has infoldings.

Notice that although digestion as shown in Figure 17-14 would be more efficient than that shown in Figure 17-13, there is still room for improvement. Two possibilities stand out. First, the cell could somehow selectively form infoldings around available food particles. Second, the cell could localize the release digestive enzymes into food-particle-containing infoldings. In other words, it could only build and release digestive enzymes where they would do the most good. We now discuss how cells have come to do both.

Endocytosis and exocytosis

Endocytosis involves using the ability of membrane movement (via actin and myosin) to form pockets around food particles. The pockets actually extend until membranes touch and join, forming a completely sealed container (see Figure 17-15). It is a landmark change. Prior to endocytosis, cytoplasm occupied all the space within the plasma membrane. Now a part of the outside environment is wrapped up and brought completely inside the cell (see Figure 17-16). Because nothing can escape from this internal cavity—often called a **vesicle**— cells capable of endocytosis can gain complete control over a small chunk of its environment. In terms of digestion, the advantage is marked. The cell can still perform digestion in a space that is effectively outside the cell, yet all digested food particles are prevented from escaping by being enclosed in a vesicle.

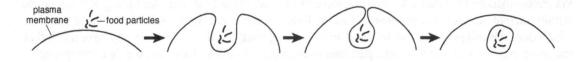

plasma membrane food particles

Figure 17-15. Endocytosis of food particles.

The evolution of endocytosis was accompanied by its reverse, **exocytosis** (see Figure 17-16). Pieces of the environment wrapped up by endocytosis are again released back into the space surrounding the cell by exocytosis. Exocytosis could release any indigestible molecules captured by endocytosis back to the surrounding environment.

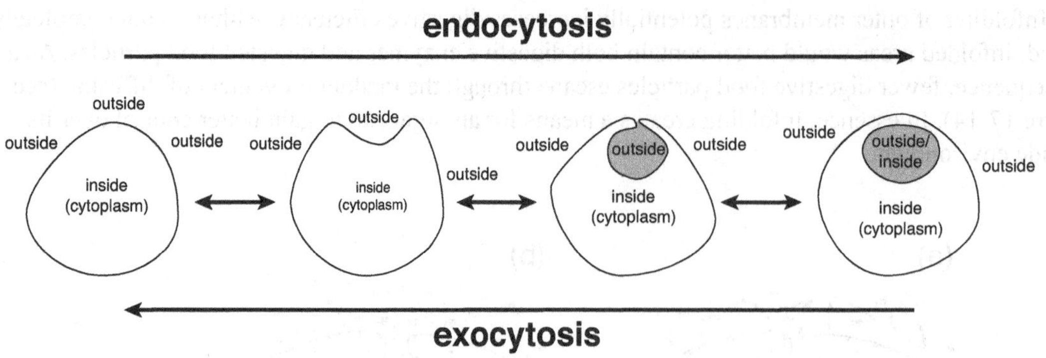

endocytosis

exocytosis

Figure 17-16. How endocytosis wraps up a piece of the environment and brings it inside the outer boundaries of the cell, while still keeping the outside separate from the cytoplasm, and how exocytosis does the reverse.

Relocating signal recognition particle (SRP) receptors

As long as signal recognition particle (SRP) receptors (that bind with the mRNA-ribosome complex when a signal peptide is present) are located along a membrane bordering the cytoplasm, synthesized digestive enzymes (or any other protein whose mRNA also codes for a signal sequence) will slip from the cytoplasm side of the membrane to the other side. Yet, exactly where this "other side" is depends on their location. If SRP receptors are located all over the plasma membrane, then digestive enzymes will be secreted from all parts of the plasma membrane. This distribution is implied in Figure 17-13. Alternatively, digestive enzymes would be release only within the pockets formed by infolding if SRP receptors were located only along the infolded regions of the plasma membrane. From the perspective of an individual cell, such a selective distribution seems like it could be advantageous because digestive enzymes would be released only where the cell is most effective at absorbing the nutrients made available by digestion (see Figure 17-14).

As it turns out, SRP receptors have been localized along certain membrane regions in eukaryotic cells, but not in any way that you might first suspect. Let me head first to the punch line, and then spend time trying to make sense of the described observation.

SRP receptors have been removed entirely from the plasma membrane in eukaryotic cells and instead are located along the membrane that forms a permanent internal cavity (called the endoplasmic reticulum). So, as any protein accompanied by a signal peptide is synthesized, it still slips outside the cytoplasm, but it does not slip outside the cell. Instead, it is held within a membrane-bounded compartment located inside the cell. This means that food particles brought into an enclosed vesicle via endocytosis and the digestive enzymes needed to break these food particles up are both contained within internal vesicles. The problem is that the food and digestive enzymes are in different vesicles, which does the cell no good. But let's add an interesting twist to this tale. We already have a cell that can use endocytosis to wrap up food particles in an enclosed vesicle. Now add the fact that through an endocytosis-like mechanism, vesicles can also bud off from these more permanent internal cavities, carrying some of their contents. All that is left is a means to fuse a vesicle loaded with digestive enzymes with a vesicle containing food to be digested. Digestion would take place outside the cell, but within a closed container. As a consequence, fewer digestive enzymes would need to be produced, and most digested food particles are potentially absorbed as the container prevents escape. Leftovers could be dumped out by exocytosis (see Figure 17-17). It is a nifty tale. It is also the basic scheme by which present-day endocytotic cells do digestion.

There is a second major theme in this relocation story. If SRP receptors are located along the membranes of an internal compartment, how will permeases and other membrane-embedded proteins needed in the plasma membrane (but now initially synthesized along these internal membranes) move

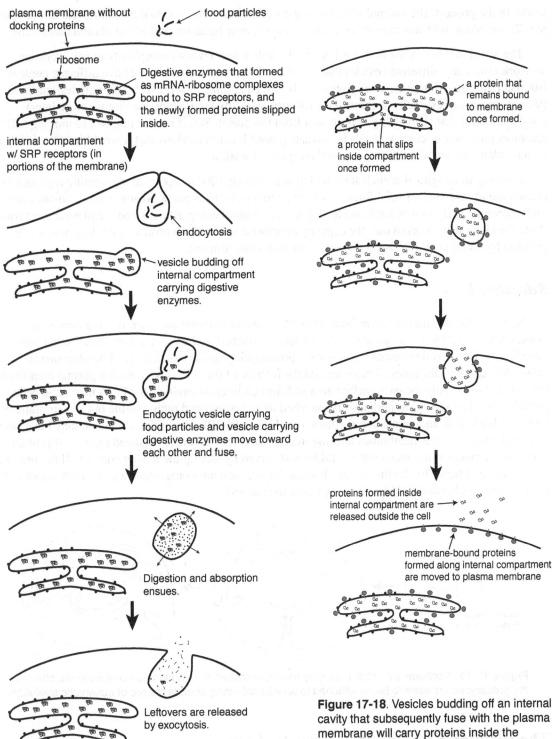

plasma membrane without docking proteins

food particles

ribosome

Digestive enzymes that formed as mRNA-ribosome complexes bound to SRP receptors, and the newly formed proteins slipped inside.

internal compartment w/ SRP receptors (in portions of the membrane)

endocytosis

vesicle budding off internal compartment carrying digestive enzymes.

Endocytotic vesicle carrying food particles and vesicle carrying digestive enzymes move toward each other and fuse.

Digestion and absorption ensues.

Leftovers are released by exocytosis.

a protein that remains bound to membrane once formed.

a protein that slips inside compartment once formed

proteins formed inside internal compartment are released outside the cell

membrane-bound proteins formed along internal compartment are moved to plasma membrane

Figure 17-17. The basic steps by which digestion occurs in endocytotic cells.

Figure 17-18. Vesicles budding off an internal cavity that subsequently fuse with the plasma membrane will carry proteins inside the compartment to outside the cell, and transfer any membrane-bound proteins formed to the plasma membrane.

to their proper position? Similarly, how will proteins that still best serve the cell when dumped into the surrounding environment, get there? The answer lies in where vesicles budding off of these internal membranes end up. In Figure 17-17, the vesicle fused with another internal vesicle formed by endocytosis, mixing their contents. Alternatively, in Figure 17-18, the vesicle fused with the plasma membrane. In the process, the internal contents of the vesicle were dumped to the outside, and the vesicle membrane, along with any membrane-bound proteins, now becomes part of the plasma membrane.

The snafu in this scheme is that it potentially adds a new level of complexity to cell workings. To work efficiently, different vesicles that move to different locations should have different contents. But that requires different types of proteins to be sorted among vesicles with different destinations. Present-day eukaryotic cells demonstrate such sorting ability (something we discuss more later), but it's doubtful that such ability was present from the outset. Yet, if it were not, would moving SRP receptors into interior compartments be advantageous? It is not obvious that it would be. One is left to wonder about the transitional steps in SRP receptor relocation.

It is easy to imagine that such steps included localizing SRP receptors along specific regions of the plasma membrane such as infoldings, or where endocytosis takes place. At some intermediate stage, SRP receptors likely moved back and forth between internal compartments and the plasma membrane. Once the kinks were worked out, the capacity to better control which proteins go where was made possible by locating all SRP receptors on an internal compartment.

Relocating DNA

So far in this discussion I have ignored DNA. In the prokaryote ancestor, it is reasonable to assume that the DNA was a single circular molecule attached to the plasma membrane. What happened to the DNA while internal cavities were proliferating inside this lineage of flexible-membraned cells? Perhaps, the DNA moved more toward the interior of the cell as well. As the plasma membrane invaginated to initially increase surface area and formed internal cavities, the DNA may have been pulled along. The DNA was perhaps first attached to an invaginated region of the outer membrane but later was hooked to an internal compartment (see Figure 17-19). The initial advantage may have been straightforward. As the membranes forming internal cavities became specialized regions of protein synthesis, it makes sense that a cell would be best served by having the master copy of all the protein recipes close at hand. Especially as cells became larger, such an arrangement would cut down on diffusion distances between DNA and sites of protein synthesis.

Figure 17-19. A scheme by which DNA may have first moved from a plasma membrane attachment in the prokaryotic ancestor to being attached to an internal cavity in early stages of eukaryotic evolution.

The Defining Features of Eukaryotic Cells

Although the simple scenario I painted earlier lacks much detail and is speculative, it creates a somewhat logical scenario of how cells changed from their prokaryotic ancestor in five important ways: becoming larger, acquiring the ability to do endo- and exocytosis, forming more permanent internal cavities, moving SRP receptors from the outer membrane to the membranes of these internal cavities, and moving DNA from an outer membrane to an inner membrane attachment. Once these were in place, evolution by natural selection could continue to elaborate. Perhaps the most fundamental change is the formation a convoluted internal cavity called the **endoplasmic reticulum** (ER), which completely encircles the cell's DNA. The DNA-containing space created is called the **nucleus**. As I already mentioned, the presence of a nucleus is considered the defining feature of eukaryotic cells.

Endoplasmic reticulum

All eukaryotic cells have a highly convoluted, membrane-bounded structure known as the endoplasmic reticulum. Whether the ER is all one single compartment or many separate compartments is difficult to tell because the folding is so extensive. Nonetheless, the ER makes up a significant portion of a eukaryotic cell. First, it may be a common feature of eukaryotic cells that the total amount of membrane within the ER exceeds the total within the plasma membrane. In two eukaryotic cells examined closely (mammalian liver and pancreatic cells), the ER had 12 and 25 times as much membrane as the plasma membrane. Furthermore, the internal cavity formed by the ER membrane (in biological speak as the **ER lumen** or the **ER cisternal space**) may comprise a significant proportion of a cell total volume. In mammalian liver cells, the ER lumen has been estimated to occupy more than 10% of the total cell volume.

The ER has two functionally distinct regions (see Figure 17-20):

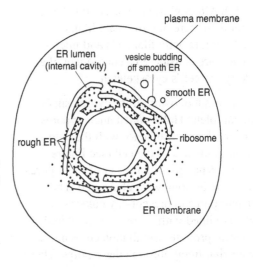

• *Rough ER*. This is the region of the ER containing SRP receptors. Due to the constant production of secretory and membrane-bound proteins—that is, the protein recipes that also code for signal peptide—within a cell, it is always studded with ribosomes. This gives it a rough appearance and also its name.

• *Smooth ER*. Ribosomes do not appear to attach to the entire ER membrane, suggesting that some portions of the ER lack SRP receptors (or at least functional SRP receptors). This region is called the smooth ER because without attached ribosomes the membrane has a smooth appearance. Membrane synthesis and other forms of lipid synthesis are thought to occur along the smooth ER, which is in contrast to prokaryotic cells, where it occurs along the outer membrane. So, this seems to be another example of an activity switched from the outer membrane to the ER membrane during the evolution of eukaryotic cells.

Figure 17-20. The basic structure of the internal compartment known as the endoplasmic reticulum or ER.

The smooth ER is also where membrane-bounded compartments called **transport vesicles** bud off. These vesicles are the means by which proteins in the ER lumen, membrane-embedded proteins, as well as the membrane itself are moved from their site of synthesis to other locations in or out of the cell.

An aside: Membranes are fluid structures, which means that proteins embedded in a membrane tend to float around. So, it is not clear how SRP receptors are kept from moving into this smooth region. Furthermore, if SRP receptors can move into smooth ER, these receptors could end up on the membranes of transport vesicles and thus be carried to the plasma membrane, or to any other membranes with which these vesicles fuse. If this happens, it would be impossible for a cell to maintain a place (the rough ER) that specializes in the synthesis of proteins destined to remain in the membrane or to slip out of the cytosol. The details of how the rough ER maintains this specialized function are not well understood.

Forming a nucleus

The hallmark compartment of a eukaryotic cell, the **nucleus**, is not an internal cavity like the ER because it is still filled with cytoplasm. Instead, a nucleus simply partitions a cell's cytoplasm into two regions: the **nuclear space**, which contains the cell's DNA, and the **cytosol**, which is the name given to all cytoplasm outside the nucleus. A portion of the ER encircling the DNA forms the partition. More specifically, the ER is draped around an almost spherical framework of protein filaments. The individual filaments are generally termed **intermediate filaments** or more specifically, **lamins**. The entire spherical structure is known as the **nuclear lamina** (see Figure 17-21). Although I will not say much more about them here, intermediate filaments, in addition to actin filaments and microtubules, are considered a component of a eukaryotic cell's cytoskeleton.

This subdivision of the cytoplasm is not complete. Holes called nuclear pores connect the nuclear space with the cytoplasm in the rest of the cell (see Figure 17-21). What goes in and out of these pores has come be somewhat controlled. The nuclear pores in present-day eukaryotic cells are lined with more than a hundred different proteins. Small molecules move somewhat freely through these pores. These proteins, however, tightly regulate the movement of larger molecules. In the course of this selective transport, the pores actually dilate to allow certain types of larger molecules to fit through. Through such selective transport, the nuclear space comes to be chemically different than the cytosol.

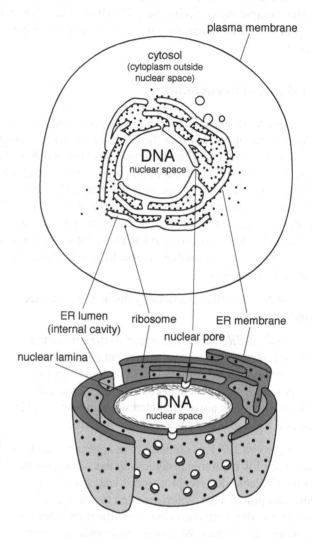

Figure 17-21. How the ER wraps around the nuclear lamina to subdivide the cytoplasm into two regions: the nuclear space and the cytosol.

We used the word *nucleus* before when we spoke about atomic nuclei (plural of nucleus). Do not let use of the same word to talk about different things confuse you. Neurobiologists use the same term to talk about parts of a nervous system. Nucleus, in general, means a central part around which other parts are grouped. The important aspect of a cell nucleus is not that it is always positioned at the center of a cell, but that it contains the cell's DNA.

Advantages

The presence of a cell nucleus raises an obvious question: Once it arose, why did it persist? What might be some advantages associated with a cell tucking its DNA inside a nucleus?

Earlier, I already suggested that a cell might benefit by having its DNA attached to the ER instead of the plasma membrane because it minimizes the distance that working protein recipes (mRNAs formed via DNA transcription) would need to diffuse to reach this specialized site of protein synthesis. The best way to minimize this diffusion distance is for the ER to completely encircle the DNA.

Other possible benefits may be summarized in one word—protection. As we discussed in Chapter 11, the protein recipes encoded in a cell's DNA are precious commodities. A damaged protein can be replaced so long as the recipe remains intact, but when the recipe itself is altered, there maybe no recourse. From what does a nucleus offer protection?

A nucleus may help a cell prevent oxygen-based chemical damage. Nucleated cells are suspected to have arisen during the time that oxygen was building up in the earth's atmosphere. Recall that oxygen has toxic effects on all organisms, especially in its free radical form. Free radicals are molecular fragments with the wrong number of electrons that act as powerful oxidants. When present, they will oxidize biological molecules and do so in a haphazard fashion. DNA molecules are particularly susceptible to this form of damage, and DNA damage is detrimental to reproduction. In the wake of increasing oxygen, all life forms were left with two options: They could retreat to areas where there was no oxygen or come up with ways to deal with oxygen's toxic properties.

One possibility is to convert reactive forms of oxygen into less reactive forms using molecules called **antioxidants**. Vitamin C is an example of a particularly good antioxidant. Even though it is likely that antioxidants evolved quickly in the lineage giving rise to nucleated cells, DNA attached to the outer membrane is still in a vulnerable position. Reactive forms of oxygen diffusing in from the outside could reach DNA before ever encountering an antioxidant. Using a nuclear envelope to separate the DNA from the chemically active cytoplasm, however, would help. In essence, a moat filled with antioxidants formed between the plasma membrane and the cell's DNA.

A relevant aside: The synthesis of steroids such as cholesterol requires oxygen, so their synthesis could not have occurred until oxygen was building up in the environment. Perhaps, even the initial advantage of steroid synthesis was its antioxidant properties. The beneficial properties associated with its assimilation into membranes may have only come secondarily.

Tucking DNA in a nucleus may also help protect it from physical damage associated with actin-myosin based movement. Once an actin-myosin system of membrane movement had evolved, DNA hanging out around the cell would be like children playing in the street because the DNA would be in the line of potentially damaging forces. Cars could collide into the children. Actin and myosin could collide into DNA. A nucleus offers a solution to this problem. The DNA is simply kept out of the way, fenced off by the nuclear envelope.

Separation of DNA transcription and RNA translation

In prokaryotes, ribosomes are right next to where DNA is being transcribed. Ribosomes can jump on a forming mRNA and begin RNA translation before DNA transcription is complete. The close association between ribosomes and DNA changed with the evolution of a nucleus, but not because the ribosomes are formed somewhere else and then prevented from getting into the nucleus. Ribosomes are actually assembled *in* a specialized region of the nucleus termed the **nucleolus** (see Figure 17-22). After assembly, however, they are actively transported through the nuclear pores and into the cytosol. Prior to transport, ribosomes are somehow prevented from binding with mRNAs that, through DNA transcription, are also formed in the nucleus. All of this leads up to the separation of DNA transcription and RNA translation. DNA transcription takes place within the nuclear space, whereas RNA translation takes place outside the nucleus. Specifically, newly formed mRNAs first exit the nucleus through one of the nuclear pores before being bound by a ribosome (see Figure 17-23).

This is wild. Two parts of protein synthesis form in the same space, and then the cell goes to the trouble of moving both elsewhere before they interact to form proteins. But why? It is likely that separating DNA and protein synthesis helps protect DNA from all the chemical activity orchestrated by proteins. And if protein recipes are to be separated from protein activity, something has to be shipped out from the nucleus. Perhaps proteins could be formed in the nucleus and then subsequently shipped out to function. In contrast, shipping out mRNAs is simpler. To build proteins, first all the tools, parts, and space required would need to be added to the nucleus. The end result is that the nucleus becomes less a place to isolate DNA and more like the rest of the cell. By the same logic, I find it puzzling that ribosome synthesis takes place in the nucleus. Moving ribosome synthesis outside would allow the nucleus to be smaller and avoid the complication of bringing proteins back in (remember that ribosomes are made of both RNA and proteins) after being synthesized outside. Perhaps, keeping ribosome synthesis within the nucleus is somewhat of a relic. Proximity to the DNA coding for ribosomal RNA may have already become too integral a component of ribosome synthesis to move it elsewhere.

Regardless of the reason that DNA transcription was separated from RNA translation, it seemingly set the stage for something fundamentally new to evolve. Somehow meaningless DNA sequences, called **introns**, came to be inserted within many of the genes making up eukaryotic genomes. Whether introns were the work of some type of parasitic DNA, or whether cells did it to themselves is still debated. Nonetheless, introns entering any gene rendered it useless—it cannot be used to make functional proteins—unless some countering move also evolved. That countering move was the addition of an entire new step called **RNA processing**, between DNA transcription and RNA translation (see Figure 17-23). RNA processing removes the regions of a newly formed mRNA coded for by introns and then splices the pieces of the functional protein recipe, called **exons**, back together. It sounds crazy. It is crazy. It was not something biologists expected to find, which is what makes the presence of introns and RNA processing so intriguing. But because of the complexity of the topic, I am not going to pursue it any further here.

Figure 17-22. The nucleolus is a nonmembrane-bound region within a nucleus that specializes in the production of ribosomes. The DNA within this region contains rRNA genes, and after transcription the rRNA produced is immediately packaged with ribosome proteins (which are produced in the cytosol and move into the nucleus through nuclear pores) to form ribosomes. The newly form ribosomes then move into the cytosol through nuclear pores. The size of a cells nucleolus can change within a cell, increasing in size as when the rate of protein synthesis increases. It can occupy up to 25% of the total nuclear volume in cells with exceptionally high rates of protein systhesis.

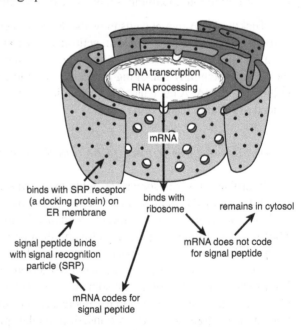

Figure 17-23. A closer look at the separation of DNA transcription and RNA translation in eukaryotic cells.

Golgi apparatus

In all but the most primitive forms of eukaryotic cells, a companion structure to the ER called the **Golgi apparatus** is present. Like the ER, the Golgi apparatus consists of complexly folded membrane-bounded compartments. In fact, most likely the Golgi apparatus was initially derived from pinching off parts of the ER. The folding forms a stack of four to six flattened disc-shaped compartments called **cisternae** (see Figure 17-24).

As mentioned earlier, transport vesicles budding off the smooth ER would work best if different types of molecules could be sorted among vesicles going to different locations. Evidence suggests that such sorting evolved prior to the evolution of Golgi apparatus. **Lysosomes**—vesicles loaded with digestive enzymes that fuse with endocytotically formed vesicles containing food items—have been found in single-celled eukaryotic organisms lacking Golgi apparatus despite the fact that they require sorting to form.

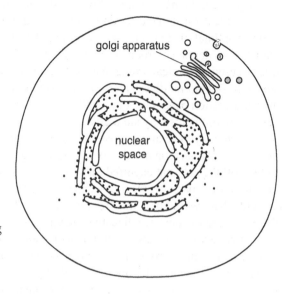

Figure 17-24. A eukaryotic cell with a golgi apparatus.

But in cells containing Golgi apparatus, sorting shifted locations. In these cells, proteins are placed in vesicles budding from the ER in an unselective fashion. These vesicles then move to the Golgi apparatus, where they fuse with the first in the series of compartments. Once inside the Golgi apparatus, molecules move from one cisternae to the next, and many are chemically modified along the way. Different types of modification tend to occur in each cisternae. Sorting then occurs in the last cisternae, which is the one facing the plasma membrane. The sorting is based on the presence of chemical tags on certain proteins.

Interestingly, the most basic pathway is a default pathway. Proteins lacking any chemical tag end up in transport vesicles that move directly to, and subsequently fuse with, the plasma membrane. Exocytosis occurs on fusion. Molecules inside the transport vesicle are dumped outside, and the piece of membrane that formed the vesicle, along with any embedded proteins, is added to the plasma membrane. Movement of proteins formed in the ER to outside the plasma membrane is referred to as the **biosynthetic-secretory pathway**.

Tagged molecules have come to be diverted into the two other options: **lysosomes** or **secretory vesicles**.

Lysosomes are packed with digestive enzymes of all sorts—nucleases, proteases, glycosidases, lipases, phosphatases, phospholipases—that work best in an environment much more acidic (pH around 5) than found in the cytoplasm (pH commonly around 7.2). Lysosomes also have a unique assembly of membrane-embedded proteins. For one, they have ATP-driven hydrogen ion pumps. These pump hydrogen ions from the cytoplasm into the lysosome, making it possible for lysosomes to maintain a pH best for their enzymes. Lysosomes also have transport proteins capable of moving products of digestion such as amino acids, simple sugars, and nucleotides into the cytoplasm. They carry out digestion and absorption when they fuse with other internal cavities within the cell, especially compartments bringing in a food source by endocytosis (as shown in Figure 17-17). Digestion ensues, and the useful products are then transported into the cytoplasm by simple diffusion, facilitated diffusion, or active transport.

Something to think about: Why would a pH difference between lysosomes and the rest of the cell have evolved? Or stated differently, why would the digestive enzymes within lysosomes have evolved a lower optimal pH than enzymes working elsewhere in the cell? One possibility is that the chemical nature of an acidic environment better supports digestion. Clearly, acidic environments can be disruptive to certain chemical arrangements, and you have a very acidic region in your digestive tract—your stomach. But not all digestive enzymes work best at lower pH values. In fact, most of your enzyme-driven digestion occurs in your small intestine, where the pH is over 7. So, although increasingly acidic environments may aid digestion, it does not appear to be essential. Another theme, namely, protection, may have also played an important role. This protection could come in two forms. First, if not killed, any bacteria or other organism brought in by endocytosis could potential invade and begin to feed off the cell that engulfed them. In other words, the prey could turn the table and become the predator or the parasite. Of course, attempting to kill the engulfed organisms by dousing them with an acidic bath would help this from occurring. The second form of protection picks up on an idea that exposure to your own digestive enzymes is not a good thing. So far, prevention of such exposure has boiled down to means to build digestive enzymes on the other side of a membrane. Sequestering digestive enzymes within a lysosome is a clear example of this. Interestingly, changing the optimal pH of lysosome enzymes adds another level of protection. If somehow these digestive enzymes leaked into the cell, they would spill into an environment where they do now work well. Recall that I just mentioned that a cell's pH is around 7.2, whereas the optimal pH for lysosomal enzymes is around 5. Due to pH being on a logarithmic scale, this means the enzymes would move into an environment where the hydrogen ion concentration was over a 100 times less.

Secretory vesicles, like default transport vesicles, dump their contents outside the cell by fusing with the plasma membrane. The added feature is a means to regulate the timing. Transport vesicles move to the plasma membrane once formed. On the other hand, fusion of secretory vesicles with the plasma membrane occurs only when triggered by some change within the cell. This change is potentially triggered by a change in external circumstance. In other words, cells may respond to some form of external change by releasing secretory vesicles. As we will discuss later, this is big stuff. For example, it is the basis underlying all your responses to changes to both external and internal circumstance.

Although increasing the efficacy of chemical sorting likely contributed to the evolution of Golgi apparatus, it is not the whole story. Here I make brief mention of a second component. Membrane-embedded proteins in eukaryotic cells are commonly glycoproteins, a protein with a carbohydrate attached. Relatively simple glycoproteins are formed in the ER. It is only after further modification within the cisternae of the Golgi apparatus that more complex glycoproteins are formed. Golgi apparatus opened an avenue for eukaryotic cells to increase the chemical complexity of their outer membrane. And as eukaryotic cells diversified, it is a potential that has been used.

New forms of motility

As mentioned in the previous chapter, there is no doubt that motility (or mobility) can be biologically important. It increases a cell's control over its environment because (in combination with sensors) it makes it possible for an organism to move toward favorable conditions and away from unfavorable ones. The underlying question, however, is how do different types of organisms generate propulsive forces? So far we have discussed cell-walled prokaryotes using stiff flagella attached to a rotating motor to propel the organism. Other prokaryotes seemingly glide along surfaces in an unknown manner. Here we add two new mechanisms of motion. Both use the combination of a dynamic cytoskeleton and a flexible outer membrane to generate propulsive forces.

Crawling-like movements

At some point, the capacity to change the shape of the outer membrane gave rise to a form of crawlinglike motion. It involves two basic steps: First, a protrusion called a pseudopodium (a false foot) extends some distance outward from the cell. In some cells, this protrusion always comes out in the same place, whereas in others it seemingly emerges from any part of the cell. Then, at some point later, the rest of the cell is pulled along. The cell crawls along by repeating these two steps over and over.

The tricky part is how the forces needed to perform these steps are actually accomplished. Clearly, the dynamic nature of the actin cortex is involved, but exactly how the combination of actin filaments changing lengths (via polymerization and depolymerization), changing orientation (via association with different cross-linking proteins), and being pulled about by myosin protein motors is coordinated into a cohesive motion is not known.

It has been observed that as a pseudopodium develops, actin filaments attached to the membrane get longer in the direction that the protrusion is extending. This observation suggests that the lengthening of actin filaments itself is generating the pushing force needed to extend the pseudopodium. However, there are some problems with this idea. For one, it is the growing end (the plus end) of microfilaments attached to the membrane—so how does growth push out the membrane when the membrane needs to be pushed out to make room to add more actin molecules to grow? Plus to be able to generate pushing forces, actin filaments needs to be able to resist compression, something they are not very good at (although being arranged into parallel bundles—an arrangement found in membrane protrusions—does at least somewhat increase their stiffness). Furthermore, myosin motors have also been observed at the leading edge of a developing pseudopodium, leading to the impression that the relative movement of actin filaments with each other and with the surrounding membrane is involved in generating the necessary forces. Yet, both of these suggestions assume that the pushing forces are created at the leading edge. There is a completely different possibility that uses contraction elsewhere in the cell to generate pushing forces at the leading edge. (And note that generating contraction depends on actin filaments being able to resist tension, which they are better at.) Combine one region of the cytoplasm underlying the membrane being more fluid (perhaps by this area lacking a cross-linked actin network) with the workings of actin and myosin squeezing the cell, and this more fluid region would more readily push out, generating a pseudopodium.

Once a pseudopodium extends outward, overall movement depends on the cell being able to somehow attach to the substrate and pull the rest of the cell along. Again, actin and myosin are clearly involved, but the details are not obvious, and there are no general points that I want to make by considering some of the possibilities, so I stop here.

Eukaryotic flagella

Earlier I made the point that because of their increased stiffness, microtubules could support longer, thinner projections extending out from the cell. Such projections may have been initially advantageous because they increase the surface area to volume ratio or because they create a more extensive network with which they could capture prey. Some extant single-celled organisms seem to use such projections in this manner.

Somewhere along the line, long, thin microtubule-supported projections were converted into whiplike devices that created propulsive forces in a water medium by waving back and forth somewhat like the tail of a fish. And evidence suggests that this occurred fairly early in the evolution of eukaryotic cells. What to call these structures is somewhat up in the air right now. Historically, they have been called **flagella**, although that is the same name used for the stiff rotating structures found in some prokaryotes. Based on the logic that fundamentally different structures should have different names, some have strongly suggested that the term **undulipodia** (waving feet) replace flagella. I actually agree with the suggestion, although I find the term *undulipodia* too complicated sounding for easy usage. So I will stick with the term *flagella*, but preface it by referring to these different structures as either prokaryotic flagella or eukaryotic flagella.

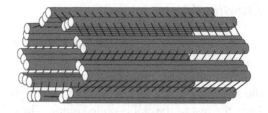

Figure 17-25. The microtubule arrangement within a kinetosome.

To begin to understand the structure of eukaryotic flagella, an additional fact about microtubules is needed. The most difficult part of forming a microtubule is getting it started—a process called **nucleation**. The microtubules that form eukaryotic flagella nucleate from a structure called **kinetosomes** (although you may find them referred to as **basal bodies**). Kinetosomes are cylindrical structures made from nine sets of three microtubules held together by a protein matrix (see Figure 17-25).

The microtubule structure that grows out of a kinetosome, called the **axoneme**, has a similar but not identical microtubule arrangement (see Figure 17-26). One difference is that only two of the three microtubules in each kinetosome triplet extend out, so the axoneme is composed of nine sets of two microtubules. Every axoneme also has a pair of microtubules positioned in the center of the cylinder. How this central pair is formed in unknown. Each microtubule within this "9 + 2" arrangement extends the entire length of the eukaryotic flagellum. The "9 + 2" arrangement has been found in eukaryotic flagella examined in a large variety of organisms, extending from protists to humans.

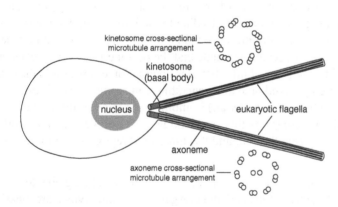

kinetosome cross-sectional microtubule arrangement

kinetosome (basal body)

nucleus

eukaryotic flagella

axoneme

axoneme cross-sectional microtubule arrangement

Figure 17-26. A eukaryotic cells with one set of two eukaryotic flagella. The cross-sectional view of how microtubule are arranged in kinetosomes and axonemes is also included.

Although typically larger than prokaryotes, flagellated eukaryotic cells are still very small (typically ranging from 5 to 200 micrometers) and consequently still live a low Reynolds number world. Recall that living in a low Reynolds number world means motility cannot take advantage of gliding. The stopping distance after propulsive forces cease is so small that maintaining movement requires a constant generation of propulsive forces. Eukaryotic flagella accomplish this in an interesting way. Although, flagella are short from our perspective, rarely exceeding 50 micrometer in length (with the range extending from 10 to 500 micrometers), they are long in a relative sense. Commonly, they are two or three times the length of the cell that they are propelling. Propulsive forces are created by prop-

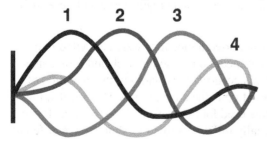

1   2   3

4

Figure 17-27. Movement pattern of an eukaryotic flagellum across a repeating temporal sequence (going from darkest to lightest before starting again). Waves generated push against the surrounding medium as they move from the base to the tip.

agating either two-dimensional (like a wavy line) or three-dimensional (like a corkscrew) waves along the length of the flagella. It is the moving wave itself that pushes against the surrounding medium to generate propulsive forces (see Figure 17-27). The relatively long length makes it possible for a new wave to start before an old one reaches the end of the flagella, creating a constant propulsive force.

Flagellar waves are generated by the actions of certain types of other proteins associated with the core microtubule structure (the axoneme). Some of these **MAPs (microtubule-associated proteins)** form cross-links between the microtubule bundles, holding them together. A walking protein known as **ciliary dynein** generates the needed forces. Other proteins create a relay system that coordinates dynein activation to generate an oscillating wave. The basic mechanics of generating a wave are to get the microtubule array to begin to bend, and the means to generate this initial bending is rather straightforward. When activated, each dynein is positioned to walk along one set of two microtubules while being attached to another microtubule set. If the microtubules were not bound together by other proteins, this would results in microtubule doublets sliding past each other. But because they are cross-linked, the force causes the microtubules to bend. The axoneme as a whole bending back and forth is what powers the flagella to wave back and forth.

As shown in Figure 17-27, waves generated along a flagellum moving from base to tip push against the surrounding medium. Accordingly, the cell would be propelled in the opposite direction—that is, in the direction opposite of where the flagellum is attached (see Figure 17-28(a)). If you are a male, this is how your sperm swim, as well as the sperm or spermlike cells produced by some (but not all) other organisms. Some flagellated single-celled eukaryotic organisms also swim in this manner, but strikingly most do not. Generally, flagellated single-celled organisms are propelled in the same direction that the flagella are attached to the cell. In other words, as the organism swims, the cell trails after the flagellum. There may be a good reason for this. Flagellated single-celled organisms that use endocytosis to ingest food particles do so only at a specialized region of the cell (called the cytostome). The cytostome is commonly located near the location where flagella emerge. This makes sense. The organism can use the actions of their flagella to help steer food particles toward their cytostome as they are propelled forward.

The question remaining is: How can a eukaryotic flagellum generate propulsive forces in the same direction in which they are attached? It turns out there are several methods, of which I mention three major ones. First, the patterns of wave propagation can be reversed. Instead of waves moving from base-to-tip, which will push outward, waves can be generated that move from tip-to-base, creating a push toward the site of flagellar attachment (Figure 17-28(b)). Second, flagella of some flagellated single-celled organism are not smooth structures, but instead are covered by numerous stiff structures,

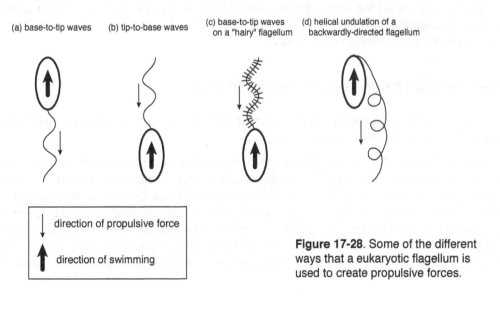

Figure 17-28. Some of the different ways that a eukaryotic flagellum is used to create propulsive forces.

called mastigonemes, that are oriented perpendicular to the flagellum. Although I do not understand the technical details of how this exactly works, the bottom line is that the direction of net thrust generated is opposite of that of a smooth flagella. So, a "hairy" flagella generating a base-to-tip wave generate a propulsive force toward the cell (Figure 17-28(c)), while a smooth flagella generating the same type of wave generates a propulsive force away from the cell. Third, long flagella can be attached in the front (in the direction of movement), but bend backward along the organism so that effectively they extend out the back. Base-to-tip waves will then propel the organism in the direction of attachment (Figure 17-28(d)).

To wrap up this beginning discussion of eukaryotic flagella, let me make two more points. One concerns speed and the other concerns structure.

So how fast are flagellated eukaryotic cells? They are a step up from flagellated prokaryotic cells. The swimming speed of flagellates, approximately 0.1 to 0.2 millimeters per second, which is around four times faster than prokaryotes.

So far I have represented the structure of a eukaryotic flagellum as an axoneme growing from a kinetosome located at its base. It is as if the entire structure is dangling on its own on the outskirts of the cell. This, of course, cannot be true. There is no way that such a long extension could start wiggling around without breaking free unless it was anchored to the rest of the cell. Microtubules form the framework of this anchoring system, commonly known as the **flagellar root system**. (Some more terminology: Kinetosomes in combination with their root system are called **kinetids**. Kinetids always have at least one kinetosome, but kinetids with two (dikinetid) or more (polykinetid) are common.)

Although the pattern by which rootlet microtubules extend out from around the kinetosomes to other parts of the cell varies considerably among different organisms, two points are worth noting. First, these rootlets create connections between the kinetosome and other cell parts such as a nucleus. These connections seem to play an important role in cell division (discussed further later). Second, these microtubules often play a major role in determining cell shape (see Figure 17-9), which connects back to helping a cell swim in the first place. An oscillating flagellum will be much more efficient at pushing or pulling a cell through water if it has a streamlined shape. (These microtubules arrays are also commonly used to create a pocket shape within the cell used to help funnel food particles into.)

I mentioned earlier that the most difficult aspect of forming a microtubule is getting it started. To overcome this difficulty, eukaryotic flagella microtubules grow out of a kinetosome and take on the very distinct "9 + 2" arrangement. But what is used to nucleate all these other rootlet microtubules? The answer is not so clear-cut, because there is no apparent preexisting microtubule structure to get it all started. What we are left with is the observation that microtubules nucleate out of a seemingly less-distinct protein matrix surrounding kinetosomes. Although this region has been given a lot of names, I use **microtubule-organizing center (MTOC)**.

Mitosis and Other Accompanying Stories

Moving DNA into a nucleus could not persist unless there was also some way to distribute duplicated DNA to daughter cells during cell division.

Recall that in prokaryotes all DNA is typically contained in one circular chromosome attached to the outer membrane. After duplication, the membrane attachment is used to pull one copy of this single chromosome into each daughter cell. Presumably, as DNA first moved into a nucleus, it was still distributed in a similar way. A single circular chromosome remained attached by proteins to a membrane, only the membrane switched from the plasma membrane to the inner nuclear membrane. Duplicates of this chromosome were pulled apart by the entire nucleus dividing in two. Membrane expansion coupled by actin and myosin generated movement may have generated the needed forces.

Yet somewhere, sometime, and somehow one of the truly landmark changes in the history of life occurred. A new way of distributing duplicated DNA called mitosis evolved in nucleated cells. Why was mitosis such a landmark change? It could effectively distribute more DNA, which then opened the door to the evolution of more complex organisms. A better mechanism of distribution means that more DNA can be distributed in a relatively error-free way, thus lifting an imposing constraint on genome size. Larger genomes create the potential for more information. The self-building of a complex organism requires more information than relatively simple ones. It is no different than the fact that more information is needed to guide the construction of a large bridge spanning a major river than to build a small footbridge over a tiny creek.

The evolutionary story of mitosis is actually a story of microtubules and associated structures that make up a mitotic spindle. But as we have discussed already, microtubules are involved in more than just mitosis. Most significantly, microtubules form the structural core of eukaryotic flagella and are a major component of the flagellar rootlet system. An important evolutionary question is, Which came first? Did the evolution of eukaryotic flagella give rise to mitotic spindles, or vice versa? Although arguments have gone both ways, next I develop a scenario where eukaryotic flagella came first. It could be wrong, but nonetheless, it gets you to see the important issues.

Duplicating and distributing kinetosomes

The issue raised here is: How does a cell with eukaryotic flagella give rise to two daughter cells, each with the same number of eukaryotic flagella? Because eukaryotic flagella grow out of kinetosomes embedded in a MTOC, this question boils down to how do the same number of kinetosomes end up in each daughter cell?

If this kinetosome–MTOC complex can be built from scratch, the question seems somewhat trivial. The main issue would be duplicating and distributing the necessary DNA. With the needed information present, an MTOC with the appropriate number of kinetosomes could be resynthesized after each round of cell division. The problem is that it is not completely clear how new kinetosome–MTOC complexes are formed. Much evidence points to the idea that kinetosome–MTOC complexes act as replicators—that is, that one somehow serves as a template for the formation of a second. New kinetosomes, for example, generally form in close proximity to a preexisting one. (Although it is curious that the second does not grow out the first, but instead tends to form at a right angle to the preexisting one.) Does the preexisting kinetosome in some unknown way carry information needed to form the second one? Although it is an intriguing possibility, it is difficult to reconcile this idea with the few known cases where kinetosomes appear to form de novo. What can be said is that generally some form of relationship exists between the presence of one kinetosome and the formation of a second. This may also be true with other components of a MTOC. Accordingly, the main route for passing eukaryotic flagella across generations involves using existing kinetosomes to form duplicates, and then distributing them into daughter cells.

Some speculation: Perhaps, preexisting kinetosomes do not act as a replicating template per se, but are one of the components needed to activate the machinery involved in kinetosome synthesis. This arrangement would help a cell produce the correct number of new kinetosomes with each round of cell division. If preexisting ones are needed to trigger synthesis, then the number of new kinetosomes synthesized will be limited to duplicating preexisting ones. Another potential advantage is that by constraining new kinetosomes to form near preexisting ones, they start off being assembled in the correct location.

To accomplish the distribution of duplicated kinetosomes into daughter cells, MTOCs took on another role (in addition to nucleating the microtubules that form the flagellar root system). As kinetosomes duplicate prior to cell division, the MTOC reforms around each set of duplicated kinetosomes—that is, MTOCs also duplicate in some sense of the word. Next, microtubules have been found to sprout from each MTOC, forming a structure commonly referred to as a spindle. As microtubules extend from the two MTOCs, a region of overlap forms between the two spindles. Within this region, forces are created that push the two spindles apart, carrying each set of kinetosomes with them. Likely, the same protein motors found to slide microtubules past each other in eukaryotic flagella create these forces.

Figure 17-29 sketches three themes by which present-day cells use this means to duplicate and separate kinetosomes to pass eukaryotic flagella across cell generations.

Figure 17-29(a) shows the basic steps by which eukaryotic flagellated cells give rise directly to eukaryotic flagellated daughter cells. It starts with a single cell with a pair of eukaryotic flagella. Duplication starts by existing kinetosomes being used as a nucleating site to double the amount of kinetosomes. Note that only the number of kinetosomes has doubled at this point, not the number of eukaryotic flagella. Interacting spindles then push an equal number of kinetosomes in opposite directions along the cell surface. Subsequently, the cell divides along the plane in between these two sets of kinetosomes, so that one set ends up in each daughter cell. Finally, eukaryotic flagella grow out of each of the newly duplicated kinetosomes to restore the original number in each daughter cell.

The major difference in Figure 17-29 (b) is that the eukaryotic flagella are not retained during cell division. They are either shed or withdrawn back into the cells. The cost of doing so is that motility is lost during cell division. However, there could also be benefits. Withdrawal may allow the whole process to be either energetically cheaper or to occur faster. During withdrawal, microtubules are disas-

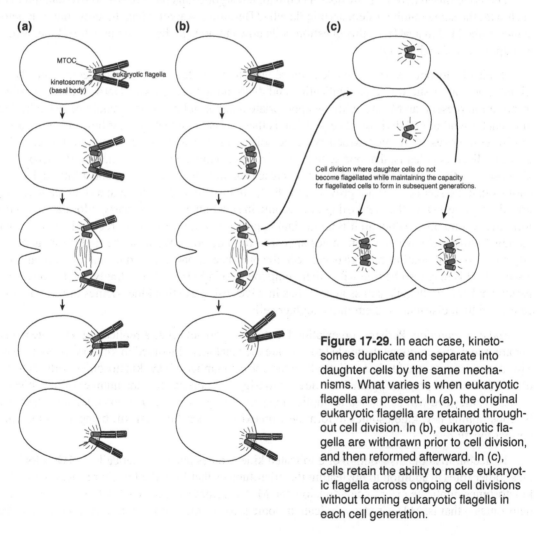

(a) **(b)** **(c)**

MTOC
eukaryotic flagella
kinetosome
(basal body)

Cell division where daughter cells do not become flagellated while maintaining the capacity for flagellated cells to form in subsequent generations.

Figure 17-29. In each case, kinetosomes duplicate and separate into daughter cells by the same mechanisms. What varies is when eukaryotic flagella are present. In (a), the original eukaryotic flagella are retained throughout cell division. In (b), eukaryotic flagella are withdrawn prior to cell division, and then reformed afterward. In (c), cells retain the ability to make eukaryotic flagella across ongoing cell divisions without forming eukaryotic flagella in each cell generation.

sembled from the tip of each flagellum downward and the tubulin subunits are returned to the cellular pool. These subunits can now be used to build the spindles involved in pushing each set of duplicated kinetosomes apart. After the cell divides and microtubule arrays are disassembled, these subunits can once again be used to build new eukaryotic flagella. Reusing the same tubulin molecules at each step of the process potentially reduces the number of tubulin molecules that need to be synthesized overall, saving on both the energetic and material costs of synthesis. Because additional synthesis may also take longer, such reuse may allow duplication and division to occur more quickly.

One more variation observed in present-day cells builds on a simple fact: Although kinetosomes are needed to build eukaryotic flagella, cells with kinetosomes are not constrained to build eukaryotic flagella. Once flagella are withdrawn, this sets up an interesting possibility. So long as kinetosomes continue to be passed across cell divisions, each daughter cell retains the potential to grow eukaryotic flagella, even if it does not do so itself. Through this process, a cell line may remain without eukaryotic flagella for many generations and then at some point later give rise to a flagellated cell (see Figure 17-29(c)). Although it probably only adds confusion, a second term is used for a kinetosome within a cell that is not presently being used to form flagella. They are referred to as **centrioles**.

Mitosis and chromosome changes

The evolution of mitosis may have involved cells taking advantage of the microtubule-based kinetosomes/eukaryotic flagella distribution system to also distribute DNA into daughter cells. The way in which mitosis still occurs in certain groups of single-celled eukaryotic organisms (e.g., Parabasalians) is suggestive of how mitosis may have first started. Each chromosome remains permanently anchored by protein complexes to the nuclear membrane. After chromosome duplication, the attachment site divides and begins to separate, apparently by membrane growth. The new twist is that microtubules from each spindle then attach to the outside of these membrane-embedded proteins anchors. As the spindles push apart, the attached microtubules act like towlines helping to hoist chromosome copies into daughter cells (see Figure 17-30)

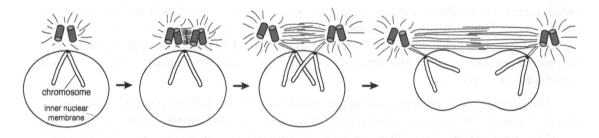

Figure 17-30. A simplified diagram illustrating how microtubule attachments assist the distribution of membrane-bound chromosomes in some types of eukaryotic cells. The nucleus eventually pinches in two, which may be accompanied by the rest of cell (not shown) dividing.

One can imagine that as microtubule-aided distribution first started, the genome was still linked into a single circular chromosome. As mentioned earlier, the advantage of confining the entire genome to a single chromosome is that it reduces the chance of distribution error. When the entire genome is hooked together as a single molecule, distribute that one molecule correctly and the job is complete. The disadvantage is that it constrains genome size. DNA replication in circular prokaryotic chromosomes, for instance, is seemingly constrained to start at a single point (there is only one special DNA sequence known as the replication origin) and then proceeds in both directions. So, the larger the chromosome, the longer it takes for the entire genome to be duplicated. At some point, the disadvantage of slowing reproduction will outweigh any advantages of increased information.

One way to circumvent the increasing information/slower duplication trade-off is to break the genome up into more than one chromosome. Each chromosome would need its own replication origin, which means that each chromosome can be duplicated simultaneously. Yet, until an efficient means to distribute more than one chromosome is in place, the advantages of breaking up the genome would be readily countered by increasing distribution error. This is where hooking chromosome distribution on to the evolving kinetosome distribution system enters the picture. So long as microtubules from each separating spindle effectively attach to each chromosome, increasing the number of chromosomes poses no special problem. Freed from this constraint, chromosome number increased. No mitotically dividing cell that I am aware of has only one chromosome.

Other shifts in chromosome structure also accompanied this mitosis-based change in chromosome number and genome size. Next I mention three, although not in any implied order of occurrence:

• Chromosomes switched from being circular (no ends) to linear (two ends). It in an intriguing change because it is not clear what advantages facilitated the shift. One idea has to do with keeping chromosomes from getting tangled up as they separate. In Chapter 19, we discuss something called crossing-over, which can occasionally happen to separating chromosomes. If crossing-over happens in circular chromosomes, the two chromosomes become hooked together and cannot separate. In contrast, linear chromosome can still separate after crossing-over occurs. On the other hand, there is a disadvantage with being linear. In a linear chromosome, a few nucleotides are lost at each end every time a chromosome replicates due to the mechanistic details of DNA replication. Over time, this gradual loss will have disastrous consequences as genes located on the ends of chromosomes disappear. Cells with linear chromosomes that have persisted have added telomeres on to each end of their chromosomes. **Telomeres** are simple repeating sequences that can be periodically extended by an enzyme named **telomerase**, thus compensating for gradual loss.

• In most mitotic cells, chromosomes have also lost their permanent attachment with the nuclear membrane. Microtubules replaced membranes in separating duplicate chromosomes, making this change possible. Evolution of the protein complex that hooks chromosomes to whatever is used to pull them apart made it happen. There were likely two major steps in the transition. First, the protein complex changed from one that hooks chromosomes to membranes to one that hooks chromosomes to both membranes and microtubules. Next, the protein complex, now called a **kinetochore**, retained its capacity to attach to microtubules while losing its membrane affinity. Chromosomes moved into the nuclear space, only forming microtubule attachments during cell division. Assuming this sequence is accurate, kinetochores evolved from the protein complex first connecting chromosomes to the plasma membrane in prokaryotes.

• The increase in the genome size from prokaryotic to mitotically dividing eukaryotic cells is marked. A typical prokaryotic genome is around three million nucleotide pairs (each A-T or G-C combination is one nucleotide pair, which is also called a base pair). Genomes in present-day eukaryotic cells, on the other hand, range between ten million to almost a hundred billion nucleotide pairs. You, for instance, are composed of eukaryotic cells, and each cell contains roughly three billion nucleotide pairs. A book containing three billion letters would have at least a million pages.

• In contrast to prokaryotes, eukaryotic DNA forms a more compact structure because it is wrapped around several types of proteins collectively called histones. Within chromatin—the name given to this DNA–protein combination—the proteins make up roughly as much of the combination as does DNA. Without histones, it is difficult to imagine fitting the massive amount of DNA found in eukaryotic cells inside a nucleus. A eukaryotic nucleus is generally no larger than 10 μm (micrometers—1 millionth of a meter) and may be much smaller. On the other hand, lined up end-to-end, the three billion nucleotides of the human genome would span around 1.5 to 1.8 meters—around 100,000 times the diameter of a nucleus. At first glance, this seems impossible, like trying to fit an elephant inside a shoebox. Yet DNA is very thin and so tightly wound around histones—which reduces DNA length at least 1,000-fold—that a lot of DNA can be tucked inside a very small space. A fun fact:

Seventy-five trillion human cells (which is approximately the number of cells that make up the body you are wearing) contain more than seventy-five billion miles of DNA—enough to go back and forth to the sun more than four-hundred times!

• There is a downside to adding histones. With chromatin, the speed of DNA replication is around 1/10th that found in prokaryotes (going from around 500 nucleotides per second to 50 nucleotides per second). Likely, this reduced speed is a result of the added complication of the replication machinery needing to negotiate around histones. But again, cells that have persisted have compensated. In addition to breaking up the genome into more than one chromosome, multiple replication origins per chromosomes have been found in extant eukaryotic cells. Being able to start replication at more than one place obviously reduces the time needed to replicate an entire chromosome.

Textbook mitosis

Mitosis may be monophyletic (evolved once), but if so, the details have diversified along different lineages. I already discussed one version. It was singled out because it is seemingly primitive—both microtubules and membrane attachments are involved in chromosome distribution. In all other versions, spindle microtubules attach to the kinetochore of free-floating chromosomes. What still varies are such things as whether the spindles form outside or inside the nucleus, whether nuclear membranes remain intact during cell division, and whether eukaryotic flagella are present during cell division or not. All this variation makes mitosis confusingly interesting. Here, however, my focus is not on the differences, but on the general means by which separating spindles have come to distribute free-floating chromosomes equally into daughter cells.

Mitotic cell division begins with each linear chromosome being duplicated by DNA replication, although the two copies remain attached. Phosphorylation of certain histones then leads to conformational changes that result in DNA winding around these proteins even more tightly. The packaging condenses the large amount of DNA contained in each chromosome into an incredibly compact form. Furthermore, in one region (the exact position being variable among chromosomes) a constriction forms called the **centromere**. The centromere contains DNA sequences that kinetochores bind with. One kinetochore forms on each attached chromosome, forming a kinetochore pair that hooks together. The entire structure is a **duplicate chromosome** (see Figure 17-31).

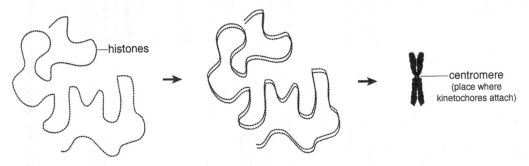

Figure 17-31. A eukaryotic chromosome first replicates and then winds even further around histones to form a compact duplicate chromosome.

The fact that the two copies of each chromosome stay hooked together plays an essential role in cell division. Remaining attached keeps track of which chromosomes are duplicates of which. It would otherwise be impossible to move one copy of each chromosome into the two daughter cells.

The example of mitosis pictured in Figure 17-32 is no more typical than other versions. It is, however, the version that is most commonly shown in textbooks. Why? Because it is how mitosis takes place in your, as well as other animal, cells. It starts with a cell lacking eukaryotic flagella, but

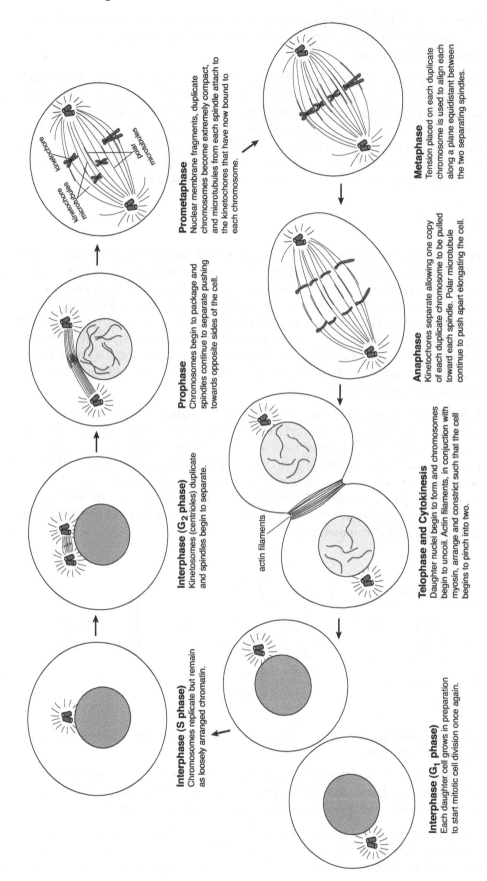

Prometaphase
Nuclear membrane fragments, duplicate chromosomes become extremely compact, and microtubules from each spindle attach to the kinetochores that have now bound to each chromosome.

Metaphase
Tension placed on each duplicate chromosome is used to align each along a plane equidistant between the two separating spindles.

Prophase
Chromosomes begin to package and spindles continue to separate pushing towards opposite sides of the cell.

Anaphase
Kinetochores separate allowing one copy of each duplicate chromosome to be pulled toward each spindle. Polar microtubule continue to push apart elongating the cell.

Interphase (G₂ phase)
Kinetosomes (centrioles) duplicate and spindles begin to separate.

Telophase and Cytokinesis
Daughter nuclei begin to form and chromosomes begin to uncoil. Actin filaments, in conjuction with myosin, arrange and constrict such that the cell begins to pinch into two.

Interphase (S phase)
Chromosomes replicate but remain as loosely arranged chromatin.

Interphase (G₁ phase)
Each daughter cell grows in preparation to start mitotic cell division once again.

Figure 17-32. The basic scheme by which mitosis occurs in animal cells. (See text for further discussion.)

bearing a pair of centrioles (non-flagellar-bearing kinetosomes) positioned near the cell's nucleus. (So although the cell has retained the means to make eukaryotic flagella, tucked away from the outer membrane, the centrioles are not in position to do so. I discuss the significance of this later.)

Like other versions of mitosis, after chromosomes begin to become duplicate chromosomes, centrioles, and their surrounding MTOCs duplicate and begin to push apart as hundreds of microtubules grow out of each MTOC, forming two spindles. As overlapping microtubules, referred to as **polar microtubules**, continue to both elongate and slide back past each other, the spindles begin to separate.

In the animal version of mitosis, at some point during spindle separation, the nuclear membrane abruptly breaks up into smaller vesicles. The breakup is initiated by phosphorylation of the protein filaments that form the nuclear lamina. On phosphorylation, this spherical framework breaks into individual filaments (which reform when phosphates are removed). Microtubules from each spindle then invade the nuclear region, some of which form connections with the kinetochores (called **kineto-chore microtubules**) on each chromosome. Specifically, each side of the kinetochore pair attaches to microtubules from opposing spindles.

Once these kinetochore–microtubule attachments form, forces pulling toward each spindle are generated, placing each duplicate chromosome under tension. The duplicate chromosomes do not split at this point. Instead, each duplicate chromosome is moved until they all line up along a plane halfway between the two spindles in the center of the cell. Just like each runner lining up in its own lane, each duplicate chromosome is now positioned so that one copy of each can be pulled into daughter cells without colliding or in any way interfering with the movement of others. Apparently, this alignment is achieved by a potential force asymmetry. The further away a duplicate chromosome is from a spindle, the greater the pulling force generated. Duplicate chromosomes not currently positioned along this midplane will therefore be pulled toward it by unequal tension. Once this midplane is reached, movement will stop as each duplicate chromosome is being pulled equally in both directions.

The next phase of mitosis is triggered by a specific chemical change within the cell that results in the paired kinetochores separating. Each duplicate chromosome can now be pulled apart—one copy moving toward each spindle. Protein motors within each kinetochore "walking" along kinetochore microtubules apparently generate the force. These protein motors are like little tugboats that pull one copy of each chromosome into opposite ports. The kinetochore microtubules shorten as the chromosomes are pulled along. As each set of chromosomes gathers near each spindle, the kinetochore microtubules disappear, a nucleus reforms around each chromosome set, and each chromosome unwinds from its tightly packaged state. Only in this less-wound form can various genes within the chromosomes be transcribed.

While this is all happening, polar (overlapping) microtubules continue to lengthen and slide back past each other, pushing the spindles further apart, which elongates the cell. The actual division of the cytoplasm into two cells, a process called **cytokinesis**, is powered by actin filaments in conjunction with its protein motor, myosin. A ring of actin filaments forms perpendicular to the orientation of the two spindles. As it shortens, it acts like a drawstring, which eventually pinches one cell into two.

The confusing world of MTOCs

From the perspective that I have presented here, MTOCs first played both a structural and distribution role. Structurally, they generated an anchoring system for flagella. Then they generated a means to distribute kinetosomes among daughter cells through the formation of spindles. Only afterward was this spindle-based distribution system hijacked to distribute genome copies among daughter cells. In many cases, such as mitosis in animal cell division (highlighted previously) both kinetosomes and chromosomes are distributed simultaneously. Yet strikingly, the simultaneous distribution of chromosomes and kinetosomes is not dependent directly on either one being present. Experiments removing one or the other still observe spindles forming and separating as normal. Actually, with kinetosomes this experiment has also been performed naturally. The cells in higher plants and most fungi have lost kinetosomes (along with the ability to ever form eukaryotic flagella), yet they still do MTOC-based mitosis.

Because eukaryotic flagella are microtubule-reinforced extensions of a cell's surface, the kinetosomes along with the surrounding MTOC must always be near the cell's periphery in lineages of eukaryotic cells that have flagella in every generation. But in lineages of eukaryotic cells that do not reform flagella every generation—that is, in eukaryotic cells where kinetosomes have become centrioles—the MTOC position is not caught in the same constraint. In such cases, MTOCs have commonly taken up a position near the cell center either inside or along the outside of the nucleus (see Figure 17-33). (To add to what already seems like a terminological nightmare, centrally placed MTOCs are commonly called **centrosomes**.) This central position works well for its distribution role because by being near or within the nucleus, it is near the cell's chromosomes. In cells with centrally placed MTOCs that still have kinetosome/centrioles, the kinetosomes/centrioles are embedded within the MTOC.

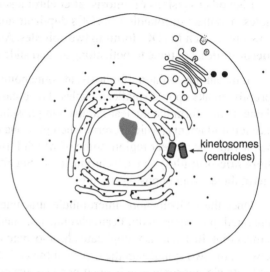

Figure 17-33. A pair of kinetosomes (centrioles) located centrally within the cell. In this location the kinetosomes cannot be used to grow flagella, but the surrounding MTOC can generate a support structure by nucleating an array of microtubules that radiate throughout the cell.

A central position does not exclude MTOCs from still playing a structural role, especially when a cell is not currently dividing. By continually nucleating microtubules in various directions, centrally placed MTOCs (or **centrosomes**) can generate a dynamic microtubule scaffold within the cell. Recall that any single microtubule nucleating from an MTOC tends to exist in one of two states: steadily growing, or rapidly falling apart. As a consequence, microtubules are inherently unstable structures. They persist for any length of time only if both ends are protected from depolarization. The MTOC protects the more stable minus end. The expanding plus end, however, is much more vulnerable. Unless it runs into a protein able to cap and stabilize it, the microtubule will eventually unravel. Cells have come to exploit this feature to direct the formation of microtubule connections. Microtubules grow out every which way from the centrally placed MTOC, but only those reaching capping proteins will last. Any means to position capping proteins within the cells becomes a means to select the shape of the microtubule framework, which in turn can have an effect on the cell's shape. For example, animal nerve cells are commonly very elongated cells, and microtubules extended from an MTOC forms the structural core of these elongations.

The microtubule scaffold emerging from centrally placed MTOCs have also become lines of transport. Two chemical families of protein motors (walking proteins) have been found to move along microtubules: the dyneins (which were mentioned in conjunction with eukaryotic flagella motion) and the kinesins. Dyneins can be used to drag things toward the cell's center (as they "walk" along microtubules toward the end embedded in the MTOC—the minus end). Kinesins can be used to pull things away from the cell center (as they walk along microtubules toward the end closer to the cell periphery—the plus end). What is being moved depends on the exact type of kinesin or dynein. One part of all kinesins and dyneins moves along microtubules, but what else these protein motors attach to, hence what they transport, varies considerable. For example, some attach to vesicles, creating a means to move these vesicles about the cell. These protein motors also play a role in positioning cell parts. The

ER stretches out from the nucleus to almost the edge of the cell. This fanning out is accomplished by kinesins pulling the ER along microtubules.

Perhaps, the most curious aspect of MTOCs is that in certain types of eukaryotic cells only one MTOC is maintained; yet it is used to play different roles. Such cells are constantly faced with either/ or situations. Its MTOC can be located at the cell periphery, where a eukaryotic flagellum can grow out of a kinetosome, or it can be located near the cell center, where microtubule arrays can create a structural framework for the cell, but not both. And when it comes time to divide, either of these roles must be abandoned. Microtubules extending to form a eukaryotic flagellum, or a centrally placed structural framework, are retracted as kinetosomes (if present) and chromosomes duplicate, and newly emerging microtubule arrays form separating mitotic spindles.

Why don't these single MTOC cells get around this trade-off by having more than one MTOC? Two always form during cell division, so the machinery to make more than one MTOC is in place. The potential complicating factor is that to make more than one MTOC within a cell, the mechanism of MTOC duplication must be separated from cell division. As we discuss in a later chapter, this separation has occurred in many single-celled eukaryotic organisms, but never in the cells of multicellular eukaryotic organisms. Curious!

Some Last Notes

Where did this line of flexible-membraned, nucleated cells come from? Evidence points to eukaryotes (Domain Eukarya) branching off the Archaea (see Figure 17-34). One extant genera—*Thermoplasma*—at least in some ways seem the most similar. Remember that many members of the Archaea domain reside in so-called extreme habitats. This particular group of Archaea lives in hot, acidic environments. (Places where temperatures range to nearly 60°C (140°F), and pH is down around 1 or 2.) When you think about it, this fact makes sense. Innovation often comes from living at the edge. As environmental challenges change, so must performance solutions. Perhaps adapting to hot, acidic environments favored performance traits that later culminated in properties conducive to forming nucleated cells.

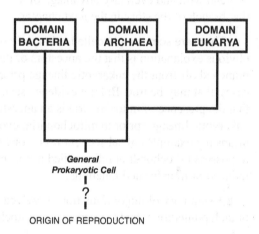

Figure 17-34. A phylogeny summarizing the ancestral relationship among Life's three domains.

Archaea living in hot acidic environments are hard to study; so much is still unknown about this group. Listed here are a few known similarities:

• The absence of a cell wall, a strong yet flexible membrane, and the means to generate the forces to move the membrane about were the suggested starting points for the evolution of nucleated cells. *Thermoplasma*, in contrast to other bacteria, have wall-less flexible membranes. There is also evidence that *Thermoplasma* can somehow control membrane movement. Individuals within this group have been observed to flatten themselves against a surface. There is also some evidence that they form actinlike filaments.

• Histones are unknown in prokaryotes with two exceptions. Histonelike proteins have been found in *Thermoplasma* and one other archaea group. In hot, acid environments, DNA's two sides can more easily separate. Binding DNA with proteins may have helped to prevent such separation. If so, histones may have first played a protective role.

•*Thermoplasma* have antioxidants in their cytoplasm and so can detoxify oxygen. The types of antioxidants found in *Thermoplasma* are similar to those that are found in present-day eukaryotic cells.

A relevant aside: The synthesis of steroids such as cholesterol requires oxygen. Their synthesis could not have occurred until oxygen was building up in the environment. Perhaps, even the initial advantage of steroid synthesis was its antioxidant properties. The beneficial properties associated with its assimilation into membranes may have only come secondarily.

Early eukaryotes

From the time that eukaryotic cells first evolved, perhaps somewhere between 1.5 billion and 1 billion years ago, eukaryotic cells have a storied history of diversifying into many different forms. As I have already mentioned, the familiar organisms such as mammals, reptiles, amphibians, insects, and plants are all composed of eukaryotic cells. Furthermore, there is a rich diversity of other multicellular and single-celled eukaryotic organisms that largely go unnoticed, mostly because they are too small to draw much attention.

Perhaps all, and at very least most, of the story of eukaryotic diversification includes the endosymbiotic evolution of an organelle called a mitochondrion, which allowed eukaryotic organisms to contend with and even take advantage of a world now filled with molecular oxygen. But, I wait to start that branch of the story in the next chapter.

There are some single-celled eukaryotic organisms still around today that lack mitochondria. One obvious explanation is that the ancestors of the current amitochondrians (mitochondria-lacking cells) branched off from the eukaryotic lineage prior to the evolution of mitochondria. And, at least in some cases, that may be true. But the evidence seems to be leaning, perhaps strongly so, toward the claim that the presence of mitochondria is an ancestral trait in all modern eukaryotes. This suggests that any eukaryotic lineages prior to mitochondrial evolution have gone extinct and that all current amitochondrians are examples of subsequent loss. For example, some amitochondrial groups have been found to possess mitochondrial relics called mitosomes or hydrogenosomes, both of which have radically reduced or transformed functions.

A summary of major transitions involved in early eukaryotic evolution, including the alternative branch points for extant (present-day) amitochondrial eukaryotes, is shown in Figure 17-35.

Mitosis and karyomastigonts

The metamonads are a large group (phylum) of single-cell flagellates that lack functional mitochondria. So, they have been part of the never-had-mitochondria versus the lost-mitochondria questions. But that issue is not why they are mentioned here. Earlier I suggested a link between evolving a system to distribute kinetosomes and then subsequently using this distribution system to distribute DNA broken into chromosomes. Although perhaps not clearly resolving the question of which came first, certain metamonads strongly point to the distribution of kinetosomes and chromosomes being linked. In fact, this link is physical. Throughout the life cycle, each nucleus remains in close proximity to a set of kinetosomes because they are connected by a cross-banded microtubular ribbon, called a rhizoplast. This entire complex (one nucleus, kinetosome set, and associated microtubules) is called a **karyomastigont**. Each kinetosome set consists of one or two kinetosome pairs (so either two or four kinetosomes in total) with two pairs seeming to be most common. And as you might expect, many members of this group have a single karyomastigont per organism, although more than one is also common. Metamonads in the subgroup known as the diplomonads commonly have two per organism, whereas members of a different subgroup, the parabasalians, may have as many as a thousand or more karyomastigonts per organism, spirally arranged around the cell's anterior end (see Figure 17-36).

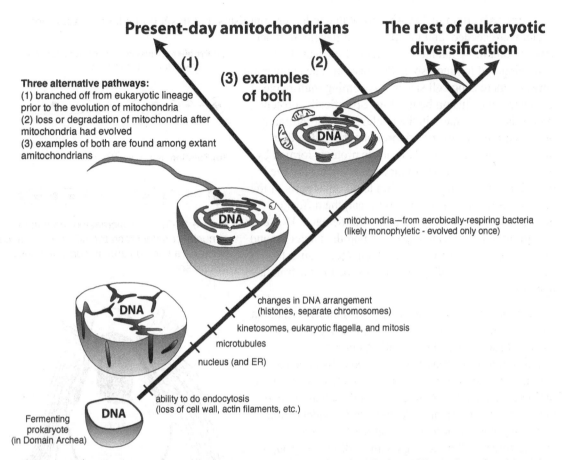

Present-day amitochondrians

The rest of eukaryotic diversification

(1)

(2)

(3) examples of both

Three alternative pathways:
(1) branched off from eukaryotic lineage prior to the evolution of mitochondria
(2) loss or degradation of mitochondria after mitochondria had evolved
(3) examples of both are found among extant amitochondrians

DNA

DNA

mitochondria—from aerobically-respiring bacteria (likely monophyletic - evolved only once)

DNA

changes in DNA arrangement (histones, separate chromosomes)

kinetosomes, eukaryotic flagella, and mitosis

microtubules

nucleus (and ER)

ability to do endocytosis (loss of cell wall, actin filaments, etc.)

Fermenting prokaryote (in Domain Archea)

DNA

Figure 17-35. A phylogeny summarizing early eukaryotic evolution (as discussed throughout the chapter), leading to three alternative ancestral pathways for the evolution of extant eukaryotes lacking mitochondria. Mitchondrial evolution, along with other major steps in eukaryotic diversification, are the emphasis of the next chapter.

The origin of a single-celled organism with more than one karyomastigont is straightforward. Karyomastigonts typically reproduce as a unit, which means that as long as cytokinesis (cell division) occurs simultaneously, karyomastigont numbers will remain the same across generations. However, if some mutation or other malfunction ever decouples cytokinesis from karyomastigont duplication, such that karyomastigont duplication occurs in the absence of cell division, the number of karyomastigotes per cell will increase. This presumably happened once in the ancestry of diplomonads, but in diplomonad lineages found today, both karyomastigonts typically duplicate simultaneously, and these duplications are coupled with cytokinesis, resulting in two single-celled diplomonads with two karyomastigonts.

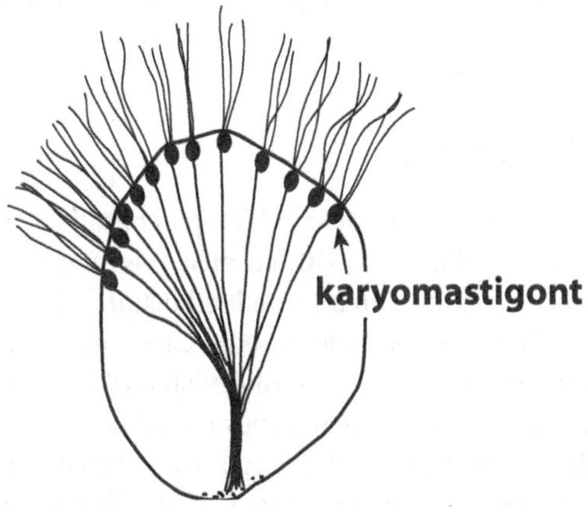

It is more difficult to understand the functional significance of increasing karyomastigont number.

karyomastigont

Figure 17-36. Simple sketch of a Parabasalian in the family Calonymphidae showing numerous karyomastigonts at the anterior end of the single-celled organism.

The reason is that three things increase simultaneously as karyomastigont number increases: the number of nuclei per cell, the number of flagella per cell, and cell size.

Perhaps, certain niches were available to larger organisms, but to support a larger size, more nuclei were needed, and the increase in flagella number was nothing more than a by-product of nucleus duplication being tied to kinetosome duplication. The connection between increasing cell size and becoming multinucleate goes back to diffusion being slow. Specifically, protein synthesis always starts in the nucleus; so, for internally produced proteins to spread throughout a cell, either mRNA formed in the nucleus or the proteins formed by transcription of nuclear-produced mRNA must move by diffusion from the nuclear region to all other parts of the cell. If this distance becomes too great, the diffusion-dependent supply cannot keep up with demand. However, becoming multinucleate and spreading the nuclei around the cell can help resolve this problem (see Figure 17-37). That way no chunk of cytoplasm will be too far from a nucleus.

On the other hand, increasing the number of flagella may have been the key alteration. More flagella will change, in some way, how a cell can move, and these changes in motility may have allowed cells to better exploit some food source, or lead to some other form of biological advantage. A group of parabasalians, called the hypermastigotes, provide one line of evidence that increasing flagella number can, at least at times, be the driving force. Individual organisms within this group have hundreds to thousands of flagella clustered at their anterior end, but have only one nucleus (see Figure 17-38). These organisms still have a karyomastigont unit that duplicates and distributes as a whole during cell division. But these organisms have also come up with some means to make more kinetosomes, independent of karyomastigont replication.

(a) Problem: diffusion distance from nucleus increases with increasing size

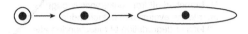

(b) Solution: multinucleate cells

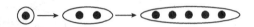

Figure 17-37. How increasing the number of nuclei can decrease the diffusion distance between a nucleus and any part of a cell's cytoplasm.

Figure 17-38. Simple sketch of a Parabasalian in the family Hypermastigida showing numerous flagella, but only one nucleus at the anterior end of the single-celled organism.

Mitotic details

The basic pattern by which parabasalians duplicate their karyomastigonts was discussed briefly earlier (see Figure 17-30) because it is suggestive of a primitive form of mitosis. Here, I provide an overview again with a few added details. Kinetosomes (and MTOCs) duplicate (typically increasing from four to eight), and in some cases, new flagella grow prior to being pushed apart. Spindles then form, and the central axis of division (the line between the two separating spindles) lies between the separating sets of kinetosomes (flagella). On the other hand, the chromosomes are off to the side. So, only microtubules that diverge from this central axis connect with chromosomes. This generates the appearance that using spindles to distribute chromosomes was added on secondarily, reinforcing the idea that this secondary addition reflects how mitosis first evolved. Chromosomes remain attached to the nuclear membrane, and spindle microtubules attach to the protein complexes (kinetochores) that hold chromosomes to the nuclear membrane. The nuclear membrane stays intact throughout, eventually budding into two nuclei. As a whole, one karyomastigont has become two.

A seemingly more efficient means to simultaneously distribute duplicated kinetosomes and duplicated chromosomes would be to somehow align both along the central axis of division. That is what we see in two other distinct forms of metamonad mitosis. In one, karyomastigont division begins with duplicated kinetosomes embedded in developing spindles first moving along the outside of the nucleus until they reach opposite sides (of the nucleus). Growing out from each spindle are microtubules that penetrate through the nucleus through small openings (nuclear fenestrae), as well as passing along the outside of the nuclear membrane. As the two spindles push apart, the kinetosomes are carried along, and the nucleus divides into two. The details of how spindle microtubules are used to distribute duplicated chromosomes within the nucleus are unknown. The major difference of the second observed version of mitosis is that the spindles first form on the inside of the nucleus. Again, kinetosomes separate and then migrate to opposing nuclear poles, where they attach to the outside of each internal spindle. (Some species retain their flagella during this migration, whereas others do not.) As these two spindles push apart, the nucleus elongates as duplicate chromosomes are separated and the attached kinetosomes are separated as well. In at least one species with two pair of kinetosomes per karyomastigont, the pairs initially separate, and then duplicate at the end of cell division (instead of at the beginning).

Although I suggested that parabasalian mitosis may reflect a primitive form of mitosis, it has been suggested that the last version of mitosis discussed earlier represents the most primitive form. This evolutionary scenario starts with spindlelike arrangements of microtubules first forming in the nucleus and initially used to distribute chromosomes. Only later were microtubules used outside the nucleus to do things like forming flagella and affecting cell shape. So, only later were separating spindles used to distribute kinetosomes. A scenario where spindles were first used to distribute kinetosomes among dividing cells is easier for me to visualize, but that, in and of itself, is relatively meaningless. The truth is not always convenient for our minds to put together.

Some key terms:

actin filaments - rope-like structures composed of two intertwined polymers of the protein actin. Their location is concentrated just beneath, and often attached to, the plasma membrane where they become an important part of a eukaryotic cell's cytoskeleton.

myosin - a class of motor proteins where one part catalyzes the hydrolysis of ATP to "walk" along actin filaments and another part binds to something else.

microtubules - cylindrical (tubular) structures composed of the protein tubulin. Due to their tubular nature they are stiff structures that form an important part of a eukaryotic cell's cytoskeleton.

kinesins - a class of motor proteins where one part catalyzes the hydrolysis of ATP to "walk" along microtubules towards the plus end and another part binds to something else.

dyneins - a class of motor proteins where one part catalyzes the hydrolysis of ATP to "walk" along microtubules towards the minus end and another part binds to something else.

endocytosis - invagination of the outer membrane to the point that materials outside the cell are brought into the cell enclosed in a membrane-bounded vesicle.

exocytosis - when the contents of a membrane-bounded vesicle inside the cell are released to the outside by fusion of the vesicle with the plasma (cell) membrane.

endoplasmic reticulum - a highly convoluted membrane-bounded cavity that surrounds the nuclear space in eukaryotic cells.

lumen - the inside of any cavity formed by a membrane (e.g., ER lumen) or by a sheet of cells (e.g., lumen of the digestive tract).

nucleus - a membrane-bound compartment of a eukaryotic cell that contains DNA and is connected to the rest of the cytoplasm by nuclear pores.

biosynthetic-secretory pathway - the path by which proteins that initially form inside the ER are moved outside the cell.

lysosomes - membrane-bounded vesicles in eukaryotic cells that typically contain a whole suite of digestive enzymes that fuse with endocytotically formed food vesicles.

kinetosome - a short cylindrical array of microtubules (plus their associated proteins) found at the base of eukaryotic flagella (or cilia). It serves as the nucleation site for the growth of a flagella's microtubule core (the axoneme).

axoneme - a "9 + 2" microtubule arrangement (and their associated proteins) that forms the supportive structure of eukaryotic flagella (or cilia) and is responsible for their movement.

(eukaryotic) chromosome - a linear (the two ends are not connected) two-side DNA molecule that contains only a portion of a cell's genome. (In other words, when the DNA that makes up a cell's genome is broken up into more than one two-sided DNA molecules, and each linear molecule is called a chromosome.)

duplicate chromosome - the structure that forms when a chromosome replicates, and the two copies of the chromosome stay attached.

kinetochores - complex protein structure that forms around the centromere of a duplicate chromosome to which spindle microtubules attach and which play an active role in the movement of chromosomes during cell division.

mitosis or **mitotic cell division** - cell division that uses a microtubule-based distribution system to move DNA, and each daughter cell ends up with all the DNA present in the original cell. (Ploidy level remains constant across cell division.)

microtubule organizing center (MTOC) - regions in the cell (commonly surrounding kinetosomes) from which microtubules start growth (are nucleated). Growth of microtubules from MTOCs can form a flagellar root system (when associated with kinetosomes bearing flagella), a dynamic microtubule scaffold throughout the cell (when located in as central location), or the separating spindles during cell division.

Some study questions:

1. Discuss how each of the following could have played a role in a prokaryotic cell with a rigid cell wall evolving into a wall-less cell that can control the shape of its outer membrane.
   - sodium ion pumps
   - cholesterol
   - actin filaments
   - myosin
   - microtubules

2. How can the capacity to change the shape of the outer membrane make it possible for a cell to become larger? (Note: to answer this question you need to understand how changing shape can be used to keep surface area increasing as fast as volume as a cell becomes large.)

3. In terms of resisting deforming forces, what is the advantage associated with a having a cytoskeleton containing both actin filaments and microtubules?

4. Explain how the capacity to do endocytosis made each of the following possible:
   - To create membrane bound spaces that are inside the cell but outside the cytoplasm.
   - To allow one cell to become a predator on other cells.

5. Trace the basic steps by which a eukaryotic cell engulfing a bacteria via endocytosis could produce digestive enzymes that end up in the vesicle containing the bacteria (starting with the transcription of a gene for a digestive enzyme, and including the role of signal sequences, SRPs, SRP receptors, and translocons). Then continue on to explain how the useful products of digestion are moved into the cytoplasm of the cell, and the indigestible parts are released back out into the environment.

6. Eukaryotic cells are broken up into three major spaces: nuclear space, cytosol, and inside cell/outside cytoplasm. Be able to answer each of the following questions.
   • Why are both the nuclear space and cytosol considered to be part of the cytoplasm?
   • List some things that happen inside the nuclear space that do not happen in the cytosol, and vice versa.
   • Is the inside (often called the lumen) of the endoplasmic reticulum and golgi apparatus part of the cytoplasm of the cell? Explain. How does your answer relate to the role that these two cell parts play in a biosynthetic-secretory pathway?
   • A nucleus is considered to be the defining feature of eukaryotic cells. Explain how endocytosis may have been involved in the evolution of nuclei. What advantages may be associated with a nucleus?

7. What are some differences between a eukaryotic cell moving by pseudopodia and a eukaryotic cell moving by flagella?

8. Three questions concerning mitosis:
   • What are kinetosomes? Understand a possible connection between the evolution of a system to distribute kinetosomes and the evolution of mitosis.
   • Focussing on a eukaryotic cell's DNA, be able to go through the basic steps involved in mitotic cell division (mitosis).
   • Discuss some of the major changes in the DNA of eukaryotic cells made possible by mitosis.

9. Why do larger single-celled organisms need more than one nucleus?

Symbiosis and the Evolution of Some Eukaryotic Organelles

Consider a single-celled eukaryotic organism that is about to engulf a smaller prokaryotic cell by endocytosis. In the process, the prokaryote will be wrapped up in a food vacuole made from the eukaryote's outer membrane and then tucked inside. What tends to happen next was discussed in the previous chapter and is shown in Figure 18-1(a). Lysosomes fuse with the food vacuole, flooding it with digestive enzymes that break many of prokaryote's molecules into smaller molecules. Many of these smaller molecules then move out of the food vacuole and into the eukaryote's cytoplasm by simple diffusion, facilitated diffusion, or active transport. Molecules remaining in the food vacuole after digestion and absorption are complete, are then removed to the environment by exocytosis.

Now let's think about a different scenario, one in which the eukaryote does not digest the prokaryote after encasing it in a food vacuole (see Figure 18-1(b)). It would happen if the mechanism that directs lysosomes to fuse with food vacuoles somehow fails. But the important question is: Would it ever benefit the eukaryote to keep a potential prey alive and tucked away inside itself? Put more generally: Would it ever benefit an organism to maintain an **endosymbiont**? (*Symbiosis* means living together, and *endo-* means inside, so **endosymbiosis** refers to one organism living inside another.) The answer is that it depends.

To consider this question, we need to return to an idea developed earlier that metabolic differences underscore interspecific interactions. Recall the two major forms of such interactions. Predators commonly feed on prey to steal prey-built molecules (or the molecules built by the prey of their prey in longer food chains) that can be broken down for energy or used to build their own molecular machinery. On the other hand, waste connections form when, due to metabolic differences, members of one species can make use of a molecule that is useless to, hence freely released by, members of the species that generate it. For reasons that hopefully become apparent as this chapter unfolds, we are going to consider waste connections first.

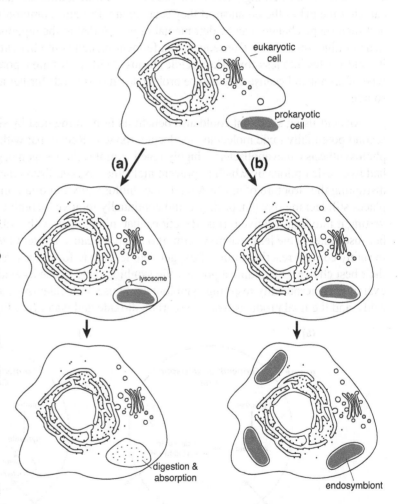

Figure 18-1. The two options that a eukaryotic cell after taking in a prokaryotic cell by endocytosis. In (a) the prokaryote is digested by a lysosome containing digestive enzymes fusing with the food vacuole. In (b) the prokaryote is allowed to remain alive and even reproduce within the host cell.

Waste Connections and Endosymbionts

Is it possible for a waste connection to create a reason for a eukaryote to not digest a captured prey? In other words, would it ever be in the best interest of a eukaryote to keep alive a "swallowed" prokaryote that can utilize its waste? It is not immediately obvious why the answer would ever be yes. Wastes are products of metabolism released freely because the organism that generated them has no further use for them. So how would a waste-generating organism benefit by keeping around another organism able to use something that it has no use for? It turns out that are at least three potential benefits.

Some forms of waste have toxic effects on the organisms that generated them, especially as they accumulate. Keeping another organism close by that can use these wastes would help prevent such accumulation by chemically converting waste molecules into different and potentially less-toxic types of molecules. Early single-celled eukaryotic organisms were likely primed to gain this type of benefit. Early eukaryotic cells are suspected to have generated ATP solely by fermentation. (One line of evidence is that the seeming closest prokaryotic relatives to eukaryotes, the Archaea in the genus *Thermoplasma*, are fermenting.) The waste products of fermentation are acids (see Figure 18-2(a)), which can alter the pH of the organism if they accumulate. Proteins commonly change shape as pH changes, and such shape changes can be detrimental or even lethal to the organism if functional proteins shift to a nonfunctional shape. Consequently, a fermenting cell could benefit from another cell, converting its acid wastes into less-toxic (less acidic) forms. Acid wastes are a potentially useful input to another type of organism because they can be broken down (oxidized) further and thus used as an energy source.

An acid-using symbiont could also benefit its fermenting host by simultaneously detoxifying a second potentially toxic molecule—molecular oxygen. Recall that with the evolution of water-splitting photosynthesis (in cyanobacteria) highly reactive molecular oxygen began to accumulate. Organisms had two basic options by which to prevent molecular oxygen from reacting with and consequently disrupting the structure of its DNA (and other biologically important molecules). They could retreat to places still lacking oxygen, or they could continually remove incoming oxygen by chemically converting it into less-reactive forms. Reactions that mix oxygen with hydrogen to form water are best because water is the least-reactive form of oxygen. Because fermenting cells lack any apparent means to safely convert reactive forms of oxygen into less-toxic forms, retreating to anoxic areas was likely their best choice. But adding a prokaryotic symbiont able to use its acid wastes could change that. For example, an aerobically respiring symbiont could use molecular oxygen in the further oxidation of acids, and the final products would be carbon dioxide and water (see Figure 18-2(b)).

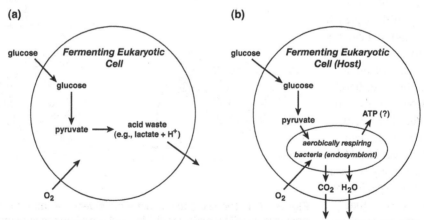

Figure 18-2. (a) A fermenting cell generates acids wastes that could alter the cell's pH unless hydrogen ions are removed as fast as they are produced. (b) A fermenting cell could potentially benefit from the presence of an aerobically respiring endosymbiont in three ways: (1) acid wastes are converted to nontoxic molecules (carbon dioxide and water), (2) any molecular oxygen present is also converted into the same nontoxic molecules, and (3) the host cell may be able to acquire some of the ATP made by the endosymbiont from its wastes.

In addition to detoxifying both acid wastes and molecular oxygen, there is one more way a fermenting eukaryote could benefit from keeping an aerobically respiring prokaryote trapped inside. An aerobically respiring prokaryote trapped inside a eukaryote is able to use its captor's waste to make more of a molecule that its captor could use—ATP. Maintaining an aerobically respiring symbiont thus creates the opportunity for the fermenting eukaryote to boost its ATP supply. The problem with this scenario is that an aerobically respiring prokaryote makes ATP for its own use. At least at the outset, there is no reason to expect that it would export some of its ATP supply to the host cell.

Endosymbiosis and waste connections: An example

Pelomyxa is a genus of large amitochondrial multinucleate amoeboid protists found in bottom sediments of stagnant freshwater ponds or slow-moving streams. The first described member of this group, *Pelomyxa palutris,* also has at least three distinct types of endosymbiotic prokaryotes, all of which tend to be housed in their own vacuoles. These permanent residents reproduce inside *Pelomyxa* and are maintained across host generations by taking up positions that result in them being distributed to all daughter cells during cell division.

The exact nature of the interaction between *Pelomyxa* and these prokaryotes is unknown, but evidence suggests that the interaction with at least two of the three prokaryotes centers around further oxidation of a *Pelomyxa*-generated waste called lactic acid. *Pelomyxa* generates ATP from glucose by fermentation, generating lactic acid as a waste product. To further oxidize lactic acid, some other molecule must be used as an electron acceptor. One of these prokaryotes is apparently able to use oxygen as this electron acceptor, generating water in the process, whereas another prokaryote seems to be able to use carbon dioxide as an electron acceptor, generating methane in the process. Methane-producing prokaryotes are called **methanogens**. Having two different types of bacteria that utilize its wastes in two different ways may help *Pelomyxa* to function well in both aerobic and anaerobic conditions. Although fermenting organisms tend to be vulnerable to the toxic effects of molecular oxygen, *Pelomyxa* is somewhat oxygen tolerant during parts of its life cycle. During this same portion of its life cycle, the population of the presumably oxygen-using prokaryotic endosymbiont increases within its host. On the other hand, the presence of methanogens makes it possible for acid wastes to be further oxidized even when oxygen is unavailable. And during anaerobic conditions, the population of the suspected methanogen increases within its host.

The evolution of mitochondria

Besides *Pelomyxa*, other examples of eukaryotic cells maintaining prokaryotic endosymbionts because of waste connection may exist, although I am not aware of any. If they do exist, it is clear that this type of relationship is extremely rare. Most likely, such rarity has little to do with the difficultly of such relationships forming. Instead, the rarity of waste-using prokaryotic symbionts is likely due to the fact that the vast majority of eukaryotic cells have at least one **mitochondrion** (see Figure 18-3). **Mitochondria** (the plural of mitochondrion) are cellular organelles that perform all the potential functions of a waste-gobbling endosymbiotic prokaryote. Through the ability to perform aerobic respiration, mitochondria use oxygen to further oxidize acid wastes and convert both potentially harmful acids and molecular oxygen into more innocuous carbon dioxide and water.

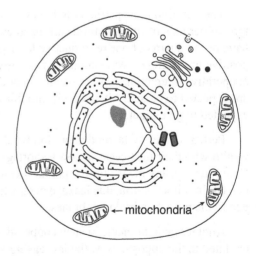

Figure 18-3. A simple sketch of a eukaryotic cell (patterned after an animal cell) that contains several mitochondria.

Furthermore, a substantial proportion of the ATP molecules formed by aerobic respiration are shipped out to be used by the rest of the cell. So, not only are potentially harmful molecules detoxified, but also mitochondria provide the rest of the cell with a significant additional source of ATP. Once mitochondria evolved, the benefit to keeping a waste-gobbling prokaryote tucked inside disappeared because something better had arrived.

But the presence of mitochondria raises a new question: How did eukaryotic cells come to have mitochondria in the first place? In other words, how did mitochondria evolve?

A symbiotic origin?

The idea most strongly supported by the evidence is that mitochondria started as free-living aerobically respiring bacteria that took up residence inside a eukaryotic cell. The association was probably initiated by the eukaryotic host as described earlier —endocytosis followed by a failure to digest the bacteria. However, it is also possible that this association started with bacteria invading eukaryotic cells to feed off them. In other words, it may have started with a bacterial infection.

Regardless of how the association started, the important point has already been established—from the perspective of an early eukaryote, keeping an aerobically respiring prokaryote trapped inside is potentially beneficial from the outset. The eukaryote can more readily venture in to aerobic habitats because the prokaryote can continually dip into the ongoing stream of acidic wastes and incoming oxygen and convert them both into less-harmful products.

Whether the prokaryote also benefited initially or was in essence a trapped slave is less clear. Potential benefits of living within a host could include residing in a more controlled and thus more protected environment, having greater access to nutrients (especially those synthesized within the host), and/or increased mobility (if the host is more mobile than the prokaryote). But even if the host cell was the only benefactor, it is easy to imagine this association becoming permanent. Once a symbiont is confined to live and reproduce entirely within the host cell, the host controls the prokaryote's fate. Once such control is established, it is the host's perspective that matters (most). (Note: a prokaryotic endosymbiont could be maintained across host cell generations by reproducing within the host, and then as any host cell divides, at least some of the increasing number of prokaryotes would end up in each of the two new host cells.)

The question most pertinent to the evolution of mitochondria is, Once established, how might this type of permanent endosymbiotic arrangement evolve in the future? The key is that both cell types have become parts of one reproductive loop. Any modification of one that affects its partner—be it positive or negative—will similarly affect itself. The stage is thus set for the evolution of increasingly cooperative interactions. Modifications in one that aid the reproductive whole by aiding its partner are expected to persist. Alternatively, modifications that negatively affect the reproductive whole are expected to go extinct.

Perhaps, an early favored alteration would be the prokaryotes sharing some of their ATP-based wealth with their host because now a shortage in ATP for the host is an ATP shortage for the whole. Consequently, any means for the prokaryote to leak some its ATP out to the host would be expected to persist. In mitochondria, this leakage occurs through the presence of specific transport proteins embedded in the mitochondrial membranes.

Another general theme in such cooperative evolution would be the **elimination of redundancy**, or stated in the opposite way, the **increasing specialization** of each cell type resulting in a **division of labor**. Resources are wasted whenever both spend time doing the same thing. Some possible examples of redundancies that could be eliminated:

• *Glycolysis.* Both a fermenting eukaryote and an aerobically respiring bacterium can synthesize the enzymes needed to perform glycolysis. But once trapped inside, an aerobically respiring bacterium will not need to break down glucose. It will be confined to feed off the end products of glycolysis coming from the host. As a consequence, it would be a waste of resources for the endosymbiont to continue to manufacture glycolytic enzymes. Only the host needs to be able to do glycolysis.

• *Cell wall.* To persist, the wall-less host cell must be in some way dealing with the too much water problem discussed in Chapter 12. Within this protected environment, the prokaryote would not need a cell wall, so its construction could be eliminated.

• *Genome.* The genes that code for all the glycolytic enzymes, all the proteins involved in cell wall construction, and any other proteins involved in functions now taken over by the host cell could be lost from prokaryotes's genome without consequence. This opens the door for the prokaryotes's genome to be reduced, which would reduce the cost of DNA replication.

In addition, coordinating the function of the whole may be made difficult by the simultaneous operation of two independent genomes—the too many bosses syndrome. Perhaps, the greatest risk is coordinating reproductive rates. If the host cell reproduces too fast, the aerobically respiring prokaryote would be diluted out across generations. On the other hand, the prokaryote's population could overwhelm the host if it grows too fast. The solution lies in converting independence to interdependence. DNA shifting from one genome to another—a process known as **gene transfer**—would accomplish just that. After such gene transfer, neither genome could leave the other behind because the two would need to work together to create a functional whole. A most obvious example (and one commonly found) is genes for different polypeptide subunits of a protein complex operating within the endosymbiont being separated between the nucleus and the endosymbiont. The production of a functional protein complex thus depends on the coordinated production of proteins whose genes are in two different locations. And if protection against oxygen damage is at least part of why nuclei persist, the favored direction gene transfer is clear. DNA moving from the oxygen-using prokaryote to the nucleus is better off than DNA moving in the other direction. The overall result would be increasing centralization of control.

Through the processes of DNA loss and gene transfer, an endosymbiont would lose its separate identity and become a **cellular organelle**. It would have evolved not only in ways that made it impossible for it to ever return to a free-living existence (i.e., live outside the host), but also in ways that made it a highly integrated part of a single organism. Or stated even more accurately, through DNA loss and gene transfer both the host and endosymbiont would have been converted into two parts of a single organism (see Figure 18-4).

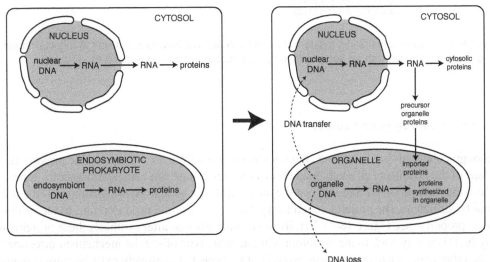

Figure 18-4. The processes of DNA loss and DNA transfer (gene transfer) convert an endosymbiont into a highly integrated cell organelle.

If over the course of time all the modifications suggested earlier actually occurred, an endosymbiotic prokaryote would become a double membrane-bounded compartment specializing in aerobic respiration—starting with the Krebs cycle and including oxidative phosphorylation—within a larger cell. The inner of the two membranes would have originally come from the prokaryote's plasma membrane. The outer of the two membranes would have originally come from the membrane of the endocytotically formed food vacuole. The DNA that remains in this compartment after eliminating redundancy and gene transfer would be too sparse to support existence outside the host or to even still consider it a prokaryotic cell. In other words, what was once a free-living prokaryotic cell would become a completely integrated cell part that would look and act very much like present-day mitochondria (see Figure 18-5).

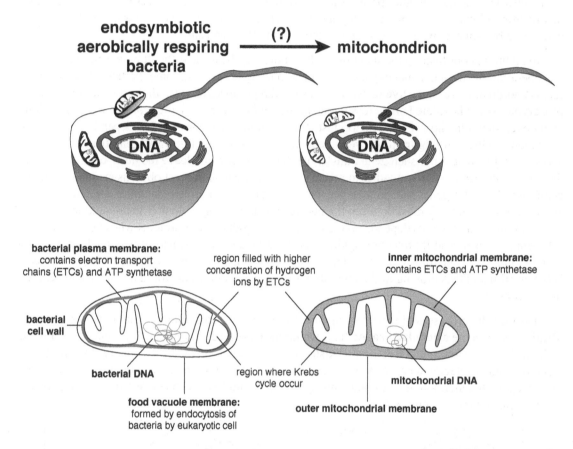

Figure 18-5. Besides containing considerable less DNA and not having a cell wall, a mitochondrion shares many similarities with an aerobically respiring bacteria enclosed within a food vacuole.

Further discussion of gene transfer

Although potentially advantageous, the transfer of genes from an endosymbiotic prokaryote to the nucleus of the host is not an easily made transition. First, how can copies of organelle genes be moved into the nuclear DNA? Second, just the movement of a gene from the symbiont to the nucleus would not be sufficient. The proteins coded for by these genes would need to return to the symbiont to function properly (see Figure 18-4). Yet, its seems unlikely that after synthesis these proteins would regularly find their way back to the symbiont without some type of special mechanism directing traffic. On the other hand, such a mechanism would not be expected to already exist because it wouldn't have been needed prior to endosymbiosis followed by gene transfer. Plus, even if a trafficking mechanism existed for one gene, how would every transferred gene acquire it?

Evidence gathered by scientists studying gene transfer hint at how cells have gotten around these difficulties. The first step, moving genes from symbiont to the nucleus, appears to be the easiest part of the process. DNA, it turns out, is a more fluid molecule than one might first suspect. We know that DNA can be copied, but a mechanism called *reverse transcription* has also been discovered. Here the RNA transcribed from a gene can be used to synthesize a corresponding chunk of DNA. Furthermore, as we discussed with viruses earlier, mechanisms exist through which small pieces of DNA (made by reverse transcription) are incorporated into a larger DNA molecule. So, any DNA coding for a symbiont gene that gets into the nucleus could be integrated into a nuclear chromosome. The second step could be thought of as a transition or intermediate stage in which copies of the same gene are present in both the endosymbiont and the nucleus. During this time, only the organelle gene may be functional, as the copy located in the nucleus may lack a promoter that triggers its expression at that right times and would be expected to lack the means to direct the protein back to the organelle. (Note: Similar to proteins that move into the endoplasmic reticulum (ER), present-day nuclear genes that code for mitochondrial proteins also code for a special sequence of amino acids at one end of the protein that acts a "transit signal." This signal is recognized by receptors located on mitochondrial membranes that facilitate the movement of these proteins inside.) This transition period is thus really an evolutionary waiting period—waiting for these other parts to evolve. One key to this transition, however, is that it does not need to be a unique evolutionary process for every symbiont gene transferred to the nucleus. As we have already established, DNA sequences can be copied and then moved to other locations along a chromosome. As a consequence, once a functional transit signal evolves, other organelle-to-nucleus genes could acquire the same signal sequence by this mechanism. It would still involve chance components and thus would still not be expected to occur quickly, but as a whole makes repeated transfers much more plausible. Evidence also supports its occurrence. The final step is the elimination of redundancy. Once a previously transferred nuclear gene is coding for a protein that makes its way back to the organelle, the functional copy of the same gene in the symbiont is not necessary. The occurrence of disruptive mutations within the symbiont copy would thus not be selected against.

One thing is clear: If mitochondria evolved from an endosymbiotic prokaryote, then gene transfer coupled with a mechanism to direct proteins back into the mitochondria played a major role in the conversion. Genes (e.g., protein genes, tRNA genes, and ribosomal genes) and the needed machinery to synthesize proteins are all present within mitochondria. However, of the hundreds of functional proteins found in a mitochondrion, only a small portion are actually synthesized there. For example, human mitochondria have only 13 protein-coding genes (and a total genome size of only 16,569 base pairs). Although some other mitochondria have considerably larger genomes (especially the mitochondria in plant cells) these genomes appear to code for only a few more proteins. The significance of all this other extra DNA is not clear, and it is possible that at least some of it serves no useful function—that is, it could be removed without consequence. Most of the genes that code for mitochondrial proteins are found in the nucleus. The synthesis of the proteins coded for by these genes occurs in the cytoplasm of the host cell, and these proteins then move into the mitochondria by the mechanism described above.

Some evidence of symbiotic origin

The fact that most mitochondrial proteins are synthesized elsewhere in the cell is why mitochondria are considered to be a cellular organelle. They are too integrated with the rest of cellular function to be seen as a distinct symbiotic organism. Furthermore, the fact that gene transfer coupled with appropriate protein trafficking would be difficult to evolve should make you skeptical of the symbiont to mitochondria evolutionary scenario. But despite this difficulty, mitochondria are still too much like a symbiont to throw the idea out. In fact, although other forms of explanations for the evolution of mitochondria exist, most biologists agree that the endosymbiotic explanation best explains the available data.

The compelling evidence starts with the fact that new mitochondria are never produced *de novo*; they always arise by the growth and division of existing ones. In other words, mitochondria reproduce just as a bacterial symbiont would. Furthermore, although much more DNA is found in free-living or symbiotic bacteria, like an endosymbiont, mitochondria have their own DNA along with all the needed protein-synthesis machinery (e.g., ribosomes, tRNAs). This small amount of DNA could have originally been nuclear DNA that was transferred to a new compartment (within in the cell) that specializes in aerobic respiration; but the advantage of doing so is not obvious. Given that oxygen can react with DNA in disruptive ways, it makes little sense to move DNA from the nucleus to a compartment that requires a continual input of molecular oxygen (for aerobic respiration). It would be like purposely putting a fox in the henhouse. On the other hand, a remnant amount of DNA would still be present if gene transfer to the nucleus was incomplete. The fact that structurally mitochondrial DNA along with the mitochondrial protein-synthesis machinery such as the ribosomes present are more similar to prokaryotes than what is found elsewhere in the same cell (only micrometers away) suggests that incomplete gene transfer is a better explanation. For example, unlike nuclear DNA but like prokaryotic DNA, mitochondrial DNA lacks histones. Furthermore, when the nucleotide sequence from mitochondrial genes is compared to genes in other organisms coding for the same thing (such as ribosomal genes), mitochondrial gene sequences are more similar to certain types of prokaryotes than those found within the nucleus of same cell. Specifically, the gene sequences are most similar to a group of eubacteria (Bacteria domain) called α-proteobacteria.

The seeming difficulty of coupling the evolution gene transfer and protein trafficking may actually help explain another observation of mitochondria. Mitochondria appear to be monophyletic—that is, mitochondria from all different types of eukaryotic cells are sufficiently similar to suggest that they all can be traced back to a single common ancestor. In other words, the evolution of all mitochondria found in all types of eukaryotic cells started with a single case of converting a prokaryote into an endosymbiont. One would expect that mitochondria-like organelles would have evolved independently many times if this was an easy evolutionary pathway.

Although the presence and nature of remnant amounts of DNA in mitochondria makes a strong argument that mitochondria started as bacterial endosymbionts, it also raises the question: Why weren't all the endosymbiont's genes transferred to the nucleus? There certainly are some disadvantages of incomplete transfer. Most obvious is that the cell has to maintain two genetic systems, each with their own protein-synthesizing machinery. Recall that one of the expected directions of evolutionary change within a cell containing an endosymbiont is the elimination of redundancy. Not only is having two complete systems more complicated, but it is also likely to be more energetically expensive. So, are there advantages of having two complete systems that override the disadvantages? Some ideas on possible advantages include: (1) Some genes may code for proteins difficult to import back into the organelle. For example, two genes found in all mitochondrial genomes (so far examined) code for highly hydrophobic proteins that would be difficult (impossible?) to transport across the mitochondrial membranes. Such genes would need to remain in the organelle. (2) Perhaps, retaining some degree of genetic autonomy is needed to maintain mitochondria's ability to reproduce within the host environment. Although this idea has an intuitive appeal, it is not obvious why it would be true. Proteins do all the work of splitting a mitochondria into two, so why would it make any difference whether the proteins were synthesized internally or synthesized outside a mitochondrion and then imported? (3) Before gene transfer was complete, the two systems may have evolved in ways that made them incompatible. The genetic code (what nucleotide triplet codes for what amino acids) in present-day mitochondria is slightly different from that found elsewhere in the cell or in other prokaryotes. If these differences evolved within mitochondria before gene transfer was complete, further gene transfer could have been blocked. Genes coding for functional proteins within the mitochondria may not be translated correctly if the same gene was located in the nucleus and translated in the cytosol.

Food Connections and Endosymbionts

Food connections create a seemingly obvious way that a eukaryote could benefit from keeping a prokaryote trapped inside a food vacuole alive. When a trapped prey is killed by digestion, the eukaryotic predator gets a quick burst of some of the molecules that it needs but cannot make. But eventually the supply of these molecules runs out, and the predator needs to find and capture another prey—which is a potentially difficult task, especially if prokaryote prey are scare. Consuming one prey may be followed by a long and costly search for the next. If so, not killing a prey outright may be a better decision, especially if the prey is photosynthetic (such as a cyanobacteria). Keeping around an organism that can continually use solar energy to synthesize carbohydrates (along with other molecules) opens the door to the host having a long-term carbohydrate supply. In other words, the stage is set for the beginning of an endosymbiotic relationship between a eukaryotic cell and a photosynthetic bacterium.

Although it is not required for an endosymbiotic association to evolve (discussed earlier), photosynthetic bacteria may also gain some form of benefit from this association such as a more protected environment (from other potential predators), increased access to some important nutrients such as carbon dioxide (see next), or increased mobility (due to being swallowed by a more mobile host). If so, herbivory would be replaced by a developing mutualism.

There are, however, two potential snags in the conversion of a photosynthetic prey into an endosymbiont.

First, the photosynthetic prey must be able to live inside the predator. Just because a prey is not digested does not mean that it will live for any length of time trapped inside. The trapped prokaryote, like any other organism, requires certain conditions to survive. So unless those conditions are present within the eukaryotic cell, the prokaryote will die. It is thus striking that there are no known examples of a eukaryotic cell that hosts photosynthetic prokaryotes (or a photosynthetic organelle) that lacks mitochondria. Although the association between mitochondria and photosynthetic symbionts could be a product of chance—that is, chance alone could lead to all photosynthetic symbionts landing in mitochondria-bearing cells because a large majority of eukaryotic cells have mitochondria—it seems more likely that the association is a result of the fact that aerobic respiration occurs in mitochondria. A mitochondria-bearing host that generates ATP by aerobic respiration would better create conditions conducive to a photosynthetic prokaryote than one that generates ATP by fermentation. Photosynthetic bacteria need a supply of CO_2, and CO_2 is an output of aerobic respiration but not fermentation (see Figure 18-6).

The second snag is that photosynthetic prokaryotes would not be expected to provide sugars or any other molecules that they build to their new host. The photosynthetic prokaryotes are making these molecules for their own use, so it is unlikely that a mechanism to export these molecules to a host would be in place. Yet, unless the host can gain access to these molecules, keeping a photosynthetic prokaryote alive serves no purpose. At the expense of killing the prey, digestion solves this problem because it breaks apart the cell, creating access to internal molecules. One way to rather easily get around this access problem is to combine digestion with keeping photosynthetic endosymbionts. It would be analogous to growing a garden. The host would allow a photosynthetic prokaryote to grow and reproduce inside itself and then periodically digest some portion of the population. ***Evolution of chloroplasts***

Photosynthetic prokaryotes (most commonly cyanobacteria) have been found inside (mitochondria-containing) eukaryotic cells in a diverse array of single-celled and multicellular organisms. This

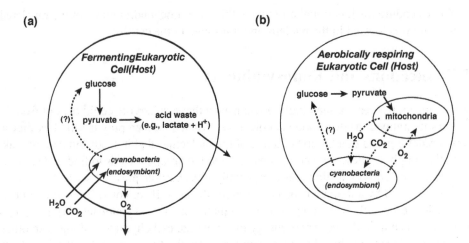

Figure 18-6. Comparing (a) and (b) illustrates why a cyanobacteria could more readily survive a endosymbiont in a host that also has mitochondria. Two outputs of mitochondria are needed inputs of cyanobacteria, so the supply of these molecules (especially carbon dioxide) would be higher in a mitochondria-bearing host. Furthermore, from the host's perspective, the advantage of having a photosynthetic endosymbiont increases with having mitochondria. The advantage of an increased supply of glucose (and other forms of reduced carbon molecules) may be even greater because aerobic respiration can generate more ATP. Plus, the negative of having to contend with more molecules (an output of photosythesis) will be lessened because mitochondria can covert it into less harmful molecules.

suggests that the conversion of a free-living cyanobacterium into an endosymbiont can occur rather easily and has likely occurred on many different occasions. However, most of the photosynthesis that occurs with eukaryotic cells does not take place within endosymbiotic photosynthetic prokaryotes, but within a cellular organelle called a **chloroplast**. Both noncyclic photophosphorylation and the Calvin cycle (carbon reduction cycle) occur inside this organelle.

Chloroplasts may have come into existence in basically the same manner as mitochondria. The evidence suggests that chloroplast evolution started with an aerobically respiring (mitochondria-containing) eukaryotic cell engulfing a photosynthetic bacteria—specifically a cyanobacteria—by endocytosis; but instead of digesting it, the photosynthetic bacteria was allowed to live and reproduce within membrane-bounded vacuoles inside the (host) cell. Once this endosymbiotic relationship was in place, the host and endosymbiont evolved in ways that increased the interdependence of their relationship. This included genes being transferred from the photosynthetic bacteria to the host cell's nucleus and the increasing specialization of function by eliminating redundancy. Through this process, the endosymbiotic cyanobacteria eventually lost its ability to function and reproduce outside the host environment. What remained was a photosynthetic organelle that we call a **chloroplast** (see Figure 18-7).

A little more information on cyanobacteria

Cyanobacteria, the group that came up with oxygen-liberating photosynthesis, are the largest group of photosynthetic prokaryotes. They are widespread in occurrence and are still responsible for a considerable proportion of photosynthetic oxygen evolution in the ocean. They are also morphologically diverse, and this diversification has occurred both through modification of individual cell structure and by more than one cell grouping into generally filamentous colonies.

The most striking modification has been to increase the membrane area along which photosynthesis can occur. In the most primitive form of cyanobacteria found today, called *Gloeobacter*, photosynthesis is confined solely to the plasma membrane, for there are no other membrane infoldings. However, such membrane infoldings, referred to as thylakoids, are characteristic of most other cyanobacteria.

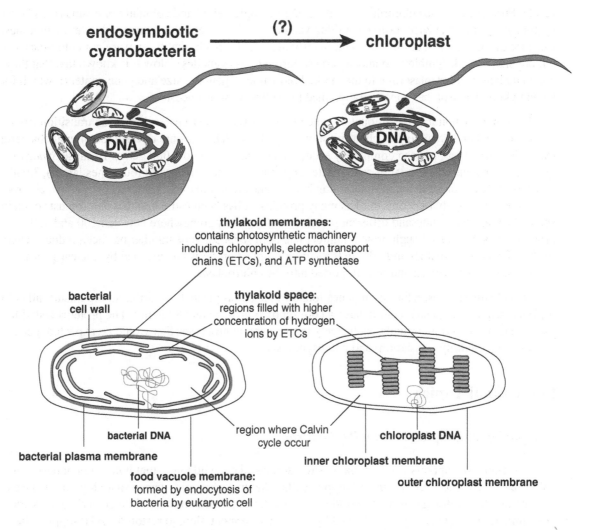

endosymbiotic cyanobacteria → (?) → chloroplast

thylakoid membranes:
contains photosynthetic machinery
including chlorophylls, electron transport
chains (ETCs), and ATP synthetase

bacterial cell wall

thylakoid space:
regions filled with higher
concentration of hydrogen
ions by ETCs

bacterial DNA

region where Calvin
cycle occur

chloroplast DNA

bacterial plasma membrane

inner chloroplast membrane

food vacuole membrane:
formed by endocytosis of
bacteria by eukaryotic cell

outer chloroplast membrane

Figure 18-7. Besides containing considerablly less DNA, generally not having a cell wall, and in some cases having a different thylakoid arrangement, a chloroplast shares many similarities with a cyanobacteria enclosed within a food vacuole. (Note: the stacked thylakoid arrangement illustrated is found in the chloroplasts of green algae and land plants, while other chloroplasts, such as in red or brown algae, have a more cyanobacteria-like thylakoid arrangement.)

These infoldings, which are often arranged as a series of single elongated compartments that follow the same contour as the outer membrane, provide much more membrane for photosynthesis. At least in chloroplasts, the thylakoids are sealed off from the outer membrane and connected with each other, forming a tubelike compartment. In some chloroplasts, these tubes are squeezed close together to form what is referred to as a stacked arrangement (see Figure 18-7).

The evidence

The type of evidence supporting the scenario that chloroplasts were once free-living cyanobacteria is the same as that found in aerobic-respiring bacteria to mitochondria scenario. Although much reduced in amount (in comparison to a free-living cyanobacteria), chloroplasts contain DNA along with all the needed protein-synthesis machinery (e.g., ribosomes, tRNAs). In terms of their DNA, ribosomes, and proteins produced, there is greater molecular similarity between chloroplasts and modern-day cyanobacteria than between chloroplasts and the rest of the eukaryotic cell in which they reside. Furthermore, the chloroplasts in one group of single-celled and colonial organisms (the glauco-cystophytes) have a eubacteria-like peptidoglycan cell wall between their inner and outer membranes. Because of the presence of this cell wall, investigators first thought that these were not chloroplasts at all, but simply endosymbiotic cyanobacteria (referred to as cyanelles). Now it is known that that they are an authentic chloroplast (due to the marked reduction in genome size and gene content), which for some unknown reason has apparently retained the cell wall of its ancestor.

Like in mitochondria, the amount of gene reduction and gene transfer during the transition from cyanobacterial endosymbiont to chloroplast was significant. The genome of one type of cyanobacteria (*Synechocystis*) that has been completely sequenced contains around 3,000 genes. Because *Synechocystis* contains one of the smaller cyanobacterial genomes (many are two to four times larger), 3,000 genes is probably close to the minimum number of genes found in cyanobacteria. In contrast, chloroplasts contain roughly only one-third as many proteins (it has been estimated that chloroplasts contain somewhere around a thousand different proteins) and typically somewhere between 100 and 250 protein genes. So even though protein number has been reduced, gene number has been reduced even further. This means that around 80% to 90% of chloroplast proteins are encoded by nuclear genes, synthesized in the cytosol, and then imported into the chloroplast.

Despite differences in the set of genes found in the chloroplasts from different organisms, all chloroplasts (sequenced so far) seem to have a core set of approximately 80 genes. The proteins coded for by these genes function virtually exclusively in two general processes that would be expected: gene expression (primarily translation) and photosynthesis.

Some Final Topics

Comparing chloroplasts and mitochondria

The evidence supports what, in many ways, sounds like a wild tale—that both mitochondria and chloroplast were once free-living prokaryotic cells. That mitochondria, whose shared-common ancestor was capable of doing aerobic respiration, was the first to be incorporated into an early eukaryotic host limited to using glycolysis, followed by lactic acid fermentation, to restore its ATP supply. The incorporation and subsequent domestication of a free-living bacteria into an interdependent cellular organelle expanded the metabolic options. Most significant is that the end product of glycolysis (pyruvate) could now enter into a mitochondrion, where its three carbons could be oxidized completely to carbon dioxides, via an initial conversion into two carbon acetate, followed by entry into a repeating metabolic path known as the Krebs cycle. The molecules reduced in the process could then pass electrons and protons into electron transport chains located along what was historically the endosymbionts outer or plasma membrane. The twist added was that although the hydrogen ions were still pumped to the outside, they were now pumped into an enclosed space—the space formed between the endosymbiont's outer membrane and the membrane wrapped around the endosymbiont during endocytosis by the host cell. By limiting the movement of hydrogen ions in all directions via diffusion, this enclosed space increased the efficiency that operating ETCs could build and maintain a sufficient hydrogen ion concentration gradient to power ATP synthesis via the spinning of ATP synthase. Use the different highlighted regions of mitochondria shown in Figure 18-8 to help you visualize all the different spaces and membranes mentioned in this story.

The endosymbiotic tale added another twist when a photosynthetic cyanobacteria was endocytosed and subsequently domesticated by a cell already inhabited by mitochondria. The resultant cells could now use sunlight and water (as an electron and hydrogen ion source) to run ETCs , build hydrogen ion gradients, and then use the gradient to synthesize ATP again via the spinning of ATP synthase. The membranes and spaces in which these events occur, however, seem, at least at first, completely different than mitochondria (see Figure 18-8). But this seeming difference is not fundamental. It stems from the fact that most cyanobacteria form invaginations of their outer membrane that apparently seal off to form inner compartments called thylakoids. Confining ETCs to thylakoid membranes has an efficiency advantage. Hydrogen ions are still pumped to the space outside the membrane, but now they enter into the enclosed space of the thylakoid, which again limits the movement of hydrogen ions in all directions via diffusion. Having multiple layers of thylakoids adds further advantage by increasing the surface area to arrange the photosystems able to intersect and utilize incoming light. Furthermore, chloroplasts brought a unique metabolic ability to the mix from their cyanobacteria past—the ability to use the ATP and NADPH generated in noncyclic photophosphorylation, along with carbon dioxide brought in from the environment, and build sugars via the Calvin–Benson cycle. Within a single cell, the outputs of the Calvin–Benson cycle (in chloroplasts) are potential inputs to glycolysis (within the cytoplasm of the host cell), whose outputs, in turn, are potential inputs of the Kreb cycle (in mitochondria). Within this metabolic circuit, the carbon in carbon dioxide and the hydrogens in water are both incorporated into biological molecules and again reformed into carbon dioxide and water. Fundamental components of an ecosystem-level nutrient cycle were now enclosed within a single cell. Perhaps, the scariest part of these scenarios is that once one starts connecting the pieces, it all makes so much sense!

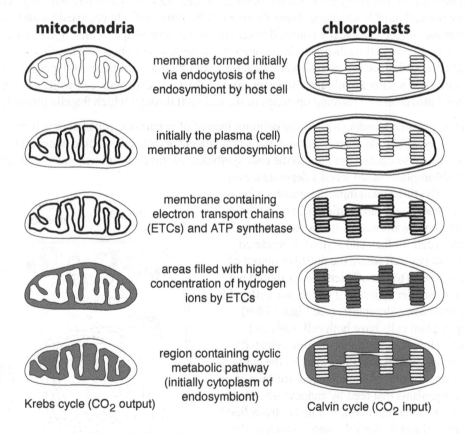

Figure 18-8. A comparative summary of structural and functional aspects of mitochondria and chloroplasts.

Cell walls

Earlier, I made a big deal about the loss of a cell wall as a likely prerequisite in the evolution of eukaryotic cells. All eukaryotic cells, however, do *not* lack cell walls. In fact, among the four commonly recognized kingdoms within the Eukarya (Protista—which include all single-celled and some multicellular eukaryotic organisms, Plantae, Fungi, and Animalia) only some protists and all animal cells lack cell walls.

It seems that after the original loss of cell walls, they evolved a second time within certain groups of organisms. The evidence does not support the alternative—that cells walls were never lost in the first place. The chemical structure of all eukaryotic cell walls is drastically different than prokaryotic cell walls. Prokaryotic cell walls are basically one large molecule—a cross-linked polymer that forms a jacket around the cell. In contrast, the walls of eukaryotes have a microfibrillar structure. Many parallel arrays of long, tightly packed, polysaccharide chains—a microfibril—are cemented together by a matrix of proteins and polysaccharides. The microfibrils give these cell walls tensile strength, whereas the matrix is resistant to compression. The two most common types of polysaccharide chains found in microfibrils are cellulose and chitin.

Why would cell walls evolve in certain lines of eukaryotic cells and not others? Looking at the trade-offs should provide clues. Recall from Chapter 12 that wall-less cells constantly expend energy running ions pumps and, in some cases, constantly forming contractile vacuoles to maintain water balance—that is, to keep water moving out of the cell as fast as it is moving into the cell. Alternatively, a rigid cell wall can prevent a cell from taking on too much water by not allowing the cell to swell past a certain point. And, building a cell wall may be a cheaper way to deal with this problem because it needs to be built only once. On the other hand, cell walls also interfere with any activities that involve the cell quickly changing shape. Once a cell becomes entirely enclosed behind a cell wall, a cell's outer membrane is basically confined to remain in the same shape as this rigid outer covering. As a consequence, cell walls preclude endocytosis along with crawling-like motility. In a completely walled-in cell, even use of eukaryotic flagella would be ruled out because flagella are mobile extensions of a cell's outer membrane. However, some eukaryotic cells with cell walls have retained flagella-based movement by creating openings in the cell wall through which flagella protrude.

If, as I have argued, endocytosis is the defining feature of eukaryotic cells because it made a predatory lifestyle possible, then it seems curious that any eukaryotic cells would abandon this ability. But, endocytosis also opened the door to the endosymbiotic evolution of mitochondria and chloroplasts, and chloroplasts eased a cell's dependence on endocytosis. The three main inputs to photosynthesis are sunlight, water, and carbon dioxide, and all three do not need to be swallowed by endocytosis to be brought into a cell. In fact, endocytosis is rendered unnecessary in any cell where the nutritive output of chloroplasts proves to be sufficient. So, it should not be surprising that the majority of eukaryotic cells with cell walls also have chloroplasts (see Figure 18-9). For example, plant cells have both cell walls and chloroplasts. However, not all eukaryotic cells with chloroplasts have cell walls. For example, the euglenoids are a small group of single-celled, freshwater, flagellated organisms that feed by endocytosis. They lack cells walls, although to retain a more streamlined shape for propulsion through the water, much of their outer membranes are reinforced by a series of proteinaceous strips to form a structure called a pellicle. A significant proportion of euglenoids also have chloroplasts. These euglenoids use a mix of the photosynthetic output of their chloroplasts and food capture by endocytosis to meet their nutritional needs.

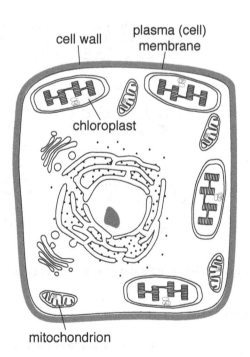

Figure 18-9. A simple sketch of a eukaryotic cell (patterned loosely after a plant cell) that has both chloroplast and a cell wall.

A combination that is harder to understand is the presence of cell wall-bearing eukaryotic cells that lack chloroplasts (but have mitochondria). Although a cell wall may be the cheapest way to maintain water balance, in addition to confining motility, a cell wall also confines a heterotrophic eukaryotic cell to feed in the same manner as a heterotrophic prokaryotic cell. Digestive enzymes are dumped outside the organism, and then digested nutrients are absorbed back in. Because of the relative inefficiency of performing digestion in an uncontrolled space, reverting back to an absorptive mode of nutrition would seemingly be favored only in environments where available nutrients do not readily escape. Dead organisms would fill this bill, and heterotrophic eukaryotic organisms with cell walls tend to be **saprophytic** (obtain their carbon and energy from dead organic matter). Such organisms are most generally referred to as fungi or fungilike organisms.

A brief overview of different types of eukaryotic cells

From our discussion so far, it is hopefully obvious that eukaryotic cells are not all the same. Some have mitochondria, whereas others do not. Some have chloroplasts, whereas others do not. Some have kinetosomes, whereas others do not. Some have cell walls, whereas others do not. In fact the only features that really unify all eukaryotic cells are the presence of at least one nucleus and cytoskeleton elements, such as actin filaments and microtubules.

Recall from Chapter 7 that the theory of evolution tries to make sense of differing degrees of similarity by suggesting that more similar organisms share a more recent common ancestor. To develop this logic a little further, recognize that from an evolutionary perspective there are two scenarios through which two organisms share the same trait: (1) they could share a common ancestor that had the trait, or (2) they could have both evolved the trait independently. Although the latter is always possible, common ancestry is the simplest (most parsimonious) explanation because it requires the trait to evolve only once instead of twice. So, unless there is considerable compelling evidence to the contrary, common descent is more likely to be true. There are also two explanations of why two different organisms do not share a trait: The trait evolved in only one of the two branching lineages after the two organisms shared a common ancestor. In other words, one lineage branched off prior to the evolution of a particular trait. Alternatively, the common ancestor of both organisms could have had the trait, but the trait was lost in one of the two lineages after the branch point. Again, unless there is compelling evidence to the contrary, the first scenario is considered to be the better explanation because it is the simpler. Although both scenarios only require the trait to evolve once, the second scenario has the added complication of requiring the subsequent loss of the trait in certain lineages.

The phylogeny presented in Figure 18-10 summarizes an evolutionary scenario for mitochondria-containing eukaryotic cells developed in the previous two chapters. Interestingly, all the aforementioned reasons why two organisms could either share or not share a trait are found within this phylogeny. I mention an example of each. The phylogeny suggests that mitochondria evolved only once and that lineage gave rise to all the eukaryotic cells that have mitochondria. In other words, animal cells, fungi cells, plant cells, and many different types of single-celled eukaryotic organisms all have mitochondria because they all share a common ancestor. In contrast to mitochondria, the phylogeny does not suggest that the cell walls found in eukaryotic cells evolved just one. The chitin-based cell wall found in fungi and the cellulose-based cell wall found in plants and many forms of algae are suggested to be independent evolutionary events. And finally, secondary loss is invoked several times to explain the absence of kinetosome (and the eukaryotic flagella that can grow out of them) in a variety of different eukaryotic cells—most specifically higher fungi, most higher plants, and red algae.

endocytosis	YES	NO	YES	NO
eukaryotic flagella (possible)	YES	NO (except aquatic forms)	YES	YES/NO (absent in red algae and most higher plants)
mitochondria	YES	YES	YES	YES
cell wall	NO	YES	NO	YES
chloroplasts	NO	NO	YES	YES
examples	many single-celled protists, animal cells	fungi-like cells, fungi cells	some single-celled photosynthetic protists	many (but not all) algae cells plant cells

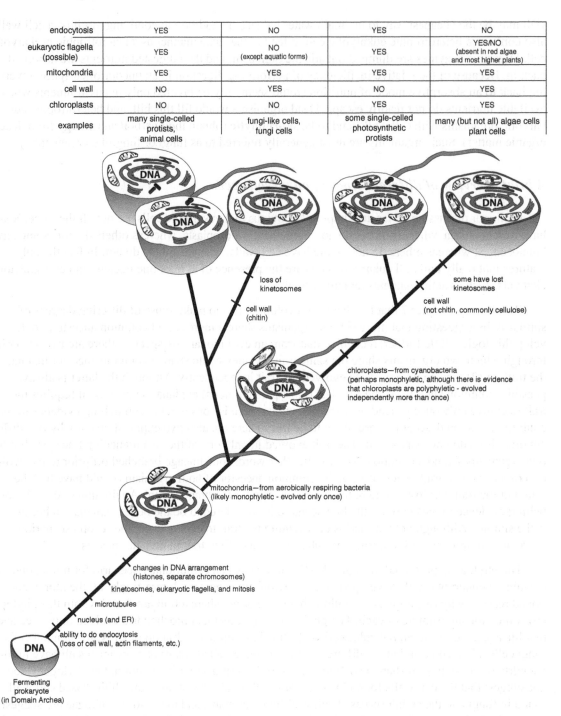

Figure 18-10. An extremely simplified and broad phylogeny for different mitochondria-containing eukaryotic cell types. (See Figure 17-35 for possible ancestries of amitochondrial eukaryotes.) The position of each trait along the phylogeny reflects where it was suggested to evolve.

Some key terms:

endosymbiont - symbiosis means living together , and endo- means inside, so and endosymbiont is an organism that lives inside another organism.

mitochondrion (plural **mitochondria**) - membrane-bounded organelle, about the size of bacteria and containing DNA and the machinery of protein synthesis, where the Krebs cycle and oxidative phosphorylation takes place and is consequently the site where most of the ATP production in eukaryotic cells takes place.

chloroplast - membrane-bounded organelle, about the size of bacteria and containing DNA and the machinery of protein synthesis, where water-splitting photosynthesis—both light phase (noncyclic photophosphorylation) and dark phase (Calvin-Benson cycle)—takes place in eukaryotic cells.

Some study questions:

1. Some questions concerning the evolution of mitochondria via endosymbiosis:
   • How might a fermenting eukaryote benefit by keeping an aerobically respiring prokaryote as an endosymbiont?
   • In what general ways might a host and an endosymbiont be expected to evolve over time?
   • Why is gene transfer the seemingly most difficult step in the evolution of mitochondria from an endosymbiotic aerobically respiring bacteria?
   • What is some of the evidence that supports the idea that mitochondria were once free-living aerobically respiring bacteria?
   • Could a mitochondria survive as a free-living organism? Explain why or why not.
   • Do all eukaryotic cells have mitochondria?

2. Ask yourself similar questions (as in #1) concerning the evolution of chloroplasts via endosymbiosis. In addition, be able to explain why a mitochondria-bearing eukaryotic cell would be a better host for a photosynthetic prokaryote than a fermenting eukaryotic cell.

3. What is the potentially link between a eukaryotic cell having chloroplasts and the evolution (again) of a cell wall? Do all eukaryotic cells bearing chloroplasts have cells walls? Do all eukaryotic cells lacking chloroplasts also lack cell walls?

4. Know which of the following are found, and generally where are they found, in these different types of the following cell types: a fermenting prokaryote, an aerobically respiring prokaryote, a photosynthetic prokaryote (more specifically a cyanobacteria), a heterotrophic eukaryote with mitochondria (see Figure 19-3), and a photosynthetic eukaryote with mitochondria and chloroplasts (see Figure 19-8).

   • DNA, DNA transcription, RNA processing, RNA translation, ribosomes, ribosome synthesis
   • signal recogniztion particle (SRP) receptors, protein synthesis of proteins that stay in the cytoplasm, protein synthesis of proteins exported from the cells, lysosome formation
   • electron transport chains (ETCs), ATP synthetase (oxidative phosphorylation)
   • glycolysis, Calvin-Benson cycle (carbon reduction cycle), Krebs cycle
   • kinetosomes, microtubule-organizing centers (MTOCs), actin filaments, intermediate filaments
   • cell walls (How are cell walls found in prokaryotes and eukaryotes different?)

5. What are the three basic functional forms of single-celled eukaryotic organisms? How does each of these types move? Which one of these three is the fastest?

Why Sex?

In Chapter 3 I claimed that reproduction was one of the two fundamental loops of Life because making more individuals counteracts the tendency for each individual to fall apart. What is curious, however, is that the mechanics of reproduction commonly include a strange twist called sex. But why? The standard assumption would be that adding sex on to reproduction further facilitates persistence. But how?

Although questions concerning the origin and maintenance of sexual reproduction have stirred many ideas, this chapter focuses mostly on one: Sex evolved as a means to repair a certain form of genetic error. Although I favor this explanation over others, that is not the only impetus for presenting it. Most important, it creates a forum to introduce several important aspects of biology.

Although reproduction is an ongoing interaction between information and activity, it is information (by having the potential to be copied and passed on) that potentially persists across generations. Yet like any other physical arrangement, arrangements of DNA containing genetic information have a tendency to accumulate errors (to fall apart). To persist, a DNA arrangement must code for activities (proteins) that counteract this tendency. The most basic activity is reproduction itself. Only if copies are made (and passed to offspring) faster than genetic information accumulates lethal errors will the information persist. But reproduction can be helped by activities that repair genetic errors before they are converted into mutations. Recall that mutations have two main problems. First, they are most likely bad. Rarely are random changes within a functional genome beneficial. Second, once a mutation has occurred, it cannot be repaired to the former sequence. Repair requires the ability to first locate where the change occurred, but this is not possible because an altered nucleotide sequence does not disrupt DNA replication (or DNA transcription) so does not leave any telltale signs of its occurrence. The best way to contend with mutation is thus to prevent them from occurring in the first place. The only other alternative is to hide the effects of a deleterious mutation by having a second good copy of the gene around. We will expand on this idea later.

In Chapter 11 we discussed means to repair two forms of genetic error: copy errors made during DNA replication and single-stranded damage—normal deoxyribonucleotides undergoing chemical conversion into something else on one side of a two-sided DNA molecule. But as of yet we have not discussed any means to repair double-stranded damage (see Figure 19-1). That is our task in this chapter.

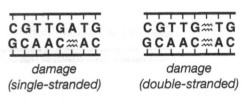

Figure 19-1. The difference between single-sided and double-sided damage.

Repairing double-stranded damage

One way to begin to contend with damage, whether it is single-stranded or double-stranded, is to limit its occurrence in the first place. Any means that reduces a cell's DNA exposure to environmental agents that can induce damage, such as ultraviolet radiation or highly reactive superoxide radicals and hydroxyl radicals, will help accomplish this. For example, that some humans tan with sun exposure is all about better blocking UV radiation. That most of the DNA in eukaryotic cells is located inside a nucleus separated from most metabolism and surrounded by antioxidants also helps prevent damage because it reduces a cell's DNA exposure to reactive molecules formed during the constant hum of metabolism.

But damage still occurs, and it has been estimated that for every 60 instances of single-stranded damage, one case of double-stranded damage pops up— frequent enough to pose a serious problem for cells. The problem is that when both sides are damaged, a two-sided DNA molecule has lost any record of what was formerly there. However, a sequence record is still available if a cell has a second double-sided DNA molecule with an identical or nearly identical nucleotide sequence. And most cells are able to use this second so-called **homologous** piece of DNA to pull off a new form of DNA repair called **recombination**. Although the details are not emphasized here, recombination's basic steps are summarized as follows (see also Figure 19-2):

• A double-stranded DNA molecule suffers double-stranded damage.
• Special enzymes leaving a double-strand gap cut out both complementary strands of a DNA.
• DNA with the double-strand break initiates a recombination event with homologous DNA.
• After repair synthesis takes place, crossing DNA strands must be cut and then spliced for the homologous pieces of DNA to separate. In the process, some DNA moves from one molecule to the other.
• Homologous DNA can align in four distinct ways. In two of them, not only does cutting and splicing result in a small portion of DNA being swapped, but also he two homologous pieces of DNA swap places across the break—an event termed **crossing-over**. You may recall, however, that there was a second version of damage introduced in Chapter 11

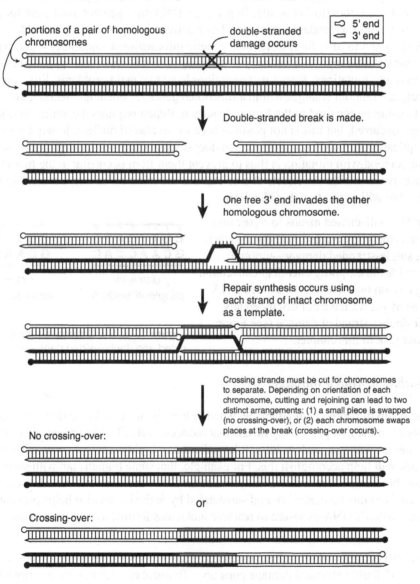

Figure 19-2. Basic scheme by which double-stranded damage is repaired by recombination.

Sex

The question surrounding recombinational repair is, Where does this second homologous piece of DNA come from? This is where sex enters the picture.

Sex in prokaryotes

When cells break apart, some prokaryotic cells are able to uptake leftover DNA fragments floating in the environment. Such uptake is called **transformation**. It has been learned that many types of bacteria have membrane-bound proteins specialized for DNA uptake, some of which seem to be able to distinguish between sequences and restrict uptake to fragments that are similar to their own. And evidence exists that similar sequenced DNA fragments are sometimes used for recombination repair (see Figure 19-3).

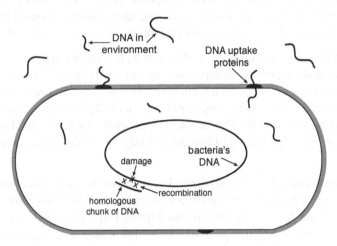

Figure 19-3. Transformation and recombination in a prokaryotic cell.

Sex is any process that combines genetic material from more than one individual into a single individual. As curious as this might sound, transformation plus recombination in prokaryotes is sex. Sex in this form stands in sharp contrast to common conceptions. For one, there were not two consenting partners. In fact, the DNA brought in was from an already-dead-broken-up cell. Plus it is not associated with reproduction. Pieces of DNA brought in may fuse into a prokaryotic chromosome during recombination, but no new individual is generated in the process. And finally, the amount of DNA incorporated into a prokaryote's genome is small compared to the amount already in the cell.

The obvious limitation of transformation-recombination is that there is no guarantee that a cell will uptake DNA homologous to the region or regions of its chromosome suffering double-stranded damage. Without such repair, the cell will most likely die and take all the functional parts of its genome with it.

Diploid versus haploid

An alternative is for a cell to become **diploid**. Recall that a cell's **ploidy level** refers to the number of complete genomes contained within a cell. A diploid cell has two complete genomes, which means every gene comes with a backup copy. Each of the chromosomes that help make up a complete genome come in pairs called **homologous chromosomes**.

Being diploid not only sets the stage for recombinational repair; it can also mask the potential harmful effects of either double-stranded damage or mutations. The likelihood that both copies of any gene succumb to error is much less than for just one copy, and the remaining good copy can cover if the other turns faulty.

There is, however, a downside to being diploid. Every time the cell reproduces there is twice as much DNA to replicate. Not only will this potentially slow down cell division, but it also adds extra costs. For instance, twice as many nucleotides need to be synthesized. Furthermore, although being diploid is a prerequisite to recombinational repair, it is no assurance that it can take place efficiently. Efficient recombination repair depends on some mechanism to align homologous chromosomes in close proximity and then separate them once repair is complete. Diploidy itself does not ensure such a mechanism is in place.

Haploid is the term used for cells containing only a single genome. The costs and benefits of a cell remaining haploid are just the opposite of being diploid. There is less DNA to replicate, so cell division is potentially faster and not as expensive. Unfortunately, double-stranded damage can never be repaired, and the effects of a faulty gene cannot be hidden without a second still-functional copy.

So which is better, haploidy or diploidy? In other words, is it more important to be able to divide faster and cheaper, or to make it possible to repair double-stranded damage? The best answer is: It depends. It depends on exactly what obstacles a particular cell type faces. But before getting too locked into thinking in terms of one or the other, recognize there is a third alternative—switching back and forth between being haploid and diploid. Prokaryotes are generally haploid cells, but transformation of homologous DNA fragments is a partial shift toward diploidy. Haploidy returns as unused fragments degrade.

Complete switching between haploid and diploid starts when two haploid cells with homologous genomes **fuse** to form one diploid cell. The return trip is made possible by **meiosis**—two rounds of cell division that convert one diploid cell back to four haploid cells. This combination of fusion and meiosis in a population of single-celled haploid organisms introduces an intriguing possibility: Cells that commonly reproduce asexually by undergoing mitotic cell division (to take advantage of being haploid) can on occasion switch to sexual reproduction (fusion/meiosis) to repair double-stranded damage (see Figure 19-4 (a)). *Chlamydomonas*, a single-celled green algae, is an example of a single-celled organism whose life cycle follows this pattern (see Figure 19-4(b)). The details lie in how often this switch is made and what detectable change organisms use to trigger the switch. Details will be under the constant scrutiny of natural selection because those variants that take the best advantage of

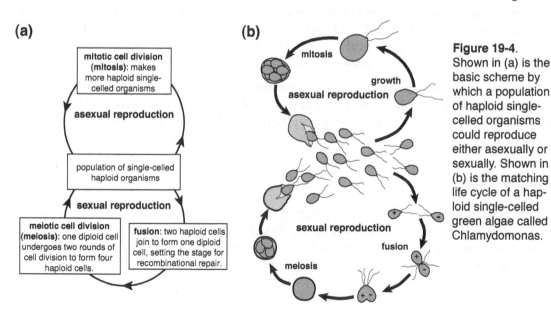

(a)

(b)

Figure 19-4. Shown in (a) is the basic scheme by which a population of haploid single-celled organisms could reproduce either asexually or sexually. Shown in (b) is the matching life cycle of a haploid single-celled green algae called Chlamydomonas.

both haploidy and diploidy will, all else being equal, win the ongoing reproductive race. Furthermore, in comparison to being always diploid, the basic workings of meiosis serve to make recombinational repair more efficient. It is possible that increasing repair efficiency is what drove the evolution of meiosis in the first place. Before speculating further it would help to understand the basic mechanics behind meiotic cell division.

The mechanics of meiosis

Meiosis, or **meiotic cell division**, seemingly evolved as a modification of mitosis because in many ways they are similar. Like mitosis, meiosis in most organisms begins with each chromosome forming a compact duplicate chromosome via chromosome replication and packaging, and microtubule spindles duplicate and separate moving to opposite sides of a dividing cell. Also like mitosis microtubules extending from each spindle form attachments used to position and then pull chromosomes into separate cells.

The major difference is that in meiosis something new was added. Normally in diploid cells, each pair of homologous chromosomes behaves like completely independent chromosomes. This is why diploidy alone is no assurance that double-stranded damage will be fixed by recombinational repair. Homologous chromosomes must first align in close proximity for such repair to occur. It is in the first stages of meiosis that this type of alignment was added. After each chromosomes replicates and begins to package (by some still unknown mechanism) homologous pairs of duplicate chromosomes are brought together. Similar DNA sequences are thought to facilitate the initial interaction. This alignment of homologous pairs of chromosomes in their duplicate form is called a **tetrad** or **bivalent** (see Figure 19-5). Recombinational repair can proceed once each tetrad forms. That chromosome duplication occurs prior to this pairing may actually facilitate recombinational repair because damaged regions cannot be replicated, so damage on the preexisting chromosome will show up as gaps on the newly formed duplicate. As shown earlier in Figure 19-2, recombination is triggered by such gaps.

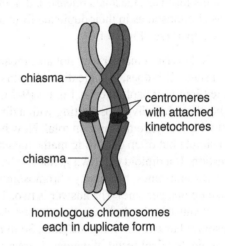

Figure 19-5. A tetrad that forms during the first stages of meiosis by the alignment of two homologous chromosomes each in their duplicate form. Each chiasma is a point where recombination occurs between homologous chromosomes.

Each spot along a tetrad where recombination takes place forms an even tighter coupling known as a **chiasma** (plural **chiasmata**; see Figure 19-5). One too many chiasmata may form in each tetrad. It is at each chiasma that crossing-over between homologous chromosomes can occur. (Note: If you study biology further, especially genetics, crossing-over will be used as a means to map the relative locations of genes on chromosomes, and its occurrence will often be interpreted as a means to promote novel combinations of genes. But if the repair of double-stranded damage was and still is the evolutionary driving force behind the formation of tetrads during meiosis, crossing-over is simply an unavoidable consequence.)

The rest of meiosis involves pulling this tetrad back apart. This is done in two stages. First the two sets of duplicate homologous chromosomes that earlier aligned to form each tetrad are pulled apart. Next each duplicate chromosome is pulled apart, returning chromosomes to their singular form (see Figure 19-6).

Mitotic mechanisms are used to generate the forces needed at each stage. In fact, the only real difference between mitosis and meiosis comes in the first separation. Recall that microtubules from opposing spindles attach to opposite sides of the two kinetochores, which hold duplicate chromosomes together during mitosis. The two duplicate chromosomes are pulled apart as the kinetochores unhinge. The same thing occurs in the second stage of meiosis. In contrast a tetrad has two sets of kinetochores, one hooking each of the two sets of duplicate chromosomes together. Microtubules from one spindle attach to one kinetochore set, and microtubules from the other spindle attach to the other set. Each set remains fused as chiasmata release and homologous chromosomes in their duplicate form are pulled apart (see Figure 19-6).

Cell division may or may not accompany each stage. If it does, a single diploid cell is converted into four haploid cells. Figure 19-7 highlights these two divisions starting with a diploid cell with four chromosomes in total. Now here is a simple but often confusing mathematical question: If a diploid cell (two genomes) has four chromosomes, how many chromosomes make up one genome? The answer is two. This also means that the diploid cell with four chromosomes has two homologous pairs. So in this example, the final result of meiosis is four cells each with a single copy of the two chromosomes making up a genome. Stated differently, each of the four cells is haploid.

Sex is rejuvenating

Like mitosis, the combination of fusion of two haploid cells followed by meiotic cell division still involves reproduction. One cell gives rise to two cells in mitosis. Fusion followed by meiosis starts with two cells and ends with four cells. In both cases, twice as many cells are made. The difference is that fusion with meiosis adds recombinational repair. Two haploid cells with lethal double-stranded damage could fuse and then undergo recombinational repair in conjunction with meiosis to produce four healthy (no lethal double-stranded damage) haploid cells (see Figure 19-8). In other words, sex is rejuvenating because to repair is to renew. (Have you ever wondered why parents that have been accumulating damage throughout their lives can combine to produce offspring that are truly younger—that is, have less genetic damage?)

Adding sex (fusion/meiosis) to reproduction adds costs such as the extra effort and danger associated with finding a mate (a suitable cell with which to fuse). From a cost-benefit perspective organ-

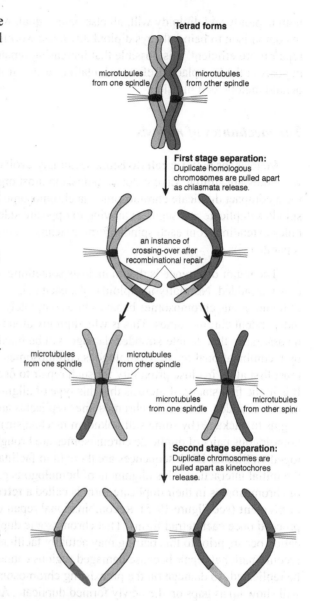

Figure 19-6. The two stages by which tetrads formed in the early stages of meiosis are separated into single chromosomes.

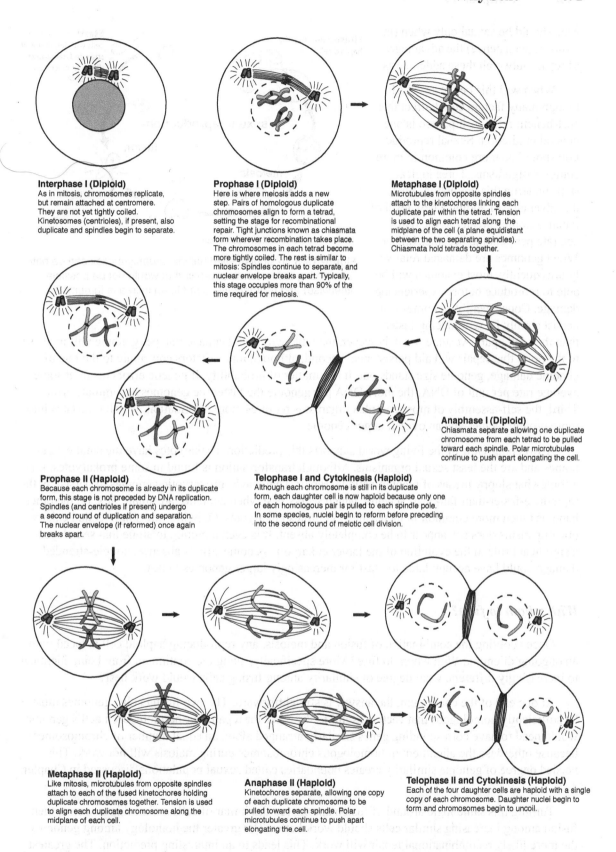

Interphase I (Diploid)
As in mitosis, chromosomes replicate, but remain attached at centromere. They are not yet tightly coiled. Kinetosomes (centrioles), if present, also duplicate and spindles begin to separate.

Prophase I (Diploid)
Here is where meiosis adds a new step. Pairs of homologous duplicate chromosomes align to form a tetrad, setting the stage for recombinational repair. Tight junctions known as chiasmata form wherever recombination takes place. The chromosomes in each tetrad become more tightly coiled. The rest is similar to mitosis: Spindles continue to separate, and nuclear envelope breaks apart. Typically, this stage occupies more than 90% of the time required for meiosis.

Metaphase I (Diploid)
Microtubules from opposite spindles attach to the kinetochores linking each duplicate pair within the tetrad. Tension is used to align each tetrad along the midplane of the cell (a plane equidistant between the two separating spindles). Chiasmata hold tetrads together.

Anaphase I (Diploid)
Chiasmata separate allowing one duplicate chromosome from each tetrad to be pulled toward each spindle. Polar microtubules continue to push apart elongating the cell.

Prophase II (Haploid)
Because each chromosome is already in its duplicate form, this stage is not preceded by DNA replication. Spindles (and centrioles if present) undergo a second round of duplication and separation. The nuclear envelope (if reformed) once again breaks apart.

Telophase I and Cytokinesis (Haploid)
Although each chromosome is still in its duplicate form, each daughter cell is now haploid because only one of each homologous pair is pulled to each spindle pole. In some species, nuclei begin to reform before preceding into the second round of meiotic cell division.

Metaphase II (Haploid)
Like mitosis, microtubules from opposite spindles attach to each of the fused kinetochores holding duplicate chromosomes together. Tension is used to align each duplicate chromosome along the midplane of each cell.

Anaphase II (Haploid)
Kinetochores separate, allowing one copy of each duplicate chromosome to be pulled toward each spindle. Polar microtubules continue to push apart elongating the cell.

Telophase II and Cytokinesis (Haploid)
Each of the four daughter cells are haploid with a single copy of each chromosome. Daughter nuclei begin to form and chromosomes begin to uncoil.

Figure 19-7. Meiotic cell division. Separation of tetrads into single chromosomes is accompanied by two rounds of cell division, resulting in one diploid cell being converted into four haploid cells.

isms should be sexual only when (in terms of persistence) the advantages of repair outweigh these added costs.

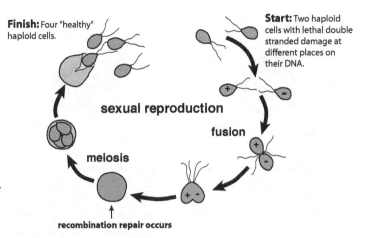

When will this be the case? Although many factors could affect this cost-benefit relationship, here is one general prediction: Sexual reproduction should be more common in more complex organisms. Three logical steps underlie this prediction. First, the advantage of adding a new level of repair becomes greater as the damage rate per genome becomes higher. When genomes are damaged relatively infrequently, most genomes will be able to reproduce before experiencing damage. Consequently, genomes can persist simply by reproducing faster than they fall apart. At some point, however, the table will turn. Damage rate per genome will increase to the point that repair will aid persistence. Second, although many factors contribute to the rate of genome damage, genome size stands out. It is a matter of probability. If genetic errors occur at some average rate per unit of DNA, the more DNA per genome the faster the genomes accumulate error. Third, the self-assembly of more complex organisms requires more information, which translates into more protein recipes and an overall larger genome.

Figure 19-8. In single-celled haploid organisms sex can be both rejuvinating (allow forms of repair that would not be possible otherwise) and reproductive (lead to an increase in number).

A sweeping view of the living world supports this prediction. Prokaryotes have the smallest genomes and are the least sexual organisms. Although transformation is found in some prokaryotes, it is a somewhat sloppy means of recombinational repair. That leaves prokaryotic genomes to persist by the reproduce-faster-than-fall-apart scheme, which works best when genomes are small. Sex, on the other hand, is much more common in increasingly complex eukaryotes. Only in some single-celled eukaryotic organisms does sex appear to be completely absent. It is even tempting to argue that sex played a significant role in the evolution of the larger eukaryotic genomes. In its absence, double-stranded damage could have accumulated too fast for increasingly larger genomes to last.

With whom to fuse?

Once adopting the combination of fusion and meiosis, any reproducing haploid cell is faced with an ongoing dilemma: With whom to fuse? More specifically, along the continuum from being identical to increasingly different, what degree of similarity among fusing cells would work best?

At one end of the continuum, the answer is straightforward. The two fusing cells' genomes must be sufficiently homologous that each is useful to the other for repair. Furthermore, each cell's genome would need to have corresponding genes similarly arranged along an equal number of chromosomes because otherwise the alignment of homologous chromosomes during meiosis will not work. This needed degree of genome similarity creates boundaries called sexual populations discussed in Chapter 4.

Turning this same logic around, if fusion among too dissimilar of cells makes things worse, then fusion among increasing similar cells should work better. The greater the homology among genomes the more likely recombinational repair will work. This leads to an interesting prediction. The greatest homology exists among cells that most recently share a common ancestor. The more closely related two cells are, the less time and therefore less chance there has been for their genomes to diverge. The seemingly best scenario would be fusion of two cells from the same individual, which is known as **selfing**. **Inbreeding**, which is fusion between close relatives, would be the next best thing, and the closer the better. Mating between siblings would be better than mating between first cousins, whereas first-cousin matings would be better than second-cousin matings, and so on.

You might find this suggestion peculiar, if not even repulsive. Humans and many other organisms are **outcrossers**—organisms that tend to avoid mating with close relatives. You may even be aware of the fact that when inbreeding occurs in normally outcrossing populations, the resultant offspring are more likely to die or have other serious abnormalities. Biologists refer to this phenomenon as **inbreeding depression**. It provides a not too subtle hint that, at least in some cases, fusing with the most similar is not the best alternative. But why?

Although we could be better prepared to take on this topic, let's take a stab at it. The argument centers on the evolution of larger, more complex, multicellular organisms.

Multicellular bodies can form at one of two points in a sexual cycle. After meiosis, single haploid cells could undergo mitotic cell division, and the resultant cells could stay together to form a haploid multicellular organism—that is, each cell making up the organism's body is haploid. Or, after two haploid cells fuse, the resultant diploid cell could undergo mitotic cell division, and the resultant cells could stay together to form a multicellular organism composed of diploid cells. (Note: Because mitotic cell division produces genetically identical daughter cells, it conserves ploidy level. Haploid or diploid cells undergoing mitosis give rise to daughter cells that are haploid or diploid, respectively. Figure 19-9 illustrates this in more detail.) In fact, within many sexual species multicellular forms are generated at both places in each turn of the sexual cycle.

Yet although all these variations in where multicellular organisms show up are interesting (and will be discussed further in later chapters) the point to be emphasized here is that despite the fact that multicellular forms can either be haploid or diploid, increasingly complex forms are consistently diploid. Larger more complex multicellular organisms need more time to grow, to develop, to reach sexual maturity, to care for their young, and so on. So the only way to pull off increasing complexity is to live longer. But to live longer one must be better able to contend with the accumulation of genetic error within the cells making up one's body. This problem is further confounded by the fact that larger more complex organisms need larger genomes, and more DNA means more opportunity for errors to arise. The combination of these problems seemingly tipped the scales toward diploidy. Although diploid cells are more expensive to replicate, they can better deal with accumulating genetic error. Two copies of every gene in every cell means that if one copy becomes faulty, a good copy still remains. Of course, both copies of any one gene could fall victim to error, but given its random nature of occurrence, the likelihood is considerably smaller than if there was only a single copy—just as it is increasingly unlikely for lightning to strike twice in the same spot. Although there may be other factors involved, it is not surprising that increasingly complex multicellular organisms tend to be diploid.

There is, however, a problem that always accompanies increasing the multicellular diploid phase of a life cycle. Deleterious mutations of genes expressed only in the diploid multicellular form are potentially passed across generations. Not only can a second good copy mask the harmful effects, but mutations can also be replicated (in contrast to damage, which cannot). As a potentially replicated part of a functional diploid organism, any harmful mutation has the same chance (50%) as the functional copy to be passed into a haploid gamete. Furthermore, because this gene is only used in the diploid form, a single faulty copy inside a haploid gamete has no effect on the gamete's ability to find and then fuse with another gamete. As a consequence, a gamete with a harmful mutation has the same chance as a gamete with a functional copy of the same gene to make it into the next generation.

That functional gametes can carry harmful mutations is what generates the potential for inbreeding depression. Two gametes bearing any number of deleterious mutations can fuse and potentially give rise to a healthy diploid multicellular organism, so long as neither gamete has the same deleteri-

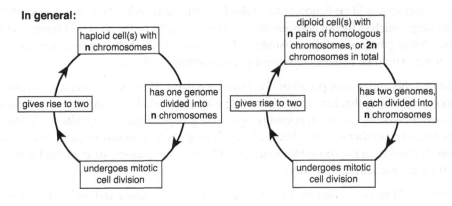

Two specific examples:

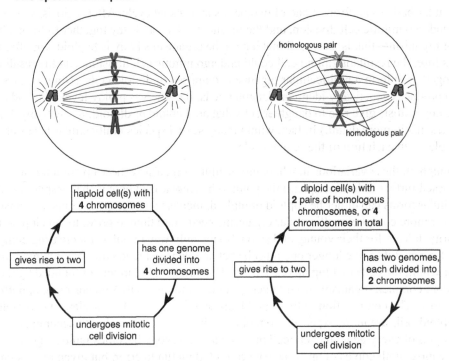

Figure 19-9. How mitosis conserves ploidy level in both haploid and diploid cells. The key point is that during mitosis each chromosome duplicates and aligns independently, regardless of whether a homologous chromosome is present or not.

ous mutations. With different deleterious mutations, the effect of each is potentially masked by the good copy provided by the other gamete. Alternatively, if two gametes fuse with any of the same deleterious mutations, no good copies are present in the developing offspring to hide the harmful effects. This sets the stage for any mechanism that helps gametes avoid such pairings to evolve. The most straightforward is to avoid breeding with close relatives. Suppose a deleterious mutation popped up in your maternal grandfather that was subsequently passed on to your mother and then to you. What other individuals have the best chance of having this same deleterious mutation? Although I am not going to work through the calculations, it turns out that any siblings have a 50% chance of inheriting it, first cousins have a 25% chance of inheriting it, whereas anyone more distantly related has a 0% of having inherited this mutation. And regardless of the details, the trend is always that the closer the relation, the greater the likelihood of having a copy of the same bad mutations. Thus employing some behavioral means to avoid breeding with close relatives (an avoidance referred to as an **incest taboo**) helps prevent this problem.

The strange twist is that outcrossing is actually a vicious cycle. The more a sexual population outcrosses, the less often deleterious mutations will be expressed, which in turn allows more deleterious mutations to accumulate at a higher frequency in the population. It is only when they are expressed that potentially masked deleterious mutations are weeded out of the population. But with more deleterious mutations around, the consequences of inbreeding will be even more severe, creating even stronger selection for outcrossing.

Alternative Views of Fusion and Meiosis

Sex, as a means to repair double-stranded damage is likely an unfamiliar idea. The idea does not have a long or well-established history. Instead, most discussions concerning the evolution of sex have focused on some benefit associated with producing variable offspring, for genetic mixing is the most obvious outcome of sex. Offspring produced sexually are almost never genetically identical to either parent or other siblings. In Chapter 6 I discussed how this mixing nature changes the basic means by which sexual populations evolve, making the obvious next question: In what circumstances is producing variable offspring an advantageous response?

A common answer to this question focuses on uncertainty. Offspring start their lives after their parents, and as a result of dispersal may also start it in a different location. As a consequence, they may not experience the same conditions as their parents. There is no guarantee that the future will be like the past, especially when living in a different locale. Producing different types of offspring would seemingly increase the chance that at least one will be well suited to deal with future conditions. Stated differently, sexual reproduction is a means to hedge bets in an uncertain world.

This same theme emerges in the idea that sex potentially speeds up evolutionary change. In sexual populations, the source of novel genotypes is not just mutations within individuals but genetic differences within a sexual population's entire gene pool. For example, two different forms of beneficial mutations arising in two individuals in a sexual population could potentially mate and produce offspring bearing both. This potential to generate more novel genetic combinations each generation in turn generates more types that either succeed or fail at reproducing. With more options, the range of change from one generation to the next would seemingly increase. The supposed advantage is that increasing evolutionary speed helps sexual populations to persist in the face of constant environmental change. In essence, sex aids persistence because sexual populations can adapt more quickly to new forms of environmental challenges. A biologist named Graham Bell termed this view of sex as the Vicar of Bray hypothesis. Apparently, the Vicar of Bray was an English cleric noted for his ability to change his religion whenever a new monarch ascended the throne.

Another line of argument concerning the evolution of sex focuses on how producing variable offspring could help reverse the accumulation of deleterious mutations. Sexual mixing between two individuals with deleterious mutations would generate offspring that fall into one of three categories: have *more* deleterious mutations than either parent, have the *same* number of deleterious mutations as either parent, or have *fewer* deleterious mutations than either parent. If offspring with fewer deleterious mutations are on average more reproductively successful, the average number of deleterious mutation can actually decrease across generations. When reproduction is *asexual*, offspring cannot be produced with fewer bad mutations than their parent. As a consequence, whenever a deleterious mutation becomes fixed in an asexual population, there is no going back. Bad mutations will instead tend to accumulate across time, resulting in a gradual and unavoidable deterioration of genetic quality that could contribute to the population going extinct. This steady accumulation of bad mutations in asexual populations is known as Muller's ratchet—named after the person who introduced the idea.

476   **Chapter 19**

Which is right?

All these ideas have a common feature—they all suggest that sex helps overcome obstacles to persistence. Strikingly, each idea focuses on a different obstacle. With the double-strand damage repair view of sex, the primary obstacle is the constant tendency for genomes to suffer damage. The basic advantage is that sex helps keep things the same by adding a new layer of repair onto reproduction. With the rate-of-evolution or bet-hedging views of sex, the primary obstacle is the constantly changing challenges imposed by an ever-changing environment. In contrast to help keeping things the same, the supposed advantage of sex here stems from facilitating change.

Although our tendency is to ask the black-and-white question of which idea is right, perhaps trying to sort each into being right or wrong may lead us astray. There may not be a completely right or wrong answer. For instance, although more efficient damage repair may best explain how and why sex first originated, the potential advantages of mixing in the face of uncertainty may have further strengthened the advantages to sex. It goes back to the principle of contradiction introduced in Chapter 5. When different perspectives lead to different views, we should embrace the contradiction. It just may be that we must be aware of all sides if we are to have a full understanding of sex.

Some key terms:

sex - any process that results in the union of genetic material from more than one source into a single individual

ploidy level - the number of complete genomes contained within a cell.

haploid cell (monoploid cell) - any cell that contains one complete genome.

diploid cell - any cell that contains two complete genomes.

homologous chromosomes - two chromosomes that contain the same portion of a cell's genome. (In sexual reproduction, a cell receives one chromosome of each homologous pair from its mom and the other from its dad.)

meiosis or **meiotic cell division** - cell division that uses a microtubule-based distribution system to move DNA, and each daughter cell ends up with one-half the number of genomes found in the original cell. (Ploidy level is reduced by one-half across cell division. Note that a haploid cell could not undergo meiotic cell division.)

tetrad – an alignment of two homologous chromosomes each in their duplicate form that occurs at the beginning (prophase I) of the first meiotic division. It is in this arrangement that recombination between homologous chromosomes can occur.

crossing over - the process where the cutting and splicing involved in separating homologous chromosomes undergoing recombination results in pieces of homologous chromosomes swapping places.

outcrossing population – a sexual population where individuals typically avoid mating with close relatives.

inbreeding depression – the increased chance of matings between close relatives producing offspring that die or suffer abnormalities. It is found in normally outcrossing populations.

Some study questions:

1. Why is double-stranded damage to DNA more difficult to repair than single-stranded damage?

2. What are the potential advantages and disadvantages (benefits and costs) of being haploid? of being diploid?

3. Understand how in single-celled haploid organisms, the combination of fusion and meiosis is able to combine recombinational repair with reproduction.

4. What are some basic similarities and basic differences between the life cycle of a land plant, such as a fern, and an animal, such as you?

5. Provide an explanation for the observed trend that increasing complex multicellular organisms tend to be diploid.

6. Use the below figure to help you understand the difference between mitotic and meiotic cell division. (The goal should be to see the patterns in a way that makes filling out all the various blanks obvious, and to understand how answers would change if the total chromosome number changed.)

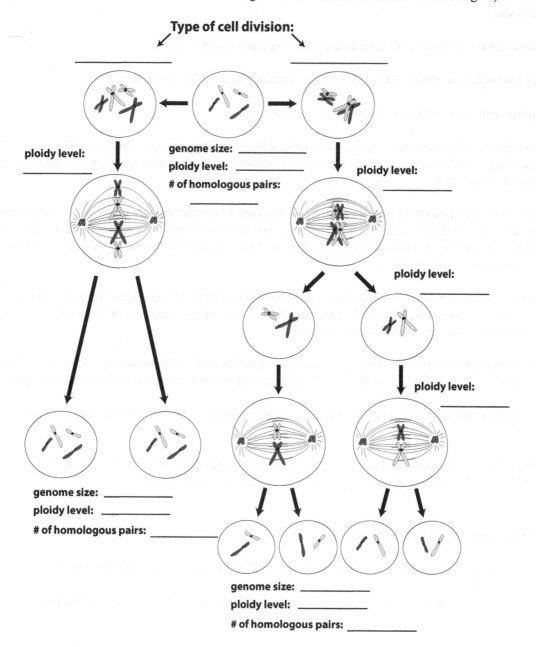

Type of cell division:

ploidy level: _____

genome size: _____
ploidy level: _____
# of homologous pairs: _____

ploidy level: _____

ploidy level: _____

ploidy level: _____

genome size: _____
ploidy level: _____
# of homologous pairs: _____

genome size: _____
ploidy level: _____
# of homologous pairs: _____

7. Explain why a haploid or diploid cell can undergo mitotic cell division, but only a diploid cell can undergo meiotic cell division.

8. In terms of the potential to be replicated, what is the difference the two forms of genetic error: damage and mutation? Explain how this difference might have contributed to the evolution of outcrossing found in many diploid multicellular organisms.

9. Besides creating the potential for recombinational repair, what is another outcome of sexual reproduction?

Becoming Multicellular

What happens after a cell divides into two daughter cells? There are two options: (1) the two cells could become two unicellular organisms by splitting apart and going their separate ways, or (2) they could remain together (see Figure 20-1). This chapter explores the option of remaining together to form a multicellular organism.

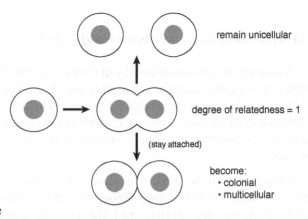

Somewhere in the backs of our minds we know that single-celled organisms do exist, but because virtually every organism large enough for us to see is multicellular, we seem to have a multicellular bias. Multicellular organisms seem so common, so normal that we don't tend to think of their existence as being at all curious. We may even assume

Figure 20-1. The two major options of what could happen after a cell undergoes cell division.

that multicellular organisms are superior to single-celled organisms. That, however, would be hard to argue. First of all, multicellular organisms were relatively late bloomers in the history of Life. Only in the last billion years or less has a diverse assemblage of multicellular forms come on the scene. Furthermore, multicellular organisms did not wipe out and subsequently replace preexisting single-celled forms. Since the advent of multicellularity, single-celled organisms are doing just fine. In fact, from a single-celled organism perspective the most significant feature about the evolution of multicellular organisms may be that they became a new habitat to exploit. Many single-celled organisms now live in abundance on and within multicellular organisms. The point of view that I stress here is that multicellularity was one of the new ways that organisms came up with of making a living—to occupy new niches. Becoming multicellular allowed organisms to use the environment in novel and successful ways. But for this to ever happen, obstacles unique to being multicellular had to be overcome. What are these obstacles? How did multicellular arrangement get around them? These are great questions, and we will at least take a stab at addressing some of the more basic issues. But let's start this chapter by focusing on four general questions:

- Why should cells "choose" to hang out together in the first place?

- So far we identified two basic cell types: prokaryotic or eukaryotic. Which of these types of cells are found in multicellular organisms?

- How do multicellular organisms deal with the fact that successful multicellular arrangements tend to get larger—that is, they tend to grow? As we have discussed in previous chapters, getting larger causes problems.

- How do multicellular arrangements reproduce?

Why Should Cells Ever Choose to Hang out Together?

Although you have likely never viewed yourself in this way, you (and all other multicellular organisms) are a "society of cells." Adult human bodies have somewhere around 75 trillion members (cells). Within this society not only do cells live together, but they also work together in a cooperative way. It is through this cooperation that you, or any other multicellular organism, function as a single entity that you call "me."

Kin selection is necessary but not sufficient

Kin selection (discussed initially in Chapter 6) sets the stage for the cooperation found in multi-cellularity to evolve. Summarized quickly, the idea of kin selection is that by selectively helping close relatives, one increases the probability that one is helping out the same type as itself. This probability is affected by the degree of relatedness between the donor and the recipient of the helping act. The more closely these two are related, the more likely that an altruistic behavior could evolve via natural selection.

Earlier we used the idea of kin selection to explain why helping behaviors such as food sharing could evolve more easily among siblings than among nonrelated individuals. The evolution of multi-cellularity was never even mentioned. But recognize that when a single cell divides into two cells, the two daughter cells are siblings. If fact barring errors in DNA replication, these two daughter cells are genetically identical, which means that there degree of relatedness is one ($R = 1$). The genetic stage is thus set for altruistic interactions to evolve between daughter cells. A cell that acts in ways that facilitates another completely related cell's reproductive success is, in essence, helping itself.

Just because cell division creates the potential for altruistic interactions to evolve among daughter cells does not mean that they always will evolve. You have heard the saying that when it comes to solving problems "two heads are better than one." Yet, that is not always the case. Unless two brains can come up with a solution at least twice as fast, it does not make economic sense. Running two brains costs twice as much without gaining more than twice the results. The same is true for cells. Clearly there is a cost to staying together because proximity intensifies competition for shared resources. So cells should stay together only if an aggregation can somehow generate more than compensating benefits. Next we consider some possibilities

Increasing size can be advantageous

Size, as we continue to emphasize, makes a difference. As a consequence, in some circumstances a larger aggregation of cells may be able to do something better than a single cell. Suppose, for example, some bacterium secretes a chemical that modifies the environment in some beneficial way, and the benefit, at least to some point, increases exponentially with the total amount secreted. If so, two daughter cells that hang together and secrete twice as much chemical would potentially receive more than twice the benefit. The same could be true for four cells or eight cells or even more. All else being equal, this would favor the evolution of an aggregation of two or more cells. The exact size favored would depend on how costs and benefits change with aggregation size.

Curiously, currents also set the stage for a size advantage. A good location for an organism to hang out remains a good location only if the nutrient supply is continually replenished and waste products are somehow removed. Currents could do both as they continuously add and remove things to any area. It turns out, however, that single-celled organisms cannot take advantage of a current. The argument goes as follows: Individual cells are restrained by physical limits to be extremely small. For example, single-celled prokaryotes typically range from 1 to 10 μm, whereas single-celled eukaryotes typically range from 10 to 100 μm. And very small organisms cannot take advantage of a current because they are faced with an intractable dilemma. First, small individual cells would be swept away by a current unless they are somehow anchored to the substrate. Yet due to the presence of a boundary layer (discussed more later), small individual cells anchored to the substrate will not experience any current. It is a no-win situation. Yet an aggregation of cells may be able to escape this dilemma. Larger multicellular forms can anchor themselves to a surface and still extend out far enough into the surrounding current to encounter sufficient nutrients and get rid of wastes. This physical consideration may have been a major feature driving the evolution of many different types of multicellular green, red, and brown algae found in the intertidal zone. All these different types of algae share basically the same growth form—a commonly branching filamentous or flattened multicellular arrangement (that extends up into the current), which is kept in place by some form of holdfast that can anchor it to a rock or some other solid part of the bottom surface (see Figure 20-2).

A brief physics lesson: The defining feature of a fluid, in contrast to a solid, is that it changes shape. As a consequence, a fluid such as water or air flowing over a solid surface does not rub up against it but instead continually changes shape as it flows around it. In the process, the fluid in direct contact with the surface is left behind, and overall fluid nearer the surface moves slower than fluid farther away. In other words, a velocity gradient forms because the closer one moves toward the surface, the slower the flow is until the flow stops altogether right next to the surface. This physical pattern is known as the **no-slip condition**. The region adjacent to the surface that experiences little or no current is called the **boundary layer**. The no-slip condition is why you cannot remove the thin film of dirt on a surface such as the body of a car by simply running water across it. The water right next to the surface of the

Figure 20-2. A typical growth form of an intertidal algae.

car is not moving, so it cannot carry these small dirt particles away. The only way to remove this dirt layer is to physically scrub it with something solid like a brush that can break through this boundary layer.

Next I list a few other potential size-based advantages:

• Larger structures are better able to travel along the direction that they want to go and get there faster. At least part of the explanation, as discussed in Chapter 16, is that larger structures exist in a higher Reynolds number world. With correspondingly greater mass a larger structure can generate larger inertial forces that can better plow through the resistance imposed by the surrounding medium (such as water or air) and thus can better incorporate gliding into their movement.

• Increasing size may help escape predation by becoming too large for a former predator to eat. For example, researchers studying a group of seemingly related organisms that extends from a single-celled form called *Chlamydomonas* to a group of multicellular green algae with thousands of cells known as *Volvox*, found that only the single-celled form is small enough to be consumed by certain filter feeders. And an upper limit to prey size is a feature common to all types of predators. For example, house cats can effectively prey on mice, likely have a bit more difficulty with rats, and anything larger is beginning to reach a house cat's size-of-prey threshold.

• If prey can avoid certain types of predators by becoming larger, then predators in turn can feed on prey that was previously too large by becoming larger. In other words, a larger group of cells may be able to feed on things that a single cell or a smaller group of cells could not.

Differences can make a difference

Let's return to the brain analogy. Earlier I introduced the idea that due to increasing costs, two heads may not always be better than one. But what if brain function encountered trade-offs—that is, being able to think in one way precludes thinking in another way? Furthermore, what if two different thinking brains are constantly sharing ideas back and forth? If so, Head A may come up with an idea that triggers a thought in Head B, that in turn triggers a thought back in Head A, and so on. Overall, each head may be able to make steps toward a solution that would be very difficult, if not impossible, for the other. In other words, two or more brains that are different in complementary ways may form a synergistic interplay able to solve problems intractable to a single brain or even a group of similar brains.

Similarly, two or more cells that function somewhat different but work together may be able to take advantage of environmental opportunities (niches) that could not be exploited by a single cell. Although a single cell may be able to perform many different tasks, some will always interfere with others. Single-celled organisms are thus always caught playing these trade-offs by doing this now and that later and perhaps neither extremely well. They must constantly "choose" between which competing activity is most important at the moment. It is not a bad way of doing things, as the success of single-celled organisms clearly testifies, but it does encounter limits. An avenue to overcome such limits and subsequently come up with novel forms of performance is to divvy up incompatible processes among different cells. That is, for cells to begin to specialize—what biologists call **cell differentiation**. Once housed in separate containers, incompatible processes can occur simultaneously. Add in some means to coordinate the activities of these different cell types into a functional whole, and novel forms of performances potentially emerge.

For example, coordinated function of differentiated cells in combination with increasing size may make it possible for a multicellular arrangement to capture and feed on prey that it could not otherwise. Social predators such as wolves clearly illustrate the idea. The advantage of wolves hunting in a pack goes beyond just an increase in the numbers chasing a prey. During a hunt, pack members do not all do the same thing. Instead they coordinate different hunting behaviors in ways that allow the group to capture prey that they would never be able to catch otherwise. In fact, it makes sense to think of a single multicellular organism composed of differentiated cells as a social predator. A society (group) of differently functioning cells work toward the common goal of capturing and consuming a prey that is shared by all.

The enigma of cell differentiation

Perhaps you noticed something. Earlier I argued that it makes sense for cells to hang out and cooperate if they are genetically identical and they can exploit available resources in novel ways by partitioning the job among different cells via cell differentiation. This sounds fine until you realize that what I just said was that the tendency to cooperate depends on being identical, whereas the usefulness of cooperation depends on being different. Yikes! Is it possible to be the same and different at the same time? In other words, wouldn't cells with the same genotype tend to give rise to cells with the same phenotype?

Actually, it is a riddle that can and has been solved. It comes down to genetic regulation. Genetically identical cells can become strikingly different if something triggers a different pattern of gene expression within them. Different genes (within the same genotype) being turned on in different cells results in different proteins being made in different cells, and because of the shape–performance trade-off, cells with different sets of proteins will function differently. Of course this explanation raises still more questions: How are these differences in genetic regulation triggered? And even more striking: How did differences in genetic regulation that led to useful cell differentiation evolve in the first place? I told you that multicellularity is puzzling.

The degree of cell differentiation separates colonies from multicellular organisms

For most biologists, not all multicellular arrangements are seen as multicellular organisms. Some are considered to be a colony. What is the difference? In both cases, cells remain together after cell division to form a larger structure. The difference lies in the degree of cell differentiation. In colonies, all the cells remain similar but form into a larger aggregation to take advantage of some aspect of increasing size. On the other hand, as cells become increasingly different, and as a consequence play increasingly different roles, the arrangement takes on more and more of the qualities of being a single organism. Multicellular organisms are not just a bunch of cells that hang out together, but a bunch of cells that become different from each other in functionally important ways. You, for instance, have muscle cells, liver cells, nerve cells, red blood cells, along with a couple of hundred more different cell types that all perform specialized tasks that combine to form the performance of you.

Where exactly is the threshold that separates colonies from multicellular organisms? That is a debatable issue. The threshold that makes the most sense is when some cells have differentiated to the point that they lose their ability to reproduce—that is, they lose their ability to be the starting cell of a new multicellular organism. (We discuss this distinction further later when we discuss the distinction between somatic cells and germ cells.) In contrast, within a colony every cell retains the ability to be the starting cell of a new colony.

A brief story—the formation of colonies in cyanobacteria

Many cyanobacteria are unicellular, such as those that live in the open ocean (planktonic forms). Water absorbs light relatively quickly, so an important issue for cyanobacteria in this open water habitat is to remain in the photic zone—the upper part of the ocean that receives enough light to sustain photosynthesis. Planktonic cyanobacteria gain some control over their position in the water column by producing buoyancy structures called gas vesicles. The strong, rigid wall of a gas vesicle is composed of protein that is permeable to gas but not to water. Consequently, gas vesicles will fill with gases to the point that the inside gases are in equilibrium with those dissolved in the surrounding cytoplasm. Buoyancy may be increased when reaching depths where light is too dim by making more gas vesicles.

Near land, the ocean takes on a very different character. The intertidal zone is a region of constantly changing water levels and powerful currents (as the tides move in and out). Here cyanobacteria commonly grouped together to form strings of cells known as filamentous colonies (see Figure 20-3). The argument presented earlier—remain in a good place and still be large enough to experience currents—likely played a major role in their evolution of these cellular aggregations. But at least in some cyanobacteria, there may have been an additional twist to the story.

Figure 20-3. Dividing cyanobacteria that remain stuck together after cell division to form a long filament of cells.

Many cyanobacteria, be they single cells or filaments, are capable of so-called gliding movements that have been clocked at speeds of up around 10 μm per second (which is not quite 1.5 inches per hour). Although mechanisms have been proposed, it is still unknown exactly how these gliding movements take place. What is known, however, is that this movement depends on cells maintaining contact with the surface, and the larger size of a filamentous colony increases the potential area of contact. As a consequence, colonies can negotiate surfaces with larger gaps, grooves, or bumps. Furthermore, light intensity has been shown to influence the direction of these gliding movements. Gliding cyanobacteria move toward places with more or less optimum light conditions and steer away from places where light intensities are deleteriously high.

Now let's add in some earth history. At the time when filamentous cyanobacteria were likely evolving in intertidal regions, the earth lacked an ultraviolet (UV)-absorbing ozone layer (in a higher region of the atmosphere called the stratosphere). Ozone (O_3) cannot form in the stratosphere until significant amounts of molecular oxygen (O_2) are present in the lower atmosphere. As discussed in

Chapter 15, cyanobacteria, or more specifically water-splitting photosynthesis, is the only process that produces O_2 as an output, and even after cyanobacteria came on the scene, it took a long time for atmospheric oxygen to build to current levels. So for literally millions of years, cyanobacteria evolved in a low-oxygen, high-UV world. Like ozone, water absorbs UV radiation, so oceanic organisms below a certain depth were better shielded from the damaging effects of UV radiation. However, as the tides go in and out, the water depth above a bottom-dwelling organism in the intertidal zone fluctuates greatly. Consequently, the UV levels potentially experienced by these organisms would also fluctuate greatly. By being able to move in and of the shadows of rocks, the ability to glide would have given filamentous bacteria a great advantage in coping with this high-UV flux. One extant type of cyano-bacteria (*Merismopedia*), for example, still creeps into the sediments during low tide and creeps back out during high tides. In doing so, it avoids times of higher light intensities and perhaps also avoids getting swept away by tidal currents.

Most Multicellular Organisms Have Eukaryotic Cells

Multicellular organisms made up of prokaryotic cells do exist. We will even discuss one example—heterocyst-forming cyanobacteria— later in this chapter. And there are other examples of a prokaryotic multicellular organism. But overall multicellularity in prokaryotes is rare. The vast majority of multicellular organisms are comprised of eukaryotic cells.

Why would eukaryotic cells be more inclined to evolve into multicellular organisms than prokaryotic cells? Although many factors may be involved, I think the evolution of mitotic cell division is the most important. The logic goes like this: The key feature of multicellularity is cell differentiation. Cell differentiation involves different genes being turned on in different cells. The more cell differentiation that takes place, the more genes needed. Mitotic cell division (mitosis) makes it possible for increasing amounts of DNA (thus increasing number of genes) to be accurately distributed between daughter cells. On the other hand, prokaryotic cell division does not as readily support increases in the amount of genetic information. So, eukaryotic cells are better set up to evolve increasingly complex multicellular organisms.

Dealing with Increasing Size

As you get better acquainted with Life, there are many things to marvel about. The size reached by some organisms is one that literally stands out. Some of the largest dinosaurs, such as *Brachiosaurus*, may have reached weights of 80 tons (that is 160,000 lbs.), and some *Diplodochus* individuals reached almost 30 m from head to tail before they died. There was even a mammal called *Baluchitherium*, a relative of modern rhinoceros, that have been estimated to have reached 30 tons and stood up to 5 m at the shoulder. Among the birds, one species of New Zealand moa weighed 500 lbs and stood 10 ft tall. And although all the species mentioned so far are extinct, the overall largest animal that ever roamed the earth—weighing up to 150 tons and spanning around 25 meters—still exists today. It is the blue whale (*Sibbaldus musculus*). Yet despite its enormous size, its cells are typically no larger than yours are or any other multicellular animal's. A blue whale just has more cells. Plants too, such as Redwood trees (*Sequoia sempervirens*) have also reached enormous sizes. Yet whereas these enormous plants and animals catch our attention, the reality is that in comparison to most single-celled organisms, multicellular organisms that grow large enough to see are relatively huge.

Basic solutions to the disruptive nature of growth

Suppose a multicellular form, be it either a colony or an organism, is doing well. By doing well I mean that the arrangement as a whole is able to gather sufficient resources from the surrounding environment to supply all its cells. What do cells do when they have adequate supplies? The answer, of course, is that they reproduce. That is their legacy; the only reason that cells exist is because they are reproductive performances. But when cells reproduce within a multicellular arrangement, something new and unique can happen—growth. The whole arrangement gets larger whenever new cells accumulate faster than existing cells die off. Why is this important? Earlier I argued that in certain environment settings increasing size is beneficial. Yet it is also true that increasing size can become disruptive. Organisms must always contend with the fact that diffusion is slow and volume increases faster than surface area as an object increases in size. And, as we will discuss later, other forms of size-based disruptions exist as well.

So multicellular forms are constantly caught in a dilemma—success creates the potential for growth, yet growth can become disruptive to success. Or stated more verbosely, because multicellular forms are made from cells that remain together, and cells have evolved to reproduce whenever they have the opportunity to do so, every successful multicellular form has the built in tendency to grow to the point that it disrupts its own success. This realization adds an important dimension to our discussion of multicellularity: Any successful foray into multicellularity is going to have to somehow contend with size-induced disruptions. The various options available are listed next:

• A multicellular form could reproduce before it gets too big—that is, before the individual reaches a size with which it cannot cope. Reproduction (regardless of the details of how it occurs) involves new individuals starting off at a smaller size. So as long as each generation reproduces before it grows beyond its size limit, persistence of a multicellular form is possible (see Figure 20-4(a)).

• Instead of forming one single structure that continues to get larger, growth past some size threshold could be channeled into a branching structure where formation of a similar structure is repeated. Stated differently, a multicellular form could grow in a modular or iterative fashion. That way total biomass could continue to accumulate without any one module growing past a disruptive size. Note that modular growth becomes a form of asexual (or clonal) reproduction whenever the connection between modules is severed to form physiologically distinct units (see Figure 20-4(b)).

• A multicellular form could come up with some means to suppress growth—that is, to stop cells from continuing to divide even when they have access to sufficient resources. The advantage of suppressing growth is longer survival because the time it takes a multicellular organism (or some part of the organism) to reach its size limit would be delayed (see Figure 20-4(c)). The occurrence of cancer is a stark reminder that multicellular organisms commonly employ means to suppress cell division. Cancer, by definition, occurs whenever cells continue to divide in circumstance that they normally would not. Cancer-caused deaths also illustrate the potentially disruptive nature of growth.

• A multicellular organism could come up with the some means to counteract a size-induced disruption. As we will explore further later, mechanisms that make it possible to overcome size limits are a common theme in multicellular function. Yet keep in mind that the presence of size-accommodating mechanisms can never completely escape the disruptive nature of growth. The argument is as follows: An organism able to function at a larger size, due to the presence of some size-accommodating mechanism, will be able to supply its cells with the resources needed for cell division and growth to continue until size again becomes disruptive (see Figure 20-4(d)). At that point function either fails or the organism begins to employ another size-accommodating mechanism, which makes it possible for a new round of growth until it becomes disruptive to start. But such cycles of growth, disruption, and accommodation cannot continue forever. Despite the impressive size to which some organisms have grown, the supply of growth-accommodating tools will eventually run out. No organism can grow forever.

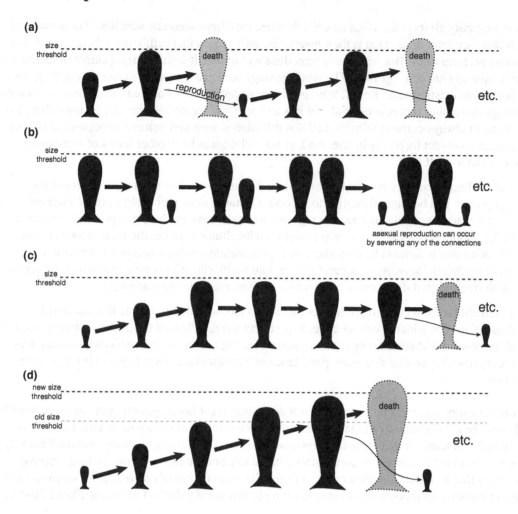

Figure 20-4. Different means by which a multicellular arrangement could deal with limits to growth. (See text for more details.)

Obviously, these solutions are not mutually exclusive. Reproducing before an organism grows to a disruptive size, or suffers some other form of disruption, is always a necessary ingredient for persistence. And the presence of mechanisms to accommodate growth and to suppress growth can work hand in hand to build organisms capable of both growing larger and living longer once they have reached their size limit. Growth-suppressing tools may even play an important role in the transition from a smaller to larger size. For any multicellular organism, getting larger while remaining functional is not a trivial task. Can this occur by simply coming up with different cell types and then letting each different cell lineage grow as fast as it can? Or does suppressing growth in some cell lineages more than others play a role?

Furthermore, given that single cells are typically pushing size limits—due to the slowness of diffusion and complicating aspects of the surface area to volume ratio—coming up with means to counteract size-induced disruptions (the last option discussed earlier) has clearly played a major role in the evolution of multicellular organisms. In fact, multicellular organisms have evolved a variety of size-accommodating mechanisms. Next, we consider three: cellular arrangements, convection systems, and support structures.

Diffusion and possible multicellular arrangements

All cells, whether they are part of a colony or a specialized cell within a multicellular organism, must perform most of their own metabolism. So each cell needs a means to get adequate inputs and get rid of its accumulating waste. Furthermore, things generally move into and out of cells (and within cells) by diffusion.

Given that, would any problems arise if a bunch of cells were grouped together into a solid ball (see Figure 20-5(a))? Each cell forming the outside of the ball is both in direct contact with other cells and the surrounding environment. Through diffusion, nutrients in the environment can thus move directly into these cells, and waste products can move directly out. But what about more interior cells (see Figure 20-5(b))? They are completely enclosed by other cells. As a consequence, access to nutrients from the environment will be considerably less for two reasons. First, the dif-fusion distance is greater, so the time it takes to replace nutrients is considerably greater (recall that the rate materials can move by diffusion goes up as a square of

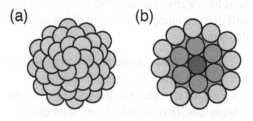

Figure 20-5. (a) A solid ball of cells. (b) A cross-section of (a) showing that the more interior a cell (increasingly darker shade), the greater the distance the separates that cell from the outside environment.

distance). Second, the overall supply of nutrients will be less as some of those available will be used by cells closer to the environment (the source). Furthermore, waste products produced by these inte-rior cells will tend to build to higher levels because it takes longer for them to move to the environ-ment by diffusion. And these problems are accentuated as cells are further and further displaced from the environment. For example, in Figure 20-5(b), the central cell will experience the lowest nutrient availability, and the highest concentration of waste products. Does that mean that interior cells will die? Not necessarily, because having less is not necessarily the same as not having enough to survive. Ultimately, however, the slowness of diffusion will set a limit to how far a cell can be from its nutrient source before supply cannot keep up with demand. And before that limit is reached, diffusion-support-ed interior cells will not be able to do as much because their overall metabolic rate will need to be set lower to match the decreasing supply.

Figure 20-6(a) displays a multicellular arrangement that deals well with diffusion-based con-straints because each cell is directly exposed to its environment—a filament. This arrangement has already been introduced in this chapter as cyanobacteria commonly stick together to form filaments. And despite the fact that branching filaments (see Figure 20-6(b)) create an overall tighter grouping of cells, this arrangement still deals well with diffusion-based constraints because again each cell is still in direct contact with the external environment. So it should not be surprising that branched or unbranched filaments are a common multicellular form. Potentially, filaments could also be grouped

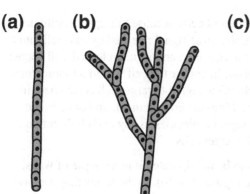 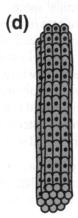

Figure 20-6. Variations of a basic multicellular arrange-ment—a filament. See text for further discussion.

together as clusters (see Figure 20-6(c) & (d)) to form a thicker structure. Yet when filaments cluster to the point that some filaments lie interior (Figure 20-6(d)), the slowness of diffusion becomes an issue. Like the solid ball of cells, the cells in the interior filaments will reside in an environment of less nutrients and increased levels of waste products. It would thus seem that larger clusters of filaments would be an uncommon arrangement. However, a familiar tissue found in most multicellular animals fits this pattern—muscles are typically large clusters of muscle fibers. And as a very active tissue, it is hard to imagine that muscles could get away with their interior fibers working at a slower rate. As we will discuss later, there is something more to this story.

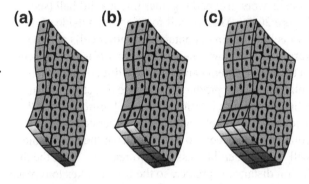

Another basic multicellular arrangement is a sheet of cells. A single sheet (Figure 20-7(a)), or two sheets adjacent to each other (Figure 20-7(b)) both deal well with diffusion-based constraints. Each cell is exposed directly to the environment. Only when cells are sandwiched between two sheets of cells (Figure 20-7(c)) do diffusion-based constraints again become an issue.

Figure 20-7. Variations of a basic multicellular arrangement—a sheet of cells. See text for further discussion.

Now let's consider a sheet of cells wrapped into a ball. Or described in a different way, considered a hollow ball of cells (see Figure 20-8(a)). This multicellular arrangement deals well with diffusion-based constraints because each cell is in contact with its environment. But it also does something else; it creates a new form of container filled with so-called **interstitial space**. Interstitial space is inside the organism, but outside any cell. And like a container formed by a cellular membrane (a lipid bilayer), the significance of this new space is that it is under the organism's control so its contents can be different than the outside. Anything that moves into or out of this interstitial space must move through the outer sheet of cells. The presence of an interstitial space makes new dimensions of performance possible. For example, an interstitial space

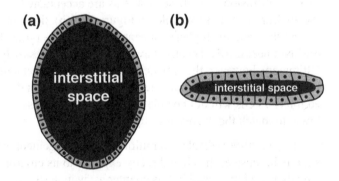

Figure 20-8. (a) Cross-section of a hollow ball of cells showing that the outer sheet of cells encloses a new space called the interstitial space. (b) is the same as (a) on the ball has taken on a flattened shape.

makes it possible to better coordinate function between different cells because this space facilitates cell-to-cell communication through chemical signaling. A chemical signal released by one cell into an interstitial space is confined to move within this space. Consequently, any signal released will sooner or later bump into any target cells elsewhere in the organism. In contrast, a cell within a filamentous arrangement would have a more difficult time getting a chemical signal to target cells elsewhere in the filament. The chemical signal would need to be dumped into the environment, and once in the environment, diffusion and currents potentially carry the signal molecules in any and all directions. Consequently little, if any, of the signal will ever reach the target cells.

Now let's allow the shape of this hollow ball of cells to be manipulated it in a couple of ways. First, the hollow ball takes on a more flattened shape (see Figure 20-8(b)). In the terms that we have been discussing, such a shape change does not really change anything. Every cell is still in contact with the environment, and an interstitial space still exists. On the other hand, another new space is created, if starting at one point, the outer cell layer folds inward (invaginates) into the interstitial space (see Figure 20-9(a)). Like the infolding of a cell's plasma membrane, a cavity is formed that is still open to the outside, but its contents are mostly under the control of the organism. This type of space is found in some multicellular animals and is typically called a **gut cavity**. It is used to digest food items too large to be used by single cells. Large food items enter into the gut cavity through the so-called **mouth**, and once inside they can be bombarded with digestive enzymes released from surrounding cells. The smaller nutrients that result from digestion are then confined to remain in the gut cavity until they can be brought into the organism by the surrounding cells.

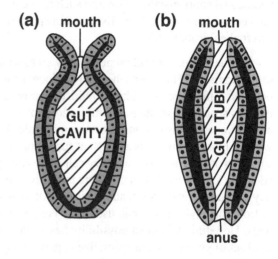

Figure 20-9. (a) Cross section of a hollow ball of cells that has invaginated (folded inward) to form a new space known as a gut cavity with one opening to the outside. (b) A gut cavity is converted to a gut tube when another opening is added. (See text for further discussion).

The fact that everything brought into the gut will not be able to be digested creates one problem for a gut cavity. With only one opening to the outside, the only way to remove these leftovers is for them to pass back through the same opening through which food is brought in. Any time one body part is used to perform two functions, the two functions potentially interfere with each other. Adding another opening to a gut cavity to form a **gut tube** eliminates such interference (see Figure 20-9(b)). One opening can be used to bring food into the tube, digestion and absorption can occur as the food moves along a tube in a specific direction, and then all the undigested materials left over can move out into the external environment through the other opening. The presence of two openings with a directional flow is known as a **complete digestive tract**. The opening where food enters is known as the mouth, and the opening where indigestible leftovers are removed is known as the **anus**. Many animals, including yourself, have a complete digestive tract.

Convection systems make new types of multicellular arrangements possible

So far we have argued that the slowness of diffusion makes it difficult for multicellular arrangements to locate cells very far from the external environment. Consequently, the interstitial space formed in some multicellular arrangements would seem to be a rather inhospitable place to locate cells because they would be separated from the environment by a surrounding cell layer. Yet in many multicellular animals, extremely metabolically active cells, such as muscle cells (fibers), are packed inside the interstitial space. How is this possible?

Materials are transported from one place to another in two basic ways. As we know, one is diffusion, which is based on random motion and concentration gradients. The second is **convection**, which is based on pressure differences that result in a mass migration of molecules moving in the same direction known as a **bulk flow**. The biologically important point is that in contrast to diffusion, the bulk flow of convection can effectively transport materials a long distance in a reasonably short time. Consequently, the evolution of any sort of convection system within a multicellular arrangement would change the rules of how cells can be distributed. Because convection can supplement the movement of materials back and forth between the external environment, cells, even those buried deep within an organism, can maintain an effective link with the external environment. (An important note: Adding a convection system does not replace diffusion. Instead they work in tandem. Diffusion still handles all short-distance transport such as the movement of materials into and out of cells, whereas convection handles the long-distance transport between each internal cell's local environment and the external environment.)

Furthermore, convection potentially creates an effective link between distant parts (cells) of the same organism. This opens the door for increasing the division of labor (the specialization of function) between different cells within a multicellular organism. Certain cells within a multicellular organism can specialize in the acquisition and/or production of molecules that all cells need, and then use convection systems to transport these molecules to all other cells. Suppose, for example, every cell within an organism needs a constant supply of molecular oxygen to run aerobic respiration. One possibility would be to position every cell close enough to the external environment that it can receive an adequate supply by diffusion. There is no division of labor here because in terms of maintaining an oxygen supply, each cell fends for itself. Alternatively, some cells could specialize in getting oxygen in from the environment and use a convection system to transport this oxygen to all other cells in the body. Hopefully this latter possibility has a familiar ring to it. Your lungs and associated tissues are a subset of your cells that specialize in getting oxygen from the environment. Once this oxygen is brought in it is transported to all your other cells by your circulatory (convection) system. The division of labor allows other cells to focus on other activities because they are freed from needing to get their own oxygen from the environment. Even cells lining an organism's outer surface, which are in the right position to get oxygen through diffusion from the environment, are freed to produce an external protective layer that concurrently acts as a diffusion barrier for oxygen because these cells can get their oxygen from elsewhere. Along a similar vein, all growing and dividing cells within a multicellular arrangement need a supply of phospholipids to build more cell membrane. One possibility is that every cell fends for itself and synthesizes its own supply. Alternatively, a convection system makes a division of labor possible. For example, one of the specialized functions performed by your liver cells is to synthesize most of the phospholipids needed, and then once produced these phospholipids are shipped to other cells through circulation.

How can organisms establish a convection system?

For any multicellular arrangement to add a convection system to its workings, it must have a means to establish the conditions needed to drive convection. There are four basic ways that organisms do so. Each is different in terms of the ways that the needed pressure differences within a fluid are created. Each is similar in that they all employ some form of pipe. A fluid, in contrast to a solid, is anything that does not have a preferred shape so that it takes on the shape of its container. In terms of directing the flow of a fluid, the most basic container is some form of pipe because it confines the directions in which the fluid can move. Establishing convective flow through a pipe simply involves creating pressure differences between the two ends of the pipe (see Figure 20-10).

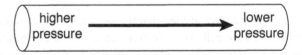

Figure 20-10. Conditions needed to establish convective flow of a fluid through a pipe.

Let's start with the most familiar way to establish convective flow along a fluid-filled pipe—somehow apply a squeezing force somewhere along the pipe. Organisms generate such a squeezing force in two general ways: They can take advantage of general body movements such as bending, stretching, and so on, or they can use the contraction of muscles wrapped around the pipe. Squeezing around the circumference of the pipe decreases the volume of the pipe at that point, which in turn increases the underlying fluid's pressure. Convective flow ensues, moving from this region of higher pressure to regions of lower pressure in both directions along the pipe (see Figure 20-11(a)). Figure 20-11(b) shows that convective flow will move back in the opposite direction if the shape of the pipe rebounds after being squeezed, either due to the elastic properties of the pipe or some other force pulling the walls of the pipe outward. Just as the decrease in volume during squeezing increases the underlying fluid pressure (relative to the pressure elsewhere in the pipe), the increase in volume due to the recoil decreases the underlying fluid pressure (relative to the pressure elsewhere in the pipe). This is basically how our lungs work. An alternation of contraction and expansion of lung volume creates an alternation of pressure differences that result in convective flow of air into and out of our lungs. In other words, a **volume-changing pump** powers breathing in and out.

Add one-way valves on both sides of the volume-changing pump, and the back-and-forth flow described earlier can be converted into a directional flow. As shown in Figure 20-11(c), so long as the one-way valves are both oriented in the same direction, the increased pressure associated with the volume-contracting phase of the pump's cycle will simultaneously close one valve and open the other. Fluid is thus constrained to flow in only one direction. Then during the volume-increasing phase of the pump's cycle, the two one-way valves continue to maintain flow in the same direction (see Figure 20-11(d)). The pressure gradient favors the flow of fluids into the pump, but the one-way valves prevent any backflow. The

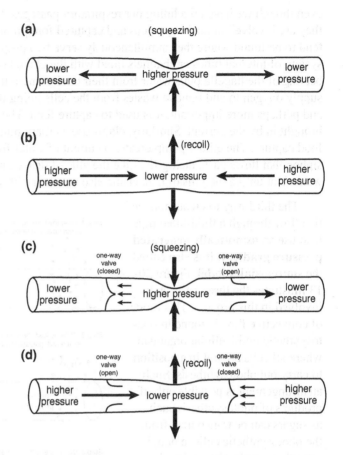

Figure 20-11. (a) & (b) show how changing shape somewhere along a pipe by both squeezing and recoil can generate convective flow. (c) & (d) show how adding one way valves can steer the convective flow generated by squeezing and recoil to move in one direction. (See text for further discussion.)

combination of a volume-changing pump and one-way valves is generically referred to as a **chamber-and-valve pump**. Your heart is a chamber-and-valve pump. Actually it is a series of four chamber-and-valve pumps—that is, you have a four-chambered heart. Two chambers make up the right heart that pumps blood to your lungs, whereas the other two chambers comprise the left heart, which pumps blood to the rest of the body. In contrast, fish have two-chambered hearts, and amphibians and reptiles have three-chambered hearts.

The second way to create a convective flow through a fluid-filled pipe is to use the coordinated beating of cilia or flagella lining the walls of the pipe (see Figure 20-12). In an energetic sense, using **ciliary** or **flagellary pumps** to move the fluid along is not nearly as efficient as a muscle-driven volume-changing pump. And such pumps can only generate slow speeds. So it is not unexpected that although ciliary pumps involved in stirring internal body fluids have been found in some organisms, they are never used as a circulatory system's major driving force. And

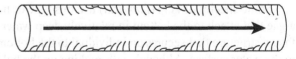

Figure 20-12. Convective flow is generated by the coordinated beating of cilia or flagella lining a pipe pushing the fluid along.

even though we have cilia lining our respiratory passages, they are not involved in pushing air. Instead they are involved in pushing mucus and captured foreign particles around. Ciliary or flagellary pumps tend to be found where they simultaneously serve two purposes. As we discuss later, sponges have a system of internal tubes or channels lined with flagellated cells that have openings to the outside. The beating of the flagella pulls water from their environment through their body. This current is used to supply oxygen to and remove wastes from the cells lining these internal channels. But simultaneously, and perhaps more important, it is used to capture food. The flagellated cells intercept food particles brought in by the current. Similarly, clams use a ciliary pump for both gas and waste exchange and food capture. The ciliary pump creates a current of water from the environment through a tube called a siphon that flows pasts their gills. Like the gills of fish, clams use their gills to extract oxygen from the water. But unlike the gills of fish, clams also use their gills as a food filtration system.

The third way to create convective flow through a fluid-filled pipe is to use an **osmotically generated pressure gradient**. It is also called the **source-sink model**. Figure 20-13 illustrates the three basic steps involved in this process. This mode of convective flow is found in photosynthetic multicellular organism where all cells are not in a position to carry out photosynthesis. Such an arrangement is possible only if products of photosynthesis such as sugars can be transported from the photosynthetic cells to nonphotosynthetic cells. Otherwise, the nonphotosynthetic cells would lack a supply of high-energy molecules. Stated more generally, photosynthetic cells become a **source**—a place of manufacture—and nonphotosynthetic cells become a **sink**—a place of use. What is striking is that what needs to be transported can be used to establish convective flow. Because sugars are solutes, actively transporting

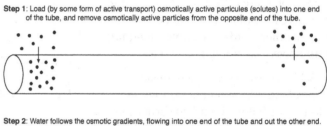

Step 1: Load (by some form of active transport) osmotically active particles (solutes) into one end of the tube, and remove osmotically active particles from the opposite end of the tube.

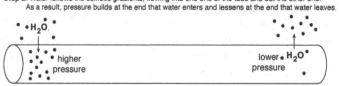

Step 2: Water follows the osmotic gradients, flowing into one end of the tube and out the other end. As a result, pressure builds at the end that water enters and lessens at the end that water leaves.

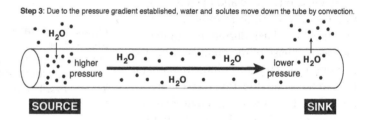

Step 3: Due to the pressure gradient established, water and solutes move down the tube by convection.

SOURCE   SINK

Figure 20-13. The three steps involved in generated convective flow through the establishment of an osmotically generated pressure gradient.

(loading) sugars produced by photosynthesis into the end of a tube surrounded by photosynthetic cells (the source), and removing (unloading) sugars at the end of the tube surrounded by nonphotosynthetic cells (the sink) will create the osmotic gradients needed to establish the pressure gradients that lead to convective flow. The tube in between is constructed of elongated cells connected to one another by porous ends (called sieve plates).

Some species of kelp (*Lamaria*) use this type of transport system. Kelp is a group of large brown algae that attach to the bottom in relatively deep water (commonly 20 to 30 meters). From the holdfast, a structure that secures an individual to the bottom, individual kelp can extend many meters up to the water surface. Although cells making up the holdfast are not buried into the bottom substrate, there are two reasons that these cells (and the cells of the stipe located just above—see Figure 20-14) may lack sufficient light to be photosynthetically active. First, water absorbs light relatively quickly, so light levels 20 to 30 meters below the surface have fallen considerably. Second, kelp often grows in groups forming what is known as a kelp forest. The extensive array of flattened kelp blades floating on and below the surface will absorb much of the incoming solar radiation before it ever has a chance to move to lower depths. As a consequence, kelp may need to transport sugars from photosynthetically active blade cells to photosynthetically inactive stipe and holdfast cells. And to accomplish this, some types of kelp have a centrally positioned group of elongated cells that are modified for transporting sugars by an osmotically generated pressure gradient.

Land plants have a similar problem because photosynthetic cells and water-gathering cells tend to function best if they are in different locations. To be hit by light photosynthetic cells need to be aboveground. On the other hand, a plant's most reliable water source is belowground. A large component of a soil's fertility is its ability to hold onto water once rain has stopped. Photosynthetic and water-gathering cells cannot be separated, however, unless there is a distribution system that goes both ways. All rooted plants are thus vascular. One part of this vascular system is called **phloem**. Similar to that found in kelp, phloem is a tubular arrangement of elongated cells that uses an osmotically generated pressure gradient to transport sugars from aboveground photosynthetically active cells to nonphotosynthetic root cells (see Figure 20-15).

How vascular plants transport water up from the roots to the leaves is the fourth and final way that organisms have been found to generate convective flow. It combines a property of water—surface tension—with solar-powered evaporation to create a pressure gradient. The steps involved are presented in Figure 20-16. Note that the tensile strength of a continuous water column plays a central role. Due to their connection via hydrogen bonds, water molecules pulled from the top will transmit this pulling force to the water molecules below.

This final means to generate convective flow may be the trickiest to understand because it almost seems both too simple and not sufficiently powerful to really work. But work it does! It is through this mechanism that all vascular land plants, including 300-foot-tall redwoods, move water and dissolved minerals brought in through their roots to the upper reaches of the plant. This part of the vascular system—that is, the system of tubes through which water and dissolved minerals flow—is known as **xylem** (see Figure 20-15). Curiously, the cells that make up xylem are dead. It is just their hardened remains that form the network of interconnecting tubes. A living component is not needed, however, because the plant does not provide the energy needed to generate convective flow. It is a solar-driven pump. Water transport in plants thus stands in

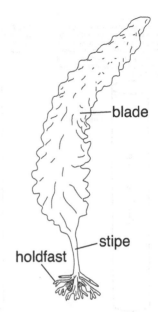

Figure 20-14. A large brown algae know as kelp (*Lamaria*). Some of them have a centrally positioned group of elongated cells that are modified for food conduction (at rates up to 60 centimeters per hour). These conduct sugars from the more photosynthetically active cells closer to the water surface to the poorly illuminated stipe and holdfast far below.

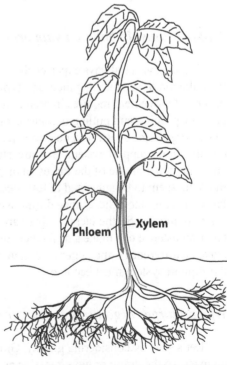

Figure 20-15. The two convection systems found in vascular plants.

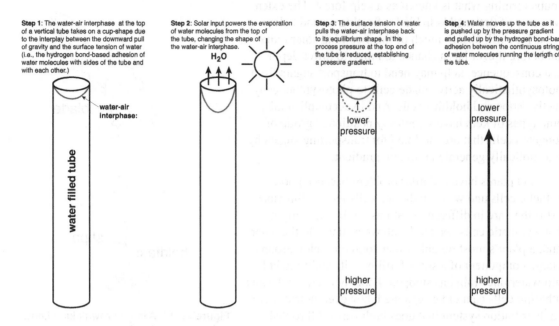

Figure 20-16. Basic steps by which surface tension and solar-powered evaporation can power convective flow of a water up a vertically-oriented tube.

contrast to the other three methods to power convection discussed earlier. The muscle contraction used in volume-changing pumps, the movement of flagella or cilia in ciliary or flagellary pumps, or the active transport used in loading or unloading solutes to form an osmotically generated pressure gradient all use organism-generated ATP as a power source.

The relationship between support and size

Organisms are always experiencing external forces, such as the gravitational pull of the earth or the collision of surrounding medium (typically water or air) into them. Furthermore, any form of self-propelled movement requires internally generated forces. All these forces cause problems—not only are they pushing and pulling organisms out of preferred shapes, but they are also literally attempting to tear organisms apart. As a consequence, organisms must counter disruptive forces with a sufficiently strong support system. But how strong is sufficiently strong? That, of course, depends on the nature and magnitude of the forces an organism encounters. For instance, perennial algae growing in the Artic seem to be subjected to less mechanical stress than comparable algae growing elsewhere. A layer of ice protects these algae during winter storms, whereas summers are characterized by relatively calm conditions. So the fact that these are relatively fragile algae makes sense. Yet while environmental circumstance can make a difference, our focus here is size; and within any set of conditions, size makes a difference—the larger an organism grows the greater the forces encountered, so the stronger the support system must become.

Why do larger organisms encounter stronger forces?

Let's start by considering gravity. Gravity is a downward (toward the earth) attractive force based on mass, so the larger or more massive an organism grows, the greater its potentially disruptive effect. But the density of the surrounding medium complicates the story. The amount of force that any organism needs to counter is not based on its mass per se, but on the gravitational pull on its mass *minus* the support provided by the surrounding medium (which is also being pulled on by gravity). And denser mediums (more mass per unit volume) provide more support. That is why it is easier to hold an arm up against gravity in water than air. In essence, an arm surrounded by water is lighter—that is, it weighs less—than when it is surrounded by air.

To better see this, envision setting out a scale where zero represents the absence of any downward force. Due to the pull of gravity, the air above will push down on the scale causing it to register a positive value. Yet the magnitude of the downward force that gravity emplaces on any organism—that is, the organism's weight—cannot be measured until the effect of surrounding air is removed. How? Set the scale to zero. Only then is the pull of gravity beyond the support provided by the surrounding medium being measured. Of course, because terrestrial organisms are typically much denser than air, the degree to which surrounding air provides support, hence lightens the load, is relatively minor. That, however, is not the case for water. Place an air-adjusted scale beneath a pool of water, and the higher density of water will push the scale down even further. So after resetting this higher starting point to zero, any organism will weigh less in water than air. And even then, only negatively buoyant organisms—that is, organisms denser than water—will register any weight at all. Neutrally buoyant organisms—organisms with the same overall density as water—will tip the scale at zero. Such organisms do not experience any downward pull of gravity because the medium provides all the support needed. And finally, the weight of positively buoyant organisms would actually be negative. They naturally rise or float, so if attached to a scale they would actually pull up on it. Like a helium balloon requires a sufficiently strong string, a positively buoyant organism attached to the bottom would thus need sufficient supportive structure to counter this upward force. No different than a helium balloon that needs to be attached with a sufficiently strong string. In other words, instead of needing to hold oneself up against gravity, a positively buoyant organism needs to hold itself down. Figure 20-17 summarizes how size and density (relative to water) affects the direction and magnitude of gravity-generated forces that a sessile organism must contend with in both air and water.

Although part of the same story, the relationship between gravity and size takes on even more significance when considering organisms that move around. To swim, walk, run, or jump requires the support structure to do more than just prevent the organism from collapsing. It must be able to withstand the forces underlying any changes in shape associated with locomotion, and magnitude of these forces will go up with organism size. Many terrestrial organisms further compound this problem because movement involves a repetitive sequence of pushing off from and then falling back to the

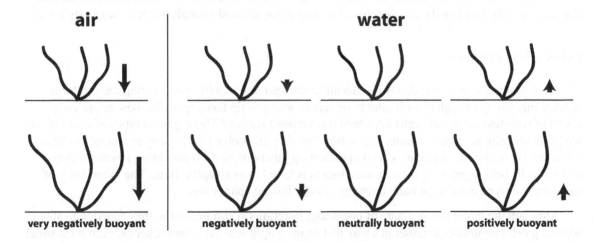

Figure 20-17. The direction (designated by the arrow) and the magnitude (length of the arrow) of gravity-based forces experienced by a sessile organism changes with the size of the organism (smaller versus larger), the medium (air versus water), and the density of the organism relative to the surrounding medium (negatively, neutrally, or positively buoyant).

ground. Obviously, larger organisms take more force to lift, and as the old saying goes, "The bigger they are, the harder they fall."

Size also makes a difference with drag. Drag is the force generated whenever an organism and the surrounding medium are traveling at different speeds. For example, a stationary organism experiences drag whenever wind or water currents are moving past, as does any self-propelled organism plowing through the surrounding medium. Drag, in essence, is the degree to which an organism is being pushed back in the direction of flow. The amount of drag an organism experiences depends on a combination of factors. First, the speed of flow—the difference between the velocity of the medium and the organism—makes a big difference, as drag increases with the square of speed. Both the viscosity and density of the medium also make a difference. Water, for instance, may provide more support against gravity than air, but at any set speed it also pushes harder on any organism in its path. Size also enters the picture because drag increases as the surface area intersecting the direction of flow increases, and surface area in any dimension tends to increase with size. For example, consider a filamentous alga attached to a rock in the intertidal zone that grows only in one dimension—it gets longer. The longer it grows the greater the surface area exposed to tidal currents, so the more drag it experiences. As a consequence, without an increased investment in support structure, such as growing thicker, it will eventually suffer mechanical failure—either breaking into two, or having its holdfast ripped from the rock. Bigger organisms may also attempt to compensate for increasing drag by becoming more streamlined. For any given cross-sectional area, a more streamlined shape experiences less drag.

Starting to build support structure in animals

Recall that replacing a prokaryotic cell wall with an internal dynamic or shape-changing cytoskeleton seemed to be a major step in the evolution of eukaryotic cells (see Chapter 17). In particular, we highlighted actin filaments and microtubules as both a means to withstand external shape-deforming forces and to generate the internal forces needed to constantly shift a cell's overall shape. The question we address here is: How could such small wall-less shape-changing cells ever generate sufficient support to evolve into large multicellular animals?

Although a diffusional perspective endorses either filaments or sheet of cells as possible initial multicellular arrangements, a key multicellular arrangement in early animal evolution appears to be a continuous sheet that wraps around on itself to form an interstitial space (as shown in Figures 20-8 & 20-9). (Note: This idea is discussed more in the next chapter.) Next I start with this arrangement and then sequentially build up the components of structure that allowed animals to get increasingly larger.

Cell–cell connections

As obvious as it may sound, any multicellular arrangement requires neighboring cells to form attachments strong enough to withstand those forces acting to rip them apart. So, how might early sheets of wall-less eukaryotic cells have held themselves together? Three general types of connections are fairly ubiquitous among animals, suggesting that they all evolved fairly early in animal evolution. These are (1) occluding junctions, (2) communicating junctions, and (3) anchoring junctions. Any sheet of cells held together by these connections is referred to as an **epithelium**. The initial story of structure is thus converting an outer covering of cells into an epithelium.

Although the molecular structure of **occluding junctions** is still uncertain, they function to stitch adjoining cell membranes together in a way that forms a tight seal. As a consequence, even most small molecules are prevented from moving from one side of an epithelium to the other by leaking through the spaces between cells. Occluding junctions, with names like *septate junctions* (found in all invertebrates except sponges) and *tight junctions* (found in vertebrates), make it possible for an animal to control the composition of its interstitial fluid. By blocking the path between cells, only molecules able to be transported through the cell layer can get in or out.

Communicating junctions are small tubelike structures that directly connect the cytoplasms of adjacent cells. Although they are too small to allow larger molecules to move through, these openings can mediate the passage of chemical or electrical (ionic) signals from one cell to next. The type of communicating junction found in practically all animal species are called *gap junctions*. They are channel proteins that span the two outer membranes of neighboring cells.

Although occluding and communicating junctions play important roles in the biology of multicellular animals, they are mentioned here more as a measure of completeness than as the means to hold cells together. It does not take much mechanical stress to rip out components attached only to each cell's outer membrane. Stronger connections, known as **anchoring junctions**, have formed by tying into

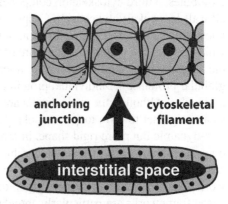

Figure 20-18. Neighboring cells in an epithelial sheet can be held together by anchoring junctions between cells hooking into each cell's cytoskeleton

each cell's cytoskeleton (see Figure 20-18). Although variation exists, all anchoring junctions follow a basic construction pattern. It starts with a *transmembrane linker protein*. The transmembrane part of this protein is that it not only crosses the membrane, but also sticks out on both sides. It is a linker protein in that the extracellular domain—the part that protrudes outside the cell—hooks together with a like protein sticking out from an adjacent cell, whereas the cytoplasmic domain—that part inside the cell—connects to the cytoskeleton through the aide of *intracellular attachment proteins*. These proteins form connections between cytoskeletal filaments and transmembrane linker proteins (see Figure 20-19).

Adherens junctions may have been the first type of anchoring junctions to evolve. They are found in nearly all animal species and hook to the network of actin filaments underlying each cell's outer membrane. Interestingly, although cross-linking actin filaments between cells adds strength, it does not preclude movement. Changing the shape of the actin cortex within any of the connected cells will change the shape of the entire arrangement. For instance, folding sheets of cells into tubes, a rearrangement that occurs during embryogenesis in many animals, is powered in this way. The transmembrane linker proteins found in adherens junctions are all sufficiently similar to each other to be considered members of one protein family known as *cadherins*.

Members of the cadherins protein family are also the transmembrane linker proteins in another type of cell–cell connection called **desmosomes**. Desmosomes are a step up in strength and rigidity and so would seemingly become increasingly important as animals got larger. The increased strength and rigidity does not come from the connection per se, but from the type of cytoskeletal filaments to which they connect. In addition to actin filaments and mi-

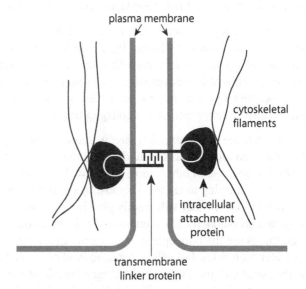

Figure 20-19. A schematic representation of the major components of an anchoring junction between two cells. (See text for further details.)

crotubules, a third cytoskeleton component, known as intermediate filaments, is found in many but not all wall-less eukaryotic cells. In Chapter 17 I briefly mentioned one class of intermediate filaments, known as the lamins. Lamins forms an interwoven spherical framework known as the nuclear lamina, which creates the underlying structure of the nuclear space. Now let's add a little more to the intermediate filament story. In contrast to microtubules and actin filaments, which are composed of linked globular proteins, the individual protein units of intermediate filaments arrange into elongated fibrous molecules. Although the exact details are not important here, these smaller thread-shaped molecules weave together to form tough nonpolar, hence insoluble, filaments. In eukaryotic cells that take on a less-dynamic but more rigid shape, intermediate filaments extend out from the nuclear lamina to the outer membrane to form a woven durable framework that reinforces a cell's shape. Desmosomes form a stronger connection between cells simply because they latch onto this intermediate filament framework. One structurally important group of cytosolic intermediate filaments are **keratins**. Keratin-based frameworks are particularly abundant in epithelia that form the outer coverings of organisms. The protective epithelium that you call skin even uses keratin left over from dying epithelia cells to knit together an even tougher more durable outer covering. Additional skin features found on some animals, such as hair, feathers, and nails, are also made from keratin.

Adding a basement membrane

Although the structure created when adjacent cells are connected together by desmosomes has strength, it alone will not support an animal of much size. This raises the question: How can an epithelium covering an interstitial space get even stronger? Curiously, nothing stronger than intermediate filaments has ever evolved within cells, so the only option is to generate structure outside of cells. But where? There is no room between epithelia cells. The only options left are thus for epithelial cells to secrete reinforcing structural components to the inside—that is, into the interstitial space—or to the outside. As we will find out, both options have been used. But here I focus next on adding a so-called **basement membrane**, also known as the basal lamina, on the inside.

A basement membrane is a thin (40–120 nm thick) tough continuous sheet made from materials secreted by the same sheet of epithelial cells that gain structure by tying into it. It reinforces an epithelium's ability to resist both tensile and compressive forces.

Tensile strength comes from the secretion of a form of collagen (known as type IV collagen). Collagens, as mentioned in Chapter 10, are proteins containing sizable regions in which three polypeptide chains coil together to form rope-like fibers. Once secreted, type IV collagen molecules self-assemble into a multilayered "chicken wire"-like arrangement due to the characteristic triple-stranded helix being interrupted periodically by bendable regions. As a consequence, a basement membrane can resist pull in any direction across this collagen framework.

Resistance to compression largely comes from a very familiar molecule—water. Water, like other liquids, is an incompressible fluid, which means that a fixed volume of water cannot be squeezed into a smaller volume. In other words, water will not shrink in the face of compression. It will, however, do its best at trying to escape. Liquids, by definition, do not have any fixed shape, so unless something holds it in place, water will readily give in to compression by squirting elsewhere. The most obvious way to hold onto a fixed volume of water is to surround it with some form of impermeable container. Yet, that is not the only option. A nexus of large soluble molecules will not only soak up large amounts of water molecules, but will continue to hold on to many of them in the face of compression. This is the "strategy" used by cells secreting a basement membrane. Along with insoluble collagen, they secrete long chemically modified polysaccharides called *glycosaminoglycans* (or GAGs). Figure 20-20 shows that a GAG's core structure is similar to a polymer of glucose. GAG chains are always a repeating disaccharide where one of each pair is called an amino sugar due to the addition of a nitrogen group, and the other is typically an acid (specifically a type of urionic acid) due to the addition of a

negatively charged carboxyl or acid group. All
GAGs except one—called *hyaluronan*—also
have negatively charged sulfate groups added to
one or more places along each disaccharide pair.
The negative charges of carboxyl and sulfate
groups are GAGs key feature. Not only do they
pull on the positive region of water molecules,
but the attraction of positive charged solutes,
such as sodium ions, also generates an osmotic
gradient. As a consequence, large amounts
of water will be sucked in, forming a gel-like
structure able to withstand a certain measure of
compressive forces. The gel is usually further
reinforced by GAGs being covalently linked
to a polypeptide backbone, generically called a
core protein, that is produced by the same cells.
The entire structure is known as a *proteoglycan*
(see Figure 20-20). Proteoglycans are commonly
around 95% carbohydrates and 5% protein. The
protein backbone in turn binds to type IV collagen. Overall, this combination of a collagen
framework filled in by an interconnected and
highly hydrated gel lying outside cells is one
example of what is commonly referred to as an
extracellular matrix.

For a basement membrane to help support
an epithelial sheet of cells, the cells must be teth-
ered to it. Here is where **hemidesmosomes** (or
half desmosomes) come into play. They resemble desmosomes morphologically, but instead of
joining adjacent epithelial cell membranes, they
connect the basal surface of epithelial cells to
the underlying basement membrane. Specifically, they hook into a component of a basement
membrane not yet mentioned—a glycoprotein named *laminin*. (Note: Glycoproteins are
proteins with sugars or sugar chains branching
off certain amino acids. Although the sugar to
protein ratio is extreme, technically proteoglycans are a type of glycoprotein.) In fact, the

Glucose polymer:

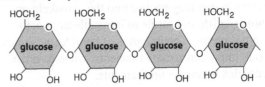

Glycosaminoglycans (GAG):

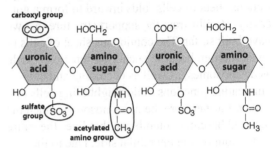

Proteoglycan:

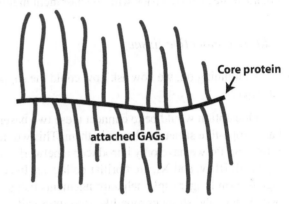

Figure 20-20. On top, the structure of a glucose polymer and a GAG (known as heparin sulfate, which is
commonly found in basement membranes) are drawn
to show the similarities. On bottom, the basic structure
of a large water-absorbing molecule called a proteoglycan. In actuality, a proteoglycan is a 3-dimensional
structure, where GAGs extend out from the core protein
like bristles of a bottle-brush.

original basement membrane may have been largely composed of laminin, as these molecules, like
type IV collagen, will self-assemble into a mat-like arrangement. Still to this day the basement membranes first formed in a developing embryo are mostly composed of laminin. Collagen is then added
to further strengthen the matrix. The laminin network ties cells and basement membrane together by
possessing binding sites for the other major molecules of the basement membrane—collagen and proteoglycans—as well as the transmembrane linker proteins found in hemidesmosomes.

Different than desmosomes, the transmembrane linker proteins of hemidesmosomes are not
similar enough to be considered members of the cadherin protein family. Instead, they have been
grouped into another protein family called *integrins*. Integrins form a strong linkage with the basement
membrane in a way analogous to Velcro—they form numerous weak connections with the laminin

framework. Inside the cell, integrins are like cadherins in that they anchor into the cytoskeleton through different forms of intracellular attachment proteins. The integrins of hemidesmosomes hook into intermediate filaments, whereas other integrins tie into actin filaments.

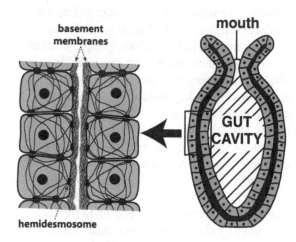

Figure 20-21 uses a diffusion-friendly cellular arrangement—specifically where a continuous sheet of cells folds inward to form a gut cavity—to illustrate the support structure that we have built so far. The continuous sheet of cells is an epithelium because anchoring junctions, such as desmosomes, as well as occluding and communicating junctions, hold neighboring cells together. Furthermore, hemidesmosomes attach the secreted basement membrane that lines the entire epithelium on the interstitial side. Due to the

Figure 20-21. A schematic illustration of the support structure that has been built so far.

infolding, the basement membrane underneath the region of epithelium that covers the outside of the organism lies back-to-back with the basement membrane of the epithelium surrounding the gut cavity.

Adding connective tissue

Continuing on, we now ask how could the support structure shown in Figure 20-21 be made even stronger?

One option would be to connect these two basement membranes together by stringing collagen-based rope-like structures between them. This would make the organism even more resistant to tensile forces. So far we have only introduced a network-forming type of collagen. Other collagens, such as type I, II, III, V, and XI, are fibrillar collagens. Instead of taking periodic bends and turns, fibrillar collagens form longer triple-helix arrangements that subsequently group together, via cross-links, to form even longer and stronger rope-like structures called collagen fibrils. Often collagen fibrils aggregate even further into cable-like structures known as collagen fibers. Collagen fibrils or fibers can then be attached to a basement membrane by anchoring fibrils, which are composed of type VII collagen. To

further resist compression, it would also make sense to fill in the space around these collagen fibers with water held in place by GAGs. The question that remains is: How could this additional extracellular matrix get in between the basement membranes? Epithelial cells cannot secrete both a basement membrane and the filler in between. Instead, cells would need to migrate into this space between basement membranes and then secrete this extracellular matrix from there. Cells able to wander through extracellular matrix are generically called **mesenchyme** cells. Some mesenchyme cells subsequently differentiate into *fibroblasts*—cells that specialize in secreting the components of the extracellular matrix described earlier (along with other components described later). **Connective tissue** is the name given to regions of interstitial space filled by fibroblasts surrounded by this extracellular matrix (see Figure 20-22).

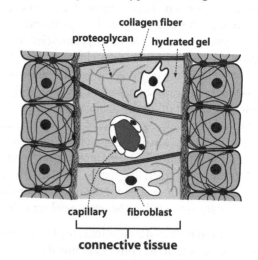

Figure 20-22. Connective tissue sandwiched in between two epithelial layers.

In an addition to collagen and GAGs, fibroblasts are also known to secret *elastin* and *fibronectin*. Elastin self-assembles into elastic fibers that, as their name implies, are both compliant (can be stretched) and elastic (will return to their original shape). Creating parts of an organism that can recoil to its original shape after experiencing stretch is a property that can be put to use in a variety of ways. Elastic fibers are commonly interwoven with inelastic collagen fibers to limit stretch from occurring to the point of damage. Fibronectin, like the laminin in basement membranes, is a glycoprotein used to connect fibroblasts (along with other mesenchyme cells) to the extracellular matrix.

The "diffusion is slow" mantra may make you start wondering how fibroblasts, along with any other mesenchyme cells, can wander off into interstitial space and still get the resources they need from the environment. There are, however, a few points to their advantage. First, much of the interstitial space is occupied by noncellular, hence nonmetabolizing, extracellular matrix. So, it does not need to be supplied. Furthermore, the watery nature of the polysaccharide gel provides a good medium for nutrients and other metabolites to diffuse between the environment and these inner cells. And finally, as animals with more and more cells move into this interstitial space, the extracellular matrix provides both the space and the support structure needed to build the tubes of a circulatory system. Once a circulatory system is in place, areas of so-called vascular connective tissue can grow extensively as materials can be shuttled in and out by convection. (Note: I added a capillary—a small vascular tube made from a sheet of cells wrapped together—to Figure 20-22.)

Adding muscles

Animals exist whose support structure stops at each of the steps described so far. These are not inferior animals, just ones that make a living in a way that does not require additional support. Typically they are small, although some living in water are able to grow to a fairly large size. But in addition to size and environment (aquatic versus terrestrial), the amount of support needed is also affected by how an organism moves, and most animals use some form of muscle to power movement. So before adding further to structure, let's briefly discuss how the support structure discussed so far set the stage for the evolution of muscles. Then we can turn around and discuss how muscles played a role in the evolution of additional support structure.

We have already seen that actin filaments in conjunction with myosin—the class of walking proteins that move along actin filaments—can be used to change the shape of a cell. The notion of a muscle is just a more specialized extension of this idea. Specifically, actin and myosin are arranged such that they pull a cell into a shortened or contracted state. And interestingly, the original contracting arrangement may have not been confined to distinct muscle cells. Animals known as cnidarians (e.g., sea anemones, jellyfish) have cells called epithelio-muscular cells. Here, the base (the side next to the interstitial space) of certain epithelial cells extends out to form long fibrous arrangements that can contract. The formation of distinct muscle cells, however, is much more common. In more primitive muscle cells the entire cell bunches up, so the cell is shortened across many lines of direction. In contrast, increasingly specialized muscle cells arrange their actin and myosin so that contraction is limited to a single direction. Muscle cells can also be hooked together as sheets (generally more primitive muscle cells) or as fibers (generally more derived muscle cells) to form structures able to shorten further and with more power.

Regardless of the details, for any contracting unit to change an organism's shape it must somehow connect to the rest of the organism. Here is where the extracellular matrix enters the picture. For example, the contracting part of epitheliomuscular cells found in cnidarians can form connections with other epithelial cells and the underlying basement membrane. Tugging on the basement membrane's collagen framework will spread this pulling force to more distant parts of the body. Embedding distinct muscle cells even deeper in interstitial space (within the connective tissue) would increase the range of muscle-orchestrated movements even further. Here mesenchyme cells again enter the picture.

So far they have been introduced as cells that wander into interstitial space and after differentiating into fibroblasts secrete additional extracellular matrix in between epithelial basement membranes. The new twist is that mesenchyme cells have also evolved the ability to differentiate into muscle cells. Furthermore, developing muscle cells secrete a basement membrane around them that connects into the surrounding extracellular matrix. By tying into the rope-like collagen fibers, muscle contractions could selectively pull on different parts of the organism. It all depends on where the collagen fibers hooked to muscle in turn connect.

Adding hydroskeletons

Here is something peculiar. Skeletons are commonly thought of as the support systems that keep animals from collapsing and provide structure on which muscles can act. Yet we have already spent considerable time building up support structure, and even introduced muscles, without mentioning skeletons per se (except cytoskeletons). Is the extracellular matrix of basement membranes and connective tissue a skeleton? And if so, are all skeletons composed of similar extracellular matrix? I ask these questions, in part, to raise notice of semantic problems. Whether basement membranes are considered to be a skeleton depends on how skeletons are defined. So although I am not looking to get into a semantic tangle, be warned that the notion of what is or isn't referred to as a skeleton can be confusing. I, however, just want to keep asking the question: How could support structure be made even stronger, so that organisms could grow even bigger? Plus I add in consideration of how to build support structure that can better take advantage of muscles to generate movement.

Perhaps you have heard that some animals, such as earthworms, have a hydroskeleton. To me, the important part of this statement is that it suggests that other animals do not. But the presence of water-binding GAGs in the interstitial extracellular matrix is a universal (or at least nearly so) feature in animals. So shouldn't all these animals be considered to have a hydroskeleton? This is part of that semantic confusion that I alluded to earlier. We can, however, ask: What do earthworms (along with other hydroskeleton-bearing animals) have in addition to the presence of GAGs to warrant the hydroskeleton distinction? The answer is that they build one or more fluid-filled cavities within their interstitial space. Such cavities, called **coeloms**, are formed by nothing more than an enclosed epithelial sheet of cells. In other words, they use an internal epithelium—often called the mesothelium—to hold in a fairly fixed volume of water (along with some other solutes). We have already developed the idea that the incompressible nature of water makes it a good structural material as long as there is a means to keep it from leaking away when compressed. So, internal bags of fluid would provide additional structural support. They can also create a new means for muscles to generate movement. The muscles in organisms with hydrostatic skeletons are commonly arranged in both longitudinal and circular layers (see Figure 20-23). Longitudinal contraction squeezes coelomic cavities lengthwise. Due to the incompressible nature of the fluids inside, decreasing a cavity's length must simultaneously increase its diameter, which in turn increases the diameter of the organism that encloses it. On the other hand, contraction of the circularly arranged muscle layer results in the organism being lengthened as each coelomic cavity is squeezed in the middle. (Note: Although perhaps starting as hydrostatic skeletons, coelomic

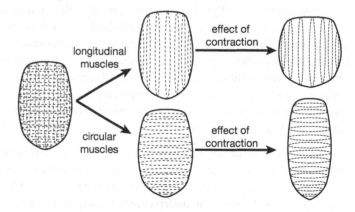

Figure 20-23. The effect that contraction of either the longitudinal or circular layer of muscles has on the body shape of an organism with a hydrostatic skeleton.

cavities have taken on many other roles in the course of animal evolution. For instance, your coelomic cavities create space for your internal organs. Separating your interior organs from your body wall also allows body parts to move independently. This is why your heart can continuously beat without your whole chest pulsating.)

A major branch point

Now we come to a fork in the road. So far the theme underlying the addition of basement membranes, connective tissue, and even fluid filled coelomic cavities has been building extracellular structure on the inside of the organism—that is, within interstitial space. But from here the addition of even more support has taken two contrasting paths in animal evolution.

One path has structure being added on the outside of organisms. To at least a limited extent, this path started early in animal evolution and thus has accompanied some of the internal changes described so far. One group of fairly primitive animals, the stony corals, even build rather extensive rigid external skeletons composed of the mineral calcium carbonate. In fact, some of these external skeletons (encasing many small modular structures called polyps) continue to accumulate to the point that they weigh several tons. The sessile nature of these organisms prevents this excessive weight from being as issue. Animals like stony corals, however, are not our focus here. Somewhere along the line mobile animals with distinct muscle cells surrounded by connective tissue started to build a hardened, but jointed structure on the outside of their bodies known as an *exoskeleton* We know these animals today as the arthropods (along with some other closely related groups). There are five common classes of arthropods—Insecta (e.g., butterflies, grasshoppers, and beetles), Arachnida (e.g., spiders, ticks, and scorpions), Chilopoda (e.g., centipedes), Crustacea (e.g., crawdads, shrimps, and crabs), and Diplopoda (e.g., millipedes)—which in total make up a substantial portion of the animals found on this planet.

The other path continued to build mostly on the inside. Regions of connective tissue evolved into even stiffer structures known as cartilage and bone, materials that made the formation of an articulating *endoskeleton* possible. The group of animals that followed this path is known as the Vertebrates, named for the presence of a backbone or spinal column. You, of course, are a vertebrate.

Adding exoskeletons

In animals that form an exoskeleton, the outer epithelium still secretes a basement membrane on the inside. What is new is that these cells also secrete molecules to the outside that subsequently link into a rigid arrangement. Of particular significance is a molecule called **chitin**. Like the GAGs secreted to the inside, chitin is a polysaccharide. In fact, the same amino sugar (called N-acetylglucosamine) commonly found in each of the repeating disaccharides in GAGs is strung together in a new way—what chemists call β-1,4 linkages—to form chitin (see Figure 20-24). The significance of these linkages is that the

Glycosaminoglycan (GAG):

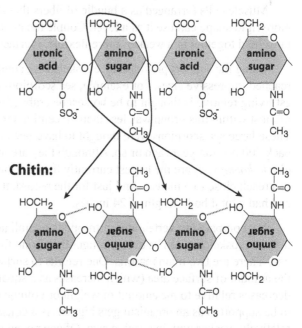

Figure 20-24. Chitin, a major structural component of arthropod exoskeletons, is a polymer of the same amino sugar commonly found in GAGs.

180-degree rotation of each amino sugar added allows the formation of a hydrogen bond that further stabilizes the connection. The result is a long, straight chain with high tensile strength. Embedding chitin microfibers in a matrix of secreted proteins forms an exoskeleton's basic structure. More specifically, a succession of thin layers of this matrix is laid down, and like plywood—where the direction of the grain changes with each layer—strength is added by the orientation of the chitin microfibers, changing some with each new layer. A process called *sclerotization* hardens the outer layers of certain regions of this exoskeletal matrix even further. Chemical reactions with molecules called quinones increases the stability of the protein matrix, creating rigid plates called *sclerites*.

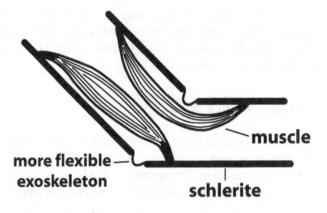

Figure 20-25. A simple diagram as to how hardened exoskeleton plates (schlerites) bordering regions of softer more flexible exoskeleton, along with internal muscle bundles, can be arranged to form a joint that can either flexed (bent further) or extended (straighted) via muscle contraction.

The increased stiffness or rigidity of sclerites made building bigger, stronger organisms possible. They also created a new option for using muscles to generate movement. Attaching muscle cells (arranged as a bundle of fibers that all shorten in the same direction) to the basement membrane underlying two sclerites connected by a more flexible region of exoskeleton creates a bendable joint (see Figure 20-25). Flexible regions in between sclerites form due to the presence of high concentrations of an elastic protein called *resilin* and the lack of quinone cross-linkages. Not only did articulating joints give rise to new forms of core body movements, but it also opened the door for the evolution of rigid yet mobile appendages. And once that occurred, both literally and figuratively, arthropod movement began to take all kinds of new strides.

Muscle cells (arranged as a bundle of fibers that all shorten in the same direction) pulling on a more rigid shape can use it as a lever. Couple the attachment of muscle bundles to two stiffer structures held together at a weaker, more flexible interface, and contraction leads to a bending joint.

Using the support provided by exoskeletons, some arthropods, especially aquatic ones, have reached impressive sizes. For example, sea scorpions are an extinct group of arthropods whose closest living relative is thought to be horseshoe crabs (*Limulus polyphemus*). Whereas the body length of most within this group was less than 20 centimeters, the largest reached lengths of 2 to 3 meters. These large sea scorpions were thought to have been one of the major predators of early evolving fish back 400 million years ago or so. Although they are mostly just legs, Japanese spider crabs (*Macrocheria kaempferi*) are the largest currently living arthropod as the span between the tips of their legs can reach close to 5 meters. And just for the record, the largest lobster ever caught weighed 42.4 lbs and had a total body length of 24 inches.

Yet compared to vertebrates, arthropods overall are relatively small organisms, despite the fact that an exoskeleton can be even stronger than bone for its weight. So why haven't they gotten bigger? There are two main reasons. One returns to surface area to volume considerations. Specifically, the amount of surface area (which increases as a square of length) to build a supportive exoskeleton decreases relative to the amount of weight or volume (which increases as a cube of length) that needs to be supported as an organism gets bigger. As a consequence, exoskeletons of the same thickness get relatively weaker with increasing size. Of course, an organism could attempt to compensate by building an increasingly thicker, hence stronger exoskeleton. And to some degree this occurs. But fairly quickly, especially for terrestrial arthropods, the increase in thickness required becomes too cumbersome and too costly to be worth it. The other drawback associated with exoskeletons and increasing size is the inability of exoskeletons to continually grow with the organism inside them. Continued growth would be possible if reabsorption of previously deposited exoskeleton could be coupled with the deposition of new exoskeleton even further out. No arthropod, however, has come up with the means to do this. Instead, exoskeleton-bearing organisms periodically shed or molt their old exoskeleton and then grow a new, larger one. Each molt, however, creates a window of extreme vulnerability. From the time that the old exoskeleton is shed until a new one can be made and subsequently harden, the organism lacks protection, support, and a rigid structure to pull against to effectively generate motion. And those problems are exacerbated at larger sizes. Can you imagine growing to your present size if periodically you kept losing your entire skeleton?

Adding a cartilaginous endoskeleton

You likely have heard of cartilage, and you probably even know that cartilage supports your ears and the tip of your nose. But did you know that cartilage is largely water enveloped in the same basic ingredients as the connective tissue described earlier? Cartilage-producing fibroblasts, known as *chondrocytes*, secrete an extracellular matrix composed of fibrillar collagen and GAGs, some of which are arranged as proteoglycans. The major difference is that the unique composition of proteoglycans, GAGs, and proteins join together to form aggregate structures that can be as large as an entire bacterium (see Figure 20-26). The increased connectiveness of these large aggregates makes them even better at holding onto water when subjected to mechanical stress. As a consequence, cartilage is stiffer

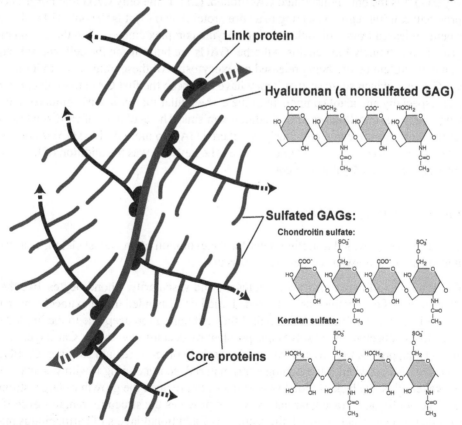

Figure 20-26. The basic structure of the large GAG aggregate found in cartilage. Many proteoglycans (GAGs connected to a core protein) are periodically attached by link proteins to the GAG called hyaluronan, which through a unique assembly process can be made into extremely long chains. Arrows indicate that the structure is typically longer than what is shown.

and even more compression resistant than other GAG, collagen mixtures. Accordingly, cartilage formation opened the same type of doors as a more rigid exoskeleton. It provided the support needed to build bigger, stronger organisms. Plus, it made an articulating skeleton possible. Attaching muscle bundles to two cartilaginous rods held together at a weaker, more flexible interface results in a bendable joint (see Figure 20-27).

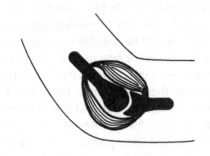

Figure 20-27. Muscle bundles attached to two articulating endoskeleton elements forms a bendable joint.

In fact, evidence suggests that the signature feature of vertebrates—a backbone—was not originally built out of bone at all. The first spinal or vertebral column was likely a completely cartilaginous structure. Even today the seemingly most primitive fish have a cartilaginous endoskeleton. (Although the complete absence of bone in at least some of these fish may be a degenerate rather than a primitive feature, as very early fishes with bony tissue are known from the fossil record.) And in addition to protecting the dorsal nerve cord, the jointed nature of this axial structure facilitated a new form of locomotion. By simultaneously supporting and bending with muscle contractions alternating across sides, the body core would wave back and forth like seen in a swimming fish.

An aside: Hyaluronan, the GAG that forms the core of each aggregate structure is unique in three striking ways: (1) it is the only nonsulfated GAG found, (2) it is the only GAG that never becomes part of a proteoglycan (through connecting to a core protein), and (3) it is the only GAG that is built while it is being released from a fibroblast (by an enzyme complex embedded in the cell membrane), thus can grow into extremely long chains. All other GAGs are built inside the cell, and subsequently attached to a core protein before being released by exocytosis. All these traits make hyluronan the simplest GAG found, which suggests that it may have also been the first GAG to evolve. Even today it remains an especially abundant component of the extracellular matrix in early embryos and is still found throughout the extracellular matrix of adult organisms. The evolution of cartilage thus seemed to combine the most primitive and previously untethered GAG to more derived GAGs connected to core proteins to form an even larger GAG ensemble. The key step was the addition of the link proteins that tie proteoglycans to the hyaluronan core.

Some structural limits of cartilage

Although cartilage provided a starting point for the evolution of an endoskeleton, as a structural material it also has some drawbacks. Let me discuss two.

The first is a trade-off between structural integrity and vascularity. Chondrocytes, like the fibroblasts in other forms of connective tissue, become buried or suspended in the extracellular matrix that they secrete. This in turn can lead to their death if they get buried too deep due to the limited nature of diffusion. Most connective tissue solves this problem by becoming vascular. Cartilage, on the other hand, commonly suppresses the invasion of blood vessels in order to remain stronger. Cartilage's structural integrity is best when it is a homogenous material, so puncturing it with vascular channels makes it a weaker. Plus, the lack of blood vessels does not preclude the growth of large, strong regions of cartilage. The nonliving extracellular matrix, which provides the structure, remains even if chondrocytes die. Further growth occurs through the secretion of additional layers of cartilaginous matrix by chondrocytes located around the periphery. A vascular layer of connective tissue known as the *perichondrium*, which surrounds any growing cartilaginous structure, supplies these chondrocytes. What is given up by letting internal chondrocytes die is the capacity to repair and even modify the arrangement. Dead chondrocytes cannot secrete new extracellular matrix—extracellular matrix that could be used to fix damage regions, and perhaps by altering the composition of that secreted could even adjust the matrix's mix to better handle changing stresses and loads associated with increasing size.

The second problem is that even in the absence of blood vessels, cartilage is not an extremely rigid material. So even though early vertebrates were aquatic and thus did not have to provide much if any support against gravity, cartilage alone would not be able to handle the mechanical stresses generated by movement in increasingly larger organisms. Past a certain point the enlarged aggregate structures cannot hold onto water molecules tightly enough to rigidly resist the compression component of bending or shear forces.

Adding minerals

The calcification of cartilage may have been the next step in adding structure. This involves largely replacing the watery part of a cartilaginous structure with something more solid. Although the details are beyond our scope here, the key feature is that *soluble* ions, specifically calcium ions (positively charged) and phosphates (negatively charged), need to reach a high enough local concentration that they begin to complex to form small *insoluble* particles that serve as starting points for the formation of larger calcium-phosphate crystals called *apatite*. Apparently, this initial local increase in concentration occurs inside little vesicles called *matrix vesicles* that bud off chondrocytes. Then, by increasing in both number and size, these crystals eventually permeate through the matrix, forming a solid structure entangled in a network of collagen fibers.

Calcified cartilage is found in a group of the cartilaginous fish known as the elasmobranchs, which include sharks, rays, and skates. More specifically, it is found in the skeletal parts in need of extra support, such as jaws, vertebrae, and gill arches. It is not a coincidence that the largest cartilaginous fish are found in this group. In fact, the whale shark (*Rhinocodon typus*) is the largest fish in the world with lengths up to 46 feet and weighing up to 15 tons.

Calcified cartilage versus bone

Is calcified cartilage just another name for bone? The answer is no. Calcified cartilage is still a homogenous, unvascularized structure. As a consequence, once it is laid down, it cannot be maintained, modified, or repaired. Bone, on the other hand, is a living, dynamic, repairable form of connective tissue due to being vascular. Anyone who has suffered a broken bone can testify to its repairable nature.

The curious part, however, is that the original function of bone was probably not structural per se. Apatite crystals may have first been used to store calcium and phosphate, both of which play important roles in many physiological functions. Still today there are cells that nestle in and around bone known as *osteoclasts* that specialize in breaking apatite back into soluble ions, hence releasing these ions from storage. The increased stiffness associated with adding apatite crystals to the extracellular matrix, however, would not be useful everywhere. Instead, storage should be confined to areas where increased stiffness would not greatly impede function. Even better would be to put it in places where the increased stiffness would be useful.

Fossil evidence from a group of now-extinct fish called ostracoderms suggests that the first structural arrangement of bone was dermal bone—the formation of a layer of bony tissue just under the basement membrane of regions of skin (outer epithelium). With dermal bone the more interior connective tissue still retains it fluidity needed for whole body movements. But the armored appearance of ostracoderms also makes it obvious that dermal bone was used in protection. The bony plates underlying the skin could help fend off the attacks of predators like the large sea scorpions mentioned earlier. (Note: Part of your skull that forms an outer protective layer around your brain is dermal bone.)

Dermal bone forms through some mechanism of selectively positioning specialized fibroblast cells known as *osteoblasts* under regions of skin. Osteoblasts differentiate from proliferating mesenchyme cells and then secrete a specialized mix of extracellular matrix termed *osteoid*, which is composed of mostly collagen (which self-assemble into collagen fibers) along with some proteoglycans. Osteoid is unique in that somehow shortly after its formation, apatite begins to precipitate at intervals along the surface of the collagen fibers, which then subsequently grows into apatite crystals.

A tale of replacement

A bony internal skeleton evolved only after the means to form dermal bone was already in place. Different than dermal bone, the evolution of a bony skeleton is a tale of replacement. Not only were internal skeletons originally composed of cartilage, but still today the skeleton of each newly developing vertebrate (including yourself) starts out as cartilage.

Forming a bony endoskeleton by replacing cartilage had one big advantage. The mechanism to form cartilage into distinctly shaped skeletal elements, even when surrounded by a background of chemically similar connective tissue, was already in place. For instance, cartilage is "molded" into the shape of each vertebra during the formation of a vertebral column, and that basic shape is retained during growth. By bony tissue replacing cartilage there was no need to "reinvent the wheel." Bones take on the shape of the cartilage that they replace. Plus, further bone growth starts with building an enlarged cartilage framework that is subsequently replaced.

As mentioned earlier, limiting the invasion of blood vessels reinforces cartilage's structural integrity. Replacing cartilage with bone starts with a reversal of this trend. Because a calcified matrix maintains strength even when perforated with blood vessels, this switch can occur without sacrificing structural integrity. In the process the connective tissue surrounding the developing structure changes from a cartilage-forming nature, the perichondrium, to a bone-forming nature, called the *periosteum*. During this switch mesenchymal cells begin to differentiate into osteoblasts. Once attaching to spicules, osteoblasts of calcified cartilage begin to produce osteoid, which triggers the spread of more bone formation. In long bones, such as leg or arm bones, this replacement starts in three distinct places: along the shaft, and at each end. The region left in between the shaft and each end, which is called the *epiphyseal plate*, continues to lengthen as new cartilage is laid down through the formation of more chondrocytes. This cartilage is then subsequently replaced by bone. This two-step process is how long bones grow longer. Mammals, such as yourself, reach a maximum height because eventually these two bone-forming regions merge and hence completely replace the cartilaginous growth zone. A bone cannot lengthen further once the epiphysis is sealed.

Yet even bones that completely replace their cartilaginous growth zone never become static entities. Due to the maintenance of a vascular network, even osteoblasts that become encased inside the bony matrix (and are now called *osteocytes*) can remain alive. As a consequence, both bone deposition and absorption—via the workings of osteoclasts—can continue to occur to at least some degree in all bones. This capacity to continually remodel has several advantages. First, it may help bones retain their toughness for a longer time. Older bone becomes relatively brittle and weak, so any replacement of older bony matrix with newer matrix will help maintain strength. Furthermore, bones respond to not being strong enough by growing stronger. The continual presence of loads large enough to cause a bone to bend or deform in any other way trigger osteoblasts to lay down additional bony matrix. Of particular importance is every bone's ability to continue to get thicker. Osteoblasts in the surrounding periosteum can direct the deposition of additional bony matrix around the current external bone surface. This increase in diameter is called *appositional growth*. The combination of absorption and deposition can even change a bone's overall shape in ways that better resist the pattern of mechanical forces to which it is being subjected.

The dynamic nature of bones also sets them up to accommodate growth early in life. As muscles enlarge, hence pull harder on the skeletal system, or the amount of weight to be supported increases with increasing size, bones will adjust to match the structural demand.

Of course, there is a trade-off underlying how strong should any bone should become. Bones need to be able to stand up to the everyday forces, but unexpected increases in forces do occur through events like a fall or a predator attach. So how much of a safety factor should be built in? Building bones strong enough to withstand extreme but rare loads may not make sense. Increasingly stronger bones weigh more and hence require more work to move during locomotion. On the other hand, severely broken bones commonly impose a death sentence in wild animal populations, so building bones so light that they break at the slightest fall may also not be the best way to win reproductive races. Each species is thus expected to evolve somewhere in the middle of this continuum. Where exactly depends on the biology of the species.

Increasing size and getting thicker

Due to living in much more of a gravitational world, bone strength is even more of an issue in terrestrial animals than aquatic ones. This is especially true in larger animals. This raises an interesting question: How much bonier should an elephant be than a mouse? For instance, an elephant's leg bone would need to be thicker than a mouse's to support the additional weight, but how much thicker?

Consider two similar-shaped animals, where one is twice as long as the other. At first you might think that each leg bone would need to be around twice as thick to keep things the same. But that is wrong. An animal that is twice as long would be expected to weigh roughly eight times as much. Why? Weight is proportional to volume, and volume goes up as a cube of a linear dimension. So, an animal twice the length should have around 2^3 the volume or weight. Does that mean that the bone needs to be eight times as thick? Wrong again! It turns out that a bone's strength is roughly proportional to its cross-sectional area (the surface area exposed when a bone is cut in half). A bone with eight times the cross-sectional area would thus be eight times as strong. But that still does not answer how much thicker it would need to be. We tend to measure thickness in terms of the linear dimension diameter, and area is proportional to the square of a linear dimension. Given that math says you can do anything as long as you do it to both sides of an equation, applying a square root throughout will convert a square on one side of an equation to a square root on the other side. Apply that here, and the thickness needs to increase by the square root of eight, or around 2.8 times. Based on such calculation biologists would say that bone diameter—a linear dimension—is not expected to scale uniformly with organism length—another linear dimension. In other words, bigger animals need proportionately thicker bones. Exactly how much thicker, however, depends on more than just increasing standing weight. The most stress is put on bones during locomotion, and animals of different size do not move the same. For instance, elephants do not bounce like rabbits, suggesting that relative to their body weight elephants do not stress their bones during locomotion as much. This in turn may allow elephants to get away with proportionately not bulking up their skeletons as much as might first be expected. Nonetheless, larger animals are bonier: Skeletons make up around 8% of the weight of a mouse, around 13% of the weight of a dog, and around 17% of the weight of a human.

Starting to build support structure in multicellular algae and plants

As mentioned in earlier chapters, although the loss of a cell wall was a likely prerequisite in the evolution of eukaryotic cells, cell walls evolved again in certain eukaryotic groups. Part of the story involves the evolution of chloroplasts. Cell walls preclude a cell's ability to crawl about and feed by endocytosis, but the ability to photosynthesize made giving these up possible. Here we focus on multicellular arrangements of photosynthetic eukaryotic cells with cell walls. This includes most forms of aquatic multicellular algae and terrestrial plants. Considering them together makes sense because all evidence suggests that land plants evolved from certain forms of green algae. In particular, we consider the support structure used to build these multicellular arrangements.

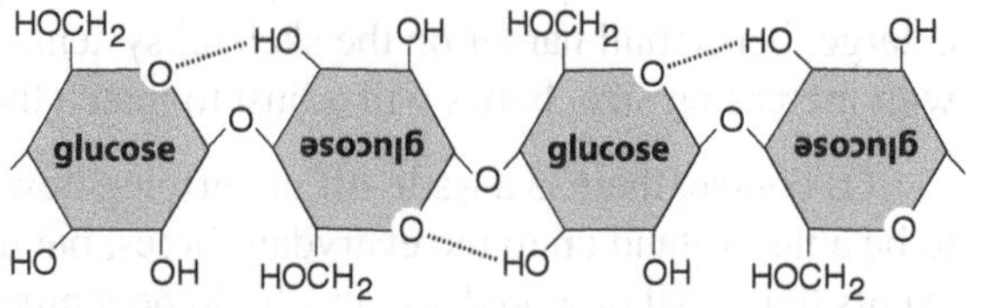

Figure 20-28. The basic structure of cellulose.

Let's start with the extracellular matrix—that is, the cell wall—that is secreted by and wraps around individual cells. Like we saw with exoskeletons, eukaryotic cells walls are composites of some form of microfibril—an aggregate of long, straight, tension-resistant polysaccharides—embedded in a matrix of other polysaccharides and proteins. In photosynthetic cells, microfibrils are commonly made from a polymer of glucose molecules called *cellulose* (see Figure 20-28). Like chitin, cellulose takes on a straight arrangement due to each glucose being bound to the next by a β-1,4 linkage. (Recall that the 180-degree rotation characteristic of these covalent bonds allows adjacent glucose molecules to also form a hydrogen bond that further stabilizes the connection.)

In a sense, the rest of the story of multicellular structure is a simple one. All multicellular arrangements are held together by somehow hooking together the cell walls of adjacent cells. The strength of the entire structure is thus the collective strength of the arrangement of cell walls. As a consequence, the stronger and more rigid the cell walls, the stronger the entire structure.

There is, however, a tricky part that results from a trade-off between cell wall strength and growth. To grow, cells must first expand, and then once reaching a large enough size, divide into two cells. The only problem is that cellulose microfibrils do not stretch. As a consequence, a cell wall can expand only if these microfibrils are not so rigidly embedded in the matrix that they can move relative to each other. Yet in this state, the cell wall is a mechanically weaker structure. This leaves multicellular arrangements with a seemingly awkward choice—they can either be weak and growing, or strong (by encasing every cell in the most rigid cell wall possible) and nongrowing. There is, however, another choice. As we have discussed, multicellularity opens the door for cells to work together by taking on different and incompatible roles. Some cells within a multicellular arrangement could thus specialize in providing increased structure by forming thicker and stronger cell walls at the cost of giving up the ability to continue to divide. Other cells within the same organism could then play the trade-off the other way. They could continue to undergo cell division at the cost of never forming extremely rigid cell walls. Together they would form a more rigid structure that still has the ability to grow. And importantly, we see this division of labor in most cell-walled multicellular organisms. Cell expansion and division is confined to one or more limited regions called **meristems**. Each meristem maintains itself by some daughter cells retaining the ability to undergo further bouts of cell expansion and division. Other daughter cells then differentiate to take on structural (or other) roles.

Single-cell thick filaments were likely the original multicellular arrangement in cell-walled photosynthetic cells. The reason goes back to the way cell walls expand prior to cell division. Typically microfibrils within a newly forming cell wall are laid down in a consistent direction. (Note: The microfibril orientation is controlled by orientation of microtubules lying just inside the cell membrane.) The tensile strength of these fibers thus prevents cells from expanding in this same direction. These microfibrils can, however, be pulled away from each other, causing cells to elongate at right angles to the microfibril orientation. In other words, a cell wrapped in microfibrils in one direction will elongate out both ends (see Figure 20-29a-b). Cell division then commonly proceeds by the cell membrane constricting in the middle, followed by an ingrowth of the cell wall (see Figure 20-29c-d). Some green algae and land plants complete the division a bit differently by forming something called a *cell plate*, but such details are not important here. The important point is that if the cell walls continue to remain attached after division while maintaining the same axis of elongation, a single cell will grow into a (diffusion-friendly) multicellular filament (see Figure 20-29e). Many different types of filamentous algae still exist today.

Although not always the case, the cell or cells that retain the ability to expand and divide are often located at the tip of anchored filamentous algae. From a structural perspective this makes sense, especially when living in a mechanically stressful environment such as the intertidal zone. As the weakest part of the cellular chain, the meristem should be located at the place experiencing the least amount of force, and that place will be the tip. Tidal currents create drag. As a consequence, each part of the chain is pulled by the drag experienced by the rest of the filament above. Cells at the base will thus experience the most pull because the entire filament is above them. Conversely, as the end of the filament the tip has nothing above, so it experiences the least pull.

No matter where the meristem is located and how strong the cell walls are, filaments in mechanically stressful environments will reach a limit to growth. Drag increases with size, so growing past a certain size will lead to mechanical failure. A single thread of cells will just not be able to withstand the forces encountered. This again raises the basic question: How could the structural support be increased? More specifically, how could an intertidal algae get stronger? The basic answer is that the base needs to get thicker. In other words, more cells need to be added. This requires the nature of the meristem to change. Instead of a single cell that always expands and divides in one direction (thus forms a filament), the meristem needs to be composed of more cells that can divide in additional directions (perhaps by changing the orientation in which microfibrils are wrapped around the cell). That way a three-dimensional array of cells could first form that could subsequently grow out into a thicker stem-like base (before growing further into some "typical" alga form).

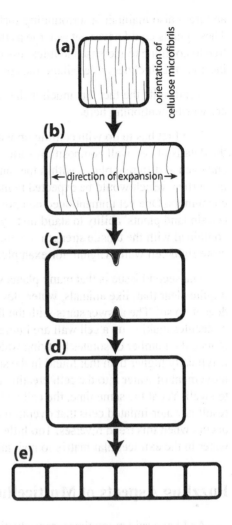

Figure 20-29. The basic steps through which the consistent orientation of cellulose microfibrils can lead to the formation of a multicellular filament. See text for more details

Yet, although a thicker base could support a larger intertidal alga, this growth form still encounters the same conceptual size limits as a single filament. Once the meristem grows out past the base, new rounds of cell division cannot increase the thickness of the "stem" further. As a consequence, the rest of the alga could grow too large for its base. Interestingly, the algae that grow the largest—a group of brown algae that we have discussed before called kelps—have overcome this limitation. They maintain a meristem around the surface of their basal region, so its girth can be increased while the rest grows larger. Basal structure can thus continue to keep up with increasing size for a longer time.

Different than algae, land plants have to hold themselves up against gravity. Yet the basic structural issues remain the same. Like multicellular algae, land plants are built by cementing the cell walls of adjacent cells together, so these cell walls form the basic structural matrix. Furthermore, growth (via cell expansion and cell division) is left to structurally less-rigid cells, which are typically found at the tips of growing shoots or branches. Although like kelp, large woody land plants such as bushes and trees also maintain a surrounding surface meristem that allows stems and trunks to get thicker. These plants could never get as large as they do without this ability. In fact, the ability of a kelp or a tree to continue to increase the thickness of its structural base is analogous to vertebrates being able to increase the thickness of cartilage rods or bones through appositional growth.

Yet despite the fact that much is the same, there are two other structural issues in land plants that are worth mentioning here.

The first has to do with coming up with new structural materials. Although a basic theme exists, the details of cell wall composition varies considerably across different types of algae and land plants and even at different places within the same organism. Different arrangements will have different properties, which would be expected to match the types of stresses each type of organism typically encounters. One yet unmentioned compound, a polymer called *lignin*, plays an important role in certain land plants' ability to stand up to gravity. Lignin has a nearly incompressible nature, so when combined with the tensile strength of cellulose—known as lignified cells—it generates even stronger, more rigid cell walls. Lignin, for example, is a common component of the cell walls that form wood.

The second issue is that many plants wilt or droop when they lack sufficient water, which makes it quite clear that, like animals, water plays an important structural role in plants. But how exactly does it do so? The answer starts with the fact that cell walls are immersed in water. In other words, the molecules making up a cell wall are immersed in water. Yet due to the abundance of polymers, which reduce the number of solutes by tying water-soluble molecules together, the osmolarity inside the cell is typically higher than that found in the surrounding cell wall. The osmotic gradient thus favors the movement of water into the cell, creating an internal hydrostatic or turgor pressure that causes the cell to swell. Yet at the same time, the cell wall prevents the cell from expanding past a certain point. The result is water-inflated cells that overall increase the mechanical rigidity of the plant's tissues. Wilting occurs when this trend reverses. Too little water in the soil decreases a plant's ability to keep enough water in the extracellular matrix to maintain the turgor pressure needed for maximal inflation.

Puzzling Aspects of Multicellular Reproduction

As I have said many times, reproduction is a fundamental component of persistence. It is true for single-celled organisms, and it is also true for multicellular organisms. This adds another complication to the whole multicellular puzzle: How can multicellular arrangements reproduce?

The means by which multicellular colonies reproduce is straightforward. Any cell or group of cells that separates from an existing colony can give rise to a new colony by repeated rounds of cell division. Reproduction in multicellular organisms must also include cell division, as offspring must start out at a smaller, fewer-celled size than the organism from which they arose. But cell differentiation introduces additional complications. Not only do *all* the different cell types have to reappear in each generation, but the relative arrangement of the different cell types must also be repeated. This reassembly of spatial arrangement is known as **pattern formation**. Furthermore, the whole process is constrained by the fact that function must be retained throughout development. A newly forming multicellular organism cannot die for awhile as it goes through some difficult transition, and then come back to life once an intact multicellular form is regenerated.

Reproduction of anything with different types of parts could work in one of two ways. One possibility, as we saw with DNA and kinetosomes during cell division, is **duplication/distribution**. Each existing part is first duplicated, and then these duplicated structures are somehow distributed to the correct position to form two separate organisms. The other option is **regeneration,** where the different parts are built anew in each generation. Although the duplication and distribution aspects of cell division were emphasized earlier, regeneration also plays an important role. For example, the supply proteins of different types are restored each generation by protein synthesis. The same is true for many other cell components. So what about multicellular organisms, do they reproduce by duplication/distribution or regeneration or some combination of both?

A first option

The evolution of multicellular organisms might be easier to think about and understand if a functional pattern of cell differentiation and pattern formation had to happen just once. That is, once a functional multicellular organism came about, it could make more copies of itself without going back to a more amorphous (less-differentiated and patterned) state. If so, reproduction could occur without regeneration of either cell type or arrangement.

Only duplication/distribution remains as an option once regeneration is thrown out, but such a scenario is at least conceivable. Duplication would occur by each cell type producing daughter cells of the same type. For example, dividing liver cells would give rise to liver cells, and so on. Reproduction would then entail simultaneous duplication of all cell types followed by some means to distribute these cells to their correct position along opposite sides. The whole process would then culminate with this cellular mass splitting down the middle into two identical multicellular organisms.

The problem with this scenario is in the details. Differentiated cells giving rise to daughter cells of the same type is known to occur, and it seems feasible that cell division could somehow be coordinated to occur synchronously. The distribution part, however, is a bit more problematic. Wouldn't cells get in the way of each other during any type of attempt to shuffle them into two separate organisms? Furthermore, the constraint of needing to retain function throughout seems rather difficult to achieve. Just think about yourself. How are all your cells (that are arranged into tissues, organs, and organ systems) going to duplicate (it is not quite clear what one looks like at this point) and then separate into two distinct individuals without disrupting the organization of either one of you? For example, how are all the components of a circulatory system supposed to duplicate and separate without getting completely entangled? When I play out this thought experiment, I end up with a bloody and thoroughly dead mess.

Of course, not all multicellular organisms have as complex of organization as you do. And interestingly, some relatively simply organized multicellular organisms are known to reproduce in ways that at least appear similar to the preceding scenario. Animals such as sea anemones and flatworms have been observed to literally pull their body apart into two or more pieces, and each piece then grows back to their original form. But this is not a duplication/distribution scenario per se. Whereas the supply of some cell types in the regrowing part may come from duplication of already differentiated types, further differentiation still occurs. Plus, parts are not duplicated and then distributed to adjacent sides prior to ripping themselves in two. Instead the cell type needed to *regenerate* a whole organism is distributed throughout these structurally simple multicellular organisms. As a consequence, the seemingly self-mutilation notion of tearing oneself into pieces can be used as a form of asexual reproduction. Such reproduction is referred to as being **fission** when the body is ripped into somewhat equal halves and **fragmentation** when the body is broken up into a bunch of variable-sized pieces.

In principle, the regenerative abilities underlying fission or fragmentation are found in all multicellular organisms. But somewhere in the evolution of increasingly complex multicellular organisms a threshold was crossed. Past that threshold, regenerative abilities could be used to repair damage to an individual, but not to make new individuals. For example, a salamander can regenerate a severed limb, but the severed limb cannot regenerate the rest of the body. Humans, as you know, are even more limited in their regenerative abilities than salamanders. Although wounds and breaks can heal, we have lost the ability to regenerate limbs or other larger-scaled body parts.

An interesting aside: Several hundred years ago another idea, called **preformation**, was introduced to explain how multicellular organisms could reproduce while retaining their differentiated organized arrangement throughout. Preformation's premise was that each new generation starts out as a miniaturized but completely intact body plan located within one of the parents—probably the female. Forming each new generation thus only entails filling out this compact "deflated" preformed body. Whereas each new generation starts out small and grows to a larger size, it does not proceed from a simple (undifferentiated) to complex (differentiated) state.

The biggest problem with this idea is that it is just not true. We now have the tools to look more closely and preformation is not found. Besides, the idea of preformation quickly heads toward absurdity when it is carried to its logical extreme. Preformation does not rid the problem of simple to complex unless all generations are preformed at the outset. This means that each miniature female form must contain even smaller preformed body plans of her potential children, which must contain even smaller preformed body plans of her potential grandchildren, and so on. Extend this idea across an unlimited number of generations, and preformation demands the absence of any limit of how small a preformed body plan could be. Such an idea is impossible to reconcile with even a rudimentary understanding of nature.

A second option

Once you rule out a preformed body plan or all existing cells being duplicated and distributed to form a new organism, the starting point for each new multicellular generation must have fewer cells, fewer cells types, and a less patterned arrangement than the more complex form that gave rise to it. As a consequence, reproduction in all multicellular organisms must involve regeneration. Not only must this smaller number of cells begin to undergo cell division to form a larger aggregation of cells, but these cells must also differentiate and arrange themselves into a new multicellular organism. Such regeneration is called **development** or **ontogeny**. *Multicellular organisms reproduce by repeating the same developmental path again and again.*

To begin to explore the nature of development I ask: Which cells within a multicellular organism are able to start the next generation. To start simply, let's focus on the case where each generation starts off as a single cell. Clearly this first cell, which we refer to as a **germ**(ination) **cell**, must have the potential to develop into all the different cell types found in the differentiated adult. Biologists refer to a cell bearing such property as being **totipotent**—which is shorthand for being totally potentialled. Because a germ cell comes from an organism with more than one cell type, the natural question is: Which of these different cell types could act as germ cells? Perhaps all of them could, but if so, cells would have to differentiate through the course of development without disrupting the totipotent properties of the original cell. It is hard, however, to become different and stay the same at the same time, and as a consequence, differentiated cells tend to lose their ability to act as a germ cell. In other words, the flip side of cell differentiation is that each cell has given up the ability to perform all aspects of reproduction. These differentiated cells become what are called **somatic cells**.

The germ cell/somatic cell distinction fits readily into the concept that multicellularity involves a division of labor where different cells specialize (differentiate) to perform different functions within a single reproductive performance. Somatic cells are all the cell types that have differentiated from the initial germ cell to form a coherently functioning multicellular organism. They make up the body that performs all the aspects of living such as foraging for resources and trying to avoid predators. Germ cells, on the other hand, are set up to play the starting role in the next generation. For history to repeat itself—that is, for development to produce a multicellular individual like the one that started it—development must start over at the same (or at least very similar) place and then be channeled in a precise way from the outset. How the first cell of a new individual begins to divide sets the stage for how development can proceed from there. Consequently, not any cell will do. Germ cells are those cells with the right ingredients arranged in the right way to play this starting role. Often germ cells are referred to as generalized cells because through the course of development they gives rise to all the different forms of specialized cells that comprise a functioning multicellular body. I tend to think of germ cells as a very specialized cell because they play a very specialized role in the persistence, generation after generation, of any multicellular form.

Somatic cells appear to make the ultimate biological sacrifice because they give up the opportunity to reproduce directly. Instead they differentiate from germ line cells to *help* germ line cells reproduce (start a new generation). But in reality the altruism goes both ways. It is a cooperative effort that makes new types of performance possible. Somatic cells serve germ cells and germ cells serve somatic cells because neither is able to pull off reproduction on its own. It is a new level of interdependence that once it starts, forces all participants to maintain their respective roles. Cancer helps us to see that quite clearly. When and where somatic cells divide is necessarily tightly regulated because adding new cells must fit with the workings of the organism. Cancer is somatic cells breaking free from such regulation and returning to do what cells do best when resources are available—undergo cell division. The only problem is such renegade somatic cells cannot persist. They cannot form new individuals, and such unchecked reproduction will eventually destroy the body of which they are a part. I have experienced the tragedy of cancer firsthand, as my father died from it. But still, as I wonder about multicellular organisms, I find myself amazed by the other side of the coin—that cancer does not happen more often. How can this cooperative division of labor among cells work as well as it does? It points to kin selection as a powerful evolutionary force.

More on the relationship between differentiation and totipotency

We now know that for multicellular organisms to reproduce, germ cells are needed to start each generation, and somatic cells arise from germ cells within each generation. This raises the question: How do germ cells avoid being caught between potentially competing tasks? In other words, how can a supply of totipotent germ cells be maintained to start the next generation while germ cells are simultaneously differentiating into somatic cells?

As biologists explored this relationship they found that all multicellular organisms seem to maintain a totipotent lineage of cells, called the **germ line**, from the start of development to when the developmental path reproduces, but how somatic cell formation interacts with retaining a totipotent germ line varies across different types of multicellular organisms. Later we explore some of the evolutionary considerations that may have shaped the various twists of this relationship. More specifically, we examine the potential effects of mutations showing up at different places within a developmental path. Two new ideas called **secondary somatic differentiation** and **germ-line sequestration** will be introduced in this discussion.

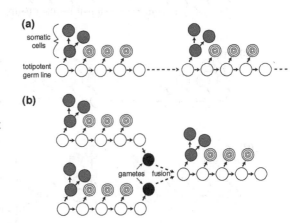

Figure 20-30 shows a simple conception of a repeatable development path. A totipotent germ line is maintained throughout development (through continual cell division), and two different types of somatic cells differentiate from these germ cells. The only difference between Figure 20-30(a) and (b) is how reproduction occurs. In Figure 20-30(a) reproduction occurs asexually. A totipotent cell somehow separates from the developing path, and the developmental path starts anew. In contrast, reproduction is sexual in Figure 20-30(b). Gametes are formed

Figure 20-30. A simple and repeatable developmental path that both retains a totipotent germ-line and forms differentiated somatic cells. In (a) reproduction occurs asexually and in (b) reproduction occurs sexually. (See text for further details.)

from the totipotent germ line, and gametes from two different individuals fuse to form a new totipotent cell from which development begins again.

There are three other aspects of Figure 20-30 that I want you to notice. First, somatic cells only differentiate from the germ-line cells. Second, one of the two somatic cell types retains the ability to divide, and the daughter cells retain the same differentiated identity—that is, the daughter cells are the same cell type as the cell from which they arose. So once this cell type arises in development it can potentially maintain itself without further participation from the germ line. In contrast, the other somatic cell type lacks the ability to continue to divide after differentiation. As a consequence, a totipotent cell line must be present throughout development for more of this cell type to be made.

In Figure 20-31 we play the evolutionary game of introducing mutations to the preceding developmental pathway. We focus, in particular, on whether the mutation's effect on the developmental pathway is heritable. Clearly the game is over if the answer is no. Any change cannot persist unless it can be passed across generations. But keep in mind that heritability is necessary but not sufficient for persistence. Selection also kicks in. The performance of the development path has to be able to negotiate the reproductive obstacle course, and perhaps even do so faster than the ancestral type.

In Figure 20-31(a) a mutation shows up in one of the somatic cells allowing this cell type to continue to divide and give rise to a new type of somatic cell. Such a mutation could have a positive or negative effect on the reproductive performance of the individual bearing the mutation. But from an evolutionary perspective the mutation's effect is irrelevant because (as we first discussed in Chapter 6) **somatic mutations** are not heritable. The genetic change has no means to show up in the totipotent cell that starts the next generation.

The last three scenarios of Figure 20-31 share an important similarity—mutations are restricted to the totipotent germ line. Given that, we focus on the differences.

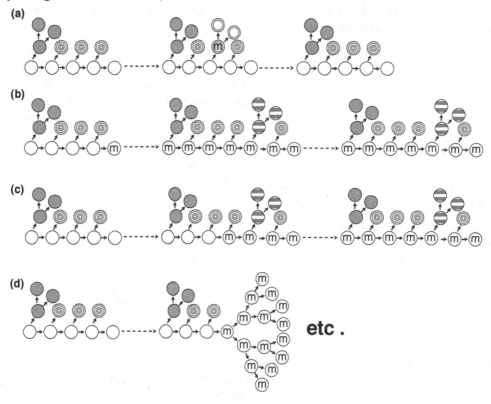

Figure 20-31. Some of the potential effects of a mutation occuring at different places within a development path is shown. Each scenario is discussed in more detail in the text.

In Figure 20-31(b) a mutation arises in a germ-line cell after cell differentiation within the initial individual has stopped. As a consequence, the mutation can influence development only if it is passed to an offspring. When this occurs, this particular mutation has pronounced developmental effects. Not only does development occur for a longer time, but also a new somatic cell type differentiates from the totipotent germ line. Because this change is potentially heritable, the question of persistence boils down to whether these developmental changes translate into a positive or negative effect on reproductive performance. If it is positive, then the stage is set for a new and more complex multicellular organism to evolve from a simpler one.

When the germ line is *developmentally active* throughout development—that is, when the totipotent cell line is involved in the formation of somatic cells throughout development—a germ-line mutation could arise that alters the developmental path of the individual within which the mutations first occur and still be potentially heritable. Figure 20-31(c) illustrates this. Furthermore, from an evolutionary perspective there is no difference between Figure 20-31(b) and (c). It does not matter whether a mutation's effects first show up in the next generation or in the individual bearing the mutation. The change is heritable and may persist because it could have positive effect on reproductive performance.

The flip side, of course, is that most mutations have a negative effect. Figure 20-31(d) illustrates this in a most extreme form—the mutation completely disrupts development by blocking the formation of somatic cells. The totipotent germ line, in essence, returns to being single-celled organisms. Other types of negative effects are also possible, but regardless of the details any developmental path bombarded with deleterious effects is expected to go extinct.

Let's add another consideration to the mix. The way development has been portrayed so far the germ line has not only been mitotically active, but it has also been developmentally active—somatic cells are continually differentiating from the dividing germ line. As a consequence, the evolution of larger and increasingly complex multicellular organisms would require a greater number of germ-line cell divisions to increase the number of somatic cell types formed during development. This seems like no big deal until mutations are considered. Because mutations tend to occur during DNA replication, the more cell divisions a germ line goes through during each bout of development (each generation) the more likely a mutation will occur. The positive side of an increasing mutation rate per generation is that it increases the chance of a beneficial mutation occurring. But remember, organisms are not trying to evolve per se. The main issue is whether a developmental pathway can persist, and to do that it must reproduce faster than it falls apart. So from a persistence perspective, a link between increasing complexity and increasing the number of germ-line cell divisions creates a problem. Because most mutations are deleterious, the main effect of increasing the mutation rate per generation is to speed up the rate that currently functional developmental pathways will fall apart. This, of course, will decrease the chance that an increasingly complex developmental pathway can persist. The evolution of increasingly complex multicellular organisms appears to be caught between a rock and a hard place.

But that is not the end of the story. **Secondary somatic differentiation**—somatic cells giving rise to different types of somatic cells—is introduced in Figure 20-32. Secondary somatic differentiation can drastically change the nature of developmental pathways because all secondarily derived somatic cells are not dependent on an actively dividing germ line. As a consequence the relationship between the germ-line and somatic cells can end before somatic development ends. In fact, Figure 20-32 portrays this relationship in its most extreme form—the germ line is separated from somatic development after the first division. All remaining somatic cell types arise directly or indirectly from the first

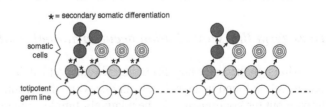

Figure 20-32. Introducing secondary somatic differentiation into a developmental pathway.

somatic cell type. In contrast, the previous two figures represent the other extreme—all somatic cell types arise directly from germ-line cells. In reality, these two extremes represent the two endpoints of a continuum because organisms range from one extreme to the other.

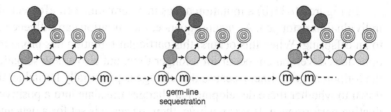

Figure 20-33. The evolution of germ-line sequestration. See text for further details.

Secondary somatic differentiation sets the stage for the evolution of **germ-line sequestration**. A totipotent germ line freed from the task of producing somatic cells throughout development is not constrained to remain mitotically active once its developmental role has ended. A sequestered germ line is one that has taken advantage of this opportunity. Figure 20-33 paints a simple-minded scenario of how germ-line sequestration could originate in a population. A mutation occurs within the germ line that terminates cell division after it stops being developmentally active. As stated earlier, such mutation would be expected to spread in the population because it would reduce the per generation mutation rate and thus reduce the rate at which deleterious mutations disrupt the currently functional developmental path. So by this argument, the earlier a germ line is sequestered the better. Yet the flip side is that even though they occur less frequently, whenever germ-line sequestration evolves it will also reduce the number of advantageous mutations per generation. As a consequence, lineages with sequestered germ lines, especially when the germ line is sequestered very early in development, would be expected to give rise to new and unique developmental paths less often.

In addition to reducing the number of cell divisions, there is another way that germ-line sequestration could reduce deleterious mutation rate per generation. Once a germ line becomes developmentally inactive, it can potentially become metabolically less active. Because metabolism produces oxidative products that can damage DNA and lead to mutation, a reduced metabolic rate should result in a reduced mutation rate.

An aside: Throughout this discussion there was one option that I did not consider. During the course of development it is conceivable that the germ line disappears—that is, the entire totipotent cell lineage differentiates into somatic cells. Such a change could still be compatible with reproduction if in at least some somatic cell lines the change is reversible. So although all somatic cells have lost the ability at the moment to act as totipotent germ cells, this ability could be restored by dedifferentiation. Each new generation could then get started by some somatic cells returning to a totipotent state. Although there are at least some examples of differentiated cells able to return to a totipotent state, I have not pushed this issue for one simple reason: I know of no cases of multicellular development that follow this path. Why? I am not sure. But recognize that such a strategy potentially plays an inherent trade-off absent in any developmental path that maintains a totipotent cell line throughout. The loss of differentiated cells means that reproduction involves a sacrifice in somatic function. In other words, such a developmental pathway gets caught in a "do this now and that later" strategy, and getting around such trade-offs may have been what drove the evolution of multicellularity in the first place.

Does germ-line sequestration occur in animals and plants?

Although the preceding discussion was theoretical, it is intriguing that the pattern of germ-line sequestration found in animals falls in line with what would be expected. Although animals vary throughout the continuum, it is the relatively simple animals that maintain a mitotically active germ line throughout development. More complex animals tend to sequester their germ line at some point, and for many animals the sequestering occurs very early. In humans, for example, the germ cells are set aside in the 56-day embryo within the developing gonad, where they remain inactive until an individual becomes sexually mature many years later.

Plants, on the other hand, are intriguing because none of them sequester their germ line. Why the difference? Although it is true that some animals are more complex than any plants, complexity is still present, and many plants also grow very large, which means that the germ line would undergo numerous cell divisions. So the complete absence of germ-line sequestration cannot be explained by the limited opportunity for deleterious mutations to arise during plant development. But what else could explain the difference? Although it sounds curious at first, the fact that all plant cells are surrounded by cell walls may be the key. The presence of cell walls alters development in one very significant way—cells walls barricade every newly formed cell from ever moving to a new location within a developing plant. In other words, each new cell arising by cell division is stuck. In contrast, animal cells can and commonly do move to new locations during development. The connection between the absence of cell movement and the lack of germ-line sequestration can be argued from one of two perspectives. I discuss both next.

When cells cannot move, sequestering a totipotent cell line would limit where a plant could place reproductive structures. For instance, after sequestration placing a flower on the tip of a newly growing shoot would be ruled out because totipotent cells could never reach the flower. In fact, if sequestration occurred early in development, reproductive structures would be confined solely to the base of the plant. Is this a plausible reproductive strategy? Perhaps, but it surely falls short of being optimal. Alternatively, totipotent cells could spread throughout a growing plant. Doing so would maintain a plant's freedom to place reproductive structures wherever works best. And that is what plants do. A totipotent cell line is continuously maintained along each axis of growth. This is accomplished in most plants, grasses being an exception, by locating a perpetually embryonic tissue called **meristem** at the tip of each shoot and root. As a tip grows by cell division, cells left in the wake may differentiate into some type of somatic cell, but the cells out front remain totipotent. Whenever a shoot or root branches, the meristem splits and grows out in front of each. Overall, whatever space a plant grows into, totipotent cells lead the way.

The other side to the story is that although cell walls take away the option of germ-line sequestration, they also make it less necessary. It is not that cell walls make mutations occur less often, or reduce the frequency that mutation are deleterious; but cell walls do reduce the ability of any deleterious mutation to disrupt a plant's development. Consider, for instance, a worst-case scenario: A deleterious mutation occurs that somehow completely disrupts a meristem's ability to continue development. For branching plants, however, disrupting one meristem is not fatal. And because plant cells cannot move, the disruptive effects of a mutation occurring within one meristem cannot spread to other meristems throughout the plant. So although the disrupted branch will die, other branches continue to grow and develop.

An aside: Note that a continuously dividing totipotent cell line in combination with less potential for deleterious mutations to be lethal opens the door for rarer advantageous mutations to occur and spread in a population more commonly. This raises an interesting question: Do plants evolve faster than animals with sequestered germ lines? It would be worth a closer look.

Another aside: The presence of totipotent cells at the growing tip along with the potential to branch explains the modular or repetitive growth pattern found in plants. Each time a shoot (or root) branches, each branch has the potential to develop into any of the differentiated structures (e.g., leaf, flower, stem) found on a plant. So the same structure could develop repeatedly. For example, a simple developmental program could result in the repetitive formation of leaves along a shoot—each time a growing shoot branches, one meristem differentiates into a leaf, and the other continues to grow as a shoot that after a set period of growth branches again.

The Evolution of Multicellular Organisms: A Primer

When I first discussed evolution back in Chapter 6, I pointed out that the subject could be loosely broken down into two parts, origin and persistence. With the evolution of multicellular organisms, development clearly plays a role in persistence because a multicellular form cannot last unless it can be built repeatedly. Yet, development also plays a seminal role in origin. The evolution of the first multicellular organisms from a single-celled lineage involves the origin of a developmental path. From there new types of multicellular organisms potentially arise when existing development paths are altered. And as you already know, whether newly altered paths can potentially persist depends on two things: (1) Is this developmental change heritable, and (2) does this development path construct an organism whose performance ability (in context to available environmental circumstance) is able to negotiate the entire reproductive obstacle course? In other words, *the evolution of multicellular organisms is really the evolution of repeatable development pathways that work.*

Understanding the evolution of multicellular organisms thus boils down to trying to understand how functional and repeatable developmental pathways came to be. To be honest, this is a challenging question. It is hard to know where to start. Should we examine adult multicellular forms and try to work backward? Should we start at the beginning of development and work forward? Here I start by attempting to do both at the same time. Have you ever heard a riddle about chickens and eggs?

The evolution of parent–offspring interactions

Which came first, the chicken or the egg? Obviously, the paradox underlying this riddle is that both seem dependent on the other, so how could either come into existence before the other> Nevertheless, here I attempt to answer the question.

First, recognize that the riddle is not about chickens per se, but about the relationship between parents and offspring. In other words, the riddle could be restated: Which came first parental care or offspring dependent on parental care? As we already stated, multicellular organisms are best thought of as a repeatable developmental path. So if offspring are simply defined as a start of any developmental path, then clearly offspring came first. Multicellularity had to start with the origin of a developmental path (see following). But such an answer fails to address the interaction between different stages of development. A parent, or more specifically parental care, is a later portion of a developmental path helping out an earlier portion of the same type of developmental path. On the other hand, an offspring dependent on parental care is an early portion of a developmental path that could not make it without parental aid.

Given those definitions, it is obvious that parental care must have come first. A dependent offspring cannot evolve in the absence of parental care. On the other hand, it is possible to help something that does not absolutely need the help. Suppose, for instance, a developmental path comes into being in which all stages are self-sufficient. Although later portions of this developmental path do not need to aid earlier stages, later stages could still help out. And doing so may increase the success that this developmental path again reaches in the later stages. In other words, parental behavior could be self-promoting—parental care would help a developmental path get back to the stages that provide parental care.

The evolution of parental care would then set the stage for the evolution of dependent offspring. Changes that allow earlier stages of a developmental path to better take advantage of parental care could be beneficial, especially when earlier stages take advantage of things that later stages do better. Say, for example, that parents are better at foraging for food. Changes that allow offspring to better rely on parentally provided resources would help offspring negotiate early development stages. This in turn would benefit the later stages by increasing the success that offspring develop into parents. And once such a loop of mutual benefit is started it is easy to imagine this division of labor evolving to the point that earlier stages are completely dependent on later stages. At that point the parent-offspring interactions captured in the chicken and the egg riddle have evolved. Earlier stages cannot continue along the developmental path without the help of later stages, and later stages cannot be repeated in the absence of earlier stages.

The evolution of a developmental path

The preceding discussion of the chicken and egg riddle skirted around discussion of how a developmental path could evolve in the first place. The only point made was that all stages need to be self-sufficient. In other words, the evolution of multicellular organisms from single-celled organisms needed to start without the benefit of parent–offspring interactions. Here I try to at least frame an argument for how this might occur. Later we will use this framework to discuss a more specific scenario.

Single-celled organisms have to be self-sufficient at all stages of their life. Parental care is not an option because once a cell divides nothing remains to further care for the daughter cells. Of course, by growing large enough prior to cell division, a cell in essence provisions each daughter cell. And resources stored within each daughter cell may support some needed conversions to a more functional form. But growth cannot occur without taking in new resources from the environment, and the only option available to daughter cells is to provision themselves.

Daughter cells remaining together to form colonies does not change the self-sufficiency requirement. Each cell within a colony, including the starting cell, must be able to care for itself. Nonetheless, colonies form a starting point for the evolution of a developmental path. The question is what could potentially favor some cells in a colony to begin to differentiate. We have raised two issues: performance trade-offs and size issues. Although both where likely involved, for the moment let's just focus on size.

Recall that successful clumps of cells will generate larger clumps of cells, and although larger size may generate advantages, it can also be disruptive. So at least some size-based benefits cannot be reaped without some means to counter size-based disruptions. The only problem is that countering size-based disruptions may require different cells in different positions doing different things, and such cell differentiation will not readily evolve. But that is not a big drawback. Colonies that face an upper size limit can still flourish. They simply need to continually break into smaller pieces before a size limit is reached. And because every cell is in essence a germ cell, every cell in every colony represents a chance for genetic changes that result in the "right type of cell differentiation" to sneak into a genome. The whole evolutionary argument is that rare but beneficial occurrences can happen given sufficient opportunity. So it is plausible that within a few colonies in the history of Life certain cells began to take on different roles in ways that countered size-based disruptions. As a consequence, the group as a whole could better take advantage of size-based benefits, and in the process, a colony would become more organism-like.

Furthermore, the development of this more organism-like arrangement would be repeatable if cell differentiation was triggered by some change associated with size-based problems. Just think about it. Reproduction starts with some cell moving to a new location and beginning to divide. Eventually the colony becomes large enough that some cells encounter size-based problems. This in turn triggers these cells to differentiate in ways that helps them solve their problem, which lets the group as a whole grow to a larger size. Overall, the progression begins to look like a developmental pathway because appearance and function change as size increases. Yet the chicken and egg trap is avoided because all stages are still self-sufficient functional arrangements.

Once a self-sufficient repeatable developmental path is set into motion, useful modification could continue to accumulate (including parental behavior followed by evolution of dependent offspring). The result of such changes may be an increasingly complex but still repeatable developmental path. In the process truly multicellular organisms would make their debut.

Some key terms:

cell differentiation – process through which cells within the same developing multicellular organism become different from each other (e.g., muscle cells, liver cells, nerve cells, etc.). The differences are generated by a unique pattern of turning on and off genes in a different cell lines.

interstitial space – the space in multicellular organisms that is inside the outer sheet of cells, but outside any cells.

anchoring junctions – structures that hold adjacent cells together by hooking into each cell's cytoskeleton. They are the relatively strongest form of cell-cell connections.

extracellular matrix – regions of interstitial space consisting of a collagen framework filled in by an interconnected and highly hydrated gel-like structure (formed from the interaction between water molecules and proteoglycans).

fibroblasts – cells that specialize in secreting the collagen and proteoglycan components of extracellular matrix.

pattern formation – the process by which the "right" cell types come to be in the "right" place to form a functional multicellular organism. (e.g., muscle cells come to be where muscles need to be, etc.)

development – the regeneration of a multicellular form from a starting point that has fewer cells, fewer cell types, and a less complex arrangement. Development commonly starts with a single cell.

germ-line cells – the lineage of cells that throughout development retains the ability to serve as a starting cell for the next generation. In sexual organisms, germ-line cells form gametes.

somatic cells – those cell types that are formed anew in each multicellular generation through differentiation from germ-line cells. A coherently functioning multicellular organism is formed by the collective action of the various forms of somatic cells.

Some study questions:

1. Comment on the following statement: Multicellular organisms are superior to single-celled organisms because they are more successful at persisting across time.

2. Briefly explain how kin selection, increasing size, and cell differentiation could have contributed to the evolution of multicellular organisms.

3. Discuss some of the ways that growth (getting bigger) in multicellular organisms can be disruptive to function. Next outline four basic ways that multicellular organisms can get around the disruptive nature of growth.

4. Discuss how cellular arrangements and convection systems can be used as a means to overcome size limits—that is, make it possible for an organism to grow larger than it could otherwise.Discuss several ways that organisms establish convection systems.

5. Why is it more difficult for a terrestrial organism to grow as large as an aquatic organism? What role do each of the following play in building support structure: desomosomes, GAGs, collagen, chitin, apatite, and cellulose?

6. Compare and contrast how movement is generated in an organism with a hydroskeleton, an exoskeleton, or an endoskeleton.

7. Single-celled organisms commonly reproduce by duplication and distribution. Why can't multicellular organisms reproduce in this same way?

8. Explain this statement: Multicellular organisms reproduce by repeating the same developmental path again and again.

9. Discuss some differences between germ cells and somatic cells? What is germ-line sequestration?

The Evolution of Animals

Earlier I made the argument that one of the potential driving forces behind the evolution of multi-cellular organisms is trade-offs that constrain a single cell from being able to simultaneously perform two useful functions. Such trade-offs generate an opportunity for cells to hang together and usefully cooperate. Here as we discuss the evolution of animals, only one trade-off, known as the **flagellation constraint**, comes into focus. So let's start there.

The flagellation constraint

Movement and cell division can occur simultaneously in a variety of single-celled organisms. For example, some single-celled organisms maintain only a single microtubule-organizing center (MTOC), but it is able to generate a spindle apparatus (for distributing kinetosomes and chromosomes) while simultaneously maintaining functional flagella (see Figure 21-1).

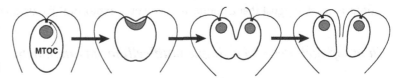

Figure 21-1. A cell with one MTOC that is able to retain flagella while undergoing cell division.

Other groups of single-celled organisms (e.g., Euglenophyta, Cryptophyta, Kinetoplastids, and Chlorophyta) are to retain flagella during cell division by maintaining more than one MTOC (see Figure 21-2). The simplest scenario is having two MTOCs: one committed to the duplication and distribution of kinetosomes (and their associated flagella) across cell division, whereas the other remains in close association with the nucleus (in some cases even moving inside the nucleus) and is committed to the formation of chromosome-distributing spindles. The ability to divide and move at the same time will be retained across generations as long as the replication and distribution of these two MTOCs are somehow coordinated to occur simultaneously.

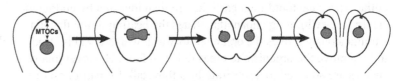

Figure 21-2. A cell with two MTOCs that is able to retain flagella while undergoing cell division.

Some groups of single-celled organisms, however, have never come up with a means to retain flagella and divide cells at the same time. Such cells are said to have a **flagellation constraint**.

One reason that this constraint may have evolved in some groups was already discussed in Chapter 17. The basic idea is that retaining flagella while producing a chromosome-dividing spindle requires a cell to synthesize enough tubulin molecules (the molecules that form microtubules) to build both structures simultaneously. It would be cheaper to reabsorb the flagella prior to spindle formation and then use the tubulin molecules that were previously part of

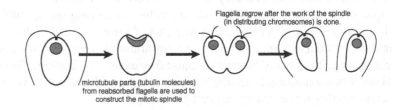

Flagella regrow after the work of the spindle (in distributing chromosomes) is done.

microtubule parts (tubulin molecules) from reabsorbed flagella are used to construct the mitotic spindle

Figure 21-3. A cell with one MTOC that experiences the flagellation constraint.

the flagellar microtubules to build spindle microtubules. For any single-celled organism whose biology is such that the temporary loss of flagella is less of a deficit than the added costs of tubulin synthesis, then the flagellation constraint makes sense (see Figure 21-3).

Yet regardless of the reason that it exists, two observations surrounding this constraint are worth noting. First, in any single-celled lineage experiencing the flagellation constraint, a multicellular arrangement is the only way that flagella-based motility and cell division can occur simultaneously. Second, the flagellation constraint appears to be a fundamental component of the cells making up the multicellular group that we call animals. In other words, none of the cells making up animals have ever been observed to divide while being flagellated, or for that matter divide while having any other unique form of microtubule-based structure. For example, animal nerve cells, with their microtubule-based axons and dendrites, cannot divide. So although it is not obvious what the flagellation constraint had to do with the evolution of frogs or other familiar multicellular animals, the preceding two observations at least suggest that a connection is worth exploring. We do so next.

Choanoflagellates and a simple multicellular arrangement

Choanoflagellates (sometimes called "collar-flagellates") are a group of eukaryotic organisms that are generally single celled and have a characteristic morphology—a single flagellum is surrounded by a ring of closely packed microvilli (i.e., slender microfilament-supported extension of the outer membrane) known as a collar (see Figure 21-4(a)). The microvilli are so closely packed that the collar appears to be a continuous transparent structure under a light microscope. The combination of flagella and collar is used to filter feed. The flagella beats in a base-to-tip wave that pushes water away from the cell, and the current created brings bacteria and other small food particles suspended in the water into contact with the collar. These captured food particles are then ingested by endocytosis. In free-swimming choanoflagellates the beating of the flagella simultaneously moves the organism forward, which is likely used to help move the organism to areas richer in food. However, many species are attached to a substrate by a thin stalk for part or all of their life cycle. In such cases the beating of the flagella is simply used to bring food to their fixed location (see Figure 21-4(b)). Some of these stalked collar flagellates form a small colony, and one possible advantage is that a greater number of flagella beating in the same area can overall create a stronger flow past each cell (see Figure 21-4(c)).

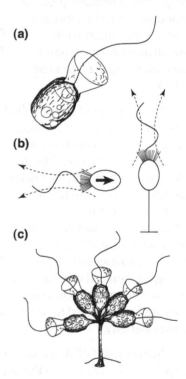

Choanoflagellates are highlighted here because they demonstrate the flagellation constraint. As a consequence, choanoflagellates cannot feed whenever they undergo cell division. Further-

Figure 21-4. Choanoflagellates. See text for further details.

more, most cells are negatively buoyant, so free-swimming species will also have the tendency to sink during cell division. Perhaps this is why stalked forms evolved in the first place; they can reproduce and still remain in a good location. This constraint has obviously not put single-celled free-swimming choanoflagellates out of business because they exist. It is, however, interesting to think for a moment about how choanoflagellates might evolve if faced with a situation where it would be beneficial to retain motility while undergoing cell division.

One option would be to become part of a somewhat spherical multicellular arrangement where the outside cells remain flagellated and the inner space is used for cell division. *Proterospongia haeckel* is an example (see Figure 21-5). Nondividing flagellated cells are connected by a gelatinous coat on the outside of a spherical arrangement, whereas amoeboid-like cells that undergo cell division occupy the interior. Although not enclosed by a definite sheet of cells, this gelatinous matrix is similar to the connective tissue discussed in the previous chapter. The amoeboid-like cells are thus at least somewhat analogous to mesenchyme cells. It is known that flagellated collar cells can change into amoeboid-like cells and vice versa. So presumably collar cells on the outside feed until they have grown enough to undergo cell division, at which point they change into amoeboid-like cells and move into the interior of the colony to divide. The daughter cells could then move back to the outside, where once again they become collar cells.

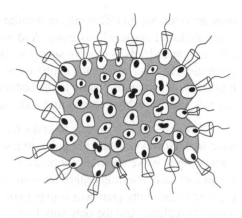

Figure 21-5. A simplified drawing of Proterospongia haeckel.

Is *Proterospongia* a colony or a multicellular organism? The best answer is not completely clear. At any slice of time it appears to be a multicellular organism because there are two distinct cell types. The outer collar cells act like somatic cells in that they differentiate into a specialized form for feeding and propulsion that cannot undergo cell division. The internal amoeboid cells would in turn qualify as germ cells. The problem is that this division of labor is not maintained across time. Amoeboid cells become collar cells and collar cell become amoeboid cells. So *Proterospongia* has colony-like properties in that any cell within this arrangement could act as a starting point to build a new *Proterospongia*.

For someone interested in the evolution of multicellular organisms the fact that *Proterospongia* sits at the crossroads between coloniality and multicellularity is anything but a problem. It may well represent a glimpse of the past. That is, historically, a structurally similar multicellular form (because it too arose to escape the flagellation constraint) may have been the transition that set the stage for the evolution of all **metazoans**—organisms that you know as animals. Next we continue to play this scenario out.

Some Speculation: The Evolution of Sponges

The key features of all animals is that they are multicellular, their eukaryotic cells lack cells walls, and they are heterotrophs—so they must bring in certain forms of preformed biological molecules. Here we focus on one group of animals known as the **Poriferans**, or sponges, which are named for their numerous pores into which water flows. Sponges are highlighted here for several reasons: First, they are the structurally simplest form of animal. Cells of only a few different types exist, and although it may be somewhat of a semantic issue, sponges are said to lack defined tissues and organs. In other words, although cells within a sponge take on different positions and roles, the interaction among cells seems to be only loosely organized. The types of cell–cell connections thought to help groups of cells work together to perform a specific task, such as communicating, occluding, and anchoring junctions, are not found in sponges. This structural simplicity suggests that sponges might have been the first animals to evolve from a single-celled ancestor. This suggestion is supported by the fact that sponges are among the oldest known animal fossils. Second, sponges seemingly evolved from choanoflagellates, as this group of single-celled (and colonial) organisms is both morphologically and genetically the most similar to the cells of multicellular sponges. And third, as biologists have looked more closely at the molecular similarities and differences among different types of animals, the evidence is becoming more and more convincing that all animals, including sponges, share a common ancestor. Stated differently, molecular evidence increasingly supports the view that animals are a monophyletic (single origin) group. And within the animal phylogenies constructed, the most basal or earliest branch leads to modern sponges, suggesting that the earliest animals had sponge-like characteristics. In other words, the evolutionary lineage that eventually led to all other animals initially branched off somewhere early in the history of sponges. So, to begin to understand the evolution of animals, one probably needs to first understand the evolution of sponges.

Of course, there is no way to know the exact steps by which sponges evolved from single-celled ancestors. However, next I am going to take some freedom to speculate, which means that in a sense I am going to make up an evolutionary tale. One could argue that such speculation is inappropriate because certain assertions either have not been or could not be tested via the scientific method. Yet I proceed because my goal here is to get you thinking about how such an evolutionary transition might have taken place. And the only way I know to do this is to introduce a plausible evolutionary scenario.

Getting started

Envision some point in the distant past. In relatively shallow ocean waters, *Proterospongia*-like arrangements are feeding as they propel themselves along. Those able to gather sufficient resources from the surrounding environment continue to grow via further cell division. However, such growth will eventually disrupt colony function. For example, the colony will lose its ability to stay afloat once the negatively buoyant volume surpasses the collective propulsion power of the surface-bound flagella (because volume increases faster than surface area).

Sinking to the bottom is not, however, necessarily fatal. The colony could reproduce by breaking up in smaller colonies, or it could even continue to try to feed and grow while resting on the bottom. As we have already seen with stalked choanoflagellates, flagella can be used to create a current and filter feed. The only real problem is that a *Proterospongia*-like arrangement resting on the bottom (see Figure 21-6) will not escape other size-based issues. For instance, increasing size would increase the diffusion distance to interior cells, making it more difficult for these cells to get adequate supplies of things absorbed from the outside environment like oxygen and to be able to remove sufficient amounts of wastes like carbon dioxide. Furthermore, increasing size would decrease the relative amount of outer surface area to arrange food-capturing collar cells (due to decreasing SA/V).

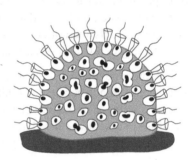

Figure 21-6. A Proterospongia-like arrangement that has sunk to the bottom.

Of course, we have already discussed the basic solution to such size-based problems—take on a more convoluted arrangement (see Figure 21-7). In this case, however, such arrangement still encounters problems. Specifically, collar cells located deep within cavities find themselves in a poor location because as water from the outside moves further into each cavity more and more of the food will have already been filtered out by other collar cells. Plus, the water will become increasing loaded with metabolic waste products released from previously encountered cells. As a consequence, a substantial increase in size may not be able to be achieved by increasing the length and number of dead-end pockets lined with collar cells.

For size to increase substantially, a bottom-dwelling arrangement must simultaneously solve two issues: (1) It must minimize

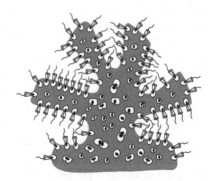

Figure 21-7. A bottom-dwelling Proterospongia-like arrangement that has folded into a more convoluted shape.

the diffusion distance between each cell and the environment, and (2) it must minimize the competition among collar cells by continually exposing each collar cell to water that has moved past at most a small number of collar cells before. Figure 21-8 shows an arrangement the meets both of these criteria. It is still a convoluted shape that minimizes diffusion distance, but now the flagellated cells have been repositioned so that they only line the inside of a vase-shaped central cavity that is connected to the outside not only by the large cavity opening at the top, but also by numerous small openings spread throughout the cavities walls. Within this arrangement the collective beating of the flagella can create a current that brings water through each of the small pores and leaves by the large opening at the top. Competition among collar cells is thus minimized because each collar cell is located close to an incurrent pore. Diffusion of oxygen and removal of metabolic wastes is also facilitated by the one-way movement of water through this central cavity.

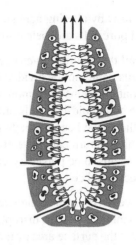

Figure 21-8. Modification of a bottom-dwelling Proterospongia-like arrangement into a shape that better resolves potential size-based disruptions.

The rearrangement of collar cells from the outside surface to lining an internal cavity is a change, but not a fundamental shift in arrangement. There are, however, some other problems that would need to be resolved before such an arrangement could function effectively. First, such a shift would leave the structure devoid of any type of cellular covering. Second, maintaining this more defined shape, especially as size increased, would be difficult unless the structural extracellular matrix became stiffer. Finally, a means to create these small openings along the cavity wall would be needed.

Interestingly, resolve these issues through additional cell differentiation, and the basic structure of a modern-day sponge arises (see Figure 21-9). For example, most modern-day sponges have cells called **pinacocytes** or **covering cells** that specialize in creating a protective outer covering. Biologists do not call this pinocyte covering an epithelium due to the lack of between-cell junctions and a basement membrane. Just underneath this pinocyte covering, however, is still a thin layer of connective-like tissue called **mesenchyme**. Here amoeboid-like cells (often call **amoebocytes**, **archaeocytes**, or **mesenchyme cells**) move around within a surrounding gelatinous extracellular matrix. These mesenchyme cells sometimes differentiate into cells that secrete additional structure. For example, some sponges form cells called **sclerocytes** that secrete skeletal-like arrangements called **spicules**, which are made out of either calcium carbonate or a siliceous (containing silicon) mixture. Spicules of either type come in a variety of shapes and can be fused together to form a rigid network. Some sponges also form cells called **spongocytes** that secrete a fibrous structural network made out of the protein keratin called **sponging**. The small openings into the central chamber are formed by another specialized cell type called **pore cells** or **porocytes**. These tube-shaped cells span the distance between the outer covering and the inner chamber. Like amoebocytes, pore cells have the ability to change shape and in so doing can

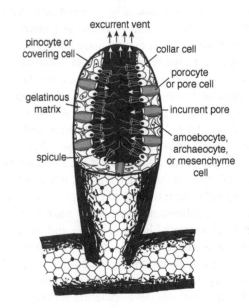

Figure 21-9. The basic structure of a multicellular animal known as a sponge.

regulate flow by altering pore size. Some sponges also have another cell type called **myocytes** that surround pore cells and help regulate pore size by contracting in a similar fashion as muscle cells.

Recall that within *Proterospongia*, collar cells can become amoeboid-like cells and vice versa, so the cells could not be divided into germ cells and somatic cells. With sponges, on the other hand, differentiation seems to be more permanent. For instance, in sponges collar cells do not seem to turn back into amoeboid-like cells once they have gathered sufficient food and then undergo cell division. Instead they have become feeding specialists that pass partially digested food particles to amoebocytes, which in turn can move about and distribute food to other types of cells as needed. The germ cell role seems to be played by generalized amoebocytes that can differentiate into any of the other more specialized cell types.

The vessel-shaped sponge introduced so far will still encounter size-based disruptions as it grows larger. Eventually the surface area available for collar cells will be insufficient to take care of the food demands of other cells or to move sufficient amounts of water through the central chamber. So for further growth to occur sponges would need to fold the flagellated internal surface in ways that still minimized competition among collar cells but allowed the internal surface area to continue to increase as fast as volume. Figure 21-10 shows two basic ways that larger sponges have accomplished this feat.

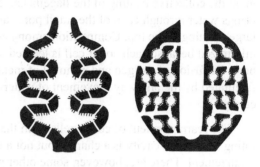

Figure 21-10. Shapes that allow sponges to grow even larger. (See text for further details.)

Reproduction

Recall that the evolution of a multicellular organism is really the evolution of a repeatable developmental path. So far our speculative evolutionary path to sponges started with single-celled choanoflagellates to *Proterospongia*-like colonial arrangement as a means to escape the flagellation constraint. This was followed by a transition to a bottom-dwelling organism with increasingly complex collar cell–lined internal chambers as a means to overcome size-based disruptions. The question, then, is could this series of evolutionary transitions become a repeatable series of developmental transitions? That is, could a single choanoflagellate-like cell that separates from a functional sponge-like arrangement repeat the series of transitions back into a sponge-like arrangement? The answer seems like it would be yes. The evolutionary part of this story is the evolution of a heritable set of tools that makes it possible to get around certain functional constraints. Given that the flagellation and size-based constraints will be encountered in a predictable and repeatable fashion, once the tool kit is in place the series of transitions around these constraints could seemingly occur over and over. Furthermore, each step along this developmental pathway is functionally independent of any other stage (see Figure 21-11).

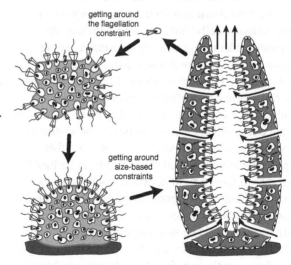

getting around the flagellation constraint

getting around size-based constraints

Figure 21-11. A plausible repeatable developmental path for a sponge-like organism in which all stages are functionally independent of each other.

However, as we discussed earlier, once a repeatable developmental pathway is present, the evolution of parental behavior would not be expected to be far behind. Anything that later stages could do to assist earlier stages make it back to later stages would be a self-promoting behavior. And perhaps the most obvious form of assistance would be to provision food. Diverting some of the resources gathered by the large somatic feeding structure to the beginning of the next generation allows early developmental transitions to occur without the added complication of needing to gather all their own resources. The evolution of dependent offspring would be expected to follow whenever changes that allow offspring to better take advantage of parentally provided resources interfere with their ability to provision themselves. Sponges show both of these expected changes (see Figure 21-12).

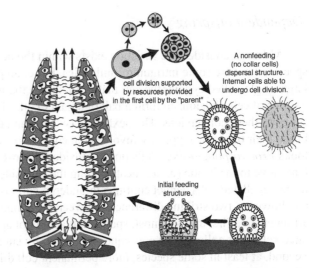

Figure 21-12. A generalized sponge life cycle that includes both parental provisioning and dependent offspring, which includes a larval stage. These are the type of transitions that would be expected to evolve from the life cycle in Figure 21-11. (See text for more detail.)

Parental provisioning in sponges

Whether reproduction occurs sexually or asexually (and both occur), sponges provision food to offspring. For example, in sexual reproduction, enlarged food-filled **eggs** are formed from specialized amoebocytes and perhaps with the help of others cells referred to as nurse cells. Smaller mobile sperm are also thought to arise from amoebocytes. In some sponges both eggs and sperm are shed into the sea so fertilization is said to occur externally, and parental care is restricted solely to the food provisioned in the egg. Development is thus restricted to occur along a path that creates self-feeding offspring by the time the parentally provided resources run out. In most sponges, however, only sperm are shed into the sea so for fertilization to occur, a sperm must move into another sponge via the water current and fuse with an egg held inside. Internal fertilization creates the opportunity for additional parental care. At the very least, early stages of development can occur within the more protected confines of the parent. Internal fertilization also creates the opportunity for a parent to provision resources after those provided within the egg run out. This extra provision appears to occur in many sponges, including those with the greatest cellular complexity. Developing offspring are brooded (held within the parent) for relatively long periods of time, and in some cases the developmental stage that exits the parent includes most of the cell types found in the adult.

Parental provisioning is also found in a means of asexual reproduction employed by many sponges. They form and release a structure called a **gemmule**, which is composed of a rounded mass of food-filled amoebocytes surrounded by a protective layer composed of additional amoebocytes and reinforced by spicules. When a released gemmule encounters favorable conditions, sponge cells emerge from a thin spot and grow into a new sponge.

An aside: Because mitotically active germ cells—the amoebocytes—are spread throughout their body, sponges can also reproduce asexually by fragmentation. Pieces breaking off an existing sponge can regenerate into a physically separate sponge.

Dependent offspring

Although considerable variation exists within the developmental details among different sponge species, there are some intriguing similarities. For example, when reproducing sexually the relatively large single-celled zygote (the cell that results from the fusion of sperm and egg) always undergoes a series of cell divisions to form a ball of smaller cells. The resources initially placed within the egg supports these conversions. The next stage (which can take longer and grow larger in species who brood their offspring) typically involves the conversion of this ball of cells into a motile structure that looks *Proterospongia*-like. Cells on the outside (or most of the outside) sprout flagella, whereas cells that move to the inside (or are located along the backside) do not. Due to the flagellation constraint, these flagellated cells cannot continue to undergo cell division, whereas those tucked away can. There are, however, two striking differences between these motile sponge **larvae** and a *Proterospongia*-like arrangement. First and foremost, sponge larvae do not appear to be feeding structures—their flagellated cells lack collars. As a consequence, parentally supplied resources must power whatever they do. Second, at least in some species, more permanent cell differentiation is beginning to take place. Flagellated cells located externally in larvae tend to move inward and become collar cells lining an internal cavity in a feeding sponge. Nonflagellated cells are the totipotent germ line because they become the generalized amoebocytes that can differentiate into all the other cell types. The term *larvae* is used for this stage of development because this motile structure does not look like a miniature "adult" sponge. After swimming for a couple of hours, sponge larvae come to rest on the bottom. There they develop into a sessile feed and reproducing structure through a series of cell rearrangements and further cell differentiation. Due to the somewhat dramatic nature of the transition between larvae and adult, the term **metamorphosis** is sometimes used to describe it.

A reasonable question is: If these Proterospongia-like larvae cannot feed, why should they continue to be included in the developmental path? The fact that the developmental path of some sponges lacks a flagellated larval stage suggests this step could be eliminated. The key may be dispersal. Motile larvae make it possible for offspring to move away from, and thus not compete with, the parent. Plus, by moving the totipotent cells into an internal space, development can continue during this dispersal period. These cells can continue to divide and even begin to differentiate into different cell types while the flagellated cells on the outside propel the larva along.

The Evolution of Other Animals from Sponges

One difficulty with the idea of animals being a monophyletic group is trying to imagine how other animals could have evolved from a sponge-like beginning. Our view, however, can be clouded by the fact that we tend to compare adult structures, and adult sponges work and look much different than any other type of animal. Evolution within multicellular organisms comes from modifications of repeatable developmental pathways. So the key is to look at what sort of modifications within a typical sponge developmental pathway could have led to the evolution of other types of animals.

Here (as I continue to speculate) I focus on the mobile, nonfeeding, flagellated larvae found in many sponges. In sponges these larvae transform into a sessile feeding and reproducing structure. A plausible developmental twist would be a modification (or series of modifications) that transformed this type of larvae into something that used its mobility to feed in a new way (see Figure 21-13).

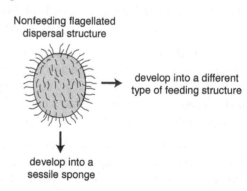

Nonfeeding flagellated dispersal structure

develop into a different type of feeding structure

develop into a sessile sponge

Figure 21-13. A possible branch point in the development pathway commonly found in sponges that could lead to the evolution of other types of animals.

As multicellular heterotrophs, all animals must seek food. Sponges solved that problem by using the beating of many collar cells to bring food particles (suspended in their local aquatic environment) to them. As a consequence, they could be sessile heterotrophs. Alternatively, mobility could be used to move to food items. All that is left is to come up with some means to detect, capture, and digest food items once they are reached—which are by no means trivial problems.

One possible example: Placozoans

One small extant organism moves and feeds in a way that could have plausibly evolved from a sponge-like larval form. It goes by its scientific name, *Trichoplax adhaerans,* and is sufficiently different than any other animal discovered that taxonomists have placed this one species in its own animal phylum—Placozoa.

Let's start with a quick physical description: As an adult, *Trichoplax* is basically a hollow ball formed from a single layer of several thousand cells compressed into a flattened shape about 1 to 2 mm in diameter (see Figure 21-14). Different from sponges, the cells in the outer layer are an epithelium as they are connected by the anchoring junctions called **desmosomes.** This rounded, flat organism has a distinct ventral and dorsal side, but lacks any head or tail region—that is, it lacks an anterior–posterior axis. The ventral epithelium consists of tall cells of two types: flagellated (one flagella per cell) and glandular. Alternatively, the dorsal epithelium consists of flat, flagellated cells. Neither epithelium, however, appears to be hooked to a definitive basement membrane lying underneath. The narrow interstitial space, which, like sponges, is called mesenchyme, is

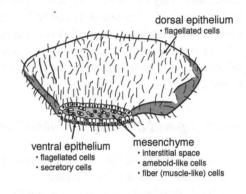

Figure 21-14. The body plan of an adult *Trichoplax adhaerens.*

connective-like tissue, as it contains amoeboid-like cells moving through a gelatinous matrix. It also contains a meshwork of fiber cells that can change the shape of the organism via contraction. This meshwork of fiber cells thus appears to be a primitive form of muscle tissue.

Now comes the interesting question: How does a *Trichoplax* move and feed?

Although little is known about their developmental pathway, the smallest observed trichoplaxes can use their coating of flagellated cells to swim. Normal-sized adults, however, are too large to do so. Instead they use their flagella on their ventral side to crawl along the bottom. So, like many sponge larvae, movement continues to be powered by flagella—it is just that flagella are used in a different way. Plus, the presence of contractile fiber cells (which may play some role in movement) foreshadows the next transition in motility—the use of muscles.

Despite being multicellular, sponges do not capture food any differently than single-celled choanoflagellates. Small food items that stick to the collar (of collar cells) are subsequently enveloped by endocytosis, where they can be broken down further by digestive enzymes. Trichoplaxes are different in that they secrete digestive enzymes into the external environment (instead of into vesicles formed by endocytosis). Specifically, trichoplaxes seem to feed by covering up a small area containing algae, bacteria, protists, and/or other forms of organic matter and then release digestive enzymes along the ventral side into the pocket

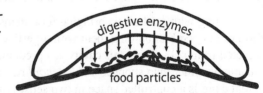

Figure 21-15. A simple cross-sectional sketch showing how Trichoplax could form a pocket with the bottom into which it could release digestive enzymes.

formed between its body and the bottom surface. The organism then absorbs the food items broken into sufficiently small pieces by the action of these enzymes (see Figure 21-15).

Like sponges, trichoplaxes reproduce both asexually and sexually. Because germ cells are spread throughout the organism, trichoplaxes can reproduce asexually by literally breaking into smaller pieces (fission or fragmentation) or by forming round buds that include dorsal, ventral, and mesen-chyme cells. Sexual reproduction seems to occur more when the population becomes dense, as egg production has been observed to greatly increase under these conditions. The details of egg and sperm production, along with postfertilization development are still somewhat unknown.

Perhaps *Trichoplax's* most striking feature is what is still missing in comparison to more familiar animals. For example, they lack any form of specialized excretory, respiratory, or circulatory system. How do they get along with out these? Hopefully, the answer is now obvious. Basically, they are so small, and every cell is in such close proximity to the environment that wastes can be gotten rid of and oxygen and other nutrients can be brought in and distributed without any of these systems. The other striking omission is any form of specialized sensory cells and an accompanying nervous system. Although some forms of cell communication and coordinated behavior must occur for this collection of cells to work as an organism, the degree to which it can respond to environmental changes is surely limited.

Another possible example: Cnidarians

Sea anemones, corals, jellyfish, and hydras represent some of the more familiar adult body forms of the 10,000 or so species of aquatic animals grouped together in the phylum Cnidaria. In terms of structural complexity, only sponges and the single placozoan are simpler. Like *Trichoplax*, most cells are arranged into a continuous epithelium. The most striking new feature is that in cnidarians this whole arrangement invaginates to form a distinct gut cavity. So although part of this continuous epi-thelial layer is still in direct contact with external environment (and basically forms the outside cover-ing of the organism), the rest that surrounds the gut cavity is tucked inside the organism. The interac-tion of the cells lining the gut cavity with the external environment is thus limited to what moves in and out of the gut cavity's external opening—the mouth. As a consequence, this inner layer surround-ing the gut, known as **endoderm**, has specialized in ways that facilitate the digestion and absorption of nutrients. On the other hand, the outer layer, known as **ectoderm** (or epidermis), has specialized in ways that facilitate both its protection from and its interaction with the external environment. In total, cnidarians are commonly referred to as having a two-layered body plan —two specialized forms of epithelium with only a narrow interstitial space sand-wiched in between (see Figure 21-16). In contrast, *Trichoplax* is basically a one-layered organism. In some cnidarians, abutting basement membranes fill most of this narrow interstitial space. In others, some additional connective-like tissue exists as a few cells wander around in a gel-like matrix. In cnidarians, the con-tents of the interstitial space are referred to as **mesoglea**.

Starting with cnidarians, bringing food items into some form of gut and bombarding them with digestive enzymes secreted from cells lining this cavity is a predominant theme in all animals other than sponges and *Trichoplax*. The advantage is that a gut is a controlled space in two senses of the word: First, any form of gut opens to the outside world through a mouth, which can exercise some control of what passes into the gut. Second, like the cellular invaginations discussed in Chapter

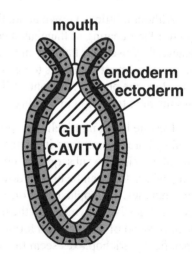

Figure 21-16. A simple cross-sec-tional sketch showing the two-lay-ered body plan found in cnidarians.

17, a multicellular gut creates a controlled space that allow the organism to absorb essentially all the nutrients made available by the action of the digestive enzymes that it released.

In addition to a gut cavity, cnidarians also have more specialized cell types, including specialized sensory cells, nerve cells, and a cell type unique to this phylum called cnidocysts —which are the stinging cells used in prey capture and protection. The "stinging" part of these cells is called a nematocyst, which discharges a small spiny harpoon-like structure (that is often accompanied by some form of toxin) on contact and/or chemical stimulation. And although most cnidarians do not have distinct muscle cells, all cnidarians have cells referred to as epitheliomuscular cells mentioned in the previous chapter. Basically, the base of certain epithelial cells in both the ectoderm and endoderm extends out in a long fibrous arrangement that is able to contract (due to the arrangement of actin and myosin).

Still missing in cnidarians are any distinct forms of excretory, respiratory, or circulatory systems. At first glance this can be puzzling, given the fact that many cnidarians grow to a large size. For example, the jellyfish *Physalia pelagica* has been reported to have individuals up to 13 meters long. However, it all boils down to the two-layered arrangement. In a two-layered arrangement every cell has sufficient access to external environment to get its needed inputs and to get rid of its outputs without any of the aforementioned systems.

An evolutionary scenario

So now let's get back to the task at hand: How could cnidarians have ever evolved from sponge-like beginnings, given that the adult forms are extremely different? Again the key appears to be to look earlier in cnidarians developmental pathways at a free-swimming larval structure called a **planula**. Planula, like many sponge larvae, are small oblong structures whose outer covering is composed of cells bearing single flagella. The potential connection is thus a transition from a nonfeeding sponge-like larva to something that feeds in a manner that could give rise to the cnidarians. More than a century ago (in 1875) a German biologist named Earnst Haeckel came up with an interesting scenario of how this could occur. His suggestion started with some type of sponge-like larva establishing an anterior–posterior axis by maintaining a forward (anterior) end as it swims (versus somewhat tumbling through the water). Note that a preferred swimming direction is observed in extant sponge larvae. Swimming is this way would subsequently set the stage for a new feeding mode as anterior cells could retain their locomotory role, whereas posterior cells could differentiate into food-acquiring, digesting cells. The assumption was that food particles encountered while moving through the water would more readily stick to the leeward side (i.e., the posterior end), increasing their opportunity to be assimilated. Furthermore, creating a pocket (by invagination) on the posterior end may help retain even more and larger food particles (see Figure 21-17). Such a pocket would, of course, be the beginning of

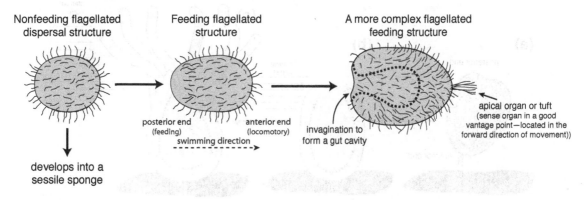

Figure 21-17. A possible transition from a sponge-like larva into a flagellated feeding structure. (see text for more details).

536   Chapter 21

a gut cavity. (Note: Although I have yet to find a detailed description of how feeding actually occurs, the fact that some forms of *feeding* planula undergo gastrulation—the formation of a two-layered organism—via invagination at the posterior end to form a gut cavity supports the preceding scenario. The opening formed by this invagination is called a **blastopore**.)

An anteriorly positioned sensory structure called an **apical tuft** is a common feature of cnidarian planula larvae. The evolution of an apical tuft accompanied the development of a flagellated structure that took advantage of a preferred swimming direction to feed. The front of the forward direction of movement is a good vantage point to gather sensory information. To take full advantage of increased sensory input, however, required some means to transmit information gathered to distant places in the body. So the evolution of nerve cells (which can be arranged into nervous systems) accompanying the evolution of apical tufts, or other forms of specialized sensory cells, would also make sense. And to add one more step, the ability of nerve cells to quickly conduct signals make them the perfect partner to muscle-like cells, such as the epitheliomuscular cells mentioned earlier. A nerve-cell-created link between specialized sensory cells and muscle-like cells positioned elsewhere in the body would allow an organism to respond to certain types of sensory input by quickly changing some component of its body shape. The fact that all animals except sponges and *Trichoplax* use nervous systems to control and coordinate muscle contraction is a testament to the usefulness of such arrangement. And perhaps more to the point, nervous systems are known to begin to form in cnidarian planula larvae.

Suppose that everything suggested here is true: Some form of sponge-like larvae evolved into a reproducing organism that used flagella to power swimming, used a posterior gut cavity to feed, and gathered sensory information through an apical tuft connected to a primitive nervous system. What might happen next? One problem that could continue to push evolution is that feeding success can translate into growth, and growth invariably makes it impossible for flagella to continue to power swimming. So this problem is either continually averted by reproducing before this size threshold is reached (and planulas giving rise to other planulas by asexual reproduction is known to occur), or something new is added on to the end of this evolving developmental pathway. Here, of course, I explore the addition of a new step, which starts with the organism sinking to the bottom.

To mimic extant cnidarians, assume the organism comes to rest along the bottom in a headstand position. In other words, its anterior end is next to the bottom and its posterior end, with the opening to the gut cavity, positioned upward (see Figure 21-18(a)). Whether such an arrangement could continue to feed depends on the interaction of two things: what food items are currently available in the environment, and how could this arrangement capture the available food supply.

Given that we are speculating that this occurred early in the evolution of animals, larger mobile animals like fish and invertebrates such as crustaceans would not have been present. Instead the po-

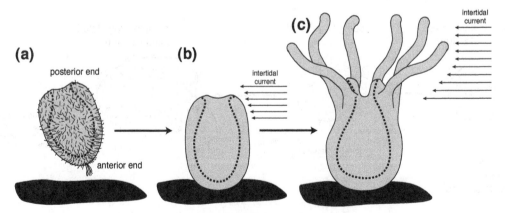

Figure 21-18. A possible transition from a flagellated feeding structure that sinks to the bottom because it grows to large to be powered by flagella to a sessile feeding polyp. (see text for more details).

tential fare would likely include bacteria, single-celled eukaryotic organisms, and perhaps some larger colonial or multicellular arrangements such as sponge-like larval forms and simple forms of algae. Could sufficient amounts of these types of potential food items be captured? Although some form of muscle-like contractile fibers may have been present and hooked to specialized sensory cells via a nervous system, it seems unlikely that an organism that just sank to the bottom would come equipped with a sufficiently sophisticated sensorimotor system to detect and capture prey while simultaneously coordinating movement. Yet how could such an arrangement feed if it was basically confined to stay in one place? One option would have been to use the moon to bring food to it. Tides are generated by the gravitational interaction between the earth and the moon, and as I have already mentioned, the in and out movement of the tides creates a nearly constant current in the shallower areas of the ocean—known as the intertidal zone. Earlier, the posterior end of this organism was postulated to have taken advantage of the current created by swimming to specialize in food capture and digestion. A bottom-end-up arrangement positioned such that it is sticking out into the intertidal current may be able to do essentially the same thing (see Figure 21-18(b)). And if so, any subsequent change in the posterior end's shape that increased the food-collecting surface area (while minimizing the increase in volume that needs to be fed) would be advantageous. In other words, sprouting tentacle-shaped convolutions to the posterior end surrounding the opening to the gut cavity would seemingly be favored by natural selection. These tentacle-shape projections would potentially intersect food items brought in from any direction by a turbulent, swirling current. A plausible next evolutionary step would then be to gain better control over the movement of these tentacle-like structures so that they could be used more effectively in food capture. This may have even set the stage for a nervous system capable of orchestrating more complex behaviors to first evolve. Tentacles that could work together in a coordinated way would seemingly facilitate their use in feeding.

The preceding scenario is particularly intriguing because it gives rise to a **radially symmetric** arrangement, known as a **polyp** (see Figure 21-18(c)), seen in many present-day adult cnidarians. (Note: Polyps are considered to be radially symmetrical because if you rotate a polyp around its anterior–posterior axis, the appearance of the organism basically stays the same. Or stated differently, a radially symmetric organism can be sliced in half anywhere along one axis, and the two resultant halves would essentially be mirror images of each other.) The only major feature found in modern cnidarians still missing in our evolutionary scenario is stinging cells, which would become increasingly useful as potential prey became more active and thus more difficult to capture. Otherwise we have begun to sketch out the basic life cycle of the group of cnidarians, called the anthozoans, which evidence suggests to be the most ancient cnidarian group. (Note: All the different species of sea anemones, with their polyp-shaped adult forms, are anthozoans.) This life cycle consists of feeding planula larvae that eventually settle to the bottom and develop into polyps, which, in addition to continuing to feed, produce sperm and eggs. Whenever fertilization occurs, the zygote begins to undergo cell division and eventually develops into a planula larva, and so on. This, of course, does not mean that all anthozoans have this exact life cycle. For example, many anthozoans have nonfeeding planula larvae, which should be expected. An emerging theme is that once a developmental pathway is in place, any modification in parental behavior that increases the success with which their offspring grow up to be parents in the next generation will be favored by natural selection. One option is to increase egg size. When offspring start off with more parentally supplied resources, they will be able to develop further before they need to forage on their own. Why haven't all anthozoans increased their initial investment per offspring? Because increasing investment per offspring comes with a trade-off—fewer offspring will be able to be produced. And whether reproductive success is maximized by producing fewer, more expensive offspring, or a greater number of cheaper offspring, depends on each species ecological circumstance. It could go either way.

Cnidarian evolution seems to have used a form of asexual reproduction known as budding to take more twists and turns. Budding occurs when a new polyp starts to grow out of the base of an existing polyp. The most important twist came when the budding polyps began to stay together to form a polyp colony (see Figure 21-19). To start, polyp colonies made it possible for a small polyp to grow into a larger organism. For example, corals are a group within the anthozoans that have tiny polyps but become larger by forming polyp colonies. In fact, many stony corals are able to grow to an extremely large size without collapsing due to the secretion of a hard external skeleton composed of calcium carbonate.

The next evolutionary twist enabled by polyp colonies introduces a theme that we discuss more later in this chapter. Polyp colonies are simply a larger organism made out of a modular growth—that is, an organism gets larger by repeating a component of a developmental pathway over and over. Modular growth sets the stage for different modules to differentiate to perform different functions. The basic idea is no different than cells that hang together differentiating to perform more specialized but complementary functions. For example, in some polyp colonies, certain polyps specialize in feeding (feeding polyps), whereas others specialize in sexual reproduction (reproductive polyps).

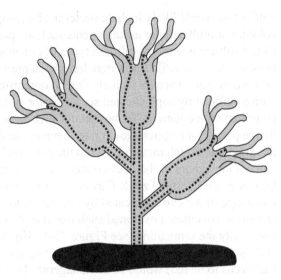

Figure 21-19. Polyps that remain together after budding can form a polyp colony. In some cases polyps differentiate to play distinct roles (e.g., feeding polyps, reproductive polyps).

There is still one feature found in certain extant cnidarian life cycles that has yet to arise from this exercise in evolutionary speculation—the structure that you know as a **jellyfish** and biologists call a **medusa**. Curiously, all types of jellyfish specialize in the production of either sperm or eggs. So later I combine this fact with the evolution of reproductive polyps within polyp colonies to add the evolution of jellyfish to our evolutionary tale.

This continuing saga starts with the question: How are sperm produced by a reproductive polyp in one colony able to find and fuse with eggs produced by a reproductive polyp in a different colony? Clearly in an aquatic environment flagellated sperm can swim. Recall, however, that single flagellated cells cannot move very fast or very far, so outcrossing—mating with another individual—will tend to occur only with individuals in close proximity. The stage is thus set for any individual that came up with a better means to transport sperm or even eggs to increase its reproductive success. But what other means of transport are available to a sessile organism? Suppose that instead of directly forming sperm or eggs, one individual's reproductive polyps started to form polyp-like buds that separated

from the colony and floated away by passive drifting. Sperm or eggs (or perhaps both) could then form in these separated structures and be released some distance from the sessile polyp colony. Assuming that it would win the reproductive race of natural selection, this reproductive strategy would then spread quickly through the population. And once that occurs the question becomes: How could this reproductive strategy be improved even further? Perhaps these floating structures could come up with some means to propel themselves. Maybe with time these separating polyp-like structures flipped over so that the mouth and the tentacles faced downward and floated off using a

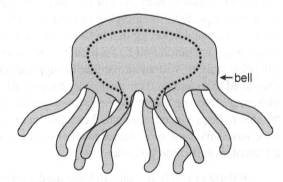

Figure 21-20. A jellyfish or medusa is basically a free floating inverted polyp that can swims by alternatively contracting and relaxing the bell.

combination of passive drifting and rhythmic contractions of the umbrella-shaped body known as the bell. Sound familiar? This is a **jellyfish** or a **medusa**, which in terms of its basic body plan is just an

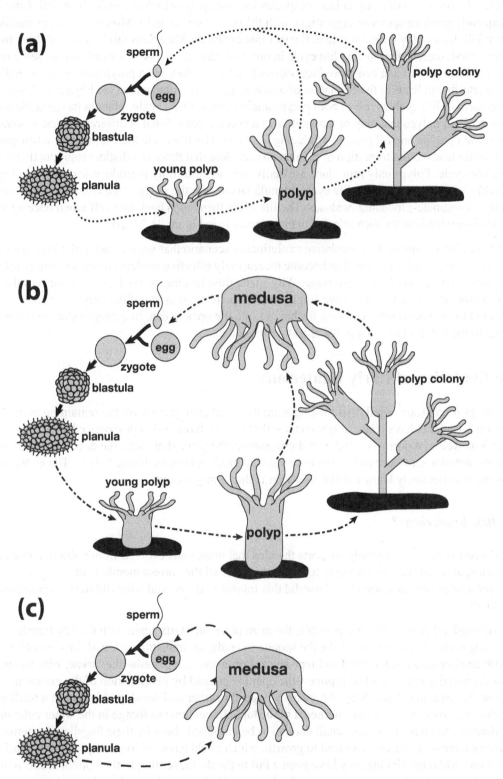

Figure 21-21. The three basic forms of life cycles found in cnidarians. While all three life cycles include planula larvae, they differ in terms of their inclusion of polyps and medusas: (a) has only polyps, (b) has both polyps and medusas, and (c) has only medusas. (See text for more details.)

inverted polyp (see Figure 21-20). Rhythmically swimming medusas may have been the first thing that ever used a nervous system hooked to muscle-like cells to power movement.

That the life cycle of many cnidarian species includes polyps budding off to form jellyfish that subsequently produce sperm or eggs aligns with the preceding scenario. Moreover, polyps budding off to form jellyfishes play a central role in the fact that cnidarian life cycles fall into one of three basic patterns. First, there is the starting life cycle in our evolutionary scenario: Planula larvae settle on the bottom to form polyps that can reproduce asexually (at times forming a polyp colony) or sexually, and gamete-fusion leads to the formation of a new round of planula larvae (see Figure 21-21(a)). The second form of life cycle involves both polyps and medusas. Once again, planula larvae settle on the bottom to form polyps that may or may not form a polyp colony. What is different is that at some point certain polyps bud off gamete-producing medusas. The life cycle then starts over when gamete-fusion again leads to the formation of planula larvae. Note that there is a distinct reproductive division in this life cycle: Polyps only reproduce asexually, and medusas only reproduce sexually (see Figure 21-21(b)). In the final cnidarian life cycle, planula larvae skip the polyp stage completely and develop directly into gamete-producing medusas. The life cycle then loops back on itself when once again gamete-fusion leads to the formation of planula larvae (see Figure 21-21(c)).

I have already outlined a speculative evolutionary scenario that would lead to the first two of these life cycles. Medusa stages that become increasingly effective feeders would seemingly set the stage for the reduction of the polyp stage. Why spend time feeding as a polyp if a medusa of the same size is a more effective feeder? Interestingly, the complete elimination of the polyp stage seems to be connected to medusa stages venturing further out into the open ocean. In a deep-water environment, settling to the bottom to form a polyp is just not possible.

The Evolution of Early Bilaterians

Except for a group of jellyfish-looking animals called ctenophores, all the remaining animals found on this planet have bilateral symmetry—that is, they have both a pronounced anterior–posterior axis as well as a dorsal–ventral axis. Furthermore, the plane that slices the dorsal–ventral midline along the anterior–posterior axis is the only one that produces mirror-image halves. The evolution of the animals collectively known as the **Bilateria** is thus a major event.

The first bilaterians?

Molecular evidence strongly supports the idea that bilaterians evolved from radially constructed organisms, and that they are monophyletic—that is, that all the current members of this group share a common bilaterian ancestor. If so, how did this transition occur, and what did the common ancestor look like?

Although other scenarios are possible, the most plausible starts again with the key transitions happening early in development. Like the sponge to cnidarian transition, a larval form would come up with an alternative way to feed and reproduce. For instance, a planula-like larvae, with an apical tuft at the anterior end and a **blastopore**—the opening created by invagination of the gut cavity—at the posterior end, may have skipped the polyp stage altogether and developed into both a feeding and reproducing structure, sometimes termed a **planuloid**. To continue to forage in the water column, planuloids would have to remain small enough to be propelled about by their flagellated exterior. But as we have seen, success can lead to growth, which could have led to some planuloids settling to the bottom. Although sinking may have been a fall to the death, settling to the bottom seems to have repeatedly opened a door to innovation in the history of Life (i.e., choanoflagellate colonies becoming sponges, sponge-like larvae becoming placozoans or cnidarian polyps). Each time the result was different largely because the history and resultant features of the settling organisms was different. In this case a planuloid would have seemingly been a small elongated organism with a distinct anterior–posterior axis.

The question then becomes how could such an organism make a living? If it were to move about on flagella power like a placozoan, instead of becoming sessile like sponges and polyps, it would presumably take advantage of its anterior sensory end to lead the way. But then food items encountered would have to have been somehow shuttled into the gut cavity opening positioned at the posterior or trailing end. Although this posterior position of the blastopore may have worked well while swimming, when crawling, moving the opening forward could have been advantageous. For instance, shifting it forward along one side would have allowed the mouth to be positioned right on top of food items found along the bottom. Tucking the blastopore to one side would also introduce a fundamental shift in the organism's symmetry. A dorsal–ventral axis, with the position of the blastopore defining the ventral side, would be added to the already existing anterior–posterior one. In essence, the organism would become bilateral (see Figure 21-22). Subsequent changes may have made it even more so. Specifically, the ventral side would be expected to flatten out to stabilize the organism—that is, to keep the organism from rolling onto a nonblastopore side—and to increase the efficiency of flagella-powered motion by increasing the surface area in contact with the bottom.

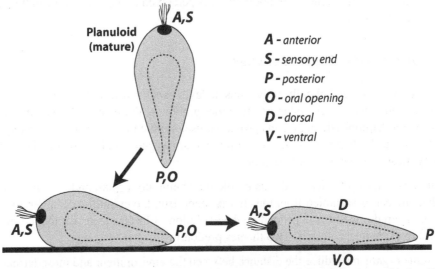

Figure 21-22. A possible set of evolutionary transitions between a radially symmetric cnidarian-like larvae (a planula) and bottom-dwelling bilaterally symmetrical organism that resembles an acoelomorph flatworm. The steps are: (1) a developing organism becoming a sexually mature organism while retaining its basic larval form (so the previous adult stage is skipped), (2) the organism settling to the bottom, and (3) the oral opening or mouth shifts to one side to form a dorsal-ventral axis. (See text for more details.)

Interestingly, the basic design just described—a small flattened flagella-powered worm-like organism with an opening to a gut cavity located on the ventral side—resembles an extant group of organisms known as the **acoelomorph flatworms**. Acoelomorph flatworms have long been considered the most primitive forms of bilaterian animals, and recent molecular evidence supports this view. In other words, acoelomorph flatworms may be structurally very similar to the first bilaterian organisms (that subsequently became the last common ancestor of all bilaterian animals—including acoelomorph flatworms).

In addition to that already discussed, the structure of acoelomorph flatworms hints at two additional changes that showed up early in bilaterian evolution. One is a distinct third tissue layer sandwiched between ectoderm and endoderm known as **mesoderm**. In other words, all bilaterians are three-layered or **triploblastic** organisms. This third layer in acoelomorph flatworms largely consists of myocytes or muscle cells. Curiously, these muscle cells are not used to actually power movement per se—forward movement is still powered by the numerous flagella along the ventral side—but are used for turning and steering movements. In other words, they make adjustments in body shape possible that help these organisms navigate. The evolution of a muscular third layer in bilaterians did, however, set the stage for an increasing commitment to muscle-powered movement, along with increasing the support structure needed to maintain an organism's shape and provide mechanical resistance against which muscles could act. In fact, the basic makeup of this third layer across bilaterians is muscle cell arrangements wrapped in connective tissue and generally attached to some form of skeleton (all of which was discussed in the previous chapter). In contrast to the epitheliomuscular cells found in cnidarians, the development of distinct muscle cells and skeletons expanded both the means and the power with which muscle contraction could change body shape.

The nervous system also underwent fundamental changes. In sessile adult cnidarians the nervous system is generally spread throughout their radially symmetric bodies in a diffuse arrangement known as a nerve net. In contrast, the nervous tissue in mobile acoelomorph flatworms, as well as all other bilaterians, accumulates near the predominant sensory area (the front end) to form a head region with a "brain"—a process known as **cephalization**. One or more larger nerve cords running along the anterior–posterior axis commonly connects the brain to the rest of the body, or more specifically to mesoderm muscle cells throughout the body. What is perceived at the front end can thus quickly affect muscles further back in the body.

Adding features that enhance exchange

The evolution of a metabolically active muscle layer separated from the environment by ectoderm on one side and endoderm on the other creates other problems. For example, given the slowness of diffusion, how could triploblastic organisms provide muscle tissue tucked inside with adequate supplies of nutrients, such as high-energy molecules or molecular oxygen? Or, how would the metabolic waste generated by muscle tissue be able to escape?

Acoelomorph flatworms deal with this problem by being both small and flat, thus minimizing the distance that any cell is separated from the environment. But, the evolution of larger and different-shaped three-layered organisms depended on the evolution of faster means for the mesoderm and the environment to exchange materials. Two themes predominate.

First, some organisms reduce the distance between the environment and mesodermal tissue by forming many small invaginations in the ectoderm that open into branching channels that permeate the mesoderm. Although convection may play a role in moving things into and out of these channels, commonly concentration gradients and diffusion are the sole means to power movement (see Figure 21-23). Some examples include the respiratory system in insects—which is involved in moving oxygen in, and carbon dioxide out—and the excretory system in flukes and turbellarian flatworms. Any form of *excretory system can be thought of as a mesoderm drain* for water-soluble waste products. (Note: Based on certain morphologically similarities, acoelomorph flatworms were once thought to be closely related to both flukes and turbellarian flatworms. However, new molecular data along with reinterpretation of morphological features support splitting these groups up. As discussed earlier, the acoelomorph flatworms seem to be the earliest extant group of bilaterians, whereas these other groups evolved later.)

Figure 21-23. In some organisms diffusion limits are countered by filling the mesoderm with branching channels that open to the outside. For example, in insects oxygen moves in and carbon dioxide moves out through branching channels called trachea.

The second theme starts with some form of circulatory system. Described most generally, a circulatory system is some form of convection system that continually stirs the interstitial fluid surrounding mesodermal cells. Commonly, the pressure gradient needed for convective flow is generated by chamber-and-value pumps such as found in hearts, and the movement of fluids is at least somewhat confined to tubes known generically as blood vessels. Circulation near any outside permeable surface makes exchange between the environment and the blood possible, which in turn creates an avenue for materials to move both to and from deeper tissues. In some animals the entire outer body functions as such an exchange surface. In others, some form of circulatory system works in conjunction with a specialized region to exchange materials with the environment. For example, in many animals high-energy molecules move into circulation after they pass through the gut's absorptive region, and then the circulatory system distributes these molecules to cells

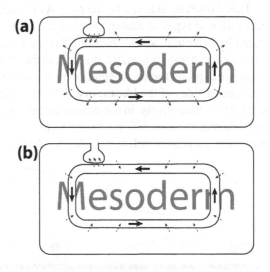

Figure 21-24. In some organisms diffusion limits are countered by combining a circulatory system with a specialized area of exchange. (See text for more details.)

throughout the body. Similarly, molecular oxygen moving through the exchange epithelium found in specialized respiratory organs such as lungs or gills is moved elsewhere in the body by a circulatory system (see Figure 21-24(a)). On the other hand, some types of excretory systems use circulation to run this scenario in reverse. The circulatory system brings water-soluble waste products produced by cells throughout the body to a place that specializes in their removal (see Figure 21-24(b)). For example, your two kidneys filter water-soluble waste products picked up by your blood and then dump these wastes into your bladder, where eventually they will released to the outside through a single opening.

Gut cavities to gut tubes

The other major rearrangement associated with the evolution of most bilaterians has to do with the gut. Although acoelomorph flatworms have a gut cavity with a ventral opening, other bilaterians typically have a gut tube instead (although there are a few exceptions). With two openings, food flows into the gut cavity through the mouth, and the indigestible remains exit through the anus. This one-way flow allows for more efficient digestion and absorption because food still to be processed never mixes with indigestible wastes. Furthermore, the mouth is typically located anteriorly, which means it is close to the major sensory area. When moving to capture prey, placing both the means to detect prey and the entrance to the digestive tract near the front end makes sense. On the other hand, the anus is typically located more posteriorly, allowing wastes to literally be left behind. So like cnidarians, a posterior opening to the gut is still commonly present, it is just not where food enters.

How did a single-opening gut cavity evolve into two separate openings? Furthermore, how did the mouth and the predominant sensory structures ever get together on the front end? Presumably the underlying developmental means by which heads and complete digestive tracts form would be shared by all bilaterians with a gut tube. That is, the basic developmental path to form a gut tube with an anteriorly located mouth would have evolved once, and this would have been the ancestral pathway from which all other bilaterians with a gut tube evolved.

This, however, may not be the case. As researchers have explored the developmental pathways of many different types of bilaterians, they have found a two-opening gut tube coupled with an anteriorly located brain form in at least two fundamentally different ways. In fact these developmental differences are used to divide bilaterians into two major groups: the **Protostomes** and the **Deuterostomes**. In the ancestral protostomes, an anterior mouth and a posterior anus is thought to have formed by fusion of the lateral sides of the **blastopore**—the opening created by invagination of the gut cavity (see Figure 21-25). Alternatively, in the deuterostome ancestor the blastopore is thought to have become the anus, whereas the mouth forms by the formation of a new anterior opening into the gut cavity. (Note: *Protostome* means "mouth first," whereas *deuterostome* means "mouth second.")

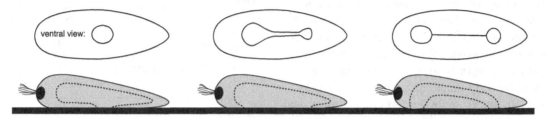

Figure 21-25. The basic scheme by which ancestral protostomes are thought to have converted a gut cavity with a ventral opening to a gut tube. (See text for more details.)

Interestingly, these developmental differences, along with molecular and other forms of evidence, suggest that the evolutionary branch point that divided protostomes and deuterostomes occurred extremely early in the evolution of bilaterians. This raises the question: Was the common ancestor of protostomes and deuterostomes a bilaterian, likely resembling acoelomorph flatworms, or did each group evolve independently from a radially symmetric ancestor? Claus Nielsen, a longtime student of the early evolution of animals, states in his book *Animal Evolution* that "I have earlier speculated that the bilateral protostomes and deuterostomes could have evolved independently from a radial common ancestor because the morphological and embryological differences between these two groups are so considerable, but new evidence from molecular studies has convinced me that there must have been a common bilaterian ancestor. The morphology of this ancestor is (however) difficult to visualize . . ." This is another way of saying that it is difficult to imagine a bilaterian developmental pathway that set the stage to branch off in both the protostome and deuterostome directions. It is also difficult to imagine what the body plan of the organism that arose from such a pathway would look like.

Using molecular evidence

Consider a mouse (a deuterostome) and a fly (a protostome). Do they seem much the same? At first glance I think most of us would say no. In fact, some may argue that they look worlds apart. Yet there are fundamental similarities. They both share all the bilaterian features discussed far: a head and tail, a front and a back, muscles tucked to the inside (a mesoderm), and some form of circulatory system. But there are other similarities as well, such as both having eyes and legs. When it comes down to it, the differences are really in the details. For instance, although both have eyes, a mouse has a single pair of movable eyes, whereas flies have compound eyes composed of hundreds of individual units, each staring out from a fixed position. Similarly, mice have four legs made sturdy by internal bones, whereas flies have six thin legs held up by a jointed exoskeleton. And we could keep going down the list. So although similarities existed, the differences seemed so profound that it was always assumed that each type of eye, leg, head, or anything else was constructed in fundamentally different ways. It was thus a big surprise when biologists found remarkably similar genes playing remarkably similar body-building roles in animals as dissimilar as mice and flies (along with everything else). Furthermore, the type of genes shared provided a new vantage point from which to glimpse at what the common ancestor of protostomes and deuterostomes looked like. To explain this, however, requires establishing some needed background.

Gene duplication

Sometimes, due to a replication error such as unequal crossing during meiosis, a second copy of a gene or even genes can be added to a chromosome (see Figure 21-26). Gene duplication can also occur by other means. Whatever the mechanism, the downside of gene duplication is that there is now more DNA to be replicated. But a second copy of a gene can also have potential benefits. We mentioned in the previous chapter the idea that a second copy can serve as a backup—a debilitating genetic error could happen to one copy, and the cell would still have a functional copy. Let's add two more potential advantages to the list.

First, suppose some important cellular process is operating below its optimal rate despite the fact that a gene that codes for the rate-limiting gene product is being transcribed as fast as possible. If so, a duplication event that added another copy of the gene would be favored by natural selection. With two (or more) copies of the same gene being transcribed simultaneously the rate-limiting gene product could be produced more quickly. Depending on the optimal rate, it may even be the case that additional duplication events would also be favored to persist.

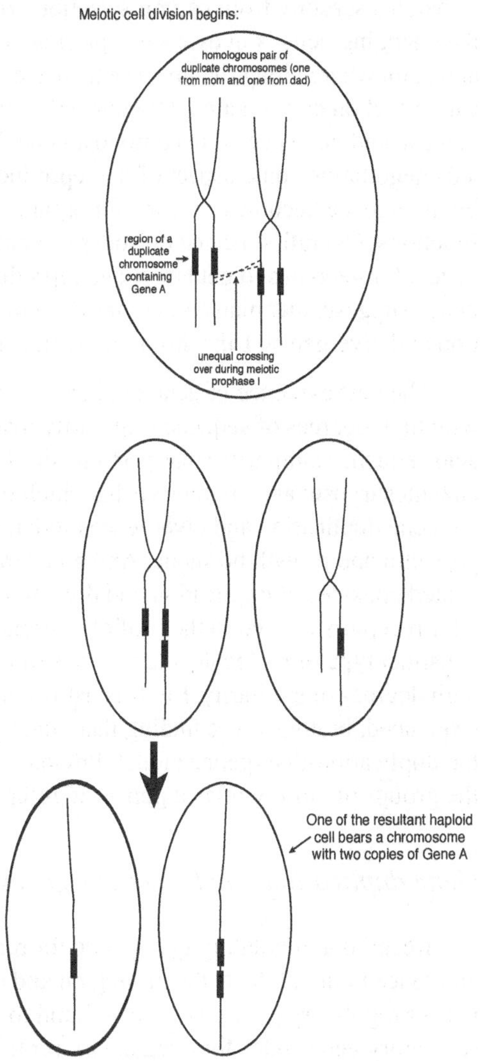

The genes that code for ribosomal RNA appear to be a common example of this phenomenon. Because a ribosome is involved in every instance of protein synthesis, cells need lots of them. In fact, it seems that commonly a cell's optimum number of ribosomes is greater than the number potentially maintained by a single copy of each rRNA gene. Multiple copies of rRNA genes have been found in many organisms. For example, *Esherichia coli*, an intestinal bacterium that has been mentioned before, seems to have around 5 to 10 copies of rRNA genes. The fruit fly *Drosophilia melanogaster* has been estimated to have around 130 copies of rRNA genes.

Figure 21-26. Uneven crossing over during meiosis can result in a gene (or genes) being duplicated in one of the resultant haploid

The second advantage comes into focus when one looks at the other side of a story. So far we saw that a duplicated gene makes it possible for a cell to survive disruption to an essential gene because a backup is present. In other words, we focused on the good copy of the gene that remained. But what about the gene copy that suffered the genetic error? For any cell with a single copy of an essential gene, only mutations that improve on its already needed function would be expected to persist. But a second copy creates a gene that can potentially persist despite suffering a deleterious mutation. If it is unneeded the fact that it does not now code for anything positive makes little difference. It can even mutate again and again and potentially still remain within the genome across generations. In other words, an unneeded duplicate gene can diverge from its starting functional form without facing nearly as harsh a scrutiny from natural selection. Yet with the introduction of each new (random) mutation, the changing gene is in essence exploring genetic space. A string of novel sequences are being formed, and somewhere along the line a sequence could again emerge that codes for a protein with a significant effect on cell function. Of course this effect could be negative, and if so this evolutionary experiment would be expected to come to an end. Yet this novel protein could also impart a new ability that aids negotiating some aspect of the reproductive obstacle course. In such cases, duplication followed by divergence becomes a means for organisms to evolve new genes that code for novel and useful functions. Overall, repeated episodes of gene duplication followed by divergence generate a simple means for genomes to get larger and reproductive performances to become more complex. In fact, evidence suggests that many—perhaps even most—genes present in all organisms arose through duplication and divergence. Like different organisms, different genes can share a common ancestor.

The best evidence of gene duplication and divergence comes from examples of two or more genes with high degrees of sequence similarity that code for proteins (that also have high degrees of amino acid sequence similarity) that perform similar but not identical functions. For example, the digestive enzymes trypsin and chymotrypsin, which perform slightly different aspects of protein digestion, fit the gene duplication and divergence model. So do the genes that code for two hormones known as prolactin and growth hormone. And on a larger scale, sequence evidence also supports the idea that repeated episodes of duplication and divergence generated the entire family of a thousand or so distinct odor receptors located in the roof of your nasal cavity. Although each distinct odor receptor binds with a distinct type of molecule, the portions of the amino acid sequence of each of these receptors show high degrees of similarity. But this list is only scratching the surface. As more and more DNA gets sequenced, biologists are finding that many genes show patterns of similarity (and difference) that fit the duplication-divergence model. Phylogenies for groups of genes are even being constructed, and the groups of closely related genes are referred to as **gene families**.

Gene duplication and homeobox genes

Recall that regulatory genes code for proteins that bind to particular sequences of two-sided DNA and, once bound, affects the turning on and off of surrounding genes. Curiously, many developmental master regulatory genes have been found to share a basic similarity. (Note: A developmental master regulatory gene codes for a regulatory protein that regulates a whole suite of other genes, which in turn influence the developmental fate of the region or regions of a developing organism in which expression occurs.) They all have a 180-base pair region that encodes the portion of the protein—60 amino acids in total—that directly binds with the DNA. (A review question: Why would a 180-base pair region of DNA code for 60 amino acids?) The 180-base sequence has been termed the **homeobox**, and the 60-amino acid sequence that it codes for is called the **homeodomain**. Furthermore, although the homeobox sequences among these genes are not identical, they are similar enough to suggest that they all share a common ancestor. That is, they arose by gene duplication followed by divergence. That the homeobox sequence has been relatively conserved across many rounds of duplication and divergence makes sense because any major alteration could easily disrupt the encoded protein's ability to bind to DNA at all, completely disrupting the protein's ability to serve a regulatory function. Most likely, loss of regulatory function would have been strongly selected against.

As would be expected within any group sharing a common ancestor, there will be even smaller clusters of increased similarity. Here is where semantics can be confusing. The whole set of homeobox-bearing regulatory genes could be considered a gene family, and these smaller clusters subfamilies. Alternatively, the entire set of homeobox genes could be considered a group comprised of different gene families. I have seen it both ways, but will use the family/subfamily distinction because it seems to conjure up a better phylogenetic image. Overall, there may be two dozen or so distinct subfamilies within the homeobox gene family. Next I discuss genes belonging to four of them in which members have been found in both the protostomes and deuterostomes lines, suggesting that they had evolved prior to the last common ancestor of both groups.

The Hox subfamily

Members of what have been called the *Hox* family were the first homeobox genes to be discovered in animals. They were first found in the fruit fly *Drosophila melanogaster* in 1983. More specifically, *Drosophila* was found to have a set of eight *Hox* genes expressed during the early stages of development in a distinct pattern along the head-to-tail (anterior–posterior) axis (see Figure 21-27). This expression pattern of regulatory genes, consequently, creates a distinct pattern of what other genes are turned on or off along this body axis; this in turn triggers different regions along this axis to develop differently. In other words, differential expression of these *Hox* developmental master regulatory genes plays an impor-

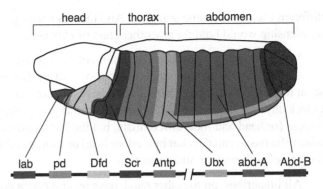

Figure 21-27. A Drosophila embryo showing the expression pattern of eight regulatory gene, known as homeotic genes, along the anterior-posterior axis. These eight genes are all found on one chromosome (chromosome 3) in two clusters. The first cluster known as the **Antennapedia complex** contains the genes labial (lab), proboscipedia (pb), De-formed (Dfd), Sex comb reduced (Scr) and Antennapedia (Antp). The second cluster known as the **Bithorax complex** contains the genes Ultrabithorax (Ubx), admoninal A (adb-A) and Abdominal-B (Abd-B). Note that the position along the chromosome of these eight genes aligns with the position along the anterior-posterior axis in which these genes are expressed.

tant role in getting one end to develop into a head, the other to develop into a tail, and the right parts to develop in the right place in the middle. Curiously, these eight genes are found in two clusters on one of Drosophila's four chromosomes, and the order of their arrangement largely parallels the order in which they are expressed along the anterior–posterior axis. Although the significance of this finding is not yet completely understood, the similarity or colinearity of these two sequences being due to chance alone is quite slim.

The discovery of *Hox* genes in *Drosophila* subsequently set into motion a remarkable discovery— *Hox* genes have been found within the genomes of every animal that has been looked at. Sponges, which grow by accretion and therefore lack a primary body axis, seem to have only one. In contrast, clusters of more than one *Hox* gene are found in organisms that grow along a fixed primary axis— that is, where the relative relationship among structures along this axis is preserved during growth. In cnidarians the fixed primary axis is top to bottom (where the top here is defined by the presence of a mouth), where it is the anterior to posterior axis in bilaterians. Coincidence? Not likely. As first found in *Drosophila*, the evidence suggests a long history of *Hox* genes being master regulatory genes involved in delimiting the primary axis in animals. In fact, the evidence suggests that the original *Hox* clusters predated the cnidarian–bilaterian split.

Presumably this increased number of *Hox* genes within organisms arose from the primordial *Hox* gene undergoing rounds of duplication and diversification. If so, some genes within any *Hox* cluster would be expected to be more similar to some than to others, due to sharing a more recent common ancestor—that is, the duplication event occurred more recently. As *Hox* gene sequences both within and across organisms have been compared and contrasted, four reasonably distinct classes—known as *anterior*, *gene-3*, *central*, and *posterior*—have been identified. Besides *gene-3*, which is a somewhat odd and harder to understand class, the three names are descriptive of their expression pattern within an organism. In other words, groups based on sequence similarity align with groups based on expression patterns. For instance, two or more *posterior Hox* genes appear to share a more recent common ancestor than *Hox* genes from any other class within the same organism. Furthermore, two *posterior Hox* genes in different organisms appear to share a more recent common ancestor than *Hox* genes of a

548   Chapter 21

different class in the same organism. And there is nothing special about the *posterior* class, the same relationship would hold for any other class of *Hox* genes.

When you look at how the distribution of *Hox* genes within different organisms fall across classes, some interesting patterns emerge. For instance, in cnidarians the body plan and the types of *Hox* genes seem to match. These organisms tend to have one anterior and one posterior *Hox* gene, but appear to lack any *Hox* genes that fall within the central group. Similarly, during development their top and bottom (or head and foot) differentiate, but the body column does not. The middle is a dynamic state where the tissue can develop into either head or foot. In other words, cnidarian bodies do not really have a defined trunk or middle section.

All bilaterians, on the other hand, have an anterior, a posterior, and a defined midsection, and all bilaterians have *Hox* genes from all classes (including *gene-3*). The origin of the *central* class thus seems to be coupled with the origin of bilaterians. Furthermore, within bilaterians the number of *Hox* genes within each class is not always the same. The seemingly most primitive extant bilaterians, the acoelomorph flatworms, have a cluster of only four *Hox* genes, one from each class. All other bilaterians, which tend to have a more complex development pattern along their anterior–posterior axis, have more. In particular, multiple representatives are found in the *anterior*, *central*, and *posterior* classes. Furthermore, at least six or seven of the Hox genes found in both protostomes and deuterostomes are sufficiently similar to suggest that they predated the protostome/deuterostome split. For example, Figure 21-28 shows five of these found in both fruit flies and mice (as well as other vertebrates such as yourself). These seemingly equivalent genes are arranged in the same order along the chromosome and are activated early in development in the same relative order along the anterior–posterior axis. Moreover, when experimenters have transferred some of these structurally similar mouse homeobox genes into a fruit fly, the mouse gene had similar effects as their fruit fly equivalent. *Yikes!* Basically the same genes are being used in the same way to build extremely different organisms.

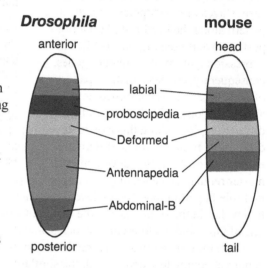

Figure 21-28. Early in embryonic development five structurally similar homeobox genes have the same order of expression along the anterior-posterior (head-to-tail) axis in fruit flies (Drosophila) and mice (as well as other vertebrates such as yourself).

I started this section with the claim that the type of genes shared between protostomes and deuterostomes provided a new vantage point from which to glimpse what their common ancestor looked like. At least six or seven shared Hox genes not only suggest that the common ancestor was a bilaterian with a distinct front, middle, and back end, but also that the developmental patterning along this axis was even more complex than that found in acoelomorph flatworms. It also very likely had a throughgut, which, if true, means that either the deuterostome or protostome means of developing a mouth and an anus evolved secondarily—that is, it represents an evolutionary branch that split from the other line.

What about eyes?

Geneticists have a potentially confusing habit of naming genes after the developmental deficit associated with a mutant form. In other words, they name the gene not after how the normal gene affects development, but after what goes wrong when it gene mutates (which is how they figure out the role played by the normal form). One such gene discovered in *Drosophila* was named *eyeless*. Fruit flies with the normal form of *eyeless* develop eyes, whereas those with the mutant form do not. *Eyeless* was also found to be a homeobox gene, although it is in a different subfamily than *Hox* genes.

Curiously, a gene known as *small eye* in mice (because the mutant form results in the reduction or elimination of eye formation) and *Aniridia* in humans (because the mutant form results in the reduction or even the elimination of iris formation—the colored portion of an eye) had sequences more similar to *eyeless* (and to each other) than to other mouse or human genes. This could be a result of chance, but it is much more likely that it is due to common ancestry. Functional similarity clearly adds strength to the common ancestry argument. In fact, although it sounds like science fiction, when researchers introduced the normal version of the mouse *small eye* gene into the part of a fruit fly destined to become a leg, it induced the formation of eye structures on the adult fly's leg.

Lots of animals have eyes, but they come in such diverse structures that it has been estimated that "the eye" has evolved independently more than 40 times. The camera-like eyes of vertebrates (deuterostomes) and the compound eyes of insects (protostomes) are just two examples. But stating that different types of image-forming optics evolved independently is not a claim that the same is true for some form of light-sensitive apparatus. When *small eye* was introduced into a fruit fly, it did not induce the development of mouse-like eyes, but compound fly-type eyes. This gene, thus, does not appear to play a role in instructing which type of eye to form, but where some type of light-sensitive apparatus should develop. Suggesting that the history of *eyeless*, *small eye*, and *Aniridia*, all the way back to their common ancestor, was that of a master regulatory gene for the development of a light-sensitive apparatus. In other words, genetic evidence supports the notion that the common ancestor of protostomes and deuterostomes developed some means to see, even if detecting the presence or absence of light was the best that they could do. It is the details of the optical equipment that then evolved differently along different evolutionary lineages past that point.

What about hearts and limbs?

The eye story is basically repeated with heart development. Fruit flies, like all insects, have an open circulatory system where a form of muscular pump or heart pushes fluid along an open-ended tube that then bathes body tissues. Some fruit fly embryos, however, were discovered that failed to develop a heart (which of course did not live very long). Geneticists subsequently found the gene that when mutated, disrupted heart development and named it *tinman* after the *The Wizard of Oz* character that lacked a heart. Once again, *tinman* turned out to also be a homeobox gene, although it was in a different subfamily than either *Hox* genes or those involved in eye development. Next, several mammalian versions of *tinman* were discovered, and they also played an important regulatory role in heart development (despite the fact that a mammalian heart is structurally much different). Genetic evidence thus supports the notion that the common ancestor of protostomes and deuterostomes had some rudimentary form of a convection system driven by a muscular pump. It is then the details that evolved differently along different evolutionary lineages past that point.

Now it is doubtful that the protostome/deuterostome common ancestor had appendages used in locomotion. Acoelomorph flatworms do not, nor do many of the worm-like groups of animals found in both the protostome and deuterostome lines. But once again genetic evidence supports the idea that they had some sort of projection from their body, like some sort of tentacle-like structure used to locate and/or capture food. And the story starts again with fruit flies, where the mutated form of another homeobox gene (in a different subfamily) was found to result in the failure of the outer or most distal parts of their limbs to develop. Using the same mutant logic introduced earlier, geneticists named this gene *distal-less*. And as you can probably already guess, versions of the *distal-less* gene have been subsequently found in animals on both sides of the protostome/deuterostome split. It turns out that the common regulatory feature of *distal-less* is not in building locomotory appendages per se, but in building anything that sticks out from the main body, from tentacles to locomotory appendages such as fish fins and legs of both lobsters and rabbits. So either the *distal-less* gene has been repeatedly picked to play a role in building protruding structures from scratch, or the common ancestor to all *distal-less* bearing animals built some form of projection. If so, then once again it would be the details that evolved differently along different evolutionary lineages past that point.

A Brief Discussion of the Rest of the Bilaterian Story

After these early beginnings, the rest of the bilaterian story is stunning, to say the least. At present, over 99 percent of described living species of animals fall into this group. Furthermore, taxonomists currently subdivide extant bilaterians into somewhere around 20 to 40 different major groups or **phyla**. Animals grouped into the same phylum are considered to share the same basic body plan and general pattern of development and consequently are assumed to represent a major line of evolutionary descent. That is, any two members of the same phylum are assumed to share a more recent common ancestor than to any animal in a different phylum. (Note: The uncertain number of phyla reflects that taxonomy is ongoing science. With further discovery of new animals, closer examination of previously described animals, along with differences of opinion among taxonomists, the number of animal phyla will likely never be set in stone.) The rest of the animals, on the other hand, are presently grouped into only four phyla: Porifera (sponges), Placozoa, Cnidiria, and Ctenophora. And the fossil record reveals many examples of bilaterians that have disappeared along the way. Some had body plans fundamentally different and thus represent a different phyla than anything found today.

What is it about bilaterians that allowed them to diversify to such a great extant? It is a great question, and it would be wonderful to be able to spell out a complete and fundamentally simple answer. I just do not know one. So let's start with a different question: Have you ever heard of a ribbon worm, a spiny-crowned worm, a horseshoe worm, a peanut worm, or an arrow worm? I am guessing for a lot of you the answer in no. Often our knowledge of worms does not extend too much beyond earthworms—those things that you can dig out of the ground, that you have probably held at least once in your life, and that you may have even tried to catch fish with. Yet each of the worms mentioned are the common name of one of the bilaterian phyla. In fact, if you look closely, a majority of bilaterian phyla are some form of worm-like animals. They are long, are thin, and generally lack any sort of projection from the body used to power movement (an appendage). Yet wouldn't all worm-like organisms be in the same phyla—that is, by being worm-like don't they share the same basic body plan. It turns out, however, that there can be significant differences within this basic design. For instances, all ribbon worms have a coiled structure at their front end called a proboscis that can be shot out of its cavity. Carnivorous ribbon worms use their proboscis to subdue prey when hunting. Some are even armed with special spines or stylets that inject toxins into prey. Spiny-crowned worms, on the other hand, set themselves apart by having 5 or 6 rings of recurved spines on their heads and rings of cuticular plates that surround the body. And horseshoe worms live in tubes that they build and have a set of flagellated tentacles that surround their mouth to filter feed. They also solve the problem of not filling up their tube with excrement by have a U-shaped gut—that is, the gut tube curls back around so that both the anus and mouth are located at the end that sticks out of the tube (which I guess should still be called the head end). One could go on, but hopefully the point has been made that there are some fundamentally different ways to build a worm-like organism. Curiously, however, most of these wormy phyla do have very many known species—often ranging in the hundreds or fewer. More will surely be discovered with more exploration, but enough of the world has been sampled to know that this basic trend will not change.

The first bilaterians were presumably soft-bodied worm-like organisms, so the majority of bilaterian phyla being rearrangements of this basic body plan is not surprising. But for a phyla to subsequently distinguish itself by diversifying into lots of different species requires that the basic body plan is such that developmental variations could lead to a lot of different functional shapes. Stated differently, the body plan needs to be comprised of basic building blocks that can be modified in ways that can lead to structurally, and thus functionally, diverse organisms. For example, I mentioned earlier that Placozoa is a phylum with just one known species, *Trichoplax adhaerans*. Perhaps this is true because this simple body plan just could not be modified in any really different ways. Similarly, the relative paucity of species in some of these wormy phyla may be due to having a basic body plan with relatively few modifiable components. That is, parts could change in size, getting somewhat bigger or smaller, but overall the body plan was not amenable to much more fundamental restructuring. It is an interesting idea. But is there something noticeably different about the basic body plans of more species diverse phyla, such as the arthropods (which are far and away the most diverse group of animals, with estimates ranging in the millions of species), the mollusks (which includes clams, snails, slugs, and squid), the chordates (which include all the vertebrates such as yourself), the round worms (phylum Nematoda), and the segmented worms (phylum Annelida)?

An idea with some history

In the late 1700s the noted philosopher Johann Wolfgang von Goethe made an interesting suggestion. It started with the recognition that many organisms are made of repeating structures—that is, an organism's body plan is not one unique structure but contains repeats of the same basic anatomical arrangement. We previously saw this type of modular arrangement in discussing the formation of cnidarian polyp colonies. Plants with multiple leaves are also an example. He then noted structural variations could occur if different repeats underwent different transformations during the course of development. For example, he suggested that a leaf and a flower petal were in essence repeats of the same structure that underwent different and major transformations.

In essence, we have been developing the theme underlying Goethe's insight throughout our discussion of multicellular organisms—that *duplication* followed by *divergence* is the basic means to construct larger more complex organisms. We first saw it at the cellular level. The evolution of multicellular organisms started with cell division creating duplicating structures that by hanging together in a cooperative association generated a new level of freedom—the freedom to diverge. Not only could the everyday tasks be divvied up between increasingly specialized cells, but also cell types could persist that took on completely novel functions that benefit the organism as a whole. I then hinted at how repeated episodes of gene duplication followed by divergence generate a simple means for genomes to get larger and reproductive performances to become more complex. Goethe simply applied this idea to repeated body parts—anatomical structures composed of many cells. In the late 1800s the English biologist William Bateson took further strides to clarify the idea that the presence of repeated structures that could be modified in number and kind set the stage for the evolution of pronounced morphological diversity.

Could this idea help explain why some bilaterian phyla are more diverse than others? Only if some bilaterians develop repeated chunks of anatomy, and at first glance how that could occur is not so obvious. The modular arrangement of cnidarian polyps or leaves sprouting off a central stem just does not fit with the maintenance of bilateral symmetry. Yet there are ways, and perhaps the most fundamental is the formation of body segments. So let's focus there.

Body segments

Some bilaterian animals grow larger by repetitively developing an organism's body or trunk region along the anterior–posterior axis (see Figure 21-29). Each serial division is known as a segment. The remaining parts of a segmental animal, which are not of segmental origin, are the anterior head and the posterior tail. When present, the head contains eyes and the portion of the nervous system (often called the brain) with which the eyes connect. Segments are typically formed sequentially and develop from growth zones just in front of the tail region, so the youngest segments are always those most posterior. Trunk structures associated with locomotion, gas exchange, and excretion are generally repeated in each segment. The gut tube, in contrast, runs through each segment. The mouth opens in or near the head, and the tail contains the anus.

Assembling a larger organism in this way may be easier than adding on a completely novel structure because the information needed to guide construction is already present. Furthermore, a segmental or serially repetitive trunk organization adds a functional design twist. A bilaterian animal's trunk is where muscles in conjunction with skeletal elements are arranged to power certain types of changes in body shape. For example, in the previous chapter we discussed how sheets of muscles wrapped both circularly and longitudinally around a fluid-filled cavity, called a coelom, which could be used to either elongate (contract circular muscles) or shorten (contract longitudinal muscles) an organism's trunk. Now envision a repetitive arrangement of the same design. Each segment bearing a separate coelom bounded by its own set of circular and longitudinal muscles. Advantageous? It may not be if all segments were all constrained to do the same thing at the same time. Like with cells, the potential advantage of duplicate body parts is increased greatly when they are able to work in different but complementary ways. Earthworms, for example, are segmental animals with the basic design just described, and they burrow through the ground by combining these two movements across segments in a coordinated way (see Figure 21-30). Similarly, if you watch a centipede, which has segmental body design (see Figure 21-31), scurry along you will see that the timing by which legs in different segments move back and forth is not the same. A wavelike pattern of leg contractions propels a centipede along.

In addition to differently regulating the timing of each segment's actions, the diversification can also be morphological. For instance, segment number could change, and an animal with 20 segments will be able to perform differently than one with 10 segments or 200 segments. Furthermore, the shape of individual segments within an organism can be modified. Not only can segments in different positions along the body axis get bigger or smaller, but also segmental structures, such as appendages, can become structurally differentiated from their counterparts on other segments. Different structures having the same segmental origin are said to be **serially homologous**. Segments can even fuse to form structurally unique arrangements. For example, in all segmental animals there is a tendency for anterior trunk segments to fuse to

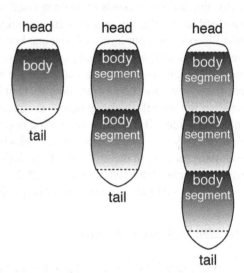

Figure 21-29. Developmental repetition of an organism's body or trunk region is one way for a larger organism to be assembled.

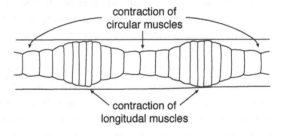

Figure 21-30. A portion of an earthworm is shown moving through an underground burrow by the coordinated contraction of circular and longitudinal muscles in different segments.

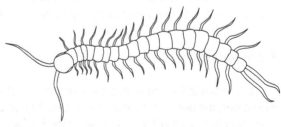

Figure 21-31. The body plan of centipedes consists largely of serially repeating structures called segments.

varying degrees with the true head region to form a "compound head." Any such changes will result in performance differences.

The two most clearly segmented animal phyla are the extraordinarily species-rich arthropods and the annelids (the segmented worms). Let's first take a closer look at arthropods.

Arthropods

The presence of segments is evident in all arthropod embryos and is a conspicuous feature of many adults. Evidence suggests that primitive arthropod segments had a few characteristic features. First the hardened plates called sclerites of the arthropod chitinous exoskeleton (discussed previous chapter) were initially confined to segments, and sclerites from adjoining segments were connected by thinner and more flexible regions of exoskeleton. These "between-segment joints," coupled with the arrangement of muscle bundles, enabled body segments to move in relationship to each other. Furthermore, each segment had a pair of jointed appendages (hence the phylum name Arthropoda, which means jointed feet), where each appendage was a forked biramous structure that emerged from a common base (see Figure 21-32). Presumably early on, the inner branch formed either a sensory structure (such as an antenna) or a structure used in movement (such

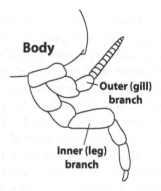

Figure 21-32. A generalized arthropod biramous appendage

as a walking leg) and the outer branch supported gills—filamentous or flattened regions that combined blood flow with increased surface area to facilitate the exchange of oxygen and carbon dioxide with the surrounding water. Movement of the outer branch was likely used to facilitate the flow of water past the gills. Gas exchange also occurred across other body surfaces, especially in regions only covered by a thin exoskeleton, but the presence of gills enhanced the exchange rate and thus enabled body sizes and activity levels to increase.

A series of these primitive segments capped on one end by a head and on the other by a tail captures the essence of the early arthropod body plan (see Figure 21-33). This body plan, however, proved amenable to an immense number of modifications. Segment

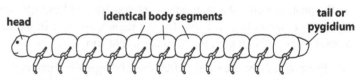

Figure 21-33. A simple conception of the early arthropod body plan.

modifications include changes in number and fusion, along with other forms of differentiation. Appendages also underwent all sorts changes such as: changes in the number and shape of leg segments; the addition of other branches or extensions that emerge from either the base, the inner branch, or the outer branch; loss of one of the two main branches; and the loss of entire appendages. In the process, arthropods have become far and away the most successful animal group in terms of both species number and range of habitats in which these different species make a living. The number of insect species alone is estimated to be somewhere in the millions. And although not to the same degree as insects, the other major arthropod groups are also diverse. These groups are the chelicerates (horseshoe crabs, spiders, and scorpions), the crustaceans (crabs, shrimp, copepods, barnacles, isopods), and the myriapods (centipedes and millipedes). You may even be familiar with the trilobites, an extinct group of marine arthropods that were once abundant and diverse inhabitants of Paleozoic seas. And several other classes of arthropods are also only known from the fossil record.

To better understand how this primitive body plan could have evolved into so many different body types, I highlight the basic body plan of some of the different types of arthropods. I start with trilobites.

Trilobites

Although trilobites (see Figure 21-34) are an early arthropod group—they first appeared in the fossil record some 540 million years ago during what geologists call the Cambrian period—they still show some pronounced alterations from the presumed ancestral body plan. For instance, the anterior region, which is called the **cephalon**, was actually a compound head composed of the head and four fused segments. The first fused segment was preoral (before the mouth opening), and the appendages were modified into a pair of antenna used in some way to "taste" the environment. On the other hand, the three postoral fused segments had pairs of basic biramous appendages (with both a gill branch and a leg branch). Furthermore, the dorsal exoskeletal plates of this compound head region had also fused to form a flattened shield-like structure with a pronounced bump running along the middle. This so-called **carapace** typically had an eye protruding from the middle of each side. The arthropod compound eye is first seen in trilobites. The exoskeleton on the underside of the cephalon was not nearly as thick. The region just posterior to a trilobite's cephalon is called the **thorax**, which was composed of separately articulating segments; each had a pair of biramous appendages. Like the shape of the cephalon, each of these segments was flattened along the dorsal–ventral axis, and the more heavily armored dorsal exoskeleton extended out past the legs on each side. At the posterior end, the segments were constructed from the same basic plan, except that the final segments commonly fused with the tail region, and like in the cephalon, the dorsal exoskeleton formed a solid shield. This region is called the **pygidium**.

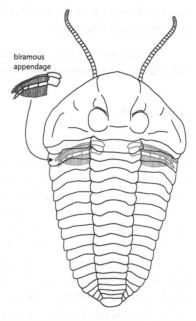

Figure 21-34. A fairly typical trilobite body plan (dorsal view). Biramous appendages are found on the ventral sided of every segment except the first, which bears antenna.

Presently, there are over 15,000 morphologically distinct types (species?) of trilobites described from the fossil record. The morphological variation of the basic body plan described earlier occurs in a number of ways. Let me list just a few: (1) The number of thoracic segments was altered from as few as 2 to over 60. (2) Overall body shape in terms of length versus width was varied, as some types were notably elongated, whereas others were widened. (3) Overall body size varied from just 1 millimeter at maturity to nearly three-quarters of a meter. (4) The shape of the cephalon was altered in many ways, such as shovel and plow shapes that seem adapted for burrowing. (5) Eyes varied considerably in size (and shape), ranging from complete loss to extremely prominent structures. (6) In some trilobites, spiny projections developed on the cephalon, thoracic segments, and/or the pygidium. These spines may have been used to defend against predation.

Crustaceans

Although two other arthropod groups contain more species (the insects, and the arachnids—spiders), the crustaceans have shaped the basic arthropod body plan into an incredible diversity of forms—from the pill bugs that reside underneath a rock in your lawn, to crabs with meter-long legs. The signature feature of crustaceans is the head region, which is a compound head formed by the fusion of the head with the first five segments. The first five pairs of appendages have also been modified to perform specialized "head-like" functions. The first two—which are preoral or before the mouth opening—are modified into two sets of antenna, and the first set is typically biramous. The third pair, called the **mandibles**, flank the mouth. They are usually short and shaped to cut and crush food items. Behind the mandibles, are two sets of accessory feeding appendages, the first and second **maxillae**, used to hold and position food.

Primitively, the crustacean trunk was likely composed of a series of similar segments capped by an anus-bearing tail, referred to in crustaceans as the **telson**. But only a very few crustaceans even approximate this condition. In most, the trunk segments have differentiated to

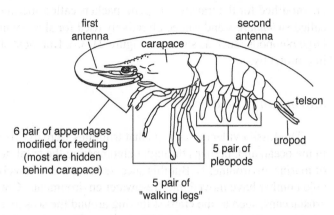

Figure 21-35. The basic structure of a shrimp as illustrated by a lateral sketch of a white shrimp (Penaeus setiferus).

varying degrees within regions of specialization called the **thorax** and **abdomen**. Yet even within this basic design there are innumerable variations. To give you the flavor of one possibility, I discuss some of the details found in shrimp (see Figure 21-35).

Shrimp have 19 segments in total, all of which bear appendages. The first 13 segments, which includes the five of the compound head and the next eight, which make up the thorax, are not apparent because they are all covered by a carapace—a shield-like outgrowth of fused exoskeleton plates—to form a **cephalothorax**. The appendages on the first three thorax segments have turned forward to form additional accessory feeding structures called **maxillipeds**. So including the mandibles, shrimp have six sets of appendages specialized in processing food. Along the next five thoracic segments the inner appendage branch has lengthened to form walking legs. In fact shrimp, along with lobsters and crabs, are called decapods because they have 10 walking legs in total. However, all walking legs are not the same. For instance, the first three pairs end as pincers that, among other things, can also be used in food processing—that is, they can start to break up prey items and then pass pieces forward to the mouthparts. (Note: In lobsters the pincers on the first pair of walking legs are greatly enlarged to form the familiar set of lobster claws used in defense and mating.) The fourth and fifth sets of walking legs, which develop sharp claws at the end, are the most specialized for locomotion. Typically some thoracic appendages also have branches that form gills. For example, the snapping shrimp *Alpheus pachychirus* has six appendages (the third maxilliped and the five walking legs) on each side that develop some form of gill branch. These gill branches do not extend below the carapace, so to function effectively, water needs to be pulled underneath the carapace and across the gills. This ventilating current is produced by the beating of a paddle-like branch (known as the gill bailer) off the second thoracic maxilliped. In shrimp, the carapace fits loosely against the side of the body allowing water to enter along its entire ventral and posterior margin. Water then exits along the anterior edge, near the gill bailer's location. (Note: In decapods with tighter-fitting carapaces, such as crayfish and crabs, water flows past gills through more defined openings and internal chambers.)

The last six segments, collectively known as the abdomen or the tail, have retained the ability to articulate. In fact, the extensive flexing muscles of the abdominal segments (familiar to anyone who has eaten shrimp) can work in conjunction with a broad tail fan to create a powerful thrust capable of propelling a shrimp backward with extraordinary speed. This darting, quick movement is used to escape predators. The broad tail fin is actually composed of two structures—a flattened telson (the terminal part of the body that arises before segmentation) is bounded on each side by the appendages of the last abdominal segments. These appendages, called **uropods**, are each a single broad and flattened structure. The five remaining abdominal segments bear biramous and commonly flattened pairs of appendages called **pleopods**. In males the first pair of pleopods (the second pair can also be involved) are modified for the transfer of sperm packets called spermatophores during mating. Pleopods are also called *swimmerets* and can be effectively used for slow swimming in species of shrimp with relatively large pleopods (such as shown in Figure 21-35). But most shrimp are bottom dwellers that only swim intermittently.

Moving on to land

The fossil evidence suggests that trilobites were exclusively marine. Crustaceans also first evolved in the ocean and, perhaps through outcompeting the trilobites, have become the dominant arthropod of marine environments. But this success has not exclusively stopped at the ocean shore. A considerable number have moved into freshwater environments. Crayfish are one well-known example. A few crustaceans, such as the crabs skittering around the seashore's edge, have been able to make at least a partial transition to a terrestrial life. Many of these shore-inhabiting forms come on land during low tide to feed on what the last high tide left behind. And a few more, including some crabs and the pill bugs mentioned previously, have completely severed their ties with the water's edge to become terrestrial organisms. How have they done so?

Two issues, in particular, must be addressed for any organism to move from water to land. First, terrestrial organisms must contend with the increase effects of gravity (discussed in the previous chapter). Commonly this involves an increase in support structure. Second, they must contend with the increased tendency to lose water. To live, all cells need to be immersed in watery surroundings. This means that terrestrial organisms need to maintain their own water supply around their cells. As a consequence, the water concentration on their insides tends to be higher than found in a gaseous environment, creating a natural tendency for water to move out of organisms. Yet to survive they must maintain water balance—that is, any water lost must be replaced by water intake. (Note: Most marine organisms, in contrast, are isotonic with their environment, whereas freshwater organisms live in a world where the problem is water gain, due to the higher water concentration being found in the surroundings.)

The presence of an exoskeleton with jointed appendages set up arthropods to literally walk out onto land. Of course, due to the increased pull of gravity, terrestrial arthropods cannot get as large as aquatic ones, and for any given size, the exoskeleton will need to be even stronger; but nonetheless, the basic arthropod body plan made the increased gravity part of the terrestrial transition very straightforward.

Part of the trick in maintaining water balance in a water-scarce environment is to reduce the rate at which water is lost (and thus reduce the rate at which water needs to be found). Covering the outer body surface with something that reduces water permeability would thus help. Exoskeletons again set the stage because this body covering, especially the hardened plates, do just that. Add an outer waxy covering, which is found in most terrestrial arthropods, and the flow will slow even further. Sealing off the entire body with a thick waxy exoskeleton to form a water impervious shield, however, is not an option. Movement requires thinner more permeable regions to form joints. Plus, any organism still needs to exchange things with the environment. Animals specifically need to get oxygen and food in, and wastes, among other things, out. Yet any surface permeable to oxygen, nutrients, or waste molecules is also permeable to water. Thus for any arthropod venturing on to land, water loss is still a major issue. What types of terrestrial environments can be invaded and still maintain water balance depends largely on how well the organism has "figured out" ways to reduce water loss during exchange with the environment. Furthermore, to stay land-bound during reproduction requires a means to get sperm and egg together and let development proceed without the aid of aquatic surroundings.

Terrestrial isopods

I suspect that most, if not all, of you are familiar with terrestrial isopods (see Figure 21-36). Some are commonly called pill bugs or roly-poly bugs because if you poke one it rolls up into a tiny, "pill-shaped" ball. Others, known as wood lice and sow bugs, cannot curl up as completely but have the same basic shape. They actually are not insects, as the name *bug* implies, but crustaceans whose ancestors seemingly crawled out of ocean. They have the typical crustacean compound head, although the first antennae are small and perhaps vestigial, and the first thoracic segment, whose appendages are modified into maxillipeds used in feeding, is fused with the head region. So there are four pairs of feeding appendages in total. The next seven thoracic articulate independently. Extensive dorsal to ventral flexion in this region is what allows pill bugs to roll up into a ball. Each of these thoracic segments bears a pair of similar-shaped walking legs, and the outer branch has been lost (so the appendages are said to uniramous). Isopods (iso = equal, pod = foot) are named after the fact that their walking legs all resemble each other. The six smaller abdominal segments each bear a pair of highly modified biramous appendages.

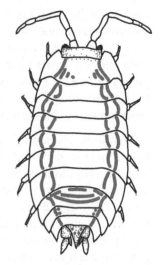

Figure 21-36. A typical body plan of a terrestrial isopod (dorsal view).

The last segment is fused with the tail or telson, and the pair of appendages is heavily sclerotized and long, except in pill bugs, where they are short enough to be included within the sphere when the animal rolls up. Like shrimp, these appendages are called uropods and are sensory and defensive in function. Also like shrimp, the appendages on the remaining five abdominal segments are called pleopods, but they perform very different functions that we discuss further later.

Terrestrial isopods are found in many different habitats throughout the world, even in desert areas. However, all species minimize exposure to hot, dry conditions behaviorally. They typically spend their days in moist, humid microhabitats such as under decaying leaves, rocks, and dead logs and venture out to feed only at night. Despite being terrestrial, they still cannot contend for too long in too dry conditions. Why not? Much can be explained just by looking at the way they acquire oxygen.

This may sound a bit curious, but isopods, as well as terrestrial crabs, use gills to acquire oxygen. Recall that crustacean gills are an appendage branch that is modified into a filamentous or flattened region that combines blood flow with increased surface area to facilitate the exchange of oxygen and carbon dioxide with their surroundings. Furthermore, gills must retain a covering film of moisture to work. So, if surrounded by air, especially drier or less humid air (humidity is a measure of the percent saturation of air with water), the high surface area will allow water to diffuse from the body at a high rate. So, how do gill-bearing isopods live on land?

As already mentioned, behavioral avoidance of dry conditions plays an important role. But there are morphological changes, as well, that reduce the rate of water loss; all of which are based on the fact that air holds about 35 times as much oxygen per unit volume as water. The higher oxygen concentration allows isopods to get adequate oxygen uptake with relatively less gill surface area, which in turns decreases the amount of evaporative water loss. It also allows gills to be positioned in a more covered protected area and still maintain a sufficient oxygen concentration to maintain uptake. In isopods the inner branch of abdominal appendages, the pleopods, are the ones modified into gas exchange surfaces. (Recall that in shrimp the gills formed from extensions off thoracic appendages.) The outer branch, which is more heavily sclerotized, is used to form a protective covering that facilitates water retention. In fact each gill lies within a depression of the outer branch to better seal it off. These outer branches can then be moved aside to better expose gills when needed. In some isopods the outer covering branch has evolved a secondary modification that facilitates increased transfer of oxygen while still covering the gill. Outer branches bear an external opening that moves into either a lung-like cavity or a system of tiny branching tubes called **pseudotracheae** within the interior. Due to decreasing the diffusion distance, these openings allow oxygen to more readily move across the outer covering branch and into the gill without pulling the outer cover aside. Interior gas exchange surfaces are more efficient at retaining water because instead of all water directly escaping to the outside, any water moving across an absorptive surface will tend to remain within the internal chamber and thus greatly reduce the concentration gradient that drives water movement. Only water able to escape through the small exterior opening will be lost. As would be expected, terrestrial isopods with these outer branch cavities can tolerate drier conditions than those lacking them.

Curiously, terrestrial isopods have never evolved a waxy exoskeletal covering to reduce water loss from other body surface areas. As previously mentioned, exoskeletons alone, especially thicker areas, already slow the flow, but a waxy layer would do an even better job. Is this an example of a missed evolutionary opportunity in that such modification would have been adaptive, but it was never introduced within the isopod lineage? Or, given that terrestrial isopods were already confined to live in moist areas, the cost of a waxy coating may have outweighed any benefits. Terrestrial isopods can acquire substantial amounts of oxygen even when their gills are covered. A waxy covering, while further reducing water loss, would also further block this avenue of oxygen input. The question comes down to which one would be more advantageous.

Perhaps one of the greatest challenges for any organism to successfully move onto land is reproduction. External fertilization, which is common in aquatic organisms, is much less of an option, as sperm released from a male's body cannot now swim through the external environment to find an egg placed nearby. Plus, development has to still occur despite the absence of watery surroundings. Copulation or internal fertilization is, however, a general rule in crustaceans, suggesting it had evolved in the isopod line prior to coming onto land. Although the details are not important here, it is noteworthy that in males the first two abdominal pleopods are not modified into gills, but into copulatory organs. Most crustaceans also brood their young to some degree after fertilization. In isopods, eggs are usually brooded in a **marsupium**—a pouch that forms on the underside of the first five thoracic segments. The marsupium of terrestrial isopods is kept filled with fluid, so that development of the young is essentially aquatic. This made a terrestrial life possible without evolving eggs that can be laid on land or returning to an aquatic environment to lay them. After a few days the eggs hatch, but the juveniles remain in the marsupium for a few hours before breaking free. Development is said to be direct, in that instead of going through a larval stage, the offspring emerge looking like miniature adults—except that they have six, instead of seven, pairs of walking legs. The seventh pair forms during the first molt.

Myriapods

The myriapodous arthropods, which contain the terrestrial centipedes and millipedes, share some similarities with terrestrial isopods. For one, they require a relatively humid environment to maintain water balance, which at least in part is due to the lack of a waxy-covered exoskeleton, so they also commonly live in places like underneath logs or leaf litter or in the soil. Their body plan also consists of a number of similar-shaped segments that each bear a pair of uniramous walking legs. And when threatened, some millipedes coil their body into a protective coil or ball-shaped arrangement.

Differences in their body plan, however, make it clear that they are not crustaceans. Perhaps the most distinct difference is that their elongated trunk is composed of numerous similar segments instead of being broken up into distinct regions, such as the thorax and abdomen. For instance in centipedes, which are predators set up for speed, 15 or more segments each bearing a pair of nearly identical walking limbs form the core part of the body. To facilitate a rapid gait, these legs progressively increase in length toward the posterior (rear) end, which reduces the potential for one leg to interfere in the movement of another. In some centipedes the last and longest pair of appendages has been modified into pinchers used in defense. Finishing off the trunk are two segments that have lost limbs altogether. Instead these two segments—the pregenital and genital—are modified for sexual reproduction. The tail end is then capped by an anus-bearing telson.

The centipede compound head in many ways resembles a crustacean head region, except that it is composed of four instead of five segments, and only the first segment's appendages are modified into antennae (instead of the first two in crustaceans). After that, like crustaceans, the remaining three sets of appendages are modified for processing food. The first pair, which are again called mandibles, are modified for cutting and crushing food items. Although somewhat variable in different species of centipedes, the next two pairs are still called maxillae, as they are always involved in holding food items. Furthermore, like crustaceans, the appendages on the next segment down (considered the first trunk segment) are called maxillipeds, as they too are involved in food capture. But in centipedes they are modified into a large pair of poison claws that are used to stun or kill prey.

Millipedes, the other major group of myriapodous arthropods, are curious animals in that they can have up to 400 leg-bearing segments, yet despite all these legs that are not very agile or fast. They typically feed on decomposing vegetation, so speed and agility are not necessary for food capture. So what is the advantage of so many legs? It is actually rather simple. If each leg can generate a certain measure of force, then the more legs, the more force that can be generated. Millipedes use their ability to generate a powerful pushing force to ram their way through humus, leaves, and loose soil. The force is generated by a wave of leg contractions along the length of the body, and the more force needed, the greater the number of legs engaged in the wave. Besides the large number of segments, the millipede body plan is also characterized by the development of doubled trunk segments, or diplosegments, that are derived from the fusion of two originally distinct segments. Because a millipede's pushing force is generated entirely by its legs, the fusion of segments into pairs may increase its ability to generate a pushing force by better stabilizing the elongated trunk.

Perhaps you noticed that the myriapod trunk region resembles the presumably primitive arthropod body plan. The striking difference is that all the trunk appendages are uniramous walking legs. The presence of a second branch modified into some form of gill-like gas exchange structure on at least some of the segments is conspicuously absent. How then do centipedes and millipedes get oxygen (and rid carbon dioxide)? Located on each side of nearly every segment near the base of the appendage are small openings—called **spiracles**—that open into a series of interconnecting and repeatedly branching tubes—called **trachea**. The smallest branches finally dead end among the animal's tissues. It is here that oxygen coming from the outside diffuses into tissues. A net flow of oxygen continues because of the constant maintenance of a favorable concentration gradient from the outside to trachea to tissues. Within cells, oxygen is constantly being converted into something else (specifically water), so tissue oxygen concentrations will continually be lower than trachea, which as oxygen diffuses into tissues, will be lower than the outside, and so goes the flow. The carbon dioxide produced in the tissues, on the other hand, escapes through these same tubes due to the direction of the concentration gradient being reversed.

The presence of a tracheal system in terrestrial myriapods helps them maintain water balance. Like we discussed with isopod pseudotrachea, gas exchange within any sort of internal cavity can greatly reduce water in drier environments. However, it is curious that centipedes and millipedes lack any means to close their spiracles. Because membranes permeable to gases are also permeable to water, the humidity inside the trachea will be near 100%. Water will thus diffuse out of an open spiracle whenever the humidity of the outside air is less. However, if spiracle openings could be regulated, and an organism opened its spiracles only when oxygen levels are getting too low (or carbon dioxide levels are getting too high) to maintain its current activity level, water loss could be reduced even further. The drier the surrounding air, the more important such regulation would be. The lack of this ability, along with absence of a waxy cuticle, helps explain why centipedes and millipedes are able to tolerate only limited exposure to drier conditions. (Note: Insects, which also have tracheal systems, can open and close their spiracles and regulate this ability in ways that minimize water loss.)

Not all terrestrial arthropods have internal fertilization. Instead some myriapods, arachnids, and insects use a form of indirect sperm transmission. Males form bundles of sperm, called **spermatophores**, which are deposited on the ground. Females then pick up the spermatophore and take it into their reproductive opening. This form of sperm transfer was likely an early adaptation to reproducing on land, although, the behavior of some primitive arthropods suggests that initially the overall scheme was a bit haphazard. Males deposited spermatophores somewhat randomly, and then "hoped" that a female would just happen to encounter one. Centipedes still have indirect sperm transmission through spermatophores, although much of the randomness has been eliminated. Males usually do not produce a spermatophore until a female is encountered. Moreover, there is often a period of courtship where the male attempts to entice the female to pick up his spermatophore.

Also different than terrestrial isopods, myriapods lay eggs on land, although many millipedes build some sort of nest out of a regurgitated material or excrement that is sealed off after the eggs are laid. Presumably this container would help prevent eggs from drying out. Although some centipede groups are exceptions, most myriapods hatch from eggs with only a part of their adult number of segments. Additional segments (and legs) are then added across molts.

Some more about trachea

Tracheal systems stand in sharp contrast to gills (or lungs) in that they break a link between circulation and gas exchange. As a consequence, tracheal systems forgo any complications associated with getting blood to pick up oxygen at the gill (or lung) and drop it off at the tissue. Water, which is always the major component of blood, does not readily absorb oxygen. This is why there is 35 times as much oxygen in air as water. It is also why so-called respiratory pigments, such as hemoglobin or hemocyanin, need to be present when blood is involved in gas exchange. On the other hand, tracheal systems have a limiting effect on body size. As the distance to interior body cells becomes greater, a diffusion-driven tracheal system will have a harder time maintaining an adequate oxygen supply for any animal weighing much more than a gram. Some larger insects raise the ceiling on this limitation a bit by adding some convective flow to their tracheal system. Air sacs coming off the trachea are positioned between muscles such that air is pushed out when these muscles contract, and back in when the muscles relax due to the air void created. It is basically the same means we use to get air to flow into and out of our lungs. But even with such a convective boost, tracheal systems are not well suited to provide even larger animals with sufficient oxygen.

Although the presence of a tracheal system makes sense in small terrestrial animals such as centipedes and insects, how did they evolve? Although gills that form from appendage branches and tracheal tubes that extend deep into the body cavity seem like fundamentally different structures, it turns out that their development may not be. To explain, let me switch gears just a little and discuss a genetic comparison made between aquatic crustaceans and a different group of terrestrial arthropods—spiders. As we already know, the gas-exchange organs in aquatic crustaceans are gill-forming appendage branches that protrude from the body. In contrast, the gas-exchange organs in spiders intrude into the body. The ancestral structure seems to be a book lung, which is an internal chamber consisting of a series of stacked plate-like structures that create extensive surface area for gases to be exchanged between blood and air. Like trachea, book lungs are connected to the outside by a small opening or spiracle. Spiders considered the most primitive have two pairs of book lungs located on each side of the second and third abdominal segments. In almost all other species of spiders the posterior pair of respiratory organs are trachea, suggesting that at least one or more times book lungs skipped the blood connection and evolved into a tracheal system. In fact, in a few groups of spiders both pairs of respiratory organs have become trachea. Nonetheless, the important point is that inward-developing book lungs or trachea seem fundamentally different than an outward-protruding appendage branch. Yet three major regulatory genes have been found to be expressed in the development of each of these structures. One is *distal-less*, the limb-building gene mentioned earlier. The two other have been named *apterous* and *nubbin* (for reasons that we won't presently discuss). Different than *distal-less*, which is expressed in all appendage branches, *apterous* and *nubbin* are only expressed in the gill branch of crustaceans. Is this simply an extraordinary coincidence? Of course it is at least possible that out of the hundreds of master regulatory genes available, crustaceans and spiders just happened to pick the same ones to be involved in regulating the development of different-looking structures that do the same job. But it is much more likely that book lungs, trachea, and gill branches are all homologous structures—that is, evolutionary modifications of ancestrally the same body part. If true, this suggests that the book lungs and trachea found in spiders are kind of like an appendage that forms inward. Although I an unaware of whether it has yet been tested, it is reasonable that the trachea of centipedes, millipedes, and insects all share the same developmental story. If true, this means that all those centipede and millipede segments with one pair of uniramous walking legs and one pair of spiracles that open near the base of the leg may in a funny way still represent a biramous appendage. It is just that one branch sticks out (the walking leg), whereas the other "branch" goes inward (the tracheal system). It is also interesting to note that at the same position on even more posterior abdominal segments, all spiders form several pairs of spinnerets—short, conical structures bearing many spigots that are connected to silk glands. Spinnerets are thus the structures from which spiders extrude a protein that hardens into the silk of their webs and drag-lines. During their development *distal-less*, *apterous*, and *nubbin* are also expressed, suggesting that spinnerets are also homologous structures to gill branches, book lungs, and trachea.

Insects: Some basic information

By far, insects are the most successful terrestrial arthropods (see Figure 21-37). Currently there are more than 800,000 known species, but this is believed to be only a small fraction of the total. No other group even comes close. So what is it about insects? The most fundamental and simplest answer is the evolution of wings. The ability to take to the air opened up a huge door in terms of different ways to make a living and thus clearly contributed to the evolutionary radiation of this lineage. In fact, the wide-ranging morphological diversity found in other insect body parts, such as the feeding ap-

Figure 21-37. Many different types of insects, such as a grasshopper, are both common and familiar.

pendages, antennae, and eyes can be directly related to increased options associated with the ability to fly. Consider, for instance, the feeding appendages in butterflies, which have been modified into a long straw-like structure that is not good for anything except sucking nectar from flowers. Imagine an insect with such a mouthpart trying to stay alive if it had to walk from one flower to the next. (Note: The large number of different types of flowering plants is also connected to insects taking wing, as many use different species of flying insects as pollinators). Or imagine a flightless mosquito, with its specialized piercing-sucking mouthparts, trying to catch larger animals to "bite" by running. Would such a mosquito worry you? The big question with insects is thus: What set them up to evolve wings? Let's start with a little background.

You have probably been taught to count legs and if there are six (three pairs) it is an insect and a spider if there are eight (four pairs). There are, however, a few groups of hexapods (six-legged arthropods) different enough to not be placed within the insects. This simply means that either some hexapod groups appear to share a more recent common ancestor with some nonhexapod groups than other hexapods, or they branched off before the defining features of the insects had evolved. In this case, both of these are likely true. But that is not our focus here.

Evidence suggest that insects evolved from an ancestor composed of 19 (20?) segments, that through the regional specialization of function came to be grouped into the three distinct areas known as the head, the thorax, and the abdomen. The more combined head and thorax region, known as the cephalothorax, found in many crustaceans is not found in insects. Embryological studies point to the original insect compound head being built from the head plus five (first six?) embryonic segments. Although through modification, fusion, and deletion, the rearrangement is so complete that the heads of present-day insects have lost all suggestion of a segmented origin. Furthermore, all insect heads have lost a pair of appendages from one head segment, and thus bear *at most* four, instead of five, pairs of modified appendages—one pair of antennae, and three pairs of modified mouthparts. I say at most four pairs because in the evolution of some specialized feeding structures, such as the siphoning structure of butterflies, one or two pairs of feeding appendages have been lost. The next three segments form the thorax, which is the body region specialized for generating movement. Not only is a pair of prominent uniramous appendages found on each segment, but the last two thoracic segments commonly bear wings. Among different groups of insects, both the legs and wings have been modified extensively. The third body region, the abdomen, varies in segment number from 9 to 11. Eleven appears to be the ancestral condition, as that is what is found in the most basal insect groups. The insect abdomen is commonly thought of as the region that lacks appendages, but it is not that clear cut. Embryogically abdominal segments bear appendages, but in some insect groups these are lost prior to hatching. Yet even in these groups, abdominal segments typically bear spiracles that open into a tracheal system whose development, as we discussed previously, may have an appendage connection. Insects can also regulate the opening of their spiracles, and some aspect of the limb was likely modified to form the closing apparatus. In some semiaquatic insects that live the early stages of their life in freshwater, gills form along abdominal segments. And in butterflies, along with some other insect groups, the abdominal region of the larvae carries several pairs of appendages called false-legs or prolegs that are unjointed fleshy structures different from the jointed legs of the thorax. Furthermore, in many insects the tenth abdominal segment bears a pair of long jointed appendages called cerci (singular cersus). Although cerci have been modified to perform different functions, in the most basal insects groups they have numerous hair-like projections that play a tactile sensory and thus permit soil and leaf litter dwellers to gather sensory information when backing up. These most basal insect groups also have an 11th abdominal segment that is also modified to form an elongated tail-like structure. In all insects the actual tail or telson is absent, and the anal opening is found in the terminal segment.

Early insect evolution

It has long been thought that among the other arthropod groups, hexapods are most closely related to terrestrial myriapods. More recent molecular evidence strongly points, however, to hexapods' closest relatives being crustaceans. However, the evidence does not suggest that insects represent a branch off a terrestrial crustacean lineage. Instead the common ancestor linking crustaceans and insects was likely aquatic, with freshwater being a distinct possibility.

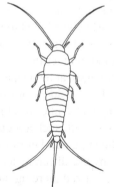

Figure 21-38. The basic silverfish body plan.

The seemingly most basal insect groups, which are commonly referred to as bristletails and silverfish (see Figure 21-38), seemingly branched off from the insect line before wings evolved. They are wingless throughout their life cycle, and there is no indication that they ever had winged ancestors. Interestingly, their entire life cycle is also terrestrial (see Figure 21-39), although too dry conditions are avoided. Eggs are laid in moist locations, and after hatching these small, scurrying organisms hide under stones and leaves during the day and emerge after dark to search for food. Hatchlings resemble small adults and feed on similar types of food, which includes algae, mosses,

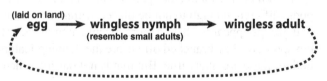

Figure 21-39. A basic life cycle of silverfish and bristletails.

lichens, and decaying organic matter. Development into reproductive adults occurs
slowly through a series of many molts. As
in many myriapods and arachnids, mating in bristletails and silverfish involves
indirect sperm transfer. Spermatophores are
deposited on the ground and then taken up
by the female, although elaborate courtship rituals have often evolved by which the
male attempts to coax the female to pick up
the spermatophore with her genital opening.

Figure 21-40. An adult mayfly.

(Note: You may be familiar with silverfish because some species have taken up residence in houses.
They are often found in damp basements and feed on the starchy paste on the back of old wallpaper
that has become detached, the gums and glues of book bindings, as well as some types of paper.)

In contrast to the terrestrial life cycle of bristletails and silverfish, the most basal groups of winged
insects, commonly referred to as mayflies (see Figure 21-40) and dragonflies, are freshwater semiaquatic insects (see Figure 21-41). Their eggs, which are not built to withstand desiccation, are laid
on water. After hatching, the so-called nymphs or naiads (aquatic nymphs) remain in the water where
they feed—mayflies commonly feed on algae and other aquatic plant life, whereas dragonflies are
voracious predators. They acquire oxygen
through abdominal appendages modified as
gills. Although they grow to an adult size in
the water, going through many molts along
the way, they do not remain in the water to
reproduce. Instead, once large enough, they
move to the surface, often crawling up
on emergent vegetation or a rock, where
they go through one (dragonflies) or two
(mayflies) more molts. In the process two

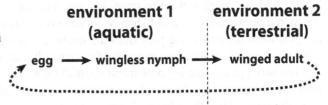

Figure 21-41. A basic life cycle of mayflies and dragonflies.

pairs of wings extend out from external pads on the last two thoracic segments. For mayflies, this adult
winged form has one function, to find a mate and reproduce. Feeding does not occur. In contrast, adult
dragonflies both feed and reproduce. In fact, like their aquatic nymphs the adult form is a voracious
predator, although they now capture food on the wing with a set of completely different mouthparts.
The lack of additional molts, however, makes it clear that the food acquired is channeled into reproduction instead of growth.

The fundamental differences
between the early wingless and
early winged insects generate some
interesting questions. Do the primitive wingless insects represent a
basal branch of the insect lineage
that emerged from freshwater, while
other insects remained in water that
later came to the surface to reproduce and subsequently evolved
a winged adult form? Or did one
branch of these early terrestrial
groups return to freshwater to lay
eggs, so that hatching and the early
stages of development could occur

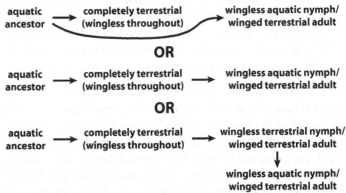

Figure 21-42. Different scenarios for the evolutionary connection
between the early wingless and early winged insects. In the first,
both only share a common aquatic ancestor, while in the next two
both share a completely terrestrial ancestor.

in an aquatic setting, but later stages still emerged back out of the water to reproduce and subsequently evolved wings? Or did the evolution of wings occur entirely within a terrestrial setting, and the return to freshwater only happened later? Figure 21-42 outlines these different potential scenarios.

Evolving wings

As a basis to further explore the evolution of wings, let's assume that the first is true—the insect line emerged from water at least twice. The first go-around, when they evolved into terrestrial wingless insects, will not be discussed further here because the basic issues have already been addressed when discussing the terrestrial emergence of other arthropods. In contrast, the second go-around involves a completely new story line—splitting time between two different environments. It is a curious way to make a living. Why at the reproductive stage of its life cycle would an ancestrally fully aquatic insect begin to go to the surface? Perhaps doing so would help them find mates, avoid predators, and/or find a particularly nutritious food source. But how? In terms of finding mates, confining mating to the surface compresses the search from a three-dimensional to a two-dimensional environment. In other words, finding something floating on the surface is easier than something located anywhere in the water column. Furthermore, if emergent vegetation is present, crawling up on a plant could also serve as a meeting place. In terms of avoiding predators, the image of an insect floating along the water surface may not seem like a great option, especially to any flyfisher reading this. But both fossil and molecular evidence suggest that this transition may have first occurred as early as 400 million years ago (mya), a time when freshwater fish may not have been present. And other predators may have not had the functional means to snag prey from the surface, or at least do so very effectively. Going up to feed would make sense if some nutritious food source collected on the surface. Fossil evidence suggests that terrestrial plants bearing pollen and seeds did not evolve until around 360 mya, but around 420 mya terrestrial vascular plants, whose reproductive cycle involved casting spores into the wind, came on to the scene. They lived in the damp conditions around water, so at times, released spores may have accumulated on the water surface, especially along the downwind shore. Feeding on floating spores may thus have been an effective means to gather large amounts of nutritious food before reproducing. Such feeding could have been the precursor to insects crawling up on these plants and feeding directly on spores within the sporangium typically produced on branch tips.

As discussed in the previous chapter, growth in arthropods requires a periodic shedding of the exoskeleton—a molt. What we have yet to point out is that periodic ridding of the skeleton not only makes growth possible, but it also makes a change in body form at almost any stage in development possible. The emergence of wings on the second to last molt in mayflies and the last molt in dragonflies is an already discussed example. And at this same time gills are replaced by trachea and mouthparts change from their nymph to adult form. Although the advantage of such shape change is straightforward—it allows a single individual to take advantage of more than one habitat throughout its life—it is a wondrous developmental twist to think about. Just imagine spending the first portion of your life crawling around on a stream bottom and then finishing off flying through the air.

But where did wings come from in the first place? Did they just all of the sudden just pop out from the back two thoracic segments? The best-supported hypothesis is that they evolved from the gill branch of the biramous appendages of their aquatic ancestors. The genetic evidence is the same as used in connecting gill branches and trachea. Not only is the previously discussed regulatory gene *distal-less* expressed in wing development, hence supporting the idea that it was derived from an appendage, but the two genes *apterous* and *nubbin*, which are expressed in only the gill branch of crustaceans, are also expressed during wing development. In fact, like other genes we have discussed, these two genes were first discovered in *Drosophila* as their mutant forms either blocked the development of wings (*apterous* means wingless) or led to the formation of only little nubs of wings (hence the name *nubbin*). Other forms of evidence also exist. For example, fossils of extinct aquatic nymph forms have been found that have gill-like appendages on all trunk (thorax and abdomen) segments.

And present-day mayfly nymphs still develop gills along their abdominal segments that resemble the two thoracic structures that later develop into wings in the adult form (see Figure 21-43). An insect wing's basic structure is also similar to the structure of gills of immature insects, as both are a body extension composed of two opposed covering layers supported by blood-filled veins. The major difference is that insect wings and walking legs do not emerge from a common base. Thus, for this scenario to work the outer and inner branches of an ancestral biramous limb would have to have separated; with part of the outer branch moving to the upper part of a thoracic segment and evolving into a wing, and the inner branch evolving into the walking leg. This seems to occur in *Drosophila*. Developing wing tissue buds off the dorsal portion of an early leg primordium, where gills are attached in crustaceans, and then migrates up to a dorsolateral position before forming wings.

Figure 21-43. A mayfly nymph bearing both wing buds (second and third thoracic segments) and abdominal gills.

Why would wings evolve from gills? So far we have only hinted at why an aquatic organism might be attracted to the surface to reproduce. But what is the connection between going to the surface and evolving wings? Two basic scenarios have emerged.

What could be called the perch-glide scenario starts with emergent nymphs climbing up vegetation to find mates and perhaps to feed on spores in branch tip sporangium or on other plant parts. But once up there, getting to a potential mate or the next sporangium on the next shoot over would pose a problem. Walking down, over, and then back up is an option, but a slow one. When small, jumping down wouldn't necessarily result in injury and would definitely save time. But any body extensions, such as remaining gill flaps could help dampen the fall by functioning as parachutes. Further extension of such flaps across a molt would seemingly be favored not only because it would further slow the fall, but it may also make gliding possible. Gliding, however, would be most useful if direction could be controlled, which would require increased motor control of these broadening appendages. Better motor control could in turn lead to the ability to move wings up and down, which if done at the right time and the right pace could create lift. That would be the start of real flight. From there natural selection could continue to steer improvement across generations at a time that there were no other flying animals. And due to trade-offs, improvements along any different dimension of flight, each of which could result in performance advantages, would contribute to the extensive radiation of flying insects.

In contrast to flight starting with animals jumping from elevated perches, the other scenario starts from the ground up. It begins with the observation that certain modern insects, especially stoneflies (another group of insects with aquatic nymphs and flying adults), engage in a winged-based form of locomotion called surface skimming. Here, instead of being used for flight, body wings are used as sails. This led to the suggestion that the advantage underlying the initial expansion of thoracic gill plates into more of winged-like structures was that they could be used in surface propulsion. Maybe as oars, as has been also observed in some insects, but especially as sails. When aquatic insects first came to the surface to find mates and/or feed, any means to help propel them around could prove advantageous. The scenario then proceeds through a series of minor modifications that, while improving the insect's capacity to undergo surface skimming, would also continue to set the stage for flight. These include (1) continuing to increase the surface area of expanding gill plates so that they would better function as sails (and subsequently as wings); (2) changes in body shape, including appendages, that would reduce surface drag by causing the insect to ride higher on top of the water (and subsequently make takeoff from water easier); (3) riding higher and higher out of the water would in turn set the stage for abdominal gills, which could continue to be used by dipping the abdomen into the water, to be converted into a tracheal system (and subsequently free the adult stage from its dependence on an aquatic environment); and (4) increasing the motor control of these appendages, so that not only could they be raised and lowered at the times that take the best advantage of wind speed and direction, but also turned and twisted in ways that increased steering ability (and subsequently led to flapping ability). Perhaps the most significant feature of this scenario is that it offers a solution to the riddle of how flight could arise through nonflying intermediate stages.

Folding wings

Have you ever noticed that when a dragonfly lands its four wings remain in flight position—stuck out to the side. Similarly, mayfly wings remain in flight position when landed, although they stick up off their backs (see Figure 21-40), instead of out to the side. In other words, the most primitive winged insects cannot fold their wings over their back (dorsal side of their thorax and abdomen). Dragonflies and mayflies also do not move around much when landed. This makes sense. Trying to run, or even walk, around with wings sticking out would be difficult. Just imagine trying to walk through a crowd or a densely vegetated area with you arms sticking out.

The rest of the winged insects, collectively called the Neoptera or "new winged" insects, can fold their wings. Although dragonflies and mayflies are still successful insect lines without this ability, wing folding—by making it possible to get wings out of the way when not in use—clearly opened new doors. Walking and running around vegetation, through crevices, or in and out of holes could be incorporated into making a living. Just watch a cockroach scamper underneath your refrigerator, and you will see the new possibilities in action. Some insects, such as stick insects and worker ants, have even lost wings altogether and thus move entirely by leg action. (Note: Some neopterous insects, such as butterflies, can no longer fold their wings against their abdomen, but evidence suggests that this was a secondary loss.)

Another landing

Although the evidence suggests that early winged insects split their life cycle between water and land, somewhere in the history of certain lineages of neopterous insects the entire life cycle moved onto land. The eggs, obviously, needed to become more resistant to dessication. And the early developmental stages (which are still wingless) needed to be able to make a living on land. In that shift, three reasonable distinct options have evolved. I briefly summarize each.

The first is similar to the aquatic/terrestrial switch in that the younger stages of development still live in a distinctly different environment than the adults (see Figure 24-44). Cicadas are a good example. Whereas the winged adults live in trees, the young—which like mayflies and dragonflies are known as nymphs—live underground. And the ability to change shape across molts is put to use, as the nymphs and adults have evolved different

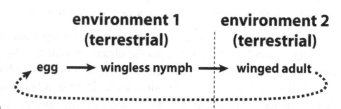

Figure 21-44. A completely terrestrial insect life cycle that is similar in structure to the water/land split found in the most primitive winged insects (mayflies and dragonflies).

shapes to better take advantage of these different environments. Eggs are actually laid in trees, but after hatching they use gravity to fall to the ground and then burrow below the surface. There they feed on sap from plant roots for a period that may last several years. In fact, some cicadas in North America spend 13 or 17 years underground. Once a cicada reaches full size, it digs upward and emerges from the soil (instead of water). It then typically climbs up a tree trunk in preparation for its final molt into an adult. In contrast to the nymph stage, the adult stage generally lasts only a few weeks. Although the adults do feed, the focus is mating. Males court females by producing a loud species-distinct mating call.

In other insects the young and adults live and feed in a similar environment (see Figure 24-45). And as might be expected, the young, which are still called nymphs, hatch out looking a lot like wingless miniature versions of the adult. Examples include grasshoppers, crickets, cockroaches, stick insects, and true bugs (such as stink bugs and box elder bugs). Clearly for this to work the adults must feed and otherwise live in a manner possible for small wingless versions to participate. Hiding out within and feeding on grasses and other vegetation, such as grasshoppers do, is an example.

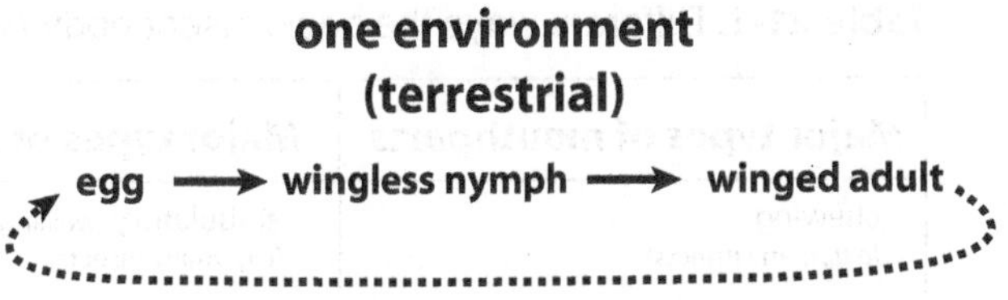

**one environment
(terrestrial)**

egg ⟶ wingless nymph ⟶ winged adult

Figure 21-45. A completely terrestrial insect life cycle in winged insects that is similar in structure to the most primitive wingless insects (mayflies and dragonflies).

Finally some insects have pushed the theme of living in two distinct environments to the extreme. To take advantage of these different habitats, the ability to change shape across molts has been pushed so far that early and late stages do not even resemble each other. Caterpillar to butterfly is the most well-known example, but there are many others including flies, beetles, and wasps. In some, like craneflies, the early stage has even returned to water. Although these more extreme changes likely started through a series of more gradual changes across molts, at some point this whole process was condensed through the evolution of a nonfeeding **pupa** stage. A pupating insect envelops itself in a casing where it spends a relatively long time undergoing the business of major body rearrangements and transformations. Such major rearrangements are known as **metamorphosis**. All stages prior to metamorphosis are termed **larvae** instead of nymphs (see Figure 24-46).

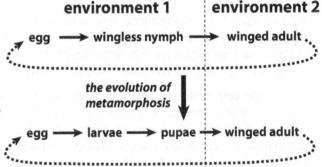

environment 1 | **environment 2**

egg ⟶ wingless nymph ⟶ winged adult

the evolution of metamorphosis

egg ⟶ larvae ⟶ pupae ⟶ winged adult

Figure 21-46. The evolution of metamorphosis involves pushing the trend of different stages of development using different environments to the extreme. See text for more details.

In essence, the theme here is that insect development ranges from minor changes to major changes between young and adults. But despite the variation, one theme found in the first water to air transitions remains the same—winged forms emerge only in the later stages of development. That is not to say that all adult insects with a winged ancestry bear wings. As mentioned previously, that is not true. The loss of adult wings has occurred in different insect lineages. And in other cases, such as found in ants and aphids, only some adult forms develop wings. Nonetheless, all insects in their earlier stages of development lack wings.

Why so many insects?

If you are familiar with a child's toy called Mr. Potato Head, you know that the more different types of eyes, noses, ears, and mouths you have, the more different types of faces you can build. The same idea applies to any group of arthropods. The more different types of mouthparts, walking legs, or any other body component available, the more different variations on the basic body plan possible. Insects are particularly adept at variation, not only because the addition of wings added another body component to be subsequently modified, but also becausee flight created the opportunity for other body parts to be modified in ways that just would not work in the absence of flight. Earlier, for instance, I mentioned that the siphoning mouthparts of butterflies would not work in the absence of flight. Although I have no intention of trying to outline all the different ways that the different modi-

Table 21-1. Different ways the basic insect body parts have been modified.

Major types of mouthparts	Major types of legs	Major types of wings
chewing (e.g., many insects)	ambulatory (walking) (e.g., many insects)	paleopterous (membranous, outstretched) (e.g., mayflies, dragonflies)
chewing-lapping (e.g., honey bees. bumble bees)	cursorial (running) (e.g., cockroaches)	neopterous (can be folded posteriorly) (e.g., all other winged insects)
sponging (e.g., houseflies)	saltatorial (jumping) (e.g., grasshopper hindlegs)	elytra (heavily sclerotized) (e.g., beetle forewings)
cutting-sponging (e.g., horse flies, black flies)	raptorial (grasping) (e.g., preying mantis forelegs)	tegmina (leathery) (e.g., grasshopper forewings)
siphoning (e.g., butterflies)	natatorial (swimming) (e.g., diving beetles)	hemelytra (hardened base, membranous tip) (e.g., true bug forewings)
		halteres (small club-like flight stabilizers) (e.g., hind wings of all flies)
piercing-sucking (e.g., cicadas, mosquitoes, assassin bugs)	fassorial (digging) (e.g., mole cricket forelegs)	scaly (covered with flattened setae or scales) (e.g., butterflies)

fied parts have been put together to form different types of insects, Table 21-1 lists the major forms of modifications of mouthparts, walking legs, and wings found in insects. (Note: Antennae are also quite variable, but I have left them out). With these lists in front of you, you can play with different combinations. Perhaps you will recognize some insects that you come up with.

The developmental twist associated with the evolution of wings, where each individual has both an early wingless stage and a later winged stages, has also added to the drama of insect evolution. In particular, flight has made it possible for both the wingless and winged stage to not only specialize, but also to do so in very different ways. Consider again caterpillars and butterflies. Wings make it possible for a butterfly to literally take off from the plant species that it fed on as a caterpillar and go feed in a completely different way. But when it comes time to reproduce, flight's increased travel range makes the return trip possible. Specifically, a butterfly can search all over to find another member of the same plant species that it fed on in its youth to lay its eggs on. And this basic pattern—the winged adult flying off to feed (and mate) in a new way, while also using flight to return to the habitat of its youth to lay eggs—is a common theme. Mayflies and dragonflies return to water to lay eggs. Parasitic wasps commonly feed on pollen and/or nectar as adults, but they also seek out specific types of insects to lay their eggs either on or within. The larva then feed off this host before again emerging as flying adults. And the list of examples goes on and on.

In most of these cases, parental care ends with hatching. That is, once the nutrients provided in the egg are used up, the nymphs or the larvae must fend for themselves. There are, however, a few exceptions. For example, in cases where the larval food source will not last long, such as dung and carrion that decompose rapidly, one or both parents of some beetle species excavate an underground chamber to store and protect the resource and the larvae developing within it. But the biggest twist is when the feeding interplay between larvae and adults goes one step further. As we have seen, wings opened the door for adults to feed differently than the younger wingless stages of development. The next step is when larval stages switch over to the adult food source. For example, larval bees often feed on pollen or a combination of pollen and nectar. Doing so may makes sense if adults can capture a more nutritious food source. The only problem is that instead of just returning back to a larval habitat to lay eggs, a parent must continual return to the "nest" to provision its larva. It is a big cost that in an evolutionary sense only a few insects have ever been willing to pay. And as I mentioned in a previous discussion of kin selection, among most larva-feeding insects—which includes many species of ants, bees, and wasps—neither mom nor dad are the major providers. Instead, dad typically does nothing, mom specializes in becoming an egg-laying machine—known as a queen, and the early produced daughters continue to hang around as adults and do the work of provisioning other siblings.

Homeotic transformations

Perhaps you are wondering about something. If two structures within an organism are different— such as a shrimp's antenna and one of its walking legs—how would one ever really know whether they are duplicate structures that have diversified or they are completely novel structures?

Homeotic transformations provide the most direct evidence for the duplication–diversification scenario. The term **homeosis** was coined by the biologist William Bateson in the late 1800s to discuss the process of making two things similar. As stated previously, Bateson was struck by the idea that transformation of repeating structures played a particular important role in the emergence of many different types of organisms. He realized that the best way to demonstrate divergence was to find structures that at times failed to diverge during development—that is, to be made similar.

In 1915 the first homeotic transformation was discovered in a laboratory setting by a *Drosophila* geneticist named Calvin Bridges. As found in mayflies and dragonflies (and many other types of insects), two sets of wings is thought to be the ancestral condition. Flies, however, normally have only one set of wings and one set of a structure used in maintaining balance during

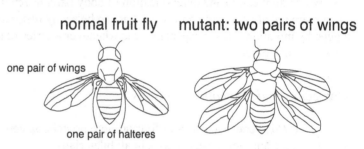

Figure 21-47. A homeotic mutation.

flight called halteres. Bridges discovered a fly with two pairs of wings and no halteres (see Figure 21-47), suggesting that halteres were once wings that have undergone developmental modification. In subsequent years other examples of homeotic transformations have been found. One of the most striking speaks to the idea that two structures found within an insect's head region—specifically antenna and mouthparts—arose via modification of a basic walking leg. Flies have been found that have grown legs where either antenna or mouthparts normally develop. Furthermore, larval flies have been found that express early patterns of leg development along abdominal segments (which normally lack any form of appendage). In other words, the abdominal segments in these larvae look like thoracic segments. These larvae have never survived and so have never developed into adults with legs on abdominal segments. Nonetheless, this homeotic transformation, along with the transformations observed in the head region, supports the idea that insects evolved from an organism that had appendages on more than just the thoracic three segments.

Homeotic mutations

Here is a simple genetic model that describes how a homeotic mutation could work.

Consider two regulatory genes called *gene A* and *gene B*. Recall that regulatory genes are ones that code for proteins that influence the turning on or off of other genes. That is, other genes have sensors that detect the presence or absence of the proteins coded for by regulatory genes. Regulatory genes can also have sensors that regulate when they are turned on. Different regulatory genes can thus be turned on within the cells of different body regions, which by influencing the overall pattern of gene expression can in turn act as developmental switches that cause different body regions to develop differently.

Viewed in that light, suppose the expression of *gene A* and *gene B* within the cells making up a repeating structure such as a segment plays a role in how this structure will develop. For example, the expression of only *gene A* within an insect segment could lead to the formation of a pair of wings. However, the expression of both *gene A* and *gene B* could modify the development of wings into something else, say halteres. If true, what would happen to an organism that suffered a disruptive mutation in *gene B*? Segments that normally develop halteres would now develop wings because such segments would only express *gene A*. Mutations that disrupt *gene B* expression would thus qualify as a **homeotic mutation**.

Two points about this model: First, the theme underlying homeotic mutations is that the disruption of one gene (or more) leads to a more ancestral pattern of gene expression within a repeating unit. Note, however, that this can occur in more than one way. For example, if *gene B* inhibits the expression of *gene A,* then both genes would not be expressed together. Yet a mutation to *gene B* could still lead to a homeotic transformation because now a segment that normally expresses only *gene B* would express *gene A* due to lack of *gene A* inhibition. Second, homeotic mutations are not possible in every case where duplication and diversification of body parts have taken place. New patterns of genetic regulation are not always formed in ways that can be easily restored to an ancestral pattern by removing a gene by mutation. This is especially true whenever a series of successive changes have been layered on top of each other.

Hox genes and homeotic mutations

Recall *Hox* genes—clusters of four or more homeobox genes that have distinct patterns of expression along the anterior–posterior axis in all bilaterians.

Hox genes were first discovered because some mutant forms lead to homeosis. For example, in *Drosophila* the *hox* gene *Ultrabithorax (Ubx)* is nomally expressed at high levels in the third thoracic segment—the segment that forms halteres instead of wings. But mutations that disrupt *Ubx* expression revert the third thoracic segment back to its ancestral state—developing wings similar to the forewings, instead of halteres. Antenna to walking legs proved to be another example of changes in a *hox* gene expression. The gene called *Antennapedia (Antp)* is normally expressed in a fruit fly's thoracic segments, but not in its head. Certain types of mutations, however, cause *Antp* expression to extend into the head region, and one effect is that a pair of legs form where antenna would normally be. Similarly, the expression of both *Ubx* and *abdominal A (abdA)* prevents the development of limbs in the abdomen, so mutations disrupting this expression pattern can lead to early patterns of leg development along abdominal segments.

Although there is simply a "gee whiz" element to homeotic mutations, the connection between homeotic mutations and *hox* genes stirred a much bigger fire in the minds of evolutionary biologists. Why? It largely comes from the alignment of three observations: (1) *Hox* genes are clusters of four or more master regulatory homeobox genes that have distinct patterns of expression along the anterior–posterior axis in all bilaterians. All arthropods seem to share 10. (2) A major difference among different arthropod groups is the pattern in which the ancestral biramous appendage is modified in different segments along the anterior–posterior axis. (3) Which *hox* genes are expressed in any segment can make a difference in what form of appendage develops. Or stated differently, changes in segment and appendage type in arthropods are usually genetically marked by boundaries between *hox* expression zones. Do you see the implication? A single mutation that shifts the pattern in which one of these master regulatory genes is expressed along segments could result in a major change in an arthropod's body plan. And the accumulating evidence lends some support for this idea. Although differences in *hox* gene expression patterns cannot be linked to all major differences in segment development patterns among arthropod groups, it does seem to explain some of them. This is remarkable. By evolving in a way that made bilaterian development possible, the basic workings of *hox* regulatory genetic tool kit also made fundamental shifts in development possible. And although the details will vary, this same pattern should hold for other regulatory gene families.

Moreover, other mutations that change how *hox* gene expression affects downstream genetic regulatory networks can lead to further developmental modifications. For example, the expression of *Ubx* in the third (but not the second) thoracic segment in insects appears to be the initial trigger for hindwings to develop differently than forewings. But it does not trigger all hindwings to develop in the same way. Butterflies, beetles, flies, along with other types of insects, develop hindwings that differ from each other—suggesting that these diverse morphologies came about by evolutionary change in their respective downstream target genes.

Annelids

The other most clearly segmented bilaterian phyla is the annelids, or segmented worms. Like arthropods, changes in both the number and kind of segments underlie annelid diversification and do not, coincidentally, display a great deal of structural variation—especially when compared to other worm-like animal phyla. One group of annelids called the polycheates even typically bear a pair of lateral, fleshy, paddle-like appendages called **parapodia** on each segment that have been modified in a variety of ways.

Yet although annelids are a species-rich group, containing somewhere around 10,000 to 15,000 known species, they don't even begin to compare to arthropods. If segmentation is a prime driver of diversification, why is there such a huge difference between these two groups? The difference appears to be the lack of an exoskeleton. Without a stiff outer covering that can both reduce water loss and provide the extra support needed to form jointed appendages, annelids have invaded land with only limited success. No terrestrial annelids run along the ground or fly through the air. Instead the earthworms and the few other terrestrial annelids are confined to live in damp areas such as soil. And even the aquatic forms are not as diverse as crustaceans and the other aquatic arthropods, whose jointed body and appendages have been modified to perform a large variety of functions.

The chordates (especially vertebrates)

One can understand a lot about chordate structure by considering what it takes to be a good swimmer. From our earlier discussion of eukaryotic flagella, as well as just watching any fish, we know that undulating back and forth can push one through the water. But how can a bilaterian generate such undulating motion? The simplest conception is to have two muscles, one running down each side, with a structural element sandwiched in between. The structure needs to flexible, in terms of side-to-side movement, yet fairly incompressible in terms of length. That way whenever a muscle on one side contracts, the whole thing bends instead of shortens. Figure 21-48 shows that alternating muscle contractions across sides would generate a rhythmic undulation. The only problem is that the type of undulations shown would not go anywhere. When both ends—head and tail—move equally, any forward propulsive forces will be met by equal and opposite backward forces.

Figure 21-48. Undulating motion created by alternating muscle contractions on two sides of a incompressible, but flexible rod.

To generate movement the tail end needs to whip back and forth while the head end remains more stable. The better this is accomplished, the better the animal can propel itself through the water. Moving muscle attachments away from the head end along with decreasing this end's ability to flex back and forth—by some combination of increasing its size and the stiffness of its structural material—are some of the means to increase head stability. On the other hand, making the structural material more flexible as it extends toward the tail, as well as breaking the muscle on each side into smaller blocks, can increase the tail end's ability to whip back and forth. Smaller units of contraction make it possible to generate an out-of-phase sequence of contraction that ripples along both sides of the body in a way that creates an even more powerful articulation of the tail end. Furthermore, each muscle block will be able to generate more torque on the whole arrangement if it is hooked into connective tissue that in turn attaches to the central structure element. Interestingly, such an arrangement (see Figure 21-49) captures the basic structural design of a chordate.

Chordates (phylum Chordata) come from the deuterostome side of the protostome/deuterostome split. At some point in their life cycle all chordates have a structural element that runs along their midline for at least a portion of the body's length and is surrounded on both sides by blocks of muscle. Among the aquatic chordates, one finds that as swimming becomes a more important component of their lifestyle, the basic components of this design are improved on. For example, the central structural element goes from just a cartilaginous rod (called a **notochord**) to a structure reinforced with articulating chunks of either cartilage, which can be calcified, or bone. Each articulating chunk is called a **vertebra**, and the whole structure is called a **vertebral column**. In vertebrates (chordates with a vertebral column), the front or head end also becomes an increasingly dynamic sensory and feeding structure used in being a mobile predator. Fins, which help in steering, also became more prominent

Figure 21-49. An arrangement of muscle blocks and structural material that could power swimming. See text for more detail.

in better swimmers and in some cases became articulating structures. In at least one of these lineages, changes associated with their particular aquatic lifestyle opened the door for a movement onto land and eventually even into the air. Two sets of articulating fins were modified into legs that in conjunction with changes to the pelvic and pectoral girdle and the vertebral column made it not only possible to support its body on land, but also to permit locomotion. In this transition to land many other features, such as the head's sensory and feeding components, the external covering (skin), and means of reproduction, were also modified in a variety of ways. What remains today among these branching lineages are animals that we call fish, amphibians, reptiles, mammals, and birds, along with some less well-known, creatures such as tunicates and cephalochordates. It is an interesting group with an interesting history. Next we explore a little further.

Are chordates segmental?

Look at any chordate from the outside, including yourself, and a segmental body plan is not apparent. However, looks at times can be deceiving. During development chordates form a series of structurally repeated, paired, block-like masses of mesoderm called **somites** running dorsally on each side of the midline. Like segment growth in annelids and arthropods, somites form sequentially along the anterior to posterior axis. Somites subsequently develop into a series of independent segments of muscle, along with their associated connective tissue (including vertebrae when present), on both sides of the body. These, of course, are the muscle blocks mentioned earlier in the discussion of how to design a more effective swimmer. So, in essence, the evolution of swimming seems to have emplaced a segmental element into chordate design.

Although the rest of the body is not segmented per se, the somitic organization does induce a segment-like arrangement in other structures, specifically the notochord and dorsal nerve tube. The notochord, as we have already learned, is a stiff, but flexible rod of connective tissue the runs between the somite pairs. But in vertebrates, the notochord gets assimilated into the segmental arrangement of vertebrae. For instance, the notochord turns into the disks between vertebrae. Early in every chordate's development the notochord also releases chemical signals that induce a **dorsal nerve tube** to develop just above it. Nerves sprouting from this nerve tube then connect to each muscle segment and thus form the means to regulate muscle contraction. Because the muscles are segmental, the arrangement of nerves along the nerve tube takes on a repeated, segmental appearance. Note that these three structures—the segmental arrangement of muscles and connective tissue, the notochord, and the dorsal nerve tube—are all parts of one motor system able to generate the type of trunk undulations useful for swimming.

Although the segmental nature of somites is different than arthropod segments, they still generate a similar axis along which body plans can diversify. The number of somites formed can vary, and the details of how each somite along a body develops can be modified. Such changes, for example, could influence both the number and the shape and size of each vertebra along the entire column, which in turn can influence a body's performance ability. You, for instance, can easily rotate your head independent of your body because, different than your chest (thoracic) vertebrae, your neck (cervical) vertebrae do not develop as long lateral projections called ribs. Snakes, on the other hand, can move as they do because they have numerous (up to a couple of hundred) similar-shaped vertebrae.

Other basic chordate features

Three basic chordate features have been introduced so far: somites, notochord, and a dorsal nerve tube.

Two other features also unite all chordates. The first, a **postanal tail**, is a muscular extension of the trunk that contributes to swimming ability by adding more flexible length to generate propelling forces. The second, **pharyngeal slits**, created a new way to filter feed. Filter feeding requires the processing of large volumes of water to get adequate food, which is why most filter-feeding animals with a gut tube have some external device to capture food before it enters the mouth. In chordates, however, the removal of small food particles from the water occurs in the pharynx, the region of the gut tube just posterior to the mouth that is lined with sticky mucus. Water is first drawn in through the mouth by the action of numerous flagella and then moves back outside through the pharyngeal slits—a series of openings between the pharynx and the outside. Large amounts of water can thus enter the mouth without having to pass through the entire gut tube. Food particles trapped in the mucus take the other route, moving into the rest of the gut tube to be digested. Figure 21-50 shows the five chordate characteristics listed.

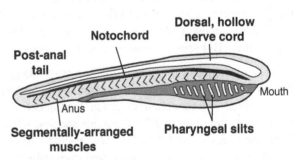

Figure 21-50. The five chordate features arranged into a simple body plan.

Cephalochordates

The cephalochordates are a small group (about 28 species) that have drawn considerable interest because they are believed to bear an uncanny likeness to the invertebrate ancestor of the vertebrates (their body plan is strikingly similar to Figure 21-50). In fact, they look like simplified fishes and are capable of swimming short distances. Cephalochordates are also known as lancelets (due to their long, pointed, blade-shaped body) or amphioxus. Their characteristic features (notochord, segmented muscles, dorsal nerve tube, etc.) arise early in development and are retained as adults. They live and feed (on plankton) in the water column by continually alternating between upward swimming and passive sinking. As they get larger—adults can be up to 5 cm long—they eventually sink to the bottom, where they burrow backward into sand and filter feed through their exposed anterior end. However, the ability to swim is still an important part of the adult lifestyle. They push out of the sand and swim to a new spot whenever feeding conditions at their current location are inadequate.

Cephalochordates are as interesting for the body feature that they lack, as the feature that they have. Let me list a few: (1) No vertebral or spinal column ever forms, so the notochord is the only structural element throughout their life. (2) Although several fins supported by fibrous fin rays are present—specifically a long dorsal fin, a posterior caudal or tail fin, and a short ventral fin—paired fins (appendages) of any type are lacking. (3) Although cephalochordates have a closed circulatory system, which facilitates the pace at which blood can be moved through tissues and thus ultimately the pace at which it can be circulated, they do not have a central or systemic heart—that is, one that collects and pumps all the blood each time through the circuit. Instead they rely on a series of smaller pumps located on main branches of the system. The blood also lacks any form of respiratory protein, such as hemoglobin, which suggests that blood likely plays a minor role in oxygen delivery. Most oxygen exchange likely occurs through the skin. Both of these circulatory features suggest that cephalochordates are not built to be very active.

The cephalochordate front or head end is also not as distinct as vertebrates. For instance, the head end of the dorsal nerve tube does not enlarge into a distinguishable structure that we commonly call a brain. Instead, the neural tube at this end is only slightly swollen. (Although, closer examination has revealed that the master regulatory genes that organize the major brain regions—forebrain, midbrain, and hindbrain—in vertebrates are both present and expressed in the same pattern. And a rudimentary version of the part of a vertebrate brain that monitors internal conditions, such as the amount of high-energy molecules present, has been found. This brain region likely plays a role in "motivating" an individual to relocate when the current food supply is inadequate.) Furthermore, familiar sensory organs are either lacking or not that sophisticated. The only evidence of visual input is a retina-like pattern of connections near a cluster of pigment cells near the very tip of the head end. In other words, cephalocordates appear to bear only a single eye, able to, at best, detect things like shadows of potential predators. The small projections or tentacles surrounding the mouth also appear to gather certain types of sensory information. In fact, some neurons hook into the brain in a similar way as vertebrate taste buds, suggesting that these animals may be able to reject or accept certain food items based on their "taste." But sensory organs associated with smell or hearing are lacking.

The existence of cephalochordates sets the stage for evolutionary inquiry to proceed in one of two directions. One is to move backward and try to understand the basic steps by which the chordate body plan evolved. Another chordate group, the tunicates, would come up in that discussion. Tunicates are a curious group of around 2,500 marine species, where the chordate features typically show up only in the larval forms, and the adults are sessile filter feeders. Other branches in the deuterostome line would also need to be scrutinized. And eventually this line of inquiry goes back to the protostome/deuterostome split. Alternatively, the forward direction would focus on how the evolution of somites, along with other chordate feature, set up the evolution of the morphological diverse group known as the vertebrates. Or stated differently, how did the chordate body plan set the stage for the evolution of all the missing features mentioned in the previous paragraph?

Inquiry in either direction is worthy of further exploration. But given that humans are members of the vertebrate clade, the forward direction begins to explore more directly who we are (along with our other vertebrate neighbors). But even then, there is much to cover and attempt to explain. A basic topic list would include the evolution of jaws, along with other features of the vertebrate head; the evolution of the vertebral column—including the diversity of shapes and functions of different vertebrae, not only among different species, but within the vertebrae found within one individual; the evolution of two sets of paired appendages; and the changes that allowed vertebrates to move onto land.

To be honest, I not sure I yet know how to put these stories together in a more effective way than the general summaries that can be found in lots of different sources. So, for the moment, I encourage you to look elsewhere (e.g., doing something as simple as an Internet search). But as you do, try to keep the central theme introduced here in mind—the connections between segmentation and the evolution of morphological diversity. Doing so will help you see basic patterns among the details.

Some key terms:

flagellation constraint – a cell that for some reason does not retain its flagella while undergoing cell division. As a consequence the cell can not "swim" and reproduce at the same time.

triploblastic organism – any organism that has an outer cell layer (known as the ectoderm), and inner cell layer surrounding the gut (known as the endoderm), and a distinct third tissue layer, consisting largely of muscle cells and connective tissue, sandwiched in between (known as the mesoderm). Also know as a three-layered organism.

Some study questions:

1. Evidence suggests that sponges evolved from choanoflagellates. Speculate as to how getting around the flagellation constraint and size-based constraints could have played a role in the evolution of sponges.

2. Provide a plausible evolutionary scenario by which the three basic forms of cnidarian life cycles shown in figure 21-21 could have evolved from sponge-like beginnings.

3. Provide a plausible evolutionary scenario by which an acoelomorph flatworm-like organism could have evolve cnidarian-like beginnings.

4. Discuss the connection between bilaterally symmetrically animals, brains, gut tubes, mesoderm, muscle cells, skeletal systems, circulatory systems, respiratory systems, and excretory systems.

5. Based on molecular evidence, sugggest what the common ancestor of protostomes and deutero-stomes may have looked like.

6. Among all animal phyla, arthropods are by far the most species rich group and its members can be found in all different types of aquatic and terrestrial habitats. What is it about arthropods that made this extensive radiation possible?

7. Speculate as to how insects may have evolved wings? How has the evolution of wings contributed to insect becoming the most species rich group of arthropods? How did the evolution of wings set the stage for the evolution of caterpillar-to-butterfly like metamorphosis?

8. What is a homeotic mutation? Provide a simple model by which a homeotic mutation could work.

9. What is a homeobox gene? Why have homeobox genes received so much attention from develop-mental and evolutionary biologists?

10. The most species rich group of deuterostomes are the vertebrates, and, like arthropods, its mem-bers can be found in all differenty types of aquatic and terrestrial habitats. What is it about vertebrates that made this extensive radiation possible?

11. What have been some of the major highlights of vertebrate evolution?

The Evolution of Multicellular Phototrophs

In the previous chapter we discussed the evolution of multicellularity in cells that lacked the ability to do photosynthesis. Starting with a single trade-off, the flagellation constraint, we ended up discussing the evolution of a seemingly monophyletic group known as animals. Here we focus on the evolution of multicellularity in photosynthetic cells, which at first glance seems like we are going to talk about the evolution of plants. It is not, however, that simple.

At the stem of this confusion are the different types of multicellular algae. Algae were traditionally regarded as simple plants adapted to living in aquatic environments. They were considered to be plants because they are photosynthetic (photoautotrophic) and simple because they lacked leaves, roots, and flowers, along with other structures that characterize higher plants. But that conception got pulled wayward by the fact that multicellularity in algae appears to have evolved many times. For example, among the three major groups of algae (red, brown, and green algae), two also have unicellular members—that is, within the green and red algae, multicellular forms are more similar to certain single-celled organisms than to multicellular members of another algal group. Such observation only makes sense if multicellularity within algae evolved more than once; or put in biology speak, if eukaryotic multicellular algae are a polyphyletic instead of monophyletic group. Evidence even points strongly to polyphyletic origins within algal groups. For example, in the green algae, multicellularity appears to have evolved many different times.

All this polyphyletic mumbo jumbo does, however, make an interesting suggestion: Multicellularity seems to evolve much more readily in phototrophic than autotrophic cells. But it also points out that if the term *plant* is constrained to represent a monophyletic or natural group, all algae cannot be plants. In fact, only by including both unicellular and multicellular forms does it make any sense to call all the various types of photosynthetic aquatic organism algae. (Although it still seems confusing!)

And even then, it would be best if at least some of the things traditionally called algae were not, specifically, the multicellular forms of cyanobacteria sometimes referred to as blue-green algae. Although they are photosynthetic and aquatic, they are also built from prokaryotic, instead of eukaryotic, cells. Clearly these organisms have a very distinct evolutionary history.

Yet, if one limits focus to just the multicellular phototrophs that fill forests and grasslands, as well as all the other terrestrial ecosystems, then the evolutionary story appears to have parallels with animal evolution. Most specifically, like animals, the ancestry of land-dwelling multicellular photosynthetic creatures appears to be monophyletic and can be traced back to an aquatic environment. These so-called land plants, or just plants, share the most similarities with one lineage of green algae called the Charophyceae. In other words, plants appear to be a branch of this evolutionary lineage that invaded the land. And in this transition, plants evolved many new features that helped them overcome the new challenges imposed by a dramatically different environment.

Two major transitions seem to underlie the evolution of multicellular phototrophs: the evolution of multicellularity in different algae groups and the movement onto land. Here we begin to explore highlights of both. Let's start with what was likely the first type of multicellular organism to ever exist on this planet.

A Multicellular Prokaryote

Cyanobacteria keep coming up in this discussion of Life. They appear to have been the first organisms to perform water-splitting photosynthesis, and they are seemingly the ancestors to the photosynthetic organelle found in some eukaryotic cells called chloroplasts. They also may have become the first truly multicellular organisms.

The basic message stays the same: Trade-offs that constrain a single cell from being able to simultaneously perform two useful functions creates an opportunity for a multicellular organism to do something that a single celled organism cannot. Here we consider a metabolic trade-off.

The trade-off between nitrogen fixation and water-splitting photosynthesis

Certain cyanobacteria evolved the ability to fix nitrogen—that is, the ability to reduce N_2, the most common molecule in the atmosphere, to NH_3 (ammonia). The advantage was potentially tremendous. Now a single cell was able to get its energy from the sun, its needed carbon from carbon dioxide, its needed hydrogen from water, and its needed nitrogen from molecular nitrogen. In other words, one organism was able to live on the most basic supplies available. Still to this day, no other organism has matched this level of self-sufficiency.

There was, however, a corresponding trade-off. The enzymes used to fix nitrogen fail to function when oxygen is present. Thus, nitrogen fixation and oxygen-liberating photosynthesis cannot occur within the same cell at the same time.

Two solutions

Some present-day cyanobacteria, and presumably the first cyanobacteria to evolve nitrogen fixation, separate these two activities temporally. They photosynthesize during most of the day and fix nitrogen at night. At first glance, it seems the ideal solution. But such temporal separation involves a continual cycle of degradation and synthesis, which is presumably energetically expensive. By the end of each day, components of the oxygen-releasing portion of photosynthesis are degraded, and synthesis of nitrogen-fixing enzymes begins. These same enzymes are then degraded once sufficient nitrogen has been fixed and stored, and synthesis of the earlier degraded photosynthetic components starts again to get ready for daytime photosynthesis.

Of course, there is another potential way to get around this trade-off—to separate these activities spatially into different cells. And such cell differentiation has happened, as some filamentous cyanobacteria generate cells called **heterocysts** (see Figure 22-1). Heterocysts form as a result of differential gene expression (in comparison to photosynthetic cells) and specialize in nitrogen fixation. Some of the ways that heterocysts are different than photosynthetic cells include (1) the formation of additional cell wall layers to reduce the diffusion of oxygen into the cell from the surrounding environment; (2) the loss of the oxygen-liberating portion of the light phase of photosynthesis (called photosystem II), while retaining the other part (called photosystem I) that can use light and a cyclic flow of electrons to generate the ATP needed to power nitrogen fixation; and (3) the loss of the Calvin cycle (carbon reduction cycle), which means that heterocysts must rely on photosynthetic cells to supply reduced forms of carbon. Furthermore, the cytoplasm of heterocysts and adjacent photosynthetic cells are connected by the formation of tiny canals. It is through these openings that reduced nitrogen moves from heterocysts to photosynthetic cells, and reduced carbon moves the other direction. To facilitate this distribution, heterocysts occur at relatively fixed intervals along these filaments.

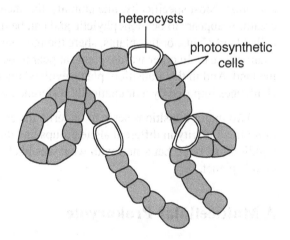

Figure 22-1. A filamentous arrangement of cyanobacteria with two different cell types that specialize in different tasks. Only photosynthetic cells perform water-splitting photosynthesis, and only heterocysts perform nitrogen fixation.

Heterocysts are a clear example of a somatic cell. Once heterocysts differentiate from "normal" photosynthetic cells due to differential gene expression, they cannot dedifferentiate back into a photosynthetic cell, nor can they undergo cell division. (Note: Biologists call this **terminal differentiation**.) Consequently, heterocysts cannot give rise to heterocysts. The only way for heterocysts to persist across generations is to be regenerated through cell differentiation in each generation. Heterocysts containing filaments are truly multicellular organisms.

A Starting Point for Eukaryotic Multicellular Algae

The apparent polyphyletic nature of eukaryotic multicellular algae makes one wonder what drove the repeated evolution of multicellularity. Was the same story repeated over and over, or was each case unique? Although more than one driving force seems likely, I find it interesting that an already familiar trade-off—the flagellation constraint—may have played a prominent role, especially among the green algae, where every multicellular line appears to have evolved from single-celled flagellates. Here, in an admittedly brief and incomplete way, I begin to discuss this possibility.

Photosynthetic flagellates and cell coverings

A photosynthetic flagellate is a general name for any flagella-bearing single-celled organism that contains chloroplasts. A means of propulsion in aquatic photosynthetic cells has several potential benefits. Perhaps most important is being able to remain in the euphotic zone—where there is sufficient light for photosynthesis. Even in the clearest water, light availability, along with harmful UV radiation, declines with depth relatively quickly as light is absorbed by water and converted into heat. Most cells also tend to sink (cells tend to be negatively buoyant or slightly more dense than water), so just to stay in regions of adequate light requires the ability to swim at least as fast as one sinks. Furthermore, the angle of the sun and the turbidity of water undergo constant change, so to remain at the best depth to photosynthesize requires constant movement up and down in the water column. Using flagella-based motility to move to places that have higher nutrient concentrations, or away from predators, would also be beneficial.

On the other hand, some form of stiff outer covering also has advantages, especially to a photosynthetic cell able to make a living in the absence of endocytosis. Not only can it play a protective or structural role (by keeping the cell in some form of preferred shape), but it can also help cells contend with their inherent osmotic or "too-much-water" problem.

Yet, although flagella and cell coverings are both good, they are not readily compatible. Recall that a eukaryotic flagellum does not extend out beyond a cell's outer membrane; it is the cell's outer membrane extending out and around a bendable microtubule-based structural core—the axoneme. So, by definition, a cell wall—a relatively rigid structure encasing *the entire* cell membrane—completely rules out flagella. Chloroplast-containing flagellates have tried to get around this dilemma in a variety of ways.

For instance, three groups of flagellates—called euglenoids, cryptomonads, and dinoflagellates—contain species with chloroplasts that have *intracellular* cell coverings. In each case, component parts fit together to form a somewhat rigid structure that lies just underneath a cell's outer membrane. Given that these structures are internal and do not completely encase the cell, flagella are still possible.

A little more information: The structural makeup of each group's intracellular cell covering is different. Euglenoids are typically narrow oblong cells whose shape is maintained by a **pellicle**—a series of interlocking strips made mostly of proteins that encircle the cell somewhat like staves of a barrel, as each strip extends from the cell's apex to its posterior. (By convention, the part of the cell directed forward during swimming is designated the apical or anterior end, whereas the opposite end is considered to be posterior.) The flagella then extend out from an invagination or pocket located at the cell's anterior end. This flagellar pocket lacks an underlying pellicle. Although still largely protein in nature, the intracellular covering of cryptomonads is made up of numerous stiff hexagonal, rectangular, oval, or round plates arranged like tiles underneath the outer membrane. Again, however, this structural support, which is known as the **periplast**, is absent underneath the anterior pocket in which flagella emerge. Dinoflagellates, on the other hand, form an almost mosaic-looking arrangement of flattened vesicles underneath the outer cell membrane. Commonly, stiff plates containing cellulose microfibrils are constructed within vesicles. These plates or **theca** usually fit closely together, even overlapping slightly, except at the flagellar pore from which two flagella emerge. Curiously, in most dinoflagellates the flagellar pore is located around the midpoint of one of the cell's sides instead of at either the anterior or posterior end.

As discussed in Chapter 20, most external cell coverings are composites of some form of microfibril—an aggregate of long, straight, tension-resistant polysaccharides, such as cellulose—embedded in an amorphous matrix of polysaccharides and proteins (which can be combined to form glycoproteins). Such microfibril-based cell walls are incompatible with flagella as they completely encase a cell's outer membrane. Flagellated cells can still, however, be included within the life cycle of organisms whose cells typically build this type of cell wall. Certain cells can undergo a type of cell division where inside an existing cell wall two or more naked or wall-less daughter cells form bearing flagella that then break free leaving the old cell wall behind. (Note: This stands in contrast to the more typical form of cell division, which involves continued growth and expansion of the existing cell wall to create a container with sufficient volume for the enclosed cell to grow and divide. Commonly, but not always, the cell wall then grows inward in between the two new daughter cells, so that each has its own complete enclosure.)

A group of green algae, often referred to as the Volvocales, took a different twist on the cell covering/flagella complication: They evolved a unique external covering compatible with flagellar motility. Specifically, every time a new cell wall is constructed a pair of well-defined channels or pores form, that then two flagella extend out through. Three features, in particular, seem to make this possible. First, their external covering lacks any microfibrils. Instead it is composed of a crystalline lattice arrangement of glycoproteins (specifically hydroxyproline-rich glycoproteins or HRGPs). Second, this exclusively glycoprotein-based cell wall is shed in each cell generation. After cell division, daughter cells digest their way out through the "mother" cell wall and leave it behind. And interestingly, cell division within this group is not always binary—one cell dividing into two daughter cells. Instead, the starting cell can undergo a series of divisions to produce a cluster of 4, 8, 16, or even more daughter cells. These daughter cells form a new cell wall only after they are released and flagellated. The new pair of flagellar pores thus form by the cell covering being assembled around already present flagella.

Cell coverings and the flagellation constraint

Naked photosynthetic flagellates—that is, those without any form of rigid covering—along with those groups of photosynthetic flagellates with an internal cell covering, do not necessarily suffer the flagellation constraint; they can, and commonly do, maintain their flagella, hence motility, while undergoing cell division. In other words, their basal bodies (kinetosomes) can be duplicated and distributed by the microtubule-based spindle into the two daughter cells while still remaining attached to flagella.

The story, however, changes among cells with external coverings.

As mentioned earlier, in lineages of cells capable of building microfibril-based cell walls, cells can either have a cell wall and no flagella, or they can have flagella and no cell walls. We use this trade-off later to discuss the evolution and life cycles of most multicellular algae.

In contrast, the volvocine algae build an external cell covering (or wall) compatible with flagella. But can they also retain their flagella during cell division? Here the answer is a bit muddled (see Figure 22-2). Due to the rigid nature of the cell covering, flagella that protrude through flagellar pores are unable to migrate along with their basal bodies during their duplication and subsequent distribution (along with the chromosomes) by the mitotic spindle.

In response, many volvocine algae species resorb their flagella during cell division and thus suffer the flagellation constraint—they cannot swim and reproduce at the same time. Curiously, these species, along with most other volvocine algae, secrete a sticky extracellular material commonly

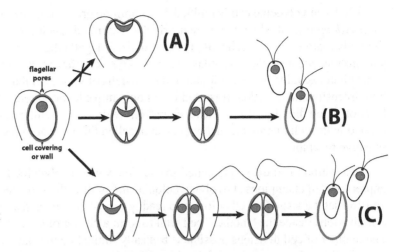

Figure 22-2. **Path A**, where basal bodies and flagella migrate together, is not a viable means for a single-celled Volvocine algal to reproduce because the rigid cell covering prevents the flagellar pore from moving along with the migrating flagella. However, both **path B** and **path C** are known to occur. In **path B** the flagella are resorbed, freeing the basal bodies to move with the mitotic spindle. This pathway suffers the flagellation constraint. In **path C**, the basal bodies separate from the flagella, freeing them to move with the mitotic spindle, while the separated flagella continue to beat for as long as they can stay attached. Whenever cell division occurs prior to flagella loss, this pathway does not suffer the flagellation constraint.

called "mucilage." And they secrete more mucilage during the time that they resorb their flagella, suggesting an attempt to compensate for flagella loss. Sticking to something may prevent a cell from sinking too far during cell division.

Other volvocine algae play this trade-off a different way. Instead of resorbing their flagella, and thus recovering all the materials used in their assembly, the basal bodies (kinetosomes) detach from the flagella, freeing them to migrate to the spindle poles during cell division. The flagella then continue to beat more or less normally in the absence of basal bodies. There is, however, an underlying problem. Most connections that anchor flagella to the rest of the cell emanate from the basal body, and the remaining connections are not strong enough to hold an oscillating flagellum for too long. So eventually the flagella will literally detach from the cell. Volvocine algae can thus retain motility temporarily during cell division, but doing so has a cost—all the materials used to assemble flagella will be lost to the cell.

Evolution of Multicellularity in the Volvocales

Volvocine algae are commonly found in calm waters of freshwater lakes and ponds, settings where cell walls and flagella are both useful. Freshwater, which generates an even more severe osmotic gradient than seawater, places a premium on a rigid container to prevent bursting. And flagella-powered motility allows an organism to both maintain and adjust its position in the water column. Yet despite these features, volvocine algae commonly face at least three major challenges: (1) not sinking too far while undergoing cell division; (2) avoid getting eaten by invertebrate filter feeders, such as rotifers and small crustaceans; and (3) getting sufficient amounts of mineral nutrients necessary for growth, especially phosphorus and nitrogen.

The basic volvocine cell is typified by a common group or genus of single-celled algae known as *Chlamydomonas*, of which there are nearly 500 described species. *Chlamydomonas* species all have a rigid, glycoprotein-based cell wall, two equal-sized flagella that power movement by a breaststroke-like motion, and a single chloroplast. They also typically have a rhodopsin-like light sensor (rhodopsin is the photoexcitable molecule found in the rod cells of your eye) that appears to somehow detect both light intensity and direction. It is used to not only move toward areas of more light when the current location is too dim, but also to move away from regions of too intense of light. This photoreceptor is located in the cell membrane just over an area called the eyespot (a pigmented shield for the light-sensitive receptor).

In addition to all the single-celled species, the various volvocine lineages also appear to be the unprecedented champions at evolving colonial and multicellular forms. Two aspects of volvocine cell division set the stage for cell colonies to readily form. The first is that cells can undergo a series of cell divisions inside the "mother" cell wall to form a cluster of 4, 8, 16, or even more daughter cells. The number of cell divisions possible is basically limited by the size of the starting cell. The larger a reproductive cell grows prior to initiating cell division, the more cell divisions can occur before falling below some minimum starting cell size threshold. The second is that these cells can secrete sticky mucilage. Daughter cells only need to secrete mucilage prior to digesting their way out of the mother cell wall to remain stuck together after emergence (see Figure 22-3).

Yet, what would be the advantage of sticking together? Like suggested in the early evolution of animals, hanging together could have been used by certain volvocine lineages to get around the flagellation constraint. But if so, the details are interestingly different than in early sponge-like colonies—where cells on the outside of a more-or-less spherical arrangement remained flagellated, and the inner space was used for cell division.

Consider, for instance, *Pandorina*. Members of this volvocine group form a globular arrangement of 16 or 32 biflagellate (*Chlamydomonas*-like) cells embedded in mucilage. Because there is no division of labor among cells, Pandorina is best seen as a colony. In fact, once any cell grows large enough to reproduce, basal bodies detach from their flagella, and the cell undergoes four (16 cells) or five (32 cells) quick cell divisions. During that time the basal-body-lacking flagella continue to work to keep the parental colony from sinking. Each new cell cluster then breaks free from the parental cell wall to form a new *Pandorina* colony. From that point on the colony's existing cells grow in size, but the number of cells never increases by further cell division (see Figure 22-3).

Why does *Pandorina* stop at 16 or 32 cells? Why not another round of division to form a 64-cell colony, or another to form a 128-cell colony? The seemingly obvious answer is that each starting cell would need

Figure 22-3. The two basic reproductive paths found in volvocine algae. In (a), once single celled algae grow large enough they resorb their flagella and go through several rounds of mitotic divisions. All the flagellated offspring then 'hatch' from the mother cell wall. In (b), the basic scenario is the same, except all the daughter cells remain stuck together to form a colony. Once each cell in a new colony has grown large enough, the cycle is repeated. It undergoes mitotic cell division in which the daughter cells remain attached and hatch out as a new colony. The means by which flagella, hence motility, is retained during cell division is discussed further in the text.

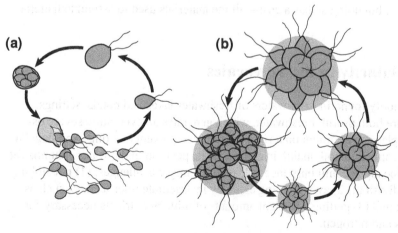

(a)   (b)

to have grown even larger to have sufficient volume to be divided into more than 32 viable cells, and for some reason spending the extra time and/or effort does not pay off. However, there may be another reason. Evidence suggests that basal-body-lacking-flagella can only reliably remain attached to the parental cell long enough for four or five rounds of cell division. Attempting more rounds of cell division would thus be accompanied by an increased risk of losing motility and sinking to a bad location.

Despite this four- to five-division limit for retaining flagella, there are lineages of volvocine algae with greater than 32 cells; but these larger groups are truly multicellular organisms, with clear somatic and germ cells. The somatic cells retain functional flagella throughout that can be used to maintain position in the water column, whereas the germ cells undergo even more rounds of cell division.

For instance, a volvocine algae group called *Pleodorina* has either 64 (six divisions), 128 (seven divisions), or 256 (eight divisions) cells arranged as a hollow sphere of mucilage-connected cells around one-half a millimeter in diameter. Early in development, all cells are the same basic size and morphology. But further cell growth is not evenly distributed. Anterior cells remain small, flagellated, and unable to reproduce. They are truly somatic cells, as their only direct fate is death. In contrast, posterior cells become the germ cells. They grow to considerably larger sizes, large enough to support seven or eight rounds of cell division, before the offspring "hatch" from the parental cell wall. While undergoing cell division, these large germ cells still contribute to motility as much as they can. They retain beating flagella until their function fails—that is, until they detach from the cell.

In terms of multicellularity, the volvocine algae group known as *Volvox* is the crown jewel. All members of this genus are hollow spheres made up of a single layer of around 500 to several thousands of *Chlamydomonas*-like flagellated cells imbedded in mucilage coat (see Figure 22-4). Most cells are terminally differentiated somatic cells (and there seems to be some cell specialization among somatic cells). The flagella of individual cells typically beat in such a way that the entire sphere rotates clockwise along the anterior–posterior axis, and this rotation pushes the anterior end forward. The cells at the front end have the largest eyespots that somehow are used to direct the organism's course. The relatively few germ cells are located along the sphere's posterior. At one to two millimeters in diameter (or over 12,000 times shorter than the length of a blue whale), these are the largest self-propelled photosynthetic multicellular organisms on the planet.

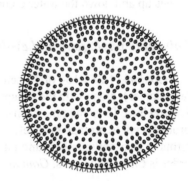

Figure 22-4. A simple drawing of the basic structure of a *Volvox*.

Different from any other volvocine algae, the space within the *Volvox* sphere, equivalent to the interstitial space in animals, is used in asexual reproduction. (Note: Although sexual reproduction does occur at times in *Volvox* species, as well as other volvocine algae, the focus here is only on asexual reproduction.) This allows the parental sphere to continue to move about while offspring form inside. Although details vary somewhat across species, the common theme is that development begins when an enlarged germ cell or gonidia begins to divide in a way that forms a pocket of cells that invaginates inward. Cell division continues until a newly developing sphere has the characteristic number of cells for the species. After that, development still involves one last step. Due to the inward invagination, cells within a developing sphere are oriented backward in the sense that flagella would sprout to the inside, resulting in an offspring unable to swim. So through a pore formed early in development, the entire multicellular arrangement turns inside out or inverts to form a properly aligned sphere. Afterward,

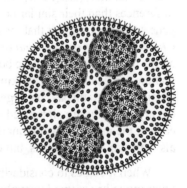

Figure 22-5. A *Volvox* with offspring forming inside the internal space.

growth continues inside the parental space. Eventually, the parental sphere is filled with somewhere between 2 and more than 10 offspring (see Figure 22-5). This raises the obvious question: How do the offspring get out? Does the parental sphere, in a sense, give birth as offspring slip through an opening that closes afterward to reform an intact parental sphere? Actually, it is more analogous to hatching, but instead of an eggshell, it is the outer parental sphere that ruptures—due to a chemical breakdown facilitated by enzymes secreted by the offspring. The offspring are then free to swim away.

A final note: The preceding discussion of the evolution of colonial and multicellular volvocine algae focused on the ability of a multicellular arrangement to maintain motility during cell division. And that may well have been the key driving force. Yet, other factors may have also contributed. For instance, it has been found that the filter-feeding invertebrates common in waters occupied by volvocine algae can consume unicellular algal cells, but all except the very smallest colonial algae are too large. Larger cellular arrangements also have at least one advantage in contending with changing nutrient levels. As algae begin to grow rapidly once favorable conditions return, such as in the spring, the supply of essential nutrients becomes quickly depleted. Although unable to reproduce as quickly as unicellular algae when nutrient levels are high, larger multicellular arrangements are able to extend their growing season by taking in and storing limiting nutrients, such as phosphorus, within their more extensive extracellular matrix. Some larger volvocine algae also seem to have coupled their increase in both swimming ability and nutrient storage capacity to come up with a novel means of contending with limiting nutrient supplies. They undergo a daily migration between the surface during the day, where light conditions are optimal for photosynthesis, and deeper waters, where phosphorus levels are higher. At the extreme, one study found that a *Volvox* species living in a deep, clear lake in Africa moves up and down the water column as much as 30 to 40 meters (at a rate of about 5 m/hr).

Volvocine phylogeny and evolutionary history

Gonium (4-, 8-, 16-, or 32-cell colonies arranged in a flat plat) and *Eudorina* (16- or 32-cell globular colonies), along with the groups mentioned earlier (*Chlamydomonas*, *Pandorina*, *Pleodorina*, and *Volvox*) have for some time been considered the major genera of volvocine algae. Curiously, all these groups seem to arrange themselves linearly along a continuum from the simplest to most complex in terms of size, cell number, amount of extracellular matrix, and the tendency to form somatic cells. The order is *Chlamydomonas*, *Gonium*, *Pandorina*, *Eudorina*, *Pleodorina*, and *Volvox*.

This order, along with the fact that all are composed of *Chlamydomonas*-like cells, suggest that *Volvox* evolved from *Chlamydomonas* in a monophyletic progression of increasing size and complexity. The groups branching off in between, in essence, record the intervening evolutionary stages. The only problem with this monophyletic scenario is that the genetic evidence does not back it up. The crux is that morphologically similar individuals have been found at times to have much larger genetic differences than their similar body plans would indicate. In fact, phylogenies based on similarities in gene sequences suggest that most, if not all, of these groups are polyphyletic. That is, instead of the *Chlamydomonas* or *Eudorina* or *Volvox* body plan evolving once, and then branching from there into all the different species, these body plans evolved more than once. If true, this is striking! It suggests that the same constraints working in different lineages have led to similar solutions. Evolutionary biologists refer to this as convergent evolution. But it also means that from an evolutionary perspective, the group names are all messed up. If, for instance, the *Volvox* body plan evolved more than once, then each of the different evolutionary groups should have a distinct group name. In other words, individuals with similar body plans, but different evolutionary histories, should be placed in different genera.

When it comes to considering the evolution of multicellularity, the volvocine algae are stars. No other group has seemed to evolve multicellularity as many times. Furthermore, the apparent polyphyletic history embedded in a linear progression of complexity underscores a dynamic evolutionary potential operating within common and biologically important constraints. Yet, when viewed from a larger perspective, they are minor players in the evolution of different life forms. *Volvox* and its relatives seem to be evolutionary dead ends; there is no evidence that this lineage has given rise to any other major groups of organisms. In fact, evidence suggests that all these experiments in the evolution of multicellular arrangements and cellular differentiation have occurred within the last 35 million years or so, perhaps at least 500 million years after similar experiments led to the evolution of plants and animals.

Multicellular Evolution in Algae with Microfibril-Based Cell Walls

Let's now return to photosynthetic cells with a more absolute form of the flagellation constraint. Cells capable of building microfibril-based cell walls can either have a cell wall and no flagella, or they can have flagella and no cell wall. The basic question is: How could cells facing such a trade-off fashion a functional life cycle? One in which they could at times enjoy the benefits of building a cell wall and still remain in a sufficiently lighted environment, and at other times be able to reproduce and move to new environments. Figure 22-6 outlines a possibility. Naked flagellated cells settle to the bottom in a sufficiently shallow area to receive adequate light and then retract their flagella and grow cell walls. Next, instead of shedding the existing cell wall after each round of cell division and generating naked flagellated cells capable of moving to a new spot, the walled cell stays put and grows by cell enlargement and cell division into a larger multicellular form. The fact that cell walls grow by the continual addition of new materials contributes to such growth, as it creates the structural basis to hold cells together. Eventually, at least some cells switch back to the type of cell division that produces naked flagellated cells, which can then disperse and settle to the bottom to start the cycle anew.

Although the preceding scenario is plausible, it is also important to explore why such a life cycle might evolve. In the ocean—where the evolution of multicellular algae likely started— shallow areas also experience tidal currents, so once a flagellated cell has settled into a suitable location, anchoring to the substrate would allow it to remain there. Growth into a multicellular form would then allow it to get large enough to break through the boundary layer associated with surrounding substrate and take advantage of the surrounding currents. Furthermore, for a flagellated cell to settle in a good spot is most likely not a trivial task. Bottom locations with the right mix of conditions compatible with growth may start off relatively rare and will become only rarer as other anchored algae begin to fill up suitable spots. Thus, for any flagellated cell "lucky" enough to settle in a good spot, it makes sense to stay awhile and grow by cell enlargement and cell division into a larger multicellular form. Not only does delaying reproduction by allocating resources toward growing larger allow one to continue

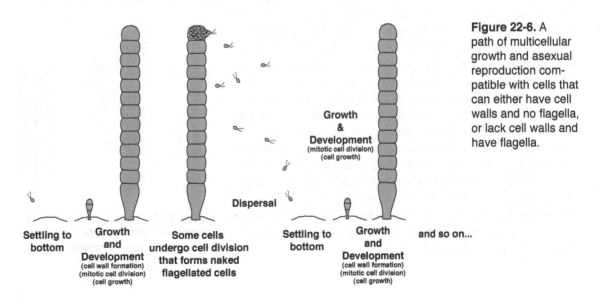

Figure 22-6. A path of multicellular growth and asexual reproduction compatible with cells that can either have cell walls and no flagella, or lack cell walls and have flagella.

Growth
&
Development
(mitotic cell division)
(cell growth)

Dispersal

Settling to bottom

Growth and Development
(cell wall formation)
(mitotic cell division)
(cell growth)

Some cells undergo cell division that forms naked flagellated cells

Settling to bottom

Growth and Development
(cell wall formation)
(mitotic cell division)
(cell growth)

and so on...

to hold onto a good location, but it also takes advantage of a rare occurrence by amplifying the number of reproductive cells potentially produced. This in turn increases the chance that one or more of its single-celled flagellated offspring will beat the odds and settle into a good location (see Figure 22-7). This concept of growing larger to amplify the advantage of rare opportunities will be a major theme.

Different growth forms

In one sense even an anchored multicellular arrangement can move—by growing. Growth allows an organism to move into, and thus interact with, new areas of their environment. The details of this interaction depend on the shape into which the organism grows. For instance, growth in one dimension produces a filament, a design that maximizes absorption ability by maximizing the surface area in contact with the local environment; growth in two dimensions creates a sheet (see Figure 22-8), a design that maximizes interception of fluxes, such as light; and growth in three dimensions generates thicker, stronger structures, while minimizing the contact that each cell has with its environment. The first two growth forms—filaments and sheets—as well as the somewhat in-between branching filamentous arrangement, are common among algae with microfibril-based cell walls. Regions of three-dimensional growth are also found in larger algae.

Microfibril-based cell walls make growing into any possible shape a bit tricky. Growth can only occur in the direction(s) in which the existing cell wall can expand. And, as discussed some in Chapter 20, the possible directions of expansion are determined by the orientation in which the microfibrils are laid down. Specifically, expansion most readily occurs along the plane located at a right angle from the microfibrils orientation. (Note: Microfibrils, such as cellulose, are formed by synthesizing-complexes embedded in a cell's outer membrane. These complexes appear to spin out long microfibrils while moving along the membrane. The orientation of each new microfibril depends on the direction in which these complexes move.) Consequently, if microfibrils are continually laid down in the simplest way possible—that is, continually laid down in the same orientation—then only one growth form is possible: a linear filament. That evidence suggests a filamentous growth form is ancestral in most, if not all, types of multicellular algae is thus not surprising. Yet, the presence of branches, along with other types of two- and three-dimensional growth in many forms of extant algae also suggest that somewhere along the line a new ability evolved—the ability to change the microfibril orientation at leading edges of cell wall expansion during development. Given that potential, the actual shape into which any multicellular algae grows will depend on the pattern and timing in which such orientation shifts occur.

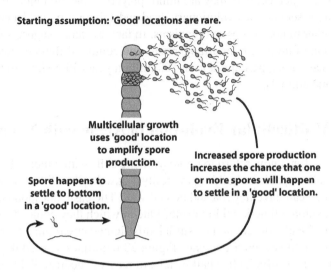

Starting assumption: 'Good' locations are rare.

Multicellular growth uses 'good' location to amplify spore production.

Spore happens to settle to bottom in a 'good' location.

Increased spore production increases the chance that one or more spores will happen to settle in a 'good' location.

Figure 22-7. The basic amplification argument for an algae to grow into a multicellular organism when reproducing asexually. (See text for further discussion.)

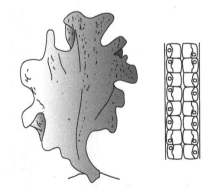

Figure 22-8. The genus *Ulva* (or sea lettuce) is a common green algae that grows as a sheet composed of two cell layers (shown on right).

The evolution of different life cycles and different types of algae

Moving to a new location can be good thing, especially during reproduction. For instance, it is generally helpful for an offspring to be able to *travel away* from parent or siblings to avoid competition. Sexual reproduction also adds a *travel toward* component; one or both gametes need to be able to move toward the other for fusion to be possible. Here, we further explore how anchored multicellular algae have evolved to deal with these travel issues.

Once a cell-wall-encased-organism becomes anchored, any form of movement requires some part to break free. The only self-propelling option is for single-celled naked flagellates to form and then break through an existing cell wall. Alternatively, any cell, whether flagellated or not, that breaks free can ride available currents —such as intertidal currents.

So the *travel away* component of reproduction does not seem a major issue for anchored algae. Once a multicellular form has grown past some threshold size, some cells would switch to allocating their resources to generating and releasing cells capable of developing into a new generation. Individual cells released could use flagella (if present) and/or currents to go off and attempt to anchor to another spot and grow into another multicellular form (see Figure 22-9). This is the scenario of asexual reproduction shown in Figure 22-6. Even groups of cells could break free and ride available currents, which occurs in some algae that at times reproduce by fragmentation.

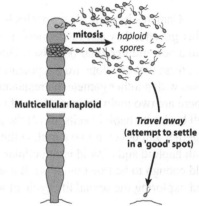

Figure 22-9. The 'travel away' component of asexual reproduction in anchored algae

An aside: If all cells, regardless of their position, are equally likely to form reproductive cells, the multicellular algae would, by definition, be a colony. Such colonies, however, may commonly suffer structural issues. Reproductive cells breaking out of the cell wall creates a weak link in filaments or two-dimensional sheets, which if generated near the base increases the risk of much of the structure breaking loose and floating away. Alternatively, confining reproductive cells at or near the tips of filaments or near the outer edges of sheets—while designating the cells making up the rest of the structure as nonreproductive (somatic) cells—would reduce that risk. It is thus not surprising that many anchored algae separate the position of germ and somatic cells in this fashion.

In Chapter 19 we started to explore some advantages of incorporating, at least at times, sexual reproduction into an organism's life cycle. The combination of fusion and meiosis is especially pervasive in multicellular organisms, and multicellular algae are no exception—despite the fact that adding sex to their life cycle is no trivial task. They must somehow get over the *travel toward* obstacle even though being anchored prevents adult forms from carrying their gametes with them as they search for a mate (see Figure 22-10). The entire task of venturing out into the world to find a compatible

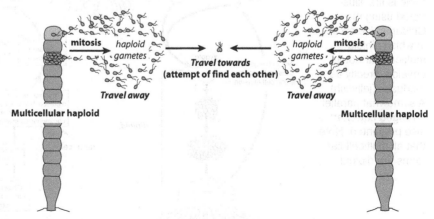

Figure 22-10. Sexual reproduction an anchored algae has both a 'travel away' and a 'travel towards' component.

partner must be left to the gametes themselves. This seems wild! How are single-celled flagellates released into the ocean supposed to track down another gamete? (Note: Depending on the type of algae,
a compatible gamete could be a flagellated cell of similar size and appearance, a flagellated cell of a
different size, or a larger nonmotile cell still attached to the algae that produced it.)

One option is that compatible gametes somehow assist each other. For example, in some species, one of the two gamete types remains stationary (as it may be harder to find a moving target) and
releases low-molecular-weight, highly volatile molecules that act as **pheromones**—chemical signals
that the more motile gametes use to zero in on the source. Curiously, this strategy of one gamete type
remaining stationary is even found in some algae species, where both gametes are flagellated. The
relatively larger gamete disperses for a short time and then settles to the bottom and begins to release
pheromones.

Gametes in some algae species have also been found to have an out: If they fail to fuse with another gamete, they can function as an asexual reproductive cell by attaching to a substrate and growing
into a new multicellular organism. This option, however, creates a puzzling scenario: A multicellular
organism that develops from a potential gamete would be haploid; yet, if this same gamete finds and
fuses with another gamete the resultant cell would be diploid. So what should have happened then?
There are two main options: (1) the first cell division could be meiotic, which would return the diploid
cell back into haploid cells, or (2) the diploid cell could undergo mitotic cell divisions that hang
together and develop into a multicellular organism. But the second option means that there would be
both haploid and diploid multicellular forms within the reproductive cycle of one organism. Sounds
odd enough to be true (and it is). But to establish a clear contrast, I want to start by first going back
and exploring the sexual life cycle of animals.

A brief discussion of animals

With *all* animals, a multicellular form only develops after fusion. So what we call the animal—
the multicellular form—is always diploid (see Figure 22-11). Why always diploid? There is not an obviously simple answer. But let's throw out some potentially important factors. For instance, in Chapter
19 we learned that one advantage of being diploid is that two copies of each gene can help protect
against deleterious mutations that occur during development. If a faulty version of an important gene
arises, a functional second copy is likely to be present. The mobile nature of animals may also play a
role. As mentioned earlier with algae, the risk of relying on sexual reproduction to restore the diploid

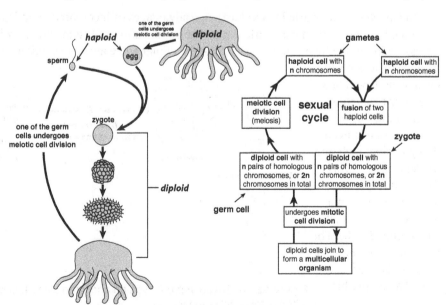

Figure 22-11. The basic animal life cycle is first illustrated using the Cnidarian life cycle, in which diploid multicellular adults develop directly as medusas (jellyfish). A somewhat parallel arranged flowchart is also presented. Note that all multicellular forms are diploid.

state each generation is that compatible gametes may not find each other. It is the inherent cost of mating. But mobile multicellular forms, which are much more capable travelers than single-celled gametes, can carry their gametes along as they search for potential mates. That way, motile gametes can be released to travel on their own only when in close proximity to other compatible gametes. The risk of gametes not being able to find each other is thus greatly reduced.

An aside: There is a potentially puzzling aspect to the argument that mobility played a role in the evolution of animals as multicellular diploids. The adult forms of the seemingly most primitive animals—sponges—are sessile. But in contrast to anchored algae, a sponge growing in one spot does not preclude movement, per se. They use the rhythmic beating of numerous flagellated cells to continually move their watery environment past them. This allows flagellated gametes (or sperm), released in large numbers by males, to be actively captured by female sponges of the same species. Furthermore, sponges, along with other forms of sessile animals—such cnidarians that do not produce a medusa—are readily able to reproduce asexually. Thus, their ability to persist does not rely solely on the ability of gamete pairs to locate one another.

Back to algae

In contrast to animals, the multicellular forms in sexual algae are not exclusively diploid, nor are they exclusively haploid. Some are only haploid, at least one group is only diploid, and many are the bizarre-seeming mixture of having both haploid and diploid multicellular forms within the same life cycle. And the reason is not as simple as multicellular haploids forming whenever a gamete fails to find another and multicellular diploids forming otherwise. Instead, many algae have a defined **alternation of generations** within their sexual cycle. That is, although certain cells within the multicellular diploid undergo meiosis and generate haploid cells that are released, these haploid cells skip acting like a gamete and act like **spores**—reproductive cells that can develop into an adult without fusion with another cell. Basically, spores *travel away* in an attempt to find a good location to anchor and grow into a multicellular haploid. These multicellular haploids in turn generate cells (by *mitosis*) that go off and act as gametes. The diploid multicellular phase is then restored when two gametes fuse and grow into a multicellular organism.

Some technical terms: Within an organism with alternating generations, multicellular diploids in which certain cells undergo meiosis to produce spores are called **sporophytes**. The unicellular or multicellular structures in which spores are produced are called **sporangia**. Alternatively, the multicellular structures in which certain cells undergo mitosis to produce gametes are called **gametophytes**. And **gametangia** are the unicellular or multicellular structure in which gametes are produced.

A sexual life cycle involving an alteration of generations raises lots of questions. Here, we focus on two: First, why is gamete formation one step removed from meiotic cell division within the multicellular diploid? Or stated differently, why does a multicellular form develop between meiosis and gamete formation? And second, if there is a good reason to grow into a multicellular haploid, then why does it also make sense to grow into a multicellular diploid (after fusion)?

Reasons for a multicellular delay between meiosis and fusion

Perhaps a potential genetic benefit is at least part of the answer to why a multicellular haploid is added between meiosis and fusion. Any faulty versions of genes important to multicellular growth introduced into the population will be quickly eliminated during this haploid stage, as the gene's deleterious effects cannot be masked by a second functional copy.

I suspect, however, that it has more to do with the inherent difficulty of compatible gametes finding each other when adults are anchored. In addition to pheromones, or other forms of tracking

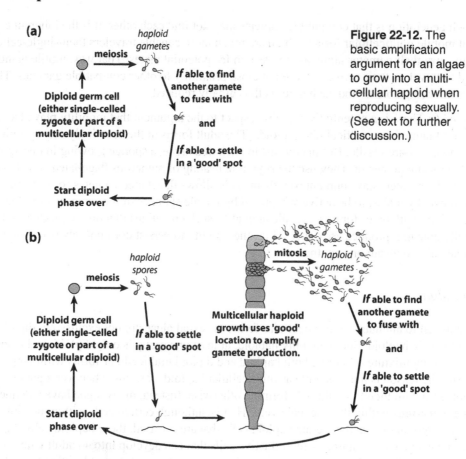

(a)

Figure 22-12. The basic amplification argument for an algae to grow into a multi-cellular haploid when reproducing sexually. (See text for further discussion.)

(b)

devices, the best way to increase the likelihood of any improbable event is to increase the number of chances. Growth of a multicellular haploid could, in essence, be a way to buy more tickets to the fusion lottery. It is another twist of the amplification argument (see Figure 22-12). For instance, suppose a multicellular diploid grows to the point that it could make and release 100 haploid cells. If these cells venture out into the world as gametes, then this organism has generated 100 chances to find and fuse with a compatible gamete that subsequently lands in a good spot to grow into another multicellular diploid. Alternatively, these 100 haploid cells could act as **spores** and go the route of attempting to anchor in a good location and grow into multicellular haploids. Again, not all will be successful, but because it is inherently easier to find a good spot to grow than to find both a compatible gamete and a good spot to grow, the number of multicellular haploids produced will tend to be greater than the number of multicellular diploids produced through the gametic route. And that is the crux of the issue. Because now if both the multicellular haploids and multicellular diploids grow to the point that they can produce 100 haploid cells that act as gametes, the life cycle with the intervening multicellular haploid stage will be more reproductively successful. The greater number of gamete-producing multicellular haploids will increase this life cycle's chance of winning the reproductive lottery.

The potential advantage of making an intervening multicellular haploid stage makes one wonder: Why stop at one? In other words, why not have another round or two (or more) where multicellular haploids release single cells that act as spores instead of gametes? That way, the population of multicellular haploids could expand even further before switching back to gamete production. In other words, wouldn't it make sense, at least under certain conditions, for a haploid organism to reproduce asexually most of the time and then switch back to a sexual phase on occasion? The answer must be yes because this life cycle exists. For example, members of the green algae genus *Ulothrix* typically grow only seasonally, such as during the spring and fall in temperate climates. During these growth periods, the population expands rapidly through asexual reproduction—multicellular haploids contin-

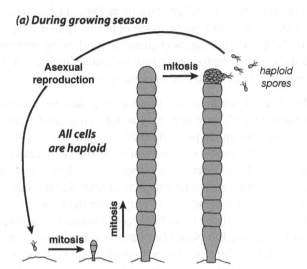

(a) During growing season

Asexual reproduction

mitosis

haploid spores

All cells are haploid

mitosis

mitosis

Figure 22-13. The different parts of the life cycle of filamentous green algae in the genus *Ulothrix*. There are several important things to notice: (1) all multicellular structures are haploid; (2) reproduction is mostly asexual, and switches to sexual only at the end of the growing season; (3) the only diploid part of the life cycle is the zygote, which develops into a dormant cell; and (4) at the beginning of the next growing season diploid zygotes undergo meiosis to form haploid spores that can settle to the bottom and grow into multicellular haploids.

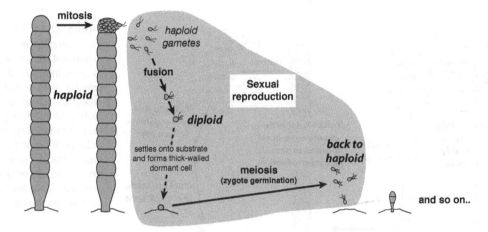

(b) End of growing season   *(c) Beginning of next growing season*

mitosis

haploid gametes

fusion

Sexual reproduction

haploid

diploid

settles onto substrate and forms thick-walled dormant cell

back to haploid

meiosis (zygote germination)

and so on..

ue to generate flagellated spores that can settle and grow into new multicellular filaments (see Figure 22-13(a)). The switch to sexual reproduction then occurs more toward the end of a growing season. Multicellular haploids begin to produce gametes, and the zygotes formed develop into thick-walled resting or dormant cells able to survive until the next growing season (see Figure 22-13(b)).

The theme of increasing the number of haploid multicellular generations is also demonstrated in those algae in which gametes that fail to fuse, act like a spore and grow into a multicellular haploid. Instead of a gamete going to waste, growth into a multicellular haploid allows it to make even more gametes in the future.

Reasons for a multicellular delay between fusion and meiosis

The other side of the alternation of generations puzzle is: Once fusion occurs, why should the resultant zygote develop into a multicellular diploid? Further validating the question is the observation that in some algae it does not. Consider, for instance, the group of green algae called the Ulotrichales, of which genus *Ulothrix* (discussed earlier) is a member. All members of this group grow seasonally and punctuate the end of the growth season by producing a sexually produced dormant cell. At the beginning of the next growing season these diploid cells could sprout into a multicellular form. But they don't. Instead, these single diploid cells undergo meiosis and produce more than one haploid, flagellated spore (see Figure 22-13(c)). This makes sense! Not only will the opportunity to undergo recombination repair, right at the beginning of the growth season, help ensure that offspring start out in good genetic shape, but it also jump-starts the seasonal reproductive race by increasing the starting number of contestants. Meiosis can convert one diploid cell into four haploid cells.

In environments that are not so seasonal (at least, from an algae's perspective), success in reproductive races may be less about trying to get out to an early lead and more about trying to take full advantage of any opportunity provided. For instance, when the population of any algae species is more stable across time, good sites to grow will tend be rare—because most good sites will already be occupied. So for any new diploid zygote "lucky" enough to land in a good spot, immediately undergoing meiosis to add a few more haploid spores to the mix may not best maximize reproductive success. Instead, the longer-term investment of growing into a multicellular form may prove the better strategy. The short-term cost of taking time to grow would seemingly be more than compensated for by holding onto the good spot longer—specifically, as long as the individual can survive—and in the interim using the greater energy harvesting capacity associated with being larger to produce and release a much greater number of haploid spores. Again it is another twist of the amplification argument. When extended to both the haploid and diploid part of a sexual life cycle, this results in an alternation of generations (see Figure 22-14).

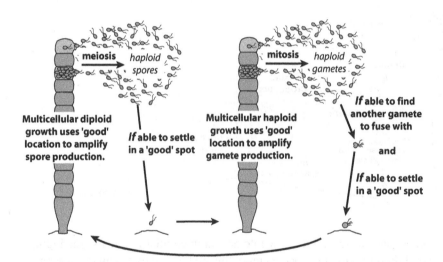

Figure 22-14. The basic amplification argument for an algae to grow into a multicellular diploid when reproducing sexually. Note that extending the amplification argument to both sides of the sexual cycle results in an alternation of generations. (See text for further discussion.)

Given that meiosis tends to scramble the available genetic information, growth as a multicellular diploid may generate a genetic advantage. It will increase an individual's ability to produce genetically variable offspring, as essentially every haploid cell produced will have a unique combination of genetic information. In a highly competitive and potentially changing environment, producing a wide diversity of offspring types may help ensure that at least some are successful.

Isomorphic versus heteromorphic

It seems a challenge for diploid animals, such as ourselves, to think about alternation of generations. The idea that instead of acting as gametes, the haploid cells that we produce would go off and grow into another multicellular form is hard to reconcile with the view of ourselves as an individual. If the multicellular diploid referred to itself as I, like we do, what would we call the multicellular haploid? He, she, or it! Somehow a third-person reference to a part of the same sexual cycle makes little sense. Yet, on the other hand, these would be two physiologically distinct multicellular forms, so it would also be hard for each to refer to the other as I.

Despite the potential confusion of who is whom (or whom is who, or who is who, or whatever), there is an important take-home message: Sexual organisms faced with certain types of constraints—such as the trade-off between cell walls and motility—may find that growing a multicellular form twice within a sexual cycle may be the best way to negotiate the reproductive obstacle course. Not that this will always be the case. For instance, it was mentioned earlier that the distinct seasonal growth periods experienced by *Ulothrix* seem to void the advantage of having a multicellular diploid phase. And for other reasons, brown algae in the genus *Fucus* generate only multicellular diploids. But the commonness of distinct alternation of generations among sexual algal species is intriguing. In addition to allowing amplification to occur twice, it allows each multicellular form to tailor its abilities to

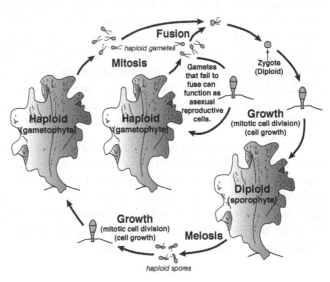

Figure 22-15. The genus *Ulva* (or sea lettuce) is a common member of the Ulvales. Members of this group have an isomorphic alternation of generations.

the needs associated with its distinct position within the sexual cycle and the specifics of the environmental conditions that it encounters.

In the green algal group known as the Ulvales (see Figure 22-15), as well as in some brown algae groups, this division of labor does not seem to go much beyond whether the haploid flagellated cells released are produced by meiosis (in the multicellular diploid) and act as spores, or produced by mitosis (in the multicellular haploid) and act as gametes. Both multicellular forms—the diploid sporophyte and the haploid gametophyte—develop into similar-looking structures that presumably interact with their environment in similar ways. This is called an **isomorphic** alternation of generations.

In contrast, in many other algal species the haploid and diploid phases exhibit distinct growth forms, often dramatically so. That is, these species display a **heteromorphic** alternation of generations. One thought is that these structural differences have been selected to better take advantage of seasonally variable habitats. However, that seems unlikely to be the entire story, given that the larger and/or structurally more complex phase tends to be diploid. Apparently, the fact that diploids are better suited to live longer and grow larger, due to having backup gene copies, is being used to take advantage of situations that haploids likely could not. Some of the kelps, which are members of the brown algae group **Laminariales**, take this dichotomy to its extreme. The diploid sporophyte commonly grows into a complex structure with holdfasts, stipes (stem-like structures), branched or unbranched long flattened leaf-like structures called blades, internal convections systems (discussed in Chapter 20), and in some cases gas-filled floats called pneumatocysts (see Figure 22-16). The entire structure can grow to many meters in length and in some cases live for years. In contrast, the haploid gametophytes are typically nothing more than short-lived microscopic branched filaments. In kelp, retention of a multicellular haploid phase may have more to do with a means of dispersal (along with some amplification) than exploiting the environ-

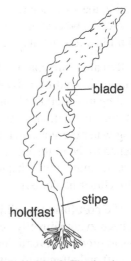

Figure 22-16. The basic growth form of the large diploid sporophyte phase of *Lamaria* or kelp, which is a member of the Laminariales.

ment in some unique way. The haploid spores produced are flagellated and thus travel away from the multicellular diploid. Once they settle they grow into multicellular haploids that are either male or female. Although the haploid males produces motile flagellated sperm, the haploid females not only produce eggs lacking flagella, but the eggs also typically remain attached. Fertilization, along with the beginning of development of the next generation multicellular diploid, occurs in association with the haploid female. (Note: The female also produces distinct pheromones to help sperm locate available eggs.) Thus, only through the initial dispersal of female spores will multicellular diploids end up developing in a different location than previous generations.

Interestingly, another group of brown algae, the **Fucales**—which although they do not grow nearly as large as kelp still generate a complex multicellular diploid—have lost the alternation of generations altogether. Basically they do so by using tidal currents as their power source for dispersal. Haploid cells produced by the multicellular diploid either form into flagellated sperm or nonflagellated eggs (that produce sperm-attracting pheromones). The release of both is timed with incoming tides, so before the tide changes and sweeps everything not held down out to sea, sperm must find eggs, and the resultant zygotes must attach to a substrate.

Some unique red algae features

In contrast to brown or green algae, red algae lacks the ability to generate flagellated cells at any point of their life cycle. Although it is not clear which came first, two morphological features are connected with this apparent loss. First, in contrast to most other eukaryotic cells, red algal cells lack basal bodies (kinetosomes). And second, there are probably no red algal cells, vegetative or reproductive, that entirely lack a cell covering.

In terms of travel, the lack of flagella may not greatly impair dispersal to new locations. Currents, such as tides, are commonly available, and red algae spores sink relatively slowly and produce a surrounding coat of mucilage that aids in the initial attachment to a substrate. In contrast, the lack of any form of self-propulsion would clearly make it more difficult for gametes to find each other. Red algae have seemingly dealt with this complication in one of a couple of ways. For one, many red algae can reproduce asexually by releasing spores that can develop into a multicellular form similar to the spore-producing parent. Furthermore, components of their sexual life cycle—sexual reproduction is still found in the vast majority of red algae—have been modified in some novel ways to amplify reproductive success whenever gametic fusion does occur. To explore how they do so, we need to step back and fill in a few details.

Red algae are commonly divided into two major groups: the more primitive **Bangiophyceae,** and the more derived **Florideophyceae.** In both groups, the nonflagellated gametes of red algae are produced by multicellular haploids and come in two distinct sizes: the smaller or male gametes (technical term: spermatium), which are released and seemingly travel toward female gametes by passively riding water currents, and the larger female gametes (technical term: carpogonium), which remain attached to the multicellular haploid. (Note: Bangiophyceans produce male and female gametes on the same multicellular haploid, whereas the florideophyceans typically have separate male and female multicellular haploids.)

The post fusion amplification in bangiophyceans occurs in a straightforward manner: Instead of a fertilized zygote directly developing into a multicellular diploid, zygotes first undergo mitotic divisions to produce several diploid spores (technical term: carpospores), which are subsequently released to go off and attempt to settle in a good spot and develop into an independent multicellular diploid. When fertilization is potentially a rare event, each zygote forming several copies of itself prior to release increases the chance of a successful gamete fusion being coupled with finding a good spot for growth.

Florideophyceans, on the other hand, have extended their postfusion amplification even further by adding a third multicellular phase to their sexual life cycle (see Figure 22-17). Nothing else on the planet has more than two. Like other algae with alternating generations, triphasic red algae have an independent multicellular diploid phase that produces haploid spores and an independent multicellular haploid phase that produces haploid gametes—although in these red algae, the haploid gametophyte is either male (relatively smaller gametes) or female (relatively larger gametes). What is new is that after fertilization the zygote undergoes mitotic division, and the cells hang together to form a multicellular diploid that remains attached to the female haploid gametophyte. This so-called carposporophyte grows as a mass of fila-

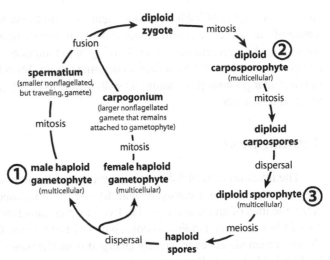

Figure 22-17. The triphasic life cycle of the florideophycean red algae. The three multicellular phases are indicated. (See text for further details.)

ments that eventually can produce *many* diploid spores. More spores being released means even more chances that rare fertilization events will be followed by the growth of an independent multicellular diploid. Some florideophyceans extend this amplification even further by a somewhat complicated mechanism that allows the formation of a single diploid zygote to lead to the development of many carposporophytes.

The fact that this new diploid stage is not independent—that is, it remains attached to the female haploid gametophyte instead of growing on its own in a new location—also plays an important part in this amplification process. Why? Think about it! The initial risk of a zygote venturing out into the world and battling the odds of settling in a good location is eliminated by growing on an already established female multicellular haploid. It is obviously already growing in a good location or it would not exist. Evidence even suggests that female haploids not only provide developing carposporophytes with a good place to grow, but they also nurture their development. Photosynthetic products are apparently transferred from the haploid female to developing carposporophytes. As far as I am aware, this is the only evidence in algae of one multicellular phase directly feeding or provisioning another multicellular phase. Such direct nutrient transfer also occurs between parents and offspring (both of which are diploid) in some animals, and in an even more analogous way (as a haploid provisioning a diploid) in land plants. This generates a good segue to next topic: the evolution of land plants.

Invading Land

Both morphological and molecular evidence strongly suggest that all multicellular terrestrial phototrophs are a monophyletic group whose closest relatives are a group of green algae known as the Charophyceae, which largely live in freshwater. In other words, apparently a branch within the charophycean algae was able to change in ways that allowed it to persist in a new environment. Yet, despite core similarities, this branch that invaded land is now different enough to not be called algae anymore. Instead we call them plants, or sometimes land plants (although adding land is a bit confusing because some plant lineages have returned to the water to live).

The invasion of multicellular phototrophs on to the terrestrial environment must be seen as both an opportunity and a challenge. The nature of the opportunity is obvious: Large portions of the earth rise above the surface of the oceans, as well as all the inland freshwater streams and lakes, creating an extensive range of habitat for any organism with the wherewithal to take advantage. In a sense, the nature of the challenge is also obvious: Algae negotiate many of life's obstacles in ways that rely on the surrounding presence of water. Moving onto land does not change the nature of the obstacles; it just changes what will be required to negotiate them. Most basically, the evolution of plants involves multicellular phototrophs coming up with means to grow, survive, and reproduce in environments with less and less water.

A starting point

The invasion of land did not start with some inventive and determined charophycean algae crawling up on the land, and staking a claim for itself and its ancestors. First, algae cannot crawl. Furthermore, the idea of an algae adapted to live in water somehow "choosing" to move to a new habitat doesn't fit our understanding of how changes in life occur. Evolution does not anticipate. Yet, if some charophycean algae never actively emerged from the water, how did some of their ancestors end up on land? It is likely a shallow water story.

Water levels in any body of water fluctuate. As a consequence, any anchored algae growing in shallow water could easily find itself going from submerged to emerged (land dwelling). This raises the question: What happens then? For one, it could quickly die. Retreating water would just be one of life's many risks that these algae are unequipped to handle. Dying quickly during periods of moisture stress would, however, make it difficult for most shallow water algae to persist. For example, algae unable to withstand periods of desiccation could not inhabit the intertidal zone, where water retreats one or more times a day. Yet, intertidal areas also make the challenge of dealing with air exposure somewhat easier as the time out of water is predictably short—water returns with every high tide. Algae growing near the edge of wetlands or freshwater lakes, however, would not experience that same predictability. Once water levels drop, an individual alga may not experience an environment flushed with water again until the next major rainfall. The wait could last hours, days, weeks, or months. So although at some point death is clearly an option, any algae bearing traits enabling it to last longer may prove to be overall better at negotiating the reproductive obstacle course. Ephemeral freshwater environments, especially unpredictable ones, would have strongly selected for traits that allowed algae to better persist during exposed periods and in the process selected for features that would have set the stage for a complete transition to land.

Changes that allowed a multicellular phototroph to continue to metabolize and grow, even when it is not completely immersed in water, would be useful. To do so, the organism would need to evolve features that allow it to **maintain water balance**—that is, to continually match water loss with water gain—in drier environments (while still being able to acquire needed supplies of carbon dioxide, along with other mineral nutrients, from the environment). Helpful changes fall into one of three general categories: (1) reduce the rate at which water is lost, (2) increase the ability to store water, or (3) increase the ability to extract or uptake water from the environment. Obviously, some modern plants are quite capable, as metabolically active plants are found even in extremely dry environments, such as deserts. But the starting point would have been much less extreme. For example, some shallow water species classified within charophycean taxa most similar to land plants—the Coleochaetales and Charales— can grow in moisture-saturated air, or in moist soil along the water's edge. These algae obviously have features that have severed their complete dependence on being immersed in water. The transition to plants would have involved continuing this trend.

Of course, regardless of how capable a vegetative structure gets at maintaining water balance, the environment could temporarily become drier than it can handle. So the evolution of **desiccation tolerance** would also be a useful component of persistence. This is the ability to switch to a dormant state capable of waiting out periods of too extreme of water stress and then switching back to a metabolically active state when wetter conditions return. Either the entire vegetative structure or specialized parts, such as reproductive cells or other forms of resting cells, could switch to the metabolically inactive or dormant state. Desiccation tolerance, like any other form of dormancy, allows an organism unable to continually relocate to favorable environmental conditions, to wait for favorable conditions to return. And although desiccation tolerance is well documented in certain plants, it appears to also be found in at least some charophycean algae. There are reports of sexual spores, produced by members of the genus *Chara* (which are in the Charales), germinating on rewetting after years of desiccation.

Reproduction will also prove a challenge in the transition to land. For instance, sexual reproduction always involves gametes being able to find each other. But whereas many algae attempt to negotiate this obstacle by casting gametes equipped with flagella out into the environment, a similar strategy will not work as readily on land. Although flagellated cells can swim, they cannot walk or fly. So new twists will need to be added.

The worts (along with other bryophytes)

Around the fifth century, people from Germanic tribes known as Angles and Saxons began to settle in the British Isles. The Anglo-Saxon language that developed became the basis of the language we now call Old English, which subsequently evolved into the version of English that I am trying to use here. The Anglo-Saxon word for plant (or herb) was "wyrt," which in a modified form is still used to name two plant groups recognized today: the liverworts and the hornworts. I find it compelling that essentially the oldest English word for *plant* is now used to name two of the oldest or most primitive lineages of plants.

Liverworts, in particular, are seemingly the simplest living plants. Comparing liverworts and charophycean algae may thus provide some information of what changes first accompanied the transition of multicellular phototrophs to land. Let's start with growth form.

Transitions in growth form

Growth forms found in extant members within the genus *Coleochaete* (which are in the Coleochaetales) basically fall into two main categories: loosely branching filaments and disc-shaped arrangements made out of a single layer of tightly packed cells (see Figure 22-18). These disc-shaped

(also called thalloid) arrangements grow by cells along the edge alternating their division planes between parallel and perpendicular to the periphery. Thalloid or disc-shaped species, in comparison to filamentous species, are also found to occur more in shallow water, suggesting that this arrangement may be better at contending with near-shore conditions, such as the increased turbulence associated with breaking waves, more intense light levels, and perhaps even being subjected more commonly to desiccation. The issue comes back to the familiar theme of surface area-to-volume ratio. Tightly packing cells together into a discoid arrangement reduces the amount of each cell's outer surface exposed to the environment and thus reduces the relative rate at which anything will enter (such as solar radiation) or be lost (such as water when exposed to air).

Figure 22-18. The basic growth form of some *Coleochaete* species. The disc-shape arrangement is one-cell thick, and grows by cell division occuring along the outer edge.

Liverworts, along with all other plants, carry this trend of packing cells tightly even further. They develop three-dimensional tissues, which means that dividing cells alternate among several division planes and subsequently generate packed clusters of cells. In terms of making the transition to land, three-dimensional tissues, in comparison to any two-dimensional shape, further reduce the amount of surface area of each cell exposed to the environment. In fact, interior cells are, by definition, completely surrounded by other cells, so they have no direct contact with the environment. Rates of water loss, in particular, will thus be reduced by the overall lower surface area-to-volume ratios.

Liverworts have been traditionally subdivided into two major groups based, in part, on growth form. One group, the thalloid liverworts, have a somewhat amorphous, sprawling, flattened, branching structure. A thallus, by definition, is a flattened growth form that *lacks* easily recognizable organs such as shoots, roots, or leaves, along with the specialized vascular or conducting system that underlies both the structure and the function of these organs. Closer inspection, however, still reveals specialized regions of function, as the thallus can be upward of 30 cells thick, but only the upper cell layers are photosynthetic (see Figure 22-19).

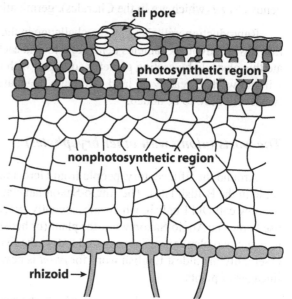

An important aside: The amount of regional specialization of function possible within any organism depends on how quickly things can be transported. For instance, a plant can separate the job of photosynthesis between photosynthetic and nonphotosynthetic tissue as long as the available means of transport can move sufficient amounts of sugars between these two tissues. The better the transport system, the further apart functions can be separated, so the more distinct functional regions can become. Thalloid liverworts lack a sufficiently capable transport system to separate photosynthetic tissue into clearly distinct regions or organs that we know as leaves.

Figure 22-19. A cross-section of a thallose liverwort, which shows some regional specialization—chloroplast-bearing (photosynthetic) cells are found in the upper layers, while lower cells layers are nonphotosynthetic.

The other group, the leafy liverworts, better fit our image of a plant. Although they still grow as a flattened arrangement along the ground and still lack distinct vascular tissue, pairs of one or two cell thick flaps grow in rows along a branching thicker axis. From the outside, each flap looks like a leaf, and each axis looks like a stem, and clearly there is some specialization of function among the different-shaped regions; but again the absence of distinct vascular systems prevents too great a separation of function. For instance, although the thin leaf-like flaps may specialize in photosynthesizing, they are found all along each stem-like axis, instead of just the best regions to intercept light.

Stuff moving in and out: Light, carbon dioxide, and water

Hopefully, you are a feeling a little confused here. Early in Chapter 20, I belabored the case against cell clusters or three-dimensional tissues because of the inherent slowness of diffusion. Yet liverworts, especially thalloid liverworts, appear to "spit in the face" of this problem. They have the seemingly lethal combination of three-dimensional tissues in the absence of a defined convection system. How is this possible?

The fact that light does not travel by diffusion is one part of the story. As long as the path is not obstructed by light-absorbing materials, photosynthetic cells buried inside a three-dimensional tissue can continually get adequate light supplies (at literally the speed of light) to their chloroplasts (see Figure 22-20). Light needing to pass further through a tissue also creates the possibility of lessening the potential damaging effects of solar radiation by better shielding of more harmful wavelengths.

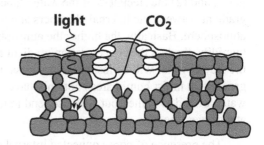

Of course, photosynthetic cells still need materials to photosynthesize, specifically water and carbon dioxide, as well as supplies of other mineral nutrients, such as nitrogen and phosphorus. And in the absence of vascular tissues, all incoming water and nutrients must be absorbed along the outer surface and then pass from cell to cell by diffusion. So how do liverworts cope with these limitations? Let's start with carbon dioxide.

Figure 22-20. The pathways by which both light and carbon dioxide can get to photosynthetic cells buried deeper within thallose liverworts. (See text for further details.)

Carbon dioxide dissolves fairly readily in water. It can also react with water molecules to form a carbon-containing molecule called bicarbonate, that is soluble in water. Aquatic multicellular phototrophs acquire their needed supply of carbon dioxide by absorbing either carbon dioxide or bicarbonate directly from their surrounding medium. Upon emerging from water, multicellular phototrophs switched to harvesting carbon dioxide from the air. Although the thallus can be many cells thick, the most photosynthetically active cells are found in the upper several layers on the light-facing or dorsal side. To facilitate carbon dioxide transport, photosynthetic cells buried below the surface cell layer grow in a loose and convoluted arrangement that fashions air spaces around a portion of each cell. This honeycomb of air spaces then connects to the outside through a barrel-shaped air opening, known as an **air pore**, composed of several layers of circular arranged cells. As carbon dioxide molecules located within these internal air spaces are taken up by cells and used to build sugars, the decreasing carbon dioxide supply creates the concentration gradient needed for new carbon dioxide molecules to diffuse through the air pore from the surrounding atmosphere into the internal chambers (see Figure 22-20). Although the overall concentrations of carbon dioxide are similar in water and air, the fact that molecules diffuse 10,000 times faster through air aids this system of carbon dioxide delivery.

An aside: Note that liverworts, along with all other terrestrial plants, have a bit of magician in them: They appear (mostly) out of thin air. Plants are around 93% carbon and oxygen, and their source is carbon dioxide—a relatively sparse atmospheric gas. Only around 3 in 10,000 air molecules are carbon dioxide (0.03 %). Further note that plants do not use any form of pump to acquire CO_2. They rely solely on a favorable concentration gradient maintained by the reduction of CO_2 to sugar once entering a chloroplast-containing cell. So despite CO_2's low atmospheric concentration, an even lower concentration can be maintained inside photosynthetic cells.

The fact that light does not travel by diffusion and that carbon dioxide travels reasonably well by diffusion along air passageways connected to the outside makes it possible for cells buried rather deep within a tissue to carry on a high photosynthetic rate. However, the ultimate advantage of this arrangement is that it reduces water loss. Any cell membrane permeable to carbon dioxide is also permeable to water—in fact, carbon dioxide may need to dissolve in a surrounding film of water before it can pass through the cell membrane. So unless the surrounding air is saturated with water (measured as 100% humidity), water loss will accompany carbon dioxide uptake. Yet, within the confines of these passageways, water molecules leaving cells are not immediately lost to the atmosphere. Instead they are held, at least temporarily, within these internal chambers, upping the surrounding humidity. The higher humidity in turn slows the rate at which other water molecules move out of cells. Water loss from buried photosynthetic cells will thus be limited to the amount of water that escapes through air pores, which will be influenced by two factors: (1) the amount of the outer surface area made up of air pores, and (2) the steepness of the water concentration gradient between the internal chambers and the outside atmosphere. Basically, the higher the atmospheric humidity, the less the concentration gradient and thus the slower water will be lost, and visa versa. Plants growing in moist humid areas not only have more water around to gather, but will also tend to lose water at a slower rate.

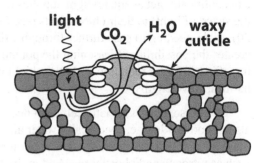

Figure 22-21. Air pores make a waxy cuticle possible. A sufficient thick waxy cuticle will block surface cells from absorbing carbon dioxide (a bad thing) or losing water (a good thing) directly to the atmosphere. Through air pores, carbon dioxide can still get to the underside of surface cells, while minimizing water loss. (See text for more details.)

The presence of pore-connected internal chambers also opened the door for another means to reduce water loss—secreting a waxy layer, known as a **waxy cuticle**, on top of the outer cell surface (see Figure 22-21). The trade-off is that although adding wax will reduce the largest potential source of water loss—movement of water molecules directly from surface cells to the environment—it will also impede the movement in of carbon dioxide. Yet, given internal air passageways, even surface layer cells can gain access to carbon dioxide from their underside. A relatively thick waxy layer is thus possible.

We have started to get an idea of how thalloid liverworts get light and carbon dioxide to their upper photosynthetic layers, yet the fact that buried even further down in the thallus are many layers of colorless or nonphotosynthetic cells still raises the question: How do these cells meet their energy needs, given the lack of a distinct vascular system to transport sugars produced in the upper photosynthetic layers to these lower positioned cells? Although the answer may involve several interacting factors, two deserve highlighting. First, these cells may have such a low metabolic rate that even diffusion across relatively long distances is adequate to met their demands. Because plants do not get up and run around, many internal cells can take on a much slower-paced structural role. (Note: The major structural components of larger woody plants are actually composed of dead cells.) Second, the transport of sugars from photosynthetic to nonphotosynthetic regions may not be solely by diffusion. When thalloid liverworts undergo cell division, the two daughter cells do not make a clean break. Instead, the cytoplasm of adjoining cells remains connected by a patchwork of membrane-bound channels, known as **plasmodesmata** (see Figure 22-22). These openings extend through the intervening cell wall. The entire multicellular arrangement is laced with an interconnected cytoplasm, making it possible for molecules to be transported between cells without passing across cell membranes (or cell walls). Therefore, sugar molecules generated in photosynthetic tissues have a route to travel to nonphotosynthetic areas by an osmotically generated pressure gradient. This is the source-sink model of convective flow discussed in Chapter 20. What is missing in liverworts, in comparison to plants with a more defined sugar transport system, are cells specialized—by their composition, shape, and arrangement—for transport.

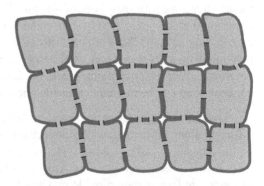

Figure 22-22. A group of cells, each surrounded by a cell wall, connected together by plasmodesmata. Plasmodesmata are generally large enough for simple sugars, amino acids, or free nucleotides to pass through, but they are generally impermeable to macromolecules such as proteins and nucleic acids. In contrast to this simple picture, single plant cells can be hooked to neighboring cells by thousands of plasmodesmata.

An important note: Plasmodesmata are not just found in liverworts. They are found in all plants and many algae. In fact, one of the similarities shared between plants and the green algae groups that seem most closely related—the Coleochaetales and Charales—is the way their plasmodesmata develop, along with the details of their structure. The cytoplasmic continuum set up throughout an entire plant by plasmodesmata (in some cases plasmodesmata can occupy as much as 50% of the area of adjoining cell walls) has led to the suggestion that plants should be considered a supercellular, instead of a multicellular, organism. For convenience, I will continue to refer to them as multicellular, but the fact that a molecule can travel from one end of a plant to the other without ever passing through a membrane is strikingly different than the multicellular arrangement of animals.

Three-dimensional tissues, air pores, and waxy cuticles all help thalloid liverworts reduce water loss to the point that they can maintain metabolically active vegetative states without being immersed in water. But, as mentioned earlier, reducing rates of water loss is only part of the water balance story. Water intake must keep up with the rate at which water is still being lost to the environment. When it is raining or the liverwort is currently residing in a moist location, a liverwort can absorb water throughout its surface. Even when lying on wet substrate, water absorbed along the base can move up through the cell layers to replace water lost through air pores. This upward movement is powered by both osmotic gradients and continuous chains of water molecules—made possible by plasmodesmata—being pulled up to replace those lost by evaporation. Yet, although these are the same driving forces used to power the upward convective movement of water in other plants, again the lack of cells arranged into a defined vascular system limits such flow. Furthermore, when surface conditions are drier, the only potential water source is that which is trapped (or in a sense stored) in the substrate below, known as soil. Although thalloid liverworts have elongate single cells or filaments called **rhizoids** (see Figure 22-19) that grow into the below substrate and potentially absorb some loosely held soil water, these are not the same as roots—multicellular structures hooked into vascular pathways through which soil water can be pulled up into the rest of the plant. In fact, rhizoids may serve as much or more as anchors than as facilitators of water uptake. As a result of these limitations, metabolically active liverworts still need to be in moist terrestrial habitats to maintain water balance.

Yet, amazingly, liverworts can persist in places that periodically (and even unpredictably) get too dry to remain metabolically active. Drier conditions won't typically kill a liverwort. Instead, as the plant dries out it slips into a dormant or desiccation tolerant state, in which it can exist for long periods (even years) while waiting for the next rain. Then once rehydrated, it quickly comes back to life. Apparently these plants produce compounds that protect their cells when they dry out and have repair mechanisms that rapidly go into effect when a plant rehydrates. In essence, liverworts are able to persist in fluctuating conditions in the same way that spore-producing bacteria do (as we discussed in Chapter 16). They literally shut down whenever conditions move out of the favorable range and then wait for better conditions to return. But, instead of the essential components of a single cell being encapsulated into a resistant spore, it is an entire multicellular structure that shifts between a dried-out dormant state and a hydrated active state. I find that remarkable!

An aside: Leafy liverworts play the trade-off between carbon dioxide uptake and water loss differently than thalloid liverworts. The one- or two-cell-thick, leafy-looking flaps composed of photosynthetic cells make air pores unnecessary—carbon dioxide can simply move in from the surrounding air by diffusion. Yet that means that their waxy cuticle cannot get too thick. Although a thicker coating will help reduce water loss, the cuticle must remain thin enough that sufficient amounts of carbon dioxide can still pass through.

Other mineral nutrients

In addition to getting in water and carbon dioxide, bryophytes also need to maintain supplies of mineral nutrients to maintain metabolic activity. Many plants get a majority of these from the soil through their roots (discussed further later). But in the absence of roots, how do bryophytes acquire their needed supply? It seems to be a diverse story.

Some nutrients still seem to come from the soil, but in the absence of a defined vascular system, movement in through rhizoids is more limited. Nutrients that dissolve in raindrops from the atmosphere are also absorbed and at least in some species may be a major source. Then there are symbiotic relationships. For example, some hornworts (a closely related group of plants) have cavities inhabited by cyanobacteria that fix nitrogen, which is subsequently acquired by the host plants. Relationships with certain bacteria likely also occur in liverworts. The most prevalent symbiotic relationship, however, is with fungi, where thin branching fungi that both hook into the plant and extend through the soil are found in liverworts (as well as all other living plants). This association (commonly known as **mycorrhizal**) is often regarded as mutualistic, with the fungus gaining sugars and the plant gaining an increased ability to obtain water and nutrients. Fungal symbionts may have played a critical role in increasing water and nutrient uptake during the colonization of land. (Note: Across time this relationship appears to have become even more entangled, as fungi seem to grow not only in and around rhizoids or roots, but also throughout the entire bodies of plants. The nature of all these fungal–plant interactions is unknown, but evidence is coming out that the fungi help protect against fast evolving pathogens—that is, they play a role at least somewhat analogous to the immune system of animals.) Finally, liverworts are known to minimize that supply of mineral nutrients needed by recycling those from old tissues to new areas of growth.

Other bryophytes

Although liverworts are the morphologically simplest plants, two other recognized groups of plants—the hornworts and mosses—are characterized by sufficiently similar features to be lumped into one broader taxonomic category know as the Bryophyta. Presumably, all three divisions of bryophytes represent early evolutionary branches after the transition to land.

Going into a more detailed discussion of hornworts or mosses here, however, would only sidetrack the more general picture of plant evolution trying to be constructed. Comments will thus be limited to general similarities shared by all three groups, along with a few important new features found in hornworts and/or mosses.

Perhaps the most striking similarity is that all three groups combine the inability to effectively pull water from soil—they all have rhizoids instead of roots—with pronounced desiccation tolerance. In other words, all three groups have a link between not being very adept at gathering water, with the ability of the multicellular form to move into a dormant state whenever it cannot get enough.

An important new feature found in hornworts and mosses, along with all other plants, are **stomata**. In effect, stomata are air pores that can open and close. This allows a plant to fine-tune the trade-off between water loss and carbon dioxide to what is best for the plant at any particular moment. Structurally, stomata are formed from two crescent-shaped cells called **guard cells** positioned within a plant's outer cell layer, or epidermis (see Figure 22-23). Due to the inner wall of each guard cell being thicker than elsewhere, guard cells tend to press up against each other, shutting off a direct opening between a loose arrangement of internal photosynthetic cells and the outside. However, whenever guard cells fill with enough water, the extra pressure causes the thinner-walled sections, in combination with the radial orientation cellulose

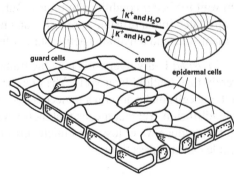

Figure 22-23. An outer or epidermal cell layer with guard cells, which under certain conditions will expand and form openings in the epidermal layer called stoma. When open, stoma provide a path for carbon dioxide to reach and water to escape from internal photosynthetic cells. See text for more information.

microfibrils, to buckle out, forcing the thickened wall sections apart and creating an opening or **stoma** (again see Figure 22-23).

Some more information: The opening and closing of stomata is regulated by anything that moves water into and out of guard cells. One obvious candidate is the amount of water in the plant as a whole. As a plant's water supply decreases, cells become more flaccid. As a result, guard cells would clamp together, closing the stomatal opening. There are problems, however, with this means of control. For instance, stomata would not close at night whenever the internal water supply was adequate. Thereby, water would continue to be lost without a compensatory benefit, as photosynthesis needs both light and CO_2. Also there would be no anticipation in reacting to water stress. A plant would shut its stomata only after water loss reached the point that guard cells become flaccid. In essence, they would react only after a plant is already in trouble. Seemingly, it would benefit plants to close their stomata earlier, especially plants potentially facing extended periods of drought. On the other side of the coin, plants solely using internal water levels to control stomatal openings would reopen their stomata only after a watered plant had brought in a sufficient amount to once again swell the guard cells. Plants may be better able to take advantage of available water if they could react when water is first present in the soil. The disadvantages associated with just using the internal water supply to control the opening and closing of stomata likely set the stage for another means of stomatal control to evolve. It turns out that extant vascular land plants use the movement of potassium ions (K^+). Darkness, for example, somehow triggers the migration of potassium ions from guard cells to neighboring cells. Water then follows by passive diffusion. The loss of water results in the cells becoming flaccid, closing the stomata. Light, on the other hand, triggers a reverse migration of potassium ions. As a consequence, water flows passively back into the guard cells, and their swelling pries open the stoma. Other factors—like the CO_2 concentration inside the leaf and water availability at the roots—have also been shown to influence the movement of potassium ions. Overall, plants control the opening and closing of their stomata via a complex regulatory system that integrates various forms of information (gathered by different forms of sensors).

In addition to guard cells, some mosses start to show development of convection or vascular systems. This, of course, means more names: the water-conducting cells are called **hydroids** and food- or sugar-conducting cells are known as **leptoids**. But the key change is the formation of thinner, more elongated cells that align together to form pathways of reduced resistance to water or sugar flow (using evaporative pulling or osmotically generated pressure gradients, respectively, as the power sources). Although mosses with vascular tracts can grow taller—water and sugar can more effectively be transported up and down the plant—they have not improved their ability to pull water out of the ground. Vascular pathways have not invaded belowground to form roots.

Reproduction and embryos

As discussed earlier, many species of algae have an alternation of generations within their sexual life cycle. All plants also have an alternation of generations. So it would make sense that plants evolved from algae that already had an alternation of generations. That may not, however, be the case. The charophycean green algae generate only multicellular haploids.

To set up how land plants may have switched to forming both multicellular haploids and diploids, let's again focus on the sexual life cycle of the extant group of charophycean green algae—members within the genus *Coleochaete*—that may be most similar to the algae that first transitioned to land.

In all *Coleochaete* species, gametes come in two distinct forms: small flagellate sperm and larger nonmotile egg cells. Some species are hermaphrodites—that is, each individual makes both sperm and eggs— whereas others have individuals with distinct genders. Nonetheless, the key aspect of sexual reproduction among *Coleochaete* species is that the egg-forming multicellular structures not only hold on to their eggs prior to fertilization, but they also continue to hold on to and *provision them* after fertilization. Thus, multicellular females can provide more extensive resources to only fertilized eggs. Vegetative cells growing around the zygote appear to transport in high-energy molecules. In the process, zygotes enlarge as they accumulate massive stores of carbohydrates and lipids. (Note: Zygotes contain chloroplasts, so they can also contribute to these accumulating stores by building their own high-energy molecules.) As zygotes mature, their walls also become lined with a compound that is presumed to help protect them from microbial attack prior to germination, which commonly occurs only after remaining dormant through winter. Interestingly, this protective compound is similar to sporopollenin, which is found in higher plant spore and pollen walls.

As mentioned earlier, *Coleochaete* species only have a haploid multicellular phase, so on germination the zygote undergoes meiotic cell division. Yet, because of the extensive energy stores, the number of spores that can be made from a single zygote is amplified. Meiosis is followed by one to a few rounds of mitotic cell division to form 8 to 32 flagellated haploid cells (that can wander off in an attempt to settle and grow into another multicellular haploid).

This is a rare story within algae. Except for certain red algae, holding onto and provisioning zygotes does not tend to happen, even in those algae that produce larger nonmotile eggs. Yet, all bryophytes (along with all other plants) start out their sexual cycle in a similar fashion. They are **oogamous**—the technical term for producing both larger nonmotile gametes (eggs) and smaller motile gametes (sperm)—and gametes of both types are produced within structures found on multicellular haploids. (Note: Gamete-producing structures, or **gametangia**, are called **antheridia** if sperm-producing and **archegonia** if egg-producing.) Furthermore, they retain their eggs within the archegonia after fertilization and subsequently provision their zygotes. But here is the new feature: The zygote, while still held within and nutritionally dependent on the multicellular haploid, begins to undergo mitotic cell divisions that hang together to form a multicellular diploid. While developing, these dependent multicellular diploids are called **embryos**. Plants with embryos are called **embryophytes**, and every single plant is an embryophyte.

Curiously, the multicellular diploid in all bryophytes never sheds its dependence on the multicellular haploid. In a sense, it grows to serve the multicellular haploid phase by increasing haploid spore production. Instead of the zygote undergoing meiosis (and perhaps a few extra rounds of mitosis) to produce spores, it uses resources garnered from the multicellular haploid, as well as its own photosynthetic tissue, to grow into a larger structure that can allocate many cells to undergo meiosis and form haploid spores (see Figure 22-24). It is the amplification argument once again. Due to the slim chance of any spore landing in a terrestrial location suitable for germination and subsequently growth into a multicellular haploid, taking the extra time to grow into a structure able to produce more spores should aid reproductive success. (Note: In addition to producing more spores, the evolution of durable protective walls that allowed spores to better tolerate dry conditions was a key event in the early invasion of the land by plants. Evolving desiccation tolerant spores allowed those that did not immediately land in a suitable spot to hang out and see if locale conditions might improve.)

Given that the multicellular diploid phase in all bryophytes grows on and is supported by a multicellular haploid, finding a good place to develop is not the issue. The difficulty is getting sperm and egg together, which is complicated by the fact that, like their algal ancestors, bryophytes still have flagellated sperm. Fertilization thus requires a water

Figure 22-24. A moss gametophyte with sporophytes growing out from it. Each diploid sporophyte started with an egg being fertilized by a flagellated sperm, and will never become independent of the gametophyte. Spores released from the sporangia disperse. Those that happen to land in a good site germinate and grow into another gametophyte.

path, commonly provided by raindrops, that connects antheridia (a sperm-producing area) with arche-gonia (an egg-producing area). So whether the multicellular haploid phase of any bryophyte species is bisexual (hermaphroditic) or unisexual, antheridia and archegonia need to be relatively close together for much chance of successful fertilization. Whether by splashing, running along a surface, or creating a continuous coat, raindrops will typically provide only relatively short avenues for sperm travel.

Seedless vascular plants

The evidence suggests that the earliest land plants shared many similarities with extant bryo-phytes—low growing, desiccation tolerant, embryophytes, with the multicellular haploid being the predominant multicellular form. Given the continued success of modern bryophytes, it is a lifestyle that works. It was also, however, a lifestyle that opened the door for further modifications. Both the haploid and diploid multicellular phases, along with the transitions in between, set the stage for com-ing up with new ways to succeed in a terrestrial setting.

Interestingly, the next major shift in plant evolution did not come within the workings of the mul-ticellular haploid—including how sperm and eggs were formed and what was needed for sperm to find eggs—but within the multicellular diploid. Changes came about that allowed the multicellular diploid to grow bigger and taller. The advantage is straightforward: A bigger and taller sporophyte can make more spores that can spread over a greater area, increasing the odds of spores landing in a site where they can germinate and grow into a new multicellular haploid.

Two changes happened, in particular, to make it possible for the sporophyte to grow bigger and taller. The first and most important change was improved vascular systems. As discussed earlier, once cells were hooked together by plasmodesmata, the power sources for moving water and mineral nutri-ents up through a plant (solar-triggered evaporation) and sugars from photosynthetic to nonphotosyn-thetic area (osmotic gradients) were present. The only "trick" needed to better utilize these gradients to generate convective flow was to modify the shape and arrangement of cells to form paths of less re-sistance. Such cell differentiation is seen to a certain degree in the gametophyte phase of some mosses (that form hydroids and leptoids). But within the plant lineage that gave rise to all plants other than bryophytes, it was within the diploid sporophyte that the evolution of vascular systems really came to fruition. This group is known, not coincidentally, as the **vascular plants**. Their vascular systems are known generally as xylem and phloem, which were mentioned briefly in Chapter 20. Next we discuss each a little more.

The second change was the sporophyte becoming independent—that is, while still starting out as an embryo supported by the gametophyte, the sporophyte eventually shed its attachment and grew on its own. It had to happen to get larger. Both in terms of structural and nutritional support, it is impos-sible to become larger than what you grow on. And, detaching the sporophyte changed everything. It was now free to evolve along any path that increased its ability to gather resources needed to produce and spread spores to viable germination sites. Eventually, this would include things like leaves, roots, and structurally more stable stems. Gaze up at a 300-foot-tall redwood tree, and you are looking at a large, independent sporophyte.

On the other hand, gametophytes remained small multicellular structures—perhaps because the advantage of getting larger is not so clear-cut. Although a larger gametophyte would be able to pro-duce more sperm or eggs or both, growing larger in a terrestrial world may not translate into increased number of fertilizations. The sperm produced by gametophytes were still flagellated, thus they need to be able to find eggs along a water-filled path. Growing higher up in the air may not have facilitated that. Growing larger also takes longer, which means that sporophytes would be started later with po-tentially less time to grow. Whether it is these or other reasons, gametophytes not only remained small, but in many plant lineages became even smaller.

Phloem and xylem

A striking difference between plant and animal vascular systems is that convective flow goes through cells in plants, whereas in animals it goes through a hollow tube (a blood vessel) made up of cells. This raises the question: How can plant cells be modified to decrease the resistance to flow?

Here, a little background knowledge is helpful. When liquid flows through any tube-like arrangement, the resistance to flow increases dramatically as tubes narrow. In fact when this pattern is stated mathematically, the relationship between flow resistance and diameter changes with the 4th power. For example, a twofold decrease in diameter increases the resistance to flow 16 times—2^4.

Structural changes that minimize flow through narrower areas are thus key for any linear arrangement of plant cells to reduce resistance to flow. Three changes, in particular, stand out. First, elongate each cell because the longer each cell within a vascular path the fewer times flow has to pass through the plasmodesmata linking cells together. Second, make the plasmodesmata as large as possible. And third, minimize cellular structures within vascular cells, as each will clog flow by effectively narrowing the pathway around them.

Both the cells making up phloem and xylem in vascular plants do all three. Of course, not all do so in exactly the same way, and such details, along with additional trade-offs associated with maintaining flow, are worth further exploration. But here I only frame in the basic ideas.

Phloem is a cytoplasmic transport path. Sugars, amino acids, signal molecules, or anything else that travels through these elongated cells (called **sieve cells** in all plant groups except the flowering plants, where they are called **sieve-tube elements**) never pass out of a cell through a cell membrane. To clear more room for flow, these cells even lose or modify basically all their parts. For instance, each nucleus either degenerates or is completely lost, as are ribosomes—thus, the cells lack the ability to do DNA-directed protein synthesis. Golgi bodies and vacuoles are also missing, and there are only relatively few mitochondria or plastids (what develop into chloroplast in photosynthetic cells). In fact, the only part that remains completely intact and functional is surrounding plasma membranes, as they are still osmotically active and responsive. These phloem cells are also in close association—spatially and via plasmodesmata connections—with helper or nurse cells (called albuminous cells or companion cells, respectively). Seemingly, these cells supply their elongated partners with whatever they need but cannot make on their own, making it possible for them to remain alive.

In contrast, the elongated cells specializing in conducting water, clear space for flow in a different way—they just die off at maturity! The cell walls left behind form the system of tubes through which water is drawn up by solar-powered evaporation (out of the plant's stomata).

An aside: Cell suicide, or what biologists call **apoptosis**, is actually a common feature of multicellular organisms. For instance, look at your hands—during development your fingers separated from each other by the cells in between committing apoptosis. In addition to developmental roles, it can be involved in maintaining healthy bodies. Damaged or virally infected cells are commonly removed by apoptosis, preventing such cells from wasting valuable nutrients or spreading and allowing them to be replaced by healthy functional cells. Apoptosis is the classic idea of an individual "taking one for the team." In multicellular organisms, the team is the rest of the body, which is typically composed of genetically identical cells. Apoptosis thus fits in with the idea of altruistic behaviors evolving by kin selection.

Although forming strands of elongated, cell-wall-bearing cells that then commit suicide is the basic means by which plants fashion water-conducting tubes, to be very effective a couple of basic issues still needed to be resolved. For one, the major component of cell walls—polysaccharides like cellulose, hemicellulose, and pectin—readily interact with and thus are permeable to water. It is hard to pull water up very far with a "leaky straw." Furthermore, the suction needed to pull up any liquid creates an inward force acting to collapse the tube. The longer the tube, the greater the inward force created. The rigidity of the surrounding walls thus sets a limit on how far a plant can draw up water and hence how tall a plant could potentially grow. And it turns out that the cellulose-based cell wall is not sufficiently rigid to support longer-distance water transport.

Lignin is a large three-dimensional spreading polymer that intertwines and forms links with basic cell wall components. In so doing it makes these cell walls both increasingly waterproof and rigid—properties that would help a plant's vascular system conduct water more efficiently. Where is lignin found? One place is the cell walls of specialized water-conducting systems of all plants except mosses. In other words, lignin-impregnated cell walls are a characteristic feature of xylem. (Note: Xylem-forming cells are called **tracheids** in all vascular plants except angiosperms, where they are called **vessel elements**—due to the fact that despite similarities, plant anatomists found them different enough to warrant a new name.) In other words, the absence of lignin is why hydroids—the specialized water-transport cells in certain mosses, which also lack living cells at maturity—are called hydroids instead of xylem. Furthermore, it is why these same mosses are not included among the vascular plants, despite the fact that there are enough similarities between conducting cells in mosses and xylem to suggest the possibility of a common origin. And finally, it is one of the reasons that these mosses are low growing—their vascular system is not efficient enough to pull water up very high.

A little more information: Lignin did not just pop out of nowhere to help land plants along. Its synthesis starts with the rearrangement of the amino acid phenylalanine (whose variable chain has a phenyl group—six-carbon ring with three alternating double bonds along with five hydrogens) along a metabolic path known as the phenylpropanoid pathway. This pathway branches in many ways to give rise to a wide array of water-soluble molecules that participate in a wide array of functions (e.g., helping defend against animal, fungal, or microbial attack, absorbing potentially damaging UV radiation, acting as antioxidants, and even generating colored pigments found in flowers and fruits). Lignin is formed by polymerizing certain molecules produced by this pathway into a macromolecule and to do it outside the cell within the cell wall.

In land plants, growing taller always has a potential advantage—the ability to better compete with surrounding plants for light. As already mentioned, one aspect of growing taller is increasing the distance that vascular tissue can transport water up from the ground. Here, the addition of lignin played a large role. But, to grow taller a plant must also be structurally stout enough to not only hold oneself up against gravity, but also to contend with mechanical stressors such as wind, rain, or snow. The increasing strength of lignified cell walls also played an important role here, although adding lignin to xylem is not the whole story. In early land plants, the vascular bundle (containing both phloem and xylem) went through the central part of the stem. Recall from Chapter 17, when we first discussed microtubules, that the outside of a tube experiences both the tensile and compressive forces associated with bending, whereas the middle surrounds the neutral plane. As a consequence, lignified cell walls positioned within a stem center are in the wrong location to provide much structural support. Increasingly taller land plants came up with two means to better position lignin. The first involved the differentiation of a new structural cell type called **sclerenchyma**, which have heavily thickened walls fortified with lignin and die at maturity. Such cells come in a variety of shapes, but one form, called fibers, seem particular important in supporting increased height. As their name implies, fibers are elongated cells whose long, tapering ends interlock to provide a strong structural framework that can be positioned wherever needed. The second involved moving the vascular tissue, along with sclerenchyma cells, to the outside of stems. Doing so not only better positions lignified xylem to play both structural and vascular roles, but when coupled with surface (or secondary) meristem—that can continually grow new outer layers of vascular tissue—generates the capacity to form **wood**. Wood is basically the accumulation of past outer layers of vascular (which is no longer functional) and support tissue.

Early vascular plants

Many plant fossils have been discovered that date back to around 430 million years ago (mya), suggesting that the simplest plants evolved even earlier. The first vascular plants found belonged to a now-extinct group called the Rhyniophyta. The oldest known rhyniophyte is called *Cooksonia*, which lived more than 400 mya. The sporophyte phase was composed of slender dichotomous branching stems ranging up to 6.5 centimeters (only a few inches) high, topped by sporangia (see Figure 22-25(a)).

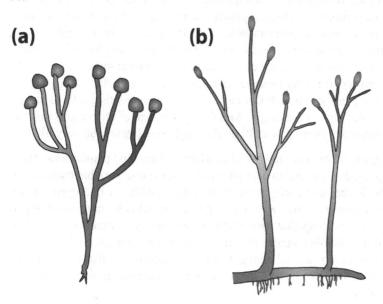

(a)   **(b)**

Figure 22-25. Drawings that show the basic growth forms of the sporophyte phase of two rhyniophytes—the earliest known group of vascular plants. Both (a) *Cooksonia* and (b) *Rhynia* lack both roots and leaves, but have branching photosynthetic stems topped by sporangia. (See text for more details.)

The best-known rhyniophyte is *Rhynia*. It too was composed solely of photosynthetic branching stems, which contained stomata and were covered by a waxy cuticle. It, however, grew taller—upward of 20 centimeters (around 8 inches)—and a single plant could spread by growing an underground stem or **rhizome** from which more photosynthetic branches could grow upward (see Figure 22-25(b)). The rhizome contained tufts of hair-like extensions or rhizoids.

Due to absence of roots and leaves, these early vascular plants would have been limited to moist habitats surrounding bodies of water. The rhizomes of some may have even extended through shallow water areas. But the limited nature of such habitats, in combination with population sizes increasing via reproduction, likely led to increasingly crowded, hence competitive, conditions. Competition for light, which is won by growing taller, would have been a driving force for improved vascular systems (such as adding lignin). The fossil record shows a general trend of these early vascular plants increasing in size and complexity of branching.

Of course, another way to deal with increasing competitive conditions is to come up with ways to colonize new terrestrial environments. This is why we discuss adding roots and leaves next.

Evolving roots and leaves

If, as the fossil evidence suggests, the earliest vascular plants were just stems, an obvious question is: How did roots and leaves come about? In essence, it is a question of how an anatomy of branching vascular stems could be modified to form flattened—but still vascular—photosynthetic areas (leaves) and ground-penetrating, highly branched filamentous—but still vascular—water-absorbing areas (roots).

The answer in both cases seems rather straightforward. Leaves appear to have formed by either flattening out photosynthetic tissues around a single small vascular branch (generating a leaf structure known as **microphylls**) or by the growth of flattened photosynthetic tissue between an array of vascular branches (generating a leaf structure known as a **macrophyll**). Most extant plants have macrophylls—as can be seen by branching leaf "veins," which are vascular bundles. The evolutionary origin of roots, on the other hand, appears to come from stems branching off a rhizome that grew down instead of up and continued to branch as they penetrated the soil.

An equally important question is: Why would leaves and roots be advantageous?

Let's start with roots. The initial advantage may have been structural. Branches growing into the ground would more firmly anchor the plant and thus help prevent it from being ripped up by wind or some other disruptive force. But growing vascular branches downward generated a new possibility. They are growing into a place with potentially more water. As water seeps into the ground after a rainfall, some of it will continue to be pulled by gravity until it reaches a rock layer through which water cannot easily move. Water then pools, filling in empty spaces and cracks within the soil, sand, or rocks. The top of this water-saturated layer is called the **water table**, and the water below is called **groundwater**. Vascular branches growing into the water table generate a conduit between a readily available water supply and photosynthetic stems above. (Of course, these underground branches would need to lose their waxy cuticle or any other form of barrier impeding the flow of water from soil into roots.) But that is not the whole story. Due to its polar nature, water has the potential to adhere to the surface of soil particles, and similar to a sponge, sufficiently small pores within soil structure can hold onto water molecules against the pull of gravity. So, even soil regions above the water table can store water from the last rain. And some of it, called **capillary water**, is held loosely enough to be absorbed by subterranean branches (roots). Although the amount of soil water available to any plant at any time is governed by a variety of factors (e.g., when it last rained, the depth of soil roots explore, and the nature of the soil material), the key point is that roots, in combination with the water storage potential of soil, increases the range of terrestrial conditions under which a plant could gather sufficient water to operate.

So far we have developed a vascular plant that gets carbon dioxide from the atmosphere through stomata and water from soil through roots. But that is not the whole input story. Quite a few other elements play essential roles in metabolism and must somehow be gathered from the environment. Rooted vascular plants do this, in large measure, by "mining" the soil for mineral nutrients. Specifically, via diffusion or active transport, roots can absorb ionic forms of needed elements that dissolve in soil water. The fertility of any soil is thus dependent on two things: (1) how readily it holds on to capillary water, and (2) whether it contains adequate supplies of needed mineral nutrients. The elements typically required, in order of needed abundance, are nitrogen, potassium, calcium, magnesium, phosphorus, sulfur, chlorine, iron, boron, manganese, sodium, zinc, copper, nickel, and molybdenum.

Some more information: The roots of vascular plants typically branch extensively, all the way down to root hairs—tiny, hair-like outgrowths of individual surface cells along a plant's root, which greatly increase the available absorptive surface area. Although more surface area increases the potential to uptake water, water cannot flow into a plant's roots unless there is favorable concentration gradient. Such gradient exists whenever the osmotic concentration—the amount of material dissolved in water—is higher in the root epidermal cells than in any water in contact with these cells. Therefore, active transport of mineral nutrients into root epidermal cells has the added benefit of increasing water uptake by increasing the osmolarity within these cells. (Note: This dependence on an osmotic gradient is also why most plants tend to dehydrate in salty soils. Even if soil water is abundant, the dissolved salts increase the soil water's osmotic concentration, making it more difficult for a plant to development a favorable water concentration gradient.) Once water flows into the epidermal cells, it will continue to flow inward because the osmotic concentration of these cells is decreased relative to the more interior cells. As a consequence, water continues to flow toward the middle of the root until it moves into the xylem.

Like with roots and their extensive branching structure, the issue of surface area again comes to the forefront when considering the evolution of leaves. Flattening any volume of aboveground tissue increases the surface area to intercept light, which in turn opens the door for more photosynthesis. But that is not the whole story. Intercepting more light also generates more heat, and tissues that get too hot can suffer "lethal overheating"—that is, they can literally get fried. So, spreading photosynthetic tissue into leaves requires a plant to be able to contend with the extra heat. One available option was evaporative cooling. More heat would lead to more **transpiration**—evaporation of water that moves out through stomata (which are typically positioned on the undersides of leaves), which will dissipate heat in the process. Being curiously sweaty mammals, we are quite familiar with evaporative cooling. But recognize that for a plant to effectively cool its leaves in this manner, several interacting factors would need to have already been in place. Basically, the climate, the soil's water-holding capacity, and the overall efficiency of a plant's root and water-transport system would need to combine such that adequate water could be delivered to leaves during drier times when the sun is shining (and heat loads are greatest). For instance, swampy areas may not have favored the evolution of leaves, not because of inadequate water supplies, but because it is normally so humid that the concentration gradient between spaces inside leaves and the surrounding atmosphere may not have been sufficient for enough water to flow out of the stomata to cool the leaves. (Note: Anyone who has experienced summertime in a humid area knows, firsthand, that higher humidity impedes evaporative cooling.) Perhaps the fact that several factors needed to be in place for leaf evolution to be favored helps explain a curiosity found in the fossil record—it appears to have taken vascular plants about 50 million years to evolve leaves.

An aside: Just to keep turning things on their head, realize that plants with the means to keep their leaves cool enough, could potentially use the extra heat gathered by leaves to facilitate growth by increasing the available supply of mineral nutrients. The causal chain goes as follows: Intercepting more light generates more heat, which will lead to more evapotranspiration, which pulls water through the xylem at a faster rate, which increases the rate at which mineral nutrients extracted from the soil are delivered to the rest of the plant. It is just one more example of the resolution of one problem opening the door for other opportunities.

Modern seedless vascular plants

The evolution of independent sporophytes, with vascular systems within structural stems connecting roots and leaves into a single functioning unit, was a huge deal in plant evolution—it extended the range of terrestrial conditions under which the sporophyte could grow. In the process, sporophytes of different plant lineages evolved into a wide variety of shapes and sizes and spread throughout much of the landscape. And all this happened without ever evolving a life cycle component, known as seeds. A familiar example is ferns, currently the most abundant and diverse group of seedless vascular plants. Other extant groups of seedless vascular plants, such as club mosses and horsetails, are not as common today, but during past times were dominant components of the earth's vegetation.

To both review and set the stage for where we are going next, I use the general life cycle of a fern (see Figure 22-26) to highlight distinctive features of how generations alternate in seedless vascular plants. The key is that whereas the sporophyte (multicellular diploid stage) still starts off as an embryo—it initially is nourished by the gametophye (multicellular haploid stage)—it eventually becomes independent of the gametophyte and grows into a rooted, vascular plant, which in this case develops large "fern-shaped" leaves. Meanwhile, the gametophyte perishes fairly quickly. The sporophyte eventually forms sporangia, which in ferns form on the underside of leaves, that give rise to haploid spores via meiotic cell division. Once released, spores that happen to disperse into sites with suitable conditions germinate and begin to undergo mitotic cell division to form a relatively small multicellular haploid that lacks roots, leaves, and a distinct vascular system. The gametophytes do, however, form both sperm-producing and egg-producing structures (antheridia and archegonia, respectively). Once these gametes mature, water stimulates antheridia to release sperm that go off in search of eggs. Water may also stimulate archegonia to release chemical signals that help guide sperm to eggs. Because of their close proximity, fertilization typically occurs between sperm and eggs produced by the same gametophyte. Self-fertilization still facilitates recombination repair. It does, however, dampen another potentially beneficial component of sexual reproduction—the continual production of genetically variable offspring through the scrambling of genetic information.

Although uncommon in ferns, one variation found in some seedless vascular plants is the production of two distinct forms (or sizes) of spores—a condition called **heterospory**. This change was associated with the evolution of two types of gametophytes. The smaller spores, or microspores, give rise to gametophytes that produce smaller (flagellated) gametes—that is, they are male. The larger

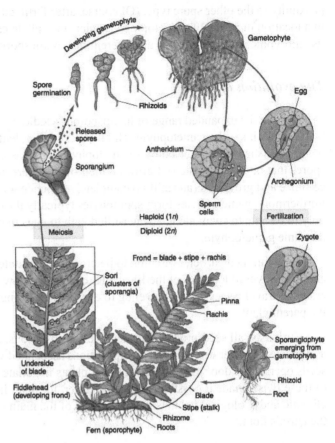

Figure 22-26. The basic life cycle of a fern. (See text for more details.)

spores, or megaspores, germinate into female gametophytes that produce larger nonmobile eggs. Presumably, heterospory evolved because it facilitated outcrossing and reaped any benefits associated with decreasing levels of self-fertilization. But it also came with the increased cost of being difficult to pull off. Think about it! The potentially rare event in homospory is not whether a sperm can locate an egg (as both are produced on the same gametophyte), but whether any dispersing spores land in a suitable location to germinate and grow. Heterospory, on the other hand, potentially compounds rare events. Outcrossing can occur only when two spores of different types, from different plants, happen to both disperse to a viable location in close enough proximity for sperm from the microgametophyte to locate and swim to an egg produced on the megagametophyte.

Interestingly, the major group of extant heterosporous seedless vascular plants, members of the genus *Selaginella*, have gametophytes that basically develop within the spore. That is, after germination they do not grow into a larger structure, which through its larger size could amplify the number of gametes produced. In fact, the male gametophytes develop wholly within the outer casing of the microspore. It consists of just a few cells in addition to an antheridium. The sperm produced within the antheridium literally emerge from a rupture in the microspore's outer casing. In contrast, the female gametophyte grows somewhat out beyond the boundaries of the megaspore's outer casing, positioning several archegonia in locations accessible to sperm in the process, but still most, if not all, of the nutrients used to support this growth come from those stored in the megaspore. The point in highlighting these details is that reducing gametophyte growth to what can be supported by resources carried in each spore removes one of the potential rare events needed for fertilization. Neither spore type requires landing in a growth-conducive site to produce gametes. They just need to land in close proximity to the other spore type. (Of course, after fertilization, the megagametophyte still needs to be in a location in which the developing vascular sporophyte can continue to grow after passing through its embryonic stage. But that is no different than homosporous plants.)

The evolution of seeds

Despite the expanded range of homosporous seedless vascular plants, their sexual life cycle still had a weak link—the gametophyte. Think about it! Big, leafy, rooted, vascular sporophytes start out being nourished and protected by a gametophyte, whereas gametophytes start out as single-celled spores that must germinate and grow on their own. Where across the landscape sporophytes could colonize and grow was (and still is) completely dependent on where gametophytes could succeed. Furthermore, gametophytes form sporophytes typically through self-fertilization, as sperm are likely only to be able to swim along a water-filled path to eggs in close proximity, such as those produced on the same gametophyte.

As mentioned earlier, switching to heterospory facilitates outcrossing, but at the cost of complicating the overall logistics of the life cycle. Especially, how a plant's life cycle incorporates the two essential travel issues: sperm traveling to eggs and offspring traveling away from or dispersing from the parent plant.

Curiously, all seed-producing plants are heterosporous. In fact, seeds may have initially evolved as a means to better deal with the complications associated with heterospory. Once present, however, seeds opened the door to new twists in how plants negotiate their life cycle. Most important, many of these twists made it possible, or at least easier, for plant lineages to inhabit an even wider range of climatic and ecological habitats. Seeds are one of the main reasons that seed plants currently dominate the earth's flora.

A new heterosporous path

Earlier we discussed an association with heterospory and reduced gametophytes. The trend continues in the evolution of seeds. What is new, however, is that instead of the haploid megaspores dispersing, they are retained by the vascular diploid sporophyte inside their production site—the megasporangium (termed the nucellus in seed plants). At some point these held megaspores begin to undergo mitotic cell division to form a relatively reduced, but still multicellular, female gametophyte, or megagametophyte. In more primitive seed plants, the developing megagametophyte still forms one or more archegonia, complete with egg. In other words, the cells that play the role of eggs within a sexual life cycle are formed by the multicellular gametophyte, which is held by the multicellular sporophyte.

There is a disadvantage associated with this new arrangement: Dispersal at this stage of the life cycle is now missing. On the other hand, retention allows large successful sporophytes to nurture and protect the egg-producing gametophyte and even in some way help guide in sperm from other individuals. Part of the protection comes from the sporophyte enveloping the megasporangium (and eventually the megagametophyte) with one or more additional layers of tissues, known as integuments. These tissue layers surround the megasporangium except for an opening on one end called the micropyle— which serves as the opening for sperm to get in. The entire integument-wrapped structure is known as an ovule. Once fertilized, an ovule can develop into a seed.

We just finished the female side of the seed story, but what about the male side? Here, we start with microsporangia that develop on mature sporophytes. These structures contain cells that are converted into microspores through meiotic cell division. Like megaspores, the microspores do not disperse at this stage. Instead each undergoes a limited number of mitotic divisions to form a few celled (commonly two or four) microgametophyte known as a pollen grain. In other words, a pollen grain is not another name for plant sperm; instead it is a greatly reduced male gametophyte. Two cell types are common to all types of pollen: tube cells and generative cells. The single tube cell is responsible for the growth of the pollen tube (discussed more later), whereas the single generative cell generally undergoes one more round of mitotic cell division to form two sperm cells. So, in contrast to all other forms of sperm-producing gametophytes, pollen grains do not develop antheridia (which you recall are distinct sperm-producing structures).

In contrast to female gametophyte, after microspores develop into male gametophytes or pollen grains, they are released out into the world, often in large numbers. The "hope" is that at least one or more of the pollen grains will be transported (by wind, animal, etc.) to within close proximity of an ovule. Whatever the transport mode, the movement of pollen from its production site to the vicinity of an ovule is known as pollination.

After pollination, sperm formed within the pollen grain must be able to reach an egg cell within the ovule for fertilization to occur. The problem is that tissues, whether just those surrounding the egg within the ovule, or even more beyond that, stand in the way. This is where the tube cell plays a role. Through a rupture in a pollen grain's outer casing, the tube cell begins to penetrate through these tissues by forming an elongated tubular outgrowth known as a pollen tube. Any pollen tube that grows along the right path becomes a conduit for sperm to travel toward and eventually fuse with an egg. In some of the most primitive seed plants, sperm are still flagellated and thus propel themselves through the pollen tube. In most others, the sperm lack flagella and are essentially pulled along by the growing pollen tube. Regardless of the details, however, the evolution of ovules and pollen grains, which combine pollination and pollen tubes to create a travel path for male gametes to reach eggs, avoided something that no other terrestrial plant had before—reliance on an external source of water. In a potentially water-scarce terrestrial world, that is a big deal. In a vertebrate analogy, it is like going from amphibian to reptiles. Amphibians still need to return to freestanding water to reproduce, whereas reptiles, via internal fertilization in combination with the so-called amniotic (or cleidoic) egg, broke that link.

The basic features of a seed

After fertilization, ovules can develop into seeds. This involves two basic steps: (1) the integument hardening to form an increasingly protective barrier known as a seed coat, and (2) the formation of an embryo within the seed. Seed plants, like all other forms of land plants, are embryophytes—early sporophyte development is supported by the gametophyte. But now the gametophytic tissue, including whatever nutrient stores they contain, are enclosed within the seed coat, and typically the zygote (fertilized egg) undergoes embryonic development while still inside the seed, to the point that the basic vascular plant body-plan forms. That is, the embryo develops seed leaves, known as **cotyledons**, an embryonic root, known as the **radicle**, and a stem-like structure, known as the **hypocotyl**, that runs in between.

Think how curious the structures of seeds are. In total, three steps of a plant's life cycle are represented: the seed coat and nucellus are diploid sporophytic tissue from the parent plant, and further inward lies haploid gametophyte tissue, which wraps around and supports the next sporophytic generation—the diploid embryo. This raises questions about how these three stages interact. Obviously, within an enclosed container an embryo can only grow so far. Furthermore, seeds form while still attached to the parent plant—not a good place to continue to grow into a full-size plant. Forming seeds thus generates two challenges: dispersal and germination. Let's discuss each in turn.

In all seedless plants, spores are the dispersal stage—that is, dispersal occurs prior to fertilization. Seed plants changed both the order and the dispersal unit: fertilization now occurs prior to dispersal, and seeds, not spores, are what disperse. In one sense, whether spores or seeds disperse seems trivial; neither spores nor seeds are actively mobile, so once released beyond falling to the ground—which gravity will take care of—any further movement away from parents and siblings requires some form of carrier. But when it comes to the most basic option—wind—spores have the advantage of being smaller (they are a single cell) and therefore more readily carried by air currents. Thus, delaying dispersal to the seed stage came with a cost. Yet, there were also potentially compensating benefits. In particular, enclosing a developing embryo, along with additional food stores, within a protective seed coat could help a young sporophyte negotiate the especially vulnerable early stages of establishment. In essence, wherever they landed they had a better chance of success because they could attain a larger, more functional size before they were own their own.

An aside: As you have likely noticed, seed plants have come up with myriad ways to increase their seed's dispersal ability. Yet despite this variety, two themes in particular are prevalent: attaching all sorts of surface-area-increasing structures that help keep wind-dispersed seeds afloat longer (think of dandelion seeds), or somehow getting mobile animals to transport their seed—such as surrounding seeds with fleshy nutritious tissue that animals will feed on, or encasing them in sticky arrangements that will adhere to an animal's outer surface.

Germination is the term used for the transition from a seed-encased embryo to a seedling—a still small but functional plant with roots extracting water and nutrients from the soil and photosynthetically active tissues aboveground. The easiest developmental path to envision is (1) the sporophyte embryo grows until its starts to be limited by seed size; (2) the seed is then released by the parent plant, where it at least drops to the ground below and perhaps via wind or some other means travels some distance away from the parent plant; and (3) the seed coat then somehow ruptures, allowing the sporophyte to continue to grow into an independent functional plant. In other words, seed release and germination are timed so that growth from zygote to independent plant proceeds along a continuous path. Yet, somewhere along the line a new twist was introduced—the ability for embryos within seeds to suspend growth and move into a quiescent or dormant state. This was a huge deal! Why? It introduced a new pause button into the life cycle of terrestrial plants. Once a seed was formed, it could wait for favorable conditions before proceeding—that is, before germinating and resuming growth. As a consequence, mature seeds could remain on the parent plant until the right conditions came along to transport them to a new, more favorable location. Or, after dispersal, seeds could wait out adverse conditions (e.g., too cold, too hot, too dry, too much competition) and germinate when favorable conditions returned.

Although the capacity for seeds to pause would be advantageous for any plant growing in any conditions, seed dormancy introduced a new possibility—the ability to persist in environments too extreme for the vascular sporophyte to survive year-round. Desert-dwelling annual plants are a classic example. After a period of sufficient rain, seeds germinate into a fast-growing sporophyte that quickly produces seeds before it dies (due to the inability to contend with extended periods of hot, dry conditions). The next generation then persists in the soil as dormant seeds until favorable germination conditions again return. Also note that persisting through harsh conditions via seed dormancy is functionally similar to desiccation tolerance in bryophytes (fleshy gametophytes able to survive water scarce conditions by drying into a dormant form that is able to come back on rehydration), but accomplished in an entirely different matter.

An amazing fact: Lotus seeds, estimated to be 10,000 years old by carbon-14 dating, were still able to germinate.

Building trees

There were two major trends in the invasion of land by plants. One was the ability to complete their life cycle in drier and drier conditions. Seeds and seed dormancy were important parts of this story. Second, was the ability to better compete for sunshine by growing taller. Interestingly, fossil evidence suggests that growing taller through forming woody tissue may have preceded seeds. Perhaps seeds even first evolved in woody plants. If true, this leads one to wonder whether there was any causal connection between getting taller and seed evolution. It is worth exploring further, starting with looking for connections between woody plants and becoming heterosporous. Here, however, we will just briefly explore the history of getting taller.

The key step in growing taller is going from an herbaceous to a woody growth form. In herbaceous plants, meristem—tissue consisting of embryonic cells in that they are undifferentiated, retain the ability to divide and ultimately can differentiate into all other plant tissues—are located only at the tips of stems (and roots). Stems can thus use cell division to grow taller but not wider and thus can only grow as tall as the initial base can support. Stem elongation is often called primary growth and the corresponding meristem called primary meristem. Although not particularly sturdy, herbaceous plants have an advantage of growing relatively quickly. Secondary retention of meristem around the outer surface, so-called secondary meristem, allowed stems to expand their diameter via cell division. This, in turn, triggered a new stage in the competition for light.

The earliest tree-like plants show up in fossil record around 50 million years after the colonization of land by plants—that is, as early as 380 mya. They are found in at least two distinct plant groups.

One group, the tree-like lycophytes, became a major component of the swamp forests that left behind the extensive fossil deposits that we call coal (which were largely deposited around 320 million plus years ago). As much of 70% of coal deposits come from this group. Yet curiously, this same group seems to have gone extinct by 300 mya. Some tree-like lycophytes, specifically the two most widespread and common ones—*Lepidondendron* and *Sigillaria*—were quite substantial in size. They grew from 20 to 40 m in height, with base diameters reaching up to 2 m. And they attained such sizes without forming wood, which can sound confusing at first. They still had secondary growth, which was clearly structural, but the growth pattern was different. In "woody" plants the secondary meristem continually differentiates into xylem and phloem, and thus, as a plant grows taller and wider, it continually restores both parts of the vascular system. In contrast, only xylem was continually formed from secondary meristem in lycophytes. This may help explain the following: Tree-like lycophytes appear to have lived most of their life as a low growing mass with an extensive root network, which on occasion shot up rapidly growing "trees." Each "tree" would produce and release spores and then die back soon afterward. The inability to continually build more phloem as a plant gets larger would have seemingly impinged on any lycophyte's ability to continue to grow and survive. It may also help explain why this group went extinct, as eventually they may have lost out in competition with woody plants. The seemingly most closely related plants that live today, known as the club mosses, are tiny—small, creeping plants that typically grow no more than 5 cm in height.

The other group is collectively known as the progymnosperms. Members of this extinct group were the first to produce woody trees with branched trunks (similar to the growth form of many of today's trees). They still, however, had fern-like leaves and produced spores instead of seeds. Some were homosporous, whereas others were heterosporous. This latter group is thought to be ancestors, or at least close relatives, of the seed plants. The most well-known progymnosperm, an extinct genus called *Archaeopteris*, is found in the fossil record around the same time span as tree-like lycophytes. It could develop a thick trunk, up to 1.5 m in diameter, and grow up to 10 m in height. Once this plant group evolved, its members appeared to have spread relatively quickly to become the most dominant tree worldwide.

Bearing sufficient similarities to suggest that they evolved from some progymnosperm lineage, around 360 to 370 mya (or even earlier) the first seed plants showed up in the fossil record. They are known as pteridosperms or seed ferns. Members of this group formed woody tissue, and some seemed to have grown upright as trees, using their stout stems to support their large fernlike fronds, whereas others seemed to take advantage of the support structure formed by other plants and grew as vines. Their seeds formed within megasporagium located on open leaves, and thus are sometimes referred to as "naked seeds" because their seeds are not encased within an enclosed structure. Similarly, pollen formed within microsporangium on open leaves. Interestingly, the evolution of trees with seeds did not lead to the rapid displacement of trees with spores. The spread of *Archaeopteris*, and the development of lycophyte-dominated coal swamp forests occurred many millions of years after seeds evolved. Instead, the most significant change may have been the increased ability to disperse and germinate in increasingly less humid and waterlogged areas, allowing plants to colonize previously inhospitable inland and upland areas. Furthermore, seed ferns were not only able to persist through the time that the spore-bearing swamp plants become extinct (around 300 mya)—perhaps largely due to major reductions in their swampy, humid habitat that resulted from climatic changes—but become abundant in certain regions over the next 100 million years. For instance, they appear to have been common in southern Pangaea—the supercontinent made from the various landmasses jamming together—during the Triassic period (250 to 205 mya). (Note: It was during the end of the Triassic period that Pangaea began to break up into the present-day landmasses.) But, by somewhere around 100 mya, seed ferns had also become extinct.

During the Permian period (300–250 mya), three other plant groups with a woody habit and "naked seeds" came on to the scene: cycadophytes, ginkos, and conifers. Based on similarities, these groups appear to have either shared a common ancestor with seed ferns or evolved from one or more branches of seed ferns. But different than seed ferns, all three groups have extant species. Collectively, these three groups, along with extinct seed ferns, are often referred to as the **gymnosperms**, which comes from the Greek word *gumnospermos*, or naked seeds. Genetic evidence suggests that cycadophytes are the oldest branch, followed by ginkos, and then conifers. That cycad and ginko pollen still retain the primitive character of producing flagellate sperm (that actively swim through the pollen tube to reach and fertilize the ovule) fits with this suggested branching pattern.

Cycadophytes have relatively short and squatty wood stems and tough leaves (and overall are similar in appearance to palms). They appear to have been most abundant during the Triassic period (250 to 200 mya), common in the Jurassic period (200 to 145 mya), and starting to decline in the Cretaceous (145 to 65 mya). (Note: These three periods make up the Mesozoic Era, which is commonly referred to as the age of dinosaurs.) Although there are still a fair number of extant species (around 300), they make up a very minor component of the overall plant flora.

Ginkos may have enjoyed some initial success by being able to colonize colder areas (higher elevations and higher latitudes), due to having deciduous leaves that could be shed during colder seasons. Similar to cycads, ginkos were most abundant in the Triassic and especially Jurassic periods and have dwindled from there. Currently, only one species still exists, whose common name is the maidenhair tree (*Ginko biloba*).

The defining feature of conifers—which include redwood, pine, cedar, hemlock, cypress, and fir trees—is the modification of the open leaves with sporangium into structures called scales, which are grouped into spiral arrangements know as a **cones**. They also typically have skinny leaves, called needles, that tend to remain on the tree throughout the year even in colder climates—a condition known as being evergreen. More than any other gymnosperm group, conifers seemed to have dominated much of the landscape during at least the first half of the Mesozoic. As such, they may have been an important food source for dinosaurs, especially larger herbivores such as the long-necked sauropods. And, in contrast, to the other gymnosperm groups, conifers are still a major component of today's flora. Although the species number is not exceedingly large, around 630, they are found basically everywhere, and in some regions, like northern boreal forest, conifers are still the dominant tree type.

Angiosperms

The vast majority of seed plants found today do not have "naked seeds." Instead, their seeds form within a megasporagium on a leaf that wraps around and fuses at the margins to form an enclosed structure called a **carpel**. Although protecting developing ovules within this modified leaf arrangement could have advantages, it also creates an obvious problem: How can the ovules get fertilized? Pollen cannot reach the micropyle—the opening within the developing seed coat—directly. Instead, carpels develop a sticky area, called a **stigma**, that holds onto pollen that lands or is placed there. The tube cell within a pollen grain then takes on a new path, as it first must grow a pollen tube through parent sporophyte tissue before even reaching an ovule. On the other hand, pollen forms on leaves with microsporangia that have been structurally modified to promote pollen dispersal. Typically, within each so-called **stamen**, the microsporangia, or pollen sacs form perched on top of thin stalk-like structures.

Most plants with carpels and stamens arrange them together to form a perfect flower, meaning that both sexes are grouped together. But where is the flower, with all of its colorful petals? Weird as it may sound, flowers, to a botanist, do not have to have petals, just carpels and/or stamens. (Note: Imperfect flowers have only one sex.) And all plant species bearing carpels and stamens are considered to be part of a single monophyletic group known as the flowering plants or **angiosperms**.

Before we delve a little further into petals (and fruits), let's add a little history. The earliest fossil of a flowering plant, *Archaefructus liaoningensis*, dates to around 125 million years ago—clearly much younger than gymnosperms. Angiosperm-like pollen has been found that dates around 140 mya. And incomplete fossils, along with other more indirect forms of evidence, such as genetic comparisons, suggest an even earlier date of origin. But so far, continuous fossil evidence that shows the intermediate steps in flower evolution is lacking. It is also still unclear exactly what plant group was ancestral to angiosperms, although, based on the most shared similarities, it is seemingly some form of gymnosperm, perhaps even a group that is now extinct. On the other hand, the fossil record clearly shows that by the mid Cretaceous period (around 100 mya) angiosperms had already radiated into a wide diversity of plant forms and habitats. By the late Cretaceous (around 70 to 75 mya) they had become the predominant form of land plant. And that remains true today. Currently, there are at least 260,000 extant species that come in a wide variety of growth forms (e.g., small herbs, shrubs, vines, trees, and even both floating and rooted aquatics) and live in nearly all possible habitats—with the highest mountaintops and extreme polar-regions being a couple of the exceptions.

Clearly something about flowers has helped lots of different plant lineages succeed. The most obvious difference is flowers opened the door to involve animals in both travel components of the life cycle. Consider, for instance, travel of pollen towards ovules. Most gymnosperms rely on wind—that is, they are typically wind pollinated. And wind pollination is still found in many angiosperms, such as in the grasses—which generally have simple flowers composed largely of carpels and stamens. But that is not the main story, nor even the original story—as some have speculated that flowers first evolved in an isolated place, such as an island or mountaintop, to take advantage of a local insect or other animal form. How could this have worked? Perhaps pigment production, and subsequent coloration, was somehow modified in leaves surrounding both macro- and microsporophylls—leaves bearing either ovule-producing macrosporangia or pollen-producing microsporangia, respectively, and these different-colored leaves, for some reason, attracted a type of insect. Via movement between plants bearing this same mutation, these insects could have begun to transfer pollen from microsporophylls of one plant to near ovules on another plant. Once started, changes that made pollen transport more efficient would have been favored. This could include changes in both the microsporophylls and macrosporophylls toward arrangements that facilitated both pollen transfer between different plants and reduced self-fertilization. The evolution of stamens, with the pollen sacs extended out on the end of a stalk, and carpels, that surround ovules with parental tissue that could influence the types of pollen grains able to form pollen tubes, may have occurred at this point. At the same time, the coloration and arrangement of the surrounding leaves could have further specialized away from being photosynthetic and toward being attractive to potential pollinators, forming a whorl of flower **petals** surrounding the stamens and carpels. The only other part found in many flowers is an additional whorl of modified leaves outside the petals knows as **sepals**. They enclose and protect the rest of the flower during its development—that is, during the bud stage. Figure 22-27 shows the four basic flower parts.

An aside: In addition to changes in structures surrounding ovules and pollen, the nature of ovules and pollen has also typically changed within angiosperms. For instance, the reduced gametophytes within gymnosperm ovules still make one or more specialized egg-producing structures or archegonia. That is not the case in angiosperms. Instead, the single haploid megaspore (that forms via meiosis and degeneration of three of the four resulting cells) commonly goes through two rounds of nuclear divisions and some curious patterns of nucleus migration and cell wall formation to form an eight-nucleus, seven-cell mature female gametophyte, or embryo sac. One cell within this structure is the egg cell. On the other hand, the male gametophyte found within pollen grains consists of only

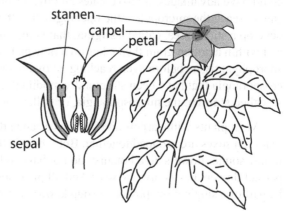

Figure 22-27. The basic parts of a flower (see text for more details).

two cells: a tube cell and a generative cell. Like in gymnosperm pollen, eventually the generative cell undergoes one more round of cell division to form two sperm cells. But afterward, something different happens. In gymnosperms, one of the two sperm degenerates, and the other fertilizes the egg. However, in angiosperms both sperm remain intact and fuse with another cell, a process called **double fertilization**. As expected, one sperm fuses with the egg cell to form a zygote—the diploid cell from which the next sporophyte generation arises. The other commonly fuses with a different cell that then undergoes rounds of cell division to form a tissue called **endosperm** that surrounds and becomes the source of food stores for the developing embryo. Something curious Is going on here! In contrast to gymnosperms, paternal genes are present in the cells acquiring nutrients for the embryo containing the same paternal genes. Given that pollen fertilizing different ovules within the same flower could easily come from different sources, one may conclude that becoming part of the genetic information used in endosperm formation could aid each male (each pollen donor) in acquiring sufficient resources for his offspring. Of course, the female filling ovules fertilized by different pollen donors may not always "agree" with each male's "perspective" in terms of how to allocate resources among her offspring. This may have led to another twist! In most angiosperms the maternal cell destined to become endosperm (after fertilization) has two maternal nuclei. In other words, endosperm is commonly triploid (two copies of maternal genome and one copy of paternal genome). Did this evolve as a means to increase the maternal "voice" in allocation decisions? It is a good question. In fact, the entire combination of double fertilization and triploid endosperm is worth puzzling over.

Once the evolutionary interaction between flowers and animals started, it makes sense that it would have exploded. Different colors and shapes would be attractive to different types of animals, and each new species would do best if it could attract either different pollinators or interact with old pollinators in a new way. Flower modifications could even facilitate speciation, as pollen and thus gene flow could become increasingly restricted from the ancestral group with a different flower morph. Additional rewards, such as nectar, to further motivate pollinators to move between flowers also makes sense. And as flowers evolved in response to animals, animals would also be selected to evolve in response to changing flowers. It is a coevolutionary tale that helps explain big patterns, like why there are so many different species of pollinating insects and pollinated plants, as well as smaller patterns, like long tube-shaped flowers and hummingbird bills.

A second flower feature also extended the interaction between animals and flowering plants to include seed dispersal. After ovules are fertilized, some plants develop the surrounding parental tissue within the carpel into a nutritious food source called a fleshy fruit. (Note: Botanists refer to any structure, whether fleshy or hard, that develops from this surrounding parental tissue as a fruit.) Any animal feeding on a fleshy fruit that moves before either spitting or defecating out the seed (or seeds) becomes a dispersal agent. Like flowers, different plant lineages have diversified widely in the size, shape, color, and contents of their fruit. And again like flowers, this diversification has been a coevolutionary tale, with fruit-eating animals (frugivores) and fleshy fruit–producing plants each evolving in response to each other.

As aside: Lots of biologists have spent lots of years studying the specific interactions between different plant species and those animals that visit their flowers or feed on their fruits. Within this search, much has been learned and myriad amazing stories have been uncovered. As the focus here cannot be to take up these topics any further, I hope you will explore some on your own. In fact, much can be learned just by paying attention to what is visiting the flowers and fruits in "your own backyard."

Another aside: Junipers and yews are two groups of conifers that produce fruit-like structures that wrap around their seeds and aid in seed dispersal through attracting animals to feed. These structures, however, are not technically fruits because the seeds are never surrounded by a carpel. Instead they are cones that have been modified to take on a berry-like appearance (and function). For instance, juniper "berries" are cones made up of fleshy, fused scales, whereas, the fleshy red structure wrapped around a single seed in yew plants is a single modified scale.

Modular growth, diversification, and homeotic mutations

Three important themes came up in the previous chapter: (1) that many multicellular animals are modular—that is, their body plan contains repeats of the same basic anatomical arrangement; (2) that lineages of modular organisms are primed to evolve into a broad range of morphologies, as both the number and the structural details of each module could be modified; and (3) that homeotic transformations provide the most direct evidence that different structures (such as legs and antenna in insects) actually originated through diversification of modules.

Did you notice that the brief discussion of flower evolution followed this exact same logic? Leaves were the repeating chunks of anatomy modified in different ways to form the four basic flower parts: sepals, petals, stamens, and carpels. And like that found in certain animal structures, the discovery of homeotic transformations lends strong support for this idea. Let me briefly explain.

When a flowering plant's meristem begins to differentiate into a flower, the cells arrange into four concentric rings, called **whorls**. Each whorl in turn gives rise to the four basic flower parts. Specifically, sepals form from the outermost whorl, petals from the next one in, stamens from the next, and finally the innermost whorl develops into carpels. The genetic underpinning of each whorl's pattern of differentiation has also been uncovered. It is called the **ABC model of flower development**, and its basic structure appears to apply to many, if not all, flowering plants. The important detail is that there are three classes of master regulatory genes—generically called A, B, and C—differentially expressed within the four whorls. Class A and Class C genes are antagonist—the expression of one turns off the expression of the other—so they are never found together. Specifically, Class A genes are turned on within cells making up the outer two whorls, whereas Class C genes are expressed in the inner two whorls. The expression pattern of Class B genes, on the other hand, crosses both boundaries, showing up in the middle two whorls. In aligning gene expression with floral development, an interesting pattern pops out: sepals develop in the whorl expressing only Class A genes, petals form where both Class A and Class B genes are expressed, stamens arise where both Class B and Class C genes are expressed, whereas carpels form where only Class C genes are expressed (see Figure 22-28).

This pattern led to a series of questions that have been experimentally tested. The most relevant to our current discussion is: What happens when the expression of all three classes of master regulatory genes are somehow blocked? The answer: All four whorls undergo a homeotic transformation—each differentiated into leaves (see Figure 22-29(a)), showing strong support that each flower part arose

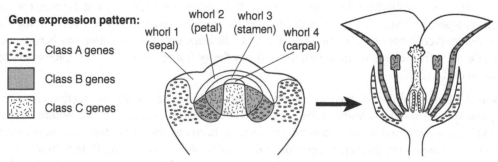

Figure 22-28. The ABC model of flower development (see text for more details).

through differential modification of leaves! The other obvious question to pose is: What happens when expression of each gene class is blocked one at a time? Figure 22-29(b-d)) summarizes these results. Note that each is predicted by the initial pattern. Also note that all the master regulatory genes involved are homeotic genes—mutations that block the building of "normal" proteins led to a shift in the development of any whorl affected.

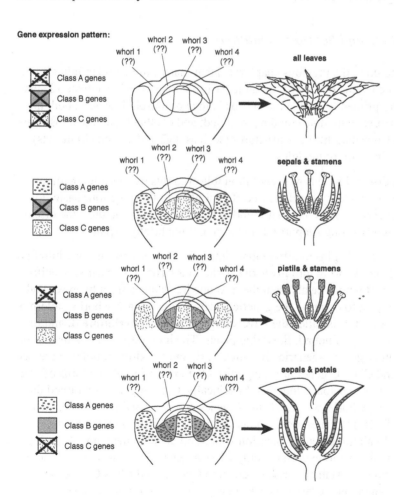

Figure 22-29. The pattern of homeotic transformations observed when the expression of different classes of master regulatory genes involved in flower development were experimentally blocked (see text for more details).

Some key terms:

alternation of generations – a form of sexual reproduction that includes both a multicellular haploid phase (organism) and a multicellular diploid phase (organism) within each reproductive cycle.

spore – a reproductive cell that can develop into a multicellular organism without fusing with another cell.

sporophyte – a multicellular diploid organism within an alternating generation reproductive cycle that produces haploid cells by meiosis that go off and act as spores.

sporangium – the structure on the sporophyte in which spores are produced.

gametophyte – a multicellular haploid organism within an alternating generation reproductive cycle that produces haploid cells by mitosis that go off and act as gametes.

gametangium – the structure on the gametophyte in which gametes are produced.

antheridium – a gametangium that produces sperm.

archegonium – a gametangium that produces an egg.

heterosporous – producing two types of spores, designated microspores (which develop into male gametophytes or microgametophytes) and megaspores (which develop into female gametophytes or megagametophytes).

plasmodesmata – membrane-bound channels that extend through openings in cell walls and connect the cytoplasm of adjacent cells.

stoma (plural **stomata**) – an opening created on the outer surface of most terrestrial plants by guard cells pulling apart. Stomata are typically found on the underside of leaves and along photosynthetic stems. Such openings allow interior cells to exchange materials (such as carbon dioxide) with their environment.

transpiration (or evapotranspiration) – the diffusional movement of water molecules out of a plant's stomata.

embryophyte – any phototroph in which early sporophyte development is supported by the gametophyte. All plants are embryophytes.

vascular plant – any plant that develops regions of conducting tissue known as phloem and xylem.

flower – the reproductive structure of angiosperms (flowering plants). A complete flower contains sepals, petals, stamens, and carpels, but all flowers have at least one stamen or one carpel.

Some study questions:

1. One might expect the evolution of multicellularity to happen when a single-cell is faced with a tradeoff—that is, when a single cell cannot simultaneously perform two (or more) biologically useful activities. Explain how such a tradeoff may help explain the evolution of multicellular cyanobacteria.

2. Discuss how their unique type of cell covering and cell division, in combination with attempting to retain motility while dividing, could have led to the evolution of both multicellular colonies and truly multicellular organisms within the Volvocine algae.

3. Outline a path of multicellular growth and asexual reproduction compatible with cells that build microfibril-based cell walls.

4. Discuss how the amplification argument may help explain why photosynthetic cells with micro-fibril-based cell walls grow into a multicellular organism. Further discuss how within a sexual life cycle, the amplification argument could lead to the alternation of generations.

5. Explain how three-dimensional tissues, air pores, waxy cuticles, plasmodesmata, and desiccation tolerance contribute to in the ability of thalloid liverworts to persist on land.

6. What is different between air pores and stomata? Why does it make sense that most extant land plands have stomata?

7. Discuss the connection between the evolution of embryos and alternating generations in plants.

8. Describe the basic life cycle of a bryophyte. Be sure to include how the two life cycle travel issues—sperm traveling toward eggs, and offspring traveling away from parents—are accomplished.

9. Discuss why the sporophyte, instead of the gametophyte, tended to get larger in the evolution of plants. Further discuss how phloem, xylem, lignin, roots, leaves, and wood played a role in increasing the size of sporophytes.

10. Describe the basic life cycle of a fern. Be sure to include how the two life cycle travel issues are accomplished.

11. What is a seed? a pollen grain? Describe the basic life cycle of a seed plant.

12. Compare and contrast dessication tolerance (found in bryophytes) and seed dormancy.

13. Compare and contrast how gymnosperms and angiosperms negotiate the two life cycle travel issues.

14. How are plants a modular structure? What is the genetic evidence that all flower parts are modified leaves?

Patterns of Inheritance

Perhaps you have heard a statement like: Betty has her mom's blue eyes. This, of course, is not a literal statement. Betty's mom is not walking around with two empty eye sockets because her eyes were transferred to her daughter.

In Chapter 20, I introduced the notion that the evolution of multicellular organisms is really the evolution of repeatable developmental pathways that work. Here we examine the notion of repeatable heritability more closely. In the broadest sense, the heritability of development refers to frogs giving rise to frogs, dogs giving rise to dogs, and so on. But really, the focus is on a finer level. Typically, members of the same species look at least somewhat different (as is very apparent among humans), which means that different individuals generally follow a somewhat unique developmental path. Accordingly, the finer level heritability question is whether frogs, dogs, humans, or any other species give rise to offspring whose developmental path more closely matches their parents than other members of the same species. Betty forming the same eye color as her mom would be an example. And if that is true, how does it happen?

Getting Started

Typically starting with a single cell, the processes of development (i.e., mitotic cell division, cell differentiation, and pattern formation) work together to generate a multicellular form that is continually being modified throughout its life. At each moment along its developmental path, an organism can be described in terms of its current physical traits and how it responds to different circumstances (different stimuli). Biologists refer to physical features such as length, weight, coloration, and so on as phenotypic traits and responses as behaviors or behavioral traits. They are, however, really two sides of the same coin because how a body is put together—that is, its physical makeup or phenotype—determines how it will react to different things.

The potential for any phenotypic/behavioral trait to be heritable—that is, for development to be repeatable—stands on a simple premise: *If something can happen once then it can happen again.* All that is required is to put into place the same factors that caused it to happen as it did before. The degree to which production of offspring can be heritable thus depends on the degree to which any parent can pass to offspring those same factors that caused the parent to develop as it did.

Way back in Chapter 4 we identified that any individual's development is steered by an interaction of four factors: its genotype (information), its current pattern of activity (its current pattern of use and disuse of its already developed body parts), its environmental circumstance, and its developmental history (how development has proceeded so far). The question of heritability of traits is thus a question about the degree to which parents can pass on these four developmental interactants.

Focusing on myopia

To frame this discussion, let's consider the development of a specific trait—the development of myopia or nearsightedness. To see something clearly, an eye's lens must be able to focus the image on the back part of the eye called the retina. As a consequence, visual clarity over a wide range of distances depends on coordinating the len's ability to focus with the distance between the lens and the retina. Getting this correct once seems tricky enough, but the fact that eyes grow through childhood means that readjustments must be continually made. Eyesight problems develop whenever someone fails to pull off this coordinated change. Specifically, myopia results when excessive growth results in too great of distance between the lens and retina to focus on more distant objects. As a consequence, distant objects begin to appear blurry.

Around 25% of the American population fails this developmental challenge and develops myopia. Yet curiously, native people in the Arctic were rarely nearsighted before outside contact, and presumably the same would be true of other hunter–gatherer societies. Currently, however, the frequency of myopia among Arctic natives is about the same as other Americans. This raises the obvious question: How has contact led to the spread of myopia? Has there been sufficient interbreeding to allow the spread of some myopia gene? Or is myopia caused by some infectious agent that spread into Arctic populations through contact? The answer appears to be no in both cases. Instead, the culprit seems to be the addition of schools. (You have probably always known that there was something wrong with going to school.) Adding schools changed how much time children spent focusing on small close objects, such as what occurs during reading. Coordinating growth of different parts of the eye appears to be regulated, at least in part, by an interaction between the eye and visual parts of the brain. Evidence suggests that when blurry images fall on the retina (due to a change in the lens), the brain sends back a signal to increase growth until the problem is corrected. In some people, however, this mechanism in conjunction with considerable close focus leads to excessive growth. These individuals become myopic.

This leaves us with an interesting conclusion. The activity of concentrated close focus appears to be a causal factor in the development of myopia, but it is *not* the sole cause. Many people that do considerable reading and other close work early in life still maintain normal vision. Instead, it appears that at least two differences are needed for myopia to develop—some form of informational or genetic difference in combination with extensive close work. In other words, the development of myopia is based on an interaction between certain genes and certain activities (see Figure 23-1).

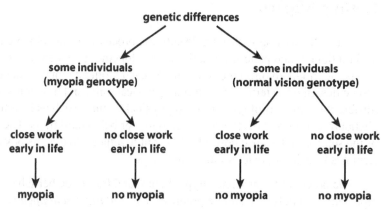

So is myopia heritable? It would depend on how readily each of the needed developmental interactants can be

Figure 23-1. A flow chart showing that the development of myopia is based on an interaction between information (the myopia genotype) and activity (close work early in life). See text for more details.

passed across generations. That is, the heritability of myopia (or any other trait) is a function of the heritability of the interactants that shaped the development of myopia (or any other trait).

Any genetic information, such as a gene associated with developing myopia, is clearly heritable because DNA can be replicated and passed on to their offspring. When reproduction is asexual, offspring will inherit the same genotype as their parent barring mutation. Due to constant mixing, the pattern through which genetic information is passed across generations in sexual populations is not as clear-cut. However, within the context of this mixing, definite patterns of inheritance still exist. Later in this chapter, we focus on trying to understand these patterns.

Although the heritability of genetic information gets most of the attention, can patterns of activity—such as doing extensive close work—be passed across generations? Although the means are more indirect, the answer is yes! As they interact with their offspring, parents are a component of their offspring's environment. Parents can thus attempt to provide their offspring with the same environment that they experienced. In doing so, parents steer their offspring to engage in the same activities. The extensive close work associated with the development of myopia provides an obvious example. Parents that were read to as children typically read to their children, along with engaging them in other activities (like learning their ABCs) that will help their offspring become readers. Similarly, parents that went to school—especially those that found it worthwhile—will generally encourage their offspring to do the same. In the process, parents that engaged in extensive close work as children encourage their children to do the same.

Furthermore, reading provides an example of how developmental history can also enter into the heritability mix—developing the ability to read opens the door to enjoying reading, which invites one to read even more. As a child, did you ever sneak in some extra reading time by hiding under your covers with a flashlight? If so, it was not your parents steering your activity. At that point, your parents wanted you to go to sleep. (Note: Of course, an old saying captures the flip side of this: You can lead a horse to water, but you cannot make them drink. While parents can introduce an environment conducive to an activity, unless at some point the offspring feels sufficiently engaged to pursue it on their own, the activity will fail to be passed across generations. This raises the question: What factors are involved in determining which parental pursuits an offspring will find appealing? It is a question that I leave you to think about.)

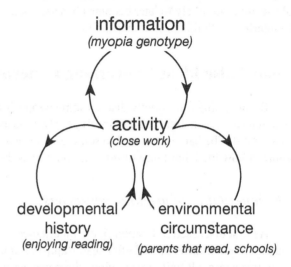

Figure 23-2 summarizes the interaction involved in the development of myopia. To review, consider each interactant and ask: Can it be passed across generations, and if so, how?

Figure 23-2. A summary of the interaction involved in the development of myopia or near-sightedness.

More on the heritability of environmental circumstance

In the myopia example, the potentially heritable component of environmental circumstance—an environment conducive to learning to read—occurred long after birth. Passing on aspects of environmental circumstance is not, however, limited to species with postnatal care. To at least some degree, it can occur in all species. For example, many offspring start out encased in a structure (typically called an egg in animals and a seed in plants) stocked with parentally supplied nutrients. Consequently, a female parent can provide her offspring with the same type and amount of nutrients that her parents provided to her. Other aspects of the early environment are also passed on whenever a female lays eggs in the same microhabitat from which she hatched. Many insects, for example, return to the same species of plant on which they developed on to lay their eggs, or sea turtles commonly voyage great distances to bury their eggs in their natal beach. Birds that incubate their eggs after laying them (instead of abandoning them) extend their range of influence even further to include fine control of early development temperatures. And by initially keeping their offspring within an internal nest called the uterus, mammals may have the greatest capacity to control and thus pass on the conditions in which their offspring first develop.

The addition of postnatal care—parents caring for the offspring after birth—some species create even more opportunity for parents to pass on aspects of environmental circumstance. Parents can provide food and/or shelter in the same way that it was provided to them. Postnatal care even creates the opportunity for parents to influence what their offspring learn. Offspring can observe how their parents hunt or do other biologically important tasks. And in the process, offspring will begin to learn how to be parents from their parents, which will enhance even further the heritability of postnatal care.

Due to the extremely long period of parental care, the potential to influence each offspring's learning environment is particularly large in humans. Over the 18 or so years of tutelage, parents expose their children to many ideas and favorite activities. As a consequence, they will have a large impact on how their children use their minds and bodies and thus how they develop. In the name of tradition, they will even emphasize ways of doing things that are deemed particularly important to pass on to the next generation. And as mentioned earlier, through all this offspring learn to treat their offspring like their parents treated them. This at times can be unfortunate because bad as well as good parenting skills can be passed on. For instance, it has been documented that victims of some form of child abuse are more likely to later become abusers. Social workers trying to stop this cycle are thus trying to interfere with this form of heritability.

Some False Ideas Concerning Patterns of Inheritance

Before going on, I briefly discuss some wrong-headed ideas on how inheritance works (some of which have been mentioned previously) for two reasons. First, I want to root out some misconceptions that may still be hanging around in some of your heads. Second, I will use these incorrect notions to contrast how the inheritance of information is now thought to work.

The inheritance of acquired characters

As first discussed in Chapter 6, the inheritance of acquired characters, or commonly called Lamarckian inheritance, named after Jean Baptiste Lamarck (1744–1829), is currently an idea in disrepute. In a sense, all traits are acquired characters as each trait develops anew in each generation. But this is not what Lamarck was speaking about. Lamarck posited that traits that develop in parents due to a particular form of interaction between an organism and its environment—specifically traits that develop due to patterns of use and disuse—would develop in the next generation *even in the absence of the same type of interaction*. For instance, Lamarckian inheritance suggests that individuals that develop myopia due to extensive early reading would give rise to offspring that developed myopia even in the absence of early reading. There is no evidence that this occurs. An offspring may receive the potential to develop myopia or any other physical or mental capacity to the same extent as their parents, but they still need to partake in the same activities to realize the same results.

A false partition

Perhaps you have heard of the **nature–nurture controversy**. People seem to want to assign certain aspects of an individual's development, such as the ability to do mathematics, to being either a product of nature (genetically based) or a product of nurture (environmentally based), or some proportion of both. As stated earlier, genes and environment affect how development turns out. They, however, never act independent of the other. The evidence is that if you remove one nothing happens. An outcome cannot be based solely, or even partially, on any one participating factor if all are needed for anything to happen. To assign any aspect of development as being genetic or environmental is thus to misrepresent development. Attempts to do so belie the interaction that took place.

Suppose, for example, two people worked together to build a barn in an interactive way—perhaps one held the pieces of wood in place and the other nailed the pieces together. Obviously, if you had removed either worker, the barn would have never been built. This does not mean that a scheme to partition the contribution of each worker could not be devised. One could measure the time each spent or the relative volumes of wood and nails in the completed barn. Time or volume can be measured; therefore, numbers partitioning the contribution of each can be generated. But the answers will differ depending on the scheme used. Which is correct? The answer is none.

When an outcome is based on an interaction, the only thing to be done is to try to determine which factors play a role—that is, which factors are interactants. The scientific method is set up to address such questions. Simply remove or alter a factor and see if the outcome is altered. Translating this idea to the interaction of development, what we want to ask is which aspects of an organism's genotype, activity patterns, environmental circumstance, and developmental history play a causal role in the development of specific phenotypic traits. But then once that is done, don't take it too far. A genetic difference that makes a difference in the development of some trait does not make that trait a product of nature.

Blending of genetic information

Sexual reproduction raises two classic patterns of inheritance questions. The first is what will the offspring look like whenever two phenotypically different individuals mate? For instance, if a male with black hair mates with a female with blond hair, what will be the offspring's hair color? The second is whether two similar-looking parents can ever produce an offspring that looks strikingly different. For instance, could an offspring develop hair color much darker than either parent? Or are offspring that develop different than either parent clear evidence that some other male (such as the mailman) was the real father?

Blending inheritance is the idea that offspring always develop traits intermediate to the two parents. Some possible examples include mating between a tall and a short person would produce offspring that grow to an intermediate height; mating between a black and a white rabbit would produce offspring that would be gray; or mating between two normal-visioned individuals would produce offspring that maintain normal vision throughout development. Being intermediate to two similar parents is to develop in the same way as both parents. Another words, the notion of blending inheritance gives clear answers to both the preceding questions. And as we will see later, there are many cases where offspring tend to develop in an intermediate fashion. But, there are also many cases where they don't. This suggests that the either "discrete" matings with very different-looking males occurs quite commonly, or that the notion blending inheritance is somehow wrong. Although I won't speculate about the former, the latter is clearly true.

Specifically, the notion of blending inheritance fails at the information level. If two parents contribute somewhat different flavors of information to an offspring, blending suggests that this information somehow mixes together to form a new intermediate form (in terms of how it would affect development). In other words, the different flavor contributed by each parent would be lost as they combine to rearrange into a single intermediate form. Only the intermediate form could then be passed to the next generation—that is, to the offspring's offspring. For example, if a plant received information that coded for red flower color from one parent and white flower color from the other, not only would the offspring develop pink flowers, but also the two forms of information would merge to form information that codes for pink flowers. So, only pink flower information could be passed to the next generation. The problem is that genetic information does not mix in this way, even in cases where the offspring develops an intermediate phenotype. Barring mutation, each component of genetic information passed to an offspring remains intact throughout its life.

An aside: Blending inheritance was the prevailing view of heredity when Darwin introduced the idea that evolution could occur by natural selection. (The notion of Lamarckian inheritance was also still around at this time.) And this view posed a problem for his idea. With blending inheritance, newly arising thus rare variants in any population would tend to quickly lose their identity. Due to their rareness, they would most likely breed with normal members of the population. Their offspring would thus be intermediates. These intermediates, in turn, would most likely breed with other normal members, producing offspring half again as variable. In essence, the observed variation would be halved in each generation, leading to its quick decay. So even if a variant had a relative reproductive advantage, it would likely be blended out of the population before it could spread through the population. The mechanism of natural selection depends on advantageous variants maintaining their identity across generations.

Some Relevant History: Mendel and Peas

Gregor Mendel and his experiments on garden peas are almost always brought up in any discussion of inheritance. Perhaps most important, Mendel's work began to undermine blending inheritance. In the history of science, find a crack in an existing paradigm, and your name goes up in lights. When what you discovered also turns out to be correct, you also get described as being brilliant. But the question remains: In what way was Gregor Mendel brilliant? Did he anticipate that there was a problem with blending inheritance, and then see that garden peas could be used to prove it? Or did Mendel just happen to stumble onto an unexpected discovery, but was then able to see the significance of his discovery and figure out how to investigate it further? It is hard to know when he worked in a remote monastery around 150 years ago. But it is at least possible that Mendel's big discovery started with a simple attempt to produce pinkish-lavender pea flowers. Let me explain. (Note: The history of science is filled with examples of someone stumbling into a big discovery.)

Gregor Mendel was a monk, but he also had training in plants and science from growing up on a farm and spending two years at the University of Vienna. At the time that he began his breeding experiments in 1857, he was also living in a monastery with a history of interest in breeding plants, including garden peas. Flower color in garden peas was notable not only because variation existed, but also becauese the variation was abruptly discontinuous. Specifically, pea flowers did not come in a range of flower colors spread across a continuum, but were either white or reddish-purple. Guided by the notion of blending inheritance, the absence of in-between colors would have seemingly struck anyone familiar with peas as odd. Except peas were known to generally self-fertilize. Pea flowers, like the flowers of many other plants, are hermaphroditic—that is they contain both male and female parts. The small, mobile male eggs, known as pollen grains, form at the end of structures called stamens. The larger, immobile female eggs, called ovules, form inside a structure called the carpel. Fertilization occurs whenever a pollen grain lands on the tip of the carpel and then burrows inside and fuses with an ovule. Self-fertilization is thus when pollen grains fuse with ova from the same flower. And a plant fertilizing itself is clearly an instance of a flower of one color mating with a flower of the same color. So the expectation of blending inheritance would match what was found, pea plants gave rise to offspring with the same flower color.

Here I am speculating: But suppose that Mendel's initial motivation to work with peas was simply to try to generate pinkish-lavender flowers. With blending inheritance as his guide, he would assume that he only needed to cross-pollinate purple-flowered and white-flowered plants. This is an experiment that he was known to have done. Specifically, he first cut the stamens off some flowers so they could not self-fertilize. Next, he used a paintbrush to transfer pollen from a different-colored flower (either purple to white, or white to purple) and waited for the cross-pollinated flowers to mature into pea pods. Finally, he planted the peas in a known location and waited for pea plants to grow up. The only twist is that I am guessing that Mendel was shocked when the plants bloomed, and none of the flowers were of intermediate color. Furthermore, none of the flowers bore any resemblance to the white-flowered parent. All the flowers developed the same reddish-purple hue as the other parent. Was this result a fluke? Did he cut the stamens too late and thus failed to prevent self-fertilization? And if it was not a fluke, how did one parent take over inheritance? These may have been some of the questions that ran through Mendel's mind.

If the scenario I just painted has even a hint of accuracy, then this was a germinal moment in the study of patterns of inheritance. And Mendel's brilliance emerged in his response to this unexpected result. If I am wrong, then his brilliance emerged earlier. Either way, he followed up this initial cross in two important ways. First, he allowed what geneticists call the F1 generation—the offspring of the initial cross—to self-fertilize and then planted their seeds to see what would happen in the next (or F2) generation. He also looked for other traits in peas that had the same pattern of "either–or" variation (i.e., each plant is *either* like this *or* like that, but nothing in between) and then performed the same experiments—cross-pollinate plants with different traits and then let the F1 generation self-fertilize, keeping track of what the offspring looked like in both the F1 and F2 generations. And finally, he did not just do this with one or two flowers, but instead created large sample sizes. This allowed him to see statistical patterns that could have been obscured by smaller numbers.

Strikingly, he found that the same basic pattern emerged in all seven traits that he investigated. First, only one form of the trait showed up in the F1 generation. He called that the dominant trait. Note that this concept of dominance added a new twist to the question: What will the offspring look like when the parents are different? Next, he found that the trait that disappeared in the F1 generation reappeared to some extent in the F2 generation. Again, that must have been a shocking result. Parents that looked the same (recall the F2 generation was produced via self-fertilization) sometimes produced offspring that looked different. Furthermore, the large sample sizes revealed a similar pattern in how frequently what he called the recessive trait showed up in the F2 generation. For all seven traits, it showed up in around one-fourth of the offspring. The other three-fourths of the F2 offspring developed the dominant trait.

Dominant and recessive traits, along with the significance of the 3:1 pattern of inheritance, will be discussed more later. The important conclusion at the moment is what Mendel called the particulate theory of inheritance. That the heritable factors transferred across generations were physical particles that could not be blended. So, although the heritable factor associated with white flowers was not expressed in the F1 generation, it was also not lost. As a consequence, it could still be passed on and potentially expressed in the F2 generation.

Diploid Sexual Genetics: The Basic Issues

So far, I have tried to disrupt the common conception that heritability and genetics are two words for the same thing. Yes, genetic information can be passed across generations, but so can other developmental interactants. Moreover, the potential heritability of other interactants plays an important role in steering development along a path taken before. Yet given that, genetics still deserves some extra attention. Not because it is more important, or in some other way more fundamental. It is simply because of sex.

Genetics is the study of the patterns by which genes get passed from one generation to the next. This turns out to be fairly trivial when reproduction occurs asexually. Barring mutation, offspring are passed the same set of genes found in their single parent. However, when reproduction occurs sexually, the patterns by which genes are passed across generations become more complicated. Due to the two steps of sexual reproduction—the making of gametes via meiosis and the joining of gametes from different individuals—the same two parents can potentially contribute different sets of genetic information to every offspring that they produce. As a consequence, it is impossible to predict the exact genetic composition that any offspring will receive from his or her parent.

Yet, although details cannot be specified for any individual, a basic pattern still exists by which genes on chromosomes are passed across generations. The task here is to first master this pattern for diploid multicellular organisms. Then, we explore the various ways that an offspring's genotype affects the development of its phenotype. Finally, we put these together to consider how the patterns in which genes move in sexual populations can affect the patterns by which phenotypic traits show up in subsequent generations.

The pattern by which chromosomes move across generations: One pair of chromosomes

Recall that diploid individuals have matched sets of chromosomes (called homologous chromosomes) that in total make up two genotypes. Because genes are located on chromosomes, to understand the pattern in which genes move across the sexual cycle (meiosis followed by fusion), one must first understand how chromosomes move across generations. Even though the genomes of diploid multicellular organisms are typically broken up into more than one chromosome, let's first focus on the movement of single pair of homologous chromosomes.

The basic pattern by which copies of homologous chromosomes move across sexual generations can be summarized by a recurrent pattern of: *come together–split–randomly toss one out–come together–split–randomly toss one out–come together–split–randomly toss one out–*and so on.

Every homologous pair of chromosomes in sexual diploid organisms is a mom–dad pair. That is, an individual's two parents each contribute one of the two chromosomes. The homologous pairs **come together** when two gametes (one from each parent) fuse to form a zygote.

The mom–dad pair, however, does not stay together when this individual gets ready to reproduce sexually. Meiosis **splits** the pair during the formation of gametes (Note: The possibility of crossing-over is not being considered here). In the process, each gamete gets either a copy of the chromosome contributed from mom (maternal origin) or a copy of the chromosome contributed from dad (paternal origin).

When this individual finds a mate and reproduces, only one gamete will fuse with a gamete from its partner to start the next generation. Accordingly, one of the two chromosomes from each homologous pair gets left behind. In other words, it is, in essence, **tossed out**. The chance that either ends up in a grandchild is generally equal (i.e., each has a 50% chance). So, in the same sense as flipping a coin, whether the chromosome of maternal or paternal origin from each pair is passed on or tossed out is a **random event**.

Figure 23-3 illustrates this pattern. The box split into four compartments at the bottom of this figure is called a **Punnet square**. It keeps track of the four possible ways that an offspring can receive a pair of homologous chromosomes from its two parents. Each box within a Punnet square has an equal probability of occurring as long as two conditions are met: (1) during meiosis, each member of any homologous pair has an equal chance of ending up in a viable gamete, and (2) all viable gametes produced by either parent have an equal chance of fusing with another gamete to form an offspring. In our discussion we will assume that both conditions are always met. So, in this Punnet square with four boxes total, each chromosome combination has a one in four or 25% chance of occurring. For example, you can use Figure 23-3 to make sense of the following statement: There is a 25% chance that neither chromosome of a homologous pair can be traced back to either grandfather (i.e., either mom's dad or dad's dad).

Consider this: You have two parents, four grandparents, eight great-grandparents, 16 great-great-grandparents, 4,096 great-great-great-great-great-great-great-great-great-great-grandparents, almost 1.5 million 20-great-grandparents, and so on. What is the chance that a specific chromosome in one of your 10-great-grandparents has been passed across the generations to you? Or asked in another way, how closely related are you to one of your ten-great-grandparents? The answer to both these questions is always $1/x$, where x is the number of parents of any type that you have. So in the case of 10-great-grandparents, you have a 1/4096 chance of having inherited any specific chromosome from one of them (ignoring the possibility of crossing-over), which also means that you are 1/4096 related to any one of them.

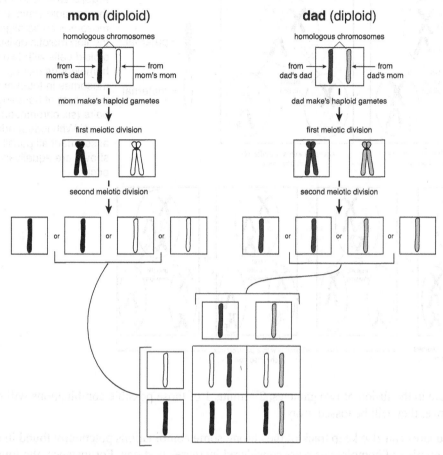

Figure 23-3. The pattern by which chromosomes within a single homologous pair are passed from diploid parents to their offspring.

The pattern by which chromosomes move across generations: Two or more pairs of chromosomes

So far, we have established that each pair of homologous chromosomes within an individual is a mom-dad pair, and that this pair separates into different gametes during meiosis. What happens when we consider two or more homologous pairs? Does meiosis always separate chromosome pairs such that the chromosomes in each gamete are either exclusively maternal or paternal in origin? Restating the question: Do maternal and paternal chromosomes from different homologous pairs stick together during meiosis? The answer is no. Chromosome pairs generally **assort independently** because they line up independently—the way that each pair aligns at beginning of meiosis does not affect the arrangement of any other homologous pair. As a consequence, any two chromosomes of the same parental origin are no more likely to end up in the same gamete as a mixture of maternal and paternal chromosomes (see Figure 23-4).

From Figure 23-4, you can also see that the number of possible chromosome combinations increases as the number of homologous pairs increases. With two sets of homologous pairs, four chromosomal combinations are possible. With three sets of homologous pairs, eight combinations are possible. The number of possible combinations for even larger numbers of homologous pairs can be calculated by 2^x, where x is number of homologous pairs. Humans, for instance, have 23 homologous pairs, which means that each of us can potentially generate gametes with 2^{23} unique chromosomal combinations. That, to put it mildly, is a large number. Or let's think about it in a different way: If you

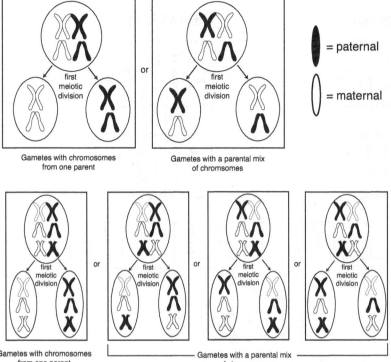

Figure 23-4. Shown are all the possible ways that chromosomes could align during the first meiotic division for diploid cells with two sets of homologous pairs (four chromosomes in total) and with three sets of homologous pairs (six chromosomes in total). With independent assortment all possibilities shown are equally likely to occur.

ever participate in the fusion of two gametes, 2^{23} minus 1 of those possible combinations will not be used. In essence, they will be tossed away.

Punnet squares can also keep track of the chromosome combinations potentially found in offspring as the number of homologous pairs considered increases past one. For instance, the four distinct chromosome combinations that arise from two homologous pairs require a four by four Punnet square to keep track of the possibilities (see Figure 23-5). The offspring combination found in any internal square has a 1/16th (1 in 16) chance of occurrence because a four by four Punnet square has 16 internal boxes. On the other hand, consideration of three pairs of homologous chromosomes requires an eight by eight Punnet square. The offspring combination found in any internal box would have a 1 in 64 chance of occurring. Of course, once the number of homologous chromosomes increases much past three, the use of Punnet squares becomes increasingly impractical. The size of the Punnet square would need to be too large to work with easily.

Focusing on Genes

Genes are located along chromosomes and thus move across generations in the same pattern as chromosomes. A gene's **locus** is a particular gene's location. The locus, thus, indicates both what chromosome the gene is on and where specifically along the chromosome the gene is positioned.

Starting to connect genes with phenotypes

The best interpretation of the expression *"a gene for a trait"* is that a particular gene, or form of a gene, makes a difference in the development of a trait. In other words, the protein coded for by the gene in some way plays a causal role in the development of a certain trait. We saw this in the myopia example; genetic differences made a difference in the development of myopia. And if those genetic differences boiled down to a single gene, then we could refer to it as the gene for myopia, or the myo-

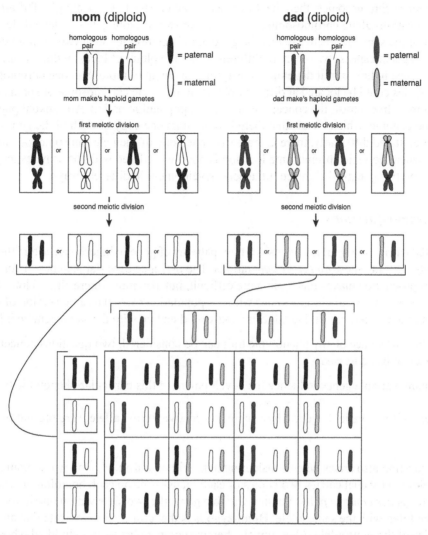

Figure 23-5. The pattern by which chromosomes within two homologous pairs are passed from diploid parents to their offspring.

pia gene. In many cases, a gene for a trait can also be viewed as a necessary, but not sufficient inter-actant in a trait's development. Again, the myopia example makes this distinction clear. The presence of a myopia gene is not sufficient because the activity of doing close work also needs to be present for myopia to develop.

More than one gene shares the distinction of being a gene for a trait whenever more than one gene makes a difference in how a specific trait develops. The only thing new is that each gene's effect is not only influenced by its interaction with activity patterns, but also by the information contained in these other genes.

Whether one or many genes play a role in the development of a specific trait, geneticists typically pay attention to only those genes that contain variation. A **variable gene** is when different versions exist in the population, and each of these different versions influences development in a noticeably different way. In geneticspeak, each different or alternative form is called an **allele**. For instance, a variable flower color gene means that more than one allele exists within a plant population, and each allele has a different effect of flower color development

Trying to figure out the difference between different genes and different alleles may have your head spinning a little right now. But if you just remember that a genome is an arrangement of genes along one or more chromosomes, then the difference is rather easy to keep straight. Different genes are different locations along chromosomes. So to say that two or more genes make a difference in the development of the same trait is to say that the genetic information found at two or more different locations (or in geneticspeak, two or more different **loci**—the plural of locus) within a single genome makes a difference in how a trait develops. In genomes made up of more than one chromosome, these two or more genes could be located at different places on the same chromosome or spread over different chromosomes. In contrast, the concept of alleles is a population notion. Any sexual population has more than one genome, which means that there is more than one copy of each of the genes that make up the genome. Stated differently, there is more than one copy of each chromosome location or locus. Alleles exist when the same chromosome location is not always filled with the same exact genetic information, and this genetic difference influences development in different ways.

Three important questions

As I stated earlier, our goal is to consider how patterns of genetic inheritance affect the pattern in which phenotypic traits show up across generations. The presence of variable genes in combination with sexual reproduction makes this topic more difficult, but also more interesting. (Note: In the absence of genetic variation, all chromosomes within a population carry the same version of each gene, so regardless of the pattern of mixing, all offspring would end up with the same genetic information.)

Before the inheritance of any phenotypic trait can be considered, two questions concerning variable genes need to be addressed:

• How many variable genes influence the development of this particular phenotypic trait?

• For each of these variable genes, how many alternative forms (**alleles**) are present in the population?

A third question also arises when considering a diploid organism. Having two genomes means that each diploid individual carries two copies of each locus—one on each homologous chromosome. In other words, *genes come in pairs*. For any variable gene, the two slots within one individual may or may not be filled with the same allele. **Homozygous** is the term used to indicate that an individual has two copies of the same allele. Alternatively, **heterozygous** refers to an individual whose two slots are filled with different alleles. Given that by definition each allele influences development differently, heterozygotes become an immediate curiosity. How will the presence of two different alleles in the same body influence development? Or stated more generally:

• What is the nature of the interaction between the set of alleles present in any diploid individual and the development of the trait in question?

Following, the issues surrounding each of these questions is discussed further.

Number of variable genes

The number of variable genes has come to form a dividing line in the study of genetics. **Mendelian genetics** focuses on situations where one variable gene affects development of two or more distinct versions of a phenotypic trait. Obviously, the name comes from Gregor Mendel, who worked out the basic patterns of inheritance of seven such traits in garden pea plants.

On the other hand, **quantitative genetics** studies phenotypic traits that vary along a continuum, such as traits like height or weight, and whose development is affected by a few to many variable genes.

Number of alleles in each variable gene

When discussing genetic-based patterns of inheritance, cases where a gene has two alleles are used commonly. Such examples are the easiest to explain, and for that reason we will follow this trend. But it is important to recognize that variable genes may have more than two alleles. For example, the gene affecting human blood type has three alleles, commonly called **A**, **B**, and **O**. At the upper extreme, some genes associated with the immune system have been found to have over 200 alleles. And that is just what has been discovered so far.

Yet, despite the number of alleles within the population, the maximum number of alleles in any diploid individual is two. So, in terms of blood types **ABO** is not a possible genotype. The only options are **AA**, **AB**, **AO**, **BB**, **BO**, and **OO**. (Note: In expressing genotypes, order does not make a difference. For example, **AB** and **BA** are the same genotypes.) In other words, there are three possible homozygous genotypes (**AA**, **BB**, or **OO**) and three possible heterozygous genotypes (**AB**, **AO**, or **BO**).

The effect that an individual's genotype—that is, what alleles it has—has on the development of its phenotype

The effect of an individual's genotype on the development of its phenotype may be **additive** or **nonadditive**. When the effect is additive, a heterozygous individual, all else being equal, will be phenotypically intermediate to the two homozygotes. In essence, an additive interaction is dosage dependent. Along some continuum, the more doses or copies of a certain allele an individual has, the stronger the phenotypic effect. Nonadditive effects, on the other hand, include all cases where dosage does not make a difference.

The classic nonadditive scenario is the **dominance-recessive** relationship first uncovered by Mendel. An allele is considered to be dominant whenever the number of copies does not seem to make a difference—that is, the phenotype of a heterozygous individual (one dose) and a homozygous individual (two doses) develop similarly. Recessive alleles are generally messed up versions of a gene that fail to have any affect on development. They can arise whenever one or more mutations alters either a gene's sequence such that it now codes for a nonfunctional protein, or a gene's regulatory components to the point that it is never translated into a protein. Functional copies of the gene within the population will thus be dominant whenever one copy codes for sufficient protein to keep development on the same course as two. In contrast, the recessive phenotype develops only in individuals homozygous for the recessive allele. Because only faulty copies of the gene are present, the recessive phenotype is that which develops in the absence of this gene's influence.

An aside: Given the faulty nature of most recessive alleles, one might assume dominant phenotypes are always functionally superior to recessive phenotypes. But it depends. Whenever the presence of a functional protein is necessary for a functional adult to develop, then the dominant phenotype will also be the functionally superior phenotype. But many genes are not necessary per se; they just change the flavor of development. For example, they may increase growth, change coloration, make hair curly, and so on. In such cases doing nothing—that is, not growing bigger, or changing color, or having curly hair—may work better. It depends on the current environmental circumstance. And whenever that proves to be true, the recessive phenotype will be functionally superior.

To better clarify the difference between an additive and a dominance-recessive interaction, consider a gene with two alleles that affects the production of a pigment deposited in a plant's flowers, a mammal's skin or hair, or anywhere else. Specifically, one allele codes for a functional enzyme that is part of the metabolic pathway that produces the pigment. The other allele does not produce a functional form of this enzyme. Homozygous individuals for the nonfunctional allele will thus not produce pigment because blocking any step of a metabolic pathway blocks the entire pathway. In contrast, pigment will be produced in individuals that are either heterozygous or homozygous for the functional allele. Whether the interaction is additive or dominance-recessive depends on whether two copies of the functional allele leads to the production of more pigment than one. For instance, suppose that this enzyme catalyzes a rate-limiting step. Having two functional copies to transcribe could lead to increased enzyme production, which in turn would increase the rate of pigment production (by speeding up this rate-limiting step). If so, the interaction would be additive—heterozygotes would be intermediate in pigmentation intensity due to the positive relationship between functional gene copy number and the amount of pigment produced. On the other hand, increasing enzyme production would not increase the rate of pigment production if this metabolic pathway's rate was being limited elsewhere. Here the interaction would be dominance-recessive. Although pigment would be produced whenever a functional allele was present, the amount produced would not be a function of copy number. Heterozygotes and homozygotes (for the functional allele) would develop the same pigmentation intensity.

Another example of a nonadditive effect is **codominance**. In codominance, both alleles in a heterozygous individual are expressed. Codominance can lead to an observed phenomenon called heterozygous superiority. This is where being heterozygous at a particular locus increases that individual's performance ability in comparison to any homozygote. For example, suppose a gene codes for an enzyme that catalyzes an important chemical reaction. Further suppose there are two versions, or two alleles, of this enzyme in the population. Both catalyze the same reaction, but one works best under one set of conditions, such as at a certain temperature, and the other works best under different conditions. A heterozygous individual would thus produce both versions of the enzyme and hence would be enzymatically more versatile. It could maintain a higher level of enzyme activity over a wider range of conditions.

The heterozygotes for blood type—**AB, AO,** and **BO**—provide examples of dominance-recessive and codominant interactions. The **A** and **B** allele both code for a specific protein called A and B, respectively. The **O** allele, on the other hand, does not code for a protein. **A** and **B** are thus dominant over **O**—**AO** individuals are blood type **A** because they only produce protein A, and **BO** individuals are blood type **B** because they only produce protein B. Yet, the **A** and **B** allele are codominant with each other—**AB** individuals are blood type **AB** because both proteins are produced. In this case, however, I am unaware of any performance advantage associated with being **AB.**

Often, gene action is not as simple as a direct correlation between the presence of certain alleles at one locus and the expression of a particular phenotypic trait. For example, some genes are **pleiotropic**. That is, one gene affects the development of several seemingly unrelated phenotypic traits. Different types of interactions among different genes also may add to the complexity. There can be an **epistatic** interaction, which is, in essence, a between gene dominance-recessive interaction. The presence of certain alleles at one locus masks the expression of other alleles at a different locus. Or certain genes act as **modifiers**—the presence of alleles at one locus alters or modifies the expression of alleles at another locus. Yet, despite their importance in understanding the genetic basis of inheritance, our task here is to get you started thinking like a geneticist. As a consequence, these interactions will not be considered further here.

Doing Genetic Problems

Now it is time to put together the patterns of chromosomal inheritance with how genotypes affect phenotypes. That is, let's do genetic problems. The goal of a genetic problem is to calculate the probability that any two sexual partners will produce an offspring with a particular phenotypic trait. The ability to calculate such probability depends on knowing two things: First, we must know the genotypes of both parents for any variable gene that affects the development of the trait in question. Knowing the parental genotypes makes it possible to calculate the probability that an offspring will inherit any particular genotype from its parents. Next we need to know the relationship between a genotype and development of the phenotypic trait. That way we can convert the probability of each genotype into the probability that an offspring will develop a specific phenotype. Don't forget, however, that the conversion from a genotypic probability to phenotypic probability depends on the assumption that the same genotype always gives rise to the same phenotype. Yet, that will be true only if the *all else being equal* assumption is met—that is, that each offspring experiences the same set of nongenetic factors that can affect development. It is important to always keep this assumption in mind.

As we are working through genetic problems, I also prod you to keep in mind two questions introduced earlier in the discussion of blending inheritance: (1) If in some respect the two parents are phenotypically different, what determines what the offspring will look like? Here we will find variety of answers. (2) If in some respect the two parents are phenotypically similar, is it possible for an offspring to look different from its parents? Here the answer will be most definitely yes.

A basic plan for doing a genetic problem

To do a genetic problem one needs to first identify the relationship between an individual's genotype and the development of the focal phenotypic trait. Specifically, one needs to know the number of variable genes, along with the number of alleles at each gene that affect this trait, and the nature of heterozygotes— that is, how do different alleles within the same individual affect development?

Next, identify all the possible ways that meiosis could divide each parent's genotype into unique gametes (i.e., unique combinations of alleles) and their probability of occurrence.

Then account for all the ways that the unique gamete types from each parent could unite to form an offspring's genotype. Punnet squares are a good way to do this (as long as all the different gamete types have an equal probability of occurring, which here we assume to be true). The probability of an offspring having a particular genotype can be expressed as a proportion by counting the number of boxes within a Punnet square containing that genotype and then divided by the total number of boxes. Note: Any proportion can be converted to percentage by multiplying by 100.

Finally, the probability that an offspring will develop some phenotypic trait can be calculated by counting the number of boxes containing the genotype or genotypes leading to the development of this phenotype, and then dividing by the total number of boxes.

First example: Flower color in garden peas

To start, let's work through Mendel's experimental results on flower colors in peas described earlier. Placing that discussion in the context of genes and alleles we can assume the following:

• Number of variable genes: 1—the flower color gene or locus.

• Number of alleles: 2—the purple flower allele (designated as **P**) and the white flower allele (designated as **W**).

• Interaction between alleles in heterozygote: Nonadditive, where **P** is dominant to **W**. (In other words, the dominant allele codes for the production of purple flower pigment, whereas the recessive allele does not. And the number of doses of this pigment-producing allele does not make a difference in flower color intensity.)

Recall that peas normally self-fertilize and produce offspring with the same flower color. As a consequence, we can assume that both parents in Mendel's first cross (where he cross-pollinated flowers of different colors) were homozygous for their respective flower color. In other words, the two homologous chromosomes bearing the flower color locus each contained the same allele. Such a cross

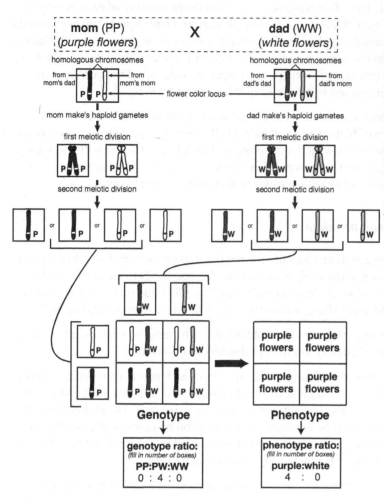

Figure 23-6. The genetics of Mendel's first cross—breeding homozygous pea plants with different flower colors—is illustrated by following the chromosomes bearing the flower color locus. The fact that all offspring develop purple flower demonstrates a dominance-recessive interaction. The genotype and phenotype ratio compares the expectations of this cross with the possible genotypes and phenotypes in the population at large.

is commonly represented as: **PP** x **WW**. Figure 23-6 follows the chromosomes bearing the flower color locus through this cross. The genotypes of all offspring turn out to be heterozygotes (instead of a blending of information). Yet, due to the dominance–recessive interaction, they all develop purple flowers.

Next, Mendel let the offspring of his first cross (the F1 generation) self-fertilize; which in genetic terms is to cross a heterozygote (**PW**) with another heterozygote (**PW**). Figure 23-7 follows the flower locus bearing chromosomes through this cross. Here there is a 50% chance (two out of four boxes) that any offspring produced from this cross will have a different genotype (either **PP** or **WW**) than their heterozygous parents. And there is a 25% chance that this mating between purple-flowered parents will produce an offspring with different colored flowers—specifically white.

The following question may at first glance seem redundant, but it is not: If this cross produced four offspring, how many of the offspring would develop white flowers? Although you may be tempted to answer *one* because one out of four boxes has the white flower genotype, that is not the correct answer. Probabilities do not keep track of history, yet an answer of one assumes otherwise. For example, answering one assumes that if the first three offspring had a red flowered genotype, then the forth offspring *must* have a white flowered genotype. Or if the first three offspring had two red and one white flowered genotypes, then the fourth offspring *must* have a red flowered genotype. It is no different than stating that because a fair coin has a 50% chance of heads or tails, a first flip coming up heads means that the next flip *must* be a tail. But each time a coin flips or gametes fuse, the outcome is not affected by what happened in the past. Instead, each instance is an independent event. The chance of

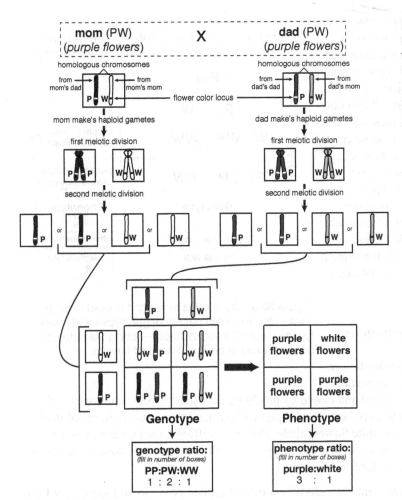

Figure 23-7. The genetics of Mendel's second cross—letting the heterozygous offspring of his first cross self-fertilize—is illustrated by following the chromosomes bearing the flower color locus.

heads on the second flip is the same as the first. So it is possible to flip two, three, four, or more heads in a row. Similarly, the chance of the next offspring having a certain genotype is the same with each offspring produced, regardless of the genotypes of past offspring. So the correct answer is: I don't know. Each of the four offspring had a 25% chance of getting a **WW** genotype, but how many actually did is unknowable. It could have been 0, 1, 2, 3, or 4. (Note: Although all options are possible, some are more likely than others. For instance, although the chance of one white flowered offspring is 25%, there is less than a 1% chance that all four offspring will inherit the white flowered genotype.)

Because of their independent nature, patterns of probability reliably reveal themselves only with large sample sizes. In other words, as sample sizes get larger—that is, the more times independent events occur—the less likely the actual results will deviate too much from what is expected by chance. Mendel obviously understood that. He followed a large number of F2 offspring—ranging from 580 to 8,023—for all seven traits studied. Of the 929 F2 offspring that he kept track of flower color, 705 (78%) had purple flowers and 224 (22%) had white flowers. The F2 generation of the other six traits was also close to this 75%:25% or 3:1 phenotypic ratio expected from a dominance–recessive interaction in combination with a heterozygous cross. And not only did he see the significance of this pattern, but also in the absence of any understanding of chromosomes, meiosis, or any other aspect of DNA, he put together essentially the same model as shown in Figure 23-7. Each individual has two copies (one from each parent) of nonblending heritable factors that may or may not be the same. During the production of sperm or eggs, these two copies separate with equal probability into different gametes. Each copy thus has an equal chance of fusing with another gamete to start the next generation.

In fact, the most common representation of genetic crosses is much more in line with Mendel's original model than what is shown in Figure 23-7. Keeping track of chromosomes and the first and second meiotic division is just too cumbersome to do every time. Pare all that out, and one is left with the shorthand method shown in Figure 23-8, which illustrates the same cross as Figure 23-7. Because of convenience, using the shorthand method makes perfect sense. The only concern is that at times people try to master the shorthand method without really understanding that genes are on chromosome that separate into gametes by meiosis, and so on. So I plead with you: Don't do it. Knowing a few tricks leads to an illusionary understanding at best.

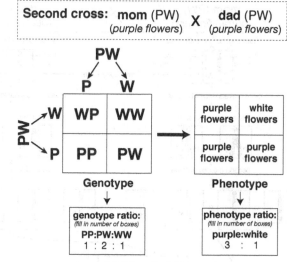

Figure 23-8. The shorthand method is used to keep track of the expected pattern of genotypes and phenotypes in Mendel's second cross—letting the heterozygous offspring of his first cross self-fertilize.

A twist: Flower color in snapdragons

Snapdragons are a common garden flower. My children call them talking flowers because the "mouth" of the flower can be opened and closed by pinching. Like garden peas, one variety of snapdragons has also been shown to have both a make-pigment (which in this case is more red than purple) and don't-make-pigment (or white flower) allele. However, different than garden peas, the interaction between the red and white allele in a heterozygote is additive. The more dosages of the red pigment allele, the redder the flowers tend to become.

This additive interaction makes them a wonderful contrast to garden peas. So, in Figure 23-9 I use the shorthand method to map out the same two genetic crosses shown previously for peas. Note that if Mendel had used snapdragons instead of garden peas, any suspicions of blending would have seemed

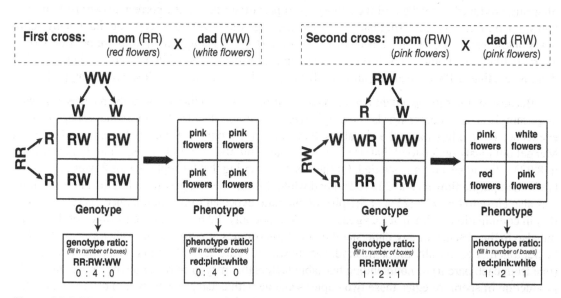

Figure 23-9. The shorthand method is used to keep track of the expected pattern of genotypes and phenotypes associated with flower color in snapdragons for the same two crosses illustrated for garden peas. Note that the additive interaction in snapdragons gives rise to different phenotypic patterns.

to be confirmed. Pink flowered offspring develop from a red and white flowered cross. Yet, also note that the second cross completely shatters any conception of blending. Although two pink flowered parents could produce pink flowered offspring (as blending would suggest), this would only be expected to occur around 50% of the time. The rest of the offspring would be expected to develop either white or red flowers (each with equal probability).

Just to test your understanding, use the shorthand method to figure out the genotype and phenotype ratio for following cross: **RW** x **WW**. What would be different if an analogous cross was made in garden peas?

Skin color in humans

As long as we have started a pigment-producing theme here, let's add another twist: human skin color.

Compared to other great apes, such as chimpanzees, human skin has two striking features: the absence of much hair, and the presence of numerous sweat glands all over the body. This difference is suggested to have started when our ancestors moved from the rain forest to the East African savanna several million years ago. To forage during the day, often traveling great distances by walking or running in this more exposed environment required a better cooling system. Sweat, which dissipates heat by evaporation, is the most effective means to cool a body. And it works best on bare skin, as hair not only adds insulation, but also retards cooling by slowing down the rate at which sweat evaporates. You know from experience that hair dries more slowly than skin.

Hair loss, however, created another problem—increased vulnerability to damage from sunlight. Here is where skin color enters the story. The darkness of a human skin is determined by the amount of a pigment called melanin produced. Darker skin better protects against DNA damage by either absorbing or dispersing UV radiation. So it is assumed that darker pigmentation evolved to help compensate for hair loss. But how dark is dark enough? And why do some groups of people have lighter skin?

Recently, Nina Jablonski, an anthropologist, suggested that human skin color variation is largely a story of two vitamins: folate (or folic acid, which is a member of the B vitamin complex) and vitamin D. Studies have shown that in lighter-skinned people, exposure to intense sunlight significantly reduces folate levels. Folate deficiencies in turn have been linked to developmental anomalies, such as neural tube defects that result in an infant being born without a full brain or spinal cord. Moreover, folate also plays a crucial role in sperm development. So, clearly reduced folate levels could significantly reduce reproductive success, generating strong selection for darker, better folate protecting skin. The relationship between sunlight and vitamin D, however, sits on the other side of the coin. Vitamin D is involved in regulating calcium uptake, which is essential for bone growth as well as many other physiological functions. And in contrast to folate, the synthesis of vitamin D (from cholesterol) involves a step that requires UV radiation. This means that as people spread to higher latitudes with less-intense sunlight, too dark skin could be detrimental. Vitamin D synthesis needs better access to the UV radiation available, whereas folate needs less protection. This suggests that people who have historically lived in areas with less UV radiation should have lighter skin. And when Jablonski compared global UV measurements with data on skin color in indigenous populations from more than 50 countries, the data supported her idea.

Genetics makes a difference in the degree to which a human's skin becomes pigmented. Like the discussion of flower color earlier, evidence suggests the presence of skin color genes with two alleles: (1) *make melanin* and (2) *do not make melanin*. Furthermore, like found in snapdragons, the effect appears to be additive—the more copies of the make melanin allele the more melanin produced. What is different is that skin color is a **polygenic trait**. There seems to be at least three independently assorting genes—that is, three different loci each located on a different chromosome—involved in melanin production. (Perhaps, there are more genes with different modes of action involved, but for simplicity, we focus on just three). Furthermore, each of these three genes appears to be functional duplicates of each other. Each has the same two alleles (*make melanin* or *don't make melanin*), and the affect appears to be additive across all three genes. Three genes in a diploid organism make a total of six slots for alleles, and the more *make melanin* alleles present the darker the skin. But as you know, genetics is not the whole story. Individuals tan, which means that increased melanin production is also triggered under any skin experiencing increased exposure to sunlight. And from a vitamin perspective, tanning makes sense for individuals living in seasonal environments. Skin not only gets darker to help protect against folate loss (and other forms of damage) during summer when UV intensity increases, but it also lightens to facilitate UV absorption for vitamin D synthesis during the winter months.

Now, let's use this background to work through the same two types of crosses performed with flower color. For each of the three genes I designate the *make melanin* allele as either **D** for darker or by a filled in circle. Alternatively, I designate the *don't make melanin* allele as either **L** for lighter or by an unfilled circle. The first cross (see Figure 23-10) considers a mating between the two extremes—that is, two individuals that sit at opposite ends of skin color. An individual with very light skin would be expected to be homozygous for lighter (**LL**) at each of the three genes. In contrast, an individual with very dark skin would be expected to be homozygous for darker (**DD**) for each of the three genes. As shown, all offspring end up being heterozygous at each of the three genes because they will always receive a darker allele (**D**) from one parent and a lighter allele (**L**) from the other parent. Due to having a total of three *make melanin* alleles, these offspring would be expected to produce an intermediate level of melanin.

First cross:

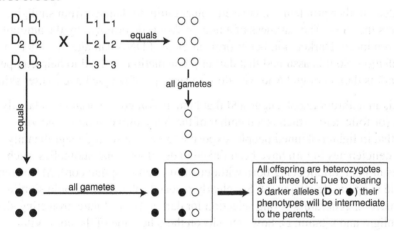

Figure 23-10. The expected outcome of a mating between a very dark skin and a very light skinned individual.

In the second cross (see Figure 23-11), two individuals heterozygous (**DL**) at each of the three genes mate with each other. The eight distinct gametes types potentially produced by each parent result from the three heterozygous genes being located on three separate, thus independently assorting, chromosomes. If one keeps track of the number of dark alleles (while ignoring the location of the dark and light alleles among the three genes) seven genotypes are possible—0, 1, 2, 3, 4, 5, or 6 dark alleles. This mating can potentially produce offspring that cover the entire range of skin color; although the bell-shaped histogram shows that offspring with more intermediate skin color are much more likely to occur than ones at either extreme.

What would be different if these three genes were all on the same chromosome? The simple answer is that they would not assort independently. Each chromosome within the homologous pair bearing these three loci would contain three alleles that are physically linked together. During meiosis, these three alleles would thus be pulled together into a gamete. So, instead of an individual heterozygous at each of three genes potentially generating eight distinct gamete types (as shown in Figure

Second cross:

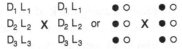

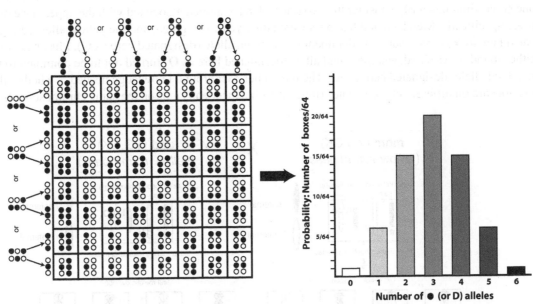

Figure 23-11. The expected outcome of a mating between two individuals that are heterozygous for the three functionally equivalent genes and independently assorting genes that play a role in the development of skin color.

23-11), only two distinct gamete types would be generated (see Figure 23-12). This in turn would change the potential outcomes of the cross (also shown in Figure 23-12). However, there is still one factor not yet considered—crossing-over. Although we will not get into the details here, more gamete types are generated whenever homologous chromosomes swap pieces in between heterozygous loci. Geneticists even use the frequency at which crossing-over occurs between two loci to estimate the distance that separates them. The further apart they are on the chromosome, the more often crossing-over is assumed to occur (because there are more places for crossing-over to occur and still exchange these loci).

Figure 23-12. The expected outcome of a mating between two individuals that are heterozygous for the three skin color genes if these genes were all located on the same chromosomes, thus did not assort independently.

Second cross:

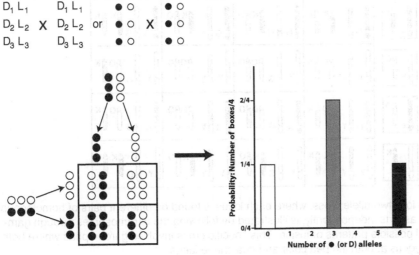

Considering patterns of inheritance of combinations of traits

As we saw with skin color, the genetics of any polygenic traits requires keeping track of how alleles move through more than one locus across generations. The same is true whenever one chooses to simultaneously follow the patterns of inheritance of more than one trait at a time. For example, one could simultaneously consider the two traits Mendel studied associated with the appearance of peas. Specifically, Mendel noted that peas were either yellow or green, and the yellow allele (designated here as **Y**) turned out to be dominant to the green allele (designated here as **G**). Plus, peas were either round or wrinkled, and the round allele (designated here as **O**) turned out to be dominant to the wrinkled allele (designated here as **K**). The only other background knowledge needed is whether these two loci are on different chromosomes (thus assort independently), or on the same chromosome (so

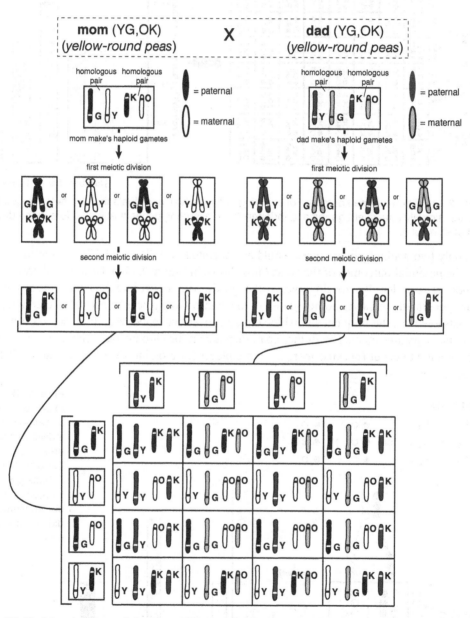

Figure 23-13. A two loci, two allele cross, where each locus is found on different pairs of homologous chromosomes, thus assorts independently, is illustrated by following the chromosomes through gamete formation and all possible patterns of fusion. This specific cross involves garden peas where both parents are heterozygous at both the pea color and pea shape locus.

do not assort independently). In turned out that all seven of Mendel's traits assort independently. This is interesting given that garden peas only have seven pairs of homologous chromosomes in total. One locus just happened to be on each of these seven chromosome pairs.

Next I consider two crosses: **YG,OK** x **YG,OK**, and **YG,OO** x **YG,OK**. Figure 23-13 goes through the details of following the chromosomes from parents to all potential offspring genotypes for the first cross. Figure 23-14 then uses the shorthand method to perform the same cross, extending the results through the expected phenotypes. Next, Figures 22-15 and 22-16 follow the same two steps for the second cross. Spend some time making sense of each of these figures.

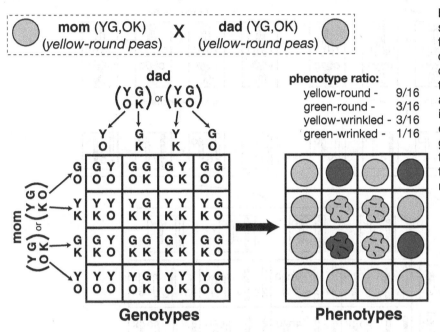

Figure 23-14. The shorthand method is first used to keep track of the expected pattern of offspring genotypes in the same two loci, two allele cross illustrated in the last figure. Next, each potential offspring genotype is converted to the expected phenotype, and the phenotype ratio is calculated.

Before leaving peas, I recommend two further exercises to test your understanding. First, figure out how the phenotype ratio would change in the preceding two crosses if pea color was an additive instead of a dominance–recessive interaction. Second, take out a piece of scratch paper and perform the following cross all the way through calculating a phenotype ratio: **YG,KK** x **YG,OK**.

Inbreeding depression

So far, the genetic problems discussed have allowed homozygous recessive individuals to develop into viable adults. For example, white-flowered peas are still completely functional plants. In fact, this recessive phenotype would even be favored by natural selection if available pollinators prefer white over reddish-purple flowers. Yet, the story changes for genes that code for a protein that plays an essential role in development. Any individuals that happen to inherit two copies of a faulty allele will not develop into reproductively competent adults. They could die before they ever reach the age of sexual maturity, or for one reason or another remain infertile even as they live to a ripe old age. In either case, the absence of reproductive capability makes this genotype lethal in terms of producing a next generation. If, however, the presence of a single good allele masks the harmful effects, such faulty alleles would still be able to hang out in the population by hiding in heterozygous individuals. In fact, as we began to discuss in Chapter 19, functional diploid individuals in outcrossing populations may commonly be heterozygous for recessive lethal alleles. And this in turn would lead to inbreeding depression—matings among close relatives in normally outcrossing populations are more likely to produce offspring that suffer some form of serious abnormality.

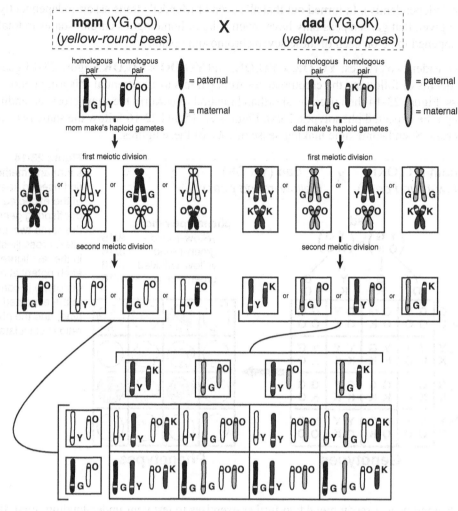

Figure 23-15. Like Figure 22-13, a two loci (pea color and pea shape), two allele cross, where each locus is found on different pairs of homologous chromosomes, thus assorts independently, is illustrated by following the chromosomes through gamete formation and all possible patterns of fusion. The difference is that the mom has a different genotype than before.

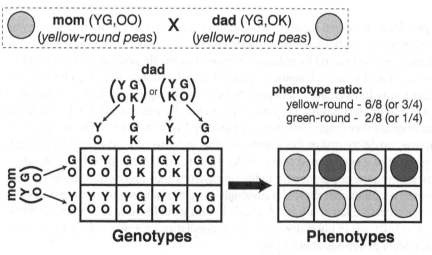

Figure 23-16. The shorthand method is first used to keep track of the expected pattern of offspring genotypes in the same two loci, two allele cross illustrated in the last figure. Next, each potential offspring genotype is converted to the expected phenotype, and the phenotype ratio is calculated.

Now let's use our increased understanding of genetics to understand inbreeding depression better. Start by considering a gene with two alleles: **F**—functional and **L**—lethal, and the interaction is non-additive with **F** being dominant over **L**. Next make sure you understand the answers to the following questions.

• Why can't a mating between a **FL** individual and a **LL** individual ever occur? (**LL** individuals die before they develop into a functional adult, and dead things cannot reproduce.)

• What is the probability that an **FF** individual mating with an **FL** individual would produce an inviable (**LL**) offspring? (0%, as only **FF** and **FL** offspring can result from this cross)

• What is the probability that an **FL** individual mating with an **FL** individual would produce an inviable offspring? (25%, as one of the four boxes in a Punnet square would yield a **LL** offspring.)

• Why does an increasing degree of relatedness among mating individuals increase the chance of an **FL x FL** cross, in comparison to an **FL x FF** cross. (The reason boils down to common ancestry. Any individual with a recessive lethal allele either experienced their own mutation, or they inherited it from one of their parents. If they inherited it, then the parent bearing this allele either experienced their own mutation or inherited it from one of their parents, and so on. And a consequence of an allele being passed along by inheritance is that closer relatives have an increased chance of being passed the same allele. For example, a full sibling has a 50% chance of being passed the same faulty allele from a parent, whereas a first cousin has a 12.5% chance of inheriting the same faulty allele from a grandparent, and the chance continues to decrease from there. As a consequence, mating with a sibling has a 50% chance of producing an **FL x FL** cross, although mating with a first cousin has a 12.5% chance, and so on. (Note: The probability steadily increases as more and more loci with recessive lethals are added to the mix.) In contrast, the only other way an **FL** individual would end up mating with another **FL** individual is to mate with someone who either themselves or one of their ancestors just happened to experience a recessive lethal mutation at the same loci. That is just not going to occur very often.

Sex Determination

Not all sexual populations have individuals with distinct genders. For instance, most plants and some animals, such as hydras and earthworms, are hermaphroditic. But note that whenever distinct males and females are present, another complication is added to patterns of inheritance. A male and a female parent must produce offspring that become either male or female. Which raises the question: How is each offspring's sex determined?

Mendel's investigation of either-or traits in peas sets the correct tone for investigating sex-determination. With his traits, the presence of a dominant allele *triggered* development to follow one of two alternative paths. Similarly, sex determination must have some form of trigger that steers development down one of two alternative paths. In animals, for instance, the trigger typically initiates a male or female pattern of sex hormone secretion. Yet, although the basic idea can be put in universal terms, the underlying mechanisms of sex determination cannot be. The nature of the trigger has been found to vary considerably across two broad categories known as **environmental sex determination** and **genetic sex determination**. I discuss each in turn.

Environmental sex determination

Environmental sex determination contrasts genetic sex determination in a couple of important ways. First, instead of the trigger being passed directly from parents to offspring at conception, every offspring "waits to decide" until a later point in development. Second, when the time comes, the trigger is external to the developing organism. Which gender path to follow is cued by some aspect of the environmental conditions encountered such as temperature, pH, or social conditions.

The following scenario reveals a potential advantage of environmental sex determination. Consider a species where males compete directly with other males for females, and size plays an important part in competitive ability. As a consequence, any offspring able to grow bigger than average could, in terms of reproductive success, be a good female but an even better male. Conversely, any offspring unable to grow to an even average size may still be able to be a reasonably successful female, but a very poor male. Next add in that how large any offspring can grow is largely determined by the environmental conditions experienced early in development, and parents have limited ability to control those conditions. If so, natural selection could favor offspring using some early environmental cue associated with faster growth to trigger male development and the absence of that cue to trigger female development.

Temperature has been to shown to be the major cue used in many species with environmental sex determination. Among vertebrates, temperature-dependent sex determination is well documented in reptiles, including many species of lizards and turtles and all crocodilians. Specifically, the temperature experienced by each egg during the middle third of embryogenesis, when gonads develop, plays a key role. Yet interestingly, no universal pattern between temperature and gender has been found. In some groups, males develop at cooler temperatures and females at warmer temperatures. In other groups, it is reversed. And sometimes one gender tends to develop within a certain temperature range, whereas the other gender develops at temperatures on either extreme.

It is perhaps not surprising that temperature has evolved as a gender cue in many reptiles. Temperature can have a pronounced affect on growth rate, along with other aspects of early development. Yet reptiles cannot maintain a constant body temperature, so in contrast to birds or mammals, they cannot use their own body heat to maintain an optimal thermal environment for their early developing offspring. The best they can do is to try to bury their eggs in a thermally conducive location. But changes in things like weather, shading patterns, or a host of other things would add significant and uncontrollable variation to the temperature each egg experiences. Add in a relationship between early growth and unequal gains in reproductive success across genders, and the evolution of temperature-dependent sex determination would be favored.

Although temperature-dependent sex determination has not been found as commonly in fish as reptiles, instances have been documented. And in one species, the Atlantic silverside (*Menidia menidea*), the biology seems to fit the logic presented earlier, although in the opposite way. Here female reproductive success seems to be more affected by size than male reproductive success. The larger volume of bigger females allows them to produce considerably more eggs. In contrast, individual males, regardless of size, cannot monopolize females because spawning occurs in large schools. The temperature cue most conducive to growth would thus be expected to induce female development. And that appears to happen. The cooler water temperatures found earlier in the growing season trigger female development, which allows females a longer time to grow before reproducing. Alternatively, the warmer waters that occur later trigger male development.

Besides temperature, changes in social environments have also been documented to trigger sex determination. Another classic example comes from fish. In Midas cichlids (*Amphilophus citrinellum*), which live in lakes in Central America, the largest members of the population are always male. This could be due to a heritable sex trigger, and males just grow larger. However, a simple, but elegant experiment by Richard Francis and George Barlow showed that instead of sex determining size, size determines sex. Specifically, those members of a brood that for whatever reason started to grow faster than their siblings became male, whereas the slower-growing members became female. Furthermore, their results suggested that it was not absolute size, but relative size that makes a difference. In other words, the gender trigger somehow takes into account each individual's size in relation to the surrounding fish. They took a brood of 74 fish and raised them together for 6 months. After that time, they measured each fish and then separated the 37 largest and the 37 smallest into two groups and then let them grow until they matured sexually. Even though the large group grew on average to a larger size, the larger half in each group tended to develop into males, whereas the others became females.

It seems obvious that an individual that develops as one gender remains that gender throughout life. It turns out, however, that sex change is widespread, occurring in plants, invertebrates, fish, and at least one amphibian. The evolutionary logic of sex change is straightforward—if an individual can reproduce more effectively as one gender when smaller and the other gender when bigger, then coupling sex change with growth would be favored by natural selection. Furthermore, in at least some sex-changing species, an environmental cue, such as changes in social interactions, is used to trigger the switch. For example, the largest female in a group of bluehead wrasses (*Thalassoma bifasciatum*), a tropical coral reef fish, will undergo female-to-male sex change if the male defending the area dies off. Other known examples also have the same flavor.

Genetic sex determination

The idea behind environmental sex determination—wait and use information from your developmental environment to determine your best gender choice—has such an appealing ring to it that it makes one wonder why it isn't used by all organisms. But there are drawbacks. First of all, environmental cues that can accurately predict which gender would be best must be available early in development. For many species, that may not be true. Furthermore, the connection between sex ratio and reproductive success has yet to be drawn into this discussion. Consider, for instance, a species where males are induced by warmer temperatures in combination with a particularly warm year. The extreme of all offspring becoming male is clearly disastrous. But as discussed in Chapter 6, even the emergence of a male (or female) biased sex ratio sets the stage for means to produce a more balanced sex ratio to be favored by natural selection. Genetic sex determination can do just that.

Evidence suggests that genetic sex determination evolved, probably several times, from environmental sex determination. If so, this switch must start with the establishment of a gene (or genes) that overrides environmental cues. Such a gender-determining gene would need to be a variable gene with two alleles, where the inheritance of a specific allele (or allelic combination) induces the development of males or females. The tricky part is that in diploid organisms, two alleles (let's call them **G** and **g**) lead to three possible genotypes (**GG**, **Gg**, and **gg**), yet there are only two sexes. With sex determination, however, that issue actually resolves itself. To see how, let's start with two genotypes (say **GG** and **Gg**) triggering female development, and the remaining genotype (**gg**) leading to male development. Under this arrangement, however, the **GG** genotype would disappear. **GG** females have to mate with males that are all **gg**, producing only heterozygous female (**Gg**) offspring. Furthermore, no new **GG** females could ever be produced because all parents with a **G** allele (either **GG** or **Gg**) are females, and two females cannot produce offspring. So the population would quickly end up with two genotypes (**Gg** and **gg**), one for each sex. And as a result, the population will tend to produce a nearly equal sex ratio in each generation. Any offspring from any mating has an equal chance of being male or female (see Figure 23-17).

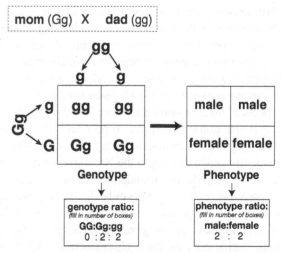

Figure 23-17. A means of genetic sex determination is shown that produces males or females with equal likelihood. Note in this scenario the female is the heterozygous sex, so the gender of each offspring is determined by which of the two alleles is present in each egg. See text for more details.

Assume that **G** codes for a functional protein, and **g** does not. If so, the protein produced could be viewed as the trigger that causes development to follow one of the two gender development paths. Alternatively, the gender that develops in the absence of **G**—that is, when the genotype is **gg**—could be considered the default sex, as it is the gender that develops in the absence of this functional protein. Curiously, which is the heterozygous (**Gg**) or triggered sex and which is the homozygous (**gg**) or default sex varies among organisms. For example, females are the triggered sex in birds, whereas males are the triggered sex in mammals. Or stated in the opposite way, males are the default sex in birds, whereas females are the default sex in mammals.

X and Y (or W and Z) sex chromosomes

Humans, along with other mammals, have a gender-determining gene called the SRY gene. It codes for the production of a protein called testis-determining factor, which among other things triggers the production of testosterone about 6 or 7 weeks after conception. The presence of testosterone at this time sets male development into motion. Alternatively, the embryo develops as a female. Yet I suspect that any previously encountered discussion of sex determination in humans centered on chromosomes instead of genes. Specifically, you have probably heard that there are two sex chromosomes, called **X** and **Y**; individuals with two **X** chromosomes develop as females, and **XY** individuals develop as male. The connection is that sex chromosomes are the homologous pair of chromosomes on which the gender-determining gene is located. Furthermore, in mammals the functional SRY allele (**G** in the preceding discussion) is only found on **Y** chromosomes, whereas **X** chromosomes have the nonfunctional allele (**g**). So **XY** individuals have a **Gg** genotype and hence are triggered to become male. Alternatively, **XX** individuals are **gg** and thus become female. (Note: All the other or nonsex chromosomes are referred to as **autosomal chromosomes**.)

But there is more to the story of sex chromosomes. In contrast to all other pairs of homologous chromosomes, the two sex chromosomes are heteromorphic—that is, they each look different than the other. For instance, in mammals the **Y** chromosome is a small, degenerate chromosome when compared to its **X** chromosome counterpart. This raises the question: Why would the chromosome bearing the functional sex-determining allele be smaller? Here is the short version of a simple model. It starts with the fact that the chromosome bearing the functional sex-determining allele (**G**), or **Y** chromosome, is only present in heterozygous sex (which is males in mammals). Alternatively, the **X** chromosome, which bears the other allele (**g**), passes through both sexes. As a consequence, natural selection would favor the accumulation of male sexually antagonistic genes—genes whose expression are advantageous for males but disadvantageous for females—on the **Y** chromosome. That way, these genes are only present in males. For example, in guppies, the fish with colorful males that we discussed earlier, 17 of the 18 genes involved in the development of the male color pattern and other aspects of male ornamentation are found on the **Y** chromosome. Yet, once this occurs, natural selection is also going to favor the suppression of recombination among sex chromosomes. Recall from Chapter 19 that recombination can lead to crossing-over, which could result in male sexually antagonistic genes moving to the **X** chromosome and being expressed in females. Whoops! Yet without recombination double-stranded repair can't occur. The **Y** chromosome in essence becomes asexual. As a consequence, it can persist only if it can reproduce faster than double-stranded damage tears it apart. This will not be possible if the chromosome is too large. So with the exception of the sex-determining allele, other sex-specific genes, and enough of the chromosome so that it can pair with the **X** chromosome during meiosis, the **Y** chromosome would be expected to degenerate. (Note: Morphologically distinct sex chromosomes are referred to as **X** and **Y** only when males are the heterozygous sex. In organisms where the female is the heterozygous sex, such as birds, the smaller chromosome bearing the allele that triggers female development is commonly referred to as the **W** chromosome, whereas the chromosome found in both sexes is called the **Z** chromosome.)

A couple other twists

Not all genetic sex determination fits into the scheme outlined. Note, for instance, that the same beginning model of a gender-determining gene with a functional and nonfunctional allele could lead to a different outcome: **GG** could induce the development of one sex, **Gg** could lead to the other, and **gg** would subsequently disappear. In such cases, the underlying mechanism of sex determination is a dosage response. Two copies of the functional allele leads to increased protein production, which triggers one gender to develop. Alternatively, one copy leads to less protein production and as a result development of the other gender is induced. This mechanism is found in some species of insects, along with other invertebrates. Typically females are the two-dose sex. Furthermore, the chromosome bearing the **G** allele is typically referred to as an **X** sex chromosome. So like mammals, females are **XX**. But it is a false similarity. **XX** individuals do not develop as females because they lack a copy of the functional allele that triggers male development, but because they have two doses of the functional gene, which triggers female development. In fact, in this scheme a chromosome analogous to a **Y** chromosome does not exist. Males are just single **X**, or typically designated as **XO**, individuals.

Sex determination in the Hymenoptera, the group of insects that includes ants, bees, and wasps, has a completely unique twist. Depending on how you look at it, either all or none of the chromosomes in these insects can be considered to be sex chromosomes. This is because they have a haplo-diploid sex determination system. Fertilized eggs—or diploid individuals—develop as females, whereas unfertilized eggs—or haploid individuals—develop as males. Furthermore, egg-laying females seem to be able to selectively release stored sperm and thus control the sex and subsequent sex ratio of her offspring. And they have been documented to use this control to produce a female-biased sex ratio in a situation known as locale mate competition. Here mating typically occurs among siblings shortly after they emerge from the site where eggs where laid. As a consequence, a female can maximize her reproductive success in the next generation by producing only a few males to fertilize the larger number of egg-laying females. Of course, the strange part of this scenario is the common occurrence of inbreeding. But in a haplo-diploid system, harmful recessive alleles will be expressed in haploid males, and thus tend to be quickly purged from the population. As a consequence, these alleles will be unavailable to cause inbreeding depression.

Sex-Linked Traits

The specialization and associated degeneration of the **Y** chromosome in mammals (or **W** sex chromosome in birds) adds another angle to genetic patterns of inheritance. In contrast to all the homologous pairs of autosomal chromosomes, only a portion of the two sex chromosomes are homologous—that is, only a portion of the **X** and **Y** chromosomes carry the same type genes. As a consequence, for many genes on the **X** chromosome there is *not* a second copy (forming a gene pair) on the **Y** chromosome. And conversely, there are genes on the **Y** chromosome that have no complement on the **X** chromosome. The presence of nonhomologous regions on both the **X** and **Y** chromosomes creates genetic differences between males and females. In males, the nonhomologous regions on both the **X** and **Y** chromosome are haploid—there is only one copy of each gene. On the other hand, females are diploid—two copies of each gene—for all genes located on the **X** chromosome, whereas genes unique to the **Y** chromosome are absent altogether. These genetic differences between the sexes can in turn influence the patterns in which phenotypic traits show up in males and females.

As I briefly discussed earlier, the story for the **Y** chromosome is fairly straightforward. Because genes unique to the **Y** chromosome (genes on the nonhomologous portion of the **Y** chromosome) are only present in males, they can only affect male phenotypes. How do they affect male phenotypes? Surprise, surprise! They are genes that set into motion the development of those traits associated with maleness. In other words, the **Y** chromosome contains genes that steer an individual to become phenotypically male.

Trying to follow the pattern of inheritance for traits influenced by genes on the **X** chromosome is less straightforward because both males and females have **X** chromosomes, but in unequal doses. For instance, recessive alleles on an **X** chromosome will always be expressed in males because there is no place for a second dominant allele to hang out. In contrast, recessive alleles will be expressed in females only if both **X** chromosomes carry the recessive allele—that is, only if the female is homozygous recessive.

To further explore the patterns of inheritance of recessive X-linked traits, let's focus on one in particular—the development of red-green color blindness.

Some background on color vision

Humans make a big deal out of color. Electromagnetic radiation comes in different wavelengths, and within the visual range wavelength differences *as little as 50 billionths of a meter* are seen as different colors.

The ability for humans to perceive different electromagnetic wavelengths as different colors starts in each eye's retina. Here light sensors of three different "electromagnetic flavors" are found. Each of the three different types of so-called **cone cells** contain light-sensitive pigments that decompose on exposure to light and in the process excite nerve fibers leading from the eye to certain regions of the brain. The three types of cone cells differ in terms of the wavelengths of light that they absorb, and based on each type's unique absorption pattern, they are referred to as **red cones**, **green cones**, or **blue cones**.

The perception of different colors is based on the degree to which each cone cell is excited by incoming light. For instance, light that excites (is absorbed by) all three types of cones equally is perceived by our brains as white light. The perception of orange starts with a wavelength of light that is maximally absorbed by the red cones, partially absorbed by the green cones (a little less than half), and not absorbed at all by the blue cones. On the other hand, the color blue is perceived when the incoming wavelength is absorbed maximally by the blue cone and not absorbed at all by the other two. In other words, each perceived color starts with a different absorption pattern among the three types of cones.

The evolution of color vision

The light-absorbing pigment found within each type of cone cell is a long chain of amino acids. Although the three genes that code for these three pigments do not specify the exact same amino acid sequence, the sequences are sufficiently similar to suggest that the three genes arose from one gene by two rounds of gene duplication followed by divergence. The differences in amino acid sequence are responsible for the spectral divergence—why each pigment absorbs slightly different wavelengths of light.

Based on the distribution pattern found among different animals, it seems that the first round of duplication and divergence occurred about the time that vertebrates originated. The result was two types of cone photoreceptors: one that preferentially responds to shorter wavelengths (blue cone), and another that preferentially responds to longer wavelengths (red cone). Animals with two cone types are called **dichromates** and possess a rudimentary form of color vision. Most mammals are dichromates.

The second round of gene duplication and spectral divergence seemed to have occurred in the common ancestor of Old World monkeys, apes, and humans (perhaps somewhere around 40 million years ago). This second round gave rise to green cones. Old World monkeys and apes are all **trichromats** and presumably perceive color in the same way as humans.

It has been suggested that trichromatic vision specifically enhanced the capacity of primates to spot different-colored food sources amid the green background coloration of leaves. For example, nearly all primates eat fruit to some extent, and some primates are also nectar eaters. Perhaps, this is why the appearance, odor, and taste of fruits and flowers are so attractive to us.

Red-green color blindness is an X sex-linked trait

The development of normal color vision requires a functional copy of each of the three cone pigment genes. Otherwise a person could not build all three types of cones, which would make it impossible to distinguish some colors from others. Having both red and green cones is particularly important in distinguishing four colors: red, orange, yellow, and green. A person lacking either of these is said to have red-green color blindness. The existence of alleles that do not code for functional red or green cone pigments is thus the genetic basis for red-green color blindness. As would be expected, functional alleles are dominant in expression, so red-green color blindness is a recessive trait. Moreover, the genes for these two different types of cone pigments are found on the **X** sex chromosome, so red-green color blindness is a recessive **X** sex-linked trait.

The fact that male mammals have only one **X** chromosome, whereas females have two, gives rise to some interesting patterns in the inheritance of faulty versions of either the red or green pigment gene. For instance, two normal-visioned parents could give rise to a color blind son, but never be able to produce a color blind daughter. Yet their color blind son could subsequently marry a normal-visioned female and never be able to produce color blind offspring of either sex. On the other hand, one of their normal-visioned daughters could marry a color blind man and potentially produce both color blind sons and daughters. In Figure 23-18, I work through all these possibilities.

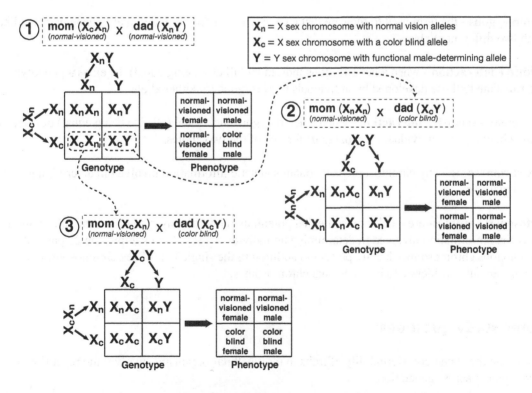

Figure 23-18. Potential patterns of inheritance of red-green color blindness are illustrated for the three crosses described in the text. Be sure that you understand what makes each outcome described in the text possible. Also make sure that you can calculate the probability of each outcome.

Some key terms:

independent assortment - when the way each pair of homologous chromosomes lines up at the beginning of meiotic cell division (i.e., how the maternally-derived and paternally-derived chromosomes of the pair align in relation to which daughter cell they will be pulled into) is not affected by how any other homologous pair lines up.

gene for a trait - a particular gene, or form of a gene, makes a difference in the development of a trait. For instance, the protein coded for by the gene in some way plays a causal role in the development of a certain trait. (In many cases, a gene for a trait can also be viewed as a necessary, but not sufficient, interactant in a trait's development.)

locus - the location of a particular gene. That is, what chromosome it is on, and where it is along that specific chromosome.

gene pair - the two locations for any gene found in a diploid organism—one on each of the homologous pair of chromosomes.

allele - one of the alternative forms of a gene found in a sexual population.

variable gene - any gene where more than one allele exists within a sexual population.

homozygous - the term used to indicate that a gene within a diploid individual (a gene pair) has two copies of the same allele.

heterozygous - the term used to indicate that a gene within a diploid individual (a gene pair) is filled with two different alleles.

additive interaction - when a heterozygous individual (all else being equal) develops a phenotype intermediate to those developed by individuals homozygous for either allele.

dominance-recessive interaction - when a heterozygous individual (all else being equal) develops the same phenotype as individuals homozygous for one of the two alleles.

sex chromosome - any chromosome that contains genetic information involved in determining an individual's sex.

autosomal chromosome - a chromosome that potentially contains any type of genetic information other than information involved in determining an individual's sex. For example, the 22 pairs of homologous chromosomes that are present in addition to the single pair of sex chromosomes in humans are all considered to be autosomal chromosomes.

Some study questions:

1. Explain the statement: Heritability of traits in multicellular organisms involves the repetition of development across generations.

2. By what avenue or avenues are three important interactants in development—genetic information, activity (patterns of use/disuse), and environment (especially early in development)—at least somewhat, heritable? How does the fact that both genetic information and environment are

interactants in any organism's development argue against trying to assign the development of some phenotypic trait (within the organism) as being either a product of nature (genetic) or nurture (environment).

3. What aspects of Lamarckian inheritance and blending inheritance appear not to be true?

4. How does meiosis and sex potentially mix up genetic information in a sexual population?

5. Know what is meant by the expression "a gene for a trait".

6. Know the difference between an additive and nonadditive effect (such as dominance-recessive) in terms of how an individual's genotype influences the development of its phenotype's.

7. The offspring of red-flowered snapdragons and white-flowered snapdragons all have pink flowers. Explain how crossing these pink flowered F1 offspring could be used to figure out whether flower color in snapdragons is an example of blending inheritance.

8. Know how to figure out the probability that any two parents will give rise to an offspring with a particular genotype or a particular phenotype for both a one locus or a two loci cross. For example, consider the following madeup scenario:

Recently, zoologists at the University of Utah discovered a new species of mammal that lives at high elevations of the Oquirrh Mountains. They have named them morcelots. Morcelots are small rodents with a peculiar color pattern. All morcelots are a spotted mixture of black and white, but significant variation exists in the population. Some individuals have black spots against a white background, while others have white spots against a black background. Also, some individuals have large spots while others have small spots.

Geneticists at this same university have since determined that this variation in color pattern is determined genetically in a straightforward Mendelian fashion. Spot size and spot color are controlled by a single locus, and in both cases one allele is dominant over the other. Specifically, large spots (L) are dominant over small spots (S), and white spots (W) against a black background are dominant over black spots (B) against a white background. The geneticists also determined that the locus for spot color and the locus for spot size are on different chromosomes. They also found that a diploid adult morcelot has 6 chromosomes in total—4 autosomal and 2 sex chromosomes. They have also determined that, like other mammals, morcelots have X and Y sex chromosomes.

a. Show how the chromosomes will initially line up in a cell of a **male** morcelot undergoing meiosis.

b. Meiosis in a male morcelot is involved in the formation of _____.

c. Next, show how the chromosomes will initially line up in a cell of a **female** morcelot undergoing mitosis.

Next, consider a cross between a male and a female morcelot that have the following genetic information.

SSWB (male) x LSWB (female)

d. In terms of color pattern, what does the above parental male and the above parental female morcelot look like?

male:

female:

e. What are the possible gamete types produced by each of the above parents?

male:

female:

f. Figure out the phenotypic ratio for the color pattern of offspring that result from the above two loci, two allele cross.

g. Use the phenotypic ratio that you derived above to figure out the probability that an offspring's color pattern will be different in terms of either color pattern trait than the **male** parent.

h. Suppose the above cross produced eight offspring. How many of them will have large white spots.

i. Now just consider the spot size locus. What would be the genotype and phenotype ratio from the above cross?

j. Think for a moment before you answer this question. When the zoologists surveyed color pattern found in morcelots in the natural population, they found that around 50% of the population had small spots. Given this observation, which of the following would be the best estimate of the frequency of the small spot allele in the population as a whole?

   a. 95%
   b. 70%
   c. 50%
   d. 25%

9. Use a simple understanding of transmission genetics (like a one locus two allele cross where one allele is a recessive lethal) to explain why in outcrossing populations the probability of producing nonviable offspring increase with incestuous matings?

10. (Returning to morcelots.) Another striking feature of morcelots is their eye color. They have either blue or green eyes. It turns out that the development of eye color is affected genetically by a single locus, and green eyes is **recessive** to blue eyes. However, there is an added complication. Eye color in morcelots is a sexlinked trait (i.e., the locus for eye color is on the X sex chromosome).

Use the above information to consider a mating between a green-eyed female and a blue-eyed male. What is the probability that such a cross will produce:

   • a male offspring with blue eyes?

   • a female offspring with green eyes?

11. Explain why red-green color blindness is a recessive trait. Next explain in general terms why recessive traits on an **X** sex chromosome, such as red-green color blindness, tend to be expressed more readily in male than in female mammals.

12. Let X_c designate an **X** chromosome that bears the information for color blindness (bears a faulty gene for the red or green pigment), and X_n designate an **X** chromosome that bears the information for normal vision. Use X_c, X_n, **Y** (to designate the **Y** chromosome), and **?** (to designate any space where there is insufficient information to know) to assist in answering the below questions.

a. Given the phenotype, fill in as much of the sex chromosome genotype as possible.

$\underline{\quad X_n \quad} \underline{\quad ? \quad}$ normal-visioned female

$\underline{\qquad} \underline{\qquad}$ color blind female

$\underline{\qquad} \underline{\qquad}$ normal-visioned male

$\underline{\quad X_c \quad} \underline{\quad Y \quad}$ color blind male

b. Taking it a step at a time, use all the information given so far to fill in as much of the sex chromosome genotype for this mating pair. Note that by the forth step you should be able to completely fill in each individual's genotype.

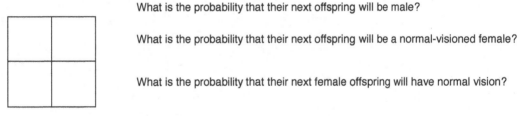

mom   dad

$\underline{\qquad} \underline{\qquad}$ $\underline{\quad ? \quad} \underline{\quad Y \quad}$ 1. no information on their vision

$\underline{\qquad} \underline{\qquad}$ $\underline{\qquad} \underline{\qquad}$ 2. had a color blind son

$\underline{\qquad} \underline{\qquad}$ $\underline{\qquad} \underline{\qquad}$ 3. also had a color blind daughter

$\underline{\qquad} \underline{\qquad}$ $\underline{\qquad} \underline{\qquad}$ 4. mom has normal vision

c. First, use the mom and dad genotypes that you uncovered in the last question to fill in the below Punnet square. Next answer each of the associated questions.

What is the probability that their next offspring will be male?

What is the probability that their next offspring will be a normal-visioned female?

What is the probability that their next female offspring will have normal vision?

What is the probability that their next offspring will be a color blind male?

d. Using the same mom and dad genotypes from question 12b, answer the below questions that involve working backwards—that is, trying to figure out the genotypes of this couple's parents.

• What do you know about the genotype of mom's mom and mom's dad?

• What more can be deduced if you know that mom's mom is color blind?

• What do you know about the genotype of dad's mom and dad's dad?

13. Suppose that both a female's maternal grandfather and her father were color blind. Is there sufficient information to calculate the probability that she will be color blind? If not, what can be concluded?

14. One textbook stated that around **8%** of all female humans are carriers for color blindness—that is, they carry a copy of a red-green color blindness allele on one of their two **X** chromosomes. If that is true, what would be a minimum estimate for the proportion of males that are color blind. (Note: Assume that all females on average produce the same number of offspring.)

658   Chapter 23

The Workings of Multicellular Organisms: Cell Perspective

Here we begin to explore how the parts— in particular organs and organ systems—making up multicellular organisms function. Or, in other words, what do the different parts do, and how do they do it? This is a broad topic. Not only are there lots of different things going on in one type of multicellular organism, but also there are many species of multicellular organisms. And each species has, to at least some degree, unique features. My concern here, however, is not to explore the vastness, but to find common ground. I start by introducing two different perspectives: cell perspective and organism perspective.

The cell perspective, the focus of this chapter, starts with realization that every living cell, whether it exists alone or as part of a multicellular organism, performs its own metabolism. Part of a multicellular organism's tasks is thus to provide each of its cells with the resources they need. This perspective starts with the question: What does an organism need to provide its cells? It then centers in on the question: How does a multicellular organism go about providing each of its cells with what it needs? In other words, the issue underlying the cell perspective is how the collective actions of the society of cells that we call a multicellular organism loops back to care for each of its members.

Alternatively, the organism perspective, which is discussed in the next chapter, focuses on how a multicellular organism's different parts are able to work together to form an organism-level performance. Or stated differently, how the pace of the different parts is regulated to best serve the organism as a whole.

Cellular Needs

Because of the ever presence of trade-offs, any cell's capacity to function will vary with its surrounding conditions. Any cell, in essence, has a niche. It functions best only within a small subset of conditions—the cell's optimal running conditions. Within a certain range outside a cell's optimal running conditions, a cell will be able to function, although increasingly less well. Beyond these tolerance limits the cell will die. Multicellular organisms thus constantly face a task. They need to strive to keep the environment of their cells at least within tolerance limits. Only then can the organism as a whole survive. Providing optimal conditions for each cell would be even better. All cells peaking in terms of performance makes for a multicellular organism at its performance peak. Or, to put it differently, an organism not maintaining optimal conditions for each of its cells will suffer losses in performance ability, perhaps to the point of death.

Some of the specific needs of cells are

• A continual supply of each cell's required nutrients.

• Removal of waste products generated within cells. Otherwise, waste products could build to levels that impede cellular performance.

• Maintenance of a proper osmotic environment. Whenever a cell's external environment is not in osmotic balance (with its inside) it is vulnerable to shrink or expand, perhaps to the point of lysing.

• Maintenance and/or the attainment of a thermal environment conducive to cellular chemistry. Enzymes within a cell tend to have a thermal optimum. Thus, a cell's metabolic activity is potentially highest at cell temperatures near this optimum.

• Protection from cell-level predators and parasites—certain bacteria and viruses—that enter the body.

Some basic issues

To begin to consider what a multicellular organism must do to care for its individual cells, envision one cell currently experiencing optimal conditions. Its surrounding environment is currently favorable in terms of nutrient supply, osmotic concentration, temperature, as well as any other aspects relevant to cell function. Now I ask: What is required to maintain these optimal conditions, even as the organism's environment and its activities change? The answer, fortunately, is easy: *Inputs to the cell's environment must continually equal outputs*. If inputs and outputs to some area are balanced, then the concentration of anything within that area will remain the same (see Figure 24-1).

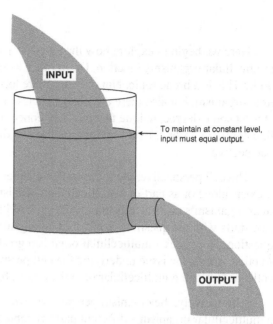

Part of the task of being a multicellular organism should thus be to attempt to continually balance inputs and outputs to each cell's environment. Yet how much control does any multicellular organism actually have over each of its cell's environment? For instance, at first glance a filamentous algae attached to a rock in the intertidal zone would seem

Figure 24-1. The conditions needed for something to remain the same, despite constant change.

to lack any control over the conditions experienced by each of its cells. Each cell within a filamentous arrangement is in direct contact with the external environment, so would seemingly experience whatever the environment dished out. But remember that just by the cells being connected and anchored to the substrate is a means to control environmental conditions. Being anchored allows all the cells to stay in a particular environment, the intertidal zone, despite tidal currents. And cells remaining hooked together after cell division allows the organism as a whole to grow large enough to move out of the boundary layer and take advantage of the continual flow of tidal current to bring in resources and remove wastes. Plus, when strung together part of each cell's surrounding environment is other cells, creating the option for cells to share resources.

Yet it is also clear that as multicellular organisms do things like coat their outside with some form of relatively impermeable protective barrier, as well as place cells further and further away from the external environment—such as when muscle cells are located within the mesoderm of three-layered animals—the environment experienced by each cell is going to be increasingly under the organism's control. In fact, increasingly isolating cells can occur only if the organism compensates by taking on the task of providing them what they need. Given that multicellular organisms may have upward of trillions of cells, this, at first glance, may seem like a daunting task. How could so many cells be cared for individually? To any great extent, they can't. It would be impossible to provide each cell with its own special mix of conditions. But cells could be cared for collectively if *different cells in the same organism have the same, or at least very similar, optimal conditions.* The task of providing all the different cells with their optimum environment would be reduced to the task of maintaining a constant internal environment throughout the body.

For animals enclosed by an epithelium, the interstitial space is, in essence, the environment surrounding cells throughout the body. Maintaining body-level homeostasis can thus be thought of in terms of keeping the interstitial environment the same throughout the body. Doing so has two basic requirements. First, an input–output balance to the interstitial environment must be maintained at the level of the organism. Second, because diffusion is so slow larger organisms need some form of convective distribution system (see Figure 24-2). Things entering or exiting a multicellular body commonly do so at specialized sites. Lungs, for instance, are the site specialized to uptake oxygen and release carbon dioxide in many multicellular animals. Consequently, lung-bearing animals need a convection system to quickly spread oxygen from the lungs to the interstitial environment throughout the body. Similarly, they need a convection system to help move the carbon released from cells throughout the body back to the lungs. Some form of circulatory system is the convection system used in larger animals. Circulatory systems prevent local accumulations or depletions of molecules by constantly moving fluids in close proximity to every cell within an animal's body. Evidence of how invasive the flow of blood is throughout your body is provided by an everyday observation: Cut yourself anywhere, and you bleed.

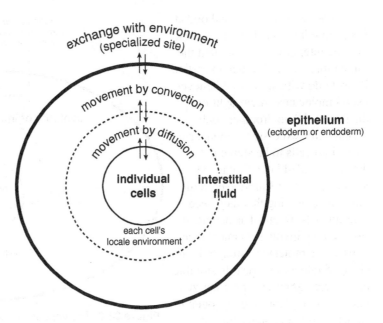

Figure 24-2. The exchange pathway used by many larger multicellular in attempt to maintain an optimal environment around each of their cells.

The fact that plant cells are hooked together by adjoining cell walls makes their multicellular design different than animals. For instance, technically they do not have an interstitial space enclosed by epithelium. But the bottom line is still similar. Much of the outer surface is coated with a protective covering. Interior cells thus must have some means to gain access to resources from the environment, and often these resources are brought in at specialized sites, so they need to be distributed to cells elsewhere by a convection system. So, despite differences in detail, the idea of maintaining a constant internal environment can be applied to plants as well as animals.

A closer look at inputs and outputs

In larger multicellular organisms, the inputs and outputs to the interstitial environment at any slice of time goes beyond what is currently moving in from or out to the environment by crossing the organism's outer (epithelial, epidermal) lining. Anything that moves into or out of cells also changes the composition of the interstitial environment (see Figure 24-3). Anything that moves into a cell is removed from, so is an output from, the interstitial environment. On the flip side, anything that moves out of a cell is added to, so is an input to, the interstitial environment.

Moreover, the inputs of cells tend to be different than the output of cells due to chemical reactions. For example, during aerobic respiration animal cells take in high-energy molecules (e.g., glucose or fatty acids) and molecular oxygen from the interstitial environment and release carbon dioxide and water back to the interstitial environment. Because the energy conversion that takes place during aerobic respiration is not perfectly efficient, heat is also released from the cell. This is why we need to keep breathing and eating. The high-energy molecules and molecular oxygen lost from the interstitial environment must be continually replaced if aerobic respiration is to continue, and the accumulating carbon dioxide needs to be removed. We will discuss what organisms do with this added heat later in the chapter.

Although is might sound odd at first, sometimes a cell releases back into the interstitial environment the same molecule that it took in earlier. It has to do with storage. Whenever useful molecules are brought into the interstitial environment only periodically, excessive amounts can move into cells to be stored until they are needed later. Storage allows organisms to survive periodic input of something that they need continuously. (Note: The details of storage may involve chemical reactions as the molecules brought in are changed into a more readily storable form—e.g., glucose is polymerized into starch in plants and glycogen in animals, and fatty acids are converted into triglycerides—which are then broken back down before release.)

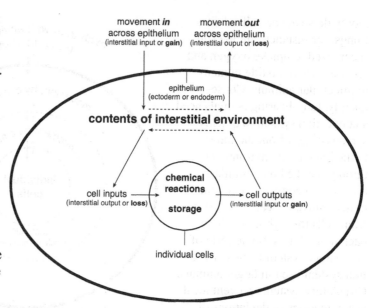

Figure 24-3. The various pathways by which something moves in or out of an organism's interstitial environment.

Scarce versus excessive resources

Maintaining an input–output balance, hence maintaining homeostasis, is an issue only when that to be balanced (call it **X**) is either **scarce** or **excessive**.

By scarce I mean that **X** tends to be lost from the body, and once lost it is difficult to replace. More **X** will enter the organism only if the organism expends energy to somehow gather it in. There are two basic reasons that something would tend to be lost from a body. First, an organism may live where the body concentration of **X** is higher than the concentration found in the surrounding environment. So as **X** moves with a concentration gradient it moves *out* of the body. For example, water is in higher concentration inside terrestrial organisms than their surrounding environment, so there is a constant tendency for water to escape to the environment. Second, **X** could be used up within the organism as it is chemically converted into something else, such as when animals break down (oxidize) glucose or fatty acids to make ATP.

Conversely, something is excessive when the problem goes the other way—**X** tends to be gained by the body, and once gained it is difficult to get rid of. Work must be done to remove the excess from the body. The two basic reasons for an increasing supply of some resource are just the opposite of those for a scarce resource. First, an organism may live where the body concentration of **X** is lower than the concentration found in the surrounding environment. So as **X** moves with a concentration gradient it moves *into* the body. Freshwater fish, for example, live where the environmental water concentration is higher than that found in their body, so there is a constant tendency for water to enter the organism. Second, **X** could be generated within the organism because it is the output of an ongoing chemical reaction, such as the constant production of carbon dioxide (CO_2) that occurs when animals break down (oxidize) glucose or fatty acids to make ATP.

Whether a resource is scarce or excessive depends on the interaction between the type of organism and its environment. That water is a scarce resource for terrestrial animals and an excessive resource for freshwater animals is one example. In Figure 24-4 I highlight this fact for three common resources—water, oxygen, and carbon dioxide. Rooted terrestrial plants are put in two categories because they live simultaneously in two different environments—their roots belowground and their shoots aboveground. As a consequence, they must contend with different issues at different places in their body. Although not simultaneously, animals that make major habitat shifts during their life—such as a mayfly moving from freshwater to air, or a salmon moving between fresh and saltwater—must be able to contend with different resources shifting from being scarce to excessive, or vice versa.

	terrestrial animal	freshwater animal	terrestrial plant leaves	roots
scarce:	O_2 H_2O	O_2	CO_2 H_2O	O_2 H_2O?
excessive:	CO_2	CO_2 H_2O	O_2	CO_2?

Figure 24-4. Whether three common resources—water, oxygen, or carbon dioxide—are scarce are excessive changes with both the type of environment and organism.

The presence of scarce or excessive resources is an unavoidable consequence of Life. Living always involves, in at least some ways, being different—hence out of equilibrium—than the surrounding environment. Furthermore, living involves activity, and the basis of activity is chemical reactions. So the inputs of chemical reactions are always becoming scarce, and the outputs of chemical reactions may build to excess. To understand how organisms actively maintain homeostasis in the face of this constant source of disruption, one must look at both the *input* and *output side* of the issue. Whatever the problem, adjusting inputs or outputs can be helpful.

Table 24-1. Maintaining balance (inputs=outputs) of scarce and excessive resources, put in terms of supply and demand.

---

scarce resource - tends to be lost from the body, and once lost is difficult to replace—work is required to get more. (The survival-based demand is to replace whatever is lost.)

supply side: (get more)

1. increase rate that X is brought in from environment.
2. increase rate the X is synthesized from other available molecules.
3. increase rate that X is released from storage.

demand side: (reduce loss)

1. reduce rate that X is lost from body
2. reduce rate that X is converted into something else (via chemical reactions)
   a. increase efficiency of use
   b. reduce activity associated with the conversion of X
   c. substitution- use something else to do the same job.

excessive resource - tends to be added to the body, and once added is difficult to get rid of—work is required to remove it. (The survival-based demand is to get rid of whatever is gained.)

supply side: (remove excess)

1. increased rate that X is moved from body to the environment.
2. increase rate the X is converted into something else by chemical reactions.
3. increase rate that X is put into storage.

demand side: (reduce gain)

1. reduce rate that X enters the body from the environment.
2. reduce rate that X is synthesized from other available molecules.

Suppose, for example, **X** is a scarce resource for some organism. How should this organism deal with this problem? The seemingly obvious answer is to work on the *input side*—to actively round up more **X** to replace all that is lost. But that is not the whole story. Working on the *output side*—that is, working to reduce the rate that **X** is lost—can be equally effective. In terms of maintaining a balance preventing the loss of a certain amount of **X** is equivalent to gathering anew that same amount. It is a simple but profound realization.

Similarly, when **X** is excessive, preventing gain (*input side*) is the same as getting rid of the same amount (*output side*). Trying to stay afloat in a leaky boat provides a good example. The water leaking in is in excess; and better plugging the holes so that less water flows in will help keep the boat afloat as well as bailing out the water once it has entered.

Attempting to maintain homeostasis can also be reworded using the economic notions of supply and demand, where demand is what drives the need for supply. The two sides of the issue are either to reduce demand or to increase supply. For example, when a resource is scarce the demand is to make up for any that is lost. An organism works on the *supply side* of scarcity whenever it actively goes out and finds more, and on the *demand side* of scarcity whenever its efforts act to reduce loss. And because both these sides are functionally equivalent, maintaining homeostasis can be accomplished by any combination of increasing supply or reducing demand that maintains an input-output balance. Alternatively, when a resource is in excess the demand is to remove all the excess that enters. Actively removing any excess that begins to accumulate is to work on the *supply side*, whereas the *demand side* involves reducing the amount of excess that enters in the first place. Table 24-1 summarizes all the various means that organisms can work on both the *supply* and *demand sides* to maintain balance.

Of course, part of maintaining such input–output balance is a regulatory issue. An organism must somehow detect that something has gone out of balance and then coordinate a response that generates a counterbalancing shift. We wait to discuss regulation until the next chapter.

The trade-off between maintenance and performance

Whenever an organism experiences scarcity or excess it is caught in a trade-off. It can either pay the costs associated with correcting the imbalance, or it can suffer the performance costs associated with not maintaining its cells at optimal conditions. Living is tough. How different organisms play this trade-off, however, is also part of what makes life so intriguing. *Organisms are caught in a perpetual juggling act.* To maintain optimal conditions for their cells they must maintain several things in balance simultaneously. This juggling act is made all the harder by the fact that restoring balance in one area always disrupts balance in another. This is true for one of two reasons. First, the act of restoring balance in one area may require the organism to dip into its supply of something else. For example, you dip into your water supply whenever you rid excess heat by sweating. Second, permeable surfaces are never exclusively permeable. So, as an organism exposes a surface to the environment in attempt to gain or lose one thing, it may—depending on the nature of the concentration gradients—gain or lose something else. Surfaces permeable to gases such as oxygen or carbon dioxide, for instance, are also permeable to water. As a consequence, an organism attempting to maintain a gas balance may have an accompanying loss or gain—depending on the environment—of water.

Because of this juggling act, the trade-off between maintenance costs and performance costs boils down to a trade-off between different forms of performance loss. Let me explain. Suppose the cost of maintaining something—call it **X**—is paid through the loss or gain of something else—call it **Y**. An organism maintaining **X**—hence maintaining the performance associated with maintaining **X**—is now put in the position of either maintaining **Y** or having performance abilities associated with maintaining **Y** at optimal levels suffer. And this chain may continue. Maintaining **Y** may be paid for through the loss or gain of something else. Figure 24-5 more clearly outlines this chain of options.

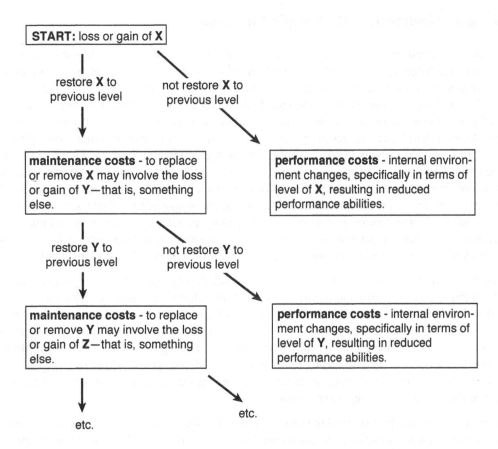

Figure 24-5. A flow chart that illustrates the ongoing tradeoff between maintenance costs and performance costs.

Despite this constant juggling act, under some conditions organisms will be able to keep all the balls in the air—that is, maintain everything at optimal levels. But what should an organism do whenever it experiences conditions under which it cannot maintain everything at optimal levels? Put in **X** and **Y** terms, how should it "choose" when it can maintain **X** or **Y** but not both? The consequence of choosing **X** is to let the performance associated with optimal **Y** levels suffer, or vice versa (see Figure 24-6). The answer is one you have likely heard before: *It should make the best of a bad situation*, where best is judged in terms of persistence. For many situations this boils down to organisms letting the aspect of performance slip that is currently *less threatening* to its survival.

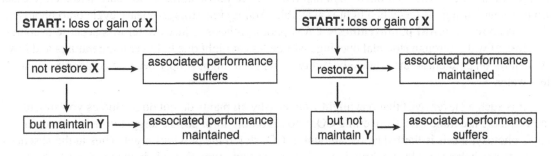

Figure 24-6. The two options when an organism is able to maintain **X** or **Y** but not both.

An example: Plants making the best of a bad situation

To survive, terrestrial plants must be able to maintain water balance while photosynthesizing—a dilemma exacerbated by the fact that in many terrestrial environments water, at least at times, is a scarce commodity. In the process of "dealing" with this dilemma, plants have evolved means on both sides of the input–output coin. Stems being modified into roots was the biggest plus on the *supply side*, and plants living in drier areas tend to not only allocate more resources toward root production, but differ in their basic root design in ways that help them bring in more water. Some plants, for instance, produce deep taproots to take advantage of local groundwater supplies. Xylem structure has also been modified in certain plants in ways that makr it possible to continue to transport water up from the roots even in scarce conditions. Terrestrial plants have also come up with many *demand-side* adjustments to minimize the amount of water lost during the uptake of CO_2. The most important is the combination of three-dimensional tissues surrounded by an outer waxy covering and numerous pairs of guard cells that can generate small openings, called stomata, that lead into an interior space of loosely packed, CO_2-permeable, photosynthetic cells (return to Chapter 22 for more details).

Despite efforts to increase supply or decrease demand, during dry, windy, sunny days, and especially during droughts, plants can be caught in situations where they cannot continue to fix carbon and still maintain water balance. That is, water loss out of the stomata exceeds water intake through the roots. This is where the ability of guard cells to close off the stomata comes into play. Plants have a "choice" between continuing photosynthesis or better maintaining water balance. Closing stomata blocks the uptake of CO_2, but also greatly slows water loss—hence greatly slows the onset of the ill effects associated with water shortage. Alternatively, keeping stomata open allows a plant access to CO_2, but at the cost of increasing water shortage.

Plants facing water shortage tend to close their stomata. This is our first example of organisms making the best of a bad situation. The sugars produced during photosynthesis are used for growth or are stored for use as an energy source during periods of energy shortage (such as at night). So plants lacking CO_2 will eventually die. But the negative consequences of blocking photosynthesis tend to not affect a plant as quickly as excessive dehydration. Slowing water loss is thus the better choice.

Another twist

It was mentioned in Chapter 22 that plants also tend to close their stomata at night. Without light CO_2 is not needed, and thus keeping stomata open would only open the avenue for wasteful water loss.

There is, however, an exception to this pattern. Cacti, along with some other plants living in arid areas, open their stomata at night and close them during the day. But how can this work? The key new ingredient is storage. CO_2 is brought in at night, converted into a storable molecule, and then released from storage during the day when light is available. Adding this storage-release cycle onto photosynthesis is known as **CAM photosynthesis**. CAM photosynthesis reduces water loss because evaporative loss of water through stomatal openings will be less at night due to lower temperatures and lower concentration gradients—the relative humidity increases at night simply because cooler air can hold less water.

It is such a clever twist that one might wonder why all plants do not do it. But, as you should expect, there are trade-offs. Converting CO_2 into a storable form costs energy. Furthermore, each day's photosynthesis is limited by the amount of CO_2 stored the previous night. Thus in the absence of severe water-balance problems, bringing in CO_2 at the same time that it is being used works best.

The Fundamental Balance: Energy

Because for any organism the task of living requires a constant processing of usable energy, maintaining an energy balance at all times is essential. Doing so, however, is no trivial matter because usable energy is always a scarce resource. In fact, every organism must expend some of its current supply of usable energy to power the capture of more usable energy. It is both the pervasiveness and the underlying difficulty of the task that makes trying to understand the various means by which different types of organisms maintain this fundamental balance intriguing. There are several aspects of the problem that stand out:

1. Even in multicellular organisms, energy balance must be maintained at the level of each and every cell because every cell generates it own ATP.

2. The cells of all eukaryotic multicellular organisms have mitochondria, which means that each cell can make ATP by aerobic respiration. But aerobic respiration requires a continual supply of two inputs: high-energy molecules to oxidize, and low-energy oxygen molecules (O_2) to serve as final acceptors. Multicellular organisms must somehow continually supply their cells with both of these.

3. The input of sources of usable energy is periodic in all organisms, so all organisms must have some means to store energy in between. The long-term energy storage molecule, however, must be something other than ATP because it is too unstable to store for more than a minute or so.

4. As high-energy molecules and molecular oxygen undergo chemical reactions (during the production of ATP), the molecular arrangements coming out of these chemical reactions will be the opposite of being scarce—they will be in excess. As a consequence, maintaining an energy balance not only involves continual bringing in the scarce inputs of ATP production, but also continually getting rid of the outputs.

Maintaining an energy balance thus boils down to maintaining three other forms of balance: (1) input of high-energy molecules must keep pace with the rate at which higher energy molecules are broken down (oxidized), (2) input of O_2 must keep pace with the rate at which O_2 is used and converted to H_2O, and (3) leftovers (such as CO_2) must be removed from the body as fast as they are being produced within the body. Figure 24-7 shows the interconnectedness between these three issues.

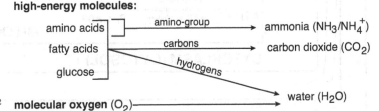

Figure 24-7. A summary of the inputs and outputs of aerobic respiration. Glucose and fatty acids are the main high-energy molecular inputs, in that they can be readily respired. Amino acids can be converted into potentially respired molecules, but in the process of doing so the amine group is cleaved off and quickly converted to ammonia (NH_3).

The fundamental nature of energy balance makes it a central theme of organism function. Most aspects of how organisms are assembled and work revolve either around maintaining each of its three components (see Figure 24-8) or contending with other forms of balance (such as water balance) that can be disrupted during the input and removal of molecules associated with maintaining energy balance. Consider, for example, topics surrounding how animals maintain a supply of high-energy molecules, such as: how sensory and motor systems are used to locate potential food items and avoid

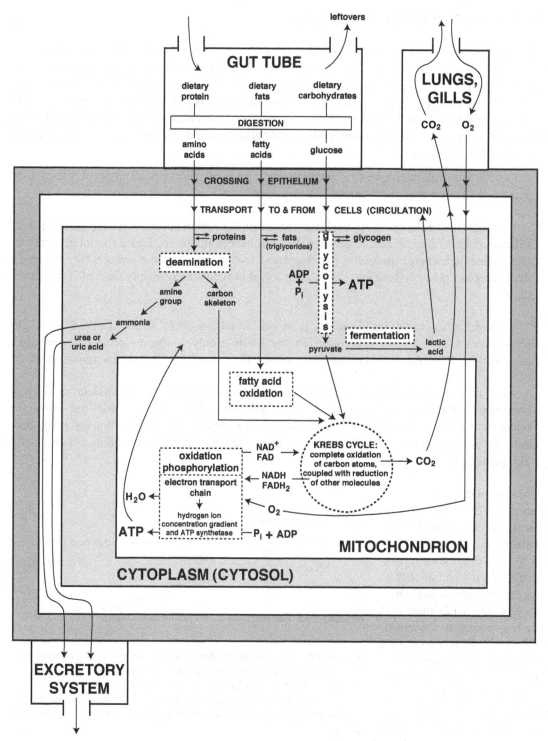

Figure 24-8. An overview of the various routes that inputs and outputs involved in maintaining ATP balance move through larger three-layered animals. Note that digestive systems, respiratory systems, circulatory systems, and excretory systems are all involved.

eating anything potentially harmful; how the digestive system works to both process and absorb high-energy molecules into the body; how the digestive and immune systems work to deal with potentially harmful things (toxic molecules, pathogenic invaders) that manage to get into the digestive tract; how high-energy molecules are stored (and released) so that they are constantly available to cells, despite being brought into a body only periodically; or how high-energy molecules are distributed to the rest of an organism's cells after absorption (a discussion that would commonly include the workings of the circulatory system). Did you notice how extensively this one aspect of energy balance incorporates different body systems? By the time one thoroughly addressed each topic mentioned, many chapters of a physiology text would be covered. Similarly, all the issues surrounding acquiring oxygen or removing wastes are equally extensive.

Covering all these topics, however, is not the focus here. (I will leave that to a physiology course.) In fact, I only briefly address a few topics to give you a flavor of some of the issues involved.

A few ways that organisms increase O_2 uptake

To convert glucose or fatty acids to ATP in the most efficient manner, molecular oxygen must be available. This means that the only way to curb an organism's demand for oxygen is to reduce its energy demands—that is, reduce its activity. Maintaining a balance between an organism's oxygen supply and demand, without cutting back on activity, thus falls all on the supply side of the balance equation. Accordingly we focus on a few different ways that organisms have come to acquire oxygen from their environment and then deliver it to its cells.

Fish gills use a countercurrent system to increase oxygen uptake

It is difficult for an organism to get sufficient oxygen from water for one simple reason. In contrast to air, water has little oxygen—somewhere around 35 times less. The lack of oxygen stems from the fact that oxygen has a low solubility in water. Some aquatic animals avoid this problem by surfacing to get oxygen. This solution, however, creates other problems. They must periodically disrupt their underwater activities to come back to the surface. This periodic, hence predictable, surfacing may also make them more vulnerable to predators. Predators could merely hang out waiting for their next rise. Others, such as fish, use gills to move oxygen from the water into their circulatory system. Actually gills are part of the circulatory system. They are an array of capillary nets exposed to the water and arranged in ways that facilitate the uptake of oxygen. First, they are filamentous structures, which increases their absorptive surface area. Also only one or two cells separate the blood flowing through the gills from the water flowing past the gills, which reduces the diffusion distance. Finally, gills use **countercurrent exchange** to increase uptake.

Countercurrent simply means that two things in close proximity are flowing in opposite directions. In gills the countercurrent flow is generated by the blood flowing through the gills moving in an opposite direction as the water flowing across the gills. And the bottom line is that this countercurrent flow, in comparison to a concurrent or parallel flow, makes a big difference. Assuming that the water first entering the gill is saturated with oxygen—that is it contains 100% of what it could potentially hold—the telltale sign of how much oxygen is extracted is then the percent saturation of the water exiting the gills. In a concurrent flow the amount remaining will tend to be around 50%, meaning that 50% was extracted. On the other hand, around 80% to 90% can be extracted in a countercurrent flow. That is, only around 10% to 20% of the oxygen dissolved in the entering water still remains. The question then is: How does this countercurrent flow between water and blood so dramatically increase potential uptake?

Blood first entering the gill has returned from circulating throughout the body. Because blood as it circulates through the body gives up oxygen to the tissues, this entering blood contains little oxygen. As it flows through the gills, however, it picks up more oxygen from the water passing by, so long as the water has higher oxygen concentration. Oxygen only enters the gills by passive diffusion. Thus, countercurrent flow can increase oxygen uptake, in contrast to concurrent flow, only by lowering the oxygen concentration of water that still encounters a concentration gradient. And it does just that.

Let me start by explaining why a concurrent flow can extract only around 50% of the water's oxygen supply. In a concurrent flow the water entering the gills first encounters blood returning from the body. In other words, the water with the most oxygen first encounters the blood with the least oxygen (see Figure 24-9). A large concentration gradient exists, and oxygen will quickly pass into the blood. But, because they are both moving in the same direction the oxygen moving into the blood moves along with the water from where it came. This means that the concentration gradient will become less and less with time until it equilibrates. And if the blood and water amounts are somewhat equal, this equilibrium will occur when about

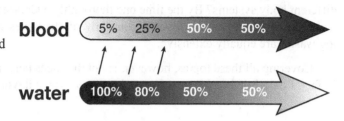

Figure 24-9. Within a fish's gills, if blood and water flowed in the same direction (a concurrent flow), the diffusion of oxygen from water to blood would only occur until the amount in each medium equilibrated.

half of the water's oxygen passes into the blood. At that point the blood and water should have nearly equal amounts of oxygen.

Alternatively, a countercurrent flow avoids the pitfalls of equilibrating concentrations. In countercurrent flow, water entering the gills first encounters blood about to exit the gill and return to the body. This means that this blood has already absorbed oxygen from water that passed through the gill earlier. Yet, as long as the oxygen concentration in the water is still greater than the blood, more oxygen will flow into the blood. Of course, as oxygen begins to move into the blood the oxygen concentration in water decreases. But because of the opposite flow, water moving through the gill continually encounters blood that has traveled a shorter and shorter distance within the gill and hence has absorbed less

oxygen. A concentration gradient is thus maintained. And it will be maintained until the water exits the gill (see Figure 24-10). Recognize that with a countercurrent flow, water flowing through the gill last passes by blood with the least possible amount of oxygen—blood just entering the gills. So the water will still have more oxygen than this mostly deoxygenated blood. Oxygen can continue to flow from the water to the point that only 10% to 20% of the initially dissolved oxygen still remains.

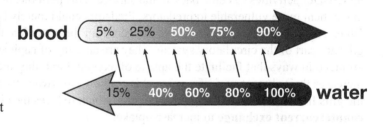

Figure 24-10. Within a fish's gills, if blood and water flowed in opposite directions (a counter-current flow), the concentration gradient needed for oxygen to diffuse from water to blood would not quickly disappear, allowing for increased oxygen intake.

The piece still missing in this countercurrent design is how fish get water to flow past their gills. When hanging out in calm water, many fish use a coordinated opening and closing of their mouth and their operculum—their two gill covers—to force water into their mouth and out past their gills. In other words, they use some of their ATP generated by aerobic respiration to run a pump that helps them get in more oxygen. But interestingly, to increase oxygen uptake when swimming, they tap into the very motion that increases oxygen demand. Instead of increasing the speed the water flows past their gills by flapping their operculum faster, they swim with their mouth and operculum open so that water is forced past their gills. In fact some fish, such as mackerel, have no pumping mechanism. Such fish rely solely on swimming to move water past the gills. Keep a mackerel from swimming, and it will suffocate.

An aside: Acquiring oxygen through gills has several forms of maintenance costs

The use of gills also continually disrupts a fish's water and salt balance. In addition to gills being permeable to oxygen, they are also permeable to water and to a smaller extent permeable to ions such as Na^+ and Cl^-. And both freshwater and saltwater bony fishes live in a medium where their osmotic concentration is different than that of their surroundings.

Freshwater bony fish live in a situation where the surrounding medium is higher in water and lower in salts. Water tends to flow into their bodies, and salts tend to flow out. Several features of freshwater fish reduce the severity of this problem. They include never drinking, making outer surfaces besides gills impermeable to water and salts, and reducing the concentration gradient between themselves and their environment by reducing the osmotic concentration of their body fluids. Freshwater fish then constantly urinate to rid the remaining excess water. Conversely, a salt balance is maintained in the face of scarcity by the presence of salt pumps in their gills that actively transport salts into their body.

Saltwater bony fish—which are thought to be descendants of freshwater fishes—have the exact opposite problem. They live in a medium that has less water and more ions than found in their bodies. Water, thus, tends to pass out of their bodies and salts tend to enter. To compensate, saltwater fish drink constantly and then use salt pumps located in their gills to actively transport excess ions from the organism—the opposite direction as freshwater fish. Because the kidneys in these organisms are unable to produce concentrated urine (urine with higher osmolarity than normal body fluids), kidney function is of little use.

Moving and breathing

Lungs are internal cavities open to the outside, containing surfaces permeable to oxygen and extensively vascularized, so that oxygen within, if in high enough concentration, can be passively transferred into the circulatory system. Lungs, in general, fall into two categories: ventilation lungs and diffusion lungs. In ventilation lungs, oxygen enters by an actively maintained airflow into and out of the lung. All terrestrial vertebrates have ventilation lungs. On the other hand, oxygen does not generally move into a diffusion lung by riding an air current, although general body movements may generate some airflow. Instead, oxygen enters by moving along concentration gradients. Snails, slugs, and spiders are examples of organisms bearing diffusion lungs.

When a reptile, bird, or mammal is stationary, an alternating sequence of contracting and relaxing of muscle attached throughout the rib cage ventilate lungs. The contraction of these muscles expands the rib cage, which concomitantly increases lung volume. As discussed in Chapter 20, the increased volume creates the pressure gradient (suction) required for air to flow into the lung. Air is then forced back out as lung volume decreases when these muscles relax. Mammals also add a diaphragm—a dome-like sheet of muscles positioned at the base of the lungs. Contraction of the diaphragm expands lung volume; relaxation does the opposite.

What about when these types of animals are moving? Like a fish, can they use the same motion that increases oxygen demand to facilitate oxygen uptake?

For most amphibians and reptiles the answer is no. In fact, they cannot even run and breathe at the same time. Their movement on land resembles the locomotory motion of fish. Their legs stick out from the sides of their body, and due to this sprawling gait, walking or running requires the trunk to flex back and forth between the right and left sides. This type of movement of the rib cage makes it impossible to expand both of their paired lungs simultaneously. Instead, each time the trunk bends, the lung on the bent side is compressed while the other is expanded. Although this interferes with normal breathing during walking, during running the cycling goes so fast that breathing is blocked. Lizards are thus constrained to run only in short bursts, as they must stop their trunk oscillations to ventilate normally.

Quadruped mammals—mammals that run on all four limbs—have escaped this running and breathing constraint by changing the axis of motion. All four limbs have moved underneath the body and hence provide vertical support, and during running the spine flexes up and down, instead of back and forth. (How would you know just by the way it swims that a dolphin is a mammal?) As a result of this shift, running not only stops interfering with breathing, but it may actually encourage it. The movement of the backbone up and down with each stride will expand and compress the rib cage evenly. It is not coincidence that mammals ranging in size from gerbils to rhinoceroses take one breath per stride. And this may not be the only way that running mammals use motion to assist ventilation. At least some (such as trotting dogs) appear to harvest the rocking back and forth of its internal organs, in particular the liver, which accompanies running. Just think about it. Each time a quadruped lands on its forelimbs during a run, its body abruptly decelerates. From screeching to a halt in your car, you know that anything not firmly attached to that decelerating keeps on going. Somewhat loosely attached internal organs will thus keep heading toward the organism's nose. This is a path that sends them colliding into, hence squeezing, the front air bags—that is, the lungs. Such a force can help push air out of the lungs. Alternatively, as the hind limbs push off, the animal quickly accelerates. Here the internal organs will do just the opposite. Things unattached to something accelerating are left behind. Accordingly, the organs, relatively speaking, start heading toward the organism's hind end. And as these organs pull back, they create forces that can help the lung to expand. Evidence even suggests that when this rocking motion is used to assist ventilation, the diaphragm takes on a new role. Instead of being solely involved in lung expansion, it also acts to keep the motion of internal organs from getting out of control. Specifically, it contracts to rein in organs whenever they begin to swing about too wildly.

Bipedal posture also relieves the running and breathing constraint. Because the chest cavity is lifted off the ground, and the forelegs are no longer used in locomotion, the rib cage does not sway laterally back and forth while moving. Breathing and running are thus possible. As a bipedal mammal you have experienced this ability firsthand. There are also other mammalian examples, such as kangaroos, but because mammalian bipeds evolved from mammalian quadrupeds, it is unlikely any mammal raised up on to its hind legs just so that it could run and breathe. But that may be the case in other evolutionary lineages. The earliest known biped is *Euparkeria*, an archosaur (the reptilian group that includes crocodiles, dinosaurs, and pterosaurs, among others), which lived around 240 mya. Though normally quadrupedal, the structure of this small reptile suggests that it was capable of shifting to a bipedal gait. Did it walk on all fours and then shift to its bipedal gait when it needed to run and breathe at the same time? It is a plausible idea. Interestingly, the earliest dinosaurs were small, fully erect, bipedal animals, suggesting that all dinosaurs evolved from a bipedal lineage. Many well-known dinosaurs, such as *Tyrannosaurus rex*, retained this bipedal posture. Was part of the dinosaur's evolutionary success based on the ability to run and breathe at the same time? Perhaps!

Birds (which all the evidence suggests evolved from dinosaurs, and many argue that they are dinosaurs) breathe quite different than mammals. Bird lungs are connected to both anterior and posterior air sacs. Inhaled air first moves into posterior air sacs. It then passes through the lungs on its way to the anterior air sacs, from where it is subsequently exhaled. Although this difference makes a difference in the efficiency in which gases are exchanged, our focus here is on whether birds are able to use some aspect of their flying motion to facilitate ventilation. Unlike mammals, flexion of the backbone is not an option. Although the neck (cervical) vertebrae of birds are highly mobile, allowing the neck to turn through a wide range of motion, the vertebrate behind the neck show areas of fusion to prevent the trunk from undulating during flight. During flapping, the forelimbs or wings need to be able to pull against a solid framework. But what about flapping itself? The flight muscles are attached ventrally to an enlarged sternum, which is hooked to the rib cage. So engaging the strongest flight muscles during each downstroke would act to compress the chest cavity more than the upstroke; suggesting that birds would benefit from exhaling with each downstroke and inhaling with each upstroke. Some birds, like pigeons, have been found to do just that. Others take much slower, presumably deeper, breaths that last across several wing beat cycles. But airflow is still influenced by wing beat, as most exhalation still occurs during the downstroke part of each cycle, and most inhalation occurs during the upstrokes.

An aside: Cold noses can minimize water loss from lungs

Air moves down into the lung and into its folding cavities where, in intimate association with the lung's tissues, oxygen is passively removed from its contents. But as it gives up oxygen, the air can also gain water, heat, and carbon dioxide. For the moment let's focus on water and temperature. Due to the exposure of so much internal surface area, air prior to leaving the lungs will be at body temperature and saturated with water. Water will thus be lost with each exhalation.

Water loss, however, could be minimized if somehow the organism could cool the exhaled air prior to exiting the body. Cool air holds less water than warm air. In fact, dramatically so, because the amount of water that air can hold increases exponentially with temperature. For instance, air around room temperature (72°F) holds less than half the water than air at a typical body temperature (around 100°F). Thus, even slight cooling could dramatically reduce water loss. No organism, however, comes equipped with a little refrigerator unit in its nasal passage. Outside temperatures below body temperature, in conjunction with breathing in and out through the same passageway, however, automatically establish the framework for **temporal countercurrent heat exchange.** (Say what?) When air below body temperature enters the nasal passages, the net heat flow is from the nasal surfaces to the air. These nasal surfaces cool as a result. This cooling is further enhanced when the entering air is dry due to the cooling effects of water being evaporated from the moist nasal surfaces. When this same and now thoroughly heated and water-laden air returns back through the same passageway, the net heat flow will be in the opposite direction. Heat moves from the air to the surfaces, cooling the air before it leaves the body. Water drops out along the way because cooler air can hold less water. How well such temporal heat exchange actually works depends on the design of the nasal passageways. The longer, the narrower, and more convoluted the nasal passages are, the more effectively they can reduce water loss. Such passages increase the incoming and outgoing air's exposure to the surrounding tissue. So, the cooling of the tissues with each inhalation and the return cooling of the air with each exhalation will be more complete.

Humans and kangaroo rats bound the two extremes. Human nasal passageways are so wide that the heat exchange between flowing air and nasal surfaces is minimal. Humans, in most circumstances, breathe out air at body temperature. Alternatively, the air leaving the nasal passages of a kangaroo rat, a small desert-dwelling rodent, is never much above ambient temperature. In fact, investigators found that air entering at 28°C came back out at 23°C when the air was completely dry. As mentioned earlier, when breathing in dry air, further cooling can occur through water evaporation.

Recognize that countercurrent heat exchangers could also play a role in an organisms heat balance. A design that effectively curbs water loss will also reduce heat loss.

Respiratory proteins and oxygen transport

In insects, the job of getting oxygen into the body and then to all the cells is accomplished simultaneously. Trachea go everywhere in the body. Gills and lungs, on the other hand, do not. Instead they hook into the circulatory system, which goes everywhere. It seems so simple. There is, however, a problem. As I have mentioned before, oxygen does not dissolve well in water (which is the major constituent of blood), and blood unable to absorb much oxygen could not effectively distribute it to the rest of the body. The evolution of respiratory proteins has thus played an important role in linking circulatory systems with oxygen transport. Respiratory proteins act as oxygen carriers by containing a metal ion capable of binding and releasing oxygen. They are often called respiratory pigments because the binding of oxygen results in a color change.

The evolution of respiratory proteins is not a monophyletic story. First, four different types of respiratory pigments have been found in animals. **Hemoglobin**, which contains iron, and **hemocyanins**, which contains copper, are the most widespread forms. **Chlorocruorins** and **hemeryhtrins**, which also contain iron, are relatively rare. These groups are sufficiently different from each other to suggest a different evolutionary history. Furthermore, respiratory proteins within each group may not even share a common ancestry. For example, although hemoglobin is the only respiratory protein found in vertebrates, it is also found in invertebrates (e.g., annelids, arthropods, and mollusks), and there its distribution does not seem to follow any phylogenetic pattern. Not only does it occur in some subgroups of a phylum but not others, but even among closely related species, one may have it while the other does not. Certain lineages losing the ability to make hemoglobin could contribute to this piecemeal pattern, but overall it seems that hemoglobin evolved independently several times. This possibility is strengthened by the fact that cytochrome pigments found in mitochondrial electron transport chains have the same basic structure of hemoglobin (a heme group plus a protein). The other widespread group of respiratory pigments, the copper-containing hemocyanins, are found in the blood of most mollusks and some arthropods. But the hemocyanins of each phyla are also different enough to suggest that they too evolved independently.

It is often stated that hemocyanins (along with the other more minor respiratory pigments) are not nearly as efficient as hemoglobin at transporting oxygen. In actuality, however, it may be difficult to compare different respiratory species in different species. Each has been tailored by evolution to best deal with the oxygen environment and oxygen demands of the species in which it is located. As a consequence, the oxygen-binding properties of both hemoglobins and hemocyanins are quite variable. Yet if this claim of overall superiority is true, it could help explain how vertebrates have become the most metabolically active animals found on the planet. Vertebrates are also the only group that puts its respiratory pigment inside (red blood) cells. Hemoglobin is a small enough molecule that sufficiently high concentrations of free-floating molecules could clog blood-filtering organs such as kidneys or excessively damage blood vessel walls. Placing it within cells could thus allow vertebrates to pack even larger concentrations of hemoglobin in their blood. (Note: Hemocyanin molecules are much larger than hemoglobin, so in a free-floating form may be able to reach higher densities without causing excessive damage. Such higher densities may even help offset its lower efficiency.)

Vertebrate hemoglobin packed inside red blood cells is typically a globulin (3-D) protein composed of four independent polypeptide chains. Each chain enfolds a heme group—a complex molecule with an iron atom at its center. Each of the four subunits can bind one oxygen molecule. Human red blood cells contain around 280 million hemoglobin molecules, so could potentially be loaded with over a billion oxygen molecules.

Hemoglobin's (or any other respiratory protein's) ability to load up with oxygen is, however, only half the story. To assist oxygen transport, hemoglobin must have the peculiar property of picking up oxygen at gas exchange surfaces, such as gills or lungs, and then let it go or dissociate at the tissues. But how could this work? The key is that metabolically active tissues, where oxygen is being consumed, will have lower oxygen concentrations than the environment surrounding gas exchange surfaces. Furthermore, the percent saturation of hemoglobin—that is, the percent of potential oxygen-binding sites that are actually bound with oxygen—varies with the concentration of oxygen in the surrounding medium. Hemoglobin will saturate with oxygen—all potential binding sites occupied—only when the surrounding oxygen concentration rises above a certain level. A typical graph of this relationship, known as an **oxygen dissociation curve** (but it could also be called an oxygen association curve), is shown in Figure 24-11. Two points on this curve are easily predicted: (1) hemoglobin cannot bind any oxygen when none is present, and (2) at some point there will be enough oxygen to essentially saturate hemoglobin. It is the shape of curve in between these two points that influences how effectively it can transport oxygen.

As the name implies, circulatory systems move blood in circles. Blood moves from a gas-exchange surface to the tissues and then back again. This means that the hemoglobin in the circulating red blood cells go back and forth between regions of higher and lower oxygen concentration. As portrayed in Figure 24-12, each time these hemoglobin molecules move past the gas exchange surface, they become almost saturated with oxygen. Yet as they continue their journey past body tissues, they encounter conditions where they cannot continue to hold onto all these oxygen molecules. The percent that dissociate depends on the concentration of oxygen encountered. Again, using Figure 24-12, about 25% dissociation is expected when blood encounters resting tissues (because the oxygen concentration encountered is still high enough that hemoglobin will continue to hold onto oxygen at around 75% of its binding sites). Yet dissociation increases to around 70% when blood moves past metabolically active tissues (because at this lower environmental oxygen concentration, hemoglobin can continue to hold onto oxygen at around 30% of its binding sites). The biological significance of the shape of hemoglobin's dissociation curve is thus that the amount of oxygen delivered to the tissues increases as demand increases. The faster oxygen is being used at any part of the body, the lower the overall oxygen concentration hemoglobin encounters will be, so the greater percent dissociation.

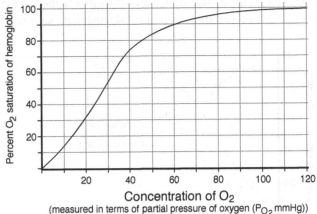

Figure 24-11. An oxygen dissociation curve for (human) hemoglobin.

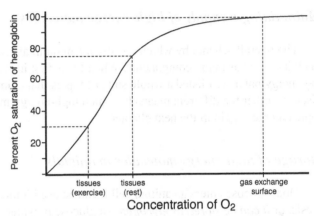

Figure 24-12. An oxygen dissociation curve where the oxygen concentration, hence percent saturation, for a gas exchange surface and both resting and metabolically active tissues are marked. The amount of oxygen delivered from the gas exchange surface to the tissues is the difference between the percent saturation at each location. (See text for more details.)

In reality, there are more details that influence the effectiveness in which hemoglobin (or any other respiratory protein) transports oxygen. Changes in environmental conditions—such as climbing up an extremely high mountain (such as Mount Everest), where oxygen becomes increasingly scarce—could influence the percent saturation at the gas exchange surface. Other changes associated with increasing a tissue's metabolic activity, such as increasing acidity (decreasing pH) and increasing temperature, are also known to decrease hemoglobin's affinity for oxygen. More oxygen will thus dissociate at a given oxygen concentration due to a right shift in the dissociation curve (see Figure 24-13). This is a good feature becausee more oxygen is needed when tissues are active. Furthermore, not all hemoglobins are alike. Different organisms have different types of hemoglobin with different association curves. And, at least in mammals, an individual's hemoglobin changes as it develops. Mammals have fetal hemoglobin early in development and adult hemoglobin later. Fetal hemoglobin has a higher oxygen affinity—the dissociation curve is shifted to the left (see Figure 24-13). This makes sense. A fetus must get its oxygen from its mom's bloodstream, so it needs to have a stronger pull.

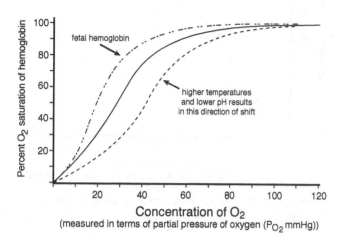

Figure 24-13. Any structural changes (fetal hemoglobin) or changes in environmental conditions (temperature and pH) that influence hemoglobin's affinity for binding oxygen will change the shape of the oxygen dissociation curve. Both the changes shown help organisms transport oxygen. (See text for more details.)

Maintaining a supply of high-energy molecules

The overall scheme by which any organism maintains a constant supply of high-energy molecules to all its cells has many components. When I was first introducing the fundamental nature of maintaining energy balance, I listed a whole suite of topics that animals must deal with. Here, however, I only discuss further the different means by which high-energy molecules are stored between meals. This topic emerges again in the next chapter.

Storage of high-energy molecules in animals

Once glucose enters an animal cell it can be used immediately as an energy source or for biosynthesis, or *it can be stored as **glycogen**—a glucose polymer. All cells are capable of storing at least some glucose, but per unit weight, liver cells store the most. Glycogen can make up 8% of a liver cell's weight. In humans this adds up to the liver being able to store about 100 grams (around 1/4 lb.) of glucose. Enough glucose—400 kcal worth—to meet your body's entire energy demands for somewhere 2 to 6 hours, depending on your activity level. The particularly intriguing aspect of liver cells is that they are only nominally storing glucose for their own use. Instead, they dispense glucose back into the bloodstream between meals for use by other tissues. In fact, liver cells actually preferentially use amino acids as an energy source.

Glucose is also stored in substantial amounts in muscle cells. The amount per cell is considerable less than liver cells—up to 1% glycogen by weight, but due to considerably greater mass muscle cells (as compared to liver cells) the total amount potentially stored is much greater—around 375–400 grams (1600 kcal) in humans. Different than liver cells, muscle cells only store glucose for themselves. Glucose stored in muscle cells is never released back into the bloodstream. Because a muscle cell's energy demands increase rapidly during times of intense activity, a locally stored—hence readily available—energy source seems beneficial. And it is during these activity bursts that muscle cells tend to use their stored glucose to make ATP. Otherwise, muscle tissue preferentially uses fatty acids to generate ATP. (Note: A one-enzyme difference is responsible for the difference between muscle and liver cells. Glucose molecules are cleaved off glycogen by a process called phosphorolysis—in contrast to hydrolysis. In a phosphorolytic cleavage, glucose comes out already phosphorylated, which among other things keeps glucose within the cell. The phosphate must be removed before stored glucose can diffuse back into the bloodstream. Due to differences in genetic regulation, however, the enzyme—glucose 6-phosphotase—that catalyzes the removal of the phosphate is synthesized in liver cells but not in muscle cells.)

Glucose levels within a body also play a role in fat storage. When glucose levels exceed a body's potential for glucose storage, liver cells begin to convert this excess glucose into triglycerides. These endogenously produced triglycerides are then transported to adipose cells for storage.

This conversion of sugars to fats raises an intriguing issue. The excess sugars being converted into fats are in excess only because the body cannot store even more glucose. Why haven't organisms upped their sugar storage capacity? This question is reinforced by the observation that organisms can store much more fat than sugar. For instance, a 70 kg (155 lbs.) human typically has around 11 kg (23 lbs.) of triglycerides in storage—around 15% body fat—with the potential to store much more. Yet the same individual can store only around 0.5 kg (1.1 lbs.) of sugar.

The answer has to do with storage efficiency. Although both fats and sugars can be stored as an energy reserve, triglycerides store much more energy per unit weight. Due to their carbons being more reduced, the complete oxidation of fatty acids yields about nine kcal/g, in contrast to four kcal/g for sugars. Furthermore, triglycerides hydrophobic (anhydrous) nature allows them to be stored in the complete absence of water. In contrast, glycogen associates with water. Each gram of glycogen holds around two more grams of water. Consequently, fats can store nearly *six times* as much energy per unit weight as glycogen.

This conversion of sugars to fats to increase storage efficiency, however, has an important asymmetry in animals. Animals cannot convert fats back to sugars. Two necessary enzymes are missing. This asymmetry poses no real issues so long as fats can be used in all ways that sugars can. As we discuss later, however, that turns out not always to be the case.

Glycogen and triglycerides are well suited for storage because they are chemically inert molecules. In other words, they are couch-potato molecules. They can be acted on, but they will not initiate activity. Most amino acids absorbed by cells are thought to be quickly converted into proteins, and proteins, as we have discussed at length earlier, are a lot like children—it is hard for them to keep their "hands" off everything. Because each protein takes on some unique shape, it may be difficult to assemble a protein that leaves everything alone in the cell—that is, it does not bind to or in any way interact with anything within its reach.

Despite this fact, in Chapter 10 I mentioned that plants are known to produce storage proteins, and I suspect that on closer examination some animal proteins will be found whose primary role is to store amino acids after meals and release them in between. Cells in the liver, kidney, and intestinal mucosa, in particular, build large amounts of proteins that can be rapidly degraded—by lysosomal digestive enzymes—back into amino acids and subsequently released back into the blood. Some of these proteins appear to be enzymes or other functional proteins, so their storage role is secondary. To qualify as a storage protein it would need to not play other roles and presumably would be the first to break apart when the overall amino acid supply is low.

Also like sugars, but somewhat unlike fats, storage of amino acids as proteins can only occur to a point. Each particular cell type has an upper limit to the amount of degradable proteins that it can store. This raises the question: What happens to the excess amino acids once this storage limit is reached?

One option is to remove these excess amino acids from the body. A seemingly reasonable alternative as long as these amino acids have no other potential uses. But that is not the case. Liver cells can deaminate amino acids—that is the amine group (NH_2) can be pulled off—resulting in a keto acid and ammonia (NH_3). The left over keto acid is useful. It can enter somewhere along the glycolysis-Krebs cycle metabolic highway, where it can then be used as a building block in the biosynthesis of glucose, fatty acids, or other types of needed molecules, or it can be used directly as an energy source.

We can now refine the earlier statement that liver cells prefer amino acids as an energy source. Liver cells preferentially oxidize keto acids derived from amino acids to generate ATP. And, given that amino acid deamination occurs in liver cells, this preference appears not to be coincidental. Overall the amount of ATP formed per gram of amino acids oxidized is close to that gained from oxidizing glucose.

The ammonia resulting from amino acid deamination, however, is a different story. Increasing levels of ammonia can be toxic. Animals tend to maintain the pH of their interstitial fluid at a fairly constant level due to the fact that fluctuations in pH can alter protein shape. Excessive amounts of ammonia can alter a body's pH because it has a relatively high affinity to bind with hydrogen ions (forming ammonium ions—NH_4^+). Nervous tissue seems especially sensitive. Deaminating amino acids thus also bears a price. Animals must allocate resources to remove excess amine groups from their body.

Getting rid of metabolic wastes

Interstitial space is, by definition, enclosed by an epithelium. This raises the question of how three-layered animals get rid of excess amine groups, which are commonly called nitrogenous wastes, along with any other potentially harmful molecules that accumulate. The simple answer is that they have an excretory system, which previously I described as a "mesoderm drain." But how does an excretory system work? It cannot just be a hole located somewhere in the epithelium, as all the interstitial contents, good and bad, would come flowing out. Excretory systems have to have some way to selectively pull out wastes without letting the good stuff, or at least too much of the good stuff, also escape.

Kidney logic

The details of excretory systems vary among different types of animals. And these different variations have been tagged with a variety of names. **Nephridia** are found in many invertebrates. They are broken down further into **protonephridia**, which are found in flatworms other than acoelomorph flatworms (that lack a excretory system altogether), and **metanephridia**, which are found in invertebrates such as annelids, mollusks, and arthropods. Insects and other terrestrial arthropods have a different variation called **Malpighian tubules**. Vertebrates, on the other hand, have excretory structures called kidneys, although not all kidneys appear as ours do. In fact during vertebrate history three variations of kidneys have evolved. The most primitive is called **pronephros** and is still seen in some fish and amphibian larvae. It develops in the most anterior position. Next in line is the **mesonephros**, which is the kidney of most fish, some adult amphibia, and many mammalian embryos. It develops more posteriorly. And finally, the **metanephros** is the kidney found in all other adult vertebrates, including us. It evolved last and develops in the most posterior position.

Yet despite this variation, all excretory systems seem to have some fundamental similarities. First, they are generally made up of small tubes or tubules that at one end have some form of internal openings among interstitial fluid, and the other end eventually drains into an external opening. Although these internal openings are big enough for waste molecules to enter, they are typically too small for larger molecules, such as interstitial proteins, to pass through. So the primary urine—what first enters into the tubules—is already a selective representation of interstitial fluid. But that cannot be the whole story, as many useful molecules are also small enough to move into the tubules. Tubes are thus lined with cells able to "recognize" useful molecules or ions and reabsorb them—that is, transport them back into interstitial space. Secondary urine—that which exits the body—is thus disproportionately composed of waste molecules or other molecules currently in excess. Cleaning your room in an analogous way would start with installing a conveyor belt positioned to carry contents from your room through a window to the outside. You then get a friend to come and pick up every object small enough to carry and place it on the moving belt (primary urine). Your job is then to survey all the objects moving toward the window and take back (reabsorb) all those you want to keep. Everything else is thus dumped outside.

Curiously, the preceding scenario is not how you typically clean your room. Instead of an arrangement where you select the things you want to keep, you usually pick out those things you do *not* want and selectively remove them. Why don't excretory systems work in the same way? That is, why do excretory systems work by recognizing good things (and transporting them back) instead of bad things (and transporting them out)? Excretory tubes could be composed of cells able to recognize waste and other harmful or excessive molecules, and then transport them from the interstitial fluid into the tube for removal. The answer may be that the first arrangement is both easier to set up and works better. Selectively bringing in needed molecules has a long history in life, so the needed transporters should already be present. Moreover, recognizing the good is the best way getting rid of anything bad that might show up. Envision, for instance, an organism coming into contact with a novel harmful molecule (perhaps newly made by one of their prey). An excretory system that filters both good and bad molecules from the interstitial space, and then selectively pulls back only what it wants is immediately set up to rid itself of this novel molecule (or any other) that gets inside. The alternative would have to wait until a means to recognize this novel molecule evolved. That could easily be too late. I refer to this backward-seeming scheme of identifying what to get rid of as *kidney logic*.

Animals rid excess amine groups in one of three forms: Ammonia, urea, or uric acid

The various means by which animals rid their excess amino groups involves a trade-off between water loss and energy loss. Ammonia is soluble in water, so an organism cannot remove its excess amino groups as ammonia without also losing water. Furthermore, to keep ammonia at safe concentrations it must be removed in a relatively dilute concentration. To set up a basis for comparison, it takes around 300 to 500 milliliters (mL) of water to safely remove a gram of nitrogen as ammonia. Alternatively, organisms can convert amino groups into molecules that can be removed safely with less water, but such reactions require an expenditure of energy.

This raises the question: How should different organisms be expected to play this trade-off? The answer: It depends on their situation. If energy is more limiting than water, it makes sense to flush excess amino groups out of their body as ammonia. Alternatively, if water is more limiting than energy, it makes sense to increase energy expenditure to conserve water.

Freshwater fish sit at one extreme of this water–energy trade-off. They live in an environment where water is in excess, as it is constantly moving into their bodies. As a consequence, energy is more limiting than water. And as expected they remove their excess amino groups by flushing ammonia out with large quantities of water.

On the other hand, terrestrial organisms are more water limited. So, it would not be surprising to find that terrestrial organisms played this water–energy trade-off differently.

Mammals, for instance, combine most of their excess ammonia with another metabolic waste product—CO_2—to form **urea**. The conversion occurs in the liver where at a cost of three ATP, two amine groups are combined with one carbon dioxide molecule. Like ammonia, urea is still a highly soluble molecule, but it is much less toxic. It takes only around 50 mL of water to safely remove a gram of nitrogen as urea. Consequently, by forming urea the amount of water loss in getting rid of excess amino groups can be reduced 6- to 10-fold (in comparison to removing it as ammonia).

Terrestrial reptiles, birds, and most arthropods commonly expend even more energy to convert some of their excess amino groups first into purines—double-ringed nitrogenous bases—which are then degraded to **uric acid**. In terms of reducing water loss the advantage of forming uric acid is that under acidic conditions it crystallizes and then precipitates out of solution. When this happens in acidic urine, uric acid crystals do not contribute to urine's osmolarity. Water in the urine can thus be more readily reabsorbed back into the body. In fact by forming uric acid, water loss can be reduced to as little as 10 mL of water per gram of nitrogen. Urine in birds and reptiles consists largely of a paste of uric acid crystals. Forming uric acid is also advantageous for birds and terrestrial reptiles because due to its relatively insoluble and nontoxic nature, it can accumulate in eggs without damaging embryos

In birds and reptiles the actual amount of excess amine groups converted to uric acid is known to vary across development and across habitats in ways that make sense in terms of the water–energy trade-off. For example, lizards and snakes switch from ammonia or urea to uric acid during development, and the switch occurs later in species that lay their eggs in moist environments. And as adults, birds that live in habitats with less water are known to remove more of their excess nitrogen as uric acid. Terrestrial birds rid about 90% of their waste as uric acid and 3% to 4% as ammonia. Semiaquatic birds, on the other hand, excrete only 50% as uric acid and 30% as ammonia.

Regulation of the Thermal Environment

The body temperature of functional multicellular organisms on this planet ranges from hovering just above 0°C—just above water's freezing point—to around 50°C (122°F). Some prokaryotes can contend with even higher temperatures, as high as 110°C (around 230°F).

Two basic issues surround an organism's body temperature: maintaining organization, and an organism's capacity to function.

Body temperature can affect organization at either extreme. For example, as temperature increases, the degree of thermal agitation within each cell increases. So, higher temperatures increase the tendency for any cellular arrangement to rearrange randomly—that is to become less organized. On the other hand, if the water within any cell cools to the point that ice crystals start to form, the forming crystals tend to rip apart cellular structures.

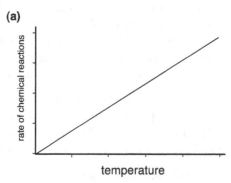

(a)

An organism's functional capacity is dependent on the rate at which chemical reaction can occur, and body temperature can affect chemical activity in two ways. First, there is a positive relationship between chemical activity and temperature. The hotter it is the greater tendency for chemical reactions to occur (see Figure 24-14(a)). Second, enzymes often have a **thermal optimum**. That is, they work best as a catalyst within a fairly narrow temperature range. Catalytic ability thus drops off at temperatures either lower or higher than an enzyme's thermal optimum (see Figure 24-14(b)).

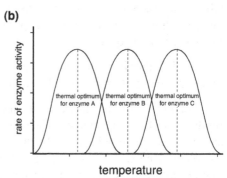

(b)

Furthermore, mutations in a protein gene can affect an enzyme's thermal optimum. Consequently, whenever more than one version of an enzyme exists in a population, and each version has a different thermal optimum, these different versions will be caught in the competition of natural selection. There are two broad expectations of how natural selection would shape the evolution of a species thermal optimum:

• The thermal optima of different enzymes are expected to converge so that they can best work together. In

Figure 24-14. The rate of any chemical reaction within living organisms depends on two factors: (a) the temperature, and (b) the thermal optimum of the enzyme catalyzing the reaction. Different enzymes can have different thermal optimums.

other words, the individuals within the population are expected to evolve toward a single thermal optimum—that is, a temperature at which an organism's performance ability as a whole is maximized. (Note: The presence of an organismal thermal optimum is another example of a shape-performance trade-off. Maximizing performance ability at some temperature precludes an organism from being able to operate well across a broad range of temperatures.)

• The thermal optimum will be a temperature that can be readily attained and maintained during periods in which maximum performance ability is important. Otherwise the thermal optimum would hinder the organism's performance.

Some terms important terms

poikilothermic—organisms that do not maintain a constant body temperature; instead body temperature fluctuates with, or is at least affected by, environmental fluctuations in temperature.

homeothermic—organisms that maintain a constant body temperature despite environmental fluctuations in temperature.

thermal conductance—a measure of how readily heat crosses a barrier. An organism's thermal conduction is thus how easily heat will move from the organism to its environment or vice versa (when the organism and the environment have different temperatures—that is, a thermal gradient exists).

endothermic—any organism that has the combination of sufficiently high internal heat production (metabolism) and/or sufficiently low thermal conductance so that it can be warmer than its environment.

ectothermic—any organism that cannot maintain a body temperature warmer than its environment because it lacks the combination of sufficiently high internal heat production and/or sufficiently low thermal conductance.

Temperature regulation in aquatic organisms—thermal selection

Aquatic organisms with gills (e.g., fish) tend to be ectotherms. Because gills bring an organism's circulating blood continually into close proximity with the water environment, a direct conduit is created for any metabolic heat generated to be carried from the body to the gills and then out into the water. This diffusion is facilitated by the fact that water is a good heat sink. In other words, water readily absorbs heat. You know this from firsthand experience if you have ever been immersed in cold water. Upon immersion you felt yourself cool down quickly. In fact, because water is such a good heat sink, it is virtually impossible for any aquatic organism with gills to maintain a body temperature different than their surrounding environment.

Earlier I argued that an organism's thermal optimum should be a readily attained and maintained temperature. For fish (along with most other aquatic organisms) this means that their thermal optimum should be close to a readily available water temperature. But for a fish to maintain a body temperature near its optimum it will still need to move around. The water in a lake or ocean is not all at the same temperature, and the location of any temperature will fluctuate seasonally and to a more limited extend daily. A mobile fish could, however, maintain body temperature near its optimum if it is equipped with a thermal sensor that allows it to search for and then stay in patches of water at its optimal temperature. Evidence suggests that at least some fish have such a thermal sensor and use it to selective stay in places at or near their thermal optimum. In doing, so these fish are behaviorally regulating their body temperature.

Temperature regulation in terrestrial organisms

Terrestrial animals tend to have thermal optima at fairly high temperatures—at least above 30°C (86°F) and commonly between 35°C (95°F) and 42°C (108°F). The reason for these high thermal optima is probably twofold. First, warmer temperatures always facilitate chemical activity. But perhaps even more important is that activity always generates heat. So for organisms typically surrounded by air—a medium that is not nearly as good a heat sink as water—it would be difficult to get rid of internally generated heat fast enough to maintain a temperature equal to or especially cooler than their environment. The thermal optimum should thus be high enough to be above common environmental temperatures, yet not so high that it would be too difficult or too energetically costly to get body temperature up to the optimum.

Poikilothermic

Because poikilothermic organisms (e.g., reptiles and insects) tend to have relatively high thermal optima, they will commonly have a body temperature lower than their optimum, a situation that at first glance seems disadvantageous. At temperatures below an organism's thermal optimum, its ability to move or be active in other ways is diminished. Loss of motility will certainly impair activities such as capturing food or escaping from predators. But there is a plus side to body temperatures lower than the performance optimum. A lower body temperature is coupled with a lower metabolic rate, which requires less energy to sustain. In other words, diminished capacity is linked with diminished demands. And in many situations the benefits associated with diminished demands may exceed the costs associated with diminished capacity. Consider, for instance, an organism facing a period of food scarcity. During this period, maintaining a high body temperature would be a losing situation if it takes more energy for an organism to maintain an optimal temperature than could be acquired by actively foraging for more food. When faced with this problem, the better alternative would be to lower its metabolic demands and wait out the period of food scarcity by surviving on its current supply of resources.

Being poikilothermic does not constrain an individual's body temperatures to be equal to the temperature of the surrounding air. In some cases poikilothermic organisms can increase body temperature above air temperature endothermically. For example, bumblebees and some moths warm themselves by flapping their wings while stationary to generate heat. The advantage is that once they warm their flight muscles sufficiently, they can fly despite cool environmental temperatures. More commonly poikilothermic organisms raise their body temperatures above air temperatures ectothermically. Generally they do so by basking in the sun. This heating process is facilitated by behaviors such as positioning oneself in a sunny location and assuming certain body postures. Color patterns can also be used to facilitate heat absorption. And once an organism reaches its thermal optimum, its body temperature can be maintained at this level by continually switching back and forth between reducing sun exposure (e.g., moving into the shade) when overheating and increasing sun exposure when cooling down. Such behavioral regulation can maintain body temperature close to optimum for extended periods.

Homeothermic

The advantage of being homeothermic is that the organism is always near its temperature optimum. It is always primed to be active. But homeothermy does have some downsides. For one it can be energetically expensive in cold environments. Despite the fact that significant heat gain can occur ectothermically at times (by basking in the sun, sitting by a fire, or drinking a hot drink), and organisms can do things like increase insulation to reduce heat loss, the bottom line is that endothermic heat generation is a necessary component of being homeothermic. And heat generations "burn up" energy. Furthermore, maintaining a constant balance between heat inputs and heat outputs across a wide range of environmental conditions and across a wide range of activity levels is a difficult proposition.

A closer look at homeothermy

It is crucial to understand the factors that affect an organism's rate of heat loss to begin to understand how organisms balance heat inputs with heat outputs. The rate heat is lost from an organism warmer than its environment depends on an interaction between two factors: the extent of the thermal gradient between an organism's body and its environment, and a body's thermal conductance. Increases in either of these factors will increase the rate at whichh a body loses heat, and vice versa. Accordingly an organism can adjust the rate of heat loss by either moving to a place with a different temperature and/or changing its thermal conductance.

An organism's **thermal conductance** depends on three main factors: the rate and pattern of blood circulation, the degree of surface insulation, and an organism's body size and shape. I discuss all three, making mention of how an organism could facultatively adjust all of them.

Being mostly made of water, blood will readily absorb heat generated in any body tissue. However, this absorbed heat will readily diffuse out of an organism only if it passes through blood vessels near the skin. So, the more extensively blood circulates past the skin, the greater the organism's thermal conductance. Blood circulating at a faster rate further increases thermal conductance because it absorbs heat internally and moves it toward the surface at a faster rate. As you know from personal experience the pattern of blood flow and the rate of blood flow are both adjustable. For example, a flushed face often accompanies exercise. The increased blood flow to surface of your face facilitates the dissipation of the excess heat generated during the increased activity of exercise.

Hair, feathers, and subcutaneous—just beneath the skin—fat can all act as good insulators. That is, they all slow the diffusion of heat. The thicker the layer the better they insulate. Hair and feathers act as insulators by trapping air next to the skin. So one way an organism can quickly change their thermal conductance is by changing the thickness of the air layer trapped by its hair or feathers. How can that be done? Change the angle at which hair or feathers emerge from the skin. Hair or feathers that lie flat will trap less air than when they are raised away from the skin. Raising hair or feathers away from the skin is an event known as **piloerection**. You probably know piloerection better as forming goose bumps. In us, however, piloerection makes little difference—we don't have sufficient body hair. In comparison to hair or feathers, organisms cannot adjust the thickness of their subcutaneous fat layer as quickly, although it is quite common for organisms to adjust this thickness seasonally.

Body size and shape affect thermal conductance because size and shape both affect an organism's surface area to volume ratio. An organism loses heat through its surface, so the greater the surface area per unit volume, the greater the opportunity for heat held within the volume to diffuse to the environment. Facultative adjustment of surface area to volume ratio can occur only if organisms can change their size or shape. To at least some extent, all homeothermic animals can change shape. For example, a common response to being cold is for an organism to become rounder—that is to curl up. Recall that round shapes have the least surface area per unit volume, so they will reduce the rate of heat loss. On the other hand, animals tend to take on a spread-out posture—which maximizes the amount of surface area per unit volume—when they are hot. It would seem that changes in body size could not be made as quickly as changes in body shape. But that is true only if one considers just one body. Two or more organisms can and commonly do snuggle together to effectively make one larger body.

Dealing with cold temperatures

There are always two sides to maintaining a balance: the supply side and the demand side. So to begin to understand how homeothermic animals maintain a constant body temperature when environmental temperatures are considerably lower we need to consider both sides of the issue.

The **supply side** of maintaining a heat balance involves all means by which organisms can adjust their rate of heat production. Organisms have a couple of options:

• *Increase basal (baseline) metabolic rate.* Living organisms are always generating heat because living always involves metabolism, and metabolism always generates heat. The minimum level of heat production will be set by an organism's resting metabolic rate, something known as its **basal metabolic rate**. So the only way an organism can increase its heat production at rest is to increase its basal metabolic rate.

Smaller homeothermic animals tend to have a higher basal metabolic rate—thus a higher base rate of heat production—than larger homeothermic animals (see Figure 24-15). If a constant body temperature is to be maintained, smaller animals need a higher rate of heat production because they will tend to lose heat more readily than larger animals. The reason is that animals lose heat to their environment through their surface, and smaller animals have a larger surface area to volume ratio than larger animals. In fact, the increased opportunity for heat loss as size decreases suggests that there would be

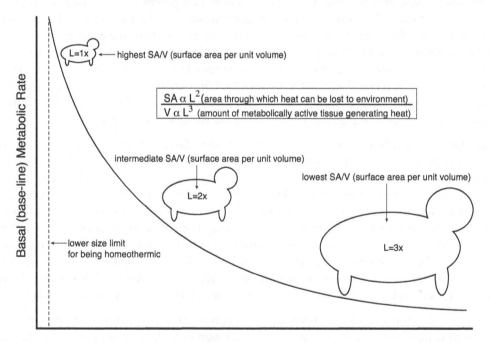

Figure 24-15. The general relationship between basal metabolic rate and body size in homeothermic animals. To maintain a constant and relatively high body temperature in a colder environment, smaller homeothermic animals must significantly increase their basal metabolic rate in comparison to larger homeothermic animals. The reason is that as the relative amount of surface area (area through which heat can be lost to environment) per unit volume (amount of metabolically active tissue generating heat) increases, the amount of heat produced per unit volume needs to increase to keep up with the increased rate of heat loss.

a lower size limit for homeothermic organisms. Below such a threshold, heat lost would be so great that to counterbalance it with heat generation (via an extremely high metabolic rate) would be too great of an energetic demand. The organism could simply not catch and process food fast enough. It turns out that the smallest homeothermic animal is a four-gram shrew. To maintain its high metabolic rate (hence maintain its body temperature) it eats its own body weight in food per day. It will starve in a matter of hours.

• *Increase muscle activity.* Whenever the basal metabolic rate is insufficient, muscle activity needs to increase to augment heat production. This is what shivering is all about. It is a sedentary way of using muscle to generate heat. Alternatively, or in addition, an organism can increase heat production by moving around at a faster pace.

• *Nonshivering thermogenesis.* Some species have brown adipose tissue—also called brown fat. This highly vascularized tissue is made up of adipose cells rich in mitochondria. Brown fat specializes in heat production. It does so by producing large amounts of a protein that uncouples the activity of electron transport chains with ATP formation. In the presence of this uncoupler protein, electron transport from NADH and O_2 proceeds as normal, but the concentration gradient of hydrogen ions formed is then used to generate heat instead of ATP.

Alternatively, the **demand side** of maintaining a heat balance involves all means by which organisms can adjust their rate of heat loss. Several options exist.

• *Behavioral avoidance.* Many species either seek shelter during the coldest times of the day or migrate elsewhere during coldest seasons.

• *Increase insulation (decrease thermal conductance).* Species that live in seasonal environments commonly have seasonal shifts in thickness of their pelage and/or their subcutaneous fat layer.

• *Spatial heterothermy.* Some animals reduce their rate of heat loss by not trying to maintain their entire body at a constant temperature. Instead they maintain their body core at a constant temperature and let more distal parts, like limbs, cool considerable. Countercurrent heat exchangers are an integral part of how spatial heterothermy can help an organism reduce its overall rate of heat loss. Figure 24-16 shows how a countercurrent heat exchanger can minimize the amount of heat lost from the legs of a duck swimming in nearly freezing water.

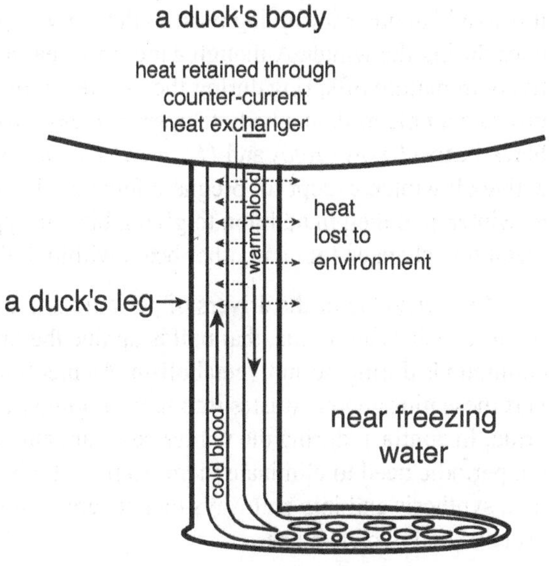

Figure 24-16. A counter-current heat exchanger in that it minimizes the amount of heat lost through a duck's legs when they are immersed in cold water. The arteries carrying blood into a duck's leg are positioned in close proximity to the veins carrying blood back into the body. As a consequence, much of the heat in the arterial blood will move into the colder venous blood and then back into the body.

• *Temporal heterothermy.* Hibernation is a temporary shift from homeothermy. During hibernation an organism's body temperature falls due to the body's thermostat being reset to as low as 20°C or more below normal. As a consequence, the organism's metabolic rate, heart rate, and respiration rate are all greatly depressed, which greatly reduces the organism's energy demand. For example, the body temperature of hibernating ground squirrels can fall within a few degrees of ambient temperature, their heart rate can slow to only one or two beats per minute (in contrast a few hundreds of beats per minute when active), and breathing rate can slow even more to less than one breath per minute (in contrast to hundreds of breaths per minute when active). Hibernation, thus, makes it possible for otherwise homeothermic organisms to survive through periods where acquiring sufficient energy to maintain body temperature would be difficult. Colder environmental temperatures and lower food availability both may contribute to hibernation being the best option. Hibernation is another case of making the best out of a bad situation. Shutting down the ability to be active is not good, but it is better than dying from an energy shortage.

Smaller homeothermic animals are more likely to be caught in this type of energetic crunch than larger ones because smaller homeothermic animals need to maintain a higher basal metabolic rate. So, it should come as no surprise that hibernation, in the strictest sense, is found only in smaller homeothermic animals. The only issue is somewhere along the line you were likely told that bears hibernate, and bears are big animals. Bears do build up fat stores prior to curling up in some protected place—their den—and, for the most part, take a winter long snooze. But whether they actually hibernate has been debated. Clearly aspects of the inner workings change during the winter. Perhaps the most striking is that in addition to not feeding, they neither defecate or urinate the whole time. Furthermore, their metabolic rate is significantly reduced, and on a per gram basis can fall within the range of much smaller hibernating mammals. Yet, in contrast to smaller hibernators, the drastic reduction in body temperature is missing in bears. Perhaps, this is solely a consequence of their decreased SA/V ratio associated with their large size—they just do not lose heat as readily. But if so, then they may have used this to add another intriguing twist to the story— pregnant female bears give birth to and nurse their cubs during the winter. Although a momma bear may not need to be very active to care for her relatively immature offspring during the first few months after birth, it is hard to imagine her being able to produce ample milk at a body temperature close to freezing. And curiously, in contrast to brown and black bears (*Ursus arctos* and *Ursus americanus*, respectively), polar bears (*Ursus maritimus*) remain active all winter, except for pregnant females. These females dig a den in a snowdrift at the beginning of winter, and then in addition to giving birth to typically two cubs, they undergo the same types of metabolic changes found in other bears within their winter dens.

An aside: One of the drivers of periodic urination is the need to get rid of certain nitrogen-based wastes, such as ammonia, that builds up due the breakdown of proteins and other nitrogen-containing compounds during normal metabolism. As mentioned in the previous chapter, mammals typically convert these nitrogenous wastes into urea, a nontoxic water-soluble compound, that can be eliminated in urine. In contrast, during the winter bears are able to reuse these nitrogen compounds and thus avoid the periodic need to eliminate them from the body. Specifically, the excess nitrogen is diverted from urea synthesis and into pathways that generate amino acids, which subsequently can be used to build proteins and nucleic acids.

Although we tend to think of homeothermic animals hibernating during the winter, the duration and periodicity of the hibernating state varies. Some species are season-long hibernators, meaning that their dormant state may last for many months. Uinta Ground Squirrels (*Citellus armatus*) are an extreme example, as they hibernate for eight or nine months. These small mammal season-long hibernators do not, however, remain in a dormant state continually for the entire hibernating period. Every couple of weeks or so a hibernating animal "wakes" from its dormant state to eliminate wastes and perhaps eat some stored food. This waking generally occurs by oxidizing brown fat to generate the necessary heat to increase body temperature.

Due to their extremely high energy demands, some very small mammals and birds encounter periods on a daily basis in which they cannot feed, yet without food they could not continue to maintain a high body temperature and survive. Some species of hummingbirds, which are extremely small homeothermic organisms, are a classic example. They cannot effectively forage for flower nectar in the dark, but could never maintain a high body temperature and last through the night without a meal. To survive, these hummingbirds lower their thermostat every night to reduce their energetic demands. Body temperature is then recovered after every nonfeeding period—every morning in hummingbirds—by the oxidation of brown fat. The fact that these hummingbirds, along with all other hibernating homeothermic animals, can internally generate the heat needed to warm themselves back to their thermal optimum is what makes them different than a strictly poikilothermic organism.

Dealing with warm temperatures

It is easier for an organism to maintain its body at a higher temperature than its surroundings, than it is for it to maintain a body temperature lower than the surroundings. As environmental temperatures approach an organism's thermal optimum, the decreasing thermal gradient makes it increasingly difficult for the organisms to dissipate a sufficient amount of the heat generated by its metabolism. Furthermore, any *activity* aimed at cooling the organism has the downside of increasing the amount of metabolic heat produced. This bad situation becomes worse if environmental temperatures exceed an organism's thermal optimum. At such temperatures heat would have to go against a thermal gradient to be lost. Movement of heat against a gradient can only happen through the evaporation of water. Even with a slightly favorable thermal gradient, heat can only be effectively dissipated through the evaporation of water. The problem with the extensive use of water in cooling is that it is practical only if the water lost can be readily replaced. And hot climates are also often dry climates. So the interesting physiological question is, how do homeothermic organisms persist in hot dry climates? It is a question worth further pursuit.

Some key terms:

tracheal system (in insects) - an extensively branching system of tubes which opens to the outside and is used to deliver oxygen to (and remove carbon dioxide from) cells throughout an insect's body.

spiracles - gated openings (that is, the openings can be closed) along the outside of an insect's body that open into an insect's tracheal system.

poikilothermic - organisms that do not always maintain body temperature at their thermal optimum.

homeothermic - organisms that maintain body temperature close to their thermal optimum despite environmental fluctuations in temperature.

thermal conductance - a measure of a barrier's permeability to the movement of heat. (Thermal conductance will affect how readily heat will move if a thermal gradient—a concentration gradient of heat—exists across the two sides of a surface. An organism's thermal conduction is how easily heat will move from the organism to its environment and vice versa.)

endothermic - any organism that can be warmer than its environment due to some combination of sufficiently high internal heat production (metabolism) and/or sufficiently low thermal conductance.

ectothermic - any organism that cannot maintain a body temperature warmer than its environment because it lacks the combination of sufficiently high internal heat production and/or sufficiently low thermal conductance.

Some study questions:

1. Briefly explain the statement: Part of the task of being a multicellular organism is taking care of all its cells.

2. Explain the concept of a cell's optimal conditions. Use this concept to explain why multicellular organisms commonly attempt to maintain a constant interstitial environment—that is, to maintain homeostasis.

3. What are the various sources of inputs to and outputs from a multicellular organism's interstitial environment? What must be true about these inputs and outputs in order to maintain a constant interstitial environment? What role can a circulatory system play in keeping the interstitial environment the same throughout an organism?

4. In terms of maintaining an input-output balance, explain what is meant by a resource being scarce or being in excess. Explain the following statement: There are always two sides to how an organism could go about maintaining an input-output balance of either a scarce or excessive resource.

5. Suppose that something within an organism is out of balance—that is there is either too much or too little of it. Why does restoring balance to one thing commonly disrupt balance of something else? Provide some examples.

6. We talked about the tradeoff between gas exchange and water loss in terrestrial plants. Discuss each of the following: Why does this tradeoff exist? Why is water loss a problem for terrestrial organisms? How do these plants acquire CO_2 in light of this tradeoff? In what situations do plants make a "choice" that is aptly described by the expression: "making the best of a bad situation"?

7. Maintaining an energy balance is something that organisms must constantly do to survive. Explain how each of the following molecules are involved in an multicellular animal attempt to maintain an energy balance: glucose, fatty acids, amino acids, O_2, CO_2, ammonia (NH_3), and water.

8. Questions about the intake of oxygen: How does a counter-current system increase a fish's ability to acquire O_2 from water? Why are lizards unable to run and breathe at the same time? How might both fish, quadruped mammals, and birds use movement to facilitate the intake of oxygen? What might be the advantage associated with early dinosaurs becoming bipedal?

9. Explain why the intake of oxygen is commonly associated with problems in maintaining water balance. How does the water balance problem differ between freshwater fish and terrestrial organisms?

10. What are the properties of hemoglobin that make it well suited for oxygen transport within an organism? To make sure that you understand how to interpret oxygen dissociation curves, rank—from highest to lowest—the four hypothetical curves in the adjacent figure in terms of the amount of oxygen that they would deliver to the tissues.

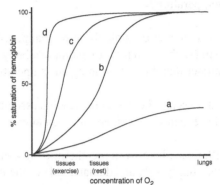

11. What is the connection between maintaining an energy balance, the periodic nature of feeding in multicellular animals, and the capacity to: store food in a stomach, store glucose (as a polymer called glycogen) in the liver and skeletal muscles, and store fatty acids (as triglycerides or also called neutral fats) in adipose cells (located throughout a body's connective tissue)? Provide an explanation as to why organisms tend to store more fat than sugar.

12. Fill out the below table:

molecule:	storage form:	storage location:	storage efficiency	amount potentially stored:
glucose				
fatty acids				
amino acids				

13. Freshwater fish rid nitrogenous wastes in the form of ammonia. Terrestrial animals rid nitrogenous wastes in the form of urea or uric acid. Why do animals have nitrogenous wastes to contend with? Give a plausible explanation as to why these different means of ridding nitrogenous wastes might have evolved.

14. In animals with circulatory systems, kidneys use filtration-reabsorption to remove certain molecules from the blood stream. The alternative would be to selectively pull "unwanted" molecules out of circulation. What is the advantage of using a filtration-reabsorption system?

15. Why do organisms tend to have a thermal optimum? (Note: answer this question in terms of the relationship between enzyme function and temperature.) Use the adjacent graphs to suggest (that is, pick **a**, **b**, or **c**) how an organism's thermal optimum should compare to common environmental temperatures depending on whether it is aquatic or terrestrial. Be sure you can justify your choice. Why does the variation in temperature change between the two graphs?

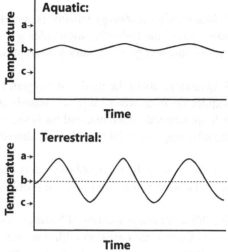

16. Explain why aquatic organisms with gills tend to be ectotherms. How can such aquatic organisms regulate their temperature?

17. Is it ever possible for terrestrial poikilothermic organism (such as a lizard) to maintain a body temperature higher than the surrounding air temperature. Explain.

18. Discuss the costs and benefits associated with being poikilothermic? homeothermic? Is one of these means of temperature regulation overall better than the other? Explain.

19. Consider how homeothermic organism maintains a thermal balance in cold condition from both the supply-side and demand-side of the issue.

20. Explain the relationship between body size, metabolic rate, and the occurrence of hibernation in endothermic/homeothermic animals.

The Workings of Multicellular Organisms: Organism Perspective

Put your two arms out in front of you, and then look at them. Now ask yourself this question: Why do I consider these arms to be *my arms*? In other words, why are these arms part of something that I call me? A common answer to this question is: They are my arms because they are attached to me. But attachment is just not sufficient. Get together with the next person you see, and sew yourselves together. The two of you are now attached, so if attachment is the essence the other person's arms should now be considered your arms. Does that seem right? No, for one simple reason: Although the two of you are now attached, you cannot control the contraction of all the muscles involved in moving the other person's arms. Your arms are yours because you can control their movement.

But what does it mean to control something? To control muscle contraction is to control the rate at which a muscle converts ATP into movement. The faster this conversion takes place the faster a muscle contracts. To apply this idea more generally, *to control* is to be able to adjust the rate at which a processor converts inputs into outputs.

The more basic question that I asked is, what makes an organism an individual? Why are each of an organism's parts (each of which performs different functions) considered to be *parts of a larger whole?* Different tissues and organs unite to form an individual only when each part performs its distinct function at a rate that creates a tightly coordinated division of labor. The fact that optimal rate (the rate best for the performance as a whole) for each part will change as both internal and external conditions change complicates this issue. To meet this challenge, each part would need to be able to be controlled in a way that *responds* to changing circumstance. Stated differently, each part would need to be able *to respond* to changing conditions by adjusting rate appropriately.

The concept of best vantage point and best effector point

To respond requires sensors because each part must have some means to detect when conditions have changed (in a way that requires a rate adjustment). Just the mention of sensors, however, is not a sufficient framework to discuss integrative control of body parts. There also is the question: Where should the sensors be located? Implicit in the preceding scenario is that each sensor would be attached to the body part that it regulates. But is that always the **best vantage point**? In other words, is the best location for a body part to perform an action—the **best effector point,** also the best place to locate the sensor that determines when that action is appropriate (the best vantage point)? Consider two examples:

• For an organism to be able to jump out of the way of a rock hurtling toward it, muscles need to be located within its limbs (as well as other places within the body). Would placing a-rock-is-coming sensors on these same muscles be the best vantage point?

• Consider a multicellular organism trying to maintain internal levels of **X** (where **X** can be anything) at a constant level. As we discussed in Chapter 3, counteracting responses form the basis of any type of homeostatic regulation. The simplest way to set up a counteracting response is to place a negative **X**-sensor (reacts to low levels of **X** by turning up the throttle) on the part that can produce more **X**. But is placing the **X**-sensor right next to the site of **X** production the best location?

The answer in both cases is no.

Muscles can best control body movement if they are located inside an organism. More specifically, in three-layered animals muscles are located in the mesoderm—the body layer sandwiched in between the ectoderm (outer layer) and the endoderm (the layer forming the gut). As a consequence, each muscle's "view" of what is going on outside the organism is blocked. Sensors located on muscles could never detect when a rock is hurtling toward the organism.

Placing an **X**-sensor right next to the site of **X** production will maintain constant **X** levels in the immediate area. But it is not clear what will happen to **X** levels elsewhere in the body. It is analogous to placing a thermostat right next to the furnace. When environmental temperatures are cold, the area close to the furnace would stay around the set temperature, but other parts of the house could dip to temperatures below the set point without initiating a response.

The solution in both of these cases is to put a sensor that detects when a body part should respond (adjust its rate) in a different place than the body part that makes the response. In other words, the body part able to detect when a response needs to be made—generically referred to as a **monitor**—should be separated from the body part that makes the response—generically termed an **effector**.

Of course, not every body part needs a monitor in a separate place. But our focus here is on those that do. And recognize that separating monitors and effectors is a theme that extends beyond the internal workings of organisms. For example, it is quite common for football teams to place some of their coaches high up in the stadium where they can overlook the entire field. This position provides them with a better overall view of what the other team is doing, which can help their team call more successful plays. Similarly, smoke detectors should not be placed close to where individuals sleep. The time to flee from a fire is long before flames are outside the bedroom door.

Despite the potential advantages, monitors and effectors can be separated only if there is an avenue by which the monitor can alter the actions of an effector at a distance. Stated differently, the monitor must have some means to communicate at a distance with the effector. Such communication depends on two things. First, upon detecting the presence of certain conditions the monitor must be able to send out a **signal** that can reach the effector. Second, the effector must have a sensor that detects the signal sent by the monitor (see Figure 25-1). Sensors that detect (pick up) a signal are often called **receptors** or **receivers**. These two requirements are easily seen in the operation of a smoke detector. Once the smoke detector—the monitor—senses smoke, it can warn individuals to leave the building only if the sound produced is loud enough to reach every individual in the building, and each individual has the needed receptors—that is, they can hear.

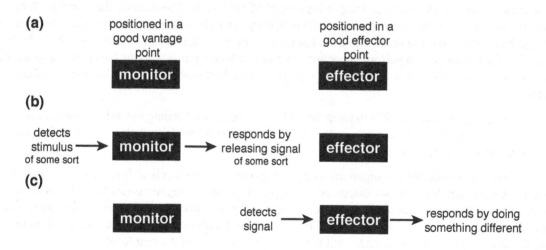

Figure 25-1. Why use signals? A good vantage point (a good location to detect some type of change) and a good effector point (a good location to respond to some type of change) may not be in the same place. This problem can be got around by placing something specialized in detecting some form of change (a monitor) in a good vantage point and placing something specialized in responding to some form of change (an effector) in a good effector point, and then connecting them by some form of signal.

Recognize that although the effector's response is directly triggered by the signal released by the monitor, to be useful an effector's action must respond to the change in conditions (the stimulus) initially detected by the monitor. That is, the change in the effector's actions must act to alter in a meaningful way the change in conditions detected by the monitor. Overall, any such response will fall into one of two familiar categories: counteracting or coacting (see Figure 25-2).

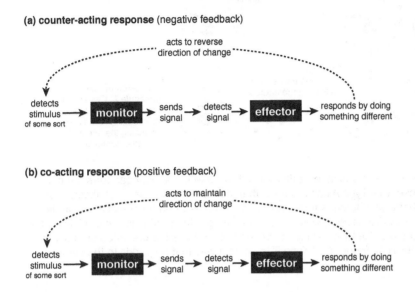

Figure 25-2. Through the use of a signal, the change in conditions (the stimulus) detected by a monitor prods an effector to act differently. This change in an effector's action is a response only if it somehow affects the change in conditions (the stimulus) that started it all. Responses fall into one of two categories: They are either (a) counter-acting or (b) co-acting.

The basic structure of biological monitor-effector responses

To place the monitor-effector idea into a biological perspective is straightforward. Every monitor is a cell or group of cells specialized in detecting some form of change and positioned within the body in a place that offers a good vantage point. The types of change biological monitors detect fall into one of four general categories: **chemoreceptors**—detect the presence (or absence) of certain chemicals, **mechanoreceptors**—detect the push or pull of physical forces, **thermoreceptors**—detect changes in temperature, and **electromagnetic receptors**—detect the presence (or absence) of certain wavelengths of electromagnetic radiation. Upon detecting certain forms of change these monitor cells produce and release signals.

We are used to the idea that signals come in a variety of basic forms. The aforementioned example of a smoke detector uses loud, distracting sounds to communicate potential danger. Police cars use both an auditory signal (a siren) and a visual signal (flashing lights) to get your attention. Perfumes or colognes are chemical-based signals also used to try to get your attention. In contrast, the signals used by one cell within a multicellular organism to communicate with another cell all fall into one class— *they are all chemical signals*.

Every effector is a specialized cell or group of cells positioned within the body such that it can generate an effective response to the stimulus detected by the monitor by changing the rate at which it does something. Detecting the presence of the chemical signal released by the monitor triggers this change in rate. So in contrast to monitors, effectors only have chemoreceptors that detect the presence (or absence) of certain chemicals released from other cells in the body—the monitors. This overall scheme is presented visually in Figure 25-3.

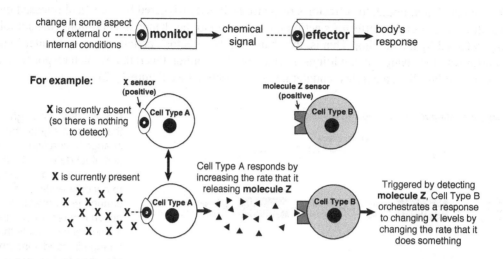

Figure 25-3. The basic scheme by which two different cell types with a sensor can form a monitor-effector based response. Cell Type A has a sensor that monitors the presence or absence of **X** (where **X** could be a chemical, a force, a temperature, or some wavelength of electromagnetic radiation—see text for further discussion), which in turn can trigger the production and release of a specific chemical—**molecule Z**. Cell Type B has a sensor that monitors the presence or absence of **molecule Z**, which in turn can trigger Cell Type B to act in a way that responds to the stimulus detected by Cell Type A.

Using chemical signals raises two issues

Two issues underlie using chemicals as signals in cell-to-cell communication within multicellular organisms. First, how do signals travel from the cell type (or types) acting as the monitor and the cell type (or types) acting as an effector? Second, how is it possible for a chemical signal to affect only a subset of the cells that it reaches? Let's answer the second question first.

Each different type of molecule has a unique shape (because each different type of molecule is a unique arrangement of protons, neutrons, and electrons). So a cell can respond to the presence of any particular signal molecule only if it has a receptor with a matching shape. For example, Figure 25-4 shows four distinctly shaped molecules floating by a receptor embedded in a piece of a cell's outer membrane. Three of the four molecules will have no effect because they are of the wrong shape to bind with the receptor. The presence of any specific receptor depends on whether a cell has assembled the specific protein (or group of proteins) that make up this receptor, which ultimately depends on whether certain genes have been turned on.

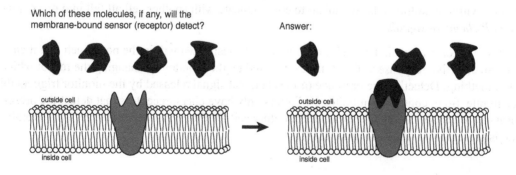

Figure 25-4. Because each type of molecule has a distinct (physical and electromagnetic) shape, the presence of any molecule will only be detected by cells with receptors specific for that molecule.

In terms of how signal molecules travel, diffusion is always an option. Any signal molecule released from a cell will spread out toward regions of lower concentration and trigger a response in any cell with a matching receptor in the signal's path. Of course, the drawback to this travel mode is that diffusion is so slow that it will be effective only when the distance between the monitor and effector is small. The **paracrine system** is the term used to distinguish when chemical signals move by diffusion to cells close by (see Figure 25-5).

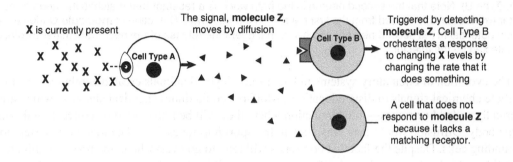

Figure 25-5. The paracrine system. **Molecule Z** is a **paracrine signal** because it moves to target cells (Cell Type B) by diffusion.

Like the paracrine system, the nervous system also relies on diffusion to move signal molecules released by one cell to other cells close by. The difference is that the **nervous system** uses elongated cells called **neurons** or nerve cells to create a link between monitors and effectors (see Figure 25-6). Nerve cells make it possible *to transmit signals long distances quickly to very specific locations*. The key is that sensors detecting a stimulus at one end of a neuron can quickly lead to the release of signal molecules at a distant end of the cell. A within-cell process called an **action potential**, that once started will travel the length of the cell, makes this possible. Detecting a particular form of stimulus (of sufficient magnitude) at one end of the nerve cell triggers an action potential to start. Upon quickly traveling the length of the cell, the action potential in turn triggers the release of a chemical signal from the other end. Depending on their effect, the signal molecules released from one end of a nerve cell are called either **neurotransmitters** or **neuromodulators**. However, acting as a neurotransmitter is the most basic and common role and thus will be discussed the most. Neuron-formed pathways using neurotransmitters can involve only one nerve cell (like seen in Figure 25-6) or more than one nerve cell lining up end to end (see Figure 25-7).

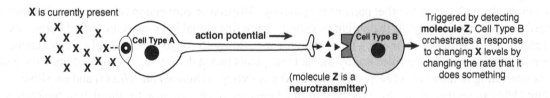

Figure 25-6. The nervous system, where Cell Type A is a nerve cell or neuron. Most of the distance between the monitor (sensor on Cell Type A) and the effector (Cell Type B) is covered by the movement of an action potential down the elongated portion of Cell Type A. Once reaching the end of the cell, the action potential triggers the release of a chemical signal (**Molecule Z**) in close proximity to the receptors on the effector (Cell Type B). So through an action potential a chemical signal is released a potentially long distance from the monitor in a very specific location. The chemical signal, known as a **neurotransmitter**, then moves the short distance to its receptor by diffusion.

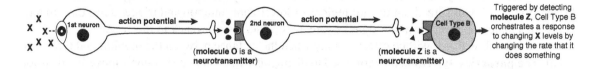

Figure 25-7. A nervous pathway where two neurons connect the monitor (the **X**-sensor) with the effector (Cell Type B). Note that the second neuron in the pathway has a receptor that matches the neurotransmitter (**molecule O**) released from the first neuron (in the pathway). Detection of **molecule O** triggers an action potential in the second neuron, which in turn triggers the release of the neurotransmitter (**molecule Z**) detected by the effector.

The evolution of circulatory systems in larger three-layered animals created another means to distribute chemical signals to distant locations. Monitors could dump chemical signals—which are generically called **hormones**—into circulation where they will be transported by convection throughout the body. Diffusion would then only need to transport hormones from the circulatory system to surrounding cells. Despite the fact that hormones will tend to go everywhere, the response initiated can still be selective because the only effectors to react will be those bearing receptors for the specific hormone released. The movement of chemical signals via circulation is referred to as the **endocrine system** (see Figure 25-8). The monitor cells that release hormones are known as **endocrine cells**. Clusters of like endocrine cells are termed **endocrine glands**.

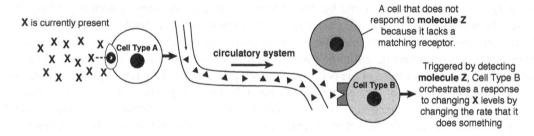

Figure 25-8. The endocrine system. **Molecule Z** is a **hormone** because it uses convection to travel to distant target cells (Cell Type B).

In contrast to animals, the term *hormone* is used more broadly in plants. Basically, it is used for all intercellular signals, despite whether they move from cell to cell via diffusion (through cells), through a convection system (xylem or phloem), or are even released into the surroundings where they can move through the air to other parts of the plant by diffusion or convection (air currents). In other words, some chemical signals that might be called a paracrine signal in animals are called hormones in plants, along with signals moving through a unique pathway (through the air). Calling any chemical signals neurotransmitters is ruled out by the fact that plants lack a definitive nervous system. However, it is interesting to note that a few plants, such as Venus flytraps (*Dionaea muscipula*) and sensitive plant (*Mimosa pudica*) demostrate the type of rapid movements in response to stimulation typically associated with a nervous system. Furthermore, an action potential, similar to those found in nerve cells, are involved in these responses.

Where to go from here?

We have just opened the door to a huge, interconnected topic. Lots of intercellular chemical signaling occurs within multicellular organisms on this planet. This means there are lots of details that have been and continue to be explored. How do cells actually work as monitors? What is the chemical structure of different signaling molecules, and how are these molecules synthesized? What is the structure of different types of receptors, and how do each of these function—specifically how do they trigger certain activities within cells operating as effectors? And this list of questions is just a starting point. But, these types of questions will not be my focus here. Instead I limit my focus to trying to create a framework to understand the nervous and endocrine system in animals. The other major multicellular groups, plants and fungi, along with paracrine signaling anywhere, will not be addressed further.

Nervous System—General Information

What biological function do the nervous systems found throughout animals play? I once asked this question to a group of students. The most common response that I received mentioned something about the brain and its processing of information, such as when we think. Some also mentioned that it is involved in the senses such as sight, touch, or hearing, and it plays a role in generating feelings such as fear, happiness, hunger, and nervousness. Although the sample size was pretty small, no one gave the response that I was looking for—that the nervous system is all about orchestrating an animal's movement (commonly, although not exclusively, in response to a stimulus). Even complex aspects of nervous system function, such as conscious thought, or generating sensations (feelings), are no exceptions. They too are just preludes to motion. For instance, you may use conscious thought to decide what to say in response to a question, but the spoken response is an act of motion. Your lips, your tongue, your vocal chords all must move in precise ways to make the sounds that form the words.

The nervous system, per se, does not move an animal's body. Body movement is powered by muscle contraction. However, the production of movement requires more than just muscles contracting. Consider, for instance, all muscles contracting at the same time. Muscles are commonly arranged antagonistically. That is, if a contracting muscle pulls a limb or some other body part in one way, another muscle is positioned to pull the same part in the opposite way. So, contraction of all muscles tends to result in a tug-of-war between the various sets of antagonistic muscles. As they pull against each other, body parts end up going nowhere. Overall the animal is a quivering mass of tensed muscles. Movement only happens when antagonist sets of muscles contract and relax at different times. Functional movements such as walking, running, swimming, or flying, depend on orchestrating in a coordinated way the contraction pattern of different sets of antagonistic muscles throughout the body. Each step of someone walking, for example, happens only if muscles in both legs, in the torso, and even the arms (to help maintain balance) contract and relax in a coordinated sequence. The nervous system is what coordinates the contractions of different muscles to generate a functional motion.

Why not use hormones?

To set the stage for explaining why the nervous system is well suited to controlling motion, I start by first trying to envision motion being controlled by hormones. Seeing the problems involved helps clarify how the structure of the nervous system makes sense.

Recall that hormones are chemical signals that travel through the circulatory system. As a consequence, every muscle within a body would be exposed to every hormone released. Attempting to coordinate motor activity with just one hormone would thus run into the problem that every muscle would contract in the order that the hormone arrived through circulation every time it was released. Clearly, this would not lead to a diverse array of coordinated motor responses. All muscles would also continue to contract until this muscle-contracting hormone was somehow removed from circulation. Yet, if one hormone will not do, exactly how many hormones would be needed? The easiest answer to envision is one hormone per muscle, so that each muscle could be controlled independently. But organisms have a lot of different muscles. Humans, for instance, have several hundred different muscles; there are twenty-some muscles just controlling each hand's movements. And a single elephant's trunk may have up to 100,000 distinct muscles. One hormone per muscle would thus entail a lot of different chemical signals. And problems associated with the number of different hormones needed are just the tip of the iceberg. How, for instance, is a body supposed to convert different sensory inputs into the release of the right hormones in the right order to get muscles to contract in the right way to generate a coordinated motor response? Furthermore, how is each hormone going to be degraded at just the right time so that each muscle contracts for just the right duration? And for oscillatory movements such as walking, how is this pattern of release and degradation supposed to be renewed over and over with each cycle? These are all mind-boggling questions.

Response time—the time between stimulus and motor response—also becomes an issue with hormones at the helm. Under resting conditions, a spot of blood takes around a minute to make one round trip through a human circulatory system. And with any animal, circulation is going to happen with the time scale of seconds to minutes. So, it may take 10 or 20 or 30 seconds for a hormone released in one part of your body to reach a muscle elsewhere. Time delays in this range would preclude many motor responses from being useful. For example, consider a small rock hurtling at one of your eyes that you see one-half second before impact. Upon detecting the oncoming rock you release a pattern of hormones that initiates the closing of your eyelid. Ten seconds later your eyelid closes, placing a protective cover over your eye. The problem, of course, is that you were nine and one-half seconds late. Escaping from predators and reacting to being tripped are among the many other examples where a quick response time would be useful.

Why use neurons?

In contrast, a nervous system is able to generate quick, coordinated motor responses because it uses elongated cells, called neurons or nerve cells, to create a link between monitors and muscles throughout the body. These so-called nervous pathways can be formed by either one nerve cell, or more than one nerve cell lined up end to end. Nervous pathways are thus analogous to stringing wires between monitors and muscles along which signals can travel. The formation of distinct pathways makes it possible for each body muscle to be individually wired into the nervous system and hence be individually controlled. Plus, action potentials can travel along nervous pathways with relative swiftness. The fastest nerve impulses (action potentials) have been clocked at traveling up to 120 meters/second—approximately 250 mph.

Some curious features

By forming neural connections between specific monitors and effectors, nervous systems can generate "if–then" behaviors called **reflexes**—*if* a certain stimulus is present, *then* a certain response will occur. For example, a neural connection can create a path for a specific stimulus in one part of a body to always activate the same muscle or set of muscles elsewhere.

Although reflexive motor responses are found in all organisms with nervous systems, what makes nervous systems particularly intriguing is that they can also generate all sorts of nonreflexive motor responses.

Consider, for example, the following two scenarios. *Scenario 1*: While running barefooted you step on a thorn. You yell "ouch" in acknowledgment of the pain felt, while reflexively stopping to raise up the injured foot to pull out the thorn. *Scenario 2*: While running barefooted away from a bear you again step on a thorn. Not only do you fail to stop to pull out the thorn, but at the moment of injury you also do not feel any pain.

Note that in each scenario the same stimulus (stepping on a thorn) did not lead to the same response (stopping to pull it out). The logic behind the change in response is easy to see. In terms of survival, continuing to run from the bear is more important than stopping to pull out the thorn. But how can a nervous system orchestrate such a **response hierarchy**—where responding to one stimulus (an approaching bear) takes priority over responding to another stimulus (a thorn impaling the foot)? It is an intriguing question.

Or think about seeing or smelling a slice of pizza (or any other food item that you enjoy eating) sitting on your kitchen counter as you walk by. Do you always respond in the same way? Of course not! If you are hungry, you will probably stop to eat it. If you are full, you may not even notice that it is there. Again, the logic behind the change in response is easy to see. If nutrients are currently in short supply, being attracted to a potential food item makes sense. However, when your nutrient tank is currently full, passing on a food item so your body has time to focus on other challenges also makes sense. Yet again, it is intriguing to consider how your nervous system's response to a food item can change with your body's fluctuating nutritional status.

An animal's response to a stimulus can also change with experience. Such change is called **learning**. Animals seem particularly good at learning to avoid dangerous situations that they had encountered previously. Recognize, however, that for the response to change with experience, the portion of the nervous system orchestrating the response must also change. But what exactly changes, and what triggers this change to happen? And, in contrast to changing response with food, which continues to fluctuate back and forth, how can learning involve a more permanent change?

Going even further, the nervous systems of some animals can even create a time warp. Instead of just reacting to present circumstance, their present behavior can also be influenced by recalling **memories** of the past and **plans** that have been made for the future. In others words, the past, present, and future can all influence current behavior. Although it seems obvious that such ability could help an organism navigate through its life, it is surely not obvious how a nervous system could orchestrate this ability.

The last curious twist of some animal's nervous systems mentioned here is **voluntary motion**, where the basis of a specific body movement has switched from reaction to action. I, for instance, can raise my arm right now not because I am responding to a particular stimulus, but because I choose to. To get some sense of why voluntary motion would be important, conceive of some future plan of action for yourself and then try to imagine carrying out this plan in its absence. It can't be done. The ability to plan and voluntary motion go hand-in-hand.

Nervous System Design

The goal here is simple: To build a basic understanding of how a nervous system, assembled from individual neurons, can do all the things mentioned earlier. Although issues like memories, planning, and voluntary motion will remain elusive, the mechanism underlying response hierarchies, fluctuating responses, and learning are conceptually straightforward. Of course, reflexes are still the place to start, and then we build from there.

To start this discussion, I have created a little organism called *Irv* (because it rhymes with nerve) that has four muscles (see Figure 25-9). *Irv* is completely fictional, as its overall arrangement is not patterned after any real organism. Despite that, we can use *Irv* to explore different ways that neurons can be used to control patterns of muscle contraction, which is to explore how different neuron arrangements can be used to create different motor or behavioral responses.

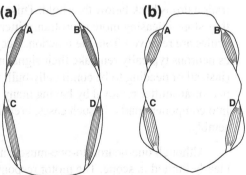

Figure 25-9. Irv's basic shape when all of its muscles are either relaxed (a) or contracted (b).

Reflexive behaviors

Previously we defined reflexes as "if–then" behaviors. Figure 25-10 shows the simplest way that neurons can be arranged to generate such behaviors. In both cases *Irv* has four neurons, each one innervating (connecting with) one of the four muscles. The two arrangements differ only in which muscle each neuron is hooked to. In either case, stimulating any of the four neurons to fire will lead the contraction of the innervated muscle.

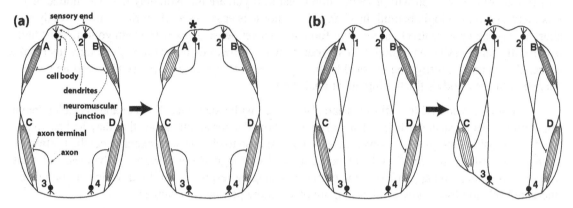

Figure 25-10. Two different four neuron arrangements in Irv that generate reflexive behaviors. In each case, the muscle that contracts when **neuron 1** is stimulated (indicated by an asterisk) is shown. See text for more details.

Let me add some more detail. The sensory-end of each neuron is located in a distinct location within *Irv*. The branches on this end that have grown out from the **cell body** (where the nucleus is located) are called **dendrites**. From this vantage point, each sensory-end continually monitors whether the stimulus it is sensitive to has reached a threshold level. A **stimulus**, by definition, is some form of chemical or energy. What form of stimulus is monitored by each neuron depends on the type of sensors present. Whenever the stimulus for any neuron rises above threshold, an action potential is triggered that travels the length of this elongated cell. The entire region of any neuron that conducts an action potential is called the **axon**. Upon reaching the end of the axon, known as the **axon terminal**, the action potential triggers the release of a chemical signal that plays the role of a neurotransmitter. The many copies of the neurotransmitter released begin to move by diffusion across the space in between the axon terminal and the muscle cell or cells that it innervates—a space generally known as the **neuromuscular junction**. Located on the muscle side of this junction are receptors able to bind with the neurotransmitter. Once the number of these signal molecules binding to muscle-bound receptors reaches a certain threshold, an action potential is triggered that spreads across the muscle cell (or connected cells) and initiates contraction. Contraction in turn stops once the neurotransmitter concentration drops back below threshold. This will occur when the neuron stops firing action potentials and thus stops releasing more neurotransmitter, and a sufficient number of already released signal molecules are removed from the junction. Recycling plays an important role in neurotransmitter removal, as neurons typically reuptake their signal molecules from the junction so that they can be used again (instead of needing to be continually built from scratch). Many neuromuscular junctions also speed up neurotransmitter removal by having many copies of an enzyme present that catalyzes its breakdown into component parts. In such cases, breakdown products can be brought back into the neuron for reassembly.

Although one-neuron-to-one-muscle arrangements will generate reflexive behaviors, they are clearly limited in scope. The motor response to any single stimulus could involve only one muscle. And, each muscle could only be involved in generating a response to one stimulus. The next task is thus to expand the design of reflexes to get around both these limitations.

A little more information: Signal molecules released from a neuron's axon terminal are called neurotransmitters whenever they play a direct transmission role—that is, they act to connect or transmit the occurrence of an action potential on a presynaptic neuron to the occurrence of an action potential on a postsynaptic cell (which in this case is a muscle cell). The details of how a neurotransmitter influences whether a postsynaptic cell fires an action potential involve binding to receptors that trigger the opening of ion channels (which will be discussed more later).

Reflexes involving more than one muscle

In Figure 25-11 the number of neurons in *Irv*'s nervous system is reduced to three, yet each of the four muscles is still hooked up. **Neuron 3** now branches so that it connects to two muscles (**A** and **D**). Branching brings up another curious aspect of action potentials. So far, an action potential has been presented as this mysterious thing that once started will travel the length of the cell. Let me build on the mystery. An action potential can travel the length of a neuron (or any other cell with the right machinery), regardless of the distance because it moves along without any diminishing of speed or strength. Action potentials are thus unlike an object, such as a ball rolling along a floor that once started will always slow to a stop with time due to friction and other forms of resistance. Furthermore, when encountering a branch point, an action potential can proceed down each branch without any loss of strength or speed. So, whenever neuron 3 is sufficiently stimulated to start an action potential, two muscles (**A** and **D**) will be involved in a single reflexive motor response. Moreover, the motor response involves a specific contraction sequence. Because the action potential has a longer distance to travel to get to **muscle A**, **muscle D** will begin to contract first.

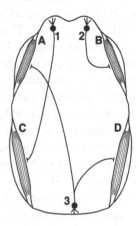

Figure 25-11. A nervous design where one of the three reflexive responses (stimulating **neuron 3**) will involve more than one muscle.

Different reflexes involving the same muscle

In Figure 25-12 the number of neurons in *Irv*'s nervous system is increased to six. Obviously, the only way that six neurons can each innervate one of four muscles is for two muscles to be innervated twice. The new dimension in motor responses added is that different stimuli can trigger the same reflexive response. For example, stimulating either **neuron 1** or **neuron 5** will cause **muscle A** to contract.

Combining both themes: Nerve nets

Reflexes in animals often combine both of the preceding twists—that is, they commonly involve more than one muscle, and individual muscles can be involved in more than one reflex. For example, a poke to a radially symmetric sea anemone, or another type of Cnidarian, is typically followed by a wave of muscle contractions that radiate out through the body from the location of the initial stimulus. A poke in a different place, and the same type of radiating wave starts from this new location. Each reflex involves lots of contracting units, and the same ones can be involved in each reflex, they just contract in a different order.

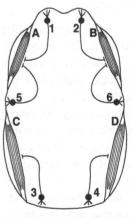

Figure 25-12. A nervous design where different stimuli can lead to the contraction of the same muscle.

Figure 25-13 wires *Irv* in two ways that would mimic this behavior. Stimulation of any of the six sensory spots will lead to all four muscles contracting, starting with closest muscle (or muscles) and radiating out from there. Yet despite orchestrating similar behaviors, these two designs are totally different. In (a), each of the six neurons sends branches to each of the four muscles. This is a simple idea that when put into practice leads to what appears to be a tangled, complicated mess. And given that real organisms typically have a much larger number of muscles and neurons than *Irv*, it is no wonder that this design does not show up in nature. It seems impossible to imagine how an organism could actually grow branches from each neuron to every contraction unit. The appearance of the design in (b) is much simpler. It is a network of neurons that connects each sensory site with each muscle. However, a new twist needs to be added for this design to work. Many of the neurons would need to be nonpolar, meaning that there is not a distinct sensory-end and transmitting end. Instead, from any innervation site, action potentials can either be started (and subsequently spread throughout the neuron) or transmitted. This allows an action started anywhere to spread throughout the network.

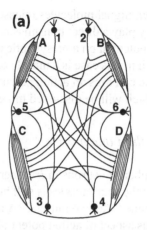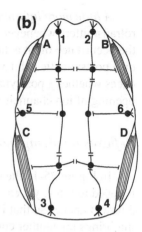

Figure 25-13. Two nervous system designs that would orchestrate the same motor response—any perceived stimulus would lead to all four muscles contracting, starting the with closest and radiating out from there. The second design (b) shares some similarities with the organization of Cnidarian nervous systems. See text for further discussion.

A little more information: All the neuron-to-neuron connections in Figure 25-13(b) are drawn with distinct gaps, which would need to be spanned by a chemical signal. For at least the nonpolar neurons, this is likely inaccurate. Nonpolar neurons likely rely on electrical transmission—where an action potential can continue across neurons, in either direction, without any chemical signal. All that is required is to physically link adjoining neurons together by gap junctions. And because, by their nature, action potentials have no preferred direction, once crossing at any junction it will spread to the rest of the neuron.

Like Figure 25-13(b) the Cnidarian nervous system is a network of neurons, called a **nerve net**. Many of the neurons are nonpolar, allowing neural impulses to radiate out in all directions from where a stimulus is first perceived. Despite their relative simplicity, there are several means by which nerve nets can orchestrate more than one type of behavior. First, a small stimulus, such as a small food particle touching one tentacle may generate a response only within that tentacle, whereas a bigger stimulus (one triggering more sensors) would cause more of the body to react. Second, different nerve cells within a nerve net conduct impulses at different rates, so one stimulus can lead to a series of responses that occur at different time intervals. For instance, in sea anemones, prodding one tentacle can provoke a twofold protective response. First, the mouth closes and the tentacles retract, then some seconds later the muscles in the body wall contract causing the entire body to shorten. Third, some Cnidarians have more the one nerve net, and each net can orchestrate different behaviors. For example, some jellyfish use one nerve net to coordinate the rhythmic, symmetric contractions of swimming, whereas a second nerve net coordinates feeding behavior.

Combining both themes: forming ganglia

The next twist to be explored is a nervous system design that can generate a greater diversity of reflexive responses than a nerve net, but still make it possible for responses to involve more than one muscle and for different reflexes to use the same muscle. Figure 25-14 shows two designs that not only accomplish this, but also orchestrate the same behaviors.

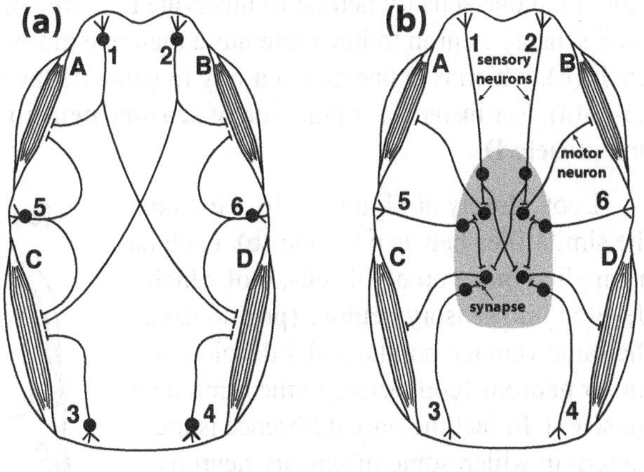

The first design uses the same logic as Figure 25-13(a). Each neuron creates a direct connection between its sensory-end, and the muscle or muscles that it will trigger to contract. For instance, stimulating **neuron 1** would lead to **muscle A** and **muscle D** contracting (with **muscle A** contracting first), whereas stimulating **neuron 5** would lead to **muscle A** and **muscle C** contracting. But also like Figure 25-13(a), this design is not found in nature. It is hard to imagine how an organism could wire itself in this way, especially as the connections that need to be formed become more wide-ranging and diverse.

Figure 25-14(b) introduces the idea of a **ganglion**. Ganglia (the plural of ganglion) have an underlying wiring simplicity, which

Figure 25-14. Two nervous system designs that would would orchestrate the same motor response. In (a) each neuron forms a direct connection with one or more muscles. The concept of a ganglion is introduced in (b). The light gray region demarks the boundary of the original cluster of neurogenic cells. As these cells grow out projections during development, the ganglion remains the location of each neuron's cell body, and is also where between neuron synapses form. See text for further discussion.

arises from their developmental history. A ganglion starts as a cluster of neurogenic cells—that is, cells with the capacity to develop into neurons. During their development, elongated projections extend out from each cell. In some cells, the sensory-end grows out past the cluster, eventually taking up a specific vantage point to monitor the occurrence of whatever stimulus it is set up to detect. Such cells are called **sensory neurons**. In contrast, the axon-terminal-end grows out from the cluster in other developing neurons, eventually connecting to (forming a neuromuscular junction with) a muscle cell (or cells). These cells are called **motor neurons**. (Note that due to these developmental differences the cell body in sensory and motor neurons is positioned differently (see Figure 25-15).) A complete circuit between monitor and effector forms whenever, within the confines of the ganglion, an axon-terminal-end of a sensory neuron extends to within close proximity of the sensory-end of the motor neuron. The space in between two neurons is called a **synapse**. Functionally synapses work in the same way as neuromuscular junctions. Whenever a sensory neuron is sufficiently stimulated to fire an action potential, it spreads to the axon terminal, where it prods the releases of a chemical signal (a neurotransmitter) into the synapse. Receptors able to bind with (detect) the specific neurotransmitter released are located on the sensory-end of the motor neuron. Once the amount of bound receptors reaches some threshold, an action potential is triggered in the motor neuron that proceeds to the neuromuscular junction.

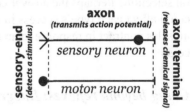

Figure 25-15. While having the same functional regions, the cell body is positioned differently in sensory and motor neurons. Although not drawn, branches or dendrites commonly extend from the cell body of a motor neuron, and become part of the sensory-end.

The close proximity of sensory and motor neurons within a ganglion opens the door for a sensory neuron to potentially innervate (form a synapse with) any motor neuron emerging from the same ganglion. Recognize the significance: *A connection can be forged between any vantage point formed within a ganglion (by the extension of a sensory neuron) and any muscle cell connected by a motor neuron extending from the same ganglion.* Furthermore, the arrangement of connections between sensory and motor neurons within a ganglion is potentially flexible. Synapses make it possible for more than one sensory neuron to innervate the same motor neuron, and branching makes it possible for a sensory neuron to innervate more than one motor neuron. All these options are shown in Figure 25-14(b), which is connected in a way to generate the same behavioral (motor) responses as Figure 25-14(a). For instance, stimulation of **sensory neuron 1** will still trigger the contraction of **muscle A** and **muscle D**.

Look closely at Figure 25-16. First note the similarities between (a) and (b). Each has a ganglion made up of 10 cells, 6 of which develop into sensory neurons (positioned at the same vantage points) and 4 develop as motor neurons (connecting to the same four muscles). In fact the only difference is the pattern in which some of sensory neurons connect to motor neurons within the ganglion. But that brings us to the punch line: *Small changes in wiring within a ganglion can make a big difference in how an organism responds to different stimuli.* In other words, how an organism behaves depends on how it is "wired." For example, in (a) activating **sensory neuron 2** will cause **muscle B** and **muscle C** to contract, whereas **muscle B**

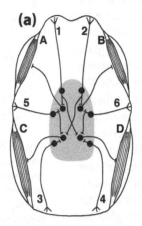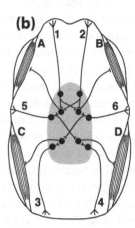

Figure 25-16. Two nervous system designs that, due to some within ganglion wiring differences, can have different motor responses to the same stimulus.

and **muscle A** will contract in (b). Similar differences occur when **sensory neurons 1**, **5**, and **6** are also stimulated.

Let's add a little biology to this scenario. Suppose that (a) and (b) are two types within the same population, and their wiring differences are heritable. Would these differences be scrutinized by natural selection? Perhaps the answer could be no, but it is hard to imagine. Clearly, behavioral differences could affect each type's success in negotiating the reproductive obstacle course. For example, which muscles contract in response to an approaching predator could surely make a difference in escape success.

Going beyond reflexes: Integration

In bilaterian nervous systems, ganglia are a basic unit of organization. In other words, bilaterians such as humans, dogs, fish, insects, earthworms, and snails all have ganglia. As a consequence, ganglia will be the centerpiece of the rest of our discussion. But to begin to move beyond reflexes, one more piece of ganglion organization needs to be added—inhibitory interneurons. This will lead us to integrative nervous pathways, which make it possible for nervous systems to orchestrate much more flexible responses.

Adding inhibitory interneurons

So far, neurogenic cells within a ganglion either extend their sensory-end or axon-terminal-end out beyond the ganglion to form sensory neurons or motor neurons, respectively. There is another possibility—becoming an interneuron. Interneurons are the neurons within a nervous pathway positioned in between sensory and motor neurons (see Figure 25-17).

Interneurons can be used to span distances between sensory and motor neurons and thus help make new connections possible. For instance, some interneurons, known as projection interneurons, form connections between different ganglia within an organism. But here I focus on interneurons that change the nature of the signal being transmitted. So far, the interaction at synapses, including the neuromuscular junction, has been *excitatory*. The chemical signal released into the synapse by the presynaptic neuron, in combination with the nature of the receptors on the postsynaptic cell, act to increase the chance that the postsynaptic cell will fire an action potential. An interaction at a synapse can also be *inhibitory*. A neurotransmitter is still released into a synapse, but the signal molecules bind to receptors that act to decrease the chance that the postsynaptic cell will fire an action potential.

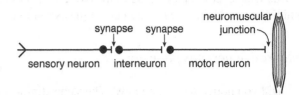

Figure 25-17. A neural pathway that includes the three basic types of neurons found in ganglion-based nervous systems.

Let's follow what would happen if the interneuron in Figure 25-17 is inhibitory. Sufficient stimulation of the sensory neuron would trigger the release neurotransmitter into the first synapse (between the sensory neuron and interneuron), which due to its excitatory nature could trigger an action potential in the interneuron. This in turn causes the release of a neurotransmitter into the second synapse (between the interneuron and the motor neuron). But in contrast to the first synapse, this chemical signal binds with receptors on the motor neuron that act to inhibit its ability to fire an action potential and thus trigger muscle contraction.

Doesn't something seem wrong with this scenario. Why go to all the trouble of telling a motor neuron not to fire when, already at rest, it was not going to fire anyway? One does not need to tell a sleeping dog to go lie down.

Irv can help provide some clarification. Suppose that for some biological reason, *Irv* would do best if it behaved in the following ways: contract **muscle A** when **sensory neuron 1** is stimulated; contract **muscle B** when **sensory neuron 2** is stimulated; and still only contract **muscle B** when both **sensory neuron 1** and **2** are stimulated. The design shown in Figure 25-18(a) would enact the first two, but not the third. Stimulating both neurons would result in both muscles contracting. It is just two simple reflexes going off at the same time. What is missing is a way to say no to one muscle, while still saying yes to another. The design in Figure 25-18(b) shows how an inhibitory interneuron can make that possible. When **sensory neuron 1** fires, it releases a neurotransmitter that binds to receptors on the **muscle A's motor neuron** that have an excitatory effect. When **sensory neuron 2** fires, it does

two things. First, it stimulates **muscle B's motor neuron** to fire. Second, it stimulates the interneuron to fire, which in turn releases a neurotransmitter that binds to receptors on **muscle A's motor neuron** that have an inhibitory effect. The question that remains is: Will **muscle A's motor neuron** fire an action potential when both sensory neurons are stimulated at the same time? The answer depends on three things: (1) the magnitude of the excitatory effect (a positive number), (2) the magnitude of the inhibitory effect (a negative number), and (3) the threshold amount of stimulation needed for this motor neuron to start an action potential (which by definition must be a positive number). Specifically, when the two effects are added together, does the result exceed the motor neuron's threshold? Clearly, this would not

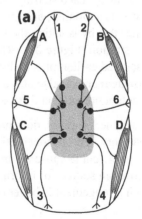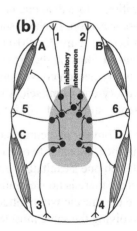

Figure 25-18. Two nervous system designs that, due to the introduction of an inhibitory interneuron in (b) will respond differently to the simultaneous stimulation of sensory neurons 1 and 2. See text for further discussion.

be true whenever the magnitude of the two effects is similar (or the inhibitory effect is even greater). Inhibition would, in essence, cancel out the excitation.

Integrative nervous pathways

Did you notice something new? The same stimulus did not always lead to the same response. Specifically, **muscle A** did not always fire when **sensory neuron 1** was stimulated. This newfound flexibility is a product of **muscle A's motor neuron** being part of an **integrative nervous pathway**.

Integration occurs whenever the action or inaction of an effector is influenced by the perception of more than one monitor. In other words, more than one source of "information" is consulted in the "decision" concerning the activity of the effector. Mechanistically, integration is possible whenever the signals released from more than one monitor somehow converge en route to a single effector (see Figure 25-19(a)). The site of convergence must then act as an **integrating center**, which is the place where a decision is made. It does so by performing two functions. First, it in some way totals up the strength of all the incoming signals from the various monitors. Second, it must have an internal threshold against which to compare the total strength of the incoming signals.

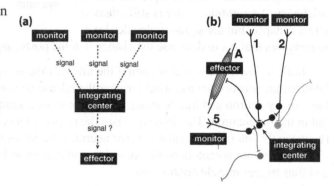

Figure 25-19. (a) The basic design of an integrative pathway. (b) How a convergent nervous pathway generates this basic plan. (Note: The pathway used came from the previous illustration. Specifically, it focuses on the pathways that converge on muscle A's motor neuron. The light gray regions represent connections to other motor neurons.) See text for further discussion.

Only if the total signal strength is greater than this threshold will the effector generate a response. Alternatively, the signal stops at the integrating center if the total signal strength is less than the threshold. In other words, any integrating center within an integrative pathway acts as a summing center that is always comparing the current total against the internal threshold

Ganglia-based nervous systems can readily establish the type of convergence necessary for integration. More than one nervous pathway, each starting with a sensory neuron, can innervate a single motor neuron. Each sensory neuron is a monitor, and the muscle hooked to the motor neuron is the effector. Figure 25-19(b) illustrates this by isolating the pathways that converge on **muscle A's motor neuron** found in the previous illustration (Figure 25-18(b)). This includes the sensory neuron and inhibitory neuron convergence discussed earlier, plus it also brings **sensory neuron 5** into the mix. The sensory-end of **muscle A's motor neuron** can also acts as the **integrating center**. Only if it is sufficiently stimulated will it fire an action potential and subsequently trigger muscle contraction.

Converging neural pathways alone, however, does not guarantee that integration is occurring. For instance, consider two or more sensory neurons innervating the same motor neuron, and the magnitude of each one's excitatory effect is sufficient to cause the motor neuron to fire. Although there is convergence, there is no weighing of different sources of information—anytime any of the sensory neurons fire the muscle will contract. Such arrangement is better described as more than one reflexive pathway involving the same muscle.

In contrast, an integrative pathway is subtler. Whether a muscle contracts or not depends on the current combination of stimuli being detected and routed through the integrating center. Convergent pathways are thus also integrative only when one or both of the following conditions are met: (1) In at least some of the converging excitatory neurons, the magnitude of their excitatory effect is *sub-*

threshold—that is, its affect alone is not large enough to trigger the postsynaptic neuron to fire an action potential. Muscle contraction will thus depend on the simultaneous stimulation of enough (at least more than one) *subthreshold* excitatory neurons to reach the postsynaptic neuron's threshold. (2) Converging neurons come in both possible flavors—some are *excitatory* and others are *inhibitory*. When inhibitory interneurons are present, the firing of the postsynaptic neuron depends not just on the tally of excitatory effects exceeding threshold, but also on the total excitation minus the total inhibition exceeding threshold.

Use Figure 25-20 to help clarify the idea of integration further. Here I added values to the same integrative pathway shown in the previous figure. There are a few things, in particular, to note. First, both scenarios demonstrate the absence of a direct relationship between the firing of an excitatory sensory neuron and muscle contraction. For example, if **sensory neuron 1** fires, whether **muscle A** contracts *depends on* what other combination of neurons are firing or at rest. Second, the concept of a subthreshold effect is introduced in Figure 25-20(b). The effect of either excitatory sensory neuron (**1 and 5**) is not large enough to trigger muscle contraction by itself. And finally, note that changes in the magnitude of effects of different neurons can greatly alter the pattern of behavioral responses—that is, what firing patterns of the three sensory neurons lead to muscle contraction? Four of the different stimulation patterns considered lead to muscle contraction in Figure 25-20(a), although that is true

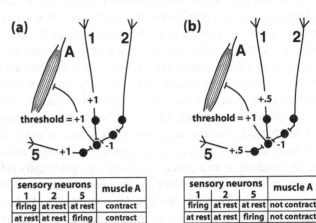

sensory neurons			muscle A
1	**2**	**5**	
firing	at rest	at rest	contract
at rest	at rest	firing	contract
firing	at rest	firing	contract
firing	firing	at rest	not contract
at rest	firing	firing	not contract
firing	firing	firing	contract

sensory neurons			muscle A
1	**2**	**5**	
firing	at rest	at rest	not contract
at rest	at rest	firing	not contract
firing	at rest	firing	contract
firing	firing	at rest	not contract
at rest	firing	firing	not contract
firing	firing	firing	not contract

Figure 25-20. The same integrative nervous pathway as the previous illustration (Figure 24-19(b)) with values added for the the effect of each converging pathway (positive is excitatory and negative is inhibitory), along with the motor neuron's threshold. In contrast to (a), in (b) the excitatory values of each innervating sensory neuron (1 and 5) are subthreshold. The tables below keep track of which of the six patterns of stimulation considered will or will not result in **muscle A** contracting.

for only one stimulation patterns in Figure 25-20(b)—only when both excitatory sensory neurons fire simultaneously, and the one inhibitory interneuron is not firing.

The magnitude of effects

By introducing the idea that some interactions between a presynaptic and postsynaptic pair of neurons can be subthreshold whereas others can meet or exceed threshold, I have introduced the idea that the magnitude of effect can vary. This variation can come in two forms: (1) the strength of interaction at any one synapse, and (2) the number of synapses. Let's discuss each in turn.

Regardless of whether it is stimulatory or inhibitory, the strength of the interaction at any synapse boils down to the number of receptors on the postsynaptic neuron bound by a neurotransmitter released by the presynaptic neuron times the overall effect of each bound receptor. Differences in the amount of neurotransmitter released, the number of receptors present, and/or the sensitivity of each receptor could thus make a difference in the magnitude of the effect. For instance, the release of more neurotransmitter by the presynaptic neuron, and/or an increase in the number of receptors on the postsynaptic neuron creates the opportunity for more binding to occur. The strength of any synapse is also influence by its position. All else being equal, the closer a presynaptic neuron forms a synapse to the postsynaptic neuron's **axon hillock** (the place where an action potential starts) the stronger its effect.

Different than an action potential, the strength of a synapse's effect decreases with distance. So, the further a synapse's distance from where an action potential starts, the less influence it can have on starting an action potential. Although important, this is not an idea that will be developed further here.

So far, axonic branching has been the means for a single neuron to forge a synapse with more than one muscle or neuron. But an axon can also branch one or more times with each axon terminal innervating the same postsynaptic neuron. In other words, through branching, a presynaptic neuron can form more than one synapse with a postsynaptic neuron. Given that an action potential, once started, moves down each and every branch with equal strength, each axon terminal has the potential to release the same amount of neurotransmitter. The number of axonic branches is thus another way that the magnitude of the effect of a presynaptic neuron can vary. A presynaptic neuron with a single axonic branch, resulting in two axonic terminals, can potentially release twice as much neurotransmitter and thus have twice the effect on the postsynaptic neuron, as one that does not branch. And even more branches means even more axon terminals, and thus an even greater effect.

Figure 25-21 illustrates how axonic branching can influence an integrative pathway. This figure uses the same basic pathway and the same value per synapse (+0.5) for the two excitatory sensory neurons (**1** and **5**) as Figure 25-20(b). The one difference is that **sensory neuron 5** now branches to form three synapses with **muscle A's motor neuron**. Note (by comparing the response tables in both figures) that in some cases this one wiring change generates different motor responses to the same stimulation pattern.

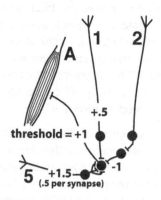

sensory neurons			muscle A
1	2	5	
firing	at rest	at rest	not contract
at rest	at rest	firing	contract
firing	at rest	firing	contract
firing	firing	at rest	not contract
at rest	firing	firing	not contract
firing	firing	firing	contract

Figure 25-21. The same integrative nervous pathway, with the same values per synapse, as Figure 24-19(b)), except that due to branching **sensory neuron 5** now forms three synapses with **muscle A's motor neuron**. The table below keeps track of which patterns of stimulation will or will not result in **muscle A** contracting.

Integrative organisms

It is time to summarize. Using all the tools that we have discussed so far, *Irv*'s ganglion was "wired" in three different ways (see Figure 25-22). In all three versions, the four motor neurons are part of an integrative pathway. More than one neuron converge on each motor neuron's sensory-end, and these neurons are both *excitatory* (sensory neurons) and *inhibitory* (interneurons) in effect. Each version, however, differs in the pattern by which sensory neurons and interneurons connect to the motor neurons within the ganglion.

The flexibility of response created by integrative pathways is evident in each version of *Irv*. Which of the muscles connected to a stimulated sensory neuron will contract depends on what other sensory neurons within the converging pathway are also stimulated. Moreover, the idea that wiring differences can lead to behavior differences is also evident. Of the six stimulation patterns examined, each version of *Irv* has at least some differences in motor response. And the wiring differences do not need to be large. The only difference between *Irv* (b) and *Irv* (c) is that in *Irv* (c) the axonic branch of **sensory neuron 1** and **sensory neuron 2** that goes to **muscle D's motor neuron** and **muscle C's motor neuron**, respectively, has branched again to form two synapses. Yet in two of the six stimulation patterns examined, *Irv* (c) responds differently than *Irv* (b).

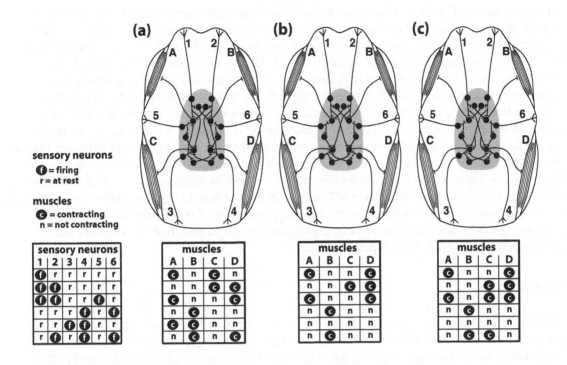

Figure 25-22. Three different versions of *Irv* wired as an integrative organism—that is, while the within ganglion connections are different, each motor neuron is part of an integrative pathway. The tables beneath each version of Irv keeps track of which muscles will contract under six different patterns of stimulation. The following values were used to calculate the motor response: (1) each sensory neuron's axon terminal contributes a +1 value toward stimulating the postsynaptic neuron, (2) each interneuron contributes a -1 value toward inhibiting the postsynaptic neuron, and (3) the threshold level of stimulation for each interneuron and each motor neuron to fire an action potential is +1.

The thorn and bear example mentioned a while ago points to the advantage of integrative nervous pathways. Although it makes sense for an organism to stop and remove a thorn that had just impaled their foot, it does not make sense to do so when an even greater danger (such as being chased by a bear) is also present. Or stated more generally, an organism's best response may often be determined by a number of factors. As we have seen, integrative pathways make accounting for more than one factor possible, as each decision is determined by a "vote" among the different converging pathways.

Just because integrative pathways incorporate more than one factor into the decision process, does not mean that they account for the right combination of factors in the right way to be biologically useful. Wiring patterns being even somewhat heritable, and thus potentially shaped by natural selection, is an important part of the story. Any time that one type responds to the environmental challenges better overall than other variants, it would be expected to spread in the population. Cumulative evolution—repeated bouts of introducing new variation followed by selection—could also continue to further fine-tune any integrative pathways toward being increasingly useful. And the nature of the voting process opens different avenues for this fine-tuning to occur. New connections can be forged, and old connections can be lost, thus, which monitors get a vote can change. The nature of the vote under a particular circumstance could also change, as any converging pathway may deliver a yes (excitatory) or no (inhibitory) vote, or any pathway can abstain by remaining at rest. Furthermore, integrative pathways are not held to the democratic ideal of all voting members having an equal voice. By changing the number of synapses via axonic branching, and/or magnitude of effect within a synapse, the weight of each converging pathway's impact on the decision can be altered. The door is thus open for stimuli that need a larger voice in the voting process (like a bear is coming!) to potentially evolve one.

A final comment: The ability of any ganglia-based nervous system to form integrative pathways opened the door for animals to have increasingly complex behavioral repertoires. In essence, it created the capacity *to think*—perhaps not in the conscious realm, as you are doing right now, but in the sense that decisions are constantly being made through the consideration of more than one factor. Every monitor hooked to an integrative pathway is always being consulted, and the sensory area of any postconvergence neuron along the way is continually tallying up the results. Some time ago a philosopher named Rene Descartes (1596–1650) made the now famous statement, "I think, therefore I am." Understanding integration, and its importance of the workings of nervous systems, suggests a modification: I think, therefore I sum. It is the mechanism behind thought. And it can occur when just two or three or four pathways converge, or if tens or hundreds or thousands of pathways converge. More pathways simply increases the range of consideration in the thought process. This in turn furthers the apparent complexity due to the increasing difficulty of predicting how an organism will respond in any situation—so many things are weighing in the thinking process. But it is still summing, nonetheless. Integrative organisms constantly have elections going on throughout their body to determine what muscles should be contracting at any point in time.

Modulation

Although integration opens the door for an organism to make better overall responses, any integrative pathway still has an element of rigidity built into its workings. Although a single stimulus will not always lead to the same response, the same response is always triggered by the same pattern of stimuli across all converging pathways (look again at Figure 25-22). As long as the response to any stimulation pattern is always appropriate, then the issue is moot. But what if it isn't? What if an increased level of behavioral flexibility would be biologically useful? The integrative answer would be to add one or more pathways into the mix that monitor the conditions under which the response should change. For example, if the best response to any particular food item changes with the nutritional status of the organism, adding pathways that monitor nutritional status would be favored by natural selection. Here, however, I introduce another way that nervous systems have increased their flexibility. It is called **modulation**. Let's take a quick step back to set up an explanation.

The addition of a pathway to any integrative network is to add a new voting member. When stimulated, it will release a chemical signal that acts as a neurotransmitter—that is, it adds a yes or no vote, of a certain magnitude, to the tally. And because every dose of neurotransmitter released has the potential to influence the outcome, a new level of responsiveness is added. In contrast, adding modulation does not add to the voting membership. Instead, it changes the magnitude of the effect of already existing pathways. For example, a converging neuron with an effect of +1, could go up or down after modulation. How much, and in which direction, depends on the details. But regardless of the details, the take-home point always stays the same: Once modulated, the same stimulation pattern will not always lead to the same result. Furthermore, because modulation can potentially influence all converging pathways, its potential effect is much greater than just adding another pathway. Perhaps it is not surprising that modulation has become an important tool in the workings of many nervous systems.

Like transmission, modulation involves a neuron releasing a chemical signal into a synapse that binds to a receptor on the postsynaptic neuron. But instead of triggering the opening of ion channels (like a neurotransmitter), the binding of a **neuromodulator** to its receptor triggers changes that influence how a neuron responds to subsequent exposure to neurotransmitters. Typically neurotransmitter receptors are altered in a way that makes them either more or less sensitive. For instance, they could undergo a shape change (commonly as a result of being phosphorylated) that causes them to bind to a neurotransmitter more readily or keep the associated ion channel open longer once bound by a neurotransmitter. Both of these changes increase the magnitude of effect of converging neurons releasing that type of neurotransmitter. The change could also go in the opposite direction and thus decrease the magnitude of effect.

An important feature is that the duration of modulatory effects are at least roughly tied to the presence or absence of the neuromodulator. That is, affected synapses are set to change strength as neuromodulator levels are adjusted up or down. As a consequence, nervous pathways, and thus behavioral responses, can be altered back and forth (by adding or removing a neuromodulator) on a fairly short time scale.

General types of neuromodulators

Although the patterns I am about to mention are probably even more general, at least in vertebrate nervous systems the molecules used as neuromodulators fall in to two basic groups.

One group consists of small molecules, commonly derived from an amino acid, that are generically called bioamines (or monoamines). Serotonin, dopamine, and norepinephrine are three common bioamines. Interestingly, in vertebrates the neurons that produce them are found in only a few areas, mostly in the brain stem, but the axons of these cells extend to widespread areas throughout the brain. In this way, a small number of highly localized neurons making a specific bioamine can influence neurons in many other locations. Because they are widely distributed they have relatively nonspecific effects. That is, they are not so much involved in precise representation of stimuli in specific circuits, but in modulating how specific stimuli are processed in different brain areas.

Neuropeptides are the other group. As their name implies, these are larger molecules consisting of a string of amino acids. In contrast to bioamines, neuropeptides are generally released by neurons that also release a neurotransmitter —usually when the firing rates of the presynaptic neuron are high— and their effects are more local, typically influencing only the pathway along which they are released. Although there are many known examples, endorphins may be the best known. Their release in certain nervous pathways is triggered by tissue damage along with other forms of stress, and after binding to their special receptors, modulate those pathways in a way that alters pain sensation and mood. This suggests that in addition to integration, modulation of pain pathways may also play a role in the bear and thorn example discussed earlier. Endorphins are also thought to play a role in the feeling achieved by runners know as "jogger's high."

A little more about serotonin

Serotonin (which is synthesized in two steps from the amino acid tryptophan) is the classic example of a bioamine that acts as a modulator in invertebrates and vertebrates. In vertebrates (including amphioxus), the cell bodies of serotonergic neurons occupy virtually the same location in the basement of the brain. This suggests that the serotonergic system was in place prior to the evolution of vertebrates and has been amazingly conserved throughout. Although their number is relatively small, axons of these localized serotonergic neurons project in rich profusion to every part of the central nervous system (brain and spinal cord), where *they influence the activity of virtually every neuron*. (Note: Overall there are only a few hundred thousand serotonergic neurons in the human brain, roughly one-millionth of the total neuron population.

Consider, for example, the effect that increasing amounts of serotonin have on a brain region called the **amygdala** (of which there are two—one on each side). The amygdala is the part of the vertebrate brain that coordinates responses to dangerous situations. Neurons within these regions constantly receive excitatory inputs started by ongoing sensory perceptions, but ignore the majority of them due to the overriding effect of tonically active inhibitory interneurons. The summing of integration is, in essence, prevented from reaching threshold. Certain types of stimuli, however, cause excitatory cells to fire rapidly for long enough periods to override the inhibitory vote and initiate a danger response. Serotonin-releasing neurons that terminate in this area influence what it takes to initiate a danger response. Specifically, serotonin acts to increase the no vote by modulating the activity of local inhibitory neurons in a way that makes it easier for them to fire action potentials. So although a danger response is still possible, the increasing strength of the no vote with increasing serotonin levels, sets the bar at a higher level. The tendency for an organism to remain calm should thus increase as serotonin levels increase.

This chain of connections explains, at least in part, the logic for taking medications such as **fluoxetine** (brand name Prozac) for mild anxiety disorders. Although feeling anxious or fearful is clearly biologically useful, this is true only if the threshold for initiating danger responses is set at the right level. For example, if it is set too low, bouts of anxiety can occur when there is nothing really present that warrants this response. Fluoxetine is a serotonin uptake inhibitory, so would seemingly amplify the effect of serotonin by slowing its removal from synapses. This, in turn, would help control unwarranted anxiety attacks by reducing the ability of inputs to the amygdala to activate danger or fear circuits. Of course, the problem with such medications goes back to our study of ecology, in particular, the ability to manipulate complex systems. Recall that it is essentially impossible to intervene in a way that merely does one thing.

A little more about dopamine

Dopamine (which is synthesized in two steps from the amino acid tyrosine) is another bioamine that seems to have long history as a modulator. In mammalian brains, the cell bodies of dopaminergic neurons are confined to a few distinct locations—known as the **substantia nigra** and **ventral tegmental area**—and although not as widespread as serotonergic neurons, the axons extending from these regions are distributed to many parts of the brain.

A brief description can never really capture the effects of any widespread modulator, but that said, modulating focus seems to be dopamine's overarching theme. Specifically, higher levels of dopamine seem to increase an organism's ability to remain focused on accomplishing a task. In other words, dopamine seems to play an important role in the motivation needed to pursue goal-directed behaviors. It may also be involved in generating a feeling of pleasure when whatever is sought after is found.

Let me use what I call the itch/scratch model to outline how changing dopamine levels could be biologically useful. Start with an organism having relatively low dopamine levels, which translates behaviorally into the organism being in a somewhat diffuse state (i.e., lacking any specific direction). Next an itch comes along—an itch being an organism's recognition (although perhaps not consciously) of either a developing problem (e.g., water or nutrient levels are getting low, tissue damage) or a developing opportunity (e.g., sexual readiness due to ovulation or increasing sperm count). The itch triggers an increase in dopamine levels, which begins to capture the nervous system's attention toward doing what is needed to scratch the itch. Moreover, this process builds on itself. The closer the organism gets to accomplishing the goal, the more intense the focus becomes, in the sense that the organism is less easily distracted. Perhaps dopamine levels continue to build throughout this process. Eventually, this intense focus is punctuated by satisfaction—the goal is accomplished—which causes the process to reverse. Dopamine levels drop, and the organism returns to a more diffuse state. Perhaps the reward—the good feelings associated with accomplishing any goal—is actually a product of this transition. That is, pleasure is found in the release from intense focus to a more relaxed state.

This model is supported by observations such as low-dopamine mice being so lethargic that they did basically nothing—they did not eat, drink, or groom themselves. However, high dopamine mice explored their surroundings like they were in the most interesting place imaginable. Higher dopamine levels has also been shown to improve working memory in monkeys. A brain region called the prefrontal cortex, which seems to play a major role in working memory, receives a rich supply of axons from one of the dopaminergic neuron regions. Dopamine makes neurons in the prefrontal cortex less responsive to incoming stimuli and thereby more likely to continue to focus on active current goals (instead of being distracted by other things). Such modulation seems to work by decreasing the strength of incoming excitatory inputs and increasing the strength of inhibitory neurons.

Peptides and feeding behavior

As mentioned earlier, how an organism reacts to a potential food item should fluctuate with its nutritional status. Although the mechanics underlying this fluctuating response include integrative pathways and widespread modulators, such as dopamine, modulation of more local pathways via peptides seem to also play an important role in the story, at least in the rodents that have been studied.

In rodent brains (and presumably other mammals, and even other vertebrates) feeding behavior is influenced by certain neural pathways found in a brain region called the hypothalamus. Three neuropeptides, in particular, have been shown to modulate these pathways and, thus, an individual's feeding behavior. Increased production of one, called **melanocortins** (which are actually a group of related peptides), act to reduce feeding. Presumably, this is by influencing these pathways to take on the pattern of activity associated with feeling satiated. In contrast, the other two peptides increase feeding behavior, although each does so in distinct ways. One called **neuropeptide Y** (NPY) appears to increase an individual's motivation to obtain food. Mice lacking the ability to make NPY will still feed sufficiently to maintain a normal body weight as long as the food is easy to get. But when challenged, they will not work very hard to obtain food. This would be a huge behavioral deficit in the real world, as obtaining food is an ongoing challenge for wild animals. Likely due to this increased motivation, animals with relatively higher levels of NPY tend to feed more frequently. On the other hand, **agouti-related protein** (AGRP) seems to increase food intake by increasing meal size. It may do so by modulating relevant pathways in a way that increases the amount of food that needs to be ingested to feel full. Interestingly, AGRP binds to the same receptor as melanocortins, but has an opposite or antagonistic effect.

Modulation and emotions

By continually adjusting the sensitivities of different parts of the nervous system, modulation has the potential to adjust behaviors in ways that help organisms negotiate life's obstacles. The key is connecting the release of different neuromodulators to the internal (within the body) and external conditions that warrant their release. For example, adjusting serotonin levels correctly may help an organism be more anxious and vigilant when placed in a more vulnerable setting and calmer otherwise. Similarly adjusting dopamine and certain neuropeptides could adjust focus and hunger/satiation, respectively, in biologically important ways.

Note that in describing modulation I have used the language of feelings or emotions. Feeling hunger, feeling easily distracted, feeling anxious, and so on. Now here is a tricky part. Evidence suggests that snails and roundworms, as well as other animals with relatively simple nervous systems, engage in modulation. But do roundworms have feelings? Clearly, they are prodded at certain times to seek food, but I doubt they feel hunger the way we do. Our different emotional states seem to be different flavors of modulation permeating into our consciousness. Conscious awareness of how our nervous system is currently being modulated is of value because we also have the conscious ability to make a plan—that is, we can think about how our own actions can be used to accomplish something. For example, we can use the self-awareness of being hungry to know that we need to begin to make a plan for how we are going to get our next meal. Without the ability to make plans, emotional information would be of little use.

An aside: Although there has been strong selection for animals to modulate their behavior correctly, the brief discussion of fluoxetin (Prozac) earlier suggests that individual humans may at times modulate in ways that interfere in running a successful life. Some examples: Evidence suggests a link between severely reduced serotonin levels in certain brain regions and suicidal behavior. Problems with dopamine regulation may make someone more vulnerable to drug abuse and other forms of addictive behavior (such as gambling). In fact, cocaine, methamphetamine, and heroine, as well as all other addictive drugs, either directly or indirectly influence a person's dopamine levels. And people that do not feel satiated as quickly will tend to eat more and thus are at greater risk of becoming obese. The apparent connection between neuromodulator levels and so-called psychiatric disorders is why drugs that influence neuromodulator levels (of which fluoxetine is just one example) have been used in attempt to treat them. In all cases, the underlying logic is an attempt to modulate the levels of a neuromodulator in a way that generates better responses.

Learning

As stated previously, learning is when an animal's response to a stimulus changes with experience. There are two basic reasons that learning would make biological sense.

First, an organism modifies its behavior in response to feedback. Specifically, behaviors followed by a positive outcome, such as finding nutritious food, would be continued and even strengthened. Conversely, behaviors followed by bad experience, such as being injured, are performed less frequently or discontinued altogether. Such trial-and-error learning is commonly called **operant conditioning**.

The second is to expand one's ability to recognize stimuli associated with either a good or bad experience. Consider, for instance, a predator attempting to track down a type of prey that gives off both a visual and auditory clue, but currently the predator only is only tuned to the visual clue. Learning to associate a second (or third, or forth . . .) type of stimuli with the prey item could increase the predator's ability to locate and subsequently capture the prey. And in general, the more cues an organism has connected to either a good or bad experience, the better it may be at negotiating life's obstacle course. The transfer of a useful behavioral pattern to another stimulus is commonly referred to as **classical conditioning** or **associated learning**. Ivan Pavlov (1849–1936) is well known for his beginning experiments in this area. He noticed that dogs responded to seeing a piece of meat by increasing salivation. He then showed that by repeatedly presenting another stimuli while showing a dog a piece of meat, the response of increased salivation could be transferred to the other stimuli. (Note: It is commonly reported that Pavlov always used a ringing bell as the other stimuli. However, his writings only mention other forms of auditory stimuli, such as whistles and tuning forks, as well as different visual stimuli. So is the bell fact or fiction? And if it is fiction, where did the idea of a bell get started?)

Learning and memory

In essence, learning requires memory. We tend to think of memory in terms of the conscious ability to recall a past image or experience. But more generally, memory is a nervous system somehow hanging on to a past experience in a way that influences how an organism will react to the same or similar experience in the future. For example, to know your best friend is to remember how they have treated you in the past, which in turn makes in a difference in how you greet them in the future.

Just for fun, think for a moment as toabout how much memory plays a role in your own life. Memory makes it possible for you to read the words on this page, to recognize the person sitting next to you, to know that you can eat the apple in your backpack, that you can put your backpack on your back, and so on and so forth. In fact, any current stimulus—whether it is coming in as a sound, sight, smell, taste, or touch—that you are not responding to as if it is your first exposure involves memory. Without memory every moment would be starting anew. We live in such a memory-based perspective of the world that its absence seems almost impossible to fathom.

The idea that a nervous system can somehow capture an experience as a memory is typically discussed in terms of storage. The biologically relevant question is: How long should a memory be stored? In other words, how long should an organism's behavior remain altered by a past experience? At first glance, it may seem that any experience worth remembering at all it is worth remembering forever. But circumstances constantly change—for instance, all animals grow older and larger—and an organism's best response to some situation may change with it. Plus, there will be limits to how much can be stored and trade-offs between what types of memories can be stored simultaneously. Storing everything forever is just not possible, so storage should have flexibility. And that is what is found. Memory is often discussed as falling into one of two broad camps: *short term*—lasting minutes to hours, or *long-term*—lasting days, weeks, or even the lifetime of the organism. But notice that there is considerable variation within both groups, and when put together they roughly make up a broad-ranging continuum. The reason, along with the mechanism, by which any memory ends up lasting a certain length of time has stirred much interest.

A similarity, a difference, and a connection between modulation and learning

Modulation and learning share a basic similarity: The response to the same stimulus can change. This means that like modulation, learning must involve altering nervous pathways by changing the strength of various synapses.

Yet there is an important difference. Instead of a response that fluctuates in accordance with changing levels of some molecule (the neuromodulator), learning must somehow leave a mark on the relevant portion of the nervous system after the experience has passed. The learning process must thus involve the generation of synaptic changes with some lasting power—changes that remain after the stimulus that triggers the change is gone. Such change is to create a memory. The length of time that this memory is stored is simply how long these synaptic changes remain intact.

The difference between modulation and learning is biologically important. For instance, for an animal to successfully nourish itself it needs to know both *when to feed* and *what to eat*. Modulation handles the "when to feed" part by adjusting the motivation to feed back and forth between hunger and satiation. On the other hand, learning can help with the "what to eat" part. Both trial-and-error and associative learning are commonly used to help an organism figure out what is good (and not good) to eat, as well as how to capture different food items.

Modulation also seems to play a role in motivating an animal to learn. Here is a simple example: Think about what you remember from yesterday. Really, take a moment and do it! I would bet that what came to mind was associated with a strong emotional experience, either good or bad. Perhaps you remember asking someone that interests you out on a date (which you were really nervous about), along with them saying yes (which you were extremely excited about). Or maybe you remember the lower score you got on your English paper (which you felt bad about, especially because you know that you really did not try very hard). Why should modulation—which enters into our consciousness as different emotions—influence what to remember? Every day organisms are bombarded with a huge amount of sensory input. Somehow each animal with any ability to learn has to decide what is worth storing for the future. But how is that decided? In a sense, that question has already been answered. Trial-and-error learning emphasizes learning from the feedback of good and bad experiences, so that in the future the good can be repeated and the bad avoided. Implicit in this idea is that all neutral experiences, neither good nor bad, should be ignored completely. However, the question not yet addressed is: How does an organism sense whether an experience is good, bad, or neutral? This is where modulation enters the scene. If a nervous system is continually being modulated in response to certain experiences, then tying learning to certain modulated (emotional) states—along with the absence of learning in other modulated states—would do the trick. Moreover, due to affecting the nervous system in different ways, each different flavor of modulation will steer an organism to focus on and thus learn different things in different ways. For instance, feeling hungry is going to focus an organism on learning what is useful to eat, whereas the modulation associated with fear is going to steer learning toward potential dangers. (*Note*: Following I briefly discuss a mechanism by which modulation could affect learning.)

Learning and synapses

Two questions, in particular, underlie the learning process. First, how are specific synapses identified as ones to be altered? And second, what is the mechanism by which targeted synapses are altered?

Although practice might not ever make it perfect, we all know that we get better at doing almost anything that we do over and over. Improvement through repetition is a form of learning. We also know that we tend to get worse at things that we do not continue to practice. Maybe this is unlearning, or learning in the opposite direction, it all depends on how you want to think about it. Nonetheless, these simple observations point out that patterns of use and disuse are at least part of the tale of how certain synapses are targeted for change. And the underlying mechanisms are at least partially known, as activity-dependent forms of synaptic change have been discovered.

Although modulation may also influence learning in other ways, how it could influence activity-dependent learning is straightforward. By altering sensitivity, changing neuromodulator levels can affect how frequently any synapse within a neural pathway fires, which in turn will influence how activity-dependent mechanisms alter the synapse. For example, a neuromodulator that increases sensitivity will make it easier for activity-dependent mechanisms to strengthen a pathway and thus fire more readily in the future. Modulation may even help a single good or bad experience make a lasting impression. Have you ever noticed that right after a bad experience, you tend to keep replaying it over and over in your mind. Doing so may help generate the needed repetition to hook the experience into a memory (and thus help one avoid repeating the same mistake). And by changing sensitivities, modulation may aid your nervous system's ability to fire the same pathways over and over again. (But if this is true, it makes you wonder what other animals do the same thing. Does your dog or your goldfish?)

The most common name you will hear associated with activity-dependent forms of synapse-specific facilitation is **long-term potentiation** (LTP). This term can be confusing because it is used for more than one variation of a similar process. These variations, however, are all united by the following themes: The process is triggered by periods of frequent activity within a synapse (or more specifically, by frequent release of the neurotransmitter), it enhances the connection strength between neurons, and this change will last for at least a while after whatever triggered the frequent activity has passed.

The details of LTP commonly involve NMDA or NMDA-like receptors, different types of protein kinases, and a protein call CREB that through acting as a gene transcription factor triggers the production of new proteins. Longer-lasting forms of LTP, in particular, involve CREB-triggered protein synthesis. The details, however, are not the focus here. On the other hand, two observations about LTP are highlighted. First, LTP acts as a *coincidence detector*, in that it only strengthens the synapses that were active when the postsynaptic cell was firing. (We will discuss the significance of this more later.) And second, the targeted synapses are facilitated in three main ways that should all sound familiar by now. These are (1) The postsynaptic neuron's sensitivity to exposure to future doses of excitatory neurotransmitter is enhanced by making currently available receptors more sensitive (through being phosphorylated), and/or triggering the synthesis of more receptors. The latter is generally the longer-lasting change. (2) The axon terminals on presynaptic neurons may release neurotransmitters more efficiently as a result of a retrograde messenger passed back from the postsynaptic cell. And (3) the number of synapses can be increased. LTP can trigger the release of growth factors called **neurotrophins** from the postsynaptic cells that influence currently active presynaptic axons to branch and form new synaptic connections. This effect is limited to active presynaptic neurons by the fact that only axon terminals that just released neurotransmitter take up neurotrophins and sprout new connections. *A final note*:

LTP can be self-reinforcing because making a pathway fire more easily can continually trigger the same types of changes that caused LTP in the first place.

A weakening of neuron-to-neuron connections can occur by reversing any of the previous three. Pairing a weakening of connection with a lower frequency of use could happen in a couple of ways. For one, the maintenance of connective strength may be coupled with activity level. As a consequence, decreasing activity would lead to the connection strength slipping. For example, many neurons will undergo so-called programmed cell death unless they continually receive life-sustaining shots of neurotrophins from their postsynaptic partner. So, although high levels of neurotrophins can promote axonic branching, lower levels are often needed just to maintain already existing neural connections, and inactive to even marginally active neurons within pathways may not stimulate sufficient neurotrophin release to even survive. The loss of a connection due to a neuron's death is the weakening of a connection all the way to zero. A process called **long-term depression** (LTD) has also been discovered in some neurons. Here low-frequency stimulation actually triggers a change in the postsynaptic neuron that decreases its sensitivity to future doses of neurotransmitter.

A simple model of classical conditioning

We have only hit some highlights of learning. There is a lot more that is already known, and there is a lot more waiting to be discovered. Many neurobiologists spend their days trying to delve deeper. But before going on, I point out one more thing: With just the addition of LTP, an organism wired as simple as *Irv* could do associative learning (classical conditioning)

Figure 25-23 is similar to other *Irv* integrative pathways that we have focused on. The one new wiring twist is that **sensory neuron 2** connects directly to **muscle A's motor neuron**, instead of an inhibitory interneuron sitting in between. The other important difference needs to be imagined: that the machinery needed to do LTP is present at each of the sensory-to-motor neuron synapses. The time sequence (a–c) illustrates a Pavlov-like experiment being performed on this pathway. But instead of salivating, the behavioral response being monitored here is whether **muscle A** contracts.

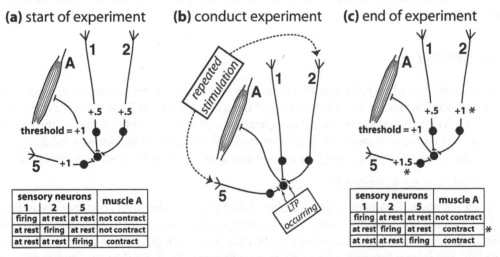

Figure 25-23. A hypothetical experiment in classical condition. It starts with a simple integrative pathway (from Irv) capable of long-term potentiation (LTP). The experimental design involves the repeated coupling of a stimulus (activiting sensory neuron 5) that can initiate a behavioral response (muscle A contracting) with a stimulus (activiting sensory neuron 2) that cannot initiate the same response. Because of LTP, by the end, activating sensory neuron 2 alone can now trigger muscle contraction. An asterisk marks all things that have changed over the course of the experiment. See text for more details.

At the start (Figure 25-23(a)), stimulating **sensory neuron 5** is like Pavlov showing a dog a piece of meat, as this is the only sensory neuron that can fire alone and trigger muscle contraction. Its magnitude of effect is above the motor neuron's threshold. On the other hand, stimulating **sensory neuron 1** or **2** would be like Pavlov's auditory stimulus (a whistle or a bell, or whatever). Although each is connected to the same motor neuron, its magnitude of effect is not great enough alone to trigger a response.

The experimental procedure (Figure 25-23(b)) involves repeatedly coupling the stimulus that is detected by either **sensory neuron 1** or **sensory neuron 2** (and causing it to fire) with the one detected by **sensory neuron 5**. **Sensory neuron 2** was chosen, meaning throughout the experiment **sensory neuron 1** will remain at rest. Note that each time **2** and **5** are stimulated, the motor neuron will fire (and **muscle A** contracts). Due to the repeated firing of the motor neuron, LTP is also initiated. However, because LTP is a coincidence detector, only the active synapses are strengthened. So although the synapses between the motor neuron and **sensory neurons 2** and **5** will be strengthened, the **sensory neuron 1** synapse will remain unaffected.

By the end of the experiment (Figure 25-23(c)) the strength of each of the affected synapses was increased by 0.5. This value was chosen because it is the minimum increase that demonstrates classical conditioning. Just like in Pavlov's experiment, where after a while the auditory stimulus alone could cause the dog to salivate, sensory neuron 2 now has the strength to cause muscle A to contract on its own. On the other hand, the effect of any nonconditioned stimulus, such as what would cause sensory neuron 1 to fire, would still be the same. *Irv* just did some learning!

A Closer Look at a Single Neuron

Here we examine how nervous signals are both initiated and then transmitted within a single nerve cell. To set this up, recall two general features: First, the two ends of polar nerve cells are different. One end is a sensory-end and the other end is a chemical-signal-releasing-end called the axon terminal. Second, what occurs at the sensory-end can lead to the release of neurotransmitters at the opposite end. The connection is forged by the sensory-end being able to initiate something called an action potential or nerve impulse, which in turn triggers the release of chemical signals once it reaches the axon terminal.

Action potential

Two features of action potentials are particularly striking. First, the movement of a nerve impulse does not involve the movement of some physical thing down the axon. This raises the question: What is actually moving? Second, once initiated, an impulse will travel the entire length of the neuron—which can be up to several meters in length—without the strength of the impulse weakening. The transmission of nerve impulses along the axon is thus an all-or-none (or yes/no) proposition.

So what is an action potential?

To set the stage, think back to your childhood. Did you ever play with dominoes—standing a bunch on end in a line, and then watching as you nudged the first one. The first domino collided into the next knocking it over, which collided into the next, and so on, only stopping when the last domino in line fell. You were witnessing a traveling positive feedback loop. All the way down the line, the falling over of a domino promotes the occurrence of the same event—the falling over of a domino.

The curious part of playing with dominoes is that it takes a whole lot longer to set them up than to knock them down. Why go to all the effort for such a short-lived reward? Perhaps because the movement seems to break everyday rules. Travel usually implies some object moving across distance. Plus, we tend to think of a traveling object always encountering resistance or friction. Anything traveling will, thus, eventually slow to a stop without a continual input of usable energy. With dominoes, however, neither of these notions apply. Something moves, but it is not any object. Each domino does nothing more than simply fall over. As mentioned earlier, it is the loop of events that travels. Furthermore, this traveling positive feedback loop will keep going and going, without any slowing or weakening, for as far as anyone is willing to line up dominoes. The last domino falls with as much force as the first one did.

An action potential is analogous to the domino effect—dominoes knocking over dominoes. The difference is that voltage-gated ion channels replace dominoes. A traveling positive feedback loop is formed by the fact that the opening of a voltage-gated ion channel embedded in the surface of a cell membrane can lead to the opening of other near-by voltage-gated ion channels and so on.

All that we have left is to explain more about how this all works. Unfortunately, such an explanation takes a little time. In particular, I need to step back a minute and talk about voltage and membranes in more general terms before I can explain how voltage-gated ion channels act like dominoes.

Ion distribution, membrane potential, and voltage

The outer membranes of all animal cells are polarized—meaning that there is a separation of charge across the membrane. The charge separation is due to a slight excess of **anions**—negatively charged ions—on the inside of cells and a corresponding slight excess of **cations**—positively charged ions—on the cell exterior. **Membrane potential** is the name given to this electric gradient across the membrane.

Membrane potential, as discussed in Chapter 12, indirectly results from the way animal cells deal with their "too much water problem." Following is a brief review.

Due to DNA, proteins, amino acids and other biological molecules—which overall tend to be negatively charged—being kept inside, water tends to be in lower concentration on the inside than on the outside of any cell. Water thus tends to diffuse inward until the cell explodes. Animal cells contend with this problem by actively pumping sodium ions (Na^+) out of the cell. By dissolving in the extracellular fluid, the added sodium ions reduce the water concentration of the extracellular fluid. Pump out enough, and the extracellular water concentration equilibrates with the intracellular concentration.

Pumping out positively charged sodium ions also creates a charge disparity across the membrane. Other ions—especially chloride ions (Cl^-) and potassium ions (K^+)—however, normally move somewhat freely through animal cell membranes. They thus begin to move in ways to balance the charge imbalance generated by pumping out sodium ions. Due to being pulled by negatively charged biological molecules trapped inside the cell, positively charged potassium ions flow inward. In contrast, negatively charged chloride ions are pulled outward by the excess of positively charged sodium ions. Despite these flows, however, a charge balance is never achieved. The building concentration of chloride ions on the outside and potassium ions on the inside creates a concentration gradient that pulls each of these freely moving ions in the opposite direction as they are being pulled by charge. Consequently, charge is unable to equilibrate on each side of the membrane. Instead, the excess of negative charges on the inside and positive charges on the outside will line up on opposite sides of the membrane. The result is a polarized membrane.

The degree of membrane potential present in a cell is measured in terms of voltage. Specifically, a volt is a unit of potential energy associated with opposite charges being separated by distance (due to their mutual attraction). A cell's normal level of charge imbalance—commonly called its **resting membrane potential**—is usually somewhere in between –50 and –90 millivolts (1 mV = 1/1000th of a volt). (Note: Because voltage is measured by comparing the inside of a cell to the outside, the negative voltage measure indicates that the inside of the cell is more negatively charged than the outside.)

Calcium ions are also pumped out

Calcium ions (Ca^{++}) are also actively pumped out of animal cells. In fact, active transport of calcium ions is so effective that extracellular calcium levels have been recorded to be 10,000 times greater (or more) than calcium levels within cells.

Unlike sodium ions, however, calcium ions are not pumped out of cells to help maintain osmotic balance. In contrast to the other common ions (sodium, potassium, and chloride ions), calcium ions are biologically active. Certain proteins are allosterically modulated by their presence. In other words, when calcium ions are present at high enough concentrations, certain proteins bind with calcium ions and correspondingly undergo a shape change that "turns on" these proteins.

Controlling calcium levels within the cell thus regulates the activity of these calcium-binding proteins. Pumping out calcium ions to low levels acts to turn off these proteins. Once intracellular calcium ion levels drop below some threshold, calcium-binding proteins will generally be free of calcium and hence return to their unbound not functional shape. On the other hand, turning back on these calcium-binding proteins can be accomplished solely by opening up channels through which calcium ions can cross the cell membrane. Given the extreme concentration gradient between the outside and inside of cells, once these channels open (and increase the membrane's permeability to calcium ions), calcium ions will move back into the cell by diffusion.

What are voltage-gated ion channels?

Let's learn about voltage-gated ion channels by dissecting its name piece by piece. An *ion channel* is a channel protein (often consisting of more than one protein) embedded in a membrane that creates an opening that at least one type of ion can pass through. Which type of ion can pass through the opening depends both on the opening's size in combination with the arrangement of charges lining the opening. In certain cases, when ions are sufficiently similar, more than one type of ion can pass through the same ion channel. *Gated* indicates that this channel can be opened and closed. *Voltage-gated* means that the opening and closing of the gate is regulated by changes in voltage across the membrane—that is changes in membrane potential. Normal membrane potentials—resting membrane potentials—or higher, keep the gate shut. Reduce membrane potential past a certain point, and the gate opens (see Figure 25-24).

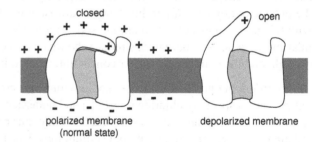

Figure 25-24. A voltage-gated ion channel in both its closed and open states.

Changes in membrane potential, relative to a cell's resting membrane potential, are commonly discussed using the following two terms: **depolarization** (of a membrane) and **hyperpolarization** (of a membrane). The direction of change is indicated in the name. Depolarization is a reduction in the separation of charge across a membrane. In other words, the measured membrane potential goes toward zero. Conversely, hyperpolarization is an increase in the separation of charge across a membrane—that is, an increase in the measured membrane potential. Voltage-gated ion channels, thus, are opened by depolarization (past a certain threshold) and kept closed by hyperpolarization.

Return to the subject at hand: Action potential

To envision how voltage-gated ion channels can generate a traveling positive feedback loop, just consider the following: Suppose the opening of one of these ion channels results in depolarization of the surrounding membrane. If so, the opening of one voltage-gated ion channel can result in the opening of an adjacent voltage-gated ion channel (and so on).

Such depolarization will occur if voltage-gated ion channels, when open, are permeable to either sodium ions or calcium ions. Both sodium and calcium ions are positively charged ions poised to rush into the cell due to a favorable concentration gradient. The excess of negative ions inside the cell also creates an electromagnetic tug on these positively charged ions. And when either of these ions moves inward, due to opening of voltage-gated ion channels, local depolarization ensues. The movement of positive ions inward starts to electrically balance the initial excess of negative ions. Once local depolarization reaches the opening threshold, the next voltage-gated ion channel opens, starting once again the same cycle of events, only further down the membrane. And like dominoes, the action potential will keep moving down the membrane until it runs out of lined-up voltage-gated ion channels. Figure 25-25 illustrates this sequence of events with voltage-gated sodium ion channels.

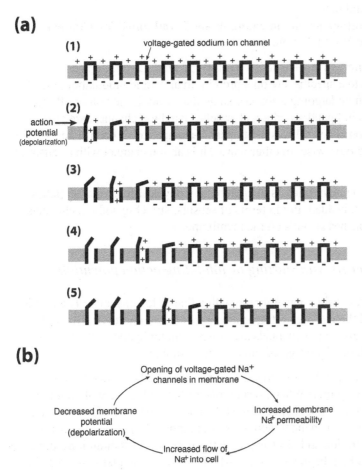

(a)

(1) voltage-gated sodium ion channel

(2) action potential (depolarization)

(3)

(4)

(5)

(b)

Opening of voltage-gated Na⁺ channels in membrane

Decreased membrane potential (depolarization)

Increased membrane Na⁺ permeability

Increased flow of Na⁺ into cell

Figure 25-25. The traveling positive feedback loop of an action potential.

Each step in (a) focuses on a small section of membrane along a neuron's axon that is currently transmitting an action potential. At first (1) the action potential has yet to reach this section, so all the voltage-gated ion channels remain closed (due to the membrane being sufficiently polarized). In (2) the action potential (moving from left to right) has just reached this section, depolarizing the membrane at the left side enough for the first voltage-gated sodium ion channel to open. As it opens, sodium ions move into the cell causing the trend of depolarization to spread even farther. In (3) through (5) the story continues to repeat itself. The next channel in line opens due to the spreading depolarization, which allows more sodium ions to enter and depolorization to spread further. Note that this trend will continue for as far as voltage-gated sodium ion channels are lined along a membrane.

The second illustration (b) summarizes the sequence of events involved in an action potential (using voltage-gated sodium ion channels).

Nonvoltage-gated ion channels and getting an action potential started

Before getting into the biological importance of action potentials spreading along cell membranes, I need to answer one more basic question: How is an action potential ever started? So far we have only talked about how an action potential keeps itself going. But the topics are related. What opens the first, middle, or last voltage-gated ion channel in line is the same—local depolarization of the membrane. Just like what knocks over the first, middle, or last domino in line is the same—a contact force. The difference with the first domino in line is that the contact force must come from something other than another domino falling into it. Your finger poking the first domino is one example of a force that could get it all started. Similarly, to start an action potential, something other than the opening of a voltage-gated (sodium or calcium) ion channel must cause local depolarization of the membrane. A common substitute is still a gated sodium ion channel—so when it opens, sodium will rush in and locally depolarize the surrounding membrane—but one that is opened (and closed) by something other than changes in membrane

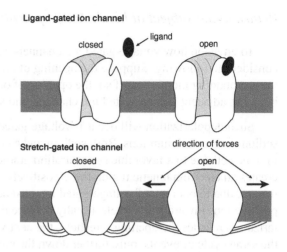

Figure 25-26. Two different types of nonvoltage gated ion channels. See text for more details.

potential. Two common forms of **nonvoltage-gated ion channels** are **ligand-gated ion channels** and **stretch-gated ion channels** (see Figure 25-26). Let me discuss each in turn.

Ligand is a word that came up earlier when we discussed allosteric modulation. Ligand is a generic name for a molecule that binds to a specific site on a protein. In allosteric modulation, the binding of a ligand results in the protein undergoing a shape change that either turned on or off the protein's function. The same idea holds in ligand-gated ion channels. Gated ion channels are also composed of proteins. A ligand-gated ion channel is one that opens—changes to its open shape—when bound by a specific ligand and is closed otherwise. In other words, it is an ion channel with a sensor to the presence of a specific molecule.

A stretch-gated ion channel, as the name implies, is opened by any physical force that stretches the membrane in which the channel is embedded. Put in terms of sensors, stretch-gated ion channels sense the presence of physical forces: pushes or pulls on the membrane.

Linking nonvoltage-gated ion channels with starting or inhibiting action potentials

Although this is a bit too simplistic, consider a membrane with a line of ion channels. The first in line is a **ligand-gated ion channel**, and the rest are **voltage-gated sodium ion channels**. But at the moment nothing is happening—that is, all the ion channels are closed, and no ligands—the specific molecule of the right shape to bind with the ligand-gated ion channels—are present.

Now, introduce some of this specific ligand. (How this ligand has come to be around is an important question, but one that I presently ignore.) When present, one of the molecules will bind to the ligand-gated ion channel, causing it to open. What happens next depends on the type of ion that can pass through the channel. If it is a sodium ion channel then the sodium ions (Na^+) poised to diffuse in—because of both a favorable concentration and electric gradient—now do. As sodium ions move into the cell the surrounding electric gradient begins to lessen, which can open the first voltage-gated sodium ion channel. And like with knocking over the first domino, opening the first voltage-gated sodium ion channel will start an action potential (see Figure 25-27). This arrangement of two different types of ion channels thus generates a mechanism that monitors (detects) the presence of a certain type of chemical (the specific ligand) and starts an action potential whenever it is present.

Strikingly, the preceding scenario is reversed if the ligand-gated ion channel is permeable to chloride ions (Cl^-) instead of sodium ions. Although the details of why this is so are a little tricky, increasing a membrane's permeability to chloride ions acts to either locally maintain a cell's membrane potential or even polarize the membrane even further—that is, **hyperpolarize** the membrane. Either way, opening a chloride channel has an inhibitory effect on an action potential. Maintaining or increasing the membrane potential will act to keep the first domino from being knocked over by acting to keep voltage-gated ion channels shut.

Recall that in our discussion of integration nervous pathways, some presynaptic neurons had a stimulatory effect on an action potential whereas others had an inhibitory effect. Now we have started to open the door onto how this opposite effect could be manifested. Any presynaptic neuron that releases a neurotransmitter that binds to ligand-gated sodium ion channels would have a stimulatory effect on starting an action potential in the postsynaptic neuron. In contrast, any presynaptic neuron that releases a neurotransmitter that binds to ligand-gated chloride channels will act to inhibit the starting of an action potential.

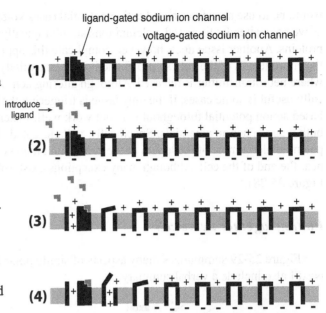

Figure 25-27. An arrangement of two types of ion channels that can trigger an action potential in response to detecting a specific type of molecule. At first (1) both types of gated ion channels are closed. In (2) type of molecule that will bind to the ligand-gated ion channel—that is, the molecule that will act as the ligand—is introduced. In (3) and (4) the opening of the ligand-gated sodium ion channels causes sufficient local depolarization to open the first voltage-gated sodium ion channel. At that point the action potential has started.

Note that the same basic scenario holds if the ligand-gated ion channel is replaced with a stretch-gated ion channel. The difference is that it is now the presence of pressure, instead of the presence of a certain type of molecule, will either stimulate or inhibit the starting of an action potential.

Linking an action potential with releasing neurotransmitter

So far we know that once an action potential starts at one end of a neuron, it will continue on until it reaches the other end. The question that we address here is: How can the arrival of action potential trigger the release of neurotransmitter from the axon terminal? The answer is that it couldn't if it is solely a sodium-based action potential (uses voltage-gated sodium ion channels). Sodium ions are not known to be biologically active, so entering ions will not affect the cell other than beginning to disrupt the osmotic balance. One solution to that problem

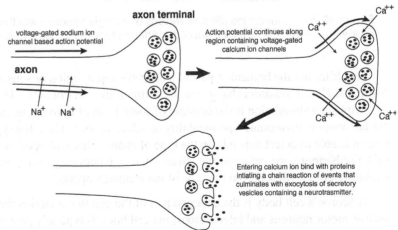

Figure 25-28. The steps through which an action potential travelling down an axon leads to the release of a chemical signal at the axon terminal.

would be to use a calcium-based action potential (uses voltage-gated calcium ion channels) because, as we have already discussed, calcium ions are biologically active—they bind with and turn on certain proteins. Another issue does, however, complicate this approach. Now calcium ions are entering along the entire length of the cell, so protein activity is potentially altered all along the neuron instead of just where neurotransmitter is released. Although altering activity along an entire neuron could be biologically useful is some cases, if the only issue is triggering the release of neurotransmitter then a calcium-based action potential throughout may not work well. Instead, the best option would be to combine both types of action potentials. Specifically, voltage-gated sodium ion channels could carry an action potential along most of the length of the cell, which then switch voltage-gated calcium ion channels near the end of the cell. Although many exceptions exist, this is the way a classic neuron works (see Figure 25-28).

Putting together nerve cells

Figure 25-29 summarizes many aspects of single polar neurons that we have discussed so far. Next I also include a verbal summary.

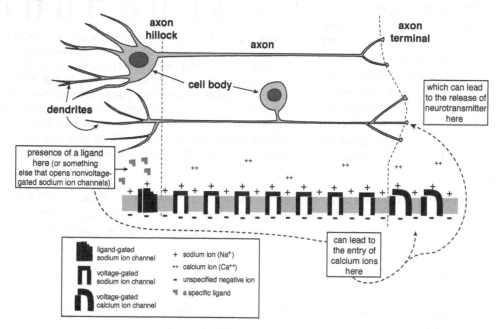

Figure 25-29. Connects the different regions of a single neuron—whether it be a motor, sensory, or interneuron—with the arrangement of the different types of ion channels in a classic neuron.

Dendrites are the branching part of a neuron's input region or sensory-end. This region can be "stimulated" as it monitors changes in the surrounding environment. The physical occurrence associated with such stimulation is the opening of some form of nonvoltage-gated ion channels, increasing the surrounding membrane's permeability to selective ions. Thus, the type of environmental changes a neuron is able to detect depends on the type of change that will open its nonvoltage-gated ion channels. Furthermore, the nature of the effect—that is, whether opening ion channels has a stimulatory or inhibitory effect—depends on the type of ion channels opened.

A neuron's cell body is the enlarged part of the cell that contains the nucleus. In some neurons, such as motor neurons and interneurons, the cell body is typically part of the input region because like the dendrites that emerge from it, its membrane contains nonvoltage-gated ion channels. In other neurons, such as sensory neurons, the cell body is located in the conducting region of the cell. (Note: The sensory neuron in this figure is drawn like a vertebrate sensory neuron where the cell body is shifted off to one side.) As we discussed, the differences in cell body position are a developmental issue that does not alter neuronal function.

The axon hillock marks the end of a neuron's input region and the start of its conducting region. The boundary is formed by the first appearance of voltage-gated Na^+ channels along a neuron. In fact, it is here that voltage-gated Na^+ channels are in their highest concentration.

In essence, the axon hillock is where the decision of whether a neuron fires is actually made. Stimulation at different places along the input region leads to either local depolarization or hyperpolarization. All these stimuli are then considered together or integrated as the cumulative effects move toward the axon hillock. The answer is yes—that is, an action potential is set into motion—whenever membrane depolarization below the voltage-gated threshold extends to the axon hillock. Otherwise the answer is no. Nerve impulses travel along the conducting region of a neuron—called the axon.

Each branch of an axon ends with a slight swelling known as the axon terminal. It is here that the release of neurotransmitter is triggered by the influx of calcium ions moving in through voltage-gated calcium ion channels.

Resetting nerve cells after they fire

So far we have created a nerve cell that could be used once. We have not discussed any means for dominoes to be set back up after the first action potential has passed. And clearly a nerve cell that could be used only once would not be very useful. So the question remains: How are neurons continually being reset so that they can fire action potentials again and again?

Part of the answer has to do with the sodium and calcium pumps that we have already discussed. The sodium and calcium ions that enter during the firing of each action potential must continually be pumped back out. But in the moment-to-moment workings of a neuron, pumping these ions back out is only a very small part of the story. In fact, it has been shown that neurons can fire numerous action potentials even after these ion pumps are blocked. Although these pumps are needed to keep a neuron fully charged, like a battery a neuron can be used for extended time without any recharging.

The resetting story actually involves a couple of components working together. The voltage-gated sodium channels have a second gate that closes very quickly after the first gate opens, shutting off the flow of sodium ions before the membrane becomes too depolarized. Voltage-gated potassium ion (K^+) channels are also located all along the membrane. They open about the time that the second gate on the sodium channels closes, which allows potassium ions to move out of the cell. It is this movement of positively charged ions out of the cell that resets the membrane potential. However, putting this all together in a way that really makes sense requires a more in-depth understanding of membrane potential than we have time to or would even want to attempt to cover here. So I leave the resetting of neurons as a topic you can look forward to exploring in the future.

The Endocrine System in Multicellular Animals

We have already discussed what an endocrine system would *not* be good at doing—it would not be good at controlling coordinated muscle-based movement. So what would a circulatory-based signal system be good at doing? In turns out that the endocrine system regulates the occurrence of many of the internal functions of multicellular organisms. Although the following examples focus on vertebrates in general, and humans in particular, the basic issues and ideas should apply to all animals.

Regulating blood contents

Counteracting regulation of blood contents is perhaps the most general theme underlying endocrine system function. The significance of doing so is clear—because blood travels throughout the body, acting to maintain blood contents around certain levels is a means to maintain the conditions experienced by all cells. The basic design is also straightforward. Endocrine cells or glands are positioned somewhere along the circulatory system to monitor some aspect of blood contents. Specifically, they respond to chang-

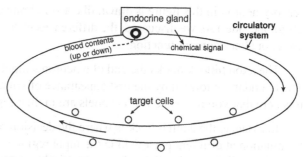

Figure 25-30. The basic design of a blood content monitoring endocrine gland. The circulatory systems is represented simply as a loop. See text for further details.

ing levels of what they detect by changing the rate at which they release a chemical signal (a hormone) into circulation. Changes in hormone levels then prods target cells (those cells bearing receptors for the specific hormone released) to act in counteracting ways (see Figure 25-30).

The regulation of blood calcium levels

A classic counteracting response orchestrated by the endocrine system in vertebrates is found in blood calcium regulation. Calcium, which an organism acquires through its diet, plays an important role in the function of nerves and muscles. In fact, blood calcium levels need to be kept within a fairly narrow range for the nervous system and muscles to function properly. Calcium regulation is largely controlled by the parathyroid glands. The parathyroid glands are negative sensors in that as

calcium ions levels decrease below normal, the parathyroid glands increase the rate at which they release a chemical signal called parathyroid hormone into circulation. Through its effect on target cells, parathyroid hormone orchestrates three body responses that act to elevate blood calcium levels: It increases the rate at which calcium ions are released from storage in bones, it indirectly increases the rate at which dietary calcium is absorbed into the body through the small intestine, and it reduces the rate at which calcium ions are lost through kidney filtration by increasing the rate at which calcium ions entering the filtrate are reabsorbed back into the body (see Figure 25-31).

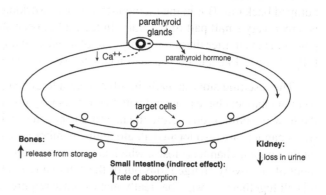

Figure 25-31. The basic design by which vertebrates regulate blood calcium levels. See text for further details.

The regulation of blood water levels

Organisms that live in environments with lower water concentration than their bodies—like terrestrial organisms—constantly lose water. Water is lost during the intake of gases, the removal of wastes, and whenever cooling occurs by water evaporation. So to maintain water balance, an organism needs to have a sensor that detects water shortage and then prods the organism into appropriate responses.

In mammals, cells that monitor blood water levels are found within a structure called the hypothalamus. Specifically, these cells detect when the osmotic concentration of the blood is too high—that is, when there is too little water (or too much solute) in the blood. Increasing stimulation of these cells initiates two responses.

One is an endocrine-based response. When blood water concentration is too low, **antidiuretic hormone**—often referred to as **ADH**—is released into the bloodstream from an adjacent and directly connected structure called the posterior pituitary gland (see Figure 25-32). Receptors for ADH are located on the collecting tubules within the kidneys. In the presence of ADH these collecting tubules become more permeable to water, which due the details of mammalian kidneys, allow more of the kidney filtrate water to be absorbed back into the body. In other words, ADH helps minimize the water loss from excretion when water is in short supply. (A side note: Ethyl alcohol blocks the release of antidiuretic hormone, which explains why increased urination and feeling dehydrated later are often associated with drinking alcoholic beverages.)

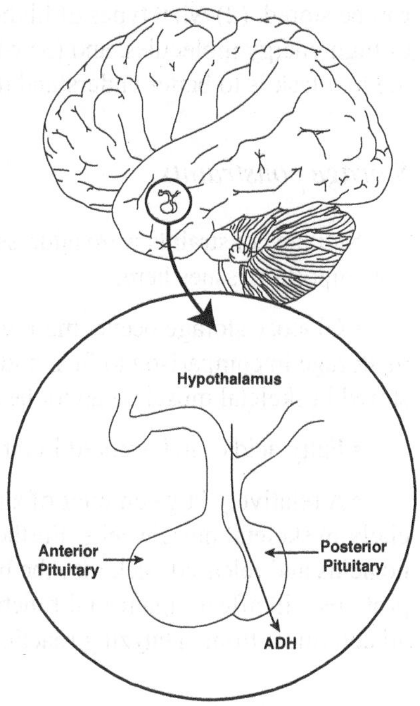

The problem with this hormone-initiated response is that it never solves the problem. Once water is in short supply, minimizing the rate of loss helps to slow the rate at which the problem gets more severe. But decreasing supplies must eventually be replenished. This is where the second response comes in.

The hypothalamus is actually a part of the nervous system—specifically part of the brain. The significance is that in addition to initiating an endocrine response, it also can initiate a familiar nervous system-based response. Through modulatory effects, it generates the sensation of thirst. (Low blood water levels stimulate nerve cells in a region of the hypothalamus called the thirst center.) As we discussed earlier, sensations inform the organism what is going on inside and in doing so help the organism set its priorities. So as an organism becomes thirstier and thirstier, it is informing itself that getting water is becoming more and more of a priority. Perhaps you have even experienced thirst to the point that getting a drink seems like all that you can think about. If so, adding more water has basically become the number one priority. If your thirst sensation is working well, feeling intense thirst should correlate with when blood water level is approaching dangerously low levels.

Figure 25-32. The hypothalamus and its associated endocrine glands. Different than the anterior pituitary, the posterior pituitary, from which ADH is released, is developmentally part of the nervous system. Its approximate position within the human brain is shown. Think of the circle as a window that shows deeper structures, as the hypothalamus is tucked underneath the extensively folded outer cortex.

The regulation of blood energy-molecule levels

As mentioned in the previous chapter, in larger multicellular animals with circulatory systems, part of the trick of maintaining an ATP balance at each cell is maintaining a continual supply of high-energy molecules in the blood—that is, molecules that can be brought into the cells and converted into ATP, preferably by aerobic respiration. Yet sugars, fats, and amino acids are only inputted into the body periodically—that is, only after meals. So some system is needed to regulate the storage of these high-energy molecules when they are in excess and to trigger their release back to the blood when they are in short supply. We take up the regulatory aspect of this issue here because the endocrine system plays a major role. The regulatory story here is particularly interesting because it must operate in the face of three types of constraints: (1) how much of the different forms of high-energy molecules can be stored, (2) what types of high-energy molecules can be metabolically converted to other types of high-energy molecules, and (3) what body tissues "prefer" what types of high-energy molecules. So the first task is to better understand these constraints.

Storage constraints

Storage constraints were addressed in some detail in the previous chapter, but let me summarize a few important issues here:

• Glucose storage occurs mainly in the liver and skeletal muscles, but due to the increased weight of storage in comparison to fats, bodies store a relatively small amount. Furthermore, the glucose stored in skeletal muscles cannot be released back into the bloodstream.

• Fatty acids can be stored in fat (adipose) cells in large amounts.

• A relatively large amount of amino acids are stored within proteins throughout the body, especially in skeletal muscle cells. Furthermore, all proteins located in cells can be broken down into amino acids and released back into the blood. But beyond some limited amount, breaking down cellular proteins will affect organismal function. As we have stated many times, proteins orchestrate basically all activities, from catalyzing reactions to generating motion via muscle contractions.

Metabolic constraints

• Although animals can convert sugars to fats, the reverse is not true. Animals do not make two of the enzymes needed for fatty acids to be converted into glucose. (Note: As discussed in Chapter 12, fatty acids are stored as triglycerides, and the glycerol portion of each triglyceride can be used to make glucose. So in this way a very small portion of fat stores can be converted to glucose.)

• Fatty acids can be converted into a group of smaller water-soluble molecules known as **ketone bodies** that can be readily used to generate ATP in other cells in the body (a process known as **ketogenesis**). In essence, ketone bodies are formed when liver cells perform the initial steps involved in breaking down fatty acids to make ATP and then release the resultant molecules into circulation. The final steps—Krebs cycle and oxidative phosphorylation—take place in the mitochondria of cells using ketone bodies. (*Some details*: Ketone bodies are formed especially when glucose is in short supply. It turns out that two-carbon acetate molecules cleaved off a fatty acid—they attach to coenzyme A to form acetyl-CoA—can enter the Krebs cycle only if a four-carbon molecule called oxaloacetate is available. Yet when glucose is in short supply, supplies of oxaloacetate are used to synthesize more glucose. Liver cells then begin converting acetyl-CoA into a two types of four-carbon compounds: acetoacetate, and D-3-hydroxybutyrate, which are sometimes collectively termed ketone bodies. Acetone—a three-carbon molecule—may also appear due to a slow but spontaneous decarboxylation of acetoacetate.)

• Eighteen of the 20 amino acids can be, at least in part, converted into glucose. This process is known as **gluconeogenesis** and occurs in liver cells. The other two can only be converted into fatty acids or ketone bodies.

"Preference" constraints

• Most cells making up a human body (and presumably many other animals) can use either glucose, fatty acids, or ketone bodies as an energy source. Although each of these in not completely interchangeable—as all cells need at least some glucose to maintain adequate supplies of oxaloacetate, the molecule needed to start the Krebs cycle—all can be used to make ATP by aerobic respiration. And in certain situations, molecules other than glucose can be used preferentially. For example, skeletal muscles tend to use fatty acids as an energy source except during quick bursts of activity (when glucose is preferred).

• Brain cells are unique in that they seem to never use fatty acids as an energy source. It has been suggested that this is true because fatty acids are unable to pass from the bloodstream to nerve cells, due to the unique characteristics of the brain's blood vessels—known as the blood–brain barrier. That, however, does not appear to be the case (nor does it make sense given that lipid soluble fatty acids can pass through membranes.) Alternatively, brain cells may have been selected to not use fatty acids because it is poor fuel for their energy demands. For one, many brain neurons do not get their high-energy molecules directly from the bloodstream. Instead, the molecules used to make ATP pass first through supportive cells called astrocytes. Glucose is the only molecule that allows to astrocytes to make some ATP by glycolysis-fermentation and then pass the lactate leftovers to neurons, which then use this substrate to make ATP by aerobic respiration. Furthermore, brains cells not only use energy at a very high rate on average—at rest your three-pound brain uses 25% of your energy—but also their energy demand fluctuates widely. This is due to some details associated with oxaloacetate only being made from glucose—cells constantly adjusting their rate of mitochondrial ATP production cannot use fatty acids.

A little more information on the blood–brain barrier: Generally, the cells making up capillary walls are attached such that an opening exists between cells. Thus, many molecules reach surrounding cells by moving out of these openings. In contrast, most brain capillaries have no such openings. The cells are tightly bound together, making it impossible for anything in the blood to reach nerve cells unless it can first pass through the cells. The potential advantage of this so-called blood–brain barrier is that access of blood-borne molecules to brain cells is selective. For instance, molecules such as epinephrine, acetylcholine, dopamine, and glycine are denied access. All these molecules act as neurotransmitters or neuromodulators; hence, their indiscriminate access could have devastating effects on brain function.

• Given that glucose is the best molecule to meet the brain's unique and fluctuating ATP demand, brains prefer to use glucose all the time—despite the fact that they can store only around a two-minute supply. Glucose transportors are thus always ready to move glucose across the blood–brain barrier.

• Whenever glucose is in short supply, brain cells can use more and more ketone bodies to produce ATP. But the switch can never be complete, as some glucose must also be available (it goes back to the issue of providing for both astrocytes and neurons, along with maintaining adequate supplies of oxaloacetate). Because ketone bodies are made from fatty acids, this provides an indirect route for the fatty acid component of fat stores to help feed the brain in case of an emergency. Given that ketone bodies are water soluble, use by the brain also requires transporters to shuttle them across the blood–brain barrier.

After a meal

Both the nervous system and the pancreas, by monitoring what passes by in the blood, monitor the presence of the fed state. This detection generates signals that lead to the storage of fuels and protein synthesis in a variety of ways. Central to generating this response is the production of a hormone called **insulin** in a region of the pancreas termed the *islets of langerhan*. Specifically, the surge in blood glucose levels following a carbohydrate meal stimulates the production of insulin from the so-called beta islet cells and concurrently inhibits the production of another hormone called glucagon from the alpha islet cells.

Insulin has several effects. First and foremost, it increases the uptake of glucose into all cells except the brain and the liver (which always readily absorb glucose). Glucose enters cells by facilitated diffusion, but the presence of insulin increases the uptake by more than 10 times. As a result, cells

switch more toward using glucose, instead of fats, as an energy
source. Second, it promotes glucose storage as glycogen in liver
and muscle cells. Insulin indirectly
leads to the turning on of enzymes
involved in glycogen synthesis in
both cell types. Third, it inhibits
the synthesis of additional glucose
from other molecules by indirectly
turning off gluconeogenic enzymes in liver cells. Forth, again
by enzyme regulation, it stimulates
fatty acid synthesis in liver cells.
These fatty acids then travel to
adipose cells, which in the presence

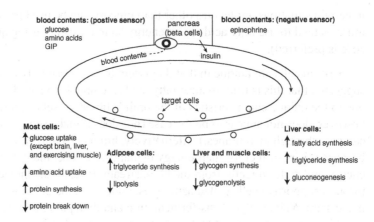

Figure 25-33. A summary of insulin's effects. See text for further details.

of glucose are converted into triglycerides and stored. Fifth, it stimulates protein synthesis, at least in part, by stimulating the movement of amino acids into cells. And finally, it inhibits the degradation of proteins already formed within the cell back into amino acids (see Figure 25-33).

High glucose levels in the blood, along with some other molecules released by the body during digestion, also trigger another homeostatic control mechanism. Specifically the hypothalamus gets involved as a monitor where, like with blood water regulation, it plays a role in generating an appro-priate sensation—*satiation*. The feeling of being full keeps an organism from eating more than it can presently handle.

In between meals

After the initial surge in glucose has either been consumed or stored, blood sugar levels begin to fall. And the production of hormones in the pancreas changes in response. Lower levels of glucose stimulate the production of glucagon and inhibit the production of insulin.

Glucagon's main target is the liver, where it prods liver cells to release glucose into the blood-stream. It does so by several means. It indirectly turns on enzymes involved in degradation of glyco-gen back into glucose and enzymes involved in synthesizing glucose from nonsugar molecules such as amino acids. At the same time, it indirectly turns off enzymes that convert glucose into glycogen. Furthermore, it inhibits enzymes involved in fatty acid synthesis, and it stimulates enzymes in the liver that convert some of the fatty acids into ketone bodies (see Figure 25-34).

Given that glucose storage is
limited and nonbrain tissues can
use fatty acids, just promoting the
release of glucose would not make
sense. When the next meal is coming is always somewhat uncertain,
so promoting fatty acid use would
help conserve the remaining glucose supply for the brain. Both the
absence of insulin and the presence
of glucagon facilitate this switch.
For one, glucagon in combination
with low insulin levels leads to an

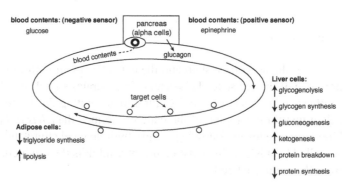

Figure 25-34. A summary of glucagon's effects. See text for further details.

enzyme found in adipose cells, called **hormone-sensitive lipase**, to turn on. This enzyme catalyzes the breakdown of triglycerides into fatty acids and glycerol, which can then be released into the blood. Furthermore, low insulin levels make it more difficult for nonbrain cells to use glucose. Without insulin, glucose cannot readily cross these cells' membranes. As a consequence, nonbrain cells increase their use of fatty acids as a fuel. Low insulin levels also contribute to the glucose supply by allowing the release of amino acids from cells, which can be converted to glucose in the liver.

As blood sugar levels continue to drop, the hypothalamus once again gets involved as a monitor. Its most direct effect is that it triggers the creation of another sensation—*hunger*. Decreasing supplies of high-energy molecules must eventually be replenished, and by creating the sensation of hunger the body directs itself to go out and get more. Specifically low blood sugar stimulates hypothalamic neurons in the hunger or feeding center to release more peptide neuromodulators, such as neuropeptide Y and agouti-related protein (which were discussed previously).

Acute Stress

I imagine everyone can relate to the expression: "I feel stressed out." Current demands on you seem so overwhelming that it is not clear how you are going to get through it all. The biological notion of stress captures the same notion. An organism is said to be stressed whenever it encounters situations so dangerous that it is not clear whether the organism will be able to make it, to survive. A zebra being chased by a lion is "stressed out." The same could be said for an organism with a severe injury or facing extremely hot or cold conditions.

How organisms respond to stressful situations (stressors) has a common theme. They alter their physiology in ways that help it contend with the current dangerous situation, but they do so at the cost of discounting the future. It is another example of organisms making the best of a bad situation. Growth, repair, immune responses, reproduction, and even digestion are important biological activities that cost resources now but only benefit the organism in the future. A zebra, however, that does not escape the lion now has no future. So stress responses should take resources away from growth and other future-based activities and channel them toward attempting to solve the immediate problem. Stress responses cannot afford to hold back because the cost of failure is too high.

The classic fight-or-flight response is a stress response involving the release of the hormone **epinephrine** (which is often called **adrenaline**). Although this response typically plays only a small role in normal blood sugar regulation, I discuss it briefly here because it can further support a body's efforts to spare blood glucose supplies for the brain.

The fight-or-flight response starts with the perception of a stressful experience by the nervous system, which quickly orchestrates a whole gamut of body changes. One part of this story is that the hypothalamus is prodded to send nervous signals to the two **adrenal medulla** glands—which are located just above the kidneys. The adrenal medullas then release **epinephrine** into the bloodstream. As epinephrine travels through the body, it orchestrates a suite of effects that help prepare for action. One of these effects is to mobilize needed resources. (Other effects include increasing heart rate and opening up the airways to the lungs—the bronchioles.) Specifically, epinephrine has similar effects as glucagon. Like glucagon it promotes the release of fatty acids from adipose cells by stimulating hormone-sensitive lipase. Also like glucagon, epinephrine promotes the breakdown of stored glycogen into glucose. The difference is that epinephrine targets glycogen breakdown in skeletal muscle, whereas glucagon targets the liver. This difference makes sense from a fight-or-flight perspective because epinephrine acts to directly increase the glucose supply of muscles throughout the body, which can be used to rapidly make the ATP needed for a quick and powerful response (see Figure 25-35). Interestingly, epinephrine's effects on skeletal muscles can also help an organism maintain a glucose supply for the brain, but only indirectly. Recall that unlike liver cells, glucose freed from storage in skeletal muscles can never return to the bloodstream, so this stored sugar can never be used directly to feed the brain. Yet the increasing the supply of glucose within muscle cells reduces the need for muscles to remove glucose from the blood, which in turn leaves more glucose for the brain. Finally, epinephrine reinforces all the preceding effects by further promoting the release of glucagon and inhibiting the release of insulin.

Chronic starvation

Different than running away from a predator, the stress response to chronic starvation will largely involve metabolic shifts. As an animal goes a longer time without a meal, at some point it exhausts both its glucose stores and its supply of proteins that can be broken down into amino acids (and then converted to glucose) without impairing body function. This raises an important question: How can this individual continue to feed its brain?

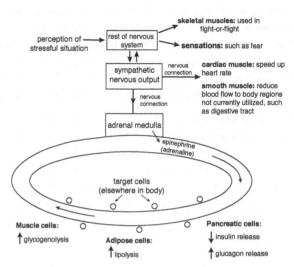

Figure 25-35. A summary of the fight-or-flight response, including epinephrine's metabolic effects.

There are two possibilities. It can either begin to cannibalize its muscles to feed its brain, or it could seemingly switch over to fueling the brain with ketone bodies. Remember that ketone bodies can be made from fatty acids, and given that a typical animal stores much more energy in fat than in glucose, fat stores will commonly still be available when a body reaches this point. All else being equal, I would expect organisms to switch quickly and completely to ketone bodies. Using fat stores seems preferable to breaking apart muscles to generate glucose. Although if it ever came down to either muscles or brain, the best of the bad situation choice would be to keep feeding the brain. Losing muscle mass and its associated strength is a bad situation that will eventually kill an animal, but the brain is even higher on the priority list. If the brain starves, the rest of the animal will die with it.

At least in humans, the body's response to chronic starvation is complicated by factors such as whether someone is experiencing complete starvation (no food intake) or semistarvation (energy intake is less than energy use). Nonetheless, the bottom line is that the brain never seems to completely switch to ketone bodies. Cannibalizing muscles to supply the brain with its needed glucose is thus always part of the starvation story.

The details of this muscle cannibalization are in the hormones. Once the hypothalamus detects dangerously low levels of glucose, it releases a hormone known as CRH that travels the short distance to the anterior pituitary and prods certain cells to release a hormone known as **ACTH**. ACTH in turn stimulates the release of third hormone, a **glucocorticoid** such as **cortisol**, from the two adrenal cortex glands (located on the outside of the adrenal medullas). Glucocorticoids, which are also known as the **stress hormone**, initiate a large number of changes in the body (see Figure 25-36). One of them is to promote protein breakdown, increasing the amino acid supply in the blood. These amino acids can then be converted to glucose in the liver.

Some speculation: When glucose becomes too scarce within brain cells (or any other cell type), the oxaloacetate supply within the mitochondria will begin to dwindle (as it is used in metabolic pathways other than the Krebs cycle). This will reduce the ability of these cells to run the Krebs cycle, which in turn will reduce the ability of these cells to use ketone bodies as an energy source. Yet, as mentioned previously, low glucose levels also trigger ketone body production in the liver. This can lead to ketone bodies accumulating in the blood, as inputs are greater than outputs. Because at normal body pH levels ketone bodies act as hydrogen ion (H^+) donors —that is, they act as acids—accumulating levels will tend to increase the acidity of body fluids. This can seriously, even fatally, disrupt organism function because proteins tend to change shape as pH changes, which can inhibit them from carrying out their "normal tasks." Maintaining at least minimal glucose levels during chronic starvation by continually cannibalizing at least small amounts of muscle may be a means to avoid this trap.

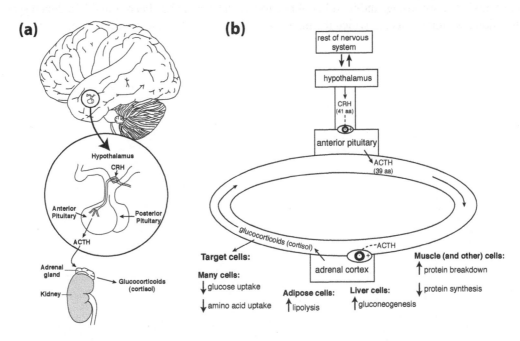

Figure 25-36. The chain of events that lead to the release of glucocorticoids are summarized in two different ways. In (b) the metabolic effects of glucocorticoids are also included.

Some curious aspects of human stress physiology

As stated earlier, an organism that cannot appropriately initiate an appropriate stress response when a dangerous situation is encountered will suffer bad if not lethal consequences. Yet because stress responses channel resources away from the future, an organism that cannot appropriately terminate a stress response or that activates the system too much because of repeated chronic stressors can also suffer problems—stress-related diseases could emerge (see Table 25-1).

Table 25-1.

Stress response:	Stress related disorder (due to chronic stress):
Mobilization of high-energy molecules	Muscle loss, fatigue, steriod-induced diabetes
Increased cardiovascular tone	Stress-induced hypertension
Suppression of digestion	Increased tendency to develop ulcers
Suppression of growth	Psychogenic dwarfism
Suppression of reproduction	Suppression of menstruation, impotency, loss of sex drive
Enhanced immune system (short-term)	Suppressed immune system—increased disease risk
Sharpening of cognition (short-term)	Neuroendangerment (especially in hippocampus), memory loss

Along these lines, humans may be particularly vulnerable. Unlike less cognitively sophisticated species, humans can turn on the stress response by thinking about stressors that we could potentially encounter in the future. So in addition to turning on the stress response when faced with issues like being chased by a predator, starvation, injury, blood loss, or temperature extremes, we can become stressed over an exam next week, whether we will get into medical school or some other program several years from now, or whether we will ever find the mate of our dreams. The realization that some-day we are going to die can even stress us out.

An interesting aside: Just after spawning, salmon (of different species) have huge adrenal glands and tremendously high levels of glucocorticoids in their blood. Remove the adrenal glands from a salmon just after spawning, and it will continue to live. The same has been found in a dozen species of Australian marsupial mice, in which the male mice die shortly after the mating season.

Some key terms:

monitor - a generic name for any body part that upon detecting a specific type of change, either within or outside the body, releases some form of signal.

effector - a generic name for any body part that adjusts its rate of action in response to receiving a signal from a monitor.

hormone - any chemical signal that uses the circulatory system to travel between the monitor that released it and whatever effectors respond to it.

integration - whenever the actions of a single effector is influenced by the perceptions of more than one monitor.

neurotransmitter - any chemical signal released from the end of a nerve cell that has a direct effect on whether the postsynaptic cell will fire an action potential.

neuromodulator - any chemical signal released from the end of a nerve cell that influences how the postsynaptic cell will respond to neurotransmitters.

long-term potentiation - a mechanism by which frequent activity within a synapse enhances the connection strength of the synapse that will last for at least a while after that which triggered the frequent activity has passed.

membrane potential - the electric gradient (separation of charge) across a cell's membrane due to a slight ionic concentration gradient. (The inside of a cell has a slight excess in negatively charged ions, and the outside a slight excess of positively charged ions).

resting membrane potential - a cell's normal level of charge imbalance across its membrane.

depolarization - a reduction in the separation of charge across a cell's membrane relative to its resting membrane potential.

hyperpolarization - an increase in the separation of charge across a cell's membrane relative to its resting membrane potential.

voltage-gated sodium ion channel - a gated channel protein that opens when membrane potential is reduced (depolarization) beyond a certain threshold, and when open is permeable to sodium ions.

ligand-gated sodium ion channel - a gated channel protein that opens when a specific ligand is present hence binds to a specific site on the ion channel, and when open is permeable to sodium ions.

dendrites - that branching part of a neuron's (nerve cell's) input region—that is the region containing nonvoltage-gated ion channels.

axon hillock - where a neuron's input region ends and its conducting regions begins. More specifically it is where the distribution of nonvoltage-gated ion channels stops and the distribution of voltage-gated ion channels begins.

action potential - a traveling positive feedback loop formed by the opening of voltage-gated sodium (or calcium) ion channels leading to the opening of next voltage-gated sodium ion channels in line and so on.

axon - starting at the axon hillock it is the elongated conducting region of a nerve cell. It is here that action potentials, once started, travel to a neuron's output end.

axon terminal - the output end of a nerve cell. It is here that action potentials indirectly trigger the release of neurotransmitters.

ADH (antidiuretic hormone) - the hormone released (from the posterior pituitary) when (a region in) the hypothalamus detects low blood water levels. It increases water reabsorption (movement of water back into the circulatory system) from kidney filtrate (by increasing water permeability of a kidney's collecting tubules).

blood-brain barrier - the tightly sealed nature of (most of) the brain's capillaries, which prevents certain molecules from being able to diffuse from the blood into the brain. (The brain's capillaries lack openings between the cells making up capillaries.)

ketone bodies - water soluble four-carbon compounds that can be made from fatty acids. (Such chemical conversion, like many other chemical conversions, occurs within the liver.)

islets of langerhan - region of the pancreas that secrete insulin (beta islet cells) or glucagon (alpha islets cells) in response to changes in blood sugar levels.

insulin - the hormone whose main effects are to increase the rate that glucose diffuses (via facilitated diffusion) from blood to cells throughout a body, and promotes glucose storage in liver and skeletal muscle cells. (Insulin indirectly leads to the turning on the enzymes that convert glucose into its storage form glycogen in both cell types).

glucagon - the hormone whose main effect is to promote the release of glucose stored in liver cells back into the blood stream.

Some study questions:

An important point: For the different cells making up a body to function as a coordinated unit—that is as an organism—as internal and external conditions continually change, different cell types in different positions must be constantly adjusting their rate (of function) in ways that best serve the organism.

An important complication: Each cell type must, in some way, be able to detect when changes that they "should" respond to, actually occur. Yet there may commonly be a tradeoff that makes this difficult. Based on functional considerations, cells of different types are best located in certain places in the body. Some of these locations, however, would put cells in places that make detection of the changes they need to respond to difficult, if not impossible. Muscle cells tucked inside an organism, for example, are not in a position to detect what is going on outside the organism. The paracrine, the endocrine, and the nervous system are means by which organisms have come to deal with this tradeoff.

The first four questions attempt to get you to see some basic issues.

1. Commonly in multicellular organisms, a cell or cells having a sensor to some external or internal circumstance (a monitor) is in a different location than the cell or cells that responds to the situation (the effector). Explain some benefits of separating a monitor and an effector.

2. Explain how both signals and receptors are needed for a monitor to communicate with an effector. What are the three basic ways that signals travel from monitor cells to effector cells?

3. Explain why in the endocrine system different responses depend on the use of different hormones, while in the nervous system the same signal molecule (same neurotransmitter) can be used to initiate different responses.

4. Explain how the actions of an effector can feedback to a monitor? Be able to design a counter-acting or co-acting response that incorporates a monitor, a signal, and an effector.

The next question is the "see the big picture" question about the nervous system.

5. In general, what activity is the nervous system involved in regulating? Explain how the nervous system is better suited to regulate this activity than the endocrine system.

The next two questions focus on some basic issues of nervous system design.

6. What is the simplest way to design a reflex involving one muscle, more than one muscle.

7. Explain how a ganglion makes it possible for a reflexive responses to involve more than one muscle and for different reflexes to use the same muscle. What is different about how a sensory neuron and a motor neuron develop?

These next seven questions focus on integrative nervous pathways.

8. Know the basic ways that the magnitude of a neuron's effect on the postsynaptic cell can vary.

9. What are some ways that an inhibitory interneuron differ from a sensory neuron. Explain how a motor neuron innervated by one sensory neuron and one inhibitory motor neuron can be an integrative nervous pathway. (Or more generally, know what distinguishes an integrative nervous pathway from a nonintegrative nervous pathway.)

10. Be sure you understand Figure 25-22, along with all the other examples of how to think about the workings of integrative nervous pathways. Understand how within an integrative pathway, some stimuli can have a larger influence over the decision made than others.

11. Understand how increasingly integrative nervous pathways can increase an organism's behavioral flexibility—that is, increase the range of responses to a particular stimulus.

12. What is modulation? How can modulation change how an organism responds to a specific set of stimuli? Why would modulation be biologically useful?

13. How is learning different than modulation? How could activity-dependent forms of synapse-specific facilitation give rise to learning? How could modulation influence what is learned?

14. Be sure you understand Figure 25-23.

The next seven questions focus on the various parts of one phenomenon: How some form of stimulus at one end of a neuron can lead to the release of a chemical signal (a neurotransmitter) at the other end.

15. What two types of ions are actively pumped out of cells?

16. Define membrane potential, depolarization of a membrane, and hyperpolarization of a membrane. Explain how the opening of sodium ion (Na^+) or calcium ion (Ca^{++}) channels leads to depolarization of a membrane.

17. Explain what is different about letting more calcium ions into a cell in comparison to letting more sodium ions into a cell. In other words, explain what is meant by the expression: Calcium ions are biologically active.

18. Explain how an action potential, once started, is able to spread across the membrane of a cell. In other words, describe how a series of voltage-gated sodium ion channels can generate an action potential.

19. Explain how the presence of a specific type of molecule can start an action potential. (Note: Be sure to include a ligand-gated ion channel in your answer.) Alternatively, explain how the presence of pressure can start an action potential. (Note: Be sure to include a stretch-gated ion channel in your answer.)

20. Explain how an action potential based on voltage-gated Na^+ channels once started could lead to the opening of voltage-gated Ca^{++} channels elsewhere in the cell.

21. Where is each of the following commonly located within a neuron: voltage-gated Na^+ channels, voltage-gated Ca^{++} channels, nonvoltage-gated (e.g., ligand-gated, stretch gated) Na^+ channels.

22. A summary question: Explain how the presence of a specific molecule or pressure at the dendrite end of a neuron could lead to the release of neurotransmitter at an axon terminal.

The next three questions focus on the endocrine system and blood sugar regulation.

23. Define hormone. How is it that hormones released in one part of the body (from an endocrine gland) effect the actions of some parts of the body but not others?

24. Explain in some detail how the body regulates blood sugar level as the body goes longer and longer without a carbohydrate meal. Be sure to distinguish when the pancreas and the hypothalamus acts as a monitor in this scenario, and the significance of the switch from one to the other.

25. Know the effects of the following hormones: insulin, glucagon, epinephrine, and glucocorticoids (cortisol).